PEARSON

ALWAYS LEARNING

Developmental Mathematics with Intermediate Algebra

Second Custom Edition for Bristol Community College

Taken from:
Developmental Mathematics, Second Edition
by Elayn Martin-Gay

Intermediate Algebra, Fourth Edition
by Elayn Martin-Gay

Developmental Mathematics
by Elayn Martin-Gay

Cover Art: Courtesy of Photodisc/Getty Images.

Taken from:

Developmental Mathematics, Second Edition
by Elayn Martin-Gay
Copyright © 2011, 2007 by Pearson Education, Inc.
Published by Prentice Hall
Upper Saddle River, New Jersey 07458

Intermediate Algebra, Fourth Edition
by Elayn Martin-Gay
Copyright © 2012, 2007, 2003 by Pearson Education, Inc.
Published by Prentice Hall, Inc.

Developmental Mathematics
by Elayn Martin-Gay
Copyright © 2007 by Prentice Hall, Inc.
Published by Prentice Hall, Inc.

This special edition published in cooperation with Pearson Learning Solutions.

All trademarks, service marks, registered trademarks, and registered service marks are the property of their respective owners and are used herein for identification purposes only.

Pearson Learning Solutions, 501 Boylston Street, Suite 900, Boston, MA 02116
A Pearson Education Company
www.pearsoned.com

Printed in the United States of America

7 16

000200010271806007

SR

ISBN 10: 1-269-42250-2
ISBN 13: 978-1-269-42250-5

Contents

Whole Numbers

1

Objectives

1.1 TIPS FOR MATHEMATICS

Before reading this section, remember that your instructor is your best source of information. Please see your instructor for any additional help or information.

Objective Ⓐ Getting Ready for This Course

Now that you have decided to take this course, remember that a *positive attitude* will make all the difference in the world. Your belief that you can succeed is just as important as your commitment to this course. Make sure you are ready for this course by having the time and positive attitude that it takes to succeed.

Next, make sure that you have scheduled your math course at a time that will give you the best chance for success. For example, if you are also working, you may want to check with your employer to make sure that your work hours will not conflict with your course schedule.

On the day of your first class period, double-check your schedule and allow yourself extra time to arrive on time in case of traffic problems or difficulty locating your classroom. Make sure that you bring at least your textbook, paper, and a writing instrument. Are you required to have a lab manual, graph paper, calculator, or some other supplies besides this text? If so, also bring this material with you.

Objective Ⓑ General Tips for Success

Below are some general tips that will increase your chance for success in a mathematics class. Many of these tips will also help you in other courses you may be taking.

Exchange names and phone numbers or e-mail addresses with at least one other person in class. This contact person can be a great help if you miss an assignment or want to discuss math concepts or exercises that you find difficult.

Choose to attend all class periods. If possible, sit near the front of the classroom. This way, you will see and hear the presentation better. It may also be easier for you to participate in classroom activities.

Do your homework. You've probably heard the phrase "practice makes perfect" in relation to music and sports. It also applies to mathematics. You will find that the more time you spend solving mathematics exercises, the easier the process becomes. Be sure to schedule enough time to complete your assignments before the next due date assigned by your instructor.

Check your work. Review the steps you made while working a problem. Learn to check your answers in the original problems. You may also compare your answers with the "Answers to Selected Exercises" section in the back of the book. If you have made a mistake, try to figure out what went wrong. Then correct your mistake. If you can't find what went wrong, don't erase your work or throw it away. Bring your work to your instructor, a tutor in a math lab, or a classmate. It is easier for someone to find where you had trouble if he or she looks at your original work.

Learn from your mistakes and be patient with yourself. Everyone, even your instructor, makes mistakes. (That definitely includes me—Elayn Martin-Gay.) Use your errors to learn and to become a better math student. The key is finding and understanding your errors.

Was your mistake a careless one, or did you make it because you can't read your own math writing? If so, try to work more slowly or write more neatly and make a conscious effort to carefully check your work.

Did you make a mistake because you don't understand a concept? Take the time to review the concept or ask questions to better understand it.

Helpful Hint

MyMathLab® and **MathXL®**

If you are doing your homework online, you can work and re-work those exercises that you struggle with until you master them. Try working through all the assigned exercises twice before the due date.

Helpful Hint

MyMathLab® and **MathXL®**

If you are completing your homework online, it's important to work each exercise on paper before submitting the answer. That way, you can check your work and follow your steps to find and correct any mistakes.

Did you skip too many steps? Skipping steps or trying to do too many steps mentally may lead to preventable mistakes.

Know how to get help if you need it. It's all right to ask for help. In fact, it's a good idea to ask for help whenever there is something that you don't understand. Make sure you know when your instructor has office hours and how to find his or her office. Find out whether math tutoring services are available on your campus. Check on the hours, location, and requirements of the tutoring service.

Organize your class materials, including homework assignments, graded quizzes and tests, and notes from your class or lab. All of these items will make valuable references throughout your course and when studying for upcoming tests and the final exam. Make sure that you can locate these materials when you need them.

Read your textbook before class. Reading a mathematics textbook is unlike reading a novel or a newspaper. Your pace will be much slower. It is helpful to have paper and a pencil with you when you read. Try to work out examples on your own as you encounter them in your text. You should also write down any questions that you want to ask in class. When you read a mathematics textbook, sometimes some of the information in a section will be unclear. But after you hear a lecture or watch a lecture video on that section, you will understand it much more easily than if you had not read your text beforehand.

Don't be afraid to ask questions. You are not the only person in class with questions. Other students are normally grateful that someone has spoken up.

Turn in assignments on time. This way you can be sure that you will not lose points for being late. Show every step of a problem and be neat and organized. Also be sure that you understand which problems are assigned for homework. If allowed, you can always double-check the assignment with another student in your class.

Objective C Using This Text

There are many helpful resources that are available to you. It is important that you become familiar with and use these resources. They should increase your chances for success in this course.

- *Practice Exercises.* Each example in every section has a parallel Practice exercise. As you read a section, try each Practice exercise after you've finished the corresponding example. This "learn-by-doing" approach will help you grasp ideas before you move on to other concepts. Answers are at the bottom of the page.
- *Chapter Test Prep Videos.* This supplement is very helpful before a test or exam.
- *Interactive DVD Lecture Series.* Exercises marked with a 📀 are fully worked out by the author on the DVDs. The lecture series provides approximately 20 minutes of instruction per section.
- *Symbols at the Beginning of an Exercise Set.* If you need help with a particular section, the symbols listed at the beginning of each exercise set will remind you of the numerous supplements available.
- *Objectives.* The main section of exercises in each exercise set is referenced by an objective, such as A or B, and also an example(s). There is also often a section of exercises entitled "Mixed Practice," which is referenced by two or more objectives or sections. These are mixed exercises written to prepare you for your next exam. Use all of this referencing if you have trouble completing an assignment from the exercise set.
- *Icons (Symbols).* Make sure that you understand the meaning of the icons that are beside many exercises. 📀 tells you that the corresponding exercise may be viewed on the video segment that corresponds to that section. ✏ tells you that this exercise is a writing exercise in which you should answer in complete sentences. △ tells you that the exercise involves geometry.

MyMathLab® and **MathXL®**

When assignments are turned in online, keep a hard copy of your complete written work. You will need to refer to your written work to be able to ask questions and to study for tests later.

MyMathLab® and **MathXL®**

Be aware of assignments and due dates set by your instructor. Don't wait until the last minute to submit work online. Allow 6–8 hours before the deadline in case you have technology trouble.

MyMathLab®

In MyMathLab, you have access to the following video resources:

- Lecture Videos for each section
- Chapter Test Prep Videos

Use these videos provided by the author to prepare for class, review, and study for tests.

- *End of Chapter Opportunities.* There are many opportunities at the end of each chapter to help you understand the concepts of the chapter.

  Chapter Highlights contain chapter summaries and examples.

  Chapter Reviews contain review problems. The first part is organized section by section and the second part contains a set of mixed exercises.

- *Student Resources in Your Textbook.* You will find a **Student Resources** section at the back of this textbook. It contains the following to help you study and prepare for tests:

  Study Skill Builders contain study skills advice. To increase your chance for success in the course, read these study tips, and answer the questions.

  Bigger Picture—Study Guide Outline provides you with a study guide outline of the course, with examples.

  Practice Final provides you with a Practice Final Exam to help you prepare for your final. The video solutions to each question are provided in the Interactive DVD Lecture Series and within MyMathLab®.

- *Resources to Check Your Work.* The **Answers to Selected Exercises** section provides answers to all odd-numbered section exercises.

Helpful Hint

MyMathLab® and MathXL®

- Use the **Help Me Solve This** button to get step-by-step help for the exercise you are working. You will need to work an additional exercise of the same type before you can get credit for having worked it correctly.
- Use the **Video** button to view a video clip of the author working a similar exercise.

Objective ⓓ Getting Help

If you have trouble completing assignments or understanding the mathematics, get help as soon as you need it! This tip is presented as an objective on its own because it is so important. In mathematics, usually the material presented in one section builds on your understanding of the previous section. This means that if you don't understand the concepts covered during a class period, there is a good chance that you will not understand the concepts covered during the next class period. If this happens to you, get help as soon as you can.

Where can you get help? Many suggestions have been made in this section on where to get help, and now it is up to you to get it. Try your instructor, a tutoring center, or a math lab, or you may want to form a study group with fellow classmates. If you do decide to see your instructor or go to a tutoring center, make sure that you have a neat notebook and are ready with your questions.

Helpful Hint

MyMathLab® and MathXL®

Review your written work for previous assignments. Then, go back and re-work previous assignments. Open a previous assignment, and click **Similar Exercise** to generate new exercises. Re-work the exercises until you fully understand them and can work them without help features.

Objective ⓔ Preparing for and Taking an Exam

Make sure that you allow yourself plenty of time to prepare for a test. If you think that you are a little "math anxious," it may be that you are not preparing for a test in a way that will ensure success. The way that you prepare for a test in mathematics is important. To prepare for a test:

1. Review your previous homework assignments.
2. Review any notes from class and section-level quizzes you have taken.
3. Review concepts and definitions by reading the Chapter Highlights at the end of each chapter.
4. Practice working out exercises by completing the Chapter Review found at the end of each chapter. *Don't stop here!*
5. It is important that you place yourself in conditions similar to test conditions to find out how you will perform. In other words, as soon as you feel that you know the material, get a few blank sheets of paper and take a sample test. You can work selected problems from the Chapter Review. Your instructor may also provide you with a review sheet. During this sample test, do not use your notes or your textbook. Then check your sample test. If you are not satisfied with the results, study the areas that you are weak in and try again.
6. On the day of the test, allow yourself plenty of time to arrive at where you will be taking your exam.

When taking your test:

1. Read the directions on the test carefully.
2. Read each problem carefully as you take the test. Make sure that you answer the question asked.
3. Watch your time and pace yourself so that you can attempt each problem on your test.
4. If you have time, check your work and answers.
5. Do not turn your test in early. If you have extra time, spend it double-checking your work.

Objective (F) Managing Your Time

As a college student, you know the demands that classes, homework, work, and family place on your time. Some days you probably wonder how you'll ever get everything done. One key to managing your time is developing a schedule. Here are some hints for making a schedule:

1. Make a list of all of your weekly commitments for the term. Include classes, work, regular meetings, extracurricular activities, etc. You may also find it helpful to list such things as laundry, regular workouts, grocery shopping, etc.
2. Next, estimate the time needed for each item on the list. Also make a note of how often you will need to do each item. Don't forget to include time estimates for the reading, studying, and homework you do outside of your classes. You may want to ask your instructor for help estimating the time needed.
3. In the exercise set that follows, you are asked to block out a typical week on the schedule grid given. Start with items with fixed time slots like classes and work.
4. Next, include the items on your list with flexible time slots. Think carefully about how best to schedule items such as study time.
5. Don't fill up every time slot on the schedule. Remember that you need to allow time for eating, sleeping, and relaxing! You should also allow a little extra time in case some items take longer than planned.
6. If you find that your weekly schedule is too full for you to handle, you may need to make some changes in your workload, classload, or in other areas of your life. You may want to talk to your advisor, manager or supervisor at work, or someone in your college's academic counseling center for help with such decisions.

1.1 Exercise Set

1. What is your instructor's name?

2. What are your instructor's office location and office hours?

3. What is the best way to contact your instructor?

4. Do you have the name and contact information of at least one other student in class?

5. Will your instructor allow you to use a calculator in this class?

6. Why is it important that you write step-by-step solutions to homework exercises and keep a hard copy of all work submitted?

7. Is there a tutoring service available on campus? If so, what are its hours? What services are available?

8. Have you attempted this course before? If so, write down ways that you might improve your chances of success during this second attempt.

9. List some steps that you can take if you begin having trouble understanding the material or completing an assignment. If you are completing your homework in MyMathLab® and MathXL®, list the resources you can use for help.

10. How many hours of studying does your instructor advise for each hour of instruction?

11. What does the ✎ icon in this text mean?

12. What does the ▯ icon in this text mean?

13. What does the △ icon in this text mean?

14. Search the minor columns in your text. What are Practice exercises?

15. When might be the best time to work a Practice exercise?

16. Where are the answers to Practice exercises?

17. What answers are contained in this text and where are they?

18. What and where are the study skills builders?

19. How many times is it suggested that you work through the homework exercises in MathXL® before the submission deadline?

20. How far in advance of the assigned due date is it suggested that homework be submitted online? Why?

21. Chapter Highlights are found at the end of each chapter. Find the Chapter 1 Highlights and explain how you might use it and how it might be helpful.

22. Chapter Reviews are found at the end of each chapter. Find the Chapter 1 Review and explain how you might use it and how it might be useful.

23. Explain how the Chapter Test Prep Videos may help. If you are working in MyMathLab® and MathXL®, how can you use previous homework assignments to study?

24. Read or reread objective ⓕ and fill out the schedule grid on the next page.

	Monday	Tuesday	Wednesday	Thursday	Friday	Saturday	Sunday
4:00 a.m.							
5:00 a.m.							
6:00 a.m.							
7:00 a.m.							
8:00 a.m.							
9:00 a.m.							
10:00 a.m.							
11:00 a.m.							
12:00 p.m.							
1:00 p.m.							
2:00 p.m.							
3:00 p.m.							
4:00 p.m.							
5:00 p.m.							
6:00 p.m.							
7:00 p.m.							
8:00 p.m.							
9:00 p.m.							
10:00 p.m.							
11:00 p.m.							
Midnight							
1:00 a.m.							
2:00 a.m.							
3:00 a.m.							

Objectives

A Find the Place Value of a Digit in a Whole Number.

B Write a Whole Number in Words and in Standard Form.

C Write a Whole Number in Expanded Form.

D Read Tables.

1.2 PLACE VALUES, NAMES FOR NUMBERS, AND READING TABLES

The **digits** 0, 1, 2, 3, 4, 5, 6, 7, 8, and 9 can be used to write numbers. For example, the **whole numbers** are

0, 1, 2, 3, 4, 5, 6, 7, 8, 9, 10, 11, . . .

and the **natural numbers** are 1, 2, 3, 4, 5, 6, 7, 8, 9, 10, 11, . . .

The three dots (. . .) after the 11 mean that this list continues indefinitely. That is, there is no largest whole number. The smallest whole number is 0.

Objective **A** Finding the Place Value of a Digit in a Whole Number

The position of each digit in a number determines its **place value.** For example, the distance (in miles) between the planet Mercury and the planet Earth can be represented by the whole number 48,337,000. Below is a place-value chart for this whole number.

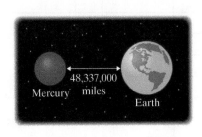
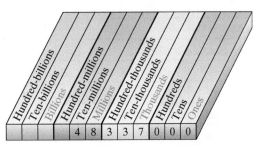

The two 3s in 48,337,000 represent different amounts because of their different placements. The place value of the 3 on the left is hundred-thousands. The place value of the 3 on the right is ten-thousands.

Examples Find the place value of the digit 3 in each whole number.

1. 396,418
↑
hundred-thousands

2. 93,192
↑
thousands

3. 534,275,866
↑
ten-millions

Work Practice 1–3

PRACTICE 1–3

Find the place value of the digit 8 in each whole number.
1. 38,760,005
2. 67,890
3. 481,922

Objective **B** Writing a Whole Number in Words and in Standard Form

A whole number such as 1,083,664,500 is written in **standard form.** Notice that commas separate the digits into groups of three, starting from the right. Each group of three digits is called a **period.** The names of the first four periods are shown in red.

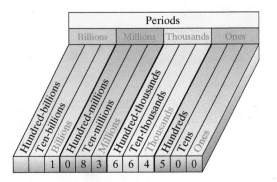

Answers
1. millions **2.** hundreds
3. ten-thousands

Writing a Whole Number in Words

To write a whole number in words, write the number in each period followed by the name of the period. (The ones period is usually not written.) This same procedure can be used to read a whole number.

For example, we write 1,083,664,500 as

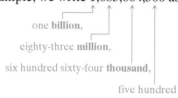

one **billion,**

eighty-three **million,**

six hundred sixty-four **thousand,**

five hundred

> **Helpful Hint** Notice the commas after the name of each period.

> **Helpful Hint**
>
> The name of the ones period is not used when reading and writing whole numbers. For example,
>
> 9,265
>
> is read as
>
> "nine **thousand,** two hundred sixty-five."

Examples Write each number in words.

4. 85   eighty-five
5. 126   one hundred twenty-six
6. 27,034   twenty-seven thousand, thirty-four

● Work Practice 4–6

> **Helpful Hint** The word "and" is *not* used when reading and writing whole numbers. It is used when reading and writing mixed numbers and some decimal values, as shown later in this text.

Example 7 Write 106,052,447 in words.

Solution: 106,052,447 is written as

one hundred six **million,** fifty-two **thousand,** four hundred forty-seven

● Work Practice 7

✓**Concept Check** True or false? When writing a check for $2600, the word name we write for the dollar amount of the check is "two thousand sixty." Explain your answer.

Writing a Whole Number in Standard Form

To write a whole number in standard form, write the number in each period, followed by a comma.

PRACTICE 4–6

Write each number in words.
4. 67
5. 395
6. 12,804

PRACTICE 7

Write 321,670,200 in words.

PRACTICE 8–11

Write each number in standard form.

8. twenty-nine

9. seven hundred ten

10. twenty-six thousand, seventy-one

11. six million, five hundred seven

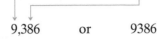 Write each number in standard form.

8. sixty-one   61   **9.** eight hundred five   805

10. nine thousand, three hundred eighty-six

9,386   or   9386

11. two million, five hundred sixty-four thousand, three hundred fifty

2,564,350

● **Work Practice 8–11**

 Helpful Hint

A comma may or may not be inserted in a four-digit number. For example, both

9,386   and   9386

are acceptable ways of writing nine thousand, three hundred eighty-six.

Objective ⓒ Writing a Whole Number in Expanded Form

The place value of a digit can be used to write a number in expanded form. The **expanded form** of a number shows each digit of the number with its place value. For example, 5672 is written in expanded form as

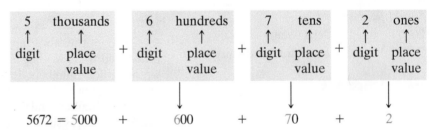

$$5672 = 5000 + 600 + 70 + 2$$

PRACTICE 12

Write 1,047,608 in expanded form.

Example 12 Write 2,706,449 in expanded form.

Solution: $2{,}000{,}000 + 700{,}000 + 6000 + 400 + 40 + 9$

● **Work Practice 12**

We can visualize whole numbers by points on a line. The line below is called a **number line.** This number line has equally spaced marks for each whole number. The arrow to the right simply means that the whole numbers continue indefinitely. In other words, there is no largest whole number.

Number Line

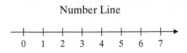

We will study number lines further in Section 1.5.

Answers

8. 29   **9.** 710

10. 26,071   **11.** 6,000,507

12. $1{,}000{,}000 + 40{,}000 + 7000 + 600 + 8$

Objective D Reading Tables

Now that we know about place value and names for whole numbers, we introduce one way that whole numbers may be presented. **Tables** are often used to organize and display facts that involve numbers. The following table shows the ten countries with the most Nobel Prize winners since the inception of the Nobel Prize in 1901, and the categories of the prizes. The numbers for the Economics prize reflect the winners since 1969, when this category was established. (The numbers may seem large for two reasons: first, the annual Nobel Prize is often awarded to more than one individual, and second, several award winners hold dual citizenship, so they are counted in two countries.)

Countries with Most Nobel Prize Winners, 1901–2008							
Country	Physics	Chemistry	Literature	Physiology and Medicine	Peace	Economics	Total
United States	88	59	11	96	22	44	320
United Kingdom	21	27	11	31	13	7	110
Germany	25	28	8	16	4	1	82
France	13	8	14	11	10	2	58
Sweden	4	4	8	7	5	2	30
Switzerland	3	6	2	6	4	0	21
Russia (USSR)	10	1	5	1	3	1	21
Austria	3	4	1	7	2	1	18
Italy	3	1	6	4	1	1	16
Netherlands	8	3	0	2	1	2	16
Japan	7	5	2	1	1	0	16

Source: Based on data from official website of the Nobel Prize Committee

For example, by reading from left to right along the row marked "United States," we find that the United States has 88 Physics, 59 Chemistry, 11 Literature, 96 Physiology and Medicine, 22 Peace, and 44 Economics Nobel Prize winners.

Example 13 Use the Nobel Prize Winner table to answer each question.

a. How many total Nobel Prize winners are from Sweden?
b. Which countries shown have fewer Nobel Prize winners than Austria?

Solution:

a. Find "Sweden" in the left column. Then read from left to right until the "Total" column is reached. We find that Sweden has 30 Nobel Prize winners.
b. Austria has 18 Nobel Prize winners. Italy, Netherlands, and Japan each has 16, so they have fewer Nobel Prize winners than Austria.

● Work Practice 13

PRACTICE 13

Use the Nobel Prize Winner table to answer the following questions:

a. How many Nobel Prize winners in Literature come from France?

b. Which countries shown have more than 60 Nobel Prize winners?

Answers

13. **a.** 14 **b.** United States, United Kingdom, and Germany

Vocabulary and Readiness Check

Use the choices below to fill in each blank.

standard form   period   whole
expanded form   place value   words

1. The numbers 0, 1, 2, 3, 4, 5, 6, 7, 8, 9, 10, 11, 12, . . . are called _____ numbers.
2. The number 1,286 is written in _____.
3. The number "twenty-one" is written in _____.
4. The number 900 + 60 + 5 is written in _____.
5. In a whole number, each group of three digits is called a(n) _____.
6. The _____ of the digit 4 in the whole number 264 is ones.

1.2 Exercise Set

FOR EXTRA HELP  PRACTICE   WATCH   DOWNLOAD   READ   REVIEW

Objective Ⓐ *Determine the place value of the digit 5 in each whole number. See Examples 1 through 3.*

1. 657   **2.** 905   **3.** 5423   **4.** 6527

5. 43,526,000   **6.** 79,050,000   **7.** 5,408,092   **8.** 51,682,700

Objective Ⓑ *Write each whole number in words. See Examples 4 through 7.*

9. 354   **10.** 316   **11.** 8279   **12.** 5445

13. 26,990   **14.** 42,009   **15.** 2,388,000   **16.** 3,204,000

17. 24,350,185   **18.** 47,033,107

Write each number in the sentence in words. See Examples 4 through 7.

19. As of this writing, the population of Iceland is 304,367. (*Source:* The World Factbook)

20. Between 2000 and 2005, Brazil lost 13,382 acres of rainforest.

21. Due for completion in 2010, the Burj Dubai, in Dubai, United Arab Emirates, a hotel and office building, will be the tallest in the world at a height of more than 2600 feet. (*Source:* Council on Tall Buildings and Urban Habitat)

22. In a recent year, there were 99,769 patients in the United States waiting for an organ transplant. (*Source:* United Network for Organ Sharing)

23. Each day, UPS delivers an average of 15,800,000 packages worldwide. (*Source:* UPS)

24. Each year, 350,000,000 Americans visit a local carnival. (*Source:* Outdoor Amusement Business Association)

25. The highest point in Colorado is Mount Elbert, at an elevation of 14,433 feet. (*Source:* U.S. Geological Survey)

26. The highest point in Oregon is Mount Hood, at an elevation of 11,239 feet. (*Source:* U.S. Geological Survey)

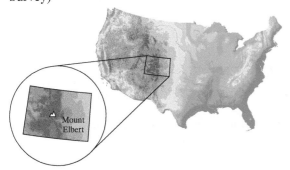

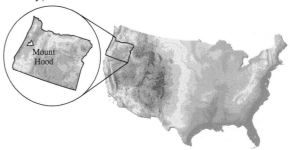

27. In a recent year, the Great Internet Mersenne Prime Search, a cooperative computing project, helped find a prime number that has nearly 13,000,000 digits. (*Source:* Science News)

28. The Goodyear blimp *Eagle* holds 202,700 cubic feet of helium. (*Source:* The Goodyear Tire & Rubber Company)

Write each whole number in standard form. See Examples 8 through 11.

29. Six thousand, five hundred eighty-seven

30. Four thousand, four hundred sixty-eight

31. Fifty-nine thousand, eight hundred

32. Seventy-three thousand, two

33. Thirteen million, six hundred one thousand, eleven

34. Sixteen million, four hundred five thousand, sixteen

35. Seven million, seventeen

36. Two million, twelve

37. Two hundred sixty thousand, nine hundred ninety-seven

38. Six hundred forty thousand, eight hundred eighty-one

Write the whole number in each sentence in standard form. See Examples 8 through 11.

39. The Mir Space Station orbits above Earth at an average altitude of three hundred ninety-five kilometers. (*Source:* Heavens Above)

40. The average distance between the surfaces of Earth and the Moon is about two hundred thirty-four thousand miles.

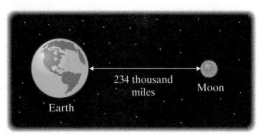

41. La Rinconada, Peru, is the highest town in the world. It is located sixteen thousand, seven hundred thirty-two feet above sea level. (*Source:* Russell Ash: *Top 10 of Everything*, 2009)

42. The world's tallest free-standing tower is the Guangzhou TV Tower in China. Its completed height is two thousand one feet tall. (*Source: The World Almanac*)

43. The Summit Entertainment film *The Twilight Saga: New Moon* set the U.S. and Canada record for opening day income when it took in approximately seventy-two million, seven hundred four thousand dollars in one day in 2009. (*Source:* wikipedia.org)

44. The Warner Brothers film *The Dark Knight* set the U.S. and Canada record for second-highest opening day income when it took in approximately sixty-seven million, one hundred sixty-five thousand dollars in one day in 2008. (*Source:* wikipedia.org)

45. As of 2009, there were one thousand, three hundred seventeen species classified as either threatened or endangered in the United States. (*Source:* U.S. Fish & Wildlife Service)

46. Morten Anderson, who played football for New Orleans, Atlanta, N.Y. Giants, Kansas City, and Minnesota between 1982 and 2007, holds the record for the most points scored in a career. Over his 25-year career he scored two thousand, five hundred forty-four points. (*Source:* NFL.com)

Objective C *Write each whole number in expanded form. See Example 12.*

47. 406   **48.** 789   **49.** 3470   **50.** 6040

51. 80,774   **52.** 20,215   **53.** 66,049   **54.** 99,032

55. 39,680,000   **56.** 47,703,029

Objectives B C D **Mixed Practice** *The table shows the six tallest mountains in New England and their elevations. Use this table to answer Exercises 57 through 62. See Example 13.*

Mountain (State)	Elevation (in feet)
Boott Spur (NH)	5492
Mt. Adams (NH)	5774
Mt. Clay (NH)	5532
Mt. Jefferson (NH)	5712
Mt. Sam Adams (NH)	5584
Mt. Washington (NH)	6288
Source: U.S. Geological Survey	

Elevation in feet

57. Write the elevation of Mt. Clay in standard form and then in words.

58. Write the elevation of Mt. Washington in standard form and then in words.

59. Write the height of Boott Spur in expanded form.

60. Write the height of Mt. Jefferson in expanded form.

61. Which mountain is the tallest in New England?

62. Which mountain is the second tallest in New England?

The table shows the top ten popular breeds of dogs in a recent year according to the American Kennel Club. Use this table to answer Exercises 63 through 68. See Example 13.

Top Ten American Kennel Club Registrations in 2007				
	Breed	Number of Registered Dogs	Average Dog Maximum Height (in inches)	Average Dog Maximum Weight (in pounds)
	Beagle	39,384	15	30
	Boxer	35,388	25	70
	Bulldog	21,037	26	90
	Dachshund	36,033	9	25
	German shepherd dog	43,575	26	95
	Golden retriever	42,962	24	80
	Labrador retriever	123,760	25	75
	Poodle (standard, miniature, and toy)	29,939	standard: 26	standard: 70
	Shih Tzu	27,282	11	16
	Yorkshire terrier	48,346	9	7
(*Source:* American Kennel Club)				

63. Which breed has fewer dogs registered, Boxer or Dachshund?

64. Which breed has more dogs registered, Golden retriever or German shepherd dog?

65. Which breed has the most American Kennel Club registrations? Write the number of registrations for this breed in words.

66. Which of the listed breeds has the fewest registrations? Write the number of registered dogs for this breed in words.

67. What is the maximum weight of an average-size Dachshund?

68. What is the maximum height of an average-size standard poodle?

Concept Extensions

69. Write the largest four-digit number that can be made from the digits 1, 9, 8, and 6 if each digit must be used once. _____ _____ _____ _____

70. Write the largest five-digit number that can be made using the digits 5, 3, and 7 if each digit must be used at least once. _____ _____ _____ _____ _____.

Check to see whether each number written in standard form matches the number written in words. If not, correct the number in words. See the Concept Check in this section.

71.

```
                                    60-8124/7233         1401
                                    1000613331
                                          DATE _____
        PAY TO
        THE ORDER OF                          $ 105.00
        One Hundred Fifty and 00/100 ~~~~~~
                                                  DOLLARS
        FIRST STATE BANK
        O F   F A R T H I N G T O N
           FARTHINGTON, IL 64422
        MEMO _____    _____
        ⑆621497260⑆ 1000613331⑈ 1401
```

72.

```
                                    60-8124/7233         1402
                                    1000613331
                                          DATE _____
        PAY TO
        THE ORDER OF                          $ 7030.00
        Seven Thousand Thirty and 00/100 ~~~~~~
                                                  DOLLARS
        FIRST STATE BANK
        O F   F A R T H I N G T O N
           FARTHINGTON, IL 64422
        MEMO _____    _____
        ⑆621497260⑆ 1000613331⑈ 1402
```

73. If a number is given in words, describe the process used to write this number in standard form.

74. If a number is written in standard form, describe the process used to write this number in expanded form.

75. Called "Roadrunner" by its users, a computer built by IBM for Los Alamos National Laboratory topped the list of the 500 fastest computers, burning up the bytes at 1.026 petaflops, or more than 1000 trillion arithmetic operations per second. Look up "trillion" (in the American system) and use the definition to write this number in standard form. (*Source:* TechWorld)

76. A Hurricane Katrina victim was seeking $3 quadrillion from the U.S. government. Look up "quadrillion" (in the American system) and write 3 quadrillion in standard form. (*Source:* Associated Press)

77. The Pro Football Hall of Fame was established on September 7, 1963, in this town. Use the information and the diagram to the right to find the name of the town.
- Alliance is east of Massillon.
- Dover is between Canton and New Philadelphia.
- Massillon is not next to Alliance.
- Canton is north of Dover.

Pro Football
Hall of Fame

OHIO

1.3 ADDING WHOLE NUMBERS AND PERIMETER

Objective Ⓐ Adding Whole Numbers

According to ConsumerSearch, the iPod nano is the best overall MP3 player. (The newest nano also contains a video camera!)

Suppose that an electronics store received a shipment of two boxes of iPod nanos one day and an additional four boxes of iPod nanos the next day. The **total** shipment in the two days can be found by adding 2 and 4.

2 boxes of iPod nanos + 4 boxes of iPod nanos = 6 boxes of iPod nanos

The **sum** (or total) is 6 boxes of iPod nanos. Each of the numbers 2 and 4 is called an **addend,** and the process of finding the sum is called **addition.**

$$2 \quad + \quad 4 \quad = \quad 6$$

addend   addend   sum

To add whole numbers, we add the digits in the ones place, then the tens place, then the hundreds place, and so on. For example, let's add 2236 + 160.

```
  2236        Line up numbers vertically so that the place values correspond. Then
 +160         add digits in corresponding place values, starting with the ones place.
  2396
```
sum of ones
sum of tens
sum of hundreds
sum of thousands

Example 1 Add: 23 + 136

Solution:
```
    23
 + 136
   159
```

● Work Practice 1

When the sum of digits in corresponding place values is more than 9, **carrying** is necessary. For example, to add 365 + 89, add the ones-place digits first.

Carrying
```
     1
   3 6 5
 +   8 9    5 ones + 9 ones = 14 ones or 1 ten + 4 ones
       4    Write the 4 ones in the ones place and carry the 1 ten to the tens place.
```

Next, add the tens-place digits.
```
   1 1
   3 6 5
 +   8 9    1 ten + 6 tens + 8 tens = 15 tens or 1 hundred + 5 tens
     5 4    Write the 5 tens in the tens place and carry the 1 hundred to the hundreds place.
```

Next, add the hundreds-place digits.
```
   1 1
   365
 +  89      1 hundred + 3 hundreds = 4 hundreds
   454      Write the 4 hundreds in the hundreds place.
```

Answer
1. 7777

16

Example 2 Add: 34,285 + 149,761

Solution:
$$
\begin{array}{r}
\overset{11\ 1}{34{,}285} \\
+\ 149{,}761 \\
\hline
184{,}046
\end{array}
$$

Work Practice 2

PRACTICE 2

Add: 27,364 + 92,977

✓ Concept Check What is wrong with the following computation?

$$
\begin{array}{r}
394 \\
+\ 283 \\
\hline
577
\end{array}
$$

Before we continue adding whole numbers, let's review some properties of addition that you may have already discovered. The first property that we will review is the **addition property of 0.** This property reminds us that the sum of 0 and any number is that same number.

Addition Property of 0

The sum of 0 and any number is that number. For example,

$7 + 0 = 7$

$0 + 7 = 7$

Next, notice that we can add any two whole numbers in any order and the sum is the same. For example,

$4 + 5 = 9$ and $5 + 4 = 9$

We call this special property of addition the **commutative property of addition.**

Commutative Property of Addition

Changing the **order** of two addends does not change their sum. For example,

$2 + 3 = 5$ and $3 + 2 = 5$

Another property that can help us when adding numbers is the **associative property of addition.** This property states that when adding numbers, the grouping of the numbers can be changed without changing the sum. We use parentheses to group numbers. They indicate which numbers to add first. For example, let's use two different groupings to find the sum of $2 + 1 + 5$.

$(2 + 1) + 5 = 3 + 5 = 8$

Also,

$2 + (1 + 5) = 2 + 6 = 8$

Both groupings give a sum of 8.

Answer

2. 120,341

✓ **Concept Check Answer**

forgot to carry 1 hundred to the hundreds place

> ### *Associative Property of Addition*
>
> Changing the **grouping** of addends does not change their sum. For example,
>
> $$3 + (5 + 7) = 3 + 12 = 15 \quad \text{and} \quad (3 + 5) + 7 = 8 + 7 = 15$$

The commutative and associative properties tell us that we can add whole numbers using any order and grouping that we want.

When adding several numbers, it is often helpful to look for two or three numbers whose sum is 10, 20, and so on. Why? Adding multiples of 10 such as 10 and 20 is easier.

PRACTICE 3

Add: $11 + 7 + 8 + 9 + 13$

Example 3 Add: $13 + 2 + 7 + 8 + 9$

Solution:

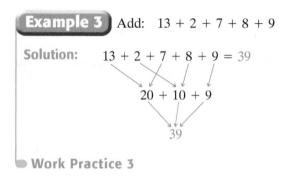

$$13 + 2 + 7 + 8 + 9 = 39$$

$$20 + 10 + 9$$

$$39$$

● Work Practice 3

Feel free to use the process of Example 3 anytime when adding.

PRACTICE 4

Add: $19 + 5042 + 638 + 526$

Example 4 Add: $1647 + 246 + 32 + 85$

Solution:

$$\begin{array}{r} {\scriptstyle 1\,2\,2} \\ 1647 \\ 246 \\ 32 \\ +85 \\ \hline 2010 \end{array}$$

● Work Practice 4

Objective ⓑ Finding the Perimeter of a Polygon

In geometry addition is used to find the perimeter of a polygon. A **polygon** can be described as a flat figure formed by line segments connected at their ends. Geometric figures such as triangles, squares, and rectangles are called polygons.

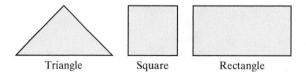

Triangle   Square   Rectangle

Answers

3. 48   **4.** 6225

The **perimeter** of a polygon is the *distance around* the polygon. This means that the perimeter of a polygon is the sum of the lengths of its sides.

Example 5 Find the perimeter of the polygon shown.

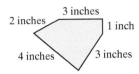

Solution: To find the perimeter (distance around), we add the lengths of the sides.

2 in. + 3 in. + 1 in. + 3 in. + 4 in. = 13 in.

The perimeter is 13 inches.

● **Work Practice 5**

To make the addition appear simpler, we will often not include units with the addends. If you do this, make sure units are included in the final answer.

Example 6 Calculating the Perimeter of a Building

The largest commercial building in the world under one roof is the flower auction building of the cooperative VBA in Aalsmeer, Netherlands. The floor plan is a rectangle that measures 776 meters by 639 meters. Find the perimeter of this building. (A meter is a unit of length in the metric system.) (*Source: The Handy Science Answer Book*, Visible Ink Press)

Solution: Recall that opposite sides of a rectangle have the same length. To find the perimeter of this building, we add the lengths of the sides. The sum of the lengths of its sides is

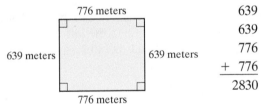

$$\begin{array}{r} 639 \\ 639 \\ 776 \\ + \ 776 \\ \hline 2830 \end{array}$$

The perimeter of the building is 2830 meters.

● **Work Practice 6**

Objective ⓒ Solving Problems by Adding

Often, real-life problems occur that can be solved by adding. The first step in solving any word problem is to *understand* the problem by reading it carefully.

Descriptions of problems solved through addition *may* include any of these key words or phrases:

Addition		
Key Words or Phrases	**Examples**	**Symbols**
added to	5 added to 7	7 + 5
plus	0 plus 78	0 + 78
increased by	12 increased by 6	12 + 6
more than	11 more than 25	25 + 11
total	the total of 8 and 1	8 + 1
sum	the sum of 4 and 133	4 + 133

PRACTICE 5

Find the perimeter of the polygon shown. (A centimeter is a unit of length in the metric system.)

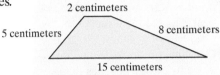

PRACTICE 6

A park is in the shape of a triangle. Each of the park's three sides is 647 feet. Find the perimeter of the park.

Answers

5. 30 cm   **6.** 1941 ft

To solve a word problem that involves addition, we first use the facts given to write an addition statement. Then we write the corresponding solution of the real-life problem. It is sometimes helpful to write the statement in words (brief phrases) and then translate to numbers.

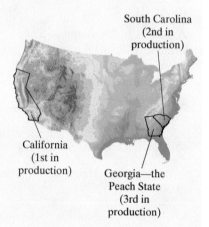

South Carolina (2nd in production)

California (1st in production)

Georgia—the Peach State (3rd in production)

Example 7 Finding a Stadium Capacity

The Darrell K Royal Memorial Stadium, located in Austin, Texas, is the largest football stadium in the Big 12 Conference. Before 2009, it could seat 94,113 fans. Recently, the capacity of the stadium was increased by 4525 permanent bleacher seats. Find the new capacity of the home of the University of Texas Longhorns for the 2009 season. (*Source:* University of Texas Athletics)

Austin

Solution: The key phrase here is "was increased by," which suggests that we add. To find the new capacity of the stadium, we add the increase, 4525, to the old capacity.

In Words		Translate to Numbers
Old capacity	$\longrightarrow$	94,113
+ increase	$\longrightarrow$	+ 4,525
New capacity	$\longrightarrow$	98,638

The number of seats in the stadium for the 2009 season was 98,638.

● **Work Practice 7**

Graphs can be used to visualize data. The graph shown next is called a **bar graph.** For this bar graph, the height of each bar is labeled above the bar. To check this height, follow the top of each bar to the vertical line to the left. For example, the first bar is labeled 146. Follow the top of that bar to the left until the vertical line is reached, not quite halfway between 140 and 160, or 146.

Example 8 Reading a Bar Graph

In the following graph, each bar represents a country and the height of each bar represents the number of endangered species identified in that country.

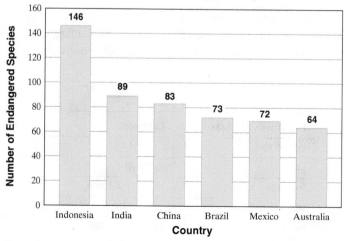

Number of Endangered Species

Source: The Top 10 of Everything, Russell Ash

a. Which country shown has the greatest number of endangered species?

b. Find the total number of endangered species for Australia, China, and India.

Solution:

a. The country with the greatest number of endangered species corresponds to the tallest bar, which is Indonesia.

b. The key word here is "total." To find the total number of endangered species for Australia, China, and India, we add.

In Words		Translate to Numbers
Australia	$\rightarrow$	64
China	$\rightarrow$	83
India	$\rightarrow$	+ 89
		Total 236

The total number of endangered species for Australia, China, and India is 236.

● **Work Practice 8**

Calculator Explorations   **Adding Numbers**

To add numbers on a calculator, find the keys marked
$+$ and $=$ or $\boxed{\text{ENTER}}$.

For example, to add 5 and 7 on a calculator, press the keys
$\boxed{5}$ $\boxed{+}$ $\boxed{7}$ $\boxed{=}$ or $\boxed{\text{ENTER}}$.

The display will read $\boxed{\quad 12 \quad}$.
Thus, 5 + 7 = 12.

To add 687, 981, and 49 on a calculator, press the keys
$\boxed{687}$ $\boxed{+}$ $\boxed{981}$ $\boxed{+}$ $\boxed{49}$ $\boxed{=}$ or $\boxed{\text{ENTER}}$.

The display will read $\boxed{\quad 1717 \quad}$.

Thus, 687 + 981 + 49 = 1717. (Although entering 687, for example, requires pressing more than one key, here numbers are grouped together for easier reading.)

Use a calculator to add.

1. 89 + 45   **2.** 76 + 97

3. 285 + 55   **4.** 8773 + 652

5.   985   **6.**   465
          1210   9888
           562   620
      +   77   +   1550

Vocabulary and Readiness Check

Use the choices below to fill in each blank. Some choices may be used more than once.

sum	order	addend	associative
perimeter	number	grouping	commutative

1. The sum of 0 and any number is the same _____.

2. The sum of any number and 0 is the same _____.

3. In $35 + 20 = 55$, the number 55 is called the _____ and 35 and 20 are each called a(n) _____.

4. The distance around a polygon is called its _____.

5. Since $(3 + 1) + 20 = 3 + (1 + 20)$, we say that changing the _____ in addition does not change the sum. This property is called the _____ property of addition.

6. Since $7 + 10 = 10 + 7$, we say that changing the _____ in addition does not change the sum. This property is called the _____ property of addition.

1.3 Exercise Set

FOR EXTRA HELP

MyMathLab ·  PRACTICE · WATCH · DOWNLOAD · READ · REVIEW

Objective A *Add. See Examples 1 through 4.*

1.
$$\begin{array}{r} 14 \\ +22 \\ \hline \end{array}$$

2.
$$\begin{array}{r} 27 \\ +31 \\ \hline \end{array}$$

3.
$$\begin{array}{r} 62 \\ +230 \\ \hline \end{array}$$

4.
$$\begin{array}{r} 37 \\ +542 \\ \hline \end{array}$$

5.
$$\begin{array}{r} 12 \\ 13 \\ +24 \\ \hline \end{array}$$

6.
$$\begin{array}{r} 23 \\ 45 \\ +30 \\ \hline \end{array}$$

7.
$$\begin{array}{r} 5267 \\ +\ 132 \\ \hline \end{array}$$

8.
$$\begin{array}{r} 236 \\ +6243 \\ \hline \end{array}$$

9. $53 + 64$

10. $41 + 74$

11. $22 + 490$

12. $35 + 470$

13. $22{,}781 + 186{,}297$

14. $17{,}427 + 821{,}059$

15.
$$\begin{array}{r} 8 \\ 9 \\ 2 \\ 5 \\ +1 \\ \hline \end{array}$$

16.
$$\begin{array}{r} 3 \\ 5 \\ 8 \\ 5 \\ +7 \\ \hline \end{array}$$

17.
$$\begin{array}{r} 6 \\ 21 \\ 14 \\ 9 \\ +12 \\ \hline \end{array}$$

18.
$$\begin{array}{r} 12 \\ 4 \\ 8 \\ 26 \\ +10 \\ \hline \end{array}$$

19.
$$\begin{array}{r} 81 \\ 17 \\ 23 \\ 79 \\ +12 \\ \hline \end{array}$$

20.
$$\begin{array}{r} 64 \\ 28 \\ 56 \\ 25 \\ +32 \\ \hline \end{array}$$

21. $62 + 18 + 14$

22. $23 + 49 + 18$

23. 40 + 800 + 70

24. 30 + 900 + 20

25. 7542 + 49 + 682

26. 1624 + 32 + 976

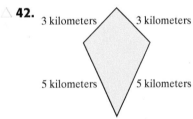 **27.** 24 + 9006 + 489 + 2407

28. 16 + 1056 + 748 + 7770

29.   627
       628
   + 629

30.   427
       383
   + 229

31.   6820
      4271
   + 5626

32.   6789
      4321
   + 5555

33.   507
       593
   + 10

34.   864
        33
   + 356

35.   4200
      2107
   + 2692

36.   5000
      1400
   + 3021

37.   49
       628
     5 762
  + 29,462

38.   26
     582
    4 763
  + 62,511

39.   121,742
     57,279
     26,586
  + 426,782

40.   504,218
   321,920
     38,507
  + 594,687

Objective **B** *Find the perimeter of each figure. See Examples 5 and 6.*

41.

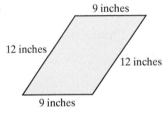

9 inches
12 inches
12 inches
9 inches

42.

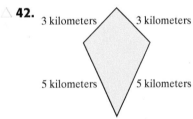

3 kilometers   3 kilometers
5 kilometers   5 kilometers

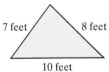 **43.**

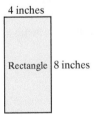

7 feet   8 feet
10 feet

44.

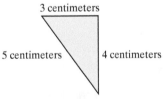

3 centimeters
5 centimeters   4 centimeters

45.

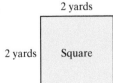

4 inches
Rectangle 8 inches

46.

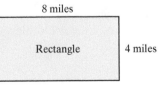

8 miles
Rectangle 4 miles

47.

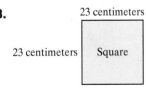

2 yards
2 yards Square

48.

23 centimeters
23 centimeters Square

49.

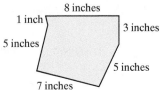

50.

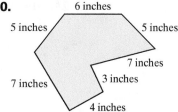

51.

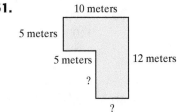

52.

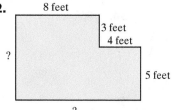

Objectives Ⓐ Ⓑ Ⓒ **Mixed Practice—Translating** *Solve. See Examples 1 through 8.*

53. Find the sum of 297 and 1796.

54. Find the sum of 802 and 6487.

55. Find the total of 76, 39, 8, 17, and 126.

56. Find the total of 89, 45, 2, 19, and 341.

57. What is 452 increased by 92?

58. What is 712 increased by 38?

59. What is 2686 plus 686 plus 80?

60. What is 3565 plus 565 plus 70?

61. The population of Florida is 19,308 thousand in 2010. It is projected to increase by 3170 thousand during the next ten years. What is Florida's projected population in 2020?

62. The population of California is 39,136 thousand in 2010. It is projected to increase by 4990 thousand during the next ten years. What is California's projected population in 2020?

63. The highest point in South Carolina is Sassafras Mountain at 3560 feet above sea level. The highest point in North Carolina is Mt. Mitchell, whose peak is 3124 feet increased by the height of Sassafras Mountain. Find the height of Mt. Mitchell. (*Source:* U.S. Geological Survey)

64. The distance from Kansas City, Kansas, to Hays, Kansas, is 285 miles. Colby, Kansas, is 98 miles farther from Kansas City than Hays. Find the total distance from Kansas City to Colby.

65. Leo Callier is installing an invisible fence in his backyard. How many feet of wiring are needed to enclose the yard below?

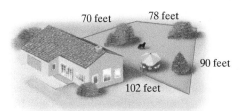

70 feet   78 feet

90 feet

102 feet

66. A homeowner is considering installing gutters around her home. Find the perimeter of her rectangular home.

60 feet   45 feet

67. The highest waterfall in the United States is Yosemite Falls in Yosemite National Park in California. Yosemite Falls is made up of three sections, as shown in the graph. What is the total height of Yosemite Falls? (*Source:* U.S. Department of the Interior)

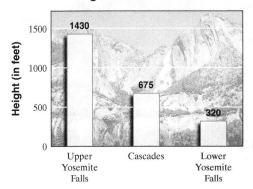

Highest U.S. Waterfalls

Height (in feet)

1430 — Upper Yosemite Falls
675 — Cascades
320 — Lower Yosemite Falls

68. Jordan White, a nurse at Mercy Hospital, is recording fluid intake on a patient's medical chart. During his shift, the patient had the following types and amounts of intake measured in cubic centimeters (cc). What amount should Jordan record as the total fluid intake for this patient?

Oral	Intravenous	Blood
240	500	500
100	200	
355		

69. In 2008, Harley-Davidson sold 235,441 of its motorcycles domestically. In addition, 78,328 Harley-Davidson motorcycles were sold internationally. What was the total number of Harley-Davidson motorcycles sold in 2008? (*Source:* Harley-Davidson, Inc.)

70. Hank Aaron holds Major League Baseball's record for the most runs batted in over his career. He batted in 1305 runs from 1954 to 1965. He batted in another 992 runs from 1966 until he retired in 1976. How many total runs did Hank Aaron bat in during his career in professional baseball?

71. During one month in a recent year, the two top-selling automobiles in the United States were the Honda Accord and the Toyota Camry. There were 41,382 Accords and 44,064 Camrys sold that month. What was the total number of Accords and Camrys sold in that month? (*Source:* Toyota Corp. and Honda Corp.)

72. In a recent year, the country of New Zealand had 29,719,969 more sheep than people. If the human population of New Zealand in 2008 was 4,280,031, what was the sheep population? (*Source:* Statistics: New Zealand)

73. The largest permanent Monopoly board is made of granite and located in San Jose, California. Find the perimeter of the square playing board.

31 ft

31 ft

74. The smallest commercially available jigsaw puzzle (with the greatest number of pieces) is a 1000-piece puzzle manufactured in Spain. Find the perimeter of this rectangular-shaped puzzle.

12 in.

18 in.

75. In 2008, there were 2677 Gap Inc. (Gap, Banana Republic, Old Navy) stores located in the United States and 493 located outside the United States. How many Gap Inc. stores were located worldwide? (*Source:* Gap Inc.)

76. Wilma Rudolph, who won three gold medals in track and field events in the 1960 Summer Olympics, was born in 1940. Tirunesh Dibaba, who won two gold medals in track and field events but in the 2008 Summer Olympics, was born 45 years later. In what year was Tirunesh Dibaba born?

The table shows the number of Target stores in ten states. Use this table to answer Exercises 77 through 82.

The Top States for Target Stores in 2009	
State	**Number of Stores**
Pennsylvania	53
California	236
Florida	124
Georgia	56
Illinois	85
New York	62
Michigan	60
Minnesota	73
Ohio	64
Texas	146
(*Source:* Target Corporation)	

77. Which state has the most Target stores?

78. Which of the states listed in the table has the fewest Target stores?

79. What is the total number of Target stores located in the three states with the most Target stores?

80. How many Target stores are located in the ten states listed in the table?

81. Which pair of neighboring states has more Target stores combined, Florida and Georgia or Michigan and Ohio?

82. Target operates stores in 49 states. There are 739 Target stores located in the states not listed in the table. How many Target stores are in the United States?

83. The state of Delaware has 2029 miles of urban highways and 3865 miles of rural highways. Find the total highway mileage in Delaware. (*Source:* U.S. Federal Highway Administration)

84. The state of Rhode Island has 5193 miles of urban highways and 1222 miles of rural highways. Find the total highway mileage in Rhode Island. (*Source:* U.S. Federal Highway Administration)

Concept Extensions

85. In your own words, explain the commutative property of addition.

86. In your own words, explain the associative property of addition.

87. Give any three whole numbers whose sum is 100.

88. Give any four whole numbers whose sum is 25.

89. Add: 56,468,980 + 1,236,785 + 986,768,000

90. Add: 78,962 + 129,968,350 + 36,462,880

Check each addition below. If it is incorrect, find the correct answer. See the Concept Check in this section.

91.
```
    566
    932
+   871
   2369
```

92.
```
    773
    659
+   481
   1913
```

93.
```
     14
    173
     86
+   257
    520
```

94.
```
     19
    214
     49
+   651
    923
```

1.4 SUBTRACTING WHOLE NUMBERS

Objective **A** Subtracting Whole Numbers

If you have $5 and someone gives you $3, you have a total of $8, since $5 + 3 = 8$. Similarly, if you have $8 and then someone borrows $3, you have $5 left. **Subtraction** is finding the **difference** of two numbers.

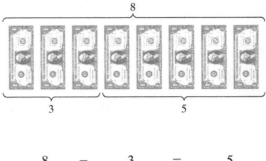

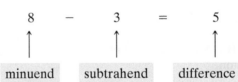

In this example, 8 is the **minuend,** and 3 is the **subtrahend.** The **difference** between these two numbers, 8 and 3, is 5.

Notice that addition and subtraction are very closely related. In fact, subtraction is defined in terms of addition.

$8 - 3 = 5$ because $5 + 3 = 8$

This means that subtraction can be *checked* by addition, and we say that addition and subtraction are reverse operations.

PRACTICE 1

Subtract. Check each answer by adding.
a. $14 - 6$
b. $20 - 8$
c. $93 - 93$
d. $42 - 0$

Example 1 Subtract. Check each answer by adding.

a. $12 - 9$ b. $22 - 7$ c. $35 - 35$ d. $70 - 0$

Solution:

a. $12 - 9 = 3$ because $3 + 9 = 12$
b. $22 - 7 = 15$ because $15 + 7 = 22$
c. $35 - 35 = 0$ because $0 + 35 = 35$
d. $70 - 0 = 70$ because $70 + 0 = 70$

◗ Work Practice 1

Look again at Examples 1(c) and 1(d).

1(c) $35 - 35 = 0$ 1(d) $70 - 0 = 70$

same number | difference is 0 | a number minus 0 | difference is the same number

These two examples illustrate the subtraction properties of 0.

Answer
1. a. 8   b. 12   c. 0   d. 42

Subtraction Properties of 0

The difference of any number and that same number is 0. For example,

$$11 - 11 = 0$$

The difference of any number and 0 is that same number. For example,

$$45 - 0 = 45$$

To subtract whole numbers we subtract the digits in the ones place, then the tens place, then the hundreds place, and so on. When subtraction involves numbers of two or more digits, it is more convenient to subtract vertically. For example, to subtract 893 − 52,

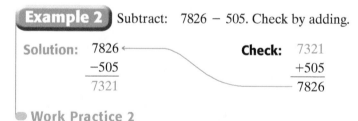

```
  893  ←── minuend          Line up the numbers vertically so that the minuend is on top and
 − 52  ←── subtrahend       the place values correspond. Subtract in corresponding place values,
  841  ←── difference       starting with the ones place.
        │ 3 − 2
        │ 9 − 5
        8 − 0
```

To check, add.

```
  difference   or      841
+ subtrahend         +  52
    minuend            893  ←── Since this is the original minuend,
                               the problem checks.
```

Example 2 Subtract: 7826 − 505. Check by adding.

Solution:
```
   7826               Check:   7321
  −505                        +505
   7321                        7826
```

● Work Practice 2

Subtracting by Borrowing

When subtracting vertically, if a digit in the second number (subtrahend) is larger than the corresponding digit in the first number (minuend), **borrowing** is necessary. For example, consider

```
   8│1
 − 6│3
```

Since the 3 in the ones place of 63 is larger than the 1 in the ones place of 81, borrowing is necessary. We borrow 1 ten from the tens place and add it to the ones place.

Borrowing

```
                     7 11
  8  −  1  =  7  →   8̸ 1̸   ←── 1 ten + 1 one = 11 ones
 tens   ten   tens  − 6 3
```

PRACTICE 2

Subtract. Check by adding.
a. 9143 − 122
b. 978 − 851

Answer
2. a. 9021 **b.** 127

Now we subtract the ones-place digits and then the tens-place digits.

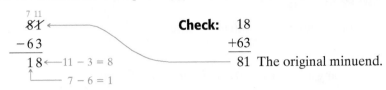

$$\begin{array}{r} \overset{7\ 11}{\cancel{8}\cancel{1}} \\ -63 \\ \hline 18 \end{array} \quad \leftarrow 11 - 3 = 8$$
$$ \leftarrow 7 - 6 = 1$$

Check:
$$\begin{array}{r} 18 \\ +63 \\ \hline 81 \end{array} \quad \text{The original minuend.}$$

Example 3   Subtract: 543 − 29. Check by adding.

Solution:
$$\begin{array}{r} \overset{3\ 13}{54\cancel{3}} \\ -29 \\ \hline 514 \end{array}$$

Check:
$$\begin{array}{r} 514 \\ +29 \\ \hline 543 \end{array}$$

● Work Practice 3

Sometimes we may have to borrow from more than one place. For example, to subtract 7631 − 152, we first borrow from the tens place.

$$\begin{array}{r} \overset{2\ 11}{76\cancel{3}\cancel{1}} \\ -\ 152 \\ \hline 9 \end{array} \quad \leftarrow 11 - 2 = 9$$

In the tens place, 5 is greater than 2, so we borrow again. This time we borrow from the hundreds place.

6 hundreds − **1 hundred** = 5 hundreds

1 hundred + 2 tens
or
10 tens + 2 tens = 12 tens

$$\begin{array}{r} \overset{5\ \overset{12}{\cancel{2}}\ 11}{7\cancel{6}\cancel{3}\cancel{1}} \\ -152 \\ \hline 7479 \end{array}$$

Check:
$$\begin{array}{r} 7479 \\ +152 \\ \hline 7631 \end{array} \quad \text{The original minuend.}$$

Example 4   Subtract: 900 − 174. Check by adding.

Solution: In the ones place, 4 is larger than 0, so we borrow from the tens place. But the tens place of 900 is 0, so to borrow from the tens place we must first borrow from the hundreds place.

$$\begin{array}{r} \overset{8\ 10}{\cancel{9}\cancel{0}0} \\ -174 \end{array}$$

Now borrow from the tens place.

$$\begin{array}{r} \overset{9}{\overset{8\ \cancel{10}10}{\cancel{9}\cancel{0}\cancel{0}}} \\ -174 \\ \hline 726 \end{array}$$

Check:
$$\begin{array}{r} 726 \\ +174 \\ \hline 900 \end{array}$$

● Work Practice 4

PRACTICE 3

Subtract. Check by adding.

a.
$$\begin{array}{r} 697 \\ -\ 49 \\ \hline \end{array}$$

b.
$$\begin{array}{r} 326 \\ -245 \\ \hline \end{array}$$

c.
$$\begin{array}{r} 1234 \\ -\ 822 \\ \hline \end{array}$$

PRACTICE 4

Subtract. Check by adding.

a.
$$\begin{array}{r} 400 \\ -164 \\ \hline \end{array}$$

b.
$$\begin{array}{r} 1000 \\ -\ 762 \\ \hline \end{array}$$

Answers

3. a. 648   **b.** 81   **c.** 412
4. a. 236   **b.** 238

Objective ⓑ Solving Problems by Subtracting

Often, real-life problems occur that can be solved by subtracting. The first step in solving any word problem is to *understand* the problem by reading it carefully.

Descriptions of problems solved through subtraction *may* include any of these key words or phrases:

Subtraction		
Key Words or Phrases	**Examples**	**Symbols**
subtract	subtract 5 from 8	8 − 5
difference	the difference of 10 and 2	10 − 2
less	17 less 3	17 − 3
less than	2 less than 20	20 − 2
take away	14 take away 9	14 − 9
decreased by	7 decreased by 5	7 − 5
subtracted from	9 subtracted from 12	12 − 9

✓**Concept Check** In each of the following problems, identify which number is the minuend and which number is the subtrahend.

a. What is the result when 6 is subtracted from 40?

b. What is the difference of 15 and 8?

c. Find a number that is 15 fewer than 23.

To solve a word problem that involves subtraction, we first use the facts given to write a subtraction statement. Then we write the corresponding solution of the real-life problem. It is sometimes helpful to write the statement in words (brief phrases) and then translate to numbers.

Example 5 Finding the Radius of a Planet

The radius of Jupiter is 43,441 miles. The radius of Saturn is 7257 miles less than the radius of Jupiter. Find the radius of Saturn. (*Source:* National Space Science Data Center)

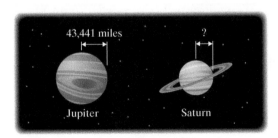

43,441 miles   ?

Jupiter   Saturn

Solution:

In Words		Translate to Numbers
radius of Jupiter	⟶	43,441
− 7257	⟶	− 7257
radius of Saturn	⟶	36,184

The radius of Saturn is 36,184 miles.

● Work Practice 5

PRACTICE 5

The radius of Uranus is 15,759 miles. The radius of Neptune is 458 miles less than the radius of Uranus. What is the radius of Neptune? (*Source:* National Space Science Data Center)

Helpful Hint Since subtraction and addition are reverse operations, don't forget that a subtraction problem can be checked by adding.

Answer

5. 15,301 miles

✓ **Concept Check Answers**

a. minuend: 40; subtrahend: 6

b. minuend: 15; subtrahend: 8

c. minuend: 23; subtrahend: 15

PRACTICE 6

During a sale, the price of a new suit is decreased by $47. If the original price was $92, find the sale price of the suit.

Example 6 Calculating Miles per Gallon

A subcompact car gets 42 miles per gallon of gas. A full-size car gets 17 miles per gallon of gas. Find the difference between the subcompact car miles per gallon and the full-size car miles per gallon.

Solution: **In Words** **Translate to Numbers**

$$\begin{array}{r} \overset{3\ \ 12}{\cancel{4}\ \cancel{2}} \\ -1\ 7 \\ \hline 2\ 5 \end{array}$$

subcompact miles per gallon ⟶

− full-size miles per gallon ⟶

difference in miles per gallon

The difference in the subcompact car miles per gallon and the full-size car miles per gallon is 25 miles per gallon.

● **Work Practice 6**

Helpful Hint

Once again, because subtraction and addition are reverse operations, don't forget that a subtraction problem can be checked by adding.

 Calculator Explorations Subtracting Numbers

To subtract numbers on a calculator, find the keys marked [−] and [=] or [ENTER].

For example, to find 83 − 49 on a calculator, press the keys [83] [−] [49] [=] or [ENTER].

The display will read [34] . Thus, 83 − 49 = 34.

Use a calculator to subtract.

1. 865 − 95   **2.** 76 − 27

3. 147 − 38   **4.** 366 − 87

5. 9625 − 647   **6.** 10,711 − 8925

Answer

6. $45

Vocabulary and Readiness Check

Use the choices below to fill in each blank.

0	minuend	difference
number	subtrahend	

1. The difference of any number and that same number is _____ .

2. The difference of any number and 0 is the same _____ .

3. In 37 − 19 = 18, the number 37 is the _____, and the number 19 is the _____ .

4. In 37 − 19 = 18, the number 18 is called the _____ .

Find each difference.

5. 6 − 6   **6.** 93 − 93   **7.** 600 − 0   **8.** 5 − 0

1.4 Exercise Set

FOR EXTRA HELP

MyMathLab
Powered by CourseCompass™ and MathXL®

PRACTICE   WATCH   DOWNLOAD   READ   REVIEW

Objective Ⓐ *Subtract. Check by adding. See Examples 1 and 2.*

1.
$$\begin{array}{r} 67 \\ -23 \\ \hline \end{array}$$

2.
$$\begin{array}{r} 72 \\ -41 \\ \hline \end{array}$$

3.
$$\begin{array}{r} 389 \\ -124 \\ \hline \end{array}$$

4.
$$\begin{array}{r} 572 \\ -321 \\ \hline \end{array}$$

5.
$$\begin{array}{r} 167 \\ -32 \\ \hline \end{array}$$

6.
$$\begin{array}{r} 286 \\ -45 \\ \hline \end{array}$$

7. 2677 − 423

8. 5766 − 324

9. 6998 − 1453

10. 4912 − 2610

11.
$$\begin{array}{r} 749 \\ -149 \\ \hline \end{array}$$

12.
$$\begin{array}{r} 257 \\ -257 \\ \hline \end{array}$$

Subtract. Check by adding. See Examples 1 through 4.

13.
$$\begin{array}{r} 62 \\ -37 \\ \hline \end{array}$$

14.
$$\begin{array}{r} 55 \\ -29 \\ \hline \end{array}$$

15.
$$\begin{array}{r} 70 \\ -25 \\ \hline \end{array}$$

16.
$$\begin{array}{r} 80 \\ -37 \\ \hline \end{array}$$

17.
$$\begin{array}{r} 938 \\ -792 \\ \hline \end{array}$$

18.
$$\begin{array}{r} 436 \\ -275 \\ \hline \end{array}$$

19.
$$\begin{array}{r} 922 \\ -634 \\ \hline \end{array}$$

20.
$$\begin{array}{r} 674 \\ -299 \\ \hline \end{array}$$

21.
$$\begin{array}{r} 600 \\ -432 \\ \hline \end{array}$$

22.
$$\begin{array}{r} 300 \\ -149 \\ \hline \end{array}$$

23.
$$\begin{array}{r} 142 \\ -36 \\ \hline \end{array}$$

24.
$$\begin{array}{r} 773 \\ -29 \\ \hline \end{array}$$

25.
$$\begin{array}{r} 923 \\ -476 \\ \hline \end{array}$$

26.
$$\begin{array}{r} 813 \\ -227 \\ \hline \end{array}$$

27.
$$\begin{array}{r} 6283 \\ -560 \\ \hline \end{array}$$

28.
$$\begin{array}{r} 5349 \\ -720 \\ \hline \end{array}$$

29.
$$\begin{array}{r} 533 \\ -29 \\ \hline \end{array}$$

30.
$$\begin{array}{r} 724 \\ -16 \\ \hline \end{array}$$

31.
$$\begin{array}{r} 200 \\ -111 \\ \hline \end{array}$$

32.
$$\begin{array}{r} 300 \\ -211 \\ \hline \end{array}$$

33.
$$\begin{array}{r} 1983 \\ -1904 \\ \hline \end{array}$$

34.
$$\begin{array}{r} 1983 \\ -1914 \\ \hline \end{array}$$

35.
$$\begin{array}{r} 56,422 \\ -16,508 \\ \hline \end{array}$$

36.
$$\begin{array}{r} 76,652 \\ -29,498 \\ \hline \end{array}$$

37. 50,000 − 17,289   **38.** 40,000 − 23,582   **39.** 7020 − 1979

40. 6050 − 1878    **41.** 51,111 − 19,898   **42.** 62,222 − 39,898

Objective **B** *Solve. See Examples 5 and 6.*

43. Subtract 5 from 9.   **44.** Subtract 9 from 21.

45. Find the difference of 41 and 21.   **46.** Find the difference of 16 and 5.

47. Subtract 56 from 63.   **48.** Subtract 41 from 59.

49. Find 108 less 36.   **50.** Find 25 less 12.

51. Find 12 subtracted from 100.   **52.** Find 86 subtracted from 90.

53. Professor Graham is reading a 503-page book. If she has just finished reading page 239, how many more pages must she read to finish the book?

54. When a couple began a trip, the odometer read 55,492. When the trip was over, the odometer read 59,320. How many miles did they drive on their trip?

55. In 2002, the hole in the Earth's ozone layer over Antarctica was about 22 million square kilometers in size. In 2008, the hole had grown to 25 million square kilometers. By how much did the hole grow from 2002 to 2008? (*Source:* U.S. Environmental Protection Agency EPA)

56. Bamboo can grow to 98 feet while Pacific giant kelp (a type of seaweed) can grow to 197 feet. How much taller is the kelp than the bamboo?

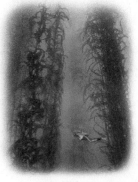

Bamboo   Kelp

A river basin is the geographic area drained by a river and its tributaries. The Mississippi River Basin is the third largest in the world and is divided into six sub-basins, whose areas are shown in the following bar graph. Use this graph for Exercises 57 through 60.

57. Find the total U.S. land area drained by the Upper Mississippi and Lower Mississippi sub-basins.

58. Find the total U.S. land area drained by the Ohio and Tennessee sub-basins.

59. How much more land is drained by the Missouri sub-basin than the Arkansas Red-White sub-basin?

60. How much more land is drained by the Upper Mississippi sub-basin than the Lower Mississippi sub-basin?

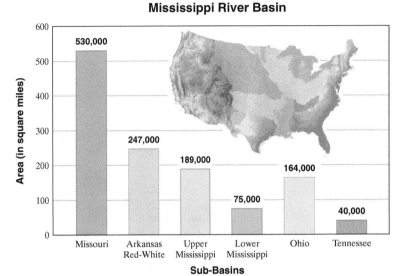

Mississippi River Basin

61. The peak of Mt. McKinley in Alaska is 20,320 feet above sea level. The peak of Long's Peak in Colorado is 14,255 feet above sea level. How much higher is the peak of Mt. McKinley than Long's Peak? (*Source:* U.S. Geological Survey)

62. On January 12, 1916, the city of Indianapolis, Indiana, had the greatest temperature change in a day. It dropped 58 degrees. If the high temperature was 68° Fahrenheit, what was the low temperature?

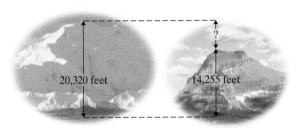

20,320 feet   14,255 feet

Mt. McKinley, Alaska   Long's Peak, Colorado

63. The Oroville Dam, on the Feather River, is the tallest dam in the United States at 754 feet. The Hoover Dam, on the Colorado River, is 726 feet high. How much taller is the Oroville Dam than the Hoover Dam? (*Source:* U.S. Bureau of Reclamation)

64. A new iPhone with 32 GB costs $299. Jocelyn Robinson has $713 in her savings account. How much will she have left in her savings account after she buys the iPhone? (*Source:* Apple, Inc.)

65. The distance from Kansas City to Denver is 645 miles. Hays, Kansas, lies on the road between the two and is 287 miles from Kansas City. What is the distance between Hays and Denver?

66. Pat Salanki's blood cholesterol level is 243. The doctor tells him it should be decreased to 185. How much of a decrease is this?

67. A new DVD player with remote control costs $295. A college student has $914 in her savings account. How much will she have left in her savings account after she buys the DVD player?

68. A stereo that regularly sells for $547 is discounted by $99 in a sale. What is the sale price?

69. The population of Oklahoma is projected to grow from 3648 thousand in 2009 to 4100 thousand in 2025. What is Oklahoma's projected population increase over this time?

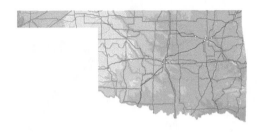

70. In 1996, the centennial of the Boston Marathon, the official number of participants was 38,708. In 2009, there were 12,322 fewer participants. How many official participants were there for the 2009 Boston Marathon?

The decibel (dB) is a unit of measurement for sound. Every increase of 10 dB is a tenfold increase in sound intensity. The bar graph below shows the decibel levels for some common sounds. Use this graph for Exercises 71 through 74.

71. What is the dB rating for live rock music?

72. Which is the quietest of all the sounds shown in the graph?

73. How much louder is the sound of snoring than normal conversation?

74. What is the difference in sound intensity between live rock music and loud television?

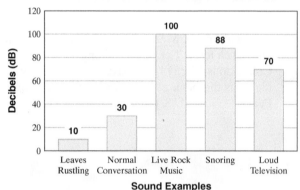

Decibel Levels for Common Sounds

75. The 111th Congress has 539 senators and representatives. Of these, 219 were registered Boy Scouts at some time in their lives. How many members of the 111th Congress were never Boy Scouts? (*Source:* Boy Scouts of America, U.S. Senate)

76. In the United States, there were 23,729 tornadoes from 1990 through 2008. In all, 13,205 of these tornadoes occurred from 1990 through 2000. How many tornadoes occurred during the period after 2000? (*Source:* Storm Prediction Center, National Weather Service)

77. Until recently, the world's largest permanent maze was located in Ruurlo, Netherlands. This maze of beech hedges covers 94,080 square feet. A new hedge maze using hibiscus bushes at the Dole Plantation in Wahiawa, Hawaii, covers 100,000 square feet. How much larger is the Dole Plantation maze than the Ruurlo maze? (*Source: The Guinness Book of Records*)

78. There were only 25 California condors in the entire world in 1987. To date, the number has increased to an estimated 127 living in the wild. How much of an increase is this? (*Source:* California Department of Fish and Game)

The bar graph shows the top five U.S. airports according to number of passengers arriving and departing in 2007. Use this graph to answer Exercises 79 through 82.

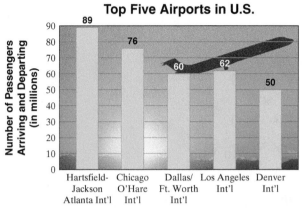

Top Five Airports in U.S.

Source: Airports Council International

79. Which airport is the busiest?

80. Which airports have fewer than 70 million passengers per year?

81. How many more passengers per year does the Chicago O'Hare International Airport have than the Denver International Airport?

82. How many more passengers per year does the Hartsfield-Jackson Atlanta International Airport have than the Dallas/Ft. Worth International Airport?

Solve.

83. Two seniors, Jo Keen and Trudy Waterbury, were candidates for student government president. Who won the election if the votes were cast as follows? By how many votes did the winner win?

	Candidate	
Class	**Jo**	**Trudy**
Freshman	276	295
Sophomore	362	122
Junior	201	312
Senior	179	18

84. Two students submitted advertising budgets for a student government fund-raiser.

	Student A	**Student B**
Radio ads	$600	$300
Newspaper ads	$200	$400
Posters	$150	$240
Handbills	$120	$170

If $1200 is available for advertising, how much excess would each budget have?

Mixed Practice (Sections 1.3 and 1.4)   *Add or subtract as indicated.*

85. 986
      + 48

86. 986
      − 48

87. 76 − 67

88. 80 + 93 + 17 + 9 + 2

89. 9000
      − 482

90. 10,000
      − 1786

91. 10,962
       4851
     + 7063

92. 12,468
       3211
     + 1988

Concept Extensions

For each exercise, identify which number is the minuend and which number is the subtrahend. See the Concept Check in this section.

93. 48
      − 1

94. 2863
      − 1904

95. Subtract 7 from 70.

96. Find 86 decreased by 25.

Identify each answer as correct or incorrect. Use addition to check. If the answer is incorrect, then write the correct answer.

97. 741
       − 56
       ‾‾‾‾
        675

98. 478
       − 89
       ‾‾‾‾
        389

99. 1029
       − 888
       ‾‾‾‾‾
        141

100. 7615
        − 547
        ‾‾‾‾‾
         7168

Fill in the missing digits in each problem.

101.   526_
         − 2_85
         ‾‾‾‾‾‾
          28_4

102.   10,_4_
         − 8_5_4
         ‾‾‾‾‾‾‾
          _710

103. Is there a commutative property of subtraction? In other words, does order matter when subtracting? Why or why not?

104. Explain why the phrase "Subtract 7 from 10" translates to "10 − 7."

105. The local college library is having a Million Pages of Reading promotion. The freshmen have read a total of 289,462 pages; the sophomores have read a total of 369,477 pages; the juniors have read a total of 218,287 pages; and the seniors have read a total of 121,685 pages. Have they reached a goal of one million pages? If not, how many more pages need to be read?

1.5 ROUNDING AND ESTIMATING

Minnesota Population: 5,197,621 or about 5 million

Objective **A** Rounding Whole Numbers

Rounding a whole number means approximating it. A rounded whole number is often easier to use, understand, and remember than the precise whole number. For example, instead of trying to remember the Minnesota state population as 5,197,621, it is much easier to remember it rounded to the nearest million: 5,000,000, or 5 million people. (*Source: World Almanac*)

Recall from Section 1.2 that the line below is called a number line. To **graph** a whole number on this number line, we darken the point representing the location of the whole number. For example, the number 4 is graphed below.

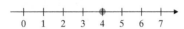

On the number line, the whole number 36 is closer to 40 than 30, so 36 rounded to the nearest ten is 40.

The whole number 52 is closer to 50 than 60, so 52 rounded to the nearest ten is 50.

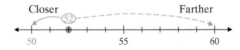

In trying to round 25 to the nearest ten, we see that 25 is halfway between 20 and 30. It is not closer to either number. In such a case, we round to the larger ten, that is, to 30.

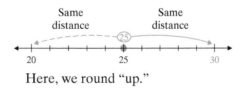

Here, we round "up."

To round a whole number without using a number line, follow these steps:

Rounding Whole Numbers to a Given Place Value

Step 1: Locate the digit to the right of the given place value.

Step 2: If this digit is 5 or greater, add 1 to the digit in the given place value and replace each digit to its right by 0.

Step 3: If this digit is less than 5, replace it and each digit to its right by 0.

PRACTICE 1

Round to the nearest ten.
a. 57
b. 641
c. 325

Example 1 Round 568 to the nearest ten.

Solution: 5 6⑧   The digit to the right of the tens place is the ones place, which is circled.

↑
tens place

5 6⑧   Since the circled digit is 5 or greater, add 1 to the 6 in the tens place and replace the digit to the right by 0.

Add 1.   Replace with 0.

We find that 568 rounded to the nearest ten is 570.

● Work Practice 1

PRACTICE 2

Round to the nearest thousand.
a. 72,304
b. 9222
c. 671,800

Example 2 Round 278,362 to the nearest thousand.

Solution:

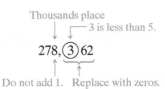

Thousands place
3 is less than 5.

278,③62

Do not add 1.   Replace with zeros.

The number 278,362 rounded to the nearest thousand is 278,000.

● Work Practice 2

PRACTICE 3

Round to the nearest hundred.
a. 3474
b. 76,243
c. 978,965

Example 3 Round 248,982 to the nearest hundred.

Solution:

Hundreds place
8 is greater than or equal to 5.

248,9⑧2

Add 1.   9 + 1 = 10, so replace the digit 9 by 0 and carry 1 to the place value to the left.

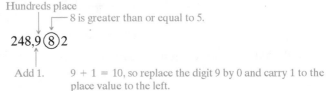

2 4 8̸, 9̸ 8 2

Add 1.   Replace with zeros.

The number 248,982 rounded to the nearest hundred is 249,000.

● Work Practice 3

✔ **Concept Check**   Round each of the following numbers to the nearest *hundred*. Explain your reasoning.
a. 59   b. 29

Answers
1. a. 60   b. 640   c. 330
2. a. 72,000   b. 9000   c. 672,000
3. a. 3500   b. 76,200   c. 979,000

✔ **Concept Check Answers**
a. 100   b. 0

Objective ⓑ Estimating Sums and Differences

By rounding addends, minuends, and subtrahends, we can estimate sums and differences. An estimated sum or difference is appropriate when the exact number is not necessary. Also, an estimated sum or difference can help us determine if we made a mistake in calculating an exact amount. To estimate the sum below, round each number to the nearest hundred and then add.

768	rounds to	800
1952	rounds to	2000
225	rounds to	200
+ 149	rounds to	+ 100
		3100

The estimated sum is 3100, which is close to the **exact** sum of 3094.

Example 4 Round each number to the nearest hundred to find an estimated sum.

$$294$$
$$625$$
$$1071$$
$$+\ 349$$

Solution:

Exact:		**Estimate:**
294	rounds to	300
625	rounds to	600
1071	rounds to	1100
+ 349	rounds to	+ 300
		2300

The estimated sum is 2300. (The exact sum is 2339.)

● **Work Practice 4**

PRACTICE 4

Round each number to the nearest ten to find an estimated sum.

$$49$$
$$25$$
$$32$$
$$51$$
$$+\ 98$$

Example 5 Round each number to the nearest hundred to find an estimated difference.

$$4725$$
$$-2879$$

Solution:

Exact:		**Estimate:**
4725	rounds to	4700
−2879	rounds to	−2900
		1800

The estimated difference is 1800. (The exact difference is 1846.)

● **Work Practice 5**

PRACTICE 5

Round each number to the nearest thousand to find an estimated difference.

$$3785$$
$$-2479$$

Objective ◉ Solving Problems by Estimating

Making estimates is often the quickest way to solve real-life problems when solutions do not need to be exact.

Answers
4. 260   **5.** 2000

PRACTICE 6

Tasha Kilbey is trying to estimate how far it is from Gove, Kansas, to Hays, Kansas. Round each given distance on the map to the nearest ten to estimate the total distance.

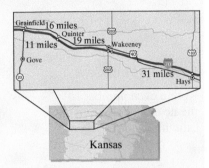

Example 6 Estimating Distances

A driver is trying to quickly estimate the distance from Temple, Texas, to Brenham, Texas. Round each distance given on the map to the nearest ten to estimate the total distance.

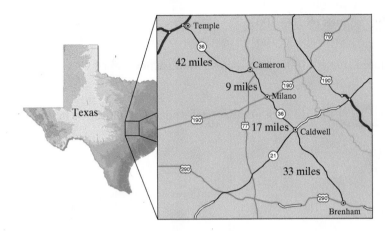

Solution:

Exact Distance:		Estimate:
42	rounds to	40
9	rounds to	10
17	rounds to	20
+33	rounds to	+30
		100

It is approximately 100 miles from Temple to Brenham. (The exact distance is 101 miles.)

● Work Practice 6

PRACTICE 7

In a recent year, there were 48,445 reported cases of chicken pox, 6584 reported cases of mumps, and 15,632 reported cases of pertussis (whooping cough). Round each number to the nearest thousand to estimate the total number of cases reported for these preventable diseases. (*Source:* Centers for Disease Control and Prevention)

Example 7 Estimating Data

In three recent months, the numbers of tons of mail that went through Hartsfield-Jackson Atlanta International Airport were 635, 687, and 567. Round each number to the nearest hundred to estimate the tons of mail that passed through this airport.

Solution:

Exact Tons of Mail:		Estimate:
635	rounds to	600
687	rounds to	700
+567	rounds to	+600
		1900

The approximate tonnage of mail that moved through Atlanta's airport over this period was 1900 tons. (The exact tonnage was 1889 tons.)

● Work Practice 7

Answers

6. 80 mi   **7.** 71,000 total cases

Vocabulary and Readiness Check

Use the choices below to fill in each blank.

    60   rounding   exact
    70   estimate   graph

1. To _____ a number on a number line, darken the point representing the location of the number.

2. Another word for approximating a whole number is _____.

3. The number 65 rounded to the nearest ten is _____, but the number 61 rounded to the nearest ten is _____.

4. A(n) _____ number of products is 1265, but a(n) _____ is 1000.

1.5 Exercise Set

Objective (A) *Round each whole number to the given place. See Examples 1 through 3.*

1. 423 to the nearest ten

2. 273 to the nearest ten

3. 635 to the nearest ten

4. 846 to the nearest ten

5. 2791 to the nearest hundred

6. 8494 to the nearest hundred

7. 495 to the nearest ten

8. 898 to the nearest ten

9. 21,094 to the nearest thousand

10. 82,198 to the nearest thousand

11. 33,762 to the nearest thousand

12. 42,682 to the nearest ten-thousand

13. 328,495 to the nearest hundred

14. 179,406 to the nearest hundred

15. 36,499 to the nearest thousand

16. 96,501 to the nearest thousand

17. 39,994 to the nearest ten

18. 99,995 to the nearest ten

19. 29,834,235 to the nearest ten-million

20. 39,523,698 to the nearest million

Complete the table by estimating the given number to the given place value.

		Tens	Hundreds	Thousands
21.	5281			
22.	7619			
23.	9444			
24.	7777			
25.	14,876			
26.	85,049			

43

Round each number to the indicated place.

27. The University of California, Los Angeles, had 83,659 Alumni Association members in 2009. Round this number to the nearest thousand. (*Source:* UCLA)

28. In 2008, there were 11,565 Burger King restaurants. Round this number to the nearest hundred. (*Source:* Burger King Holdings, Inc.)

29. Kareem Abdul-Jabbar holds the NBA record for points scored, a total of 38,387 over his NBA career. Round this number to the nearest thousand. (*Source:* National Basketball Association)

30. It takes 60,149 days for Neptune to make a complete orbit around the Sun. Round this number to the nearest hundred. (*Source:* National Space Science Data Center)

31. In 2008, the most valuable brand in the world was Wal-Mart, having just overtaken the longtime leader, Coca-Cola. The estimated brand value of Wal-Mart was $42,570,000,000. Round this to the nearest billion. (*Source: Wall Street Journal*)

32. According to the 2009 Population Clock, the population of the United States was 305,747,409 in February 2009. Round this population figure to the nearest million. (*Source:* U.S. Census population clock)

33. The average salary for a Boston Red Sox baseball player during the 2009 season was $4,089,867. Round this average salary to the nearest hundred-thousand. (*Source:* ESPN)

34. In FY 2008, the Procter & Gamble Company had $83,503,000,000 in sales. Round this sales figure to the nearest billion. (*Source:* Procter & Gamble)

35. The United States currently has 262,700,000 cellular mobile phone users, while India has 296,886,000 users. Round each of the user numbers to the nearest million. (*Source:* Cellular Telecommunications Industry Association)

36. U.S. farms produced 2,933,888,000 bushels of soybeans in 2008. Round the soybean production figure to the nearest ten-million. (*Source:* U.S. Department of Agriculture)

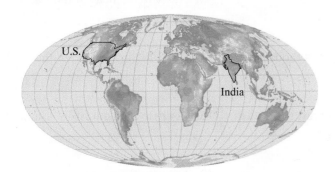

Objective B *Estimate the sum or difference by rounding each number to the nearest ten. See Examples 4 and 5.*

37.	**38.**	**39.**	**40.**
39	52	449	555
45	33	− 373	− 235
22	15		
+ 17	+ 29		

Estimate the sum or difference by rounding each number to the nearest hundred. See Examples 4 and 5.

41.	**42.**	**43.**	**44.**	**45.**	**46.**
1913	4050	1774	1989	3995	799
1886	3133	− 1492	− 1870	2549	1655
+ 1925	+ 1220			+ 4944	+ 271

Three of the given calculator answers below are incorrect. Find them by estimating each sum.

47. 463 + 219   602

48. 522 + 785   1307

49. 229 + 443 + 606   1278

50. 542 + 789 + 198   2139

51. 7806 + 5150   12,956

52. 5233 + 4988   9011

> **Helpful Hint** Estimation is useful to check for incorrect answers when using a calculator. For example, pressing a key too hard may result in a double digit, while pressing a key too softly may result in the digit not appearing in the display.

Objective **C** *Solve each problem by estimating. See Examples 6 and 7.*

53. An appliance store advertises three refrigerators on sale at $899, $1499, and $999. Round each cost to the nearest hundred to estimate the total cost.

54. Suppose you scored 89, 97, 100, 79, 75, and 82 on your biology tests. Round each score to the nearest ten to estimate your total score.

55. The distance from Kansas City to Boston is 1429 miles and from Kansas City to Chicago is 530 miles. Round each distance to the nearest hundred to estimate how much farther Boston is from Kansas City than Chicago is.

56. The Gonzales family took a trip and traveled 588, 689, 277, 143, 59, and 802 miles on six consecutive days. Round each distance to the nearest hundred to estimate the distance they traveled.

57. The peak of Mt. McKinley, in Alaska, is 20,320 feet above sea level. The top of Mt. Rainier, in Washington, is 14,410 feet above sea level. Round each height to the nearest thousand to estimate the difference in elevation of these two peaks. (*Source:* U.S. Geological Survey)

58. A student is pricing new car stereo systems. One system sells for $1895 and another system sells for $1524. Round each price to the nearest hundred dollars to estimate the difference in price of these systems.

59. In 2008, the population of Joliet, Illinois, was 142,702, and the population of Evanston, Illinois, was 75,543. Round each population to the nearest ten-thousand to estimate how much larger Joliet was than Evanston. (*Source:* U.S. Census Bureau)

60. Round each distance given on the map to the nearest ten to estimate the total distance from North Platte, Nebraska, to Lincoln, Nebraska.

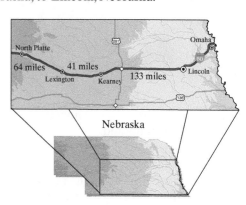

61. Head Start is a national program that provides developmental and social services for America's low-income preschool children ages three to five. Enrollment figures in Head Start programs showed an increase from 905,851 in 2004 to 908,412 in 2007. Round each number of children to the nearest thousand to estimate this increase. (*Source:* U.S. Department of Health and Human Services)

62. Enrollment figures at a local community college showed an increase from 49,713 credit hours in 2005 to 51,746 credit hours in 2006. Round each number to the nearest thousand to estimate the increase.

Mixed Practice (Sections 1.2 and 1.5)   *The following table shows the top five leading U.S. television advertisers in 2007 and the amount of money spent that year on advertising. Complete this table. The first line is completed for you.* (*Source:* Television Bureau of Advertising)

	Advertiser	Amount Spent on Television Advertising in 2007 (in millions of dollars)	Amount Written in Standard Form	Standard Form Rounded to Nearest Ten-Million	Standard Form Rounded to Nearest Hundred-Million
	General Motors, Dealers	443	$443,000,000	$440,000,000	$400,000,000
63.	Chrysler-Cerberus	391			
64.	Ford, Dealers	364			
65.	AT & T Inc.	349			
66.	Toyota, Dealers	311			

Concept Extensions

67. Find one number that when rounded to the nearest hundred is 5700.

68. Find one number that when rounded to the nearest ten is 5700.

69. A number rounded to the nearest hundred is 8600.
   a. Determine the smallest possible number.
   b. Determine the largest possible number.

70. On August 23, 1989, it was estimated that 1,500,000 people joined hands in a human chain stretching 370 miles to protest the fiftieth anniversary of the pact that allowed what was then the Soviet Union to annex the Baltic nations in 1939. If the estimate of the number of people is to the nearest hundred-thousand, determine the largest possible number of people in the chain.

71. In your own words, explain how to round a number to the nearest thousand.

72. In your own words, explain how to round 9660 to the nearest thousand.

73. Estimate the perimeter of the rectangle by first rounding the length of each side to the nearest ten.

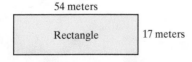

54 meters
Rectangle   17 meters

74. Estimate the perimeter of the triangle by first rounding the length of each side to the nearest hundred.

5950 miles   7693 miles
8203 miles

1.6 MULTIPLYING WHOLE NUMBERS AND AREA

Objectives

A Use the Properties of Multiplication.

B Multiply Whole Numbers.

C Multiply by Whole Numbers Ending in Zero(s).

D Find the Area of a Rectangle.

E Solve Problems by Multiplying Whole Numbers.

Multiplication Shown as Repeated Addition Suppose that we wish to count the number of laptops provided in a computer class. The laptops are arranged in 5 rows, and each row has 6 laptops.

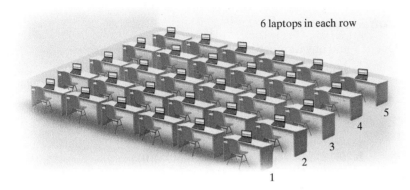

6 laptops in each row

Adding 5 sixes gives the total number of laptops. We can write this as $6 + 6 + 6 + 6 + 6 = 30$ laptops. When each addend is the same, we refer to this as **repeated addition.**

Multiplication is repeated addition but with different notation.

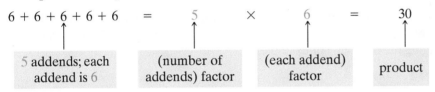

The $\times$ is called a **multiplication sign.** The numbers 5 and 6 are called **factors.** The number 30 is called the **product.** The notation 5×6 is read as "five times six." The symbols $\cdot$ and ( ) can also be used to indicate multiplication.

$$5 \times 6 = 30, \quad 5 \cdot 6 = 30, \quad (5)(6) = 30, \quad \text{and} \quad 5(6) = 30$$

✓Concept Check

a. Rewrite $5 + 5 + 5 + 5 + 5 + 5 + 5$ using multiplication.

b. Rewrite 3×16 as repeated addition. Is there more than one way to do this? If so, show all ways.

Objective **A** Using the Properties of Multiplication

As with addition, we memorize products of one-digit whole numbers and then use certain properties of multiplication to multiply larger numbers.

Notice that when any number is multiplied by 0, the result is always 0. This is called the **multiplication property of 0.**

Multiplication Property of 0

The product of 0 and any number is 0. For example,

$$5 \cdot 0 = 0 \quad \text{and} \quad 0 \cdot 8 = 0$$

When any number is multiplied by 1, the result is always the original number. We call this result the **multiplication property of 1.**

Multiplication Property of 1

The product of 1 and any number is that same number. For example,

$$1 \cdot 9 = 9 \quad \text{and} \quad 6 \cdot 1 = 6$$

PRACTICE 1

Multiply.
a. 3×0
b. $4(1)$
c. $(0)(34)$
d. $1 \cdot 76$

Example 1 Multiply.

a. 6×1 b. $0(18)$ c. $1 \cdot 45$ d. $(75)(0)$

Solution:

a. $6 \times 1 = 6$ b. $0(18) = 0$
c. $1 \cdot 45 = 45$ d. $(75)(0) = 0$

● **Work Practice 1**

Like addition, multiplication is commutative and associative. Notice that when multiplying two numbers, the order of these numbers can be changed without changing the product. For example,

$$3 \cdot 5 = 15 \quad \text{and} \quad 5 \cdot 3 = 15$$

This property is the **commutative property of multiplication.**

Commutative Property of Multiplication

Changing the **order** of two factors does not change their product. For example,

$$9 \cdot 2 = 18 \quad \text{and} \quad 2 \cdot 9 = 18$$

Another property that can help us when multiplying is the **associative property of multiplication.** This property states that when multiplying numbers, the grouping of the numbers can be changed without changing the product. For example,

$$(2 \cdot 3) \cdot 4 = 6 \cdot 4 = 24$$

Also,

$$2 \cdot (3 \cdot 4) = 2 \cdot 12 = 24$$

Both groupings give a product of 24.

Answers

1. a. 0   b. 4   c. 0   d. 76

Associative Property of Multiplication

Changing the **grouping** of factors does not change their product. From the previous page, we know that for example,

$$(2 \cdot 3) \cdot 4 = 2 \cdot (3 \cdot 4)$$

With these properties, along with the **distributive property**, we can find the product of any whole numbers. The distributive property says that multiplication **distributes** over addition. For example, notice that $3(2 + 5)$ simplifies to the same number as $3 \cdot 2 + 3 \cdot 5$.

$$3(2 + 5) = 3(7) = 21$$

$$3 \cdot 2 + 3 \cdot 5 = 6 + 15 = 21$$

Since $3(2 + 5)$ and $3 \cdot 2 + 3 \cdot 5$ both simplify to 21, then

$$3(2 + 5) = 3 \cdot 2 + 3 \cdot 5$$

Notice in $3(2 + 5) = 3 \cdot 2 + 3 \cdot 5$ that each number inside the parentheses is multiplied by 3.

Distributive Property

Multiplication distributes over addition. For example,

$$2(3 + 4) = 2 \cdot 3 + 2 \cdot 4$$

Example 2 Rewrite each using the distributive property.

a. $3(4 + 5)$ **b.** $10(6 + 8)$ **c.** $2(7 + 3)$

Solution: Using the distributive property, we have

a. $3(4 + 5) = 3 \cdot 4 + 3 \cdot 5$
b. $10(6 + 8) = 10 \cdot 6 + 10 \cdot 8$
c. $2(7 + 3) = 2 \cdot 7 + 2 \cdot 3$

Work Practice 2

Objective Ⓑ Multiplying Whole Numbers

Let's use the distributive property to multiply $7(48)$. To do so, we begin by writing the expanded form of 48 (see Section 1.2) and then applying the distributive property.

$$
\begin{aligned}
7(48) &= 7(40 + 8) && \text{Write 48 in expanded form.} \\
&= 7 \cdot 40 + 7 \cdot 8 && \text{Apply the distributive property.} \\
&= 280 + 56 && \text{Multiply.} \\
&= 336 && \text{Add.}
\end{aligned}
$$

PRACTICE 2

Rewrite each using the distributive property.
a. $5(2 + 3)$
b. $9(8 + 7)$
c. $3(6 + 1)$

Answers

2. a. $5(2 + 3) = 5 \cdot 2 + 5 \cdot 3$
   b. $9(8 + 7) = 9 \cdot 8 + 9 \cdot 7$
   c. $3(6 + 1) = 3 \cdot 6 + 3 \cdot 1$

This is how we multiply whole numbers. When multiplying whole numbers, we will use the following notation.

First:

$$\begin{array}{r} \overset{5}{4}8 \\ \times 7 \\ \hline 336 \end{array}$$ ← $7 \cdot 8 = 56$ Write 6 in the ones place and carry 5 to the tens place.

Next:

$$\begin{array}{r} \overset{5}{4}8 \\ \times 7 \\ \hline 336 \end{array}$$ $7 \cdot 4 + 5 = 28 + 5 = 33$

The product of 48 and 7 is 336.

PRACTICE 3

Multiply.

a. $\begin{array}{r} 36 \\ \times\ 4 \\ \hline \end{array}$ b. $\begin{array}{r} 132 \\ \times\ 9 \\ \hline \end{array}$

> **Example 3**   Multiply:
>
> a. $\begin{array}{r} 25 \\ \times\ 8 \\ \hline \end{array}$ b. $\begin{array}{r} 246 \\ \times\ 5 \\ \hline \end{array}$
>
> **Solution:**
>
> a. $\begin{array}{r} \overset{4}{2}5 \\ \times\ 8 \\ \hline 200 \end{array}$ b. $\begin{array}{r} \overset{23}{2}46 \\ \times\ 5 \\ \hline 1230 \end{array}$

● Work Practice 3

To multiply larger whole numbers, use the following similar notation. Multiply 89×52.

Step 1

$$\begin{array}{r} \overset{1}{8}9 \\ \times\ 52 \\ \hline 178 \end{array}$$ ← Multiply 89×2.

Step 2

$$\begin{array}{r} \overset{4}{8}9 \\ \times\ 52 \\ \hline 178 \\ 4450 \end{array}$$ ← Multiply 89×50.

Step 3

$$\begin{array}{r} 89 \\ \times\ 52 \\ \hline 178 \\ 4450 \\ \hline 4628 \end{array}$$ Add.

The numbers 178 and 4450 are called **partial products.** The sum of the partial products, 4628, is the product of 89 and 52.

PRACTICE 4

Multiply.

a. $\begin{array}{r} 594 \\ \times\ 72 \\ \hline \end{array}$ b. $\begin{array}{r} 306 \\ \times\ 81 \\ \hline \end{array}$

> **Example 4**   Multiply: 236×86
>
> **Solution:** $\begin{array}{r} 236 \\ \times\ 86 \\ \hline 1\,416 \\ 18\,880 \\ \hline 20{,}296 \end{array}$ ← 6(236) \\ ← 80(236) \\ Add.

● Work Practice 4

PRACTICE 5

Multiply.

a. $\begin{array}{r} 726 \\ \times\ 142 \\ \hline \end{array}$ b. $\begin{array}{r} 288 \\ \times\ 4 \\ \hline \end{array}$

> **Example 5**   Multiply: 631×125
>
> **Solution:** $\begin{array}{r} 631 \\ \times\ 125 \\ \hline 3\,155 \\ 12\,620 \\ 63\,100 \\ \hline 78{,}875 \end{array}$ ← 5(631) \\ ← 20(631) \\ ← 100(631) \\ Add.

● Work Practice 5

Answers

3. **a.** 144   **b.** 1188
4. **a.** 42,768   **b.** 24,786
5. **a.** 103,092   **b.** 1152

✓ Concept Check Find and explain the error in the following multiplication problem.

$$
\begin{array}{r}
102 \\
\times\ 33 \\
\hline
306 \\
306 \\
\hline
612
\end{array}
$$

Objective ⓒ Multiplying by Whole Numbers Ending in Zero(s)

Interesting patterns occur when we multiply by a number that ends in zeros. To see these patterns, let's multiply a number, say 34, by 10, then 100, then 1000.

1 zero
↓
$34 \cdot 10 = 340$ 1 zero attached to 34.

2 zeros
$34 \cdot 100 = 3400$ 2 zeros attached to 34.

3 zeros
$34 \cdot 1000 = 34{,}000$ 3 zeros attached to 34.

These patterns help us develop a shortcut for multiplying by whole numbers ending in zeros.

To multiply by 10, 100, 1000, and so on,
  Form the product by attaching the number of zeros in that number to the other factor.
  For example, $41 \cdot 100 = 4100$.
                         2 zeros

Examples Multiply.

6. $176 \cdot 1000 = 176{,}000$ Attach 3 zeros.

7. $2041 \cdot 100 = 204{,}100$ Attach 2 zeros.

● Work Practice 6–7

We can use a similar format to multiply by any whole number ending in zeros. For example, since

$$15 \cdot 500 = 15 \cdot 5 \cdot 100,$$

we find the product by multiplying 15 and 5, then attaching two zeros to the product.

$$
\begin{array}{l}
\overset{2}{15} \qquad 15 \cdot 500 = 7500 \\
\underline{\times\,5} \\
\ \ 75
\end{array}
$$

PRACTICE 6–7

Multiply.
6. $75 \cdot 100$
7. $808 \cdot 1000$

Answers
6. 7500 **7.** 808,000

✓ **Concept Check Answer**
$$
\begin{array}{r}
102 \\
\times\ 33 \\
\hline
306 \\
3060 \\
\hline
3366
\end{array}
$$

Copyright 2011 Pearson Education, Inc.

PRACTICE 8–9

Multiply.

8. $35 \cdot 3000$

9. $600 \cdot 600$

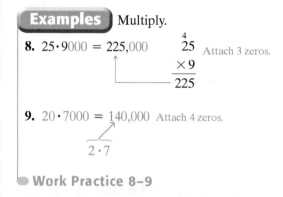

Examples Multiply.

8. $25 \cdot 9000 = 225,000$ Attach 3 zeros.

$$\begin{array}{r} \overset{4}{25} \\ \times\, 9 \\ \hline 225 \end{array}$$

9. $20 \cdot 7000 = 140,000$ Attach 4 zeros.

$2 \cdot 7$

● **Work Practice 8–9**

Objective ⓓ Finding the Area of a Rectangle

A special application of multiplication is finding the **area** of a region. Area measures the amount of surface of a region. For example, we measure a plot of land or the living space of a home by its area. The figures below show two examples of units of area measure. (A centimeter is a unit of length in the metric system.)

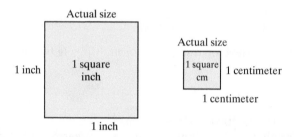

For example, to measure the area of a geometric figure such as the rectangle below, count the number of square units that cover the region.

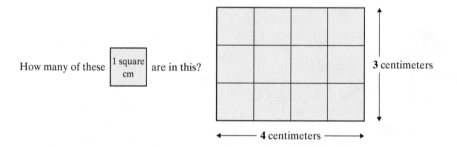

This rectangular region contains 12 square units, each 1 square centimeter. Thus, the area is 12 square centimeters. This total number of squares can be found by counting or by multiplying $4 \cdot 3$ (length · width).

$$\begin{aligned} \text{Area of a rectangle} &= \text{length} \cdot \text{width} \\ &= (4 \text{ centimeters})(3 \text{ centimeters}) \\ &= 12 \text{ square centimeters} \end{aligned}$$

In this section, we find the areas of rectangles only. In later sections, we will find the areas of other geometric regions.

Helpful Hint

Notice that area is measured in **square** units while perimeter is measured in units.

Answers

8. 105,000   **9.** 360,000

Example 10 Finding the Area of a State

The state of Colorado is in the shape of a rectangle whose length is 380 miles and whose width is 280 miles. Find its area.

Solution: The area of a rectangle is the product of its length and its width.

Area = length · width
= (380 miles)(280 miles)
= 106,400 square miles

The area of Colorado is 106,400 square miles.

● Work Practice 10

Objective ⓔ Solving Problems by Multiplying

There are several words or phrases that indicate the operation of multiplication. Some of these are as follows:

Multiplication		
Key Words or Phrases	**Examples**	**Symbols**
multiply	multiply 5 by 7	5 · 7
product	the product of 3 and 2	3 · 2
times	10 times 13	10 · 13

Many key words or phrases describing real-life problems that suggest addition might be better solved by multiplication instead. For example, to find the **total** cost of 8 shirts, each selling for $27, we can either add

27 + 27 + 27 + 27 + 27 + 27 + 27 + 27

or we can multiply 8(27).

Example 11 Finding DVD Space

A digital video disc (DVD) can hold about 4800 megabytes (MB) of information. How many megabytes can 12 DVDs hold?

Solution: Twelve DVDs will hold 12 × 4800 megabytes.

In Words	Translate to Numbers
megabytes per disc →	4800
× DVDs →	× 12
	9600
	48000
total megabytes	57,600

Twelve DVDs will hold 57,600 megabytes.

● Work Practice 11

PRACTICE 10

The state of Wyoming is in the shape of a rectangle whose length is 360 miles and whose width is 280 miles. Find its area.

PRACTICE 11

A particular computer printer can print 16 pages per minute in color. How many pages can it print in 45 minutes?

Answers
10. 100,800 sq mi **11.** 720 pages

PRACTICE 12

Ken Shimura purchased DVDs and CDs through a club. Each DVD was priced at $11 and each CD cost $9. Ken bought eight DVDs and five CDs. Find the total cost of the order.

Example 12 Budgeting Money

Suzanne Scarpulla and a friend plan to take their children to the Georgia Aquarium in Atlanta, the world's largest aquarium. The ticket price for each child is $22 and for each adult, $26. If five children and two adults plan to go, how much money is needed for admission? (*Source:* GeorgiaAquarium.org)

Solution: If the price of one child's ticket is $22, the price for 5 children is $5 \times 22 = \$110$. The price of one adult ticket is $26, so the price for two adults is $2 \times 26 = \$52$. The total cost is:

In Words		Translate to Numbers
price of 5 children	→	110
+ cost of 2 adults	→	+ 52
total cost		162

The total cost is $162.

● **Work Practice 12**

PRACTICE 13

If an average page in a book contains 163 words, estimate, rounding each number to the nearest hundred, the total number of words contained on 391 pages.

Example 13 Estimating Word Count

The average page of a book contains 259 words. Estimate, rounding each number to the nearest hundred, the total number of words contained on 212 pages.

Solution: The exact number of words is 259×212. Estimate this product by rounding each factor to the nearest hundred.

$$
\begin{array}{ll}
259 & \text{rounds to} \quad 300 \\
\times 212 & \text{rounds to} \quad \times 200
\end{array}, \quad
\begin{array}{c}
300 \times 200 = 60{,}000 \\
\hline
3 \cdot 2 = 6
\end{array}
$$

There are approximately 60,000 words contained on 212 pages.

● **Work Practice 13**

🖩 **Calculator Explorations**   **Multiplying Numbers**

To multiply numbers on a calculator, find the keys marked $\boxed{\times}$ and $\boxed{=}$ or $\boxed{\text{ENTER}}$. For example, to find $31 \cdot 66$ on a calculator, press the keys $\boxed{31}$ $\boxed{\times}$ $\boxed{66}$ $\boxed{=}$ or $\boxed{\text{ENTER}}$. The display will read $\boxed{\qquad 2046}$. Thus, $31 \cdot 66 = 2046$.

Use a calculator to multiply.

1. 72×48 **2.** 81×92

3. $163 \cdot 94$ **4.** $285 \cdot 144$

5. $983(277)$ **6.** $1562(843)$

Answers

12. $133   **13.** 80,000 words

Vocabulary and Readiness Check

Use the choices below to fill in each blank.

area	grouping	commutative	1	product	length
factor	order	associative	0	distributive	number

1. The product of 0 and any number is _____ .

2. The product of 1 and any number is the _____ .

3. In $8 \cdot 12 = 96$, the 96 is called the _____ and 8 and 12 are each called a(n) _____ .

4. Since $9 \cdot 10 = 10 \cdot 9$, we say that changing the _____ in multiplication does not change the product. This property is called the _____ property of multiplication.

5. Since $(3 \cdot 4) \cdot 6 = 3 \cdot (4 \cdot 6)$, we say that changing the _____ in multiplication does not change the product. This property is called the _____ property of multiplication.

6. _____ measures the amount of surface of a region.

7. Area of a rectangle = _____ $\cdot$ width.

8. We know $9(10 + 8) = 9 \cdot 10 + 9 \cdot 8$ by the _____ property.

1.6 Exercise Set

FOR EXTRA HELP

MyMathLab

Math XL · PRACTICE · WATCH · DOWNLOAD · READ · REVIEW

Objective A *Multiply. See Example 1.*

1. $1 \cdot 24$

2. $55 \cdot 1$

3. $0 \cdot 19$

4. $27 \cdot 0$

5. $8 \cdot 0 \cdot 9$

6. $7 \cdot 6 \cdot 0$

7. $87 \cdot 1$

8. $1 \cdot 41$

Use the distributive property to rewrite each expression. See Example 2.

9. $6(3 + 8)$

10. $5(8 + 2)$

11. $4(3 + 9)$

12. $6(1 + 4)$

13. $20(14 + 6)$

14. $12(12 + 3)$

Objective B *Multiply. See Example 3.*

15. $\begin{array}{r} 64 \\ \times\ 8 \\ \hline \end{array}$

16. $\begin{array}{r} 79 \\ \times\ 3 \\ \hline \end{array}$

17. $\begin{array}{r} 613 \\ \times\ 6 \\ \hline \end{array}$

18. $\begin{array}{r} 638 \\ \times\ 5 \\ \hline \end{array}$

19. 277×6

20. 882×2

21. 1074×6

22. 9021×3

Objectives A B Mixed Practice *Multiply. See Examples 1 through 5.*

23. $\begin{array}{r} 89 \\ \times 13 \\ \hline \end{array}$

24. $\begin{array}{r} 91 \\ \times 72 \\ \hline \end{array}$

25. $\begin{array}{r} 421 \\ \times 58 \\ \hline \end{array}$

26. $\begin{array}{r} 526 \\ \times 23 \\ \hline \end{array}$

27. $\begin{array}{r} 306 \\ \times 81 \\ \hline \end{array}$

28. $\begin{array}{r} 708 \\ \times 21 \\ \hline \end{array}$

29. (780)(20)   **30.** (720)(80)   **31.** (495)(13)(0)   **32.** (593)(47)(0)   **33.** (640)(1)(10)

34. (240)(1)(20)   **35.** 1234 × 39   **36.** 1357 × 79   **37.** 609 × 234   **38.** 807 × 127

39. 8649   **40.** 1234   **41.**   589   **42.**   426   **43.** 1941   **44.** 1876
     × 274   × 567   ×110   ×110   ×2035   ×1407

Objective **C** *Multiply. See Examples 6 through 9.*

45. 8 × 100   **46.** 6 × 100   **47.** 11 × 1000   **48.** 26 × 1000   **49.** 7406 · 10   **50.** 9054 · 10

51. 6 · 4000   **52.** 3 · 9000   **53.** 50 · 900   **54.** 70 · 300   **55.** 41 · 80,000   **56.** 27 · 50,000

Objective **D** **Mixed Practice (*Section 1.3*)** *Find the area and the perimeter of each rectangle. See Example 10.*

57.

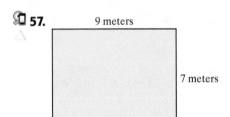

58. 3 inches

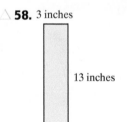

59.

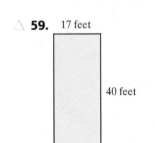

60.

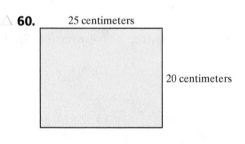

Objective **E** **Mixed Practice (*Section 1.5*)** *Estimate the products by rounding each factor to the nearest hundred. See Example 13.*

61. 576 × 354   **62.** 982 × 650   **63.** 604 × 451   **64.** 111 × 999

Without actually calculating, mentally round, multiply, and choose the best estimate.

65. 38 × 42 =   **66.** 2872 × 12 =   **67.** 612 × 29 =   **68.** 706 × 409 =
 a. 16   **a.** 2872   **a.** 180   **a.** 280
 b. 160   **b.** 28,720   **b.** 1800   **b.** 2800
 c. 1600   **c.** 287,200   **c.** 18,000   **c.** 28,000
 d. 16,000   **d.** 2,872,000   **d.** 180,000   **d.** 280,000

Objectives Ⓓ Ⓔ **Mixed Practice–Translating** *Solve. See Examples 10 through 13.*

69. Multiply 80 by 11.

70. Multiply 70 by 12.

71. Find the product of 6 and 700.

72. Find the product of 9 and 900.

73. Find 2 times 2240.

74. Find 3 times 3310.

75. One tablespoon of olive oil contains 125 calories. How many calories are in 3 tablespoons of olive oil? (*Source: Home and Garden Bulletin No. 72,* U.S. Department of Agriculture)

76. One ounce of hulled sunflower seeds contains 14 grams of fat. How many grams of fat are in 8 ounces of hulled sunflower seeds? (*Source: Home and Garden Bulletin No. 72,* U.S. Department of Agriculture)

77. The textbook for a course in biology costs $94. There are 35 students in the class. Find the total cost of the biology books for the class.

78. The seats in a large lecture hall are arranged in 14 rows with 34 seats in each row. Find how many seats are in this room.

79. Cabot Creamery is packing a pallet of 20-lb boxes of cheddar cheese to send to a local restaurant. There are five layers of boxes on the pallet, and each layer is four boxes wide by five boxes deep.

   a. How many boxes are in one layer?

   b. How many boxes are on the pallet?

   c. What is the weight of the cheese on the pallet?

80. An apartment building has *three floors*. Each floor has five rows of apartments with four apartments in each row.

   a. How many apartments are on 1 floor?

   b. How many apartments are in the building?

81. A plot of land measures 80 feet by 110 feet. Find its area.

82. A house measures 45 feet by 60 feet. Find the floor area of the house.

83. The largest hotel lobby can be found at the Hyatt Regency in San Francisco, CA. It is in the shape of a rectangle that measures 350 feet by 160 feet. Find its area.

84. Recall from an earlier section that the largest commercial building in the world under one roof is the flower auction building of the cooperative VBA in Aalsmeer, Netherlands. The floor plan is a rectangle that measures 776 meters by 639 meters. Find the area of this building. (A meter is a unit of length in the metric system.) (*Source: The Handy Science Answer Book,* Visible Ink Press)

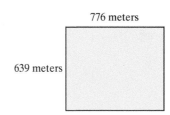

85. A pixel is a rectangular dot on a graphing calculator screen. If a graphing calculator screen contains 62 pixels in a row and 94 pixels in a column, find the total number of pixels on a screen.

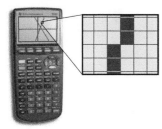

86. A certain compact disc (CD) can hold 700 megabytes (MB) of information. How many MBs can 17 discs hold?

87. A line of print on a computer contains 60 characters (letters, spaces, punctuation marks). Find how many characters there are in 35 lines.

88. An average cow eats 3 pounds of grain per day. Find how much grain a cow eats in a year. (Assume 365 days in 1 year.)

89. One ounce of Planters® Dry Roasted Peanuts has 160 calories. How many calories are in 8 ounces? (*Source:* RJR Nabisco, Inc.)

90. One ounce of Planters® Dry Roasted Peanuts has 13 grams of fat. How many grams of fat are in 16 ounces? (*Source:* RJR Nabisco, Inc.)

91. The Thespian club at a local community college is ordering T-shirts. T-shirts size S, M, or L cost $10 each and T-shirts size XL or XXL cost $12 each. Use the table below to find the total cost. (The first row is filled in for you.)

T-Shirt Size	Number of Shirts Ordered	Cost per Shirt	Cost per Size Ordered
S	4	$10	$40
M	6		
L	20		
XL	3		
XXL	3		

92. The student activities group at North Shore Community College is planning a trip to see the local minor league baseball team. Tickets cost $5 for students, $7 for nonstudents, and $2 for children under 12. Use the following table to find the total cost.

Person	Number of Persons	Cost per Person	Cost per Category
Student	24	$5	$120
Nonstudent	4		
Children under 12	5		

93. Celestial Seasonings of Boulder, Colorado, is a tea company that specializes in herbal teas, accounting for over $100,000,000 in herbal tea blend sales in the United States annually. Their plant in Boulder has bagging machines capable of bagging over 1000 bags of tea per minute. If the plant runs 24 hours a day, how many tea bags are produced in one day? (*Source:* Celestial Seasonings)

94. The number of "older" Americans (ages 65 and older) has increased twelvefold since 1900. If there were 3 million "older" Americans in 1900, how many were there in 2008? (*Source:* Administration on Aging, U.S. Census Bureau)

Mixed Practice (Sections 1.3, 1.4, 1.6) *Perform each indicated operation.*

95.   128
        + 7

96.   126
        − 8

97.   134
        × 16

98. 47 + 26 + 10 + 231 + 50

99. Find the sum of 19 and 4.

100. Find the product of 19 and 4.

101. Find the difference of 19 and 4.

102. Find the total of 19 and 4.

Concept Extensions

Solve. See the first Concept Check in this section.

103. Rewrite 7 + 7 + 7 + 7 using multiplication.

104. Rewrite 11 + 11 + 11 + 11 + 11 + 11 using multiplication.

105. a. Rewrite $3 \cdot 5$ as repeated addition.
  b. Explain why there is more than one way to do this.

106. a. Rewrite $4 \cdot 5$ as repeated addition.
  b. Explain why there is more than one way to do this.

Find and explain the error in each multiplication problem. See the second Concept Check in this section.

107.
$$
\begin{array}{r}
203 \\
\times\ 14 \\
\hline
812 \\
203 \\
\hline
1015
\end{array}
$$

108.
$$
\begin{array}{r}
31 \\
\times\ 50 \\
\hline
155
\end{array}
$$

Fill in the missing digits in each problem.

109.
$$
\begin{array}{r}
4\_ \\
\times\ \ \_3 \\
\hline
126 \\
3780 \\
\hline
3906
\end{array}
$$

110.
$$
\begin{array}{r}
\_7 \\
\times\ \ 6\_ \\
\hline
171 \\
3420 \\
\hline
3591
\end{array}
$$

111. Explain how to multiply two 2-digit numbers using partial products.

112. In your own words, explain the meaning of the area of a rectangle and how this area is measured.

113. A window washer in New York City is bidding for a contract to wash the windows of a 23-story building. To write a bid, the number of windows in the building is needed. If there are 7 windows in each row of windows on 2 sides of the building and 4 windows per row on the other 2 sides of the building, find the total number of windows.

114. During the NBA's 2007–2008 regular season, Kobe Bryant of the Los Angeles Lakers scored 150 three-point field goals, 775 two-point field goals, and 623 free throws (worth one point each). How many points did Kobe Bryant score during the 2007–2008 regular season? (*Source:* NBA)

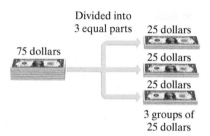
1.7 DIVIDING WHOLE NUMBERS

Suppose three people pooled their money and bought a raffle ticket at a local fund-raiser. Their ticket was the winner and they won a $75 cash prize. They then divided the prize into three equal parts so that each person received $25.

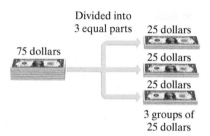

Objective A Dividing Whole Numbers

The process of separating a quantity into equal parts is called **division.** The division above can be symbolized by several notations.

$$\text{quotient} \rightarrow 25$$
$$3\overline{)75} \leftarrow \text{dividend}$$
$$\uparrow \text{divisor}$$

$$\text{dividend} \rightarrow \frac{75}{3} = 25 \leftarrow \text{quotient}$$
$$\uparrow \text{divisor}$$

$$\text{quotient}$$
$$75 \div 3 = 25$$
$$\uparrow \quad \uparrow$$
$$\text{dividend} \quad \text{divisor}$$

$$\text{dividend} \quad \text{quotient}$$
$$75/3 = 25$$
$$\uparrow$$
$$\text{divisor}$$

(In the notation $\frac{75}{3}$, the bar separating 75 and 3 is called a **fraction bar.**) Just as subtraction is the reverse of addition, division is the reverse of multiplication. This means that division can be checked by multiplication.

$$\overset{25}{3\overline{)75}} \quad \text{because} \quad 25 \cdot 3 = 75$$

| Quotient | · | Divisor | = | Dividend |

Since multiplication and division are related in this way, you can use your knowledge of multiplication facts to review quotients of one-digit divisors if necessary.

Example 1 Find each quotient. Check by multiplying.

a. $42 \div 7$　　　**b.** $\dfrac{64}{8}$　　　**c.** $3\overline{)21}$

Solution:

a. $42 \div 7 = 6$ because $6 \cdot 7 = 42$

b. $\dfrac{64}{8} = 8$ because $8 \cdot 8 = 64$

c. $3\overline{)21}^{\,7}$ because $7 \cdot 3 = 21$

● Work Practice 1

PRACTICE 1

Find each quotient. Check by multiplying.

a. $9\overline{)72}$
b. $40 \div 5$
c. $\dfrac{24}{6}$

Example 2 Find each quotient. Check by multiplying.

a. $1\overline{)7}$　　**b.** $12 \div 1$　　**c.** $\dfrac{6}{6}$　　**d.** $9 \div 9$　　**e.** $\dfrac{20}{1}$　　**f.** $18\overline{)18}$

Solution:

a. $1\overline{)7}^{\,7}$ because $7 \cdot 1 = 7$

b. $12 \div 1 = 12$ because $12 \cdot 1 = 12$

c. $\dfrac{6}{6} = 1$ because $1 \cdot 6 = 6$

d. $9 \div 9 = 1$ because $1 \cdot 9 = 9$

e. $\dfrac{20}{1} = 20$ because $20 \cdot 1 = 20$

f. $18\overline{)18}^{\,1}$ because $1 \cdot 18 = 18$

● Work Practice 2

PRACTICE 2

Find each quotient. Check by multiplying.

a. $\dfrac{7}{7}$　　　**b.** $5 \div 1$
c. $1\overline{)11}$　　**d.** $4 \div 1$
e. $\dfrac{10}{1}$　　**f.** $21 \div 21$

Example 2 illustrates the important properties of division described next:

Division Properties of 1

The quotient of any number (except 0) and that same number is 1. For example,

$$8 \div 8 = 1 \qquad \frac{5}{5} = 1 \qquad 4\overline{)4}^{\,1}$$

The quotient of any number and 1 is that same number. For example,

$$9 \div 1 = 9 \qquad \frac{6}{1} = 6 \qquad 1\overline{)3}^{\,3} \qquad \frac{0}{1} = 0$$

PRACTICE 3

Find each quotient. Check by multiplying.

a. $\dfrac{0}{7}$　　　**b.** $8\overline{)0}$
c. $7 \div 0$　　**d.** $0 \div 14$

Example 3 Find each quotient. Check by multiplying.

a. $9\overline{)0}$　　**b.** $0 \div 12$　　**c.** $\dfrac{0}{5}$　　**d.** $\dfrac{3}{0}$

Solution:

a. $9\overline{)0}^{\,0}$ because $0 \cdot 9 = 0$　　　**b.** $0 \div 12 = 0$ because $0 \cdot 12 = 0$

c. $\dfrac{0}{5} = 0$ because $0 \cdot 5 = 0$

Continued on next page

Answers
1. a. 8 **b.** 8 **c.** 4 **2. a.** 1 **b.** 5
c. 11 **d.** 4 **e.** 10 **f.** 1 **3. a.** 0
b. 0 **c.** undefined **d.** 0

d. If $\dfrac{3}{0}$ = a *number*, then the *number* times $0 = 3$. Recall from Section 1.6 that any number multiplied by 0 is 0 and not 3. We say, then, that $\dfrac{3}{0}$ is **undefined.**

◗ **Work Practice 3**

Example 3 illustrates important division properties of 0.

> ### Division Properties of 0
>
> The quotient of 0 and any number (except 0) is 0. For example,
>
> $$0 \div 9 = 0 \qquad \dfrac{0}{5} = 0 \qquad 14\overline{)0}\,^{0}$$
>
> The quotient of any number and 0 is not a number. We say that
>
> $$\dfrac{3}{0}, \quad 0\overline{)3}, \quad \text{and} \quad 3 \div 0$$
>
> are **undefined.**

Objective Ⓑ Performing Long Division

When dividends are larger, the quotient can be found by a process called **long division.** For example, let's divide 2541 by 3.

$$\text{divisor} \longrightarrow 3\overline{)2541}$$
$$\uparrow$$
$$\text{dividend}$$

We can't divide 3 into 2, so we try dividing 3 into the first two digits.

$$\begin{array}{r} 8 \\ 3\overline{)2541} \end{array}$$ $25 \div 3 = 8$ with 1 left, so our best estimate is 8. We place 8 over the 5 in 25.

Next, multiply 8 and 3 and subtract this product from 25. Make sure that this difference is less than the divisor.

$$\begin{array}{r} 8 \\ 3\overline{)2541} \\ -24 \\ \hline 1 \end{array}$$ $8(3) = 24$
$25 - 24 = 1$, and 1 is less than the divisor 3.

Bring down the next digit and go through the process again.

$$\begin{array}{r} 84 \\ 3\overline{)2541} \\ -24\downarrow \\ \hline 14 \\ -12 \\ \hline 2 \end{array}$$ $14 \div 3 = 4$ with 2 left

$4(3) = 12$
$14 - 12 = 2$

Once more, bring down the next digit and go through the process.

$$\begin{array}{r} 847 \\ 3\overline{)2541} \\ -24 \\ \hline 14 \\ -12\downarrow \\ \hline 21 \\ -21 \\ \hline 0 \end{array}$$ $21 \div 3 = 7$

$7(3) = 21$
$21 - 21 = 0$

The quotient is 847. To check, see that $847 \times 3 = 2541$.

Example 4   Divide: 3705 ÷ 5. Check by multiplying.

Solution:

$$\begin{array}{r} 7 \\ 5\overline{)3705} \\ -35\downarrow \\ \hline 20 \end{array}$$

37 ÷ 5 = 7 with 2 left. Place this estimate, 7, over the 7 in 37.

7(5) = 35

37 − 35 = 2, and 2 is less than the divisor 5.

—— Bring down the 0.

$$\begin{array}{r} 74 \\ 5\overline{)3705} \\ -35 \\ \hline 20 \\ -20\downarrow \\ \hline 05 \end{array}$$

20 ÷ 5 = 4

4(5) = 20

20 − 20 = 0, and 0 is less than the divisor 5.

—— Bring down the 5.

$$\begin{array}{r} 741 \\ 5\overline{)3705} \\ -35 \\ \hline 20 \\ -20\downarrow \\ \hline 5 \\ -5 \\ \hline 0 \end{array}$$

5 ÷ 5 = 1

1(5) = 5

5 − 5 = 0

Check:

$$\begin{array}{r} 741 \\ \times \quad 5 \\ \hline 3705 \end{array}$$

● **Work Practice 4**

PRACTICE 4

Divide. Check by multiplying.
a. 4908 ÷ 6
b. 2212 ÷ 4
c. 753 ÷ 3

Example 5   Divide and check: 1872 ÷ 9

Solution:

$$\begin{array}{r} 208 \\ 9\overline{)1872} \\ -18\downarrow \\ \hline 07 \\ -0\downarrow \\ \hline 72 \\ -72 \\ \hline 0 \end{array}$$

2(9) = 18

18 − 18 = 0; bring down the 7.

0(9) = 0

7 − 0 = 7; bring down the 2.

8(9) = 72

72 − 72 = 0

Check: 208 · 9 = 1872

● **Work Practice 5**

PRACTICE 5

Divide and check by multiplying.
a. $7\overline{)2128}$
b. $9\overline{)45,900}$

Answers
4. a. 818   **b.** 553   **c.** 251
5. a. 304   **b.** 5100

Naturally, quotients don't always "come out even." Making 4 rows out of 26 chairs, for example, isn't possible if each row is supposed to have exactly the same number of chairs. Each of 4 rows can have 6 chairs, but 2 chairs are still left over.

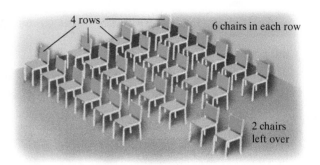
4 rows / 6 chairs in each row / 2 chairs left over

We signify "leftovers" or **remainders** in this way:

$$4\overline{)26} \quad 6 \text{ R } 2$$

The **whole number part of the quotient** is 6; the **remainder part of the quotient** is 2. Checking by multiplying,

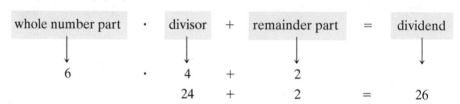

| whole number part | · | divisor | + | remainder part | = | dividend |

6 · 4 + 2
24 + 2 = 26

PRACTICE 6

Divide and check.
a. $4\overline{)939}$
b. $5\overline{)3287}$

Example 6 Divide and check: $2557 \div 7$

Solution:
$$7\overline{)2557} \quad 365 \text{ R } 2$$
$$-21$$
$$45$$
$$-42$$
$$37$$
$$-35$$
$$2$$

3(7) = 21
25 − 21 = 4; bring down the 5.
6(7) = 42
45 − 42 = 3; bring down the 7.
5(7) = 35
37 − 35 = 2; the remainder is 2.

Check: 365 · 7 + 2 = 2557

whole number part · divisor + remainder part = dividend

● **Work Practice 6**

PRACTICE 7

Divide and check.
a. $9\overline{)81,605}$
b. $4\overline{)23,310}$

Example 7 Divide and check: $56,717 \div 8$

Solution:
$$8\overline{)56717} \quad 7089 \text{ R } 5$$
$$-56$$
$$07$$
$$-0$$
$$71$$
$$-64$$
$$77$$
$$-72$$
$$5$$

7(8) = 56
Subtract and bring down the 7.
0(8) = 0
Subtract and bring down the 1.
8(8) = 64
Subtract and bring down the 7.
9(8) = 72
Subtract. The remainder is 5.

Answers
6. a. 234 R 3 **b.** 657 R 2
7. a. 9067 R 2 **b.** 5827 R 2

Check: 7089 ·   8   +   5   =   56,717

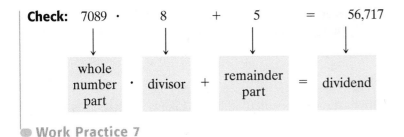

whole number part · divisor + remainder part = dividend

● Work Practice 7

When the divisor has more than one digit, the same pattern applies. For example, let's find $1358 \div 23$.

$$
\begin{array}{r}
5 \\
23\overline{)1358} \\
-115\downarrow \\
\hline
208
\end{array}
$$

$135 \div 23 = 5$ with 20 left over. Our estimate is 5.

$5(23) = 115$

$135 - 115 = 20$. Bring down the 8.

Now we continue estimating.

$$
\begin{array}{r}
59 \quad \text{R } 1 \\
23\overline{)1358} \\
-115 \\
\hline
208 \\
-207 \\
\hline
1
\end{array}
$$

$208 \div 23 = 9$ with 1 left over.

$9(23) = 207$

$208 - 207 = 1$. The remainder is 1.

To check, see that $59 \cdot 23 + 1 = 1358$.

Example 8   Divide: $6819 \div 17$

Solution:
$$
\begin{array}{r}
401 \quad \text{R } 2 \\
17\overline{)6819} \\
-68\downarrow \\
\hline
01 \\
-0\downarrow \\
\hline
19 \\
-17 \\
\hline
2
\end{array}
$$

$4(17) = 68$
Subtract and bring down the 1.
$0(17) = 0$
Subtract and bring down the 9.
$1(17) = 17$
Subtract. The reminder is 2.

To check, see that $401 \cdot 17 + 2 = 6819$.

● Work Practice 8

Example 9   Divide: $51,600 \div 403$

Solution:
$$
\begin{array}{r}
128 \quad \text{R } 16 \\
403\overline{)51600} \\
-403\downarrow \\
\hline
1130 \\
-806\downarrow \\
\hline
3240 \\
-3224 \\
\hline
16
\end{array}
$$

$1(403) = 403$
Subtract and bring down the 0.
$2(403) = 806$
Subtract and bring down the 0.
$8(403) = 3224$
Subtract. The remainder is 16.

To check, see that $128 \cdot 403 + 16 = 51,600$.

● Work Practice 9

PRACTICE 8
Divide: $8920 \div 17$

PRACTICE 9
Divide: $33,282 \div 678$

Answers
8. 524 R 12   **9.** 49 R 60

Division Shown as Repeated Subtraction   To further understand division, recall from Section 1.6 that addition and multiplication are related in the following manner:

$$\underbrace{3 + 3 + 3 + 3}_{\text{4 addends; each addend is 3}} = 4 \times 3 = 12$$

In other words, multiplication is repeated addition. Likewise, division is repeated subtraction.

For example, let's find

$$35 \div 8$$

by repeated subtraction. Keep track of the number of times 8 is subtracted from 35. We are through when we can subtract no more because the difference is less than 8.

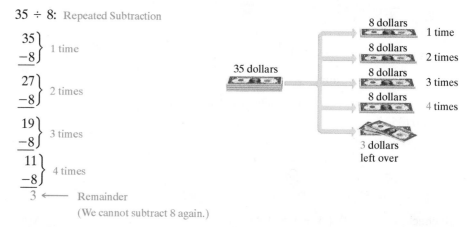

$35 \div 8$:   Repeated Subtraction

$$\left.\begin{array}{r} 35 \\ -8 \end{array}\right\} \text{1 time}$$

$$\left.\begin{array}{r} 27 \\ -8 \end{array}\right\} \text{2 times}$$

$$\left.\begin{array}{r} 19 \\ -8 \end{array}\right\} \text{3 times}$$

$$\left.\begin{array}{r} 11 \\ -8 \end{array}\right\} \text{4 times}$$

$$3 \longleftarrow \text{Remainder}$$
(We cannot subtract 8 again.)

Thus, $35 \div 8 = 4 \text{ R } 3$.

To check, perform the same multiplication as usual, but finish by adding in the remainder.

whole number part of quotient	·	divisor	+	remainder	=	dividend
↓		↓		↓		↓
4	·	8	+	3	=	35

Objective ⓒ Solving Problems by Dividing

Below are some key words and phrases that may indicate the operation of division:

Division		
Key Words or Phrases	**Examples**	**Symbols**
divide	divide 10 by 5	$10 \div 5$ or $\dfrac{10}{5}$
quotient	the quotient of 64 and 4	$64 \div 4$ or $\dfrac{64}{4}$
divided by	9 divided by 3	$9 \div 3$ or $\dfrac{9}{3}$
divided or shared equally among	$100 divided equally among five people	$100 \div 5$ or $\dfrac{100}{5}$
per	100 miles per 2 hours	$\dfrac{100 \text{ miles}}{2 \text{ hours}}$

✓**Concept Check** Which of the following is the correct way to represent "the quotient of 60 and 12"? Or are both correct? Explain your answer.

a. $12 \div 60$ **b.** $60 \div 12$

Example 10 Finding Shared Earnings

Three college students share a paper route to earn money for expenses. The total in their fund after expenses was $2895. How much is each person's equal share?

Solution:

In words:	Each person's share	=	total money	÷	number of persons

Translate:	Each person's share	=	2895	÷	3

Then

$$
\begin{array}{r}
965 \\
3\overline{)2895} \\
-27 \\
\hline
19 \\
-18 \\
\hline
15 \\
-15 \\
\hline
0
\end{array}
$$

Each person's share is $965.

● **Work Practice 10**

Example 11 Dividing Number of Downloads

As part of a promotion, an executive receives 238 cards, each good for one free song download. If she wants to share them evenly with 19 friends, how many download cards will each friend receive? How many will be left over?

Solution:

In words:	Number of cards for each person	=	number of cards	÷	number of friends

Translate:	Number of cards for each person	=	238	÷	19

$$
\begin{array}{r}
12 \;\; \text{R } 10 \\
19\overline{)238} \\
-19 \\
\hline
48 \\
-38 \\
\hline
10
\end{array}
$$

Each friend will receive 12 download cards. The cards cannot be divided equally among her friends since there is a nonzero remainder. There will be 10 download cards left over.

● **Work Practice 11**

Objective ⓓ Finding Averages

A special application of division (and addition) is finding the average of a list of numbers. The **average** of a list of numbers is the sum of the numbers divided by the *number* of numbers.

$$\text{average} = \frac{\text{sum of numbers}}{\textit{number of numbers}}$$

PRACTICE 12

To compute a safe time to wait for reactions to occur after allergy shots are administered, a lab technician is given a list of elapsed times between administered shots and reactions. Find the average of the times 4 minutes, 7 minutes, 35 minutes, 16 minutes, 9 minutes, 3 minutes, and 52 minutes.

Example 12 Averaging Scores

A mathematics instructor is checking a simple program she wrote for averaging the scores of her students. To do so, she averages a student's scores of 75, 96, 81, and 88 by hand. Find this average score.

Solution: To find the average score, we find the sum of the student's scores and divide by 4, the number of scores.

$$
\begin{array}{r}
75 \\
96 \\
81 \\
+88 \\
\hline
340 \text{ sum}
\end{array}
\qquad
\text{average} = \frac{340}{4} = 85
\qquad
\begin{array}{r}
85 \\
4\overline{)340} \\
-32 \\
\hline
20 \\
-20 \\
\hline
0
\end{array}
$$

The average score is 85.

● **Work Practice 12**

🖩 Calculator Explorations   Dividing Numbers

To divide numbers on a calculator, find the keys marked ÷ and = or ENTER . For example, to find $435 \div 5$ on a calculator, press the keys 435 ÷ 5 = or ENTER . The display will read 87 . Thus, $435 \div 5 = 87$.

Use a calculator to divide.

1. $848 \div 16$
2. $564 \div 12$
3. $95\overline{)5890}$
4. $27\overline{)1053}$
5. $\dfrac{32{,}886}{126}$
6. $\dfrac{143{,}088}{264}$
7. $0 \div 315$
8. $315 \div 0$

Answer

12. 18 minutes

Vocabulary and Readiness Check

Use the choices below to fill in each blank. Some choices may be used more than once.

1	number	divisor	dividend
0	undefined	average	quotient

1. In $90 \div 2 = 45$, the answer 45 is called the _____, 90 is called the _____, and 2 is called the _____.

2. The quotient of any number and 1 is the same _____.

3. The quotient of any number (except 0) and the same number is _____.

4. The quotient of 0 and any number (except 0) is _____.

5. The quotient of any number and 0 is _____.

6. The _____ of a list of numbers is the sum of the numbers divided by the _____ of numbers.

1.7 Exercise Set

Objective A *Find each quotient. See Examples 1 through 3.*

1. $54 \div 9$

2. $72 \div 9$

 **3.** $36 \div 3$

4. $24 \div 3$

5. $0 \div 8$

6. $0 \div 4$

 **7.** $31 \div 1$

8. $38 \div 1$

 **9.** $\dfrac{18}{18}$

10. $\dfrac{49}{49}$

11. $\dfrac{24}{3}$

12. $\dfrac{45}{9}$

 **13.** $26 \div 0$

14. $\dfrac{12}{0}$

15. $26 \div 26$

16. $6 \div 6$

 **17.** $0 \div 14$

18. $7 \div 0$

19. $18 \div 2$

20. $18 \div 3$

Objectives A B Mixed Practice *Divide and then check by multiplying. See Examples 1 through 5.*

21. $3\overline{)87}$

22. $5\overline{)85}$

23. $3\overline{)222}$

24. $8\overline{)640}$

25. $3\overline{)1014}$

26. $4\overline{)2104}$

27. $\dfrac{30}{0}$

28. $\dfrac{0}{30}$

29. $63 \div 7$

30. $56 \div 8$

31. $150 \div 6$

32. $121 \div 11$

Divide and then check by multiplying. See Examples 6 and 7.

33. $7\overline{)479}$

34. $7\overline{)426}$

35. $6\overline{)1421}$

36. $3\overline{)1240}$

37. $305 \div 8$

38. $167 \div 3$

39. $2286 \div 7$

40. $3333 \div 4$

Divide and then check by multiplying. See Examples 8 and 9.

41. $55\overline{)715}$ **42.** $23\overline{)736}$ **43.** $23\overline{)1127}$ **44.** $42\overline{)2016}$ **45.** $97\overline{)9417}$

46. $44\overline{)1938}$ **47.** $3146 \div 15$ **48.** $7354 \div 12$ **49.** $6578 \div 13$ **50.** $5670 \div 14$

51. $9299 \div 46$ **52.** $2505 \div 64$ **53.** $\dfrac{12{,}744}{236}$ **54.** $\dfrac{5781}{123}$ **55.** $\dfrac{10{,}297}{103}$

56. $\dfrac{23{,}092}{240}$ **57.** $20{,}619 \div 102$ **58.** $40{,}853 \div 203$ **59.** $244{,}989 \div 423$ **60.** $164{,}592 \div 543$

Divide. See Examples 1 through 9.

61. $7\overline{)119}$ **62.** $8\overline{)104}$ **63.** $7\overline{)3580}$ **64.** $5\overline{)3017}$

65. $40\overline{)85{,}312}$ **66.** $50\overline{)85{,}747}$ **67.** $142\overline{)863{,}360}$ **68.** $214\overline{)650{,}560}$

Objective Ⓒ **Translating** *Solve. See Examples 10 and 11.*

69. Find the quotient of 117 and 5.

70. Find the quotient of 94 and 7.

71. Find 200 divided by 35.

72. Find 116 divided by 32.

73. Find the quotient of 62 and 3.

74. Find the quotient of 78 and 5.

75. Martin Thieme teaches American Sign Language classes for $65 per student for a 7-week session. He collects $2145 from the group of students. Find how many students are in the group.

76. Kathy Gomez teaches Spanish lessons for $85 per student for a 5-week session. From one group of students, she collects $4930. Find how many students are in the group.

77. The gravity of Jupiter is 318 times as strong as the gravity of Earth, so objects on Jupiter weigh 318 times as much as they weigh on Earth. If a person would weigh 52,470 pounds on Jupiter, find how much the person weighs on Earth.

78. Twenty-one people pooled their money and bought lottery tickets. One ticket won a prize of $5,292,000. Find how many dollars each person received.

79. An 18-hole golf course is 5580 yards long. If the distance to each hole is the same, find the distance between holes.

80. A truck hauls wheat to a storage granary. It carries a total of 5768 bushels of wheat in 14 trips. How much does the truck haul each trip if each trip it hauls the same amount?

81. There is a bridge over highway I-35 every three miles. The first bridge is at the beginning of a 265-mile stretch of highway. Find how many bridges there are over 265 miles of I-35.

82. The white stripes dividing the lanes on a highway are 25 feet long, and the spaces between them are 25 feet long. Let's call a "lane divider" a stripe followed by a space. Find how many whole "lane dividers" there are in 1 mile of highway. (A mile is 5280 feet.)

83. Ari Trainor is in the requisitions department of Central Electric Lighting Company. Light poles along a highway are placed 492 feet apart. The first light pole is at the beginning of a 1-mile strip. Find how many poles he should order for the 1-mile strip of highway. (A mile is 5280 feet.)

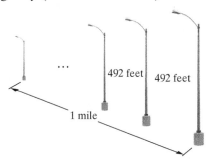

84. Professor Lopez has a piece of rope 185 feet long that she wants to cut into pieces for an experiment in her physics class. Each piece of rope is to be 8 feet long. Determine whether she has enough rope for her 22-student class. Determine the amount extra or the amount short.

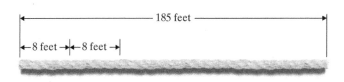

85. Broad Peak in Pakistan is the twelfth-tallest mountain in the world. Its elevation is 26,400 feet. A mile is 5280 feet. How many miles tall is Broad Peak? (*Source:* National Geographic Society)

86. DeAngelo Williams of the Carolina Panthers led the NFL in touchdowns during the 2008 football season, scoring a total of 120 points from touchdowns. If a touchdown is worth 6 points, how many touchdowns did Williams make during 2008? (*Source:* National Football League)

87. Find how many yards are in 1 mile. (A mile is 5280 feet; a yard is 3 feet.)

88. Find how many whole feet are in 1 rod. (A mile is 5280 feet; 1 mile is 320 rods.)

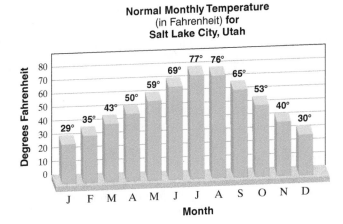

Objective Ⓓ *Find the average of each list of numbers. See Example 12.*

89. 10, 24, 35, 22, 17, 12

90. 37, 26, 15, 29, 51, 22

91. 205, 972, 210, 161

92. 121, 200, 185, 176, 163

93. 86, 79, 81, 69, 80

94. 92, 96, 90, 85, 92, 79

The normal monthly temperature in degrees Fahrenheit for Salt Lake City, Utah, is given in the graph. Use this graph to answer Exercises 95 and 96. (Source: National Climatic Data Center)

Normal Monthly Temperature
(in Fahrenheit) for
Salt Lake City, Utah

Degrees Fahrenheit

J 29° F 35° M 43° A 50° M 59° J 69° J 77° A 76° S 65° O 53° N 40° D 30°

Month

95. Find the average temperature for June, July, and August.

96. Find the average temperature for October, November, and December.

Mixed Practice (*Sections 1.3, 1.4, 1.6, 1.7*) *Perform each indicated operation. Watch the operation symbol.*

97. $82 + 463 + 29 + 8704$

98. $23 + 407 + 92 + 7011$

99. $\begin{array}{r} 546 \\ \times\ 28 \\ \hline \end{array}$

100. $\begin{array}{r} 712 \\ \times 54 \\ \hline \end{array}$

101. $\begin{array}{r} 722 \\ -\ 43 \\ \hline \end{array}$

102. $\begin{array}{r} 712 \\ -\ 54 \\ \hline \end{array}$

103. $\dfrac{45}{0}$

104. $\dfrac{0}{23}$

105. $228 \div 24$

106. $304 \div 31$

Concept Extensions

Match each word phrase to the correct translation. (Not all letter choices will be used.) See the Concept Check in this section.

107. The quotient of 40 and 8

108. The quotient of 200 and 20

a. $20 \div 200$ **b.** $200 \div 20$

109. 200 divided by 20

110. 40 divided by 8

c. $40 \div 8$ **d.** $8 \div 40$

The following table shows the top five countries with the most Nobel Prize winners through 2008. Use this table to answer Exercises 111 and 112. (Source: Nobel Prize Committee)

111. Find the average number of Nobel Prize winners for the countries shown.

112. Find the average number of Nobel Prize winners per category for Sweden.

Countries with the Most Nobel Prize Winners, 1901–2008							
Country	Physics	Chemistry	Literature	Physiology and Medicine	Peace	Economics	Total
United States	88	59	11	96	22	44	320
United Kingdom	21	27	11	31	13	7	110
Germany	25	28	8	16	4	1	82
France	13	8	14	11	10	2	58
Sweden	4	4	8	7	5	2	30

In Example 12 in this section, we found that the average of 75, 96, 81, and 88 is 85. Use this information to answer Exercises 113 and 114.

113. If the number 75 is removed from the list of numbers, does the average increase or decrease? Explain why.

114. If the number 96 is removed from the list of numbers, does the average increase or decrease? Explain why.

115. Without computing it, tell whether the average of 126, 135, 198, 113 is 86. Explain why it is possible or why it is not.

116. Without computing it, tell whether the average of 38, 27, 58, and 43 is 17. Explain why it is possible or why it is not.

117. If the area of a rectangle is 60 square feet and its width is 5 feet, what is its length?

118. If the area of a rectangle is 84 square inches and its length is 21 inches, what is its width?

119. Write down any two numbers whose quotient is 25.

120. Write down any two numbers whose quotient is 1.

121. Find $26 \div 5$ using the process of repeated subtraction.

122. Find $86 \div 10$ using the process of repeated subtraction.

1.8 AN INTRODUCTION TO PROBLEM SOLVING

Objectives

Ⓐ Solve Problems by Adding, Subtracting, Multiplying, or Dividing Whole Numbers.

Ⓑ Solve Problems That Require More Than One Operation.

Objective Ⓐ Solving Problems Involving Addition, Subtraction, Multiplication, or Division

In this section, we decide which operation to perform in order to solve a problem. Don't forget the key words and phrases that help indicate which operation to use. Some of these are listed below and were introduced earlier in the chapter. Also included are several words and phrases that translate to the symbol "=".

Addition (+)	Subtraction (−)	Multiplication (·)	Division (÷)	Equality (=)
sum	difference	product	quotient	equals
plus	minus	times	divide	is equal to
added to	subtract	multiply	shared equally	is/was
more than	less than	multiply by	among	yields
increased by	decreased by	of	divided by	
total	less	double/triple	divided into	

The following problem-solving steps may be helpful to you:

Problem-Solving Steps

1. UNDERSTAND the problem. Some ways of doing this are to read and reread the problem, construct a drawing, and look for key words to identify an operation.
2. TRANSLATE the problem. That is, write the problem in short form using words, and then translate to numbers and symbols.
3. SOLVE the problem. It is helpful to estimate the solution by rounding. Then carry out the indicated operation from step 2.
4. INTERPRET the results. *Check* the proposed solution in the stated problem and *state* your conclusions. Write your results with the correct units attached.

Example 1 Calculating the Length of a River

The Hudson River in New York State is 306 miles long. The Snake River in the northwestern United States is 732 miles longer than the Hudson River. How long is the Snake River? (*Source*: U.S. Department of the Interior)

Solution:

1. UNDERSTAND. Read and reread the problem, and then draw a picture. Notice that we are told that Snake River is 732 miles longer than the Hudson River. The phrase "longer than" means that we add.

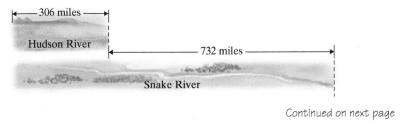

Continued on next page

PRACTICE 1

The Bank of America Building is the second-tallest building in San Francisco, California, at 779 feet. The tallest building in San Francisco is the Transamerica Pyramid, which is 74 feet taller than the Bank of America Building. How tall is the Transamerica Pyramid? (*Source: The World Almanac*)

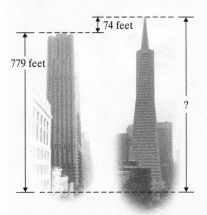

Bank of America   Transamerica Pyramid

Answer
1. 853 ft

2. TRANSLATE.

In words:	Snake River	is	732 miles	longer than	the Hudson River
	↓	↓	↓	↓	↓
Translate:	Snake River	=	732	+	306

3. SOLVE: Let's see if our answer is reasonable by also estimating. We will estimate each addend to the nearest hundred.

$$
\begin{array}{rl}
732 & \text{rounds to} \\
+306 & \text{rounds to} \\
\hline
1038 & \text{exact}
\end{array}
\qquad
\begin{array}{rl}
700 & \\
300 & \\
\hline
1000 & \text{estimate}
\end{array}
$$

4. INTERPRET. *Check* your work. The answer is reasonable since 1038 is close to our estimated answer of 1000. *State* your conclusion: The Snake River is 1038 miles long.

● **Work Practice 1**

Four friends bought a lottery ticket and won $65,000. If each person is to receive the same amount of money, how much does each person receive?

Example 2 Filling a Shipping Order

How many cases can be filled with 9900 cans of jalapeños if each case holds 48 cans? How many cans will be left over? Will there be enough cases to fill an order for 200 cases?

Solution:

1. UNDERSTAND. Read and reread the problem. Draw a picture to help visualize the situation.

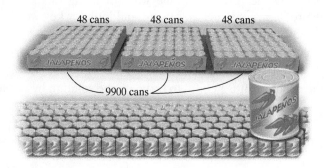

Since each case holds 48 cans, we want to know how many 48s there are in 9900. We find this by dividing.

2. TRANSLATE.

In words:	Number of cases	is	9900	divided by	48
		↓	↓	↓	↓
Translate:	Number of cases	=	9900	÷	48

3. SOLVE: Let's estimate a reasonable solution before we actually divide. Since 9900 rounded to the nearest thousand is 10,000 and 48 rounded to the nearest ten is 50, 10,000 ÷ 50 = 200. Now find the exact quotient.

$$
\begin{array}{r}
206 \text{ R } 12 \\
48\overline{)9900} \\
-96 \\
\hline
300 \\
-288 \\
\hline
12 \\
\end{array}
$$

4. INTERPRET. *Check* your work. The answer is reasonable since 206 R 12 is close to our estimate of 200. *State* your conclusion: 206 cases will be filled, with 12 cans left over. There will be enough cases to fill an order for 200 cases.

● Work Practice 2

Example 3 Calculating Budget Costs

The director of a learning lab at a local community college is working on next year's budget. Thirty-three new DVD players are needed at a cost of $187 each. What is the total cost of these DVD players?

Solution:

1. UNDERSTAND. Read and reread the problem, and then draw a diagram.

33 DVD Players

$187 $187   ... $187

From the phrase "total cost," we might decide to solve this problem by adding. This would work, but repeated addition, or multiplication, would save time.

2. TRANSLATE.

In words:	Total cost	is	number of DVD players	times	cost of a DVD player
	↓	↓	↓	↓	↓
Translate:	Total cost	=	33	×	$187

3. SOLVE: Once again, let's estimate a reasonable solution.

$$
\begin{array}{r}
187 \\
\times\ 33 \\
\hline
561 \\
5610 \\
\hline
6171
\end{array}
$$

187 rounds to 200
× 33 rounds to × 30
6000 estimate

561
5610
6171 exact

4. INTERPRET. *Check* your work. *State* your conclusion: The total cost of the DVD players is $6171.

● Work Practice 3

Example 4 Calculating a Public School Teacher's Salary

In 2008, the average salary of a public school teacher in California was $64,424. For the same year, the average salary for a public school teacher in Iowa was $17,760 less than this. What was the average public school teacher's salary in Iowa? (*Source:* National Education Association)

Solution:

1. UNDERSTAND. Read and reread the problem. Notice that we are told that the Iowa salary is $17,760 less than the California salary. The phrase "less than" indicates subtraction.

Continued on next page

PRACTICE 3

The director of the learning lab also needs to include in the budget a line for 425 blank CDs at a cost of $4 each. What is this total cost for the blank CDs?

PRACTICE 4

In 2008, the average salary for a public school teacher in Alaska was $56,758. For the same year, the average salary for a public school teacher in Hawaii was $3358 less than this. What was the average public school teacher's salary in Hawaii? (*Source:* National Education Association)

Answers
3. $1700   **4.** $53,400

2. TRANSLATE. Remember that order matters when subtracting, so be careful when translating.

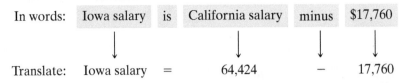

In words: | Iowa salary | is | California salary | minus | $17,760 |

Translate: Iowa salary   =   64,424   −   17,760

3. SOLVE. This time, instead of estimating, let's check by adding.

$$\begin{array}{r} 64{,}424 \\ -17{,}760 \\ \hline 46{,}664 \end{array}$$

Check:
$$\begin{array}{r} 46{,}664 \\ +17{,}760 \\ \hline 64{,}424 \end{array}$$

4. INTERPRET. *Check* your work. The check is above. *State* your conclusion: The average Iowa teacher's salary in 2008 was $46,664.

● Work Practice 4

Objective ⓑ Solving Problems That Require More Than One Operation

We must sometimes use more than one operation to solve a problem.

Example 5   Planting a New Garden

A gardener bought enough plants to fill a rectangular garden with length 30 feet and width 20 feet. Because of shading problems from a nearby tree, the gardener changed the width of the garden to 15 feet. If the area is to remain the same, what is the new length of the garden?

Solution:

1. UNDERSTAND. Read and reread the problem. Then draw a picture to help visualize the problem.

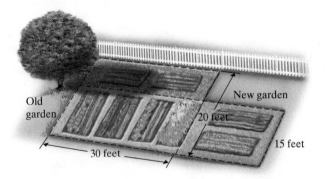

2. TRANSLATE. Since the area of the new garden is to be the same as the area of the old garden, let's find the area of the old garden. Recall that

Area = length × width = 30 feet × 20 feet = 600 square feet

PRACTICE 5

A gardener is trying to decide how much fertilizer to buy for his yard. He knows that his lot is in the shape of a rectangle that measures 90 feet by 120 feet. He also knows that the floor of his house is in the shape of a rectangle that measures 45 feet by 65 feet. How much area of the lot is not covered by the house?

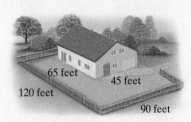

Answer
5. 7875 sq ft

Since the area of the new garden is to be 600 square feet also, we need to see how many 15s there are in 600. This means division. In other words,

In words: New length   =   Area of garden   ÷   New width

Translate: New length   =   600   ÷   15

3. SOLVE.

$$
\begin{array}{r}
40 \\
15\overline{)600} \\
-60 \\
\hline
00
\end{array}
$$

4. INTERPRET. *Check* your work. *State* your conclusion: The length of the new garden is 40 feet.

● **Work Practice 5**

1.8 Exercise Set

Objective A *Solve. Exercises 1, 2, 11, and 12 have been started for you. See Examples 1 through 4.*

1. 41 increased by 8 is what number?
Start the Solution:
1. UNDERSTAND the problem. Reread it as many times as needed.
2. TRANSLATE into an equation. (Fill in the blanks below.)

41	increased by	8	is	what number
↓	↓	↓	↓	↓
41	___	8	___	what number

Finish with:
3. SOLVE
4. INTERPRET

2. What is 12 multiplied by 9?
Start the Solution:
1. UNDERSTAND the problem. Reread it as many times as needed.
2. TRANSLATE into an equation. (Fill in the blanks below.)

what	is	12	multiplied by	9
↓	↓	↓	↓	↓
what number	___	12	___	9

Finish with:
3. SOLVE
4. INTERPRET

3. What is the quotient of 1185 and 5?

4. 78 decreased by 12 is what number?

5. What is the total of 35 and 7?

6. What is the difference of 48 and 8?

7. 60 times 10 is what number?

8. 60 divided by 10 is what number?

9. A vacant lot in the shape of a rectangle measures 120 feet by 80 feet.
  a. What is the perimeter of the lot?
  b. What is the area of the lot?

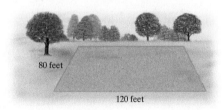

10. A parking lot in the shape of a rectangle measures 100 feet by 150 feet.
  a. What is the perimeter of the lot?
  b. What is the area of the parking lot?

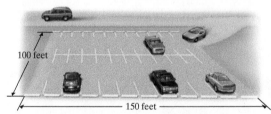

11. A family bought a house for $185,700 and later sold the house for $201,200. How much money did they make by selling the house?
Start the Solution:
1. UNDERSTAND the problem. Reread it as many times as needed.
2. TRANSLATE into an equation. (Fill in the blanks below.)

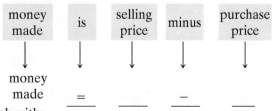

money made	is	selling price	minus	purchase price
↓	↓	↓	↓	↓
money made	=	___	−	___

Finish with:
3. SOLVE
4. INTERPRET

12. Three people dream of equally sharing a $147 million lottery. How much would each person receive if they have the winning ticket?
Start the solution:
1. UNDERSTAND the problem. Reread it as many times as needed.
2. TRANSLATE into an equation. (Fill in the blanks below.)

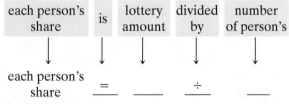

each person's share	is	lottery amount	divided by	number of person's
↓	↓	↓	↓	↓
each person's share	=	___	÷	___

Finish with:
3. SOLVE
4. INTERPRET

13. There are 24 hours in a day. How many hours are in a week?

14. There are 60 minutes in an hour. How many minutes are in a day?

15. The Verrazano Narrows Bridge is the longest bridge in New York, measuring 4260 feet. The George Washington Bridge, also in New York, is 760 feet shorter than the Verrazano Narrows Bridge. Find the length of the George Washington Bridge.

16. The Goodyear Tire &Rubber Company maintains a fleet of five blimps. The *Spirit of Goodyear* can hold 202,700 cubic feet of helium. Its smaller sister, the *Spirit of Europe*, can hold 132,700 fewer cubic feet of helium than *Spirit of Goodyear*. How much helium can *Spirit of Europe* hold? (*Source:* Goodyear Tire & Rubber Company)

17. Yellowstone National Park in Wyoming was the first national park in the United States. It was created in 1872. One of the more recent additions to the National Park System is Governors Island National Monument in New York. It was established in 2001. How much older is Yellowstone than Governors Island? (*Source:* National Park Service)

18. Razor scooters were introduced in 2000. Radio Flyer Wagons were first introduced 83 years earlier. In what year were Radio Flyer Wagons introduced? (*Source:* Toy Industry Association, Inc.)

19. Since their introduction, the number of LEGO building bricks that have been sold is equivalent to the world's current population of approximately 6 billion people owning 52 LEGO bricks each. About how many LEGO bricks have been sold since their introduction? (*Source:* LEGO Company)

20. In 2010, the average weekly pay for a home health aide in the United States was about $519. At this rate, how much will a home health aide earn working a 52-week year? (*Source:* Bureau of Labor Statistics)

21. The three most common city names in the United States are Fairview, Midway, and Riverside. There are 287 towns named Fairview, 252 named Midway, and 180 named Riverside. Find the total number of towns named Fairview, Midway, or Riverside.

22. In the game of Monopoly, a player must own all properties in a color group before building houses. The yellow color-group properties are Atlantic Avenue, Ventnor Avenue, and Marvin Gardens. These cost $260, $260, and $280, respectively, when purchased from the bank. What total amount must a player pay to the bank before houses can be built on the yellow properties? (*Source:* Hasbro, Inc.)

23. In 2007, the average weekly pay for a correctional officer supervisor in the United States was $1080. If such a supervisor works 40 hours in one week, what is his or her hourly pay? (*Source:* Bureau of Labor Statistics)

24. In 2007, the average weekly pay for a bill collector was $600. If a bill collector works 40 hours in one week, what is his or her hourly pay? (*Source:* Bureau of Labor Statistics)

25. Three ounces of canned tuna in oil has 165 calories. How many calories does 1 ounce have? (*Source: Home and Garden Bulletin No. 72,* U.S. Department of Agriculture)

26. A whole cheesecake has 3360 calories. If the cheesecake is cut into 12 equal pieces, how many calories will each piece have? (*Source: Home and Garden Bulletin No. 72,* U.S. Department of Agriculture)

27. The average estimated 2008 U.S. population was 303,800,000. Between Memorial Day and Labor Day, 7 billion hot dogs are consumed. Approximately how many hot dogs were consumed per person between Memorial Day and Labor Day in 2008? Divide, but do not give the remainder part of the quotient. (*Source:* U.S. Census Bureau, National Hot Dog and Sausage Council)

28. David Akers, a kicker with the NFL's Philadelphia Eagles, scored an average of 9 points per game during the 2008 regular season. He played in a total of 16 games during the season. What was the total number of points he scored during the 2008 football season? (*Source:* National Football League)

29. Macy's, formerly the Federated Department Stores Company, operates 810 Macy's and 40 Bloomingdale's department stores around the country. In 2007, Macy's had sales of approximately $26,313,249,400. What is the average amount of sales made by each of the 850 stores? (*Source:* Macy's)

30. In 2008, approximately 2,132,000 pounds of mail were carried by mule train for delivery to the Havasupai Indians, on their reservation inside the Grand Canyon. If mail is delivered every one of the 52 weeks of the year, what was the average number of pounds of mail delivered to the Havasupai per week in 2008? (*Source:* United States Postal Service)

31. The Museum of Modern Art in New York welcomes 1,585,000 visitors per year. The Museum of Science in Boston receives 1,429,700 visitors per year. How many more people visit the Museum of Modern Art than the science museum? (*Source:* The Official Museum Directory)

32. In 2009, Target Corporation operated 1698 stores in the United States. Of these, 146 were in Texas. How many Target Stores were located in states other than Texas? (*Source:* Target Corporation)

33. The length of the southern boundary of the conterminous United States is 1933 miles. The length of the northern boundary of the conterminous United States is 2054 miles longer than this. What is the length of the northern boundary? (*Source:* U.S. Geological Survey)

34. In humans, 14 muscles are required to smile. It takes 29 more muscles to frown. How many muscles does it take to frown?

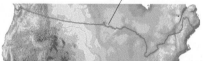

2054 miles longer

1933 miles

35. An instructor at the University of New Orleans receives a paycheck every four weeks. Find how many paychecks he receives in a year. (A year has 52 weeks.)

36. A loan of $6240 is to be paid in 48 equal payments. How much is each payment?

Objective Ⓑ *Solve. See Example 5.*

37. Find the total cost of 3 sweaters at $38 each and 5 shirts at $25 each.

38. Find the total cost of 10 computers at $2100 each and 7 boxes of diskettes at $12 each.

39. A college student has $950 in an account. She spends $205 from the account on books and then deposits $300 in the account. How much money is now in the account?

40. The temperature outside was 57°F (degrees Fahrenheit). During the next few hours, it decreased by 18 degrees and then increased by 23 degrees. Find the new temperature.

The table shows the menu from a concession stand at the county fair. Use this menu to answer Exercises 41 and 42.

41. A hungry college student is debating between the following two orders:
  a. a hamburger, an order of onion rings, a candy bar, and a soda.
  b. a hot dog, an apple, an order of french fries, and a soda.
  Which order will be cheaper? By how much?

42. A family of four is debating between the following two orders:
  a. 6 hot dogs, 4 orders of onion rings, and 4 sodas.
  b. 4 hamburgers, 4 orders of french fries, 2 apples, and 4 sodas.
  Will the family save any money by ordering (b) instead of (a)? If so, how much?

Corky's Concession Stand Menu	
Item	**Price**
Hot dog	$3
Hamburger	$4
Soda	$1
Onion rings	$3
French fries	$2
Apple	$1
Candy bar	$2

Objectives Ⓐ Ⓑ **Mixed Practice** *Use the bar graph to answer Exercises 43 through 50. (Source: Miniwatts Marketing Group)*

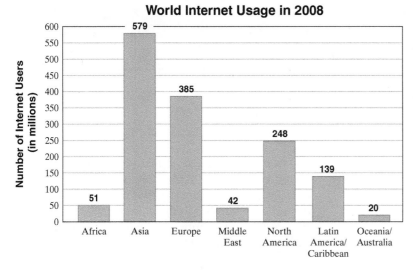

World Internet Usage in 2008

Africa: 51, Asia: 579, Europe: 385, Middle East: 42, North America: 248, Latin America/Caribbean: 139, Oceania/Australia: 20

Number of Internet Users (in millions)
Region of the World

43. Which region of the world listed had the greatest number of Internet users in 2008?

44. Which region of the world listed had the fewest number of Internet users in 2008?

45. How many more Internet users (in millions) did the world region with the most Internet users have than the world region with the fewest Internet users?

46. How many more Internet users did Africa have than the Middle East in 2008?

47. How many more Internet users did North America have than Latin America/Caribbean?

48. Which region of the world had more Internet users, Europe or North America? How many more Internet users did it have?

Find the average number of Internet users for the world regions listed in the graph on page 81.

49. The three world regions with the greatest number of Internet users.

50. The four world regions with the least number of Internet users.

Solve.

51. The learning lab at a local university is receiving new equipment. Twenty-two computers are purchased for $615 each and three printers for $408 each. Find the total cost for this equipment.

52. The washateria near the local community college is receiving new equipment. Thirty-six washers are purchased for $585 each and ten dryers are purchased for $388 each. Find the total cost for this equipment.

53. The American Heart Association recommends consuming no more than 2400 milligrams of salt per day. (This is about the amount in 1 teaspoon of salt.) How many milligrams of sodium is this in a week?

54. This semester a particular student pays $1750 for room and board, $709 for a meal ticket plan, and $2168 for tuition. What is her total bill?

55. The Meishs' yard is in the shape of a rectangle and measures 50 feet by 75 feet. In their yard, they have a rectangular swimming pool that measures 15 feet by 25 feet.
   a. Find the area of the entire yard.
   b. Find the area of the swimming pool.
   c. Find the area of the yard that is not part of the swimming pool.

56. The community is planning to construct a rectangular-shaped playground within the local park. The park is in the shape of a square and measures 100 yards on each side. The playground is to measure 15 yards by 25 yards.
   a. Find the area of the entire park.
   b. Find the area of the playground.
   c. Find the area of the park that is not part of the playground.

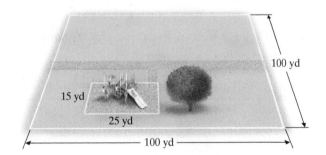

Concept Extensions

57. In 2008, the United States Postal Service issued approximately 149,100,000 money orders worth approximately $25,649,300,000. Round the number of money orders and the value of the money orders issued to the nearest ten-million to estimate the average value of each money order. (*Source:* United States Postal Service)

58. The average estimated population of the United States for 2009 was 307,607,800. The land area of the country is approximately 3,794,068 square miles. Round each number to the nearest million to estimate the population per square mile in the United States for 2009.

59. Write an application of your own that uses the term "bank account" and the numbers 1036 and 524.

1.9 EXPONENTS, SQUARE ROOTS, AND ORDER OF OPERATIONS

Objectives

(A) Write Repeated Factors Using Exponential Notation.

(B) Evaluate Expressions Containing Exponents.

(C) Evaluate the Square Root of a Perfect Square.

(D) Use the Order of Operations.

(E) Find the Area of a Square.

Objective (A) Using Exponential Notation

In the product $3 \cdot 3 \cdot 3 \cdot 3 \cdot 3$, notice that 3 is a factor several times. When this happens, we can use a shorthand notation, called an **exponent,** to write the repeated multiplication.

$$\underbrace{3 \cdot 3 \cdot 3 \cdot 3 \cdot 3}_{\text{3 is a factor 5 times}} \quad \text{can be written as}$$

3^5 Read as "three to the fifth power."

with exponent pointing to the 5 and base pointing to the 3.

This is called **exponential notation.** The **exponent,** 5, indicates how many times the **base,** 3, is a factor.

The table below shows examples of reading exponential notation in words.

Expression	In Words
5^2	"five to the second power" or "five squared"
5^3	"five to the third power" or "five cubed"
5^4	"five to the fourth power"

Usually, an exponent of 1 is not written, so when no exponent appears, we assume that the exponent is 1. For example, $2 = 2^1$ and $7 = 7^1$.

Examples Write using exponential notation.

1. $7 \cdot 7 \cdot 7 = 7^3$
2. $3 \cdot 3 = 3^2$
3. $6 \cdot 6 \cdot 6 \cdot 6 \cdot 6 = 6^5$
4. $3 \cdot 3 \cdot 3 \cdot 3 \cdot 17 \cdot 17 \cdot 17 = 3^4 \cdot 17^3$

● Work Practice 1–4

Objective (B) Evaluating Exponential Expressions

To **evaluate** an exponential expression, we write the expression as a product and then find the value of the product.

Examples Evaluate.

5. $9^2 = 9 \cdot 9 = 81$
6. $6^1 = 6$
7. $3^4 = 3 \cdot 3 \cdot 3 \cdot 3 = 81$
8. $5 \cdot 6^2 = 5 \cdot 6 \cdot 6 = 180$

● Work Practice 5–8

PRACTICE 1–4

Write using exponential notation.
1. $8 \cdot 8 \cdot 8 \cdot 8$
2. $3 \cdot 3 \cdot 3$
3. $10 \cdot 10 \cdot 10 \cdot 10 \cdot 10$
4. $5 \cdot 5 \cdot 4 \cdot 4 \cdot 4 \cdot 4 \cdot 4 \cdot 4$

PRACTICE 5–8

Evaluate.
5. 4^2 6. 7^3
7. 11^1 8. $2 \cdot 3^2$

Answers
1. 8^4 2. 3^3 3. 10^5 4. $5^2 \cdot 4^6$
5. 16   6. 343   7. 11   8. 18

Example 8 illustrates an important property: An exponent applies only to its base. The exponent 2, in $5 \cdot 6^2$, applies only to its base, 6.

Helpful Hint

An exponent applies only to its base. For example, $4 \cdot 2^3$ means $4 \cdot 2 \cdot 2 \cdot 2$.

Helpful Hint

Don't forget that 2^4, for example, is *not* $2 \cdot 4$. The expression 2^4 means repeated multiplication of the same factor.

$$2^4 = 2 \cdot 2 \cdot 2 \cdot 2 = 16, \quad \text{whereas } 2 \cdot 4 = 8$$

✔ **Concept Check** Which of the following statements is correct?

a. 3^6 is the same as $6 \cdot 6 \cdot 6$.

b. "Eight to the fourth power" is the same as 8^4.

c. "Ten squared" is the same as 10^3.

d. 11^2 is the same as $11 \cdot 2$.

Objective ⓒ Evaluating Square Roots

A **square root** of a number is one of two identical factors of the number. For example,

$$7 \cdot 7 = 49, \quad \text{so a square root of 49 is 7.}$$

We use this symbol $\sqrt{}$ (called a radical sign) for finding square roots. Since

$$7 \cdot 7 = 49, \text{ then } \sqrt{49} = 7.$$

PRACTICE 9–11

Find each square root.

9. $\sqrt{100}$
10. $\sqrt{4}$
11. $\sqrt{1}$

Examples Find each square root.

9. $\sqrt{25} = 5$ because $5 \cdot 5 = 25$
10. $\sqrt{81} = 9$ because $9 \cdot 9 = 81$
11. $\sqrt{0} = 0$ because $0 \cdot 0 = 0$

▶ **Work Practice 9–11**

Helpful Hint

Make sure you understand the difference between squaring a number and finding the square root of a number.

$$9^2 = 9 \cdot 9 = 81 \quad \sqrt{9} = 3 \text{ because } 3 \cdot 3 = 9$$

Not every square root simplifies to a whole number. We will study this more in a later chapter. In this section, we will find square roots of perfect squares only.

Answers
9. 10 **10.** 2 **11.** 1

✔ **Concept Check Answer**
b

Objective ⓓ Using the Order of Operations

Suppose that you are in charge of taking inventory at a local cell phone store. An employee has given you the number of a certain cell phone in stock as the expression

$$6 + 2 \cdot 30$$

To calculate the value of this expression, do you add first or multiply first? If you add first, the answer is 240. If you multiply first, the answer is 66.

Contents: 30 cell phones

Contents: 30 cell phones

Mathematical symbols wouldn't be very useful if two values were possible for one expression. Thus, mathematicians have agreed that, given a choice, we multiply first.

$$6 + 2 \cdot 30 = 6 + 60 \quad \text{Multiply.}$$
$$= 66 \quad \text{Add.}$$

This agreement is one of several **order of operations** agreements.

Order of Operations

1. Perform all operations within parentheses ( ), brackets [ ], or other grouping symbols such as fraction bars or square roots, starting with the innermost set.
2. Evaluate any expressions with exponents.
3. Multiply or divide in order from left to right.
4. Add or subtract in order from left to right.

Below we practice using order of operations to simplify expressions.

Example 12 Simplify: $2 \cdot 4 - 3 \div 3$

Solution: There are no parentheses and no exponents, so we start by multiplying and dividing, from left to right.

$$2 \cdot 4 - 3 \div 3 = 8 - 3 \div 3 \quad \text{Multiply.}$$
$$= 8 - 1 \quad \text{Divide.}$$
$$= 7 \quad \text{Subtract.}$$

● Work Practice 12

PRACTICE 12

Simplify: $9 \cdot 3 - 8 \div 4$

Answer
12. 25

PRACTICE 13

Simplify: $48 \div 3 \cdot 2^2$

PRACTICE 14

Simplify: $(10 - 7)^4 + 2 \cdot 3^2$

PRACTICE 15

Simplify:
$36 \div [20 - (4 \cdot 2)] + 4^3 - 6$

PRACTICE 16

Simplify: $\dfrac{25 + 8 \cdot 2 - 3^3}{2(3 - 2)}$

Example 13   Simplify: $4^2 \div 2 \cdot 4$

Solution: We start by evaluating 4^2.

$$4^2 \div 2 \cdot 4 = 16 \div 2 \cdot 4 \quad \text{Write } 4^2 \text{ as } 16.$$

Next we multiply or divide *in order* from left to right. Since division appears before multiplication from left to right, we divide first, then multiply.

$$16 \div 2 \cdot 4 = 8 \cdot 4 \quad \text{Divide.}$$
$$= 32 \quad \text{Multiply.}$$

● **Work Practice 13**

Example 14   Simplify: $(8 - 6)^2 + 2^3 \cdot 3$

Solution: $(8 - 6)^2 + 2^3 \cdot 3 = 2^2 + 2^3 \cdot 3 \quad$ Simplify inside parentheses.

$$= 4 + 8 \cdot 3 \quad \text{Write } 2^2 \text{ as 4 and } 2^3 \text{ as 8.}$$
$$= 4 + 24 \quad \text{Multiply.}$$
$$= 28 \quad \text{Add.}$$

● **Work Practice 14**

Example 15   Simplify: $4^3 + [3^2 - (10 \div 2)] - 7 \cdot 3$

Solution: Here we begin with the innermost set of parentheses.

$$4^3 + [3^2 - (10 \div 2)] - 7 \cdot 3 = 4^3 + [3^2 - 5] - 7 \cdot 3 \quad \text{Simplify inside parentheses.}$$

$$= 4^3 + [9 - 5] - 7 \cdot 3 \quad \text{Write } 3^2 \text{ as 9.}$$

$$= 4^3 + 4 - 7 \cdot 3 \quad \text{Simplify inside brackets.}$$

$$= 64 + 4 - 7 \cdot 3 \quad \text{Write } 4^3 \text{ as 64.}$$

$$= 64 + 4 - 21 \quad \text{Multiply.}$$

$$= 47 \quad \text{Add and subtract from left to right.}$$

● **Work Practice 15**

Example 16   Simplify: $\dfrac{7 - 2 \cdot 3 + 3^2}{5(2 - 1)}$

Solution: Here, the fraction bar is like a grouping symbol. We simplify above and below the fraction bar separately.

$$\frac{7 - 2 \cdot 3 + 3^2}{5(2 - 1)} = \frac{7 - 2 \cdot 3 + 9}{5(1)} \quad \text{Evaluate } 3^2 \text{ and } (2 - 1).$$

$$= \frac{7 - 6 + 9}{5} \quad \text{Multiply } 2 \cdot 3 \text{ in the numerator and multiply 5 and 1 in the denominator.}$$

$$= \frac{10}{5} \quad \text{Add and subtract from left to right.}$$

$$= 2 \quad \text{Divide.}$$

● **Work Practice 16**

Answers

13. 64   **14.** 99   **15.** 61   **16.** 7

Example 17 Simplify: $64 \div \sqrt{64} \cdot 2 + 4$

Solution: $64 \div \sqrt{64} \cdot 2 + 4 = \underline{64 \div 8} \cdot 2 + 4$ Find the square root.

$= \underline{8 \cdot 2} + 4$ Divide.

$= 16 + 4$ Multiply.

$= 20$ Add.

⬤ Work Practice 17

PRACTICE 17
Simplify: $81 \div \sqrt{81} \cdot 5 + 7$

Objective Ⓔ Finding the Area of a Square

Since a square is a special rectangle, we can find its area by finding the product of its length and its width.

Area of a rectangle = length · width

By recalling that each side of a square has the same measurement, we can use the following procedure to find its area:

Area of a square = length · width
$= $ side · side
$= $ (side)^2

Square Side

Side

Helpful Hint

Recall from Section 1.6 that area is measured in **square** units while perimeter is measured in units.

Example 18 Find the area of a square whose side measures 4 inches.

Solution: Area of a square $= $ (side)^2

$= $ (4 inches)^2

$= $ 16 square inches

4 inches

The area of the square is 16 square inches.

⬤ Work Practice 18

PRACTICE 18

Find the area of a square whose side measures 12 centimeters.

Answers
17. 52 **18.** 144 sq cm

Calculator Explorations   Exponents

To evaluate an exponent such as 4^7 on a calculator, find the keys marked $\boxed{y^x}$ or $\boxed{\wedge}$ and $\boxed{=}$ or $\boxed{\text{ENTER}}$. To evaluate 4^7, press the keys $\boxed{4}$ $\boxed{y^x}$ (or $\boxed{\wedge}$) $\boxed{7}$ $\boxed{=}$ or $\boxed{\text{ENTER}}$. The display will read $\boxed{\qquad 16384}$. Thus, $4^7 = 16{,}384$.

Use a calculator to evaluate.

1. 4^6 **2.** 5^6 **3.** 5^5
4. 7^6 **5.** 2^{11} **6.** 6^8

Order of Operations

To see whether your calculator has the order of operations built in, evaluate $5 + 2 \cdot 3$ by pressing the keys $\boxed{5}$ $\boxed{+}$ $\boxed{2}$ $\boxed{\times}$ $\boxed{3}$ $\boxed{=}$ or $\boxed{\text{ENTER}}$. If the display reads $\boxed{11}$, your calculator does have the order of operations built in. This means that most of the time, you can key in a problem exactly as it is written and the calculator will perform operations in the proper order. When evaluating an expression containing parentheses, key in the parentheses. (If an expression contains brackets, key in parentheses.) For example, to evaluate $2[25 - (8 + 4)] - 11$, press the keys $\boxed{2}$ $\boxed{\times}$ $\boxed{(}$ $\boxed{25}$ $\boxed{-}$ $\boxed{(}$ $\boxed{8}$ $\boxed{+}$ $\boxed{4}$ $\boxed{)}$ $\boxed{)}$ $\boxed{-}$ $\boxed{11}$ $\boxed{=}$ or $\boxed{\text{ENTER}}$.

The display will read $\boxed{\qquad 15}$.

Use a calculator to evaluate.

7. $7^4 + 5^3$
8. $12^4 - 8^4$
9. $63 \cdot 75 - 43 \cdot 10$
10. $8 \cdot 22 + 7 \cdot 16$
11. $4(15 \div 3 + 2) - 10 \cdot 2$
12. $155 - 2(17 + 3) + 185$

Vocabulary and Readiness Check

Use the choices below to fill in each blank.

  addition   multiplication   exponent   base

  subtraction   division   square root

1. In $2^5 = 32$, the 2 is called the _____ and the 5 is called the_____.

2. To simplify $8 + 2 \cdot 6$, which operation should be performed first? _____

3. To simplify $(8 + 2) \cdot 6$, which operation should be performed first? _____

4. To simplify $9(3 - 2) \div 3 + 6$, which operation should be performed first? _____

5. To simplify $8 \div 2 \cdot 6$, which operation should be performed first? _____

6. The _____ of a whole number is one of two identical factors of the number.

1.9 Exercise Set

Objective A *Write using exponential notation. See Examples 1 through 4.*

1. $4 \cdot 4 \cdot 4$

2. $5 \cdot 5 \cdot 5 \cdot 5$

3. $7 \cdot 7 \cdot 7 \cdot 7 \cdot 7 \cdot 7$

4. $6 \cdot 6 \cdot 6 \cdot 6 \cdot 6 \cdot 6 \cdot 6$

5. $12 \cdot 12 \cdot 12$

6. $10 \cdot 10 \cdot 10$

7. $6 \cdot 6 \cdot 5 \cdot 5 \cdot 5$

8. $4 \cdot 4 \cdot 3 \cdot 3 \cdot 3$

9. $9 \cdot 8 \cdot 8$

10. $7 \cdot 4 \cdot 4 \cdot 4$

11. $3 \cdot 2 \cdot 2 \cdot 2 \cdot 2$

12. $4 \cdot 6 \cdot 6 \cdot 6 \cdot 6$

13. $3 \cdot 2 \cdot 2 \cdot 2 \cdot 2 \cdot 5 \cdot 5 \cdot 5 \cdot 5 \cdot 5$

14. $6 \cdot 6 \cdot 2 \cdot 9 \cdot 9 \cdot 9 \cdot 9$

Objective B *Evaluate. See Examples 5 through 8.*

15. 8^2 **16.** 6^2 **17.** 5^3 **18.** 6^3 **19.** 2^5 **20.** 3^5

21. 1^{10} **22.** 1^{12} **23.** 7^1 **24.** 8^1 **25.** 2^7 **26.** 5^4

27. 2^8 **28.** 3^3 **29.** 4^4 **30.** 4^3 **31.** 9^3 **32.** 8^3

33. 12^2 **34.** 11^2 **35.** 10^2 **36.** 10^3 **37.** 20^1 **38.** 14^1

39. 3^6 **40.** 4^5 **41.** $3 \cdot 2^6$ **42.** $5 \cdot 3^2$ **43.** $2 \cdot 3^4$ **44.** $2 \cdot 7^2$

Objective C *Find each square root. See Examples 9 through 11.*

45. $\sqrt{9}$ **46.** $\sqrt{36}$ **47.** $\sqrt{64}$ **48.** $\sqrt{121}$

49. $\sqrt{144}$ **50.** $\sqrt{0}$ **51.** $\sqrt{16}$ **52.** $\sqrt{169}$

Objective Ⓓ *Simplify. See Examples 12 through 16. (This section does not contain square roots.)*

53. $15 + 3 \cdot 2$ **54.** $24 + 6 \cdot 3$ **55.** $14 \div 7 \cdot 2 + 3$ **56.** $100 \div 10 \cdot 5 + 4$

57. $32 \div 4 - 3$ **58.** $42 \div 7 - 6$ **59.** $13 + \dfrac{24}{8}$ **60.** $32 + \dfrac{8}{2}$

61. $6 \cdot 5 + 8 \cdot 2$ **62.** $3 \cdot 4 + 9 \cdot 1$ **63.** $\dfrac{5 + 12 \div 4}{1^7}$ **64.** $\dfrac{6 + 9 \div 3}{3^2}$

65. $(7 + 5^2) \div 4 \cdot 2^3$ **66.** $6^2 \cdot (10 - 8)$ **67.** $5^2 \cdot (10 - 8) + 2^3 + 5^2$

68. $5^3 \div (10 + 15) + 9^2 + 3^3$ **69.** $\dfrac{18 + 6}{2^4 - 2^2}$ **70.** $\dfrac{40 + 8}{5^2 - 3^2}$

71. $(3 + 5) \cdot (9 - 3)$ **72.** $(9 - 7) \cdot (12 + 18)$ **73.** $\dfrac{7(9 - 6) + 3}{3^2 - 3}$

74. $\dfrac{5(12 - 7) - 4}{5^2 - 18}$ **75.** $8 \div 0 + 37$ **76.** $18 - 7 \div 0$

77. $2^4 \cdot 4 - (25 \div 5)$ **78.** $2^3 \cdot 3 - (100 \div 10)$ **79.** $3^4 - [35 - (12 - 6)]$

80. $[40 - (8 - 2)] - 2^5$ **81.** $(7 \cdot 5) + [9 \div (3 \div 3)]$ **82.** $(18 \div 6) + [(3 + 5) \cdot 2]$

83. $8 \cdot [2^2 + (6 - 1) \cdot 2] - 50 \cdot 2$ **84.** $35 \div [3^2 + (9 - 7) - 2^2] + 10 \cdot 3$

85. $\dfrac{9^2 + 2^2 - 1^2}{8 \div 2 \cdot 3 \cdot 1 \div 3}$ **86.** $\dfrac{5^2 - 2^3 + 1^4}{10 \div 5 \cdot 4 \cdot 1 \div 4}$

Simplify. See Examples 12 through 17. (This section does contain square roots.)

87. $6 \cdot \sqrt{9} + 3 \cdot \sqrt{4}$ **88.** $3 \cdot \sqrt{25} + 2 \cdot \sqrt{81}$ **89.** $4 \cdot \sqrt{49} - 0 \div \sqrt{100}$

90. $7 \cdot \sqrt{36} - 0 \div \sqrt{64}$ **91.** $\dfrac{\sqrt{4} + 4^2}{5(20 - 16) - 3^2 - 5}$ **92.** $\dfrac{\sqrt{9} + 9^2}{3(10 - 6) - 2^2 - 1}$

93. $\sqrt{81} \div \sqrt{9} + 4^2 \cdot 2 - 10$ **94.** $\sqrt{100} \div \sqrt{4} + 3^3 \cdot 2 - 20$

95. $[\sqrt{225} \div (11 - 6) + 2^2] + (\sqrt{25} - \sqrt{1})^2$

96. $[\sqrt{169} \div (20 - 7) + 2^5] - (\sqrt{4} + \sqrt{9})^2$

97. $7^2 - \{18 - [40 \div (4 \cdot 2) + \sqrt{4}] + 5^2\}$

98. $29 - \{5 + 3[8 \cdot (10 - \sqrt{64})] - 50\}$

Objective Ⓔ **Mixed Practice (*Sections 1.3, 1.6*)**   *Find the area and perimeter of each square. See Example 15.*

99.
7 meters

100.
9 centimeters

101.
23 miles

102.
41 feet

Concept Extensions

Answer the following true or false. See the Concept Check in this section.

103. "Six to the fifth power" is the same as 6^5.

104. "Seven squared" is the same as 7^2.

105. 2^5 is the same as $5 \cdot 5$.

106. 4^9 is the same as $4 \cdot 9$.

Insert grouping symbols (parentheses) so that each given expression evaluates to the given number.

107. $2 + 3 \cdot 6 - 2$; evaluates to 28

108. $2 + 3 \cdot 6 - 2$; evaluates to 20

109. $24 \div 3 \cdot 2 + 2 \cdot 5$; evaluates to 14

110. $24 \div 3 \cdot 2 + 2 \cdot 5$; evaluates to 15

111. A building contractor is bidding on a contract to install gutters on seven homes in a retirement community, all in the shape shown. To estimate the cost of materials, she needs to know the total perimeter of all seven homes. Find the total perimeter.

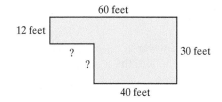

112. The building contractor from Exercise 111 plans to charge $4 per foot for installing vinyl gutters. Find the total charge for the seven homes given the total perimeter answer to Exercise 111.

Simplify.

113. $(7 + 2^4)^5 - (3^5 - 2^4)^2$

114. $25^3 \cdot (45 - 7 \cdot 5) \cdot 5$

115. Write an expression that simplifies to 5. Use multiplication, division, addition, subtraction, and at least one set of parentheses. Explain the process you would use to simplify the expression.

116. Explain why $2 \cdot 3^2$ is not the same as $(2 \cdot 3)^2$.

1 Chapter Highlights

Helpful Hint Are you preparing for your test? Use the Test Prep Videos to see the fully worked-out solutions to any of the exercises you want to review.

Definitions and Concepts	Examples

Section 1.2   Place Values, Names for Numbers, and Reading Tables

The **whole numbers** are $0, 1, 2, 3, 4, 5, \ldots$.

The position of each digit in a number determines its **place value.** A place-value chart is shown next with the names of the periods given.

0, 14, 968, 5,268,619

Periods

Billions | Millions | Thousands | Ones

Hundred-billions, Ten-billions, Billions, Hundred-millions, Ten-millions, Millions, Hundred-thousands, Ten-thousands, Thousands, Hundreds, Tens, Ones

To write a whole number in words, write the number in each period followed by the name of the period. (The name of the ones period is not included.)

9,078,651,002 is written as nine billion, seventy-eight million, six hundred fifty-one thousand, two.

To write a whole number in standard form, write the number in each period, followed by a comma.

Four million, seven hundred six thousand, twenty-eight is written as 4,706,028.

Section 1.3   Adding Whole Numbers and Perimeter

To add whole numbers, add the digits in the ones place, then the tens place, then the hundreds place, and so on, carrying when necessary.

Find the sum:

$$
\begin{array}{r}
\overset{211}{} \\
2689 \leftarrow \text{addend} \\
1735 \leftarrow \text{addend} \\
+\ 662 \leftarrow \text{addend} \\
\hline
5086 \leftarrow \text{sum}
\end{array}
$$

The **perimeter** of a polygon is its distance around or the sum of the lengths of its sides.

Find the perimeter of the polygon shown.

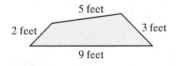

The perimeter is
5 feet + 3 feet + 9 feet + 2 feet = 19 feet.

Section 1.4   Subtracting Whole Numbers

To subtract whole numbers, subtract the digits in the ones place, then the tens place, then the hundreds place, and so on, borrowing when necessary.

Subtract:

$$
\begin{array}{r}
\overset{8\ 15}{79\cancel{8}4} \leftarrow \text{minuend} \\
-5673 \leftarrow \text{subtrahend} \\
\hline
2281 \leftarrow \text{difference}
\end{array}
$$

Definitions and Concepts	**Examples**
Section 1.5 Rounding and Estimating	

ROUNDING WHOLE NUMBERS TO A GIVEN PLACE VALUE

Step 1. Locate the digit to the right of the given place value.

Step 2. If this digit is 5 or greater, add 1 to the digit in the given place value and replace each digit to its right with 0.

Step 3. If this digit is less than 5, replace it and each digit to its right with 0.

Round 15,721 to the nearest thousand.

$$15,\underbrace{\overset{\uparrow}{\underset{\text{Add 1}}{}}\textcircled{7}21}_{\substack{\text{Replace} \\ \text{with} \\ \text{zeros.}}}$$ Since the circled digit is 5 or greater, add 1 to the given place value and replace digits to its right with zeros.

15,721 rounded to the nearest thousand is 16,000.

Section 1.6 Multiplying Whole Numbers and Area	

To multiply 73 and 58, for example, multiply 73 and 8, then 73 and 50. The sum of these partial products is the product of 73 and 58. Use the notation to the right.

$$
\begin{array}{r}
73 \ \leftarrow \ \text{factor} \\
\times\ 58 \ \leftarrow \ \text{factor} \\
\hline
584 \ \leftarrow \ 73 \times 8 \\
3650 \ \leftarrow \ 73 \times 50 \\
\hline
4234 \ \leftarrow \ \text{product}
\end{array}
$$

To find the **area** of a rectangle, multiply length times width.

△ Find the area of the rectangle shown.

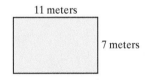

11 meters

7 meters

area of rectangle = length · width
= (11 meters)(7 meters)
= 77 square meters

Section 1.7 Dividing Whole Numbers	

DIVISION PROPERTIES OF 0

The quotient of 0 and any number (except 0) is 0.

The quotient of any number and 0 is not a number. We say that this quotient is undefined.

To divide larger whole numbers, use the process called **long division** as shown to the right.

$$\frac{0}{5} = 0$$

$$\frac{7}{0} \text{ is undefined}$$

$$
\begin{array}{r}
507 \ \text{R } 2 \ \leftarrow \text{quotient and remainder} \\
\text{divisor} \rightarrow 14\overline{)7100} \ \leftarrow \text{dividend} \\
-70\downarrow \qquad\quad 5(14) = 70 \\
\hline
10 \qquad \text{Subtract and bring down the 0.} \\
-0\downarrow \qquad 0(14) = 0 \\
\hline
100 \qquad \text{Subtract and bring down the 0.} \\
-98 \qquad 7(14) = 98 \\
\hline
2 \qquad \text{Subtract. The remainder is 2.}
\end{array}
$$

To check, see that 507 · 14 + 2 = 7100.

The **average** of a list of numbers is

$$\text{average} = \frac{\text{sum of numbers}}{\textit{number } \text{of numbers}}$$

Find the average of 23, 35, and 38.

$$\text{average} = \frac{23 + 35 + 38}{3} = \frac{96}{3} = 32$$

Definitions and Concepts	**Examples**
Section 1.8 An Introduction to Problem Solving	

PROBLEM-SOLVING STEPS	Suppose that 225 tickets are sold for each performance of a play. How many tickets are sold for 5 performances?
1. UNDERSTAND the problem.	**1.** UNDERSTAND. Read and reread the problem. Since we want the number of tickets for 5 performances, we multiply.
2. TRANSLATE the problem.	**2.** TRANSLATE.

number of tickets	is	number of performances	times	tickets per performance
↓	↓	↓	↓	↓
Number of tickets	=	5	·	225

3. SOLVE the problem.	**3.** SOLVE: See if the answer is reasonable by also estimating.

$$\begin{array}{lll} \overset{1\,2}{225} & \text{rounds to} & 200 \\ \underline{\times \quad 5} & & \underline{\times \quad 5} \\ 1125 \;\; \text{exact} & & 1000 \;\; \text{estimate} \end{array}$$

4. INTERPRET the results.	**4.** INTERPRET. **Check** your work. The product is reasonable since 1125 is close to our estimated answer of 1000, and **state** your conclusion: There are 1125 tickets sold for 5 performances.

Section 1.9 Exponents, Square Roots, and Order of Operations	

An **exponent** is a shorthand notation for repeated multiplication of the same factor.

A **square root** of a number is one of two identical factors of the number.

ORDER OF OPERATIONS

1. Perform all operations within parentheses ( ), brackets [ ], or other grouping symbols such as square roots or fraction bars, starting with the innermost set.
2. Evaluate any expressions with exponents.
3. Multiply or divide in order from left to right.
4. Add or subtract in order from left to right.

$$\overset{\text{exponent}}{3^4} = \underbrace{3 \cdot 3 \cdot 3 \cdot 3}_{4 \text{ factors of } 3} = 81$$

base

$$\sqrt{36} = 6 \quad \text{because} \quad 6 \cdot 6 = 36$$
$$\sqrt{121} = 11 \quad \text{because} \quad 11 \cdot 11 = 121$$
$$\sqrt{0} = 0 \quad \text{because} \quad 0 \cdot 0 = 0$$

Simplify: $\dfrac{5 + 3^2}{2(7 - 6)}$

Simplify above and below the fraction bar separately.

$$\frac{5 + 3^2}{2(7 - 6)} = \frac{5 + 9}{2(1)} \quad \begin{array}{l}\text{Evaluate } 3^2 \text{ above the fraction bar.} \\ \text{Subtract: } 7 - 6 \text{ below the fraction bar.}\end{array}$$

$$= \frac{14}{2} \quad \begin{array}{l}\text{Add.} \\ \text{Multiply.}\end{array}$$

$$= 7 \quad \text{Divide.}$$

The **area of a square** is $(\text{side})^2$.

Find the area of a square with side length 9 inches.

$$\begin{aligned} \text{Area of the square} &= (\text{side})^2 \\ &= (9 \text{ inches})^2 \\ &= 81 \text{ square inches} \end{aligned}$$

Chapter 1 Review

(1.2) *Determine the place value of the digit 4 in each whole number.*

1. 7640

2. 46,200,120

Write each whole number in words.

3. 7640

4. 46,200,120

Write each whole number in expanded form.

5. 3158

6. 403,225,000

Write each whole number in standard form.

7. Eighty-one thousand, nine hundred

8. Six billion, three hundred four million

The following table shows the Internet use of world regions. Use this table to answer Exercises 9 through 12.

(*Source:* International Telecommunications Union)

Internet Use by World Regions			
World Region	**2000**	**2004**	**2008**
Africa	4,514,400	21,371,600	51,065,630
Asia	114,304,000	295,852,200	578,538,257
Europe	105,096,093	241,208,100	384,633,765
Middle East	3,284,800	28,917,600	41,939,200
North America	108,096,800	217,835,900	248,241,969
Latin America/ Caribbean	18,068,919	50,661,500	139,009,209
Oceania/ Australia	7,620,480	11,805,500	20,204,331

9. Find the number of Internet users in 2008 in Europe.

10. Find the number of Internet users in Oceania/Australia in 2004.

11. Which world region had the smallest number of Internet users in 2000?

12. Which world region had the greatest number of Internet users in 2008?

(1.3) *Add.*

13. 17 + 46

14. 28 + 39

15. 25 + 8 + 15

16. 27 + 9 + 41

17. 932 + 24

18. 819 + 21

19. 567 + 7383

20. 463 + 6787

21. 91 + 3623 + 497

22. 82 + 1647 + 238

Solve.

23. Find the sum of 86, 331, and 909.

24. Find the sum of 49, 529, and 308.

25. What is 26,481 increased by 865?

26. What is 38,556 increased by 744?

27. The distance from Chicago to New York City is 714 miles. The distance from New York City to New Delhi, India, is 7318 miles. Find the total distance from Chicago to New Delhi if traveling by air through New York City.

28. Susan Summerline earned salaries of $62,589, $65,340, and $69,770 during the years 2002, 2003, and 2004, respectively. Find her total earnings during those three years.

Find the perimeter of each figure.

△ **29.**

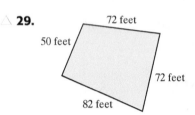

72 feet
50 feet
72 feet
82 feet

△ **30.** 11 kilometers   20 kilometers
35 kilometers

(1.4) *Subtract and then check.*

31. 93 − 79   **32.** 61 − 27   **33.** 462 − 397   **34.** 583 − 279   **35.** 4000 − 86   **36.** 8000 − 92

Solve.

37. Subtract 7965 from 25,862.

38. Subtract 4349 from 39,007.

39. Find the increase in population for San Antonio, Texas, from 2000 (population: 1,144,646) to 2007 (population: 1,328,984).

40. Find the decrease in population for Philadelphia, Pennsylvania, from 2000 (population: 1,517,550) to 2007 (population: 1,491,812).

41. Bob Roma is proofreading the Yellow Pages for his county. If he has finished 315 pages of the total 712 pages, how many pages does he have left to proof-read?

42. Shelly Winters bought a new car listed at $28,425. She received a discount of $1599 and a factory rebate of $1200. Find how much she paid for the car.

The following bar graph shows the monthly savings account balance for a freshman attending a local community college. Use this graph to answer Exercises 43 through 46.

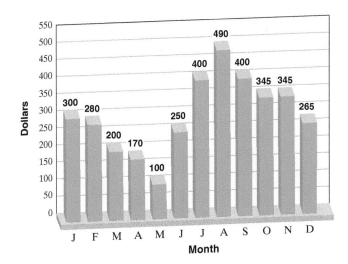

43. During what month was the balance the least?

44. During what month was the balance the greatest?

45. By how much did his balance decrease from February to April?

46. By how much did his balance increase from June to August?

(1.5) *Round to the given place.*

47. 93 to the nearest ten

48. 45 to the nearest ten

49. 467 to the nearest ten

50. 493 to the nearest hundred

51. 4832 to the nearest hundred

52. 57,534 to the nearest thousand

53. 49,683,712 to the nearest million

54. 768,542 to the nearest hundred-thousand

55. In 2008, 65,025,901 Americans voted for one of the major candidates for president. Round this number to the nearest million. (*Source:* CNN)

56. In 2007, there were 93,295 public elementary and secondary schools in the United States. Round this number to the nearest thousand. (*Source:* National Center for Educational Statistics)

Estimate the sum or difference by rounding each number to the nearest hundred.

57. 4892 + 647 + 1876

58. 5925 − 1787

59. A group of students took a week-long driving trip and traveled 628, 290, 172, 58, 508, 445, and 383 miles on seven consecutive days. Round each distance to the nearest hundred to estimate the distance they traveled.

60. According to the city population table, the 2007 population of Houston, Texas, was 2,208,180, and for San Diego, California, it was 1,336,865. Round each number to the nearest hundred-thousand and estimate how much larger Houston is than San Diego.

(1.6) *Multiply.*

61. 273
      × 7

62. 349
      × 4

63. 47
      × 30

64. 69
      × 42

65. 20(8)(5)

66. 25(9)(4)

67.   48
      × 77

68.   77
      × 22

69. 49 · 49 · 0

70. 62 · 88 · 0

71.   586
      × 29

72.   242
      × 37

73.   642
      × 177

74.   347
      × 129

75. 1026
      × 401

76. 2107
      × 302

77. 375 · 1000

78. 108 · 1000

79. 30 · 400

80. 50 · 700

81. 1700 · 3000

82. 1900 · 4000

Solve.

83. Find the product of 5 and 230.

84. Find the product of 6 and 820.

85. Multiply 9 and 12.

86. Multiply 8 and 14.

87. One ounce of Swiss cheese contains 8 grams of fat. How many grams of fat are in 3 ounces of Swiss cheese? (*Source: Home and Garden Bulletin No. 72,* U.S. Department of Agriculture)

88. The cost for a South Dakota resident to attend Black Hills State University full-time is $6112 per semester. Determine the cost for 20 students to attend full-time. (*Source:* Black Hills State University)

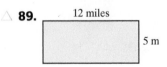

Find the area of each rectangle.

△ **89.**

12 miles

5 m

△ **90.**

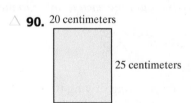

20 centimeters

25 centimeters

(1.7) *Divide and then check.*

91. $\frac{18}{6}$

92. $\frac{36}{9}$

93. 42 ÷ 7

94. 35 ÷ 5

95. 27 ÷ 5

96. 18 ÷ 4

97. 16 ÷ 0

98. 0 ÷ 8

99. 9 ÷ 9

100. 10 ÷ 1

101. $0 \div 668$ **102.** $918 \div 0$ **103.** $5\overline{)167}$ **104.** $8\overline{)159}$ **105.** $26\overline{)626}$

106. $19\overline{)680}$ **107.** $47\overline{)23{,}792}$ **108.** $53\overline{)48{,}111}$ **109.** $207\overline{)578{,}291}$ **110.** $306\overline{)615{,}732}$

Solve.

111. Find the quotient of 92 and 5.

112. Find the quotient of 86 and 4.

113. One foot is 12 inches. Find how many feet there are in 5496 inches.

114. One mile is 1760 yards. Find how many miles there are in 22,880 yards.

115. Find the average of the numbers 76, 49, 32, and 47.

116. Find the average of the numbers 23, 85, 62, and 66.

(1.8) *Solve.*

117. A box can hold 24 cans of corn. How many boxes can be filled with 648 cans of corn?

118. If a ticket to a movie costs $6, how much do 32 tickets cost?

119. Aspirin was 100 years old in 1997 and was the first U.S. drug made in tablet form. Today, people take 11 billion tablets a year for heart disease prevention and 4 billion tablets a year for headaches. How many more tablets are taken a year for heart disease prevention? (*Source:* Bayer Market Research)

120. The cost to banks when a person uses an ATM (Automatic Teller Machine) is 27¢. The cost to banks when a person deposits a check with a teller is 48¢ more. How much is this cost?

121. A golf pro orders shirts for the company sponsoring a local charity golfing event. Shirts size large cost $32 while shirts size extra-large cost $38. If 15 large shirts and 11 extra-large shirts are ordered, find the cost.

122. Two rectangular pieces of land are purchased: one that measures 65 feet by 110 feet and one that measures 80 feet by 200 feet. Find the total area of land purchased. (*Hint:* Find the area of each rectangle, then add.)

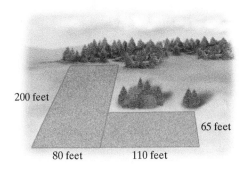

200 feet

65 feet

80 feet   110 feet

(1.9) *Simplify.*

123. 7^2 **124.** 5^3 **125.** $5 \cdot 3^2$ **126.** $4 \cdot 10^2$

127. $18 \div 3 + 7$ **128.** $12 - 8 \div 4$ **129.** $\dfrac{5(6^2 - 3)}{3^2 + 2}$ **130.** $\dfrac{7(16 - 8)}{2^3}$

131. $48 \div 8 \cdot 2$ **132.** $27 \div 9 \cdot 3$

133. $2 + 3[1^5 + (20 - 17) \cdot 3] + 5 \cdot 2$ **134.** $21 - [2^4 - (7 - 5) - 10] + 8 \cdot 2$

Simplify. (These exercises contain square roots.)

135. $\sqrt{81}$ **136.** $\sqrt{4}$ **137.** $\sqrt{1}$ **138.** $\sqrt{0}$

139. $4 \cdot \sqrt{25} - 2 \cdot 7$ **140.** $8 \cdot \sqrt{49} - 3 \cdot 9$

141. $\left(\sqrt{36} - \sqrt{16}\right)^3 \cdot [10^2 \div (3 + 17)]$ **142.** $\left(\sqrt{49} - \sqrt{25}\right)^3 \cdot [9^2 \div (2 + 7)]$

143. $\dfrac{5 \cdot 7 - 3 \cdot \sqrt{25}}{2\left(\sqrt{121} - 3^2\right)}$ **144.** $\dfrac{4 \cdot 8 - 1 \cdot \sqrt{121}}{3\left(\sqrt{81} - 2^3\right)}$

Find the area of each square.

△ **145.** A square with side length of 7 meters.

△ **146.**

3 inches

Answers to Selected Exercises

Chapter 1 The Whole Numbers

Section 1.2

Vocabulary and Readiness Check **1.** whole **3.** words **5.** period

Exercise Set 1.2 **1.** tens **3.** thousands **5.** hundred-thousands **7.** millions **9.** three hundred fifty-four **11.** eight thousand, two hundred seventy-nine **13.** twenty-six thousand, nine hundred ninety **15.** two million, three hundred eighty-eight thousand **17.** twenty-four million, three hundred fifty thousand, one hundred eighty-five **19.** three hundred four thousand, three hundred sixty-seven **21.** two thousand, six hundred **23.** fifteen million, eight hundred thousand **25.** fourteen thousand, four hundred thirty-three **27.** thirteen million **29.** 6587 **31.** 59,800 **33.** 13,601,011 **35.** 7,000,017 **37.** 260,997 **39.** 395 **41.** 16,732 **43.** $72,704,000 **45.** 1317 **47.** 400 + 6 **49.** 3000 + 400 + 70 **51.** 80,000 + 700 + 70 + 4 **53.** 60,000 + 6000 + 40 + 9 **55.** 30,000,000 + 9,000,000 + 600,000 + 80,000 **57.** 5532; five thousand, five hundred thirty-two **59.** 5000 + 400 + 90 + 2 **61.** Mt. Washington **63.** Boxer **65.** Labrador retriever; one hundred twenty-three thousand, seven hundred sixty **67.** 25 pounds **69.** 9861 **71.** no; one hundred five **73.** answers may vary **75.** 1,000,000,000,000,000 **77.** Canton

Section 1.3

Calculator Explorations **1.** 134 **3.** 340 **5.** 2834

Vocabulary and Readiness Check **1.** number **3.** sum; addend **5.** grouping; associative

Exercise Set 1.3 **1.** 36 **3.** 292 **5.** 49 **7.** 5399 **9.** 117 **11.** 512 **13.** 209,078 **15.** 25 **17.** 62 **19.** 212 **21.** 94 **23.** 910 **25.** 8273 **27.** 11,926 **29.** 1884 **31.** 16,717 **33.** 1110 **35.** 8999 **37.** 35,901 **39.** 632,389 **41.** 42 in. **43.** 25 ft **45.** 24 in. **47.** 8 yd **49.** 29 in. **51.** 44 m **53.** 2093 **55.** 266 **57.** 544 **59.** 3452 **61.** 22,478 thousand **63.** 6684 ft **65.** 340 ft **67.** 2425 ft **69.** 313,769 motorcycles **71.** 85,446 automobiles **73.** 124 ft **75.** 3170 **77.** California **79.** 506 stores **81.** Florida and Georgia **83.** 5894 mi **85.** answers may vary **87.** answers may vary **89.** 1,044,473,765 **91.** correct **93.** incorrect: 530

Section 1.4

Calculator Explorations **1.** 770 **3.** 109 **5.** 8978

Vocabulary and Readiness Check **1.** 0 **3.** minuend; subtrahend **5.** 0 **7.** 600

Exercise Set 1.4 **1.** 44 **3.** 265 **5.** 135 **7.** 2254 **9.** 5545 **11.** 600 **13.** 25 **15.** 45 **17.** 146 **19.** 288 **21.** 168 **23.** 106 **25.** 447 **27.** 5723 **29.** 504 **31.** 89 **33.** 79 **35.** 39,914 **37.** 32,711 **39.** 5041 **41.** 31,213 **43.** 4 **45.** 20 **47.** 7 **49.** 72 **51.** 88 **53.** 264 pages **55.** 3 million sq km **57.** 264,000 sq mi **59.** 283,000 sq mi **61.** 6065 ft **63.** 28 ft **65.** 358 mi **67.** $619 **69.** 452 thousand **71.** 100 dB **73.** 58 dB **75.** 320 **77.** 5920 sq ft **79.** Hartsfield Atlanta International **81.** 26 million **83.** Jo; by 271 votes **85.** 1034 **87.** 9 **89.** 8518 **91.** 22,876 **93.** minuend: 48; subtrahend: 1 **95.** minuend: 70; subtrahend: 7 **97.** incorrect: 685 **99.** correct **101.** $5269 - 2385 = 2884$ **103.** no; answers may vary **105.** no: 1089 more pages

Section 1.5

Vocabulary and Readiness Check **1.** graph **3.** 70; 60

Exercise Set 1.5 **1.** 420 **3.** 640 **5.** 2800 **7.** 500 **9.** 21,000 **11.** 34,000 **13.** 328,500 **15.** 36,000 **17.** 39,990 **19.** 30,000,000 **21.** 5280; 5300; 5000 **23.** 9440; 9400; 9000 **25.** 14,880; 14,900; 15,000 **27.** 84,000 members **29.** 38,000 points **31.** $43,000,000,000 **33.** $4,100,000 **35.** US: 263,000,000; India: 297,000,000 **37.** 130 **39.** 80 **41.** 5700 **43.** 300 **45.** 11,400 **47.** incorrect **49.** correct **51.** correct **53.** $3400 **55.** 900 mi **57.** 6000 ft **59.** Joliet is larger by approximately 60,000. **61.** The increase was 2000. **63.** 391,000,000; 390,000,000; 400,000,000 **65.** 349,000,000; 350,000,000; 300,000,000 **67.** 5723, for example **69. a.** 8550 **b.** 8649 **71.** answers may vary **73.** 140 m

Section 1.6

Calculator Explorations **1.** 3456 **3.** 15,322 **5.** 272,291

Vocabulary and Readiness Check **1.** 0 **3.** product; factor **5.** grouping; associative **7.** length

Exercise Set 1.6 **1.** 24 **3.** 0 **5.** 0 **7.** 87 **9.** $6 \cdot 3 + 6 \cdot 8$ **11.** $4 \cdot 3 + 4 \cdot 9$ **13.** $20 \cdot 14 + 20 \cdot 6$ **15.** 512 **17.** 3678 **19.** 1662 **21.** 6444 **23.** 1157 **25.** 24,418 **27.** 24,786 **29.** 15,600 **31.** 0 **33.** 6400 **35.** 48,126 **37.** 142,506 **39.** 2,369,826 **41.** 64,790 **43.** 3,949,935 **45.** 800 **47.** 11,000 **49.** 74,060 **51.** 24,000 **53.** 45,000 **55.** 3,280,000 **57.** area: 63 sq m; perimeter: 32 m **59.** area: 680 sq ft; perimeter: 114 ft **61.** 240,000 **63.** 300,000 **65.** c **67.** c **69.** 880 **71.** 4200 **73.** 4480 **75.** 375 cal **77.** $3290 **79. a.** 20 **b.** 100 **c.** 2000 lb **81.** 8800 sq ft **83.** 56,000 sq ft **85.** 5828 pixels **87.** 2100 characters **89.** 1280 cal **91.** $10, $60; $10, $200; $12, $36; $12, $36; total cost: $372 **93.** 1,440,000 tea bags **95.** 135 **97.** 2144 **99.** 23 **101.** 15 **103.** $5 \cdot 6$ or $6 \cdot 5$ **105. a.** $5 + 5 + 5$ or $3 + 3 + 3 + 3 + 3$ **b.** answers may vary **107.**

$$\begin{array}{r} 203 \\ \times\ 14 \\ \hline 812 \\ 2030 \\ \hline 2842 \end{array}$$

109.

$$\begin{array}{r} 42 \\ \times 93 \end{array}$$

111. answers may vary **113.** 506 windows

Section 1.7

Calculator Explorations **1.** 53 **3.** 62 **5.** 261 **7.** 0

Vocabulary and Readiness Check **1.** quotient; dividend; divisor **3.** 1 **5.** undefined

Exercise Set 1.7 **1.** 6 **3.** 12 **5.** 0 **7.** 31 **9.** 1 **11.** 8 **13.** undefined **15.** 1 **17.** 0 **19.** 9 **21.** 29 **23.** 74 **25.** 338 **27.** undefined **29.** 9 **31.** 25 **33.** 68 R 3 **35.** 236 R 5 **37.** 38 R 1 **39.** 326 R 4 **41.** 13 **43.** 49 **45.** 97 R 8 **47.** 209 R 11 **49.** 506 **51.** 202 R 7 **53.** 54 **55.** 99 R 100 **57.** 202 R 15 **59.** 579 R 72 **61.** 17 **63.** 511 R 3 **65.** 2132 R 32 **67.** 6080 **69.** 23 R 2 **71.** 5 R 25 **73.** 20 R 2 **75.** 33 students

77. 165 lb   **79.** 310 yd   **81.** 89 bridges   **83.** 11 light poles   **85.** 5 mi   **87.** 1760 yd   **89.** 20   **91.** 387   **93.** 79   **95.** 74°   **97.** 9278   **99.** 15,288   **101.** 679   **103.** undefined   **105.** 9 R 12   **107.** c   **109.** b   **111.** 120   **113.** increase; answers may vary   **115.** no; answers may vary   **117.** 12 ft   **119.** answers may vary   **121.** 5 R 1

Section 1.8

Exercise Set 1.8   **1.** 49   **3.** 237   **5.** 42   **7.** 600   **9. a.** 400 ft   **b.** 9600 sq ft   **11.** $15,500   **13.** 168 hr   **15.** 3500 ft   **17.** 129 yr   **19.** 312 billion bricks   **21.** 719 towns   **23.** $27   **25.** 55 cal   **27.** 23 hot dogs   **29.** $30,956,764   **31.** 155,300   **33.** 3987 mi   **35.** 13 paychecks   **37.** $239   **39.** $1045   **41.** b will be cheaper by $3   **43.** Asia   **45.** 559 million   **47.** 109 million   **49.** 404 million   **51.** $14,754   **53.** 16,800 mg   **55. a.** 3750 sq ft   **b.** 375 sq ft   **c.** 3375 sq ft   **57.** $171   **59.** answers may vary

Section 1.9

Calculator Explorations   **1.** 4096   **3.** 3125   **5.** 2048   **7.** 2526   **9.** 4295   **11.** 8

Vocabulary and Readiness Check   **1.** base; exponent   **3.** addition   **5.** division

Exercise Set 1.9   **1.** 4^3 **3.** 7^6 **5.** 12^3 **7.** $6^2 \cdot 5^3$ **9.** $9 \cdot 8^2$ **11.** $3 \cdot 2^4$ **13.** $3 \cdot 2^4 \cdot 5^5$ **15.** 64   **17.** 125   **19.** 32   **21.** 1   **23.** 7   **25.** 128   **27.** 256   **29.** 256   **31.** 729   **33.** 144   **35.** 100   **37.** 20   **39.** 729   **41.** 192   **43.** 162   **45.** 3   **47.** 8   **49.** 12   **51.** 4   **53.** 21   **55.** 7   **57.** 5   **59.** 16   **61.** 46   **63.** 8   **65.** 64   **67.** 83   **69.** 2   **71.** 48   **73.** 4   **75.** undefined   **77.** 59   **79.** 52   **81.** 44   **83.** 12   **85.** 21   **87.** 24   **89.** 28   **91.** 3   **93.** 25   **95.** 23   **97.** 13   **99.** area: 49 sq m; perimeter: 28 m   **101.** area: 529 sq mi; perimeter: 92 mi   **103.** true   **105.** false   **107.** $(2 + 3) \cdot 6 - 2$ **109.** $24 \div (3 \cdot 2) + 2 \cdot 5$ **111.** 1260 ft   **113.** 6,384,814   **115.** answers may vary; $(20 - 10) \cdot 5 \div 25 + 3$

Chapter 1 Review   **1.** tens   **2.** ten-millions   **3.** seven thousand, six hundred forty   **4.** forty-six million, two hundred thousand, one hundred twenty   **5.** $3000 + 100 + 50 + 8$ **6.** $400,000,000 + 3,000,000 + 200,000 + 20,000 + 5000$ **7.** 81,900   **8.** 6,304,000,000   **9.** 384,633,765   **10.** 11,805,500   **11.** Middle East   **12.** Asia   **13.** 63   **14.** 67   **15.** 48   **16.** 77   **17.** 956   **18.** 840   **19.** 7950   **20.** 7250   **21.** 4211   **22.** 1967   **23.** 1326   **24.** 886   **25.** 27,346   **26.** 39,300   **27.** 8032 mi   **28.** $197,699   **29.** 276 ft   **30.** 66 km   **31.** 14   **32.** 34   **33.** 65   **34.** 304   **35.** 3914   **36.** 7908   **37.** 17,897   **38.** 34,658   **39.** 184,338   **40.** 25,738   **41.** 397 pages   **42.** $25,626   **43.** May   **44.** August   **45.** $110   **46.** $240   **47.** 90   **48.** 50   **49.** 470   **50.** 500   **51.** 4800   **52.** 58,000   **53.** 50,000,000   **54.** 800,000   **55.** 65,000,000   **56.** 93,000   **57.** 7400   **58.** 4100   **59.** 2500 mi   **60.** 900,000   **61.** 1911   **62.** 1396   **63.** 1410   **64.** 2898   **65.** 800   **66.** 900   **67.** 3696   **68.** 1694   **69.** 0   **70.** 0   **71.** 16,994   **72.** 8954   **73.** 113,634   **74.** 44,763   **75.** 411,426   **76.** 636,314   **77.** 375,000   **78.** 108,000   **79.** 12,000   **80.** 35,000   **81.** 5,100,000   **82.** 7,600,000   **83.** 1150   **84.** 4920   **85.** 108   **86.** 112   **87.** 24 g   **88.** $122,240   **89.** 60 sq mi   **90.** 500 sq cm   **91.** 3   **92.** 4   **93.** 6   **94.** 7   **95.** 5 R 2   **96.** 4 R 2   **97.** undefined   **98.** 0   **99.** 1   **100.** 10   **101.** 0   **102.** undefined   **103.** 33 R 2   **104.** 19 R 7   **105.** 24 R 2   **106.** 35 R 15   **107.** 506 R 10   **108.** 907 R 40   **109.** 2793 R 140   **110.** 2012 R 60   **111.** 18 R 2   **112.** 21 R 2   **113.** 458 ft   **114.** 13 mi   **115.** 51   **116.** 59   **117.** 27 boxes   **118.** $192   **119.** 7 billion   **120.** 75¢   **121.** $898   **122.** 23,150 sq ft   **123.** 49   **124.** 125   **125.** 45   **126.** 400   **127.** 13   **128.** 10   **129.** 15   **130.** 7   **131.** 12   **132.** 9   **133.** 42   **134.** 33   **135.** 9   **136.** 2   **137.** 1   **138.** 0   **139.** 6   **140.** 29   **141.** 40   **142.** 72   **143.** 5   **144.** 7   **145.** 49 sq m   **146.** 9 sq in.

Fractions

2

Objectives

A Identify the Numerator and the Denominator of a Fraction and Review Division Properties for 0 and 1.

B Write a Fraction to Represent Parts of Figures or Real-Life Data.

C Identify Proper Fractions, Improper Fractions, and Mixed Numbers.

D Write Mixed Numbers as Improper Fractions.

E Write Improper Fractions as Mixed Numbers or Whole Numbers.

2.1 INTRODUCTION TO FRACTIONS AND MIXED NUMBERS

Objective **A** Identifying Numerators and Denominators and Reviewing Division Properties for 0 and 1

Whole numbers are used to count whole things or units, such as cars, horses, dollars, and people. To refer to a part of a whole, fractions can be used. Here are some examples of **fractions.** Study these examples for a moment.

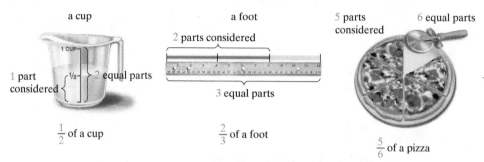

$\frac{1}{2}$ of a cup $\frac{2}{3}$ of a foot $\frac{5}{6}$ of a pizza

In a fraction, the top number is called the **numerator** and the bottom number is called the **denominator.** The bar between the numbers is called the **fraction bar.**

Names	Fraction	Meaning
numerator ⟶	$\dfrac{5}{6}$	⟵ number of parts being considered
denominator ⟶		⟵ number of equal parts in the whole

Examples Identify the numerator and the denominator of each fraction.

1. $\dfrac{3}{7}$ ← numerator
   ← denominator

2. $\dfrac{13}{5}$ ← numerator
   ← denominator

> **Helpful Hint**
> Notice the fraction $\dfrac{11}{1} = 11$, or also $11 = \dfrac{11}{1}$.

● **Work Practice 1–2**

Before we continue further, don't forget from Section 1.7 that the fraction bar indicates division. Let's review some division properties for 1 and 0.

$\dfrac{9}{9} = 1$ because $1 \cdot 9 = 9$ $\dfrac{11}{1} = 11$ because $11 \cdot 1 = 11$

$\dfrac{0}{6} = 0$ because $0 \cdot 6 = 0$ $\dfrac{6}{0}$ *is undefined* because there is no number that when multiplied by 0 gives 6.

In general, we can say the following.

> Let n be any whole number except 0.
>
> $\dfrac{n}{n} = 1$ $\dfrac{0}{n} = 0$
>
> $\dfrac{n}{1} = n$ $\dfrac{n}{0}$ is undefined.

PRACTICE 1–2

Identify the numerator and the denominator of each fraction.

1. $\dfrac{9}{2}$ **2.** $\dfrac{10}{17}$

Answers

1. numerator = 9, denominator = 2
2. numerator = 10, denominator = 17

Examples Simplify.

3. $\frac{5}{5} = 1$ **4.** $\frac{0}{7} = 0$ **5.** $\frac{10}{1} = 10$ **6.** $\frac{3}{0}$ is undefined

● Work Practice 3–6

PRACTICE 3–6

Simplify.

3. $\frac{0}{2}$ **4.** $\frac{8}{8}$

5. $\frac{4}{0}$ **6.** $\frac{20}{1}$

Objective ⓑ Writing Fractions to Represent Parts of Figures or Real-Life Data

One way to become familiar with the concept of fractions is to visualize fractions with shaded figures. We can then write a fraction to represent the shaded area of the figure.

Examples Write a fraction to represent the shaded part of each figure.

7. In this figure, 2 of the 5 equal parts are shaded. Thus, the fraction is $\frac{2}{5}$.

$\frac{2}{5}$ ← number of parts shaded
   ← number of equal parts

8. In this figure, 3 of the 10 rectangles are shaded. Thus, the fraction is $\frac{3}{10}$.

$\frac{3}{10}$ ← number of parts shaded
    ← number of equal parts

● Work Practice 7–8

PRACTICE 7–8

Write a fraction to represent the shaded part of each figure.

7.

8.

Examples Write a fraction to represent the shaded part of the diagram.

9.

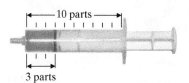

The fraction is $\frac{3}{10}$.   3 parts

10.

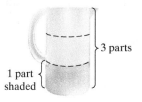

The fraction is $\frac{1}{3}$.   1 part shaded

● Work Practice 9–10

PRACTICE 9–10

Write a fraction to represent the part of the whole shown.

9. Just consider this part of the syringe

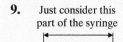

10.

Answers

3. 0   **4.** 1   **5.** undefined   **6.** 20

7. $\frac{3}{8}$ **8.** $\frac{1}{6}$ **9.** $\frac{7}{10}$ **10.** $\frac{9}{16}$

PRACTICE 11–12

Draw and shade a part of a figure to represent each fraction.

11. $\frac{2}{3}$ of a figure

12. $\frac{7}{11}$ of a figure

Examples Draw a figure and then shade a part of it to represent each fraction.

11. $\frac{5}{6}$ of a figure

We will use a geometric figure such as a rectangle. Since the denominator is 6, we divide it into 6 equal parts. Then we shade 5 of the equal parts.

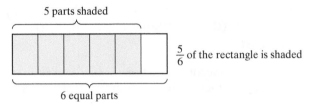

5 parts shaded

$\frac{5}{6}$ of the rectangle is shaded

6 equal parts

12. $\frac{3}{8}$ of a figure

If you'd like, our figure can consist of 8 triangles of the same size. We will shade 3 of the triangles.

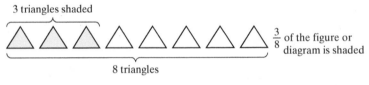

3 triangles shaded

$\frac{3}{8}$ of the figure or diagram is shaded

8 triangles

● **Work Practice 11–12**

✔ **Concept Check** If 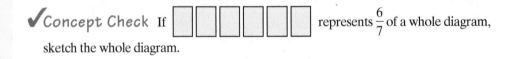 represents $\frac{6}{7}$ of a whole diagram, sketch the whole diagram.

PRACTICE 13

Of the eight planets in our solar system, five are farther from the Sun than Earth is. What fraction of the planets are farther from the Sun than Earth is?

Example 13 Writing Fractions from Real-Life Data

Of the eight planets in our solar system (Pluto is now a dwarf planet), three are closer to the Sun than Mars. What fraction of the planets are closer to the Sun than Mars?

Solution: The fraction of planets closer to the Sun than Mars is:

$\frac{3}{8}$ ← number of planets closer
 ← number of planets in our solar system

Thus, $\frac{3}{8}$ of the planets in our solar system are closer to the Sun than Mars.

● **Work Practice 13**

Answers

11. answers may vary; for example,

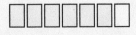

12. answers may vary; for example,

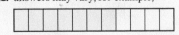

13. $\frac{5}{8}$

✔ **Concept Check Answer**

Objective ⓒ Identifying Proper Fractions, Improper Fractions, and Mixed Numbers

A **proper fraction** is a fraction whose numerator is less than its denominator. Proper fractions are less than 1. For example, the shaded portion of the triangle's area is represented by $\frac{2}{3}$.

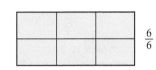

$\frac{2}{3}$

An **improper fraction** is a fraction whose numerator is greater than or equal to its denominator. Improper fractions are greater than or equal to 1. The shaded part of the group of circles' area below is $\frac{9}{4}$. The shaded part of the rectangle's area is $\frac{6}{6}$. (Recall from earlier that $\frac{6}{6}$ simplifies to 1 and notice that 1 whole figure or rectangle is shaded below.)

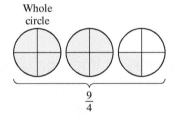

Whole circle

$\frac{9}{4}$

$\frac{6}{6}$

A **mixed number** contains a whole number and a fraction. Mixed numbers are greater than 1. Earlier, we wrote the shaded part of the group of circles below as the improper fraction $\frac{9}{4}$. Now let's write the shaded part as a mixed number. The shaded part of the group of circles' area is $2\frac{1}{4}$. (Read "two and one-fourth.")

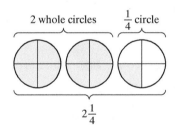

2 whole circles $\frac{1}{4}$ circle

$2\frac{1}{4}$

> **Helpful Hint**
>
> The mixed number $2\frac{1}{4}$ represents $2 + \frac{1}{4}$.

Example 14 Identify each number as a proper fraction, improper fraction, or mixed number.

a. $\frac{6}{7}$ is a proper fraction

b. $\frac{13}{12}$ is an improper fraction

c. $\frac{2}{2}$ is an improper fraction

d. $\frac{99}{101}$ is a proper fraction

e. $1\frac{7}{8}$ is a mixed number

f. $\frac{93}{74}$ is an improper fraction

● Work Practice 14

PRACTICE 14

Identify each number as a proper fraction, improper fraction, or mixed number.

a. $\frac{5}{8}$ **b.** $\frac{7}{7}$

c. $\frac{14}{13}$ **d.** $\frac{13}{14}$

e. $5\frac{1}{4}$ **f.** $\frac{100}{49}$

Answers

14. a. proper fraction **b.** improper fraction **c.** improper fraction **d.** proper fraction **e.** mixed number **f.** improper fraction

PRACTICE 15–16

Represent the shaded part of each figure group as both an improper fraction and a mixed number.

15.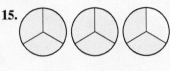

16.

Examples Represent the shaded part of each figure group's area as both an improper fraction and a mixed number.

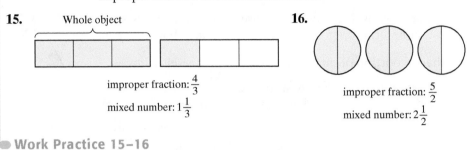

15. Whole object

improper fraction: $\frac{4}{3}$

mixed number: $1\frac{1}{3}$

16.

improper fraction: $\frac{5}{2}$

mixed number: $2\frac{1}{2}$

● Work Practice 15–16

✓**Concept Check** If you were to estimate $2\frac{1}{8}$ by a whole number, would you choose 2 or 3? Why?

Objective ⓓ Writing Mixed Numbers as Improper Fractions

Notice from Examples 15 and 16 that mixed numbers and improper fractions were both used to represent the shaded area of the figure groups. For example,

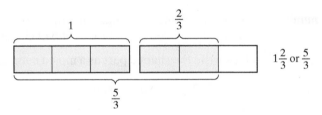

$$1\frac{2}{3} \text{ or } \frac{5}{3}$$

The following steps may be used to write a mixed number as an improper fraction:

Writing a Mixed Number as an Improper Fraction

To write a mixed number as an improper fraction:

Step 1: Multiply the denominator of the fraction by the whole number.

Step 2: Add the numerator of the fraction to the product from Step 1.

Step 3: Write the sum from Step 2 as the numerator of the improper fraction over the original denominator.

PRACTICE 17

Write each as an improper fraction.

a. $2\frac{5}{7}$ **b.** $5\frac{1}{3}$

c. $9\frac{3}{10}$ **d.** $1\frac{1}{5}$

For example,

$$1\frac{2}{3} = \frac{3 \cdot 1 + 2}{3} = \frac{3 + 2}{3} = \frac{5}{3}$$

Step 1, Step 2, Step 3

Example 17 Write each as an improper fraction.

a. $4\frac{2}{9} = \frac{9 \cdot 4 + 2}{9} = \frac{36 + 2}{9} = \frac{38}{9}$

b. $1\frac{8}{11} = \frac{11 \cdot 1 + 8}{11} = \frac{11 + 8}{11} = \frac{19}{11}$

● Work Practice 17

Answers

15. $\frac{8}{3}, 2\frac{2}{3}$ **16.** $\frac{5}{4}, 1\frac{1}{4}$

17. a. $\frac{19}{7}$ **b.** $\frac{16}{3}$ **c.** $\frac{93}{10}$ **d.** $\frac{6}{5}$

✓**Concept Check Answer**

2; answers may vary

Objective ⓔ Writing Improper Fractions as Mixed Numbers or Whole Numbers

Just as there are times when an improper fraction is preferred, sometimes a mixed or a whole number better suits a situation. To write improper fractions as mixed or whole numbers, we use division. Recall once again from Section 1.7 that the fraction bar means division. This means that the fraction

$$\frac{5}{3} \begin{array}{l} \text{numerator} \\ \text{denominator} \end{array} \text{ means } 3\overline{)5} \begin{array}{l} \uparrow \quad \uparrow \\ \text{numerator} \\ \text{denominator} \end{array}$$

Writing an Improper Fraction as a Mixed Number or a Whole Number

To write an improper fraction as a mixed number or a whole number:

Step 1: Divide the denominator into the numerator.

Step 2: The whole number part of the mixed number is the quotient. The fraction part of the mixed number is the remainder over the original denominator.

$$\text{quotient} \, \dfrac{\text{remainder}}{\text{original denominator}}$$

For example,

$$\begin{array}{cc} \text{Step 1} & \text{Step 2} \end{array}$$

$$\frac{5}{3}: \quad 3\overline{)5} \atop \begin{array}{r}\underline{3}\\2\end{array} \quad \quad \frac{5}{3} = 1\frac{2}{3} \begin{array}{l}\leftarrow \text{remainder}\\ \leftarrow \text{original denominator}\end{array}$$
$$\qquad\qquad\qquad\qquad \uparrow \text{quotient}$$

Example 18 Write each as a mixed number or a whole number.

a. $\dfrac{30}{7}$ **b.** $\dfrac{16}{15}$ **c.** $\dfrac{84}{6}$

Solution:

a. $\dfrac{30}{7}:$ $7\overline{)30} \atop \begin{array}{r}\underline{28}\\2\end{array}$ $\dfrac{30}{7} = 4\dfrac{2}{7}$

b. $\dfrac{16}{15}:$ $15\overline{)16} \atop \begin{array}{r}\underline{15}\\1\end{array}$ $\dfrac{16}{15} = 1\dfrac{1}{15}$

c. $\dfrac{84}{6}:$ $6\overline{)84} \atop \begin{array}{r}\underline{6}\\24\\\underline{24}\\0\end{array}$ $\dfrac{84}{6} = 14$ Since the remainder is 0, the result is the whole number 14.

> **Helpful Hint**
> When the remainder is 0, the improper fraction is a whole number. For example, $\dfrac{92}{4} = 23$.
>
> $4\overline{)92} \atop \begin{array}{r}23\\\underline{8}\\12\\\underline{12}\\0\end{array}$

🔵 **Work Practice 18**

Vocabulary and Readiness Check

Use the choices below to fill in each blank.

improper	fraction	proper	is undefined	mixed number	= 0
greater than or equal to 1	denominator	=1	less than 1	numerator	

1. The number $\frac{17}{31}$ is called a(n) _____. The number 31 is called its _____ and 17 is called its _____ .

2. If we simplify each fraction, $\frac{9}{9}$ _____ , $\frac{0}{4}$ _____ , and we say $\frac{4}{0}$ _____ .

3. The fraction $\frac{8}{3}$ is called a(n) _____ fraction, the fraction $\frac{3}{8}$ is called a(n) _____ fraction, and $10\frac{3}{8}$ is called a(n) _____ .

4. The value of an improper fraction is always _____, and the value of a proper fraction is always _____ .

2.1 Exercise Set

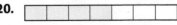

FOR EXTRA HELP

MyMathLab   Math XL   PRACTICE   WATCH   DOWNLOAD   READ   REVIEW

Objectives Ⓐ Ⓒ **Mixed Practice** *Identify the numerator and the denominator of each fraction and identify each fraction as proper or improper. See Examples 1, 2, and 14.*

1. $\frac{1}{2}$ **2.** $\frac{1}{4}$ **3.** $\frac{10}{3}$

4. $\frac{53}{21}$ **5.** $\frac{15}{15}$ **6.** $\frac{26}{26}$

Objective Ⓐ *Simplify. See Examples 3 through 6.*

7. $\frac{21}{21}$ **8.** $\frac{14}{14}$ **9.** $\frac{5}{0}$ **10.** $\frac{1}{0}$ **11.** $\frac{13}{1}$ **12.** $\frac{14}{1}$

13. $\frac{0}{20}$ **14.** $\frac{0}{17}$ **15.** $\frac{10}{0}$ **16.** $\frac{0}{18}$ **17.** $\frac{16}{1}$ **18.** $\frac{18}{18}$

Objective Ⓑ *Write a fraction to represent the shaded part of each. See Examples 7 through 10.*

19.    **20.**   **21.**

108

22.

23.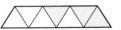

24.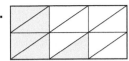

25.

26.

27.

28.

29.

1 mile

30.

Draw and shade a part of a figure to represent each fraction. See Examples 11 and 12.

31. $\frac{1}{5}$ of a figure

32. $\frac{1}{16}$ of a figure

33. $\frac{7}{8}$ of a figure

34. $\frac{3}{5}$ of a figure

35. $\frac{6}{7}$ of a figure

36. $\frac{7}{9}$ of a figure

37. $\frac{4}{4}$ of a figure

38. $\frac{6}{6}$ of a figure

Write each fraction. See Example 13.

39. Of the 131 students at a small private school, 42 are freshmen. What fraction of the students are freshmen?

40. Of the 63 employees at a new biomedical engineering firm, 22 are men. What fraction of the employees are men?

41. Use Exercise 39 to answer a and b.
   a. How many students are *not* freshmen?
   b. What fraction of the students are *not* freshmen?

42. Use Exercise 40 to answer a and b.
   a. How many of the employees are women?
   b. What fraction of the employees are women?

43. As of the beginning of 2010, the United States has had 44 different presidents. A total of seven U.S. presidents were born in the state of Ohio, second only to the state of Virginia in producing U.S. presidents. What fraction of U.S. presidents were born in Ohio? (*Source: World Almanac and Book of Facts*)

44. Of the eight planets in our solar system, four have days that are longer than the 24-hour Earth day. What fraction of the planets have longer days than Earth has? (*Source:* National Space Science Data Center)

45. The Atlantic hurricane season of 2005 rewrote the record books. There were 28 tropical storms, 15 of which turned into hurricanes. What fraction of the 2005 Atlantic tropical storms escalated to hurricanes?

46. There are 12 inches in a foot. What fractional part of a foot does 5 inches represent?

47. There are 31 days in the month of March. What fraction of the month does 11 days represent?

Mon.	Tue.	Wed.	Thu.	Fri.	Sat.	Sun.
					1	2
3	4	5	6	7	8	9
10	11	12	13	14	15	16
17	18	19	20	21	22	23
24	25	26	27	28	29	30
31						

48. There are 60 minutes in an hour. What fraction of an hour does 37 minutes represent?

49. In a basic college mathematics class containing 31 students, there are 18 freshmen, 10 sophomores, and 3 juniors. What fraction of the class is sophomores?

50. In a sports team with 20 children, there are 9 boys and 11 girls. What fraction of the team is boys?

51. Thirty-three out of the fifty total states in the United States contain federal Indian reservations.

  a. What fraction of the states contain federal Indian reservations?

  b. How many states do not contain federal Indian reservations?

  c. What fraction of the states do not contain federal Indian reservations? (*Source:* Tiller Research, Inc., Albuquerque, NM)

52. Consumer fireworks are legal in 45 out of the 50 total states in the United States.

  a. In what fraction of the states are consumer fireworks legal?

  b. In how many states are consumer fireworks illegal?

  c. In what fraction of the states are consumer fireworks illegal? (*Source:* United States Fireworks Safety Council)

53. A bag contains 50 red or blue marbles. If 21 marbles are blue,

  a. What *fraction* of the marbles are blue?

  b. How many marbles are red?

  c. What *fraction* of the marbles are red?

54. An art dealer is taking inventory. His shop contains a total of 37 pieces, which are all sculptures, watercolor paintings, or oil paintings. If there are 15 watercolor paintings and 17 oil paintings, answer each question.

  a. What fraction of the inventory is watercolor paintings?

  b. What fraction of the inventory is oil paintings?

  c. How many sculptures are there?

  d. What fraction of the inventory is sculptures?

Objective  *Write the shaded area in each figure group as (a) an improper fraction and (b) a mixed number. See Examples 15 and 16.*

55.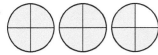

56.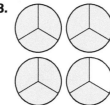

57.

58.

59.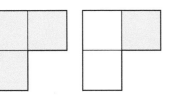

60.

61.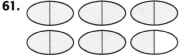

62.

Objective  *Write each mixed number as an improper fraction. See Example 17.*

63. $2\frac{1}{3}$ **64.** $6\frac{3}{4}$ **65.** $3\frac{3}{5}$ **66.** $2\frac{5}{9}$ **67.** $6\frac{5}{8}$ **68.** $7\frac{3}{8}$

69. $2\frac{11}{15}$ **70.** $1\frac{13}{17}$ **71.** $11\frac{6}{7}$ **72.** $12\frac{2}{5}$ **73.** $6\frac{6}{13}$ **74.** $8\frac{9}{10}$

75. $4\frac{13}{24}$ **76.** $5\frac{17}{25}$ **77.** $17\frac{7}{12}$ **78.** $12\frac{7}{15}$ **79.** $9\frac{7}{20}$ **80.** $10\frac{14}{27}$

81. $2\frac{51}{107}$ **82.** $3\frac{27}{125}$ **83.** $166\frac{2}{3}$ **84.** $114\frac{2}{7}$

Objective **E** *Write each improper fraction as a mixed number or a whole number. See Example 18.*

85. $\dfrac{17}{5}$ **86.** $\dfrac{13}{7}$ **87.** $\dfrac{37}{8}$ **88.** $\dfrac{64}{9}$ **89.** $\dfrac{47}{15}$ **90.** $\dfrac{65}{12}$

91. $\dfrac{46}{21}$ **92.** $\dfrac{67}{17}$ **93.** $\dfrac{198}{6}$ **94.** $\dfrac{112}{7}$ **95.** $\dfrac{225}{15}$ **96.** $\dfrac{196}{14}$

97. $\dfrac{200}{3}$ **98.** $\dfrac{300}{7}$ **99.** $\dfrac{247}{23}$ **100.** $\dfrac{437}{53}$ **101.** $\dfrac{319}{18}$ **102.** $\dfrac{404}{21}$

103. $\dfrac{182}{175}$ **104.** $\dfrac{149}{143}$ **105.** $\dfrac{737}{112}$ **106.** $\dfrac{901}{123}$

Review

Simplify. See Section 1.9.

107. 3^2 **108.** 4^3 **109.** 5^3 **110.** 3^4

Write each using exponents.

111. $7 \cdot 7 \cdot 7 \cdot 7 \cdot 7$ **112.** $5 \cdot 5 \cdot 5 \cdot 5$ **113.** $2 \cdot 2 \cdot 2 \cdot 3$ **114.** $4 \cdot 4 \cdot 10 \cdot 10 \cdot 10$

Concept Extensions

Write each fraction.

115. In your own words, explain how to write an improper fraction as a mixed number.

116. In your own words, explain how to write a mixed number as an improper fraction.

Identify the larger fraction for each pair.

117. $\dfrac{1}{2}$ or $\dfrac{2}{3}$ (*Hint:* Represent each fraction by the shaded part of equivalent figures. Then compare the shaded areas.)

118. $\dfrac{7}{4}$ or $\dfrac{3}{5}$ (*Hint:* Identify each as a proper fraction or an improper fraction.)

Solve. See the first Concept Check in this section.

119. If ⃝⃝⃝⃝ represents $\frac{4}{9}$ of a whole diagram, sketch the whole diagram.

120. If △ △ represents $\frac{1}{3}$ of a whole diagram, sketch the whole diagram.

121. The Gap Corporation owns stores with three different brand names, as shown on the bar graph. What fraction of the stores owned by The Gap Corporation are named "Banana Republic"?

122. The Public Broadcasting Service (PBS) provides programming to the noncommercial public TV stations of the United States. The bar graph shows a breakdown of the public television licensees by type. Each licensee operates one or more PBS member TV stations. What fraction of the public television licensees are universities or colleges? (*Source:* The Public Broadcasting Service)

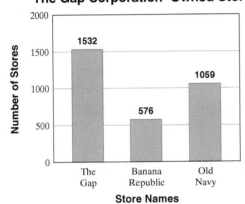

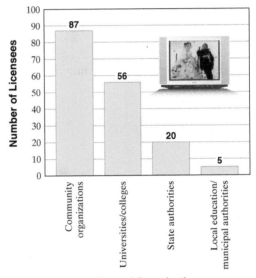

123. Habitat for Humanity is a nonprofit organization that helps provide affordable housing to families in need. Habitat for Humanity does its work of building and renovating houses through 1700 local affiliates in the United States and 550 international affiliates. What fraction of the total Habitat for Humanity affiliates are located in the United States? (*Hint:* First find the total number of affiliates.) (*Source:* Habitat for Humanity International)

124. The United States Marine Corps (USMC) has five principal training centers in California, three in North Carolina, two in South Carolina, one in Arizona, one in Hawaii, and one in Virginia. What fraction of the total USMC principal training centers are located in California? (*Hint:* First find the total number of USMC training centers.) (*Source:* U.S. Department of Defense)

2.2 FACTORS AND PRIME FACTORIZATION

To perform many operations with fractions, it is necessary to be able to factor a number. In this section, only the **natural numbers**—1, 2, 3, 4, 5, and so on—will be considered.

✓**Concept Check** How are the natural numbers and the whole numbers alike? How are they different?

Objective **A** Finding Factors of Numbers

Recall that when numbers are multiplied to form a product, each number is called a factor. Since $5 \cdot 9 = 45$, both 5 and 9 are **factors** of 45, and $5 \cdot 9$ is called a **factorization** of 45.

The two-number factorizations of 45 are

$$1 \cdot 45 \quad 3 \cdot 15 \quad 5 \cdot 9$$

Thus, we say that the factors of 45 are 1, 3, 5, 9, 15, and 45.

Helpful Hint

From our definition of factor above, notice that a **factor** of a number divides the number evenly (with a remainder of 0). For example,

$$\frac{45}{1)45} \quad \frac{15}{3)45} \quad \frac{9}{5)45} \quad \frac{5}{9)45} \quad \frac{3}{15)45} \quad \frac{1}{45)45}$$

Example 1 Find all the factors of 20.

Solution: First we write all the two-number factorizations of 20.

$$1 \cdot 20 = 20$$
$$2 \cdot 10 = 20$$
$$4 \cdot 5 = 20$$

The factors of 20 are 1, 2, 4, 5, 10, and 20.

● Work Practice 1

Objective **B** Identifying Prime and Composite Numbers

Of all the ways to factor a number, one special way is called the **prime factorization.** To help us write prime factorizations, we first review prime and composite numbers.

Prime Numbers

A **prime number** is a natural number that has exactly two different factors, 1 and itself.

The first several prime numbers are

2, 3, 5, 7, 11, 13, 17

It would be helpful to memorize these.

If a natural number other than 1 is not a prime number, it is called a **composite number.**

PRACTICE 1

Find all the factors of each number.

a. 15 **b.** 7 **c.** 24

Answers

1. a. 1, 3, 5, 15 **b.** 1, 7
c. 1, 2, 3, 4, 6, 8, 12, 24

✓ **Concept Check Answer**

answers may vary

Composite Numbers

A **composite number** is any natural number, other than 1, that is not prime.

Helpful Hint

The natural number 1 is neither prime nor composite.

Example 2 Determine whether each number is prime or composite. Explain your answers.

3, 9, 11, 17, 26

Solution: The number 3 is prime. Its only factors are 1 and 3 (itself).
The number 9 is composite. It has more than two factors: 1, 3, and 9.
The number 11 is prime. Its only factors are 1 and 11.
The number 17 is prime. Its only factors are 1 and 17.
The number 26 is composite. Its factors are 1, 2, 13, and 26.

● Work Practice 2

Objective Ⓒ Finding Prime Factorizations

Now we are ready to find **prime factorizations** of numbers.

Prime Factorization

The **prime factorization** of a number is the factorization in which all the factors are prime numbers.

For example, the prime factorization of 12 is $2 \cdot 2 \cdot 3$ because

$$12 = \underline{2 \cdot 2 \cdot 3}$$

       This product is 12 and each
       number is a prime number.

Every whole number greater than 1 has exactly one prime factorization.

Helpful Hint

Don't forget that multiplication is commutative, so $2 \cdot 2 \cdot 3$ can also be written as $2 \cdot 3 \cdot 2$ or $3 \cdot 2 \cdot 2$ or $2^2 \cdot 3$. Any one of these can be called *the prime factorization of* 12.

Example 3 Find the prime factorization of 45.

Solution: The first prime number, 2, does not divide 45 evenly (with a remainder of 0). The second prime number, 3, does, so we divide 45 by 3.

$$\begin{array}{r} 15 \\ 3\overline{)45} \end{array}$$

Because 15 is not prime and 3 also divides 15 evenly, we divide by 3 again.

$$\begin{array}{r} 5 \\ 3\overline{)15} \\ 3\overline{)45} \end{array}$$

Continued on next page

Continued on next page

PRACTICE 2

Determine whether each number is prime or composite. Explain your answers.

21, 13, 18, 29, 39

PRACTICE 3

Find the prime factorization of 28.

Answers

2. 13, 29 are prime. 21, 18, and 39 are composite.   **3.** $2 \cdot 2 \cdot 7$ or $2^2 \cdot 7$

The quotient, 5, is a prime number, so we are finished. The prime factorization of 45 is

$$45 = 3 \cdot 3 \cdot 5 \quad \text{or} \quad 45 = 3^2 \cdot 5,$$

using exponents.

● **Work Practice 3**

There are a few quick **divisibility tests** to determine whether a number is divisible by the primes 2, 3, or 5. (A number is divisible by 2, for example, if 2 divides it evenly.)

Divisibility Tests

A whole number is divisible by:

- **2** if the last digit is 0, 2, 4, 6, or 8.

    13**2** is divisible by 2 since the last digit is a 2.

- **3** if the sum of the digits is divisible by 3.

    144 is divisible by 3 since $1 + 4 + 4 = 9$ is divisible by 3.

- **5** if the last digit is 0 or 5.

    111**5** is divisible by 5 since the last digit is a 5.

Helpful Hint

Here are a few other divisibility tests you may find interesting. A whole number is divisible by:

- **4** if its last two digits are divisible by 4.

    17**12** is divisible by 4.

- **6** if it's divisible by 2 and 3.

    9858 is divisible by 6.

- **9** if the sum of its digits is divisible by 9.

    5238 is divisible by 9 since $5 + 2 + 3 + 8 = 18$ is divisible by 9.

We will usually begin the division process with the smallest prime number factor of the given number. Since multiplication is commutative, this is not necessary. As long as the divisor is any prime number factor, this process works.

PRACTICE 4

Find the prime factorization of 120.

Example 4 Find the prime factorization of 180.

Solution: We divide 180 by 2 and continue dividing until the quotient is no longer divisible by 2. We then divide by the next largest prime number, 3, until the quotient is no longer divisible by 3. We continue this process until the quotient is a prime number.

$$
\begin{array}{r}
5 \\
3\overline{)\,15} \\
3\overline{)\,45} \\
2\overline{)\,90} \\
2\overline{)\,180}
\end{array}
$$

Answer

4. $2 \cdot 2 \cdot 2 \cdot 3 \cdot 5$ or $2^3 \cdot 3 \cdot 5$

Thus, the prime factorization of 180 is

$$180 = 2 \cdot 2 \cdot 3 \cdot 3 \cdot 5 \quad \text{or} \quad 180 = 2^2 \cdot 3^2 \cdot 5,$$

using exponents.

● **Work Practice 4**

Example 5 Find the prime factorization of 945.

Solution: This number is not divisible by 2 but is divisible by 3. We will begin by dividing 945 by 3.

$$\begin{array}{r} 7 \\ 5\overline{)\ 35} \\ 3\overline{)105} \\ 3\overline{)315} \\ 3\overline{)945} \end{array}$$

Thus, the prime factorization of 945 is

$$945 = 3 \cdot 3 \cdot 3 \cdot 5 \cdot 7 \quad \text{or} \quad 945 = 3^3 \cdot 5 \cdot 7$$

● **Work Practice 5**

Another way to find the prime factorization is to use a factor tree, as shown in the next example.

Example 6 Use a factor tree to find the prime factorization of 18.

Solution: We begin by writing 18 as a product of two natural numbers greater than 1, say $2 \cdot 9$.

$$\begin{array}{c} 18 \\ \diagup\diagdown \\ 2 \cdot 9 \end{array}$$

The number 2 is prime, but 9 is not. So we write 9 as $3 \cdot 3$.

$$\begin{array}{c} 18 \\ \diagup\diagdown \\ 2 \cdot 9 \\ \downarrow \ \ \downarrow\diagdown \\ 2 \cdot 3 \cdot 3 \end{array}$$

Each factor is now prime, so the prime factorization is

$$18 = 2 \cdot 3 \cdot 3 \quad \text{or} \quad 18 = 2 \cdot 3^2,$$

using exponents.

● **Work Practice 6**

In this text, we will write the factorization of a number from the smallest factor to the largest factor.

PRACTICE 5

Find the prime factorization of 756.

PRACTICE 6

Use a factor tree to find the prime factorization of 45.

Answers
5. $2 \cdot 2 \cdot 3 \cdot 3 \cdot 3 \cdot 7$ or $2^2 \cdot 3^3 \cdot 7$
6. $3 \cdot 3 \cdot 5$ or $3^2 \cdot 5$

PRACTICE 7

Use a factor tree to find the prime factorization of each number.

a. 30   **b.** 56   **c.** 72

Example 7 Use a factor tree to find the prime factorization of 80.

Solution: Write 80 as a product of two numbers. Continue this process until all factors are prime.

All factors are now prime, so the prime factorization of 80 is

$2 \cdot 2 \cdot 2 \cdot 2 \cdot 5$ or $2^4 \cdot 5$.

● **Work Practice 7**

Helpful Hint

It makes no difference which factors you start with. The prime factorization of a number will be the same.

$$
\begin{array}{c}
80 \\
20 \quad \cdot \quad 4 \\
4 \quad \cdot \quad 5 \cdot 2 \cdot 2 \\
2 \cdot 2 \cdot 5 \cdot 2 \cdot 2
\end{array}
$$

Same factors as in Example 7

✓**Concept Check** True or false? Two different numbers can have exactly the same prime factorization. Explain your answer.

PRACTICE 8

Use a factor tree to find the prime factorization of 117.

Example 8 Use a factor tree to find the prime factorization of 175.

Solution: We begin by writing 175 as a product of two numbers greater than 1, say $7 \cdot 25$.

$$
\begin{array}{c}
175 \\
7 \cdot 25 \\
7 \cdot 5 \cdot 5
\end{array}
$$

The prime factorization of 175 is

$175 = 5 \cdot 5 \cdot 7$ or $175 = 5^2 \cdot 7$

● **Work Practice 8**

Answers

7. a. $2 \cdot 3 \cdot 5$ **b.** $2 \cdot 2 \cdot 2 \cdot 7$ or $2^3 \cdot 7$
c. $2 \cdot 2 \cdot 2 \cdot 3 \cdot 3$ or $2^3 \cdot 3^2$
8. $3 \cdot 3 \cdot 13$ or $3^2 \cdot 13$

✓**Concept Check Answer**

false; answers may vary

Vocabulary and Readiness Check

Use the choices below to fill in each blank.

    factor(s)   prime factorization   prime

    natural   composite

1. The number 40 equals $2 \cdot 2 \cdot 2 \cdot 5$. Since each factor is prime, we call $2 \cdot 2 \cdot 2 \cdot 5$ the _____ of 40.
2. A natural number, other than 1, that is not prime is called a(n) _____ number.
3. A natural number that has exactly two different factors, 1 and itself, is called a(n) _____ number.
4. The numbers $1, 2, 3, 4, 5, \ldots$ are called the _____ numbers.
5. Since $30 = 5 \cdot 6$, the numbers 5 and 6 are _____ of 30.
6. Answer true or false: $5 \cdot 6$ is the prime factorization of 30. _____

2.2 Exercise Set

FOR EXTRA HELP

MyMathLab   Math XL — PRACTICE   WATCH   DOWNLOAD   READ   REVIEW

Objective A *List all the factors of each number. See Example 1.*

1. 8   **2.** 6   **3.** 25   **4.** 30   **5.** 4   **6.** 9

7. 18   **8.** 48   **9.** 29   **10.** 37   **11.** 80   **12.** 100

13. 12   **14.** 28   **15.** 34   **16.** 26

Objective B *Identify each number as prime or composite. See Example 2.*

17. 7   **18.** 5   **19.** 4   **20.** 10   **21.** 23   **22.** 13

23. 49   **24.** 45   **25.** 67   **26.** 89   **27.** 39   **28.** 21

29. 31   **30.** 27   **31.** 63   **32.** 51   **33.** 119   **34.** 147

Objective C *Find the prime factorization of each number. Write any repeated factors using exponents. See Examples 3 through 8.*

35. 32   **36.** 64   **37.** 15   **38.** 21   **39.** 40   **40.** 63

41. 36   **42.** 80   **43.** 39   **44.** 56   **45.** 60   **46.** 84

47. 110   **48.** 130   **49.** 85   **50.** 93   **51.** 128   **52.** 81

53. 154   **54.** 198   **55.** 300   **56.** 360   **57.** 240   **58.** 836

59. 828   **60.** 504   **61.** 882   **62.** 405   **63.** 637   **64.** 539

Objectives Ⓑ Ⓒ **Mixed Practice** *Find the prime factorization of each composite number. Write any repeated factors using exponents. Write prime if the number is prime.*

65. 33   **66.** 48   **67.** 98   **68.** 54   **69.** 67   **70.** 59

71. 459   **72.** 208   **73.** 97   **74.** 103   **75.** 700   **76.** 1000

Review

Round each whole number to the indicated place value. See Section 1.5.

77. 4267 hundreds   **78.** 32,465 thousands   **79.** 7,658,240 ten-thousands

80. 4,286,340 tens   **81.** 19,764 thousands   **82.** 10,292,876 millions

General Mills produces well-known brands such as Pillsbury, Cheerios, Yoplait, Häagen-Dazs, and many others. The bar graph below shows the number of patents that General Mills has been granted over a four-year period. Use this bar graph to answer the questions below. See Section 2.1. (Source: U.S. Patent Office)

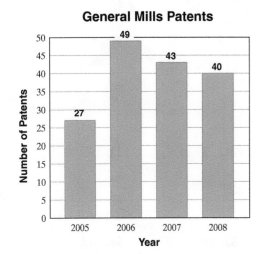

83. Find the total number of patents received by General Mills for the years shown.

84. How many fewer patents were granted in 2008 than in 2007?

85. What fraction of the patents were granted in 2005?

86. What fraction of the patents were granted in 2008?

Concept Extensions

Find the prime factorization of each number.

87. 34,020   **88.** 131,625

89. In your own words, define a prime number.   **90.** The number 2 is a prime number. All other even natural numbers are composite numbers. Explain why.

91. Why are we interested in the prime factorizations of nonzero whole numbers only?   **92.** Two students have different prime factorizations for the same number. Is this possible? Explain.

2.3 SIMPLEST FORM OF A FRACTION

Objective A Writing Fractions in Simplest Form

Fractions that represent the same portion of a whole are called **equivalent fractions.**

$$\frac{2}{3}$$

$$\frac{4}{6}$$

$$\frac{8}{12}$$

For example, $\frac{2}{3}, \frac{4}{6}$, and $\frac{8}{12}$ all represent the same shaded portion of the rectangle's area, so they are equivalent fractions.

$$\frac{2}{3} = \frac{4}{6} = \frac{8}{12}$$

There are many equivalent forms of a fraction. A special form of a fraction is called **simplest form.**

Simplest Form of a Fraction

A fraction is written in **simplest form** or **lowest terms** when the numerator and the denominator have no common factors other than 1.

For example, the fraction $\frac{2}{3}$ *is* in simplest form because 2 and 3 have no common factor other than 1. The fraction $\frac{4}{6}$ *is not* in simplest form because 4 and 6 both have a factor of 2. That is, 2 is a common factor of 4 and 6. The process of writing a fraction in simplest form is called **simplifying** the fraction.

To simplify $\frac{4}{6}$ and write it as $\frac{2}{3}$, let's first study a few properties. Recall from Section 2.1 that any nonzero whole number n divided by itself is 1.

Any nonzero number n divided by itself is 1.

$$\frac{5}{5} = 1, \quad \frac{17}{17} = 1, \quad \frac{24}{24} = 1, \text{ or, in general, } \frac{n}{n} = 1$$

Also, in general, if $\frac{a}{b}$ and $\frac{c}{d}$ are fractions (with b and d not 0), the following is true.

$$\frac{a \cdot c}{b \cdot d} = \frac{a}{b} \cdot \frac{c}{d}^*$$

These properties allow us to do the following:

$$\frac{4}{6} = \frac{2 \cdot 2}{2 \cdot 3} = \frac{2}{2} \cdot \frac{2}{3} = 1 \cdot \frac{2}{3} = \frac{2}{3}$$ When 1 is multiplied by a number, the result is the same number.

⌞ This is 1

Note: We will study this concept further in the next section.

PRACTICE 1
Write in simplest form: $\dfrac{30}{45}$

Example 1 Write in simplest form: $\dfrac{12}{20}$

Solution: Notice that 12 and 20 have a common factor of 4.

$$\frac{12}{20} = \frac{4 \cdot 3}{4 \cdot 5} = \frac{4}{4} \cdot \frac{3}{5} = 1 \cdot \frac{3}{5} = \frac{3}{5}$$

Since 3 and 5 have no common factors (other than 1), $\dfrac{3}{5}$ is in simplest form.

● Work Practice 1

If you have trouble finding common factors, write the prime factorization of the numerator and the denominator.

PRACTICE 2
Write in simplest form: $\dfrac{39}{51}$

Example 2 Write in simplest form: $\dfrac{42}{66}$

Solution: Let's write the prime factorizations of 42 and 66.

$$\frac{42}{66} = \frac{2 \cdot 3 \cdot 7}{2 \cdot 3 \cdot 11} = \frac{2}{2} \cdot \frac{3}{3} \cdot \frac{7}{11} = 1 \cdot 1 \cdot \frac{7}{11} = \frac{7}{11}$$

● Work Practice 2

In the example above, you may have saved time by noticing that 42 and 66 have a common factor of 6.

$$\frac{42}{66} = \frac{6 \cdot 7}{6 \cdot 11} = \frac{6}{6} \cdot \frac{7}{11} = 1 \cdot \frac{7}{11} = \frac{7}{11}$$

Helpful Hint
Writing the prime factorizations of the numerator and the denominator is helpful in finding any common factors.

PRACTICE 3
Write in simplest form: $\dfrac{9}{50}$

Example 3 Write in simplest form: $\dfrac{10}{27}$

Solution:

$$\frac{10}{27} = \frac{2 \cdot 5}{3 \cdot 3 \cdot 3} \quad \text{Prime factorizations of 10 and 27.}$$

Since 10 and 27 have no common factors, $\dfrac{10}{27}$ is already in simplest form.

● Work Practice 3

PRACTICE 4
Write in simplest form: $\dfrac{49}{112}$

Example 4 Write in simplest form: $\dfrac{30}{108}$

Solution:

$$\frac{30}{108} = \frac{2 \cdot 3 \cdot 5}{2 \cdot 2 \cdot 3 \cdot 3 \cdot 3} = \frac{2}{2} \cdot \frac{3}{3} \cdot \frac{5}{2 \cdot 3 \cdot 3} = 1 \cdot 1 \cdot \frac{5}{18} = \frac{5}{18}$$

● Work Practice 4

We can use a shortcut procedure with common factors when simplifying.

$$\frac{4}{6} = \frac{\overset{1}{\cancel{2}} \cdot 2}{\underset{1}{\cancel{2}} \cdot 3} = \frac{1 \cdot 2}{1 \cdot 3} = \frac{2}{3} \qquad \text{Divide out the common factor of 2 in the numerator and denominator.}$$

Answers
1. $\dfrac{2}{3}$ 2. $\dfrac{13}{17}$ 3. $\dfrac{9}{50}$ 4. $\dfrac{7}{16}$

This procedure is possible because dividing out a common factor in the numerator and denominator is the same as removing a factor of 1 in the product.

Writing a Fraction in Simplest Form

To write a fraction in simplest form, write the prime factorization of the numerator and the denominator and then divide both by all common factors.

Example 5 Write in simplest form: $\dfrac{72}{26}$

Solution:

$$\frac{72}{26} = \frac{\overset{1}{\cancel{2}} \cdot 2 \cdot 2 \cdot 3 \cdot 3}{\underset{1}{\cancel{2}} \cdot 13} = \frac{1 \cdot 2 \cdot 2 \cdot 3 \cdot 3}{1 \cdot 13} = \frac{36}{13},$$

which can also be written as

$$2\frac{10}{13}$$

● Work Practice 5

PRACTICE 5
Write in simplest form: $\dfrac{64}{20}$

✓**Concept Check** Which is the correct way to simplify the fraction $\dfrac{15}{25}$? Or are both correct? Explain.

a. $\dfrac{15}{25} = \dfrac{3 \cdot \overset{1}{\cancel{5}}}{5 \cdot \underset{1}{\cancel{5}}} = \dfrac{3}{5}$ **b.** $\dfrac{1\overset{1}{\cancel{5}}}{2\underset{1}{\cancel{5}}} = \dfrac{11}{21}$

Example 6 Write in simplest form: $\dfrac{6}{60}$

Solution:

$$\frac{6}{60} = \frac{\overset{1}{\cancel{2}} \cdot \overset{1}{\cancel{3}}}{\underset{1}{\cancel{2}} \cdot 2 \cdot \underset{1}{\cancel{3}} \cdot 5} = \frac{1 \cdot 1}{1 \cdot 2 \cdot 1 \cdot 5} = \frac{1}{10}$$

● Work Practice 6

PRACTICE 6
Write in simplest form: $\dfrac{8}{56}$

Helpful Hint

Be careful when all factors of the numerator or denominator are divided out. In Example 6, the numerator was $1 \cdot 1 = 1$, so the final result was $\dfrac{1}{10}$.

In the fraction of Example 6, $\dfrac{6}{60}$, you may have immediately noticed that the largest common factor of 6 and 60 is 6. If so, you may simply divide out that largest common factor.

$$\frac{6}{60} = \frac{\overset{1}{\cancel{6}}}{\underset{1}{\cancel{6}} \cdot 10} = \frac{1}{1 \cdot 10} = \frac{1}{10} \qquad \text{Divide out the common factor of 6.}$$

Notice that the result, $\dfrac{1}{10}$, is in simplest form. If it were not, we would repeat the same procedure until the result was in simplest form.

Answers
5. $\dfrac{16}{5}$ or $3\dfrac{1}{5}$ **6.** $\dfrac{1}{7}$

✓**Concept Check Answers**
a. correct   **b.** incorrect

PRACTICE 7

Write in simplest form: $\dfrac{42}{48}$

Example 7 Write in simplest form: $\dfrac{45}{75}$

Solution: You may write the prime factorizations of 45 and 75 or you may notice that these two numbers have a common factor of 15.

$$\dfrac{45}{75} = \dfrac{3 \cdot \overset{1}{\cancel{15}}}{5 \cdot \underset{1}{\cancel{15}}} = \dfrac{3 \cdot 1}{5 \cdot 1} = \dfrac{3}{5}$$

The numerator and denominator of $\dfrac{3}{5}$ have no common factors other than 1, so $\dfrac{3}{5}$ is in simplest form.

● **Work Practice 7**

Objective ⓑ Determining Whether Two Fractions Are Equivalent

Recall that two fractions are equivalent if they represent the same part of a whole. One way to determine whether two fractions are equivalent is to see whether they simplify to the same fraction.

Example 8 Determine whether $\dfrac{16}{40}$ and $\dfrac{10}{25}$ are equivalent.

Solution: Simplify each fraction.

$$\dfrac{16}{40} = \dfrac{\overset{1}{\cancel{8}} \cdot 2}{\underset{1}{\cancel{8}} \cdot 5} = \dfrac{1 \cdot 2}{1 \cdot 5} = \dfrac{2}{5}$$

$$\dfrac{10}{25} = \dfrac{2 \cdot \overset{1}{\cancel{5}}}{5 \cdot \underset{1}{\cancel{5}}} = \dfrac{2 \cdot 1}{5 \cdot 1} = \dfrac{2}{5}$$

Since these fractions are the same, $\dfrac{16}{40} = \dfrac{10}{25}$.

PRACTICE 8

Determine whether $\dfrac{7}{9}$ and $\dfrac{21}{27}$ are equivalent.

● **Work Practice 8**

There is a shortcut method you may use to check or test whether two fractions are equivalent. In the example above, we learned that the fractions are equivalent, or

$$\dfrac{16}{40} = \dfrac{10}{25}$$

In this example above, we call $25 \cdot 16$ and $40 \cdot 10$ **cross products** because they are the products one obtains by multiplying across.

Cross Products

$$25 \cdot 16 \qquad 40 \cdot 10$$

$$\dfrac{16}{40} = \dfrac{10}{25}$$

Notice that these cross products are equal

$$25 \cdot 16 = 400, \quad 40 \cdot 10 = 400$$

Answers

7. $\dfrac{7}{8}$ **8.** equivalent

In general, this is true for equivalent fractions.

Equivalent Fractions

$8 \cdot 6$ $24 \cdot 2$

$$\frac{6}{24} \stackrel{?}{=} \frac{2}{8}$$

Since the cross products ($8 \cdot 6 = 48$ and $24 \cdot 2 = 48$) are equal, the fractions are equivalent.

    Note: If the cross products are not equal, the fractions are not equivalent.

Example 9 Determine whether $\frac{8}{11}$ and $\frac{19}{26}$ are equivalent.

Solution: Let's check cross products.

$26 \cdot 8$ $11 \cdot 19$
$= 208$ $\frac{8}{11} \stackrel{?}{=} \frac{19}{26}$ $= 209$

Since $208 \neq 209$, then $\frac{8}{11} \neq \frac{19}{26}$.

Work Practice 9

PRACTICE 9

Determine whether $\frac{4}{13}$ and $\frac{5}{18}$ are equivalent.

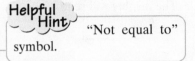

Helpful Hint

"Not equal to" symbol.

Objective C Solving Problems by Writing Fractions in Simplest Form

Many real-life problems can be solved by writing fractions. To make the answers clearer, these fractions should be written in simplest form.

Example 10   Calculating Fraction of Parks in Wyoming State

There are currently 58 national parks in the United States. Two of these parks are located in the state of Wyoming. What fraction of the United States' national parks can be found in Wyoming? Write the fraction in simplest form. (*Source: National Park Service*)

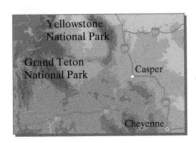

Solution: First we determine the fraction of parks found in Wyoming state.

$\frac{2}{58}$ ← national parks in Wyoming
     ← total national parks

PRACTICE 10

There are six national parks (including historic) in Washington state. See Example 10 and determine what fraction of the United States' national parks are located in Washington. Write the fraction in simplest form.

Continued on next page

Answers
9. not equivalent   **10.** $\frac{3}{29}$

Next we simplify the fraction.

$$\frac{2}{58} = \frac{\overset{1}{\cancel{2}}}{\underset{1}{\cancel{2}} \cdot 29} = \frac{1}{1 \cdot 29} = \frac{1}{29}$$

Thus, $\frac{1}{29}$ of the United States' national parks are in the state of Wyoming.

● **Work Practice 10**

 Calculator Explorations   Simplifying Fractions

Scientific Calculator

Many calculators have a fraction key, such as $\boxed{a \, b/c}$, that allows you to simplify a fraction on the calculator. For example, to simplify $\frac{324}{612}$, enter

$$\boxed{3}\ \boxed{2}\ \boxed{4}\ \boxed{a \, b/c}\ \boxed{6}\ \boxed{1}\ \boxed{2}\ \boxed{=}$$

The display will read

$$\boxed{\quad 9 \mid 17 \quad}$$

which represents $\frac{9}{17}$, the original fraction simplified.

Helpful Hint   The Calculator Explorations boxes in this chapter provide only an introduction to fraction keys on calculators. Any time you use a calculator, there are both advantages and limitations to its use. Never rely solely on your calculator. It is very important that you understand how to perform all operations on fractions by hand in order to progress through later topics. For further information, talk to your instructor.

Use your calculator to simplify each fraction.

1. $\frac{128}{224}$ 2. $\frac{231}{396}$ 3. $\frac{340}{459}$ 4. $\frac{999}{1350}$

5. $\frac{810}{432}$ 6. $\frac{315}{225}$ 7. $\frac{243}{54}$ 8. $\frac{689}{455}$

Vocabulary and Readiness Check

Use the choices below to fill in each blank.

    0   cross products   equivalent

    1   simplest form   *n*

1. In $\frac{11}{48}$, since 11 and 48 have no common factors other than 1, $\frac{11}{48}$ is in _____ .

2. Fractions that represent the same portion of a whole are called _____ fractions.

3. In the statement $\frac{5}{12} = \frac{15}{36}$, $5 \cdot 36$ and $12 \cdot 15$ are called _____ .

4. The fraction $\frac{7}{7}$ simplifies to _____ .

5. The fraction $\frac{0}{7}$ simplifies to _____ .

6. The fraction $\frac{n}{1}$ simplifies to _____ .

2.3 Exercise Set

FOR EXTRA HELP

Objective Ⓐ *Write each fraction in simplest form. See Examples 1 through 7.*

1. $\frac{3}{12}$ **2.** $\frac{5}{30}$ **3.** $\frac{4}{42}$ **4.** $\frac{9}{48}$

5. $\frac{14}{16}$ **6.** $\frac{22}{34}$ **7.** $\frac{20}{30}$ **8.** $\frac{70}{80}$

9. $\frac{35}{50}$ **10.** $\frac{25}{55}$ **11.** $\frac{63}{81}$ **12.** $\frac{21}{49}$

13. $\frac{24}{40}$ **14.** $\frac{36}{54}$ **15.** $\frac{27}{64}$ **16.** $\frac{32}{63}$

17. $\frac{25}{40}$ **18.** $\frac{36}{42}$ **19.** $\frac{40}{64}$ **20.** $\frac{28}{60}$

21. $\frac{56}{68}$ **22.** $\frac{39}{42}$ **23.** $\frac{36}{24}$ **24.** $\frac{60}{36}$

25. $\frac{90}{120}$ **26.** $\frac{60}{150}$ **27.** $\frac{70}{196}$ **28.** $\frac{98}{126}$

29. $\frac{66}{308}$ **30.** $\frac{65}{234}$ **31.** $\frac{55}{85}$ **32.** $\frac{78}{90}$

33. $\frac{75}{350}$ **34.** $\frac{72}{420}$ **35.** $\frac{189}{216}$ **36.** $\frac{144}{162}$

37. $\frac{288}{480}$ **38.** $\frac{135}{585}$ **39.** $\frac{224}{16}$ **40.** $\frac{270}{15}$

Objective **B** *Determine whether each pair of fractions is equivalent. See Examples 8 and 9.*

41. $\frac{3}{6}$ and $\frac{4}{8}$

42. $\frac{3}{9}$ and $\frac{2}{6}$

43. $\frac{7}{11}$ and $\frac{5}{8}$

44. $\frac{2}{5}$ and $\frac{4}{11}$

45. $\frac{10}{15}$ and $\frac{6}{9}$

46. $\frac{4}{10}$ and $\frac{6}{15}$

47. $\frac{3}{9}$ and $\frac{6}{18}$

48. $\frac{2}{8}$ and $\frac{7}{28}$

49. $\frac{10}{13}$ and $\frac{12}{15}$

50. $\frac{16}{20}$ and $\frac{9}{12}$

51. $\frac{8}{18}$ and $\frac{12}{24}$

52. $\frac{6}{21}$ and $\frac{14}{35}$

Objective **C** *Solve. Write each fraction in simplest form. See Example 10.*

53. A work shift for an employee at McDonald's consists of 8 hours. What fraction of the employee's work shift is represented by 2 hours?

54. Two thousand baseball caps were sold one year at the U.S. Open Golf Tournament. What fractional part of this total does 200 caps represent?

55. There are 5280 feet in a mile. What fraction of a mile is represented by 2640 feet?

56. There are 100 centimeters in 1 meter. What fraction of a meter is 20 centimeters?

57. Sixteen states in the United States have Ritz-Carlton hotels. (*Source:* Ritz-Carlton Hotel Company, LLC)

   a. What fraction of states can claim at least one Ritz-Carlton hotel?

   b. How many states do not have a Ritz-Carlton hotel?

   c. Write the fraction of states without a Ritz-Carlton hotel.

58. There are 78 national monuments in the United States. Ten of these monuments are located in New Mexico. (*Source:* National Park Service)

   a. What fraction of the national monuments in the United States can be found in New Mexico?

   b. How many of the national monuments in the United States are found outside New Mexico?

   c. Write the fraction of national monuments found in states other than New Mexico.

59. The outer wall of the Pentagon is 24 inches wide. Ten inches is concrete, 8 inches is brick, and 6 inches is limestone. What fraction of the wall is concrete? (*Source: USA Today*)

60. There are 35 students in a biology class. If 10 students made an A on the first test, what fraction of the students made an A?

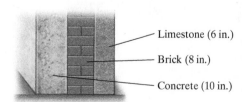

Limestone (6 in.)

Brick (8 in.)

Concrete (10 in.)

61. Kroger Company operates stores under multiple banners in 32 states in the United States. (*Source:* Kroger Company)

   a. How many states do not have a Kroger Company store?

   b. What fraction of states do not have a Kroger company store?

62. Katy Biagini just bought a brand-new 2009 Toyota Camry hybrid for $28,000. Her old car was traded in for $12,000.

   a. How much of her purchase price was not covered by her trade-in?

   b. What fraction of the purchase price was not covered by the trade-in?

63. As of this writing, a total of 320 individuals from the United States are/have been astronauts. Of these, 22 were born in Texas. What fraction of U.S. astronauts were born in Texas? (*Source:* NASA)

64. Worldwide, Hallmark employs nearly 16,000 full-time employees. About 4200 employees work at the Hallmark headquarters in Kansas City, Missouri. What fraction of Hallmark employees work in Kansas City? (*Source:* Hallmark Cards, Inc.)

Review

Multiply. See Section 1.6.

65. $\begin{array}{r} 91 \\ \times\ 4 \\ \hline \end{array}$ **66.** $\begin{array}{r} 73 \\ \times\ 8 \\ \hline \end{array}$ **67.** $\begin{array}{r} 387 \\ \times\ 6 \\ \hline \end{array}$ **68.** $\begin{array}{r} 562 \\ \times\ 9 \\ \hline \end{array}$ **69.** $\begin{array}{r} 72 \\ \times\ 35 \\ \hline \end{array}$ **70.** $\begin{array}{r} 238 \\ \times\ 26 \\ \hline \end{array}$

Concept Extensions

 **71.** In your own words, define equivalent fractions.

72. Given a fraction, say $\frac{3}{8}$, how many fractions are there that are equivalent to it? Explain your answer.

Write each fraction in simplest form.

73. $\dfrac{3975}{6625}$

74. $\dfrac{9506}{12,222}$

There are generally considered to be eight basic blood types. The table shows the number of people with the various blood types in a typical group of 100 blood donors. Use the table to answer Exercises 75 through 78. Write each answer in simplest form.

Distribution of Blood Types in Blood Donors	
Blood Type	**Number of People**
O Rh-positive	37
O Rh-negative	7
A Rh-positive	36
A Rh-negative	6
B Rh-positive	9
B Rh-negative	1
AB Rh-positive	3
AB Rh-negative	1
(*Source:* American Red Cross Biomedical Services)	

75. What fraction of blood donors have blood type A Rh-positive?

76. What fraction of blood donors have an O blood type?

77. What fraction of blood donors have an AB blood type?

78. What fraction of blood donors have a B blood type?

The following graph is called a circle graph or pie chart. Each sector (shaped like a piece of pie) shows the fraction of entering college freshmen who expect to major in each discipline shown. The whole circle represents the entire class of college freshmen. Use this graph to answer Exercises 79 through 82.

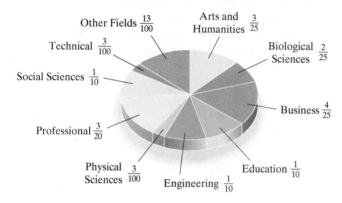

Other Fields $\frac{13}{100}$ Arts and Humanities $\frac{3}{25}$

Technical $\frac{3}{100}$ Biological Sciences $\frac{2}{25}$

Social Sciences $\frac{1}{10}$

Professional $\frac{3}{20}$ Business $\frac{4}{25}$

Physical Sciences $\frac{3}{100}$ Education $\frac{1}{10}$

Engineering $\frac{1}{10}$

Source: The Higher Education Research Institute

79. What fraction of entering college freshmen plan to major in education?

80. What fraction of entering college freshmen plan to major in biological sciences?

81. Why is the Social Sciences sector the same size as the Engineering sector?

82. Why is the Physical Sciences sector smaller than the Business sector?

Use this circle graph to answer Exercises 83 through 86.

Areas Maintained by the National Park Service

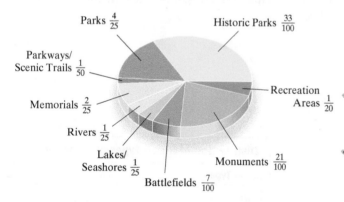

Parks $\frac{4}{25}$ Historic Parks $\frac{33}{100}$

Parkways/ Scenic Trails $\frac{1}{50}$

Memorials $\frac{2}{25}$

Rivers $\frac{1}{25}$ Recreation Areas $\frac{1}{20}$

Lakes/ Seashores $\frac{1}{25}$

Battlefields $\frac{7}{100}$ Monuments $\frac{21}{100}$

Source: National Park Service

83. What fraction of National Park Service areas are National Memorials?

84. What fraction of National Park Service areas are National Parks?

85. Why is the National Battlefields sector smaller than the National Monuments sector?

86. Why is the National Lakes/National Seashores sector the same size as the National Rivers sector?

Use the following numbers for Exercises 87 through 90.

8691   786   1235   2235   85   105   22   222   900   1470

87. List the numbers divisible by both 2 and 3.

88. List the numbers that are divisible by both 3 and 5.

89. The answers to Exercise 87 are also divisible by what number? Tell why.

90. The answers to Exercise 88 are also divisible by what number? Tell why.

2.4 MULTIPLYING FRACTIONS AND MIXED NUMBERS

Objectives

Ⓐ **Multiply Fractions.**

Ⓑ **Multiply Fractions and Mixed Numbers or Whole Numbers.**

Ⓒ **Solve Problems by Multiplying Fractions.**

Objective Ⓐ Multiplying Fractions

Let's use a diagram to discover how fractions are multiplied. For example, to multiply $\frac{1}{2}$ and $\frac{3}{4}$, we find $\frac{1}{2}$ of $\frac{3}{4}$. To do this, we begin with a diagram showing $\frac{3}{4}$ of a rectangle's area shaded.

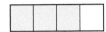 $\frac{3}{4}$ of the rectangle's area is shaded.

To find $\frac{1}{2}$ of $\frac{3}{4}$, we heavily shade $\frac{1}{2}$ of the part that is already shaded.

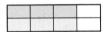

By counting smaller rectangles, we see that $\frac{3}{8}$ of the larger rectangle is now heavily shaded, so that

$$\frac{1}{2} \text{ of } \frac{3}{4} \text{ is } \frac{3}{8}, \text{ or } \frac{1}{2} \cdot \frac{3}{4} = \frac{3}{8}$$ Notice that $\frac{1}{2} \cdot \frac{3}{4} = \frac{1 \cdot 3}{2 \cdot 4} = \frac{3}{8}$.

> ### Multiplying Fractions
>
> To multiply two fractions, multiply the numerators and multiply the denominators. If $a, b, c,$ and d represent positive whole numbers, we have
>
> $$\frac{a}{b} \cdot \frac{c}{d} = \frac{a \cdot c}{b \cdot d}$$

Examples Multiply.

1. $\dfrac{2}{3} \cdot \dfrac{5}{11} = \dfrac{2 \cdot 5}{3 \cdot 11} = \dfrac{10}{33}$ Multiply numerators.
Multiply denominators.

This fraction is in simplest form since 10 and 33 have no common factors other than 1.

2. $\dfrac{1}{4} \cdot \dfrac{1}{2} = \dfrac{1 \cdot 1}{4 \cdot 2} = \dfrac{1}{8}$ This fraction is in simplest form.

● Work Practice 1–2

PRACTICE 1–2

Multiply.

1. $\dfrac{3}{8} \cdot \dfrac{5}{7}$ **2.** $\dfrac{1}{3} \cdot \dfrac{1}{6}$

Answers

1. $\dfrac{15}{56}$ **2.** $\dfrac{1}{18}$

PRACTICE 3

Multiply and simplify: $\dfrac{6}{55} \cdot \dfrac{5}{8}$

Example 3 Multiply and simplify: $\dfrac{6}{7} \cdot \dfrac{14}{27}$

Solution:

$$\frac{6}{7} \cdot \frac{14}{27} = \frac{6 \cdot 14}{7 \cdot 27}$$

We can simplify by finding the prime factorizations and using our shortcut procedure of dividing out common factors in the numerator and denominator.

$$\frac{6 \cdot 14}{7 \cdot 27} = \frac{2 \cdot \overset{1}{\cancel{3}} \cdot 2 \cdot \overset{1}{\cancel{7}}}{\underset{1}{\cancel{7}} \cdot \underset{1}{\cancel{3}} \cdot 3 \cdot 3} = \frac{2 \cdot 2}{3 \cdot 3} = \frac{4}{9}$$

● Work Practice 3

Helpful Hint

Remember that the shortcut procedure above is the same as removing factors of 1 in the product.

$$\frac{6 \cdot 14}{7 \cdot 27} = \frac{2 \cdot 3 \cdot 2 \cdot 7}{7 \cdot 3 \cdot 3 \cdot 3} = \frac{7}{7} \cdot \frac{3}{3} \cdot \frac{2 \cdot 2}{3 \cdot 3} = 1 \cdot 1 \cdot \frac{4}{9} = \frac{4}{9}$$

Helpful Hint

In simplifying a product, don't forget that it may be possible to identify common factors without actually writing the prime factorization. For example,

$$\frac{10}{11} \cdot \frac{1}{20} = \frac{10 \cdot 1}{11 \cdot 20} = \frac{\overset{1}{\cancel{10}} \cdot 1}{11 \cdot \underset{1}{\cancel{10}} \cdot 2} = \frac{1}{11 \cdot 2} = \frac{1}{22}$$

PRACTICE 4

Multiply and simplify: $\dfrac{4}{15} \cdot \dfrac{3}{8}$

Example 4 Multiply and simplify: $\dfrac{23}{32} \cdot \dfrac{4}{7}$

Solution: Notice that 4 and 32 have a common factor of 4.

$$\frac{23}{32} \cdot \frac{4}{7} = \frac{23 \cdot 4}{32 \cdot 7} = \frac{23 \cdot \overset{1}{\cancel{4}}}{\underset{1}{\cancel{4}} \cdot 8 \cdot 7} = \frac{23}{8 \cdot 7} = \frac{23}{56}$$

● Work Practice 4

After multiplying two fractions, always check to see whether the product can be simplified.

PRACTICE 5–7

Multiply.

5. $\dfrac{2}{5} \cdot \dfrac{20}{7}$

6. $\dfrac{4}{11} \cdot \dfrac{33}{16}$

7. $\dfrac{1}{6} \cdot \dfrac{3}{10} \cdot \dfrac{25}{16}$

Examples Multiply.

5. $\dfrac{3}{4} \cdot \dfrac{8}{5} = \dfrac{3 \cdot 8}{4 \cdot 5} = \dfrac{3 \cdot \overset{1}{\cancel{4}} \cdot 2}{\underset{1}{\cancel{4}} \cdot 5} = \dfrac{6}{5}$

6. $\dfrac{6}{13} \cdot \dfrac{26}{30} = \dfrac{6 \cdot 26}{13 \cdot 30} = \dfrac{\overset{1}{\cancel{6}} \cdot \overset{1}{\cancel{13}} \cdot 2}{\underset{1}{\cancel{13}} \cdot \underset{1}{\cancel{6}} \cdot 5} = \dfrac{2}{5}$

7. $\dfrac{1}{3} \cdot \dfrac{2}{5} \cdot \dfrac{9}{16} = \dfrac{1 \cdot 2 \cdot 9}{3 \cdot 5 \cdot 16} = \dfrac{1 \cdot \overset{1}{\cancel{2}} \cdot \overset{1}{\cancel{3}} \cdot 3}{\underset{1}{\cancel{3}} \cdot 5 \cdot \underset{1}{\cancel{2}} \cdot 8} = \dfrac{3}{40}$

● Work Practice 5–7

Answers

3. $\dfrac{3}{44}$ **4.** $\dfrac{1}{10}$ **5.** $\dfrac{8}{7}$ **6.** $\dfrac{3}{4}$ **7.** $\dfrac{5}{64}$

Objective ⓑ Multiplying Fractions and Mixed Numbers or Whole Numbers

When multiplying a fraction and a mixed or a whole number, remember that mixed and whole numbers can be written as fractions.

> ### *Multiplying Fractions and Mixed Numbers or Whole Numbers*
>
> To multiply with mixed numbers or whole numbers, first write any mixed or whole numbers as fractions and then multiply as usual.

Example 8 Multiply: $3\frac{1}{3} \cdot \frac{7}{8}$

Solution: The mixed number $3\frac{1}{3}$ can be written as the fraction $\frac{10}{3}$. Then,

$$3\frac{1}{3} \cdot \frac{7}{8} = \frac{10}{3} \cdot \frac{7}{8} = \frac{\overset{1}{\cancel{2}} \cdot 5 \cdot 7}{3 \cdot \underset{1}{\cancel{2}} \cdot 4} = \frac{35}{12} \quad \text{or} \quad 2\frac{11}{12}$$

● Work Practice 8

PRACTICE 8

Multiply and simplify: $2\frac{1}{2} \cdot \frac{8}{15}$

Don't forget that a whole number can be written as a fraction by writing the whole number over 1. For example,

$$20 = \frac{20}{1} \quad \text{and} \quad 7 = \frac{7}{1}$$

Example 9 Multiply.

$$\frac{3}{4} \cdot 20 = \frac{3}{4} \cdot \frac{20}{1} = \frac{3 \cdot 20}{4 \cdot 1} = \frac{3 \cdot \overset{1}{\cancel{4}} \cdot 5}{\underset{1}{\cancel{4}} \cdot 1} = \frac{15}{1} \quad \text{or} \quad 15$$

● Work Practice 9

PRACTICE 9

Multiply.

$$\frac{2}{3} \cdot 18$$

When both numbers to be multiplied are mixed or whole numbers, it is a good idea to estimate the product to see if your answer is reasonable. To do this, we first practice rounding mixed numbers to the nearest whole. If the fraction part of the mixed number is $\frac{1}{2}$ or greater, we round the whole number part up. If the fraction part of the mixed number is less than $\frac{1}{2}$, then we do not round the whole number part up. Study the table below for examples.

Mixed Number	Rounding
$5\frac{1}{4}$ $\frac{1}{4}$ is less than $\frac{1}{2}$ $\frac{1}{4}$ $\frac{1}{2}$	Thus, $5\frac{1}{4}$ rounds to 5.
$3\frac{9}{16}$ ← 9 is greater than 8 → Half of 16 is 8.	Thus, $3\frac{7}{16}$ rounds to 4.
$1\frac{3}{7}$ ← 3 is less than $3\frac{1}{2}$. → Half of 7 is $3\frac{1}{2}$.	Thus, $1\frac{3}{7}$ rounds to 1.

Answers

8. $\frac{4}{3}$ or $1\frac{1}{3}$ **9.** 12

PRACTICE 10–11

Multiply.

10. $3\frac{1}{5} \cdot 2\frac{3}{4}$ **11.** $5 \cdot 3\frac{11}{15}$

| Examples | Multiply. Check by estimating.

10. $1\frac{2}{3} \cdot 2\frac{1}{4} = \frac{5}{3} \cdot \frac{9}{4} = \frac{5 \cdot 9}{3 \cdot 4} = \frac{5 \cdot \overset{1}{\cancel{3}} \cdot 3}{\underset{1}{\cancel{3}} \cdot 4} = \frac{15}{4}$ or $3\frac{3}{4}$ Exact

Let's check by estimating.

$1\frac{2}{3}$ rounds to 2, $2\frac{1}{4}$ rounds to 2, and $2 \cdot 2 = 4$ Estimate

The estimate is close to the exact value, so our answer is reasonable.

11. $7 \cdot 2\frac{11}{14} = \frac{7}{1} \cdot \frac{39}{14} = \frac{7 \cdot 39}{1 \cdot 14} = \frac{\overset{1}{\cancel{7}} \cdot 39}{1 \cdot 2 \cdot \underset{1}{\cancel{7}}} = \frac{39}{2}$ or $19\frac{1}{2}$ Exact

To estimate,

$2\frac{11}{14}$ rounds to 3 and $7 \cdot 3 = 21$. Estimate

The estimate is close to the exact value, so our answer is reasonable.

● **Work Practice 10–11**

Recall from Section 1.6 that 0 multiplied by any number is 0. This is true of fractions and mixed numbers also.

| Examples | Multiply.

12. $0 \cdot \frac{3}{5} = 0$

13. $2\frac{3}{8} \cdot 0 = 0$

● **Work Practice 12–13**

PRACTICE 12–13

Multiply.

12. $\frac{9}{11} \cdot 0$ **13.** $0 \cdot 4\frac{1}{8}$

✓ **Concept Check**

Find the error.

$2\frac{1}{4} \cdot \frac{1}{2} = 2\frac{1 \cdot 1}{4 \cdot 2} = 2\frac{1}{8}$

Objective ⓒ Solving Problems by Multiplying Fractions

To solve real-life problems that involve multiplying fractions, we use our four problem-solving steps from Chapter 1. In Example 14, a key word that implies multiplication is used. That key word is "**of.**"

Helpful Hint

"of" usually translates to multiplication.

Answers

10. $\frac{44}{5}$ or $8\frac{4}{5}$ **11.** $\frac{56}{3}$ or $18\frac{2}{3}$
12. 0 **13.** 0

✓ **Concept Check Answer**

forgot to change mixed number to fraction

Example 14 Finding the Number of Roller Coasters in an Amusement Park

Cedar Point is an amusement park located in Sandusky, Ohio. Its collection of 68 rides is the largest in the world. Of the rides, $\frac{4}{17}$ are roller coasters. How many roller coasters are in Cedar Point's collection of rides? (*Source:* Wikipedia)

PRACTICE 14

Hershey Park is an amusement park in Hershey, Pennsylvania. Of its 60 rides, $\frac{1}{6}$ of them are roller coasters. How many roller coasters are in Hershey Park?

Solution:

1. UNDERSTAND the problem. To do so, read and reread the problem. We are told that $\frac{4}{17}$ of Cedar Point's rides are roller coasters. The word "of" here means multiplication.

2. TRANSLATE.

In words:	number of roller coasters	is	$\frac{4}{17}$	of	total rides at Cedar Point
	↓	↓	↓	↓	↓
Translate:	number of roller coasters	=	$\frac{4}{17}$	·	68

3. SOLVE: Before we solve, let's estimate a reasonable answer. The fraction $\frac{4}{17}$ is less than $\frac{1}{2}$ (draw a diagram, if needed), and $\frac{1}{2}$ of 68 rides is 34 rides, so the number of roller coasters should be less than 34.

$$\frac{4}{17} \cdot 68 = \frac{4}{17} \cdot \frac{68}{1} = \frac{4 \cdot 68}{17 \cdot 1} = \frac{4 \cdot \overset{1}{\cancel{17}} \cdot 4}{\underset{1}{\cancel{17}} \cdot 1} = \frac{16}{1} \quad \text{or} \quad 16$$

4. INTERPRET. *Check* your work. From our estimate, our answer is reasonable. *State* your conclusion: The number of roller coasters at Cedar Point is 16.

● Work Practice 14

Helpful Hint

To help visualize a fractional part of a whole number, look at the diagram below.

$\frac{1}{5}$ of 60 = ?

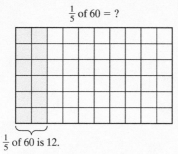

$\frac{1}{5}$ of 60 is 12.

Answer
14. 10 roller coasters

Vocabulary and Readiness Check

Use the choices below to fill in each blank. Not all choices will be used.

multiplication $\dfrac{a \cdot d}{b \cdot c}$ $\dfrac{a \cdot c}{b \cdot d}$ $\dfrac{2 \cdot 2 \cdot 2}{7}$ $\dfrac{2}{7} \cdot \dfrac{2}{7} \cdot \dfrac{2}{7}$

division   0

1. To multiply two fractions, we write $\dfrac{a}{b} \cdot \dfrac{c}{d} = $ _____ .

2. Using the definition of an exponent, the expression $\dfrac{2^3}{7} = $ _____ while $\left(\dfrac{2}{7}\right)^3 = $ _____ .

3. The word "of" indicates _____ .

4. $\dfrac{1}{5} \cdot 0 = $ _____ .

2.4 Exercise Set

FOR EXTRA HELP
MyMathLab   Math XL — PRACTICE   WATCH   DOWNLOAD   READ   REVIEW

Objective A *Multiply. Write each answer in simplest form. See Examples 1 through 7 and 12.*

1. $\dfrac{1}{3} \cdot \dfrac{2}{5}$ **2.** $\dfrac{2}{3} \cdot \dfrac{4}{7}$ **3.** $\dfrac{6}{5} \cdot \dfrac{1}{7}$ **4.** $\dfrac{7}{3} \cdot \dfrac{1}{4}$ **5.** $\dfrac{3}{10} \cdot \dfrac{3}{8}$

6. $\dfrac{2}{5} \cdot \dfrac{7}{11}$ **7.** $\dfrac{2}{7} \cdot \dfrac{5}{8}$ **8.** $\dfrac{7}{8} \cdot \dfrac{2}{3}$ **9.** $\dfrac{16}{5} \cdot \dfrac{3}{4}$ **10.** $\dfrac{8}{3} \cdot \dfrac{5}{12}$

11. $\dfrac{5}{28} \cdot \dfrac{2}{25}$ **12.** $\dfrac{4}{35} \cdot \dfrac{5}{24}$ **13.** $0 \cdot \dfrac{8}{9}$ **14.** $\dfrac{11}{12} \cdot 0$ **15.** $\dfrac{1}{10} \cdot \dfrac{1}{11}$

16. $\dfrac{1}{9} \cdot \dfrac{1}{13}$ **17.** $\dfrac{18}{20} \cdot \dfrac{36}{99}$ **18.** $\dfrac{5}{32} \cdot \dfrac{64}{100}$ **19.** $\dfrac{3}{8} \cdot \dfrac{9}{10}$ **20.** $\dfrac{4}{5} \cdot \dfrac{8}{25}$

21. $\dfrac{11}{20} \cdot \dfrac{1}{7} \cdot \dfrac{5}{22}$ **22.** $\dfrac{27}{32} \cdot \dfrac{10}{13} \cdot \dfrac{16}{30}$ **23.** $\dfrac{1}{3} \cdot \dfrac{2}{7} \cdot \dfrac{1}{5}$ **24.** $\dfrac{3}{5} \cdot \dfrac{1}{2} \cdot \dfrac{3}{7}$ **25.** $\dfrac{9}{20} \cdot 0 \cdot \dfrac{4}{19}$

26. $\dfrac{8}{11} \cdot \dfrac{4}{7} \cdot 0$ **27.** $\dfrac{3}{14} \cdot \dfrac{6}{25} \cdot \dfrac{5}{27} \cdot \dfrac{7}{6}$ **28.** $\dfrac{7}{8} \cdot \dfrac{9}{20} \cdot \dfrac{12}{22} \cdot \dfrac{11}{14}$

Objective **B** *Round each mixed number to the nearest whole number. See the table at the bottom of page 133.*

29. $7\frac{7}{8}$ **30.** $11\frac{3}{4}$ **31.** $6\frac{1}{5}$ **32.** $4\frac{1}{9}$ **33.** $19\frac{11}{20}$ **34.** $18\frac{12}{22}$

Multiply. Write each answer in simplest form. For those exercises marked, find both an exact product and an estimated product. See Examples 8 through 11 and 13.

35. $12 \cdot \frac{1}{4}$ **36.** $\frac{2}{3} \cdot 6$ **37.** $\frac{5}{8} \cdot 4$ **38.** $10 \cdot \frac{7}{8}$ **39.** $1\frac{1}{4} \cdot \frac{4}{25}$

40. $\frac{3}{22} \cdot 3\frac{2}{3}$ **41.** $\frac{2}{5} \cdot 4\frac{1}{6}$ **42.** $2\frac{1}{9} \cdot \frac{6}{7}$ **43.** $\frac{2}{3} \cdot 1$ **44.** $1 \cdot \frac{5}{9}$

45. $2\frac{1}{5} \cdot 3\frac{1}{2}$ **46.** $2\frac{1}{4} \cdot 7\frac{1}{8}$ **47.** $3\frac{4}{5} \cdot 6\frac{2}{7}$ **48.** $5\frac{5}{6} \cdot 7\frac{3}{5}$ **49.** $5 \cdot 2\frac{1}{2}$

    Exact: Exact: Exact: Exact:

    Estimate: Estimate: Estimate: Estimate:

50. $6 \cdot 3\frac{1}{3}$ **51.** $1\frac{1}{5} \cdot 12\frac{1}{2}$ **52.** $1\frac{1}{6} \cdot 7\frac{1}{5}$ **53.** $\frac{3}{4} \cdot 16 \cdot \frac{1}{2}$ **54.** $\frac{7}{8} \cdot 24 \cdot \frac{1}{3}$

55. $\frac{3}{10} \cdot 15 \cdot 2\frac{1}{2}$ **56.** $\frac{11}{20} \cdot 12 \cdot 3\frac{1}{3}$ **57.** $3\frac{1}{2} \cdot 1\frac{3}{4} \cdot 2\frac{2}{3}$ **58.** $4\frac{1}{2} \cdot 2\frac{1}{9} \cdot 1\frac{1}{5}$

Objectives **A** **B** Mixed Practice *Multiply and simplify. See Examples 1 through 13.*

59. $\frac{1}{4} \cdot \frac{2}{15}$ **60.** $\frac{3}{8} \cdot \frac{5}{12}$ **61.** $\frac{19}{37} \cdot 0$ **62.** $0 \cdot \frac{3}{31}$ **63.** $2\frac{4}{5} \cdot 1\frac{1}{7}$

64. $3\frac{1}{5} \cdot 2\frac{11}{32}$ **65.** $\frac{3}{2} \cdot \frac{7}{3}$ **66.** $\frac{15}{2} \cdot \frac{3}{5}$ **67.** $\frac{6}{15} \cdot \frac{5}{16}$ **68.** $\frac{9}{20} \cdot \frac{10}{90}$

69. $\frac{7}{72} \cdot \frac{9}{49}$ **70.** $\frac{3}{80} \cdot \frac{2}{27}$ **71.** $20 \cdot \frac{11}{12}$ **72.** $30 \cdot \frac{8}{9}$ **73.** $9\frac{5}{7} \cdot 8\frac{1}{5} \cdot 0$

74. $4\frac{11}{13} \cdot 0 \cdot 12\frac{1}{13}$ **75.** $12\frac{4}{5} \cdot 6\frac{7}{8} \cdot \frac{26}{77}$ **76.** $14\frac{2}{5} \cdot 8\frac{1}{3} \cdot \frac{11}{16}$

Objective Ⓒ *Solve. Write each answer in simplest form. For Exercises 77 through 80, recall that "of" translates to multiplication. See Example 14.*

77. Find $\frac{1}{4}$ of 200.

78. Find $\frac{1}{5}$ of 200.

79. Find $\frac{5}{6}$ of 24.

80. Find $\frac{5}{8}$ of 24.

Solve. For Exercises 81 and 82, the solutions have been started for you. See Example 14.

81. In the United States, $\frac{4}{25}$ of college freshmen major in business. A community college in Pennsylvania has a freshman enrollment of approximately 800 students. How many of these freshmen might we project are majoring in business?

Start the solution:

1. UNDERSTAND the problem. Reread it as many times as needed.

2. TRANSLATE into an equation. (Fill in the blank below.)

freshmen majoring in business	is	$\frac{4}{25}$	of	community college freshmen enrollment
↓	↓	↓	↓	↓

$$\text{freshmen majoring in business} = \frac{4}{25} \cdot \underline{\qquad}$$

Finish with:

3. SOLVE

4. INTERPRET

82. A patient was told that, at most, $\frac{1}{5}$ of his calories should come from fat. If his diet consists of 3000 calories a day, find the maximum number of calories that can come from fat.

Start the solution:

1. UNDERSTAND the problem. Reread it as many times as needed.

2. TRANSLATE into an equation. (Fill in the blank below.)

patient's fat calories	is	$\frac{1}{5}$	of	his daily calories
↓	↓	↓	↓	↓

$$\text{patient's fat calories} = \frac{1}{5} \cdot \underline{\qquad}$$

Finish with:

3. SOLVE

4. INTERPRET

83. In a recent year, there were approximately 175 million moviegoers in the United States. Of these, about $\frac{7}{25}$ were ages 16–24. Find the approximate number of people ages 16–24 who attended the movies in that year. (*Source:* Motion Picture Association of America)

84. In a recent year, movie theater owners received a total of $7660 million in movie admission tickets. About $\frac{7}{10}$ of this amount was for R-rated movies. Find the amount of money received from R-rated movies. (*Source:* Motion Picture Association of America)

85. The Oregon National Historic Trail is 2170 miles long. It begins in Independence, Missouri, and ends in Oregon City, Oregon. Manfred Coulon has hiked $\frac{2}{5}$ of the trail before. How many miles has he hiked? (*Source:* National Park Service)

86. Each turn of a screw sinks it $\frac{3}{16}$ of an inch deeper into a piece of wood. Find how deep the screw is after 8 turns.

$\frac{3}{16}$ inch

87. The radius of a circle is one-half of its diameter, as shown. If the diameter of a circle is $\frac{3}{8}$ of an inch, what is its radius?

diameter
←radius→

88. The diameter of a circle is twice its radius, as shown in the Exercise 87 illustration. If the radius of a circle is $\frac{7}{20}$ of a foot, what is its diameter?

89. A veterinarian's dipping vat holds 36 gallons of liquid. She normally fills it $\frac{5}{6}$ full of a medicated flea dip solution. Find how many gallons of solution are normally in the vat.

36 gallons
$\frac{5}{6}$ full

90. The plans for a deck call for $\frac{2}{5}$ of a 4-foot post to be underground. Find the length of the post that is to be buried.

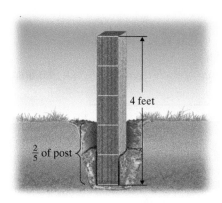

4 feet
$\frac{2}{5}$ of post

91. An estimate for the measure of an adult's wrist is $\frac{1}{4}$ of the waist size. If Jorge has a 34-inch waist, estimate the size of his wrist.

92. An estimate for an adult's waist measurement is found by multiplying the neck size (in inches) by 2. Jock's neck measures $\frac{36}{2}$ inches. Estimate his waist measurement.

93. A sidewalk is built 6 bricks wide by laying each brick side by side. How many inches wide is the sidewalk if each brick measures $3\frac{1}{4}$ inches wide?

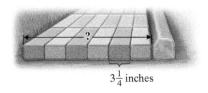

?
$3\frac{1}{4}$ inches

94. A recipe calls for $\frac{1}{3}$ of a cup of flour. How much flour should be used if only $\frac{1}{2}$ of the recipe is being made?

95. A Japanese company called Che-ez! manufactures a small digital camera, the SPYZ camera. The face of the camera measures $2\frac{9}{25}$ inches by $1\frac{13}{25}$ inches and is slightly bigger than a Zippo lighter. Find the area of the face of this camera. (Area = length · width)

$1\frac{13}{25}$ in.

$2\frac{9}{25}$ in.

96. As part of his research, famous tornado expert Dr. T. Fujita studied approximately 31,050 tornadoes that occurred in the United States between 1916 and 1985. He found that roughly $\frac{7}{10}$ of these tornadoes occurred during April, May, June, and July. How many of these tornadoes occurred during these four months? (*Source: U.S. Tornadoes Part 1*, T. Fujita, University of Chicago)

Find the area of each rectangle. Recall that area = length · width.

△ **97.**

$\frac{1}{5}$ foot

$\frac{5}{14}$ foot

△ **98.** $\frac{1}{2}$ mile

$\frac{3}{8}$ mile

△ **99.**

$1\frac{3}{4}$ yards

2 yards

△ **100.**

5 inches

$3\frac{1}{2}$ inches

Recall that the following graph is called a **circle graph** *or* **pie chart**. *Each sector (shaped like a piece of pie) shows the fractional part of a car's total mileage that falls into a particular category. The whole circle represents a car's total mileage.*

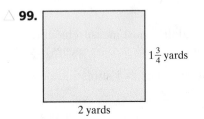

Shopping $\frac{3}{25}$

Vacation/other $\frac{3}{50}$

Work $\frac{8}{25}$

Social/ recreational $\frac{13}{100}$

Medical $\frac{1}{100}$

Family business $\frac{1}{5}$

Visit friends $\frac{3}{25}$

School/church $\frac{2}{50}$

Source: The American Automobile Manufacturers Association and The National Automobile Dealers Association

In one year, a family drove 12,000 miles in the family car. Use the circle graph to determine how many of these miles might be expected to fall in the categories shown in Exercises 101 through 104.

101. Work

102. Shopping

103. Family business

104. Medical

Review

Divide. See Section 1.7.

105. $8\overline{)1648}$ **106.** $7\overline{)3920}$ **107.** $23\overline{)1300}$ **108.** $31\overline{)2500}$

Concept Extensions

109. In your own words, explain how to multiply
  a. fractions
  b. mixed numbers

110. In your own words, explain how to round a mixed number to the nearest whole number.

Find the error in each calculation. See the Concept Check in this section.

111. $3\frac{2}{3} \cdot 1\frac{1}{7} = 3\frac{2}{21}$

112. $5 \cdot 2\frac{1}{4} = 10\frac{1}{4}$

Choose the best estimate for each product.

113. $3\frac{1}{5} \cdot 4\frac{5}{8}$
  a. 7
  b. 15
  c. 8
  d. $12\frac{1}{8}$

114. $\frac{11}{12} \cdot 4\frac{1}{16}$
  a. 16
  b. 1
  c. 4
  d. 8

115. $9 \cdot \frac{10}{11}$
  a. 9
  b. 90
  c. 99
  d. 0

116. $7\frac{1}{4} \cdot 4\frac{1}{5}$
  a. 40
  b. $\frac{7}{5}$
  c. 35
  d. 28

117. If $\frac{3}{4}$ of 36 students on a first bus are girls and $\frac{2}{3}$ of the 30 students on a second bus are *boys*, how many students on the two buses are girls?

118. In 2008, there were approximately 14,120 commercial radio stations broadcasting in the United States. Of these, approximately $\frac{33}{625}$ were news/talk stations. How many radio stations were news/talk stations in 2008? (Round to the nearest whole.) (*Source:* Corporation for Public Broadcasting)

119. There were approximately $116\frac{4}{5}$ million households in the United States in 2009. About $\frac{3}{4}$ of these households had one or more credit cards. How many American households had one or more credit cards in 2009? (*Source:* Nilson report, April 2009)

120. Approximately $\frac{1}{8}$ of the U.S. population lives in the state of California. If the U.S. population is approximately 307,607,800, find the approximate population of California. (*Source:* U.S. Census Bureau)

2.5 DIVIDING FRACTIONS AND MIXED NUMBERS

Objective **A** Finding Reciprocals of Fractions

Before we can divide fractions, we need to know how to find the **reciprocal** of a fraction or whole number.

Reciprocal of a Fraction

Two numbers are **reciprocals** of each other if their product is 1. The reciprocal of the fraction $\frac{a}{b}$ is $\frac{b}{a}$ because $\frac{a}{b} \cdot \frac{b}{a} = \frac{a \cdot b}{b \cdot a} = 1$.

Finding the Reciprocal of a Fraction

To find the reciprocal of a fraction, interchange its numerator and denominator.

For example,

The reciprocal of $\frac{2}{5}$ is $\frac{5}{2}$ because $\frac{2}{5} \cdot \frac{5}{2} = \frac{10}{10} = 1$.

The reciprocal of 7, or $\frac{7}{1}$ is $\frac{1}{7}$ because $7 \cdot \frac{1}{7} = \frac{7}{1} \cdot \frac{1}{7} = \frac{7}{7} = 1$.

Examples Find the reciprocal of each number.

PRACTICE 1–4

Find the reciprocal of each number.

1. $\frac{4}{9}$ **2.** $\frac{15}{7}$

3. 9   **4.** $\frac{1}{8}$

1. The reciprocal of $\frac{5}{6}$ is $\frac{6}{5}$. $\frac{5}{6} \cdot \frac{6}{5} = \frac{5 \cdot 6}{6 \cdot 5} = \frac{30}{30} = 1$

2. The reciprocal of $\frac{11}{8}$ is $\frac{8}{11}$. $\frac{11}{8} \cdot \frac{8}{11} = \frac{11 \cdot 8}{8 \cdot 11} = \frac{88}{88} = 1$

3. The reciprocal of $\frac{1}{3}$ is $\frac{3}{1}$ or 3. $\frac{1}{3} \cdot \frac{3}{1} = \frac{1 \cdot 3}{3 \cdot 1} = \frac{3}{3} = 1$

4. The reciprocal of 5, or $\frac{5}{1}$, is $\frac{1}{5}$. $\frac{5}{1} \cdot \frac{1}{5} = \frac{5 \cdot 1}{1 \cdot 5} = \frac{5}{5} = 1$

Work Practice 1–4

Helpful Hint

Every number except 0 has a reciprocal. The number 0 has no reciprocal because there is no number that when multiplied by 0 gives a result of 1.

Objective **B** Dividing Fractions

Division of fractions has the same meaning as division of whole numbers. For example,

10 ÷ 5 means: How many 5s are there in 10?

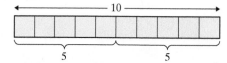

There are two 5s in 10, so
10 ÷ 5 = 2.

$\dfrac{3}{4} \div \dfrac{1}{8}$ means: How many $\dfrac{1}{8}$s are there in $\dfrac{3}{4}$?

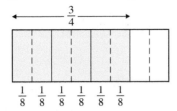

There are six $\dfrac{1}{8}$s in $\dfrac{3}{4}$, so $\dfrac{3}{4} \div \dfrac{1}{8} = 6$.

We use reciprocals to divide fractions.

Dividing Fractions

To divide two fractions, multiply the first fraction by the reciprocal of the second fraction.

If $a, b, c,$ and d represent numbers, and $b, c,$ and d are not 0, then

$$\frac{a}{b} \div \frac{c}{d} = \frac{a}{b} \cdot \underset{\uparrow\text{reciprocal}}{\frac{d}{c}} = \frac{a \cdot d}{b \cdot c}$$

For example,

multiply by reciprocal

$$\frac{3}{4} \div \frac{1}{8} = \frac{3}{4} \cdot \frac{8}{1} = \frac{3 \cdot 8}{4 \cdot 1} = \frac{3 \cdot 2 \cdot \overset{1}{\cancel{4}}}{\underset{1}{\cancel{4}} \cdot 1} = \frac{6}{1} \text{ or } 6$$

Just as when you are multiplying fractions, always check to see whether your answer can be simplified when you divide fractions.

Examples Divide and simplify.

5. $\dfrac{7}{8} \div \dfrac{2}{9} = \dfrac{7}{8} \cdot \dfrac{9}{2} = \dfrac{7 \cdot 9}{8 \cdot 2} = \dfrac{63}{16}$

6. $\dfrac{5}{16} \div \dfrac{3}{4} = \dfrac{5}{16} \cdot \dfrac{4}{3} = \dfrac{5 \cdot 4}{16 \cdot 3} = \dfrac{5 \cdot \overset{1}{\cancel{4}}}{\underset{1}{\cancel{4}} \cdot 4 \cdot 3} = \dfrac{5}{12}$

7. $\dfrac{2}{5} \div \dfrac{1}{2} = \dfrac{2}{5} \cdot \dfrac{2}{1} = \dfrac{2 \cdot 2}{5 \cdot 1} = \dfrac{4}{5}$

● Work Practice 5–7

PRACTICE 5–7

Divide and simplify.

5. $\dfrac{3}{2} \div \dfrac{14}{5}$ **6.** $\dfrac{8}{7} \div \dfrac{2}{9}$

7. $\dfrac{4}{9} \div \dfrac{1}{2}$

Helpful Hint

When dividing fractions, do *not* look for common factors to divide out until you rewrite the division as multiplication.

Do not try to divide out these two 2s.

$$\frac{1}{\mathbf{2}} \div \frac{\mathbf{2}}{3} = \frac{1}{2} \cdot \frac{3}{2} = \frac{3}{4}$$

Answers

5. $\dfrac{15}{28}$ **6.** $\dfrac{36}{7}$ **7.** $\dfrac{8}{9}$

Objective ⓒ Dividing Fractions and Mixed Numbers or Whole Numbers

Just as with multiplying, mixed or whole numbers should be written as fractions before you divide them.

> ### Dividing Fractions and Mixed Numbers or Whole Numbers
>
> To divide with a mixed number or a whole number, first write the mixed or whole number as a fraction and then divide as usual.

Examples Divide.

8. $\dfrac{3}{4} \div 5 = \dfrac{3}{4} \div \dfrac{5}{1} = \dfrac{3}{4} \cdot \dfrac{1}{5} = \dfrac{3 \cdot 1}{4 \cdot 5} = \dfrac{3}{20}$

9. $\dfrac{11}{18} \div 2\dfrac{5}{6} = \dfrac{11}{18} \div \dfrac{17}{6} = \dfrac{11}{18} \cdot \dfrac{6}{17} = \dfrac{11 \cdot 6}{18 \cdot 17} = \dfrac{11 \cdot \overset{1}{\cancel{6}}}{\underset{1}{\cancel{6}} \cdot 3 \cdot 17} = \dfrac{11}{51}$

10. $5\dfrac{2}{3} \div 2\dfrac{5}{9} = \dfrac{17}{3} \div \dfrac{23}{9} = \dfrac{17}{3} \cdot \dfrac{9}{23} = \dfrac{17 \cdot 9}{3 \cdot 23} = \dfrac{17 \cdot \overset{1}{\cancel{3}} \cdot 3}{\underset{1}{\cancel{3}} \cdot 23} = \dfrac{51}{23} \text{ or } 2\dfrac{5}{23}$

● Work Practice 8–10

Recall from Section 1.7 that the quotient of 0 and any number (except 0) is 0. This is true of fractions and mixed numbers also. For example,

$$0 \div \dfrac{7}{8} = 0 \cdot \dfrac{8}{7} = 0 \qquad \text{\small Recall that 0 multiplied by any number is 0.}$$

Also recall from Section 1.7 that the quotient of any number and 0 is undefined. This is also true of fractions and mixed numbers. For example, to find $\dfrac{7}{8} \div 0$, or $\dfrac{7}{8} \div \dfrac{0}{1}$, we would need to find the reciprocal of 0 $\left(\text{or } \dfrac{0}{1}\right)$. As we mentioned in the helpful hint at the beginning of this section, 0 has no reciprocal because there is no number that when multiplied by 0 gives a result of 1. Thus,

$$\dfrac{7}{8} \div 0 \text{ is undefined.}$$

Examples Divide.

11. $0 \div \dfrac{2}{21} = 0 \cdot \dfrac{21}{2} = 0$ **12.** $1\dfrac{3}{4} \div 0$ is undefined.

● Work Practice 11–12

✓ **Concept Check** Which of the following is the correct way to divide $\dfrac{2}{5}$ by $\dfrac{3}{4}$? Or are both correct? Explain.

a. $\dfrac{5}{2} \cdot \dfrac{3}{4}$ **b.** $\dfrac{2}{5} \cdot \dfrac{4}{3}$

Objective ⒟ Solving Problems by Dividing Fractions

To solve real-life problems that involve dividing fractions, we continue to use our four problem-solving steps.

Example 13 Calculating Manufacturing Materials Needed

In a manufacturing process, a metal-cutting machine cuts strips $1\frac{3}{5}$ inches wide from a piece of metal stock. How many such strips can be cut from a 48-inch piece of stock?

Solution:

1. UNDERSTAND the problem. To do so, read and reread the problem. Then draw a diagram:

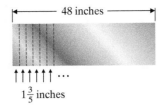

|← 48 inches →|

↑↑↑↑↑ ⋯
$1\frac{3}{5}$ inches

We want to know how many $1\frac{3}{5}$s there are in 48.

2. TRANSLATE.

In words:	Number of strips	is	48	divided by	$1\frac{3}{5}$
	↓	↓	↓	↓	↓
Translate:	Number of strips	=	48	÷	$1\frac{3}{5}$

3. SOLVE: Let's estimate a reasonable answer. The mixed number $1\frac{3}{5}$ rounds to 2 and $48 \div 2 = 24$.

$$48 \div 1\frac{3}{5} = 48 \div \frac{8}{5} = \frac{48}{1} \cdot \frac{5}{8} = \frac{48 \cdot 5}{1 \cdot 8} = \frac{\overset{1}{\cancel{8}} \cdot 6 \cdot 5}{1 \cdot \underset{1}{\cancel{8}}} = \frac{30}{1} \text{ or } 30$$

4. INTERPRET. *Check* your work. Since the exact answer of 30 is close to our estimate of 24, our answer is reasonable. *State* your conclusion: Thirty strips can be cut from the 48-inch piece of stock.

● Work Practice 13

PRACTICE 13

A designer of clothing designs an outfit that requires $2\frac{1}{7}$ yards of material. How many outfits can be made from a 30-yard bolt of material?

Vocabulary and Readiness Check

Use the choices below to fill in each blank. Not all choices will be used.

multiplication $\quad \dfrac{a \cdot d}{b \cdot c} \qquad \dfrac{a \cdot c}{b \cdot d}$

division $\qquad\qquad 0 \qquad$ reciprocals

1. Two numbers are _____ of each other if their product is 1.
2. Every number has a reciprocal except _____.
3. To divide two fractions, we write $\dfrac{a}{b} \div \dfrac{c}{d} =$ _____.
4. The word "per" usually indicates _____.

2.5 Exercise Set

FOR EXTRA HELP

MyMathLab — *Powered by CourseCompass™ and MathXL®*

 PRACTICE   WATCH   DOWNLOAD   READ   REVIEW

Objective Ⓐ *Find the reciprocal of each number. See Examples 1 through 4.*

1. $\dfrac{4}{7}$

2. $\dfrac{9}{10}$

3. $\dfrac{1}{11}$

4. $\dfrac{1}{20}$

5. 15

6. 13

7. $\dfrac{12}{7}$

8. $\dfrac{10}{3}$

Objective Ⓑ *Divide. Write each answer in simplest form. See Examples 5 through 7 and 11 and 12.*

9. $\dfrac{2}{3} \div \dfrac{5}{6}$

10. $\dfrac{5}{8} \div \dfrac{2}{3}$

11. $\dfrac{8}{9} \div \dfrac{1}{2}$

12. $\dfrac{10}{11} \div \dfrac{4}{5}$

13. $\dfrac{3}{7} \div \dfrac{5}{6}$

14. $\dfrac{16}{27} \div \dfrac{8}{15}$

15. $\dfrac{3}{5} \div \dfrac{4}{5}$

16. $\dfrac{11}{16} \div \dfrac{13}{16}$

17. $\dfrac{1}{10} \div \dfrac{10}{1}$

18. $\dfrac{3}{13} \div \dfrac{13}{3}$

19. $\dfrac{7}{9} \div \dfrac{7}{3}$

20. $\dfrac{6}{11} \div \dfrac{6}{5}$

21. $\dfrac{5}{8} \div \dfrac{3}{8}$

22. $\dfrac{7}{8} \div \dfrac{5}{6}$

23. $\dfrac{7}{45} \div \dfrac{4}{25}$

24. $\dfrac{14}{52} \div \dfrac{1}{13}$

25. $\dfrac{2}{37} \div \dfrac{1}{7}$

26. $\dfrac{100}{158} \div \dfrac{10}{79}$

27. $\dfrac{3}{25} \div \dfrac{27}{40}$

28. $\dfrac{6}{15} \div \dfrac{7}{10}$

29. $\dfrac{11}{12} \div \dfrac{11}{12}$

30. $\dfrac{7}{13} \div \dfrac{7}{13}$

31. $\dfrac{8}{13} \div 0$

32. $0 \div \dfrac{4}{11}$

33. $0 \div \dfrac{7}{8}$

34. $\dfrac{2}{3} \div 0$ **35.** $\dfrac{25}{126} \div \dfrac{125}{441}$ **36.** $\dfrac{65}{495} \div \dfrac{26}{231}$

Objective Ⓒ *Divide. Write each answer in simplest form. See Examples 8 through 11.*

37. $\dfrac{2}{3} \div 4$ **38.** $\dfrac{5}{6} \div 10$ **39.** $8 \div \dfrac{3}{5}$ **40.** $7 \div \dfrac{2}{11}$ **41.** $2\dfrac{1}{2} \div \dfrac{1}{2}$

42. $4\dfrac{2}{3} \div \dfrac{2}{5}$ **43.** $\dfrac{5}{12} \div 2\dfrac{1}{3}$ **44.** $\dfrac{4}{15} \div 2\dfrac{1}{2}$ **45.** $3\dfrac{3}{7} \div 3\dfrac{1}{3}$ **46.** $2\dfrac{5}{6} \div 4\dfrac{6}{7}$

47. $1\dfrac{4}{9} \div 2\dfrac{5}{6}$ **48.** $3\dfrac{1}{10} \div 2\dfrac{1}{5}$ **49.** $0 \div 15\dfrac{4}{7}$ **50.** $\dfrac{33}{50} \div 1$ **51.** $1 \div \dfrac{13}{17}$

52. $0 \div 7\dfrac{9}{10}$ **53.** $1 \div \dfrac{18}{35}$ **54.** $\dfrac{17}{75} \div 1$ **55.** $10\dfrac{5}{9} \div 16\dfrac{2}{3}$ **56.** $20\dfrac{5}{6} \div 137\dfrac{1}{2}$

Objectives Ⓑ Ⓒ **Mixed Practice** *Divide. Write each answer in simplest form. See Examples 5 through 12.*

57. $\dfrac{6}{15} \div \dfrac{12}{5}$ **58.** $\dfrac{4}{15} \div \dfrac{8}{3}$ **59.** $\dfrac{11}{20} \div \dfrac{3}{11}$ **60.** $\dfrac{9}{20} \div \dfrac{2}{9}$

61. $12 \div \dfrac{1}{8}$ **62.** $9 \div \dfrac{1}{6}$ **63.** $\dfrac{3}{7} \div \dfrac{4}{7}$ **64.** $\dfrac{3}{8} \div \dfrac{5}{8}$

65. $2\dfrac{3}{8} \div 0$ **66.** $20\dfrac{1}{5} \div 0$ **67.** $\dfrac{11}{85} \div \dfrac{7}{5}$ **68.** $\dfrac{13}{84} \div \dfrac{3}{16}$

69. $4\dfrac{5}{11} \div 1\dfrac{2}{5}$ **70.** $8\dfrac{2}{7} \div 3\dfrac{1}{7}$ **71.** $\dfrac{27}{100} \div \dfrac{3}{20}$ **72.** $\dfrac{25}{128} \div \dfrac{5}{32}$

Objective Ⓓ *Solve. For Exercises 73 and 74, the solutions have been started for you. Write each answer in simplest form. See Example 13.*

73. A heart attack patient in rehabilitation walked on a treadmill $12\frac{3}{4}$ miles over 4 days. How many miles is this per day?

74. A local restaurant is selling hamburgers from a booth on Memorial Day. A total of $27\frac{3}{4}$ pounds of hamburger have been ordered. How many quarter-pound hamburgers can this make?

Start the solution:

1. UNDERSTAND the problem. Reread it as many times as needed.
2. TRANSLATE into an equation. (Fill in the blanks.)

miles per day	is	total miles	divided by	number of days
↓	↓	↓	↓	↓

$$\text{miles per day} = \underline{\quad} \div \underline{\quad}$$

Finish with:

3. SOLVE and
4. INTERPRET

Start the solution:

1. UNDERSTAND the problem. Reread it as many times as needed.
2. TRANSLATE into an equation. (Fill in the blanks.)

how many quarter-pound hamburgers	is	total pounds of hamburger	divided by	a quarter-pound
↓	↓	↓	↓	↓

$$\text{how many quarter-pound hamburgers} = \underline{\quad} \div \underline{\quad}$$

Finish with:

3. SOLVE and
4. INTERPRET

75. A patient is to take $3\frac{1}{3}$ tablespoons of medicine per day in 4 equally divided doses. How much medicine is to be taken in each dose?

76. If there are $13\frac{1}{3}$ grams of fat in 4 ounces of lean hamburger meat, how many grams of fat are in an ounce?

77. The record for rainfall during a 24-hour period in Alaska is $15\frac{1}{5}$ inches. This record was set in Angoon, Alaska, in October 1982. How much rain fell per hour on average? (*Source:* National Climatic Data Center)

78. An order for 125 custom-made candle stands was placed with Mr. Levi, the manager of Just For You, Inc. The worker assigned to the job can produce $2\frac{3}{5}$ candle stands per hour. Using this worker, how many work hours will be required to complete the order?

79. At this writing, the average price of aluminum is $98\frac{1}{2}$¢ per pound. During that time, a family received 1379¢ for aluminum cans that they sold for recycling at a scrap metal center. Assuming that they received the average price, how many pounds of aluminum cans did they recycle? (*Source:* London Metal Exchange)

80. Yoko's Fine Jewelry paid $450 for a $\frac{3}{4}$-carat gem. At this price, what is the cost of one carat?

△ **81.** The area of the rectangle below is 12 square meters. If its width is $2\frac{4}{7}$ meters, find its length.

△ **82.** The perimeter of the square below is $23\frac{1}{2}$ feet. Find the length of each side.

Rectangle	$2\frac{4}{7}$ meters

Square

Mixed Practice (Sections 2.4, 2.5) *Perform the indicated operation.*

83. $\dfrac{2}{5}\cdot\dfrac{4}{7}$

84. $\dfrac{2}{5}\div\dfrac{4}{7}$

85. $2\dfrac{2}{3}\div1\dfrac{1}{16}$

86. $2\dfrac{2}{3}\cdot1\dfrac{1}{16}$

87. $5\dfrac{1}{7}\cdot\dfrac{2}{9}\cdot\dfrac{14}{15}$

88. $8\dfrac{1}{6}\cdot\dfrac{3}{7}\cdot\dfrac{18}{25}$

89. $\dfrac{11}{20}\div\dfrac{20}{11}$

90. $2\dfrac{1}{5}\div1\dfrac{7}{10}$

Review

Perform each indicated operation. See Sections 1.3 and 1.4.

91. 27
 76
+ 98

92. 811
 42
+ 69

93. 968
− 772

94. 882
− 773

95. 2000
− 431

96. 500
− 92

Concept Extensions

A student asked you to find the error in the work below. Find the error and correct it. See the Concept Check in this section.

97. $20\dfrac{2}{3}\div10\dfrac{1}{2}=2\dfrac{1}{3}$

98. $6\dfrac{1}{4}\div\dfrac{1}{2}=3\dfrac{1}{8}$

Choose the best estimate for each quotient.

99. $20\dfrac{1}{4}\div\dfrac{5}{6}$

 a. 5 **b.** $5\dfrac{1}{8}$ **c.** 20 **d.** 10

100. $\dfrac{11}{12}\div16\dfrac{1}{5}$

 a. $\dfrac{1}{16}$ **b.** 4 **c.** 8 **d.** 16

101. $12\dfrac{2}{13}\div3\dfrac{7}{8}$

 a. 4 **b.** 9 **c.** 36 **d.** 3

102. $10\dfrac{1}{4}\div2\dfrac{1}{16}$

 a. 8 **b.** 5 **c.** 20 **d.** 12

Simplify.

103. $\dfrac{42}{25}\cdot\dfrac{125}{36}\div\dfrac{7}{6}$

104. $\left(\dfrac{8}{13}\cdot\dfrac{39}{16}\cdot\dfrac{8}{9}\right)^2\div\dfrac{1}{2}$

105. The FedEx Express air fleet includes 252 Cessnas. These Cessnas make up $\dfrac{42}{109}$ of the FedEx fleet. How many aircraft make up the entire FedEx Express air fleet? (*Source:* FedEx Corporation)

106. One-third of all native flowering plant species in the United States are at risk of becoming extinct. That translates into 5144 at-risk flowering plant species. Based on this data, how many flowering plant species are native to the United States overall? (*Source:* The Nature Conservancy) (*Hint:* How many $\dfrac{1}{3}$s are in 5144?)

107. In your own words, describe how to find the reciprocal of a number.

108. In your own words, describe how to divide fractions.

2.6 ADDING AND SUBTRACTING LIKE FRACTIONS

Fractions with the same denominator are called **like fractions.** Fractions that have different denominators are called **unlike fractions.**

Like Fractions	Unlike Fractions
$\frac{2}{5}$ and $\frac{3}{5}$ — same denominator	$\frac{2}{5}$ and $\frac{3}{4}$ — different denominators
$\frac{5}{21}, \frac{16}{21},$ and $\frac{7}{21}$ — same denominator	$\frac{5}{7}$ and $\frac{5}{9}$ — different denominators

Objective (A) Adding Like Fractions

To see how we add like fractions (fractions with the same denominator), study the figures below:

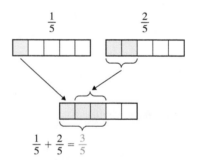

$$\frac{1}{5} + \frac{2}{5} = \frac{3}{5}$$

Adding Like Fractions (*Fractions with the Same Denominator*)

To add like fractions, add the numerators and write the sum over the common denominator.

If $a, b,$ and c represent nonzero whole numbers, we have

$$\frac{a}{c} + \frac{b}{c} = \frac{a+b}{c}$$

For example,

$$\frac{1}{4} + \frac{2}{4} = \frac{1+2}{4} = \frac{3}{4} \quad \longleftarrow \text{ Add the numerators.}$$
$$\longleftarrow \text{ Keep the denominator.}$$

Helpful Hint

As usual, don't forget to write all answers in simplest form.

Examples Add and simplify.

1. $\dfrac{2}{7} + \dfrac{3}{7} = \dfrac{2+3}{7} = \dfrac{5}{7}$ ⟵ Add the numerators.
  ⟵ Keep the common denominator.

2. $\dfrac{3}{16} + \dfrac{7}{16} = \dfrac{3+7}{16} = \dfrac{10}{16} = \dfrac{\overset{1}{\cancel{2}} \cdot 5}{\underset{1}{\cancel{2}} \cdot 8} = \dfrac{5}{8}$

3. $\dfrac{7}{13} + \dfrac{6}{13} + \dfrac{3}{13} = \dfrac{7+6+3}{13} = \dfrac{16}{13}$ or $1\dfrac{3}{13}$

● **Work Practice 1–3**

✓**Concept Check** Find and correct the error in the following:

$\dfrac{1}{5} + \dfrac{1}{5} = \dfrac{2}{10}$

Objective Ⓑ Subtracting Like Fractions

To see how we subtract like fractions (fractions with the same denominator), study the following figure:

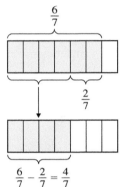

$$\dfrac{6}{7} - \dfrac{2}{7} = \dfrac{4}{7}$$

Subtracting Like Fractions (Fractions with the Same Denominator)

To subtract like fractions, subtract the numerators and write the difference over the common denominator.

If $a, b,$ and c represent nonzero whole numbers, then

$$\dfrac{a}{c} - \dfrac{b}{c} = \dfrac{a-b}{c}$$

For example,

$\dfrac{4}{5} - \dfrac{2}{5} = \dfrac{4-2}{5} = \dfrac{2}{5}$ ⟵ Subtract the numerators.
  ⟵ Keep the denominator.

Examples Subtract and simplify.

4. $\dfrac{8}{9} - \dfrac{1}{9} = \dfrac{8-1}{9} = \dfrac{7}{9}$ ⟵ Subtract the numerators.
  ⟵ Keep the common denominator.

5. $\dfrac{7}{8} - \dfrac{5}{8} = \dfrac{7-5}{8} = \dfrac{2}{8} = \dfrac{\overset{1}{\cancel{2}}}{\underset{1}{\cancel{2}} \cdot 4} = \dfrac{1}{4}$

● **Work Practice 4–5**

Objective ⒸSolving Problems by Adding or Subtracting Like Fractions

Many real-life problems involve finding the perimeters of square or rectangular areas such as pastures, swimming pools, and so on. We can use our knowledge of adding fractions to find perimeters.

PRACTICE 6

Find the perimeter of the square.

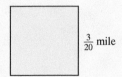

$\frac{3}{20}$ mile

Example 6 Find the perimeter of the rectangle.

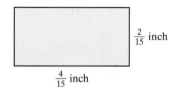

$\frac{2}{15}$ inch

$\frac{4}{15}$ inch

Solution: Recall that perimeter means distance around and that opposite sides of a rectangle are the same length.

$\frac{4}{15}$ inch

$\frac{2}{15}$ inch $\frac{2}{15}$ inch

$\frac{4}{15}$ inch

$$\text{Perimeter} = \frac{2}{15} + \frac{4}{15} + \frac{2}{15} + \frac{4}{15} = \frac{2 + 4 + 2 + 4}{15}$$

$$= \frac{12}{15} = \frac{\cancel{3} \cdot 4}{\cancel{3} \cdot 5} = \frac{4}{5}$$

The perimeter of the rectangle is $\frac{4}{5}$ inch.

● **Work Practice 6**

We can combine our skills in adding and subtracting fractions with our four problem-solving steps from Chapter 1 to solve many kinds of real-life problems.

PRACTICE 7

If a piano student practices the piano $\frac{3}{8}$ of an hour in the morning and $\frac{1}{8}$ of an hour in the evening, how long did she practice that day?

Example 7 Total Amount of an Ingredient in a Recipe

A recipe calls for $\frac{1}{3}$ of a cup of honey at the beginning and $\frac{2}{3}$ of a cup of honey later. How much total honey is needed to make the recipe?

$\frac{1}{3}$ cup $\frac{2}{3}$ cup

Solution:

1. UNDERSTAND the problem. To do so, read and reread the problem. Since we are finding total honey, we add.

Answers

6. $\frac{3}{5}$ mi   7. $\frac{1}{2}$ hr

2. TRANSLATE.

In words:	total honey	is	honey at the beginning	added to	honey later
	↓	↓	↓	↓	↓
Translate:	total honey	$=$	$\frac{1}{3}$	$+$	$\frac{2}{3}$

3. SOLVE: $\dfrac{1}{3} + \dfrac{2}{3} = \dfrac{1+2}{3} = \dfrac{\overset{1}{\cancel{3}}}{\underset{1}{\cancel{3}}} = 1$

4. INTERPRET. *Check* your work. *State* your conclusion: The total honey needed for the recipe is 1 cup.

● **Work Practice 7**

Example 8 Calculating Distance

The distance from home to the World Gym is $\dfrac{7}{8}$ of a mile and from home to the post office is $\dfrac{3}{8}$ of a mile. How much farther is it from home to the World Gym than from home to the post office?

Solution:

1. UNDERSTAND. Read and reread the problem. The phrase "How much farther" tells us to subtract distances.

2. TRANSLATE.

In words:	distance farther	is	home to World Gym distance	minus	home to post office distance
	↓	↓	↓	↓	↓
Translate:	distance farther	$=$	$\dfrac{7}{8}$	$-$	$\dfrac{3}{8}$

3. SOLVE: $\dfrac{7}{8} - \dfrac{3}{8} = \dfrac{7-3}{8} = \dfrac{4}{8} = \dfrac{\overset{1}{\cancel{4}}}{2 \cdot \underset{1}{\cancel{4}}} = \dfrac{1}{2}$

4. INTERPRET. *Check* your work. *State* your conclusion: The distance from home to the World Gym is $\dfrac{1}{2}$ mile farther than from home to the post office.

● **Work Practice 8**

PRACTICE 8

A jogger ran $\dfrac{13}{4}$ miles on Monday and $\dfrac{7}{4}$ miles on Wednesday. How much farther did he run on Monday than on Wednesday?

Answer

8. $\dfrac{3}{2}$ or $1\dfrac{1}{2}$ mi

Vocabulary and Readiness Check

Use the choices below to fill in each blank. Not all choices will be used.

    perimeter   like $\dfrac{a-c}{b}$ $\dfrac{a+c}{b}$

    equivalent   unlike

1. The fractions $\dfrac{9}{11}$ and $\dfrac{13}{11}$ are called _____ fractions while $\dfrac{3}{4}$ and $\dfrac{1}{3}$ are called _____ fractions.

2. $\dfrac{a}{b} + \dfrac{c}{b} =$ _____ .

3. $\dfrac{a}{b} - \dfrac{c}{b} =$ _____ .

4. The distance around a figure is called its _____ .

State whether the fractions in each list are like or unlike fractions.

5. $\dfrac{7}{8}, \dfrac{7}{10}$
        6. $\dfrac{2}{3}, \dfrac{4}{9}$
        7. $\dfrac{9}{10}, \dfrac{1}{10}$
        8. $\dfrac{8}{11}, \dfrac{2}{11}$

9. $\dfrac{2}{31}, \dfrac{30}{31}, \dfrac{19}{31}$
        10. $\dfrac{3}{10}, \dfrac{3}{11}, \dfrac{3}{13}$
        11. $\dfrac{5}{12}, \dfrac{7}{12}, \dfrac{12}{11}$
        12. $\dfrac{1}{5}, \dfrac{2}{5}, \dfrac{4}{5}$

2.6 Exercise Set

Objective A *Add and simplify. See Examples 1 through 3.*

**1.** $\dfrac{1}{7} + \dfrac{2}{7}$
      2. $\dfrac{9}{17} + \dfrac{2}{17}$
      3. $\dfrac{1}{10} + \dfrac{1}{10}$
      4. $\dfrac{1}{4} + \dfrac{1}{4}$

5. $\dfrac{2}{9} + \dfrac{4}{9}$
      6. $\dfrac{3}{10} + \dfrac{2}{10}$
      7. $\dfrac{6}{20} + \dfrac{1}{20}$
      8. $\dfrac{2}{8} + \dfrac{3}{8}$

9. $\dfrac{3}{14} + \dfrac{4}{14}$
      10. $\dfrac{5}{24} + \dfrac{7}{24}$
      11. $\dfrac{10}{11} + \dfrac{3}{11}$
      12. $\dfrac{13}{17} + \dfrac{9}{17}$

13. $\dfrac{4}{13} + \dfrac{2}{13} + \dfrac{1}{13}$
      14. $\dfrac{5}{11} + \dfrac{1}{11} + \dfrac{2}{11}$
      15. $\dfrac{7}{18} + \dfrac{3}{18} + \dfrac{2}{18}$
      16. $\dfrac{7}{15} + \dfrac{4}{15} + \dfrac{1}{15}$

Objective Ⓑ *Subtract and simplify. See Examples 4 and 5.*

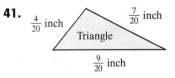 **17.** $\dfrac{10}{11} - \dfrac{4}{11}$

18. $\dfrac{9}{13} - \dfrac{5}{13}$

19. $\dfrac{4}{5} - \dfrac{1}{5}$

20. $\dfrac{7}{8} - \dfrac{4}{8}$

21. $\dfrac{7}{4} - \dfrac{3}{4}$

22. $\dfrac{18}{5} - \dfrac{3}{5}$

23. $\dfrac{7}{8} - \dfrac{1}{8}$

24. $\dfrac{5}{6} - \dfrac{1}{6}$

25. $\dfrac{25}{12} - \dfrac{15}{12}$

26. $\dfrac{30}{20} - \dfrac{15}{20}$

27. $\dfrac{11}{10} - \dfrac{3}{10}$

28. $\dfrac{14}{15} - \dfrac{4}{15}$

29. $\dfrac{86}{90} - \dfrac{85}{90}$

30. $\dfrac{74}{80} - \dfrac{73}{80}$

31. $\dfrac{27}{33} - \dfrac{8}{33}$

32. $\dfrac{37}{45} - \dfrac{18}{45}$

Objectives Ⓐ Ⓑ **Mixed Practice** *Perform the indicated operation. See Examples 1 through 5.*

33. $\dfrac{8}{21} + \dfrac{5}{21}$

34. $\dfrac{7}{37} + \dfrac{9}{37}$

35. $\dfrac{99}{100} - \dfrac{9}{100}$

36. $\dfrac{85}{200} - \dfrac{15}{200}$

37. $\dfrac{13}{28} - \dfrac{13}{28}$

38. $\dfrac{15}{26} - \dfrac{15}{26}$

39. $\dfrac{3}{16} + \dfrac{7}{16} + \dfrac{2}{16}$

40. $\dfrac{5}{18} + \dfrac{1}{18} + \dfrac{6}{18}$

Objective Ⓒ *Find the perimeter of each figure. (Hint: Recall that perimeter means distance around.) See Example 6.*

△ **41.**

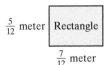

△ **42.**

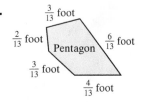

△ **43.**

△ **44.**

Solve. For Exercises 45 and 46, the solutions have been started for you. Write each answer in simplest form. See Examples 7 and 8.

45. A railroad inspector must inspect $\frac{19}{20}$ of a mile of railroad track. If she has already inspected $\frac{5}{20}$ of a mile, how much more does she need to inspect?

Start the solution:

1. UNDERSTAND the problem. Reread it as many times as needed.
2. TRANSLATE into an equation. (Fill in the blanks.)

distance left to inspect	is	distance needed to inspect	minus	distance already inspected
↓	↓	↓	↓	↓

$$\text{distance left to inspect} = \underline{\quad\quad} - \underline{\quad\quad}$$

Finish with:

3. SOLVE. and
4. INTERPRET.

46. Scott Davis has run $\frac{11}{8}$ miles already and plans to complete $\frac{16}{8}$ miles. To do this, how much farther must he run?

Start the solution:

1. UNDERSTAND the problem. Reread it as many times as needed.
2. TRANSLATE into an equation. (Fill in the blanks.)

distance left to run	is	distance planned to run	minus	distance already run
↓	↓	↓	↓	↓

$$\text{distance left to run} = \underline{\quad\quad} - \underline{\quad\quad}$$

Finish with:

3. SOLVE. and
4. INTERPRET.

47. Emil Vasquez, a bodybuilder, worked out $\frac{7}{8}$ of an hour one morning before school and $\frac{5}{8}$ of an hour that evening. How long did he work out that day?

48. A recipe for Heavenly Hash cake calls for $\frac{3}{4}$ cup of sugar and later $\frac{1}{4}$ cup of sugar. How much sugar is needed to make the recipe?

The pyramid below shows the servings of various foods that a healthy diet requires. While your age, weight, and level of physical activity may change your personal needs, the circle graph below is just one example of an average healthy college student's requirements. Use this graph for Exercises 49–52. Write your answers in simplest form. (Source: United States Department of Agriculture—mypyramid.gov)

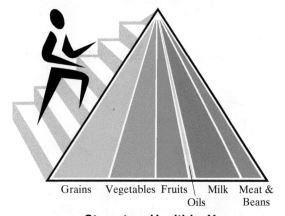

Steps to a Healthier You

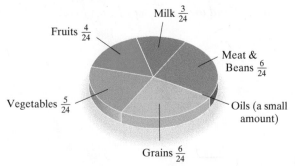

An Example of Daily Healthy Eating

49. Find the fractional part of a college student's daily servings that should come from vegetables and fruit.

50. Find the fractional part of a college student's daily servings that should come from grains and milk.

51. How much greater is the fractional part of a college student's daily servings that comes from grains than from fruit?

52. How much greater is the fractional part of a college student's daily servings that comes from vegetables than from fruit?

Solve.

53. According to a recent poll, approximately $\frac{6}{100}$ of teenagers who have cell phones do social networking tasks every day. Approximately $\frac{7}{100}$ of teenagers with cell phones do social networking tasks once a week to several times a week. What fractions of teenagers with cell phones do social networking tasks at least once a week? (*Source:* Harris Interactive Polls)

54. In a recent survey, $\frac{55}{100}$ of people said that visiting family and friends would be their pleasure trip of choice while $\frac{29}{100}$ of people surveyed said that going to a beach resort would be their pleasure trip of choice. What fraction of people surveyed said visiting family and friends or going to a beach resort? (*Source:* American Express)

55. In 2009, the fraction of states in the United States with maximum interstate highway speed limits up to and including 70 mph was $\frac{19}{25}$. The fraction of states with 70 mph speed limits was $\frac{9}{25}$. What fraction of states had speed limits that were less than 70 mph? (*Source:* Insurance Institute for Highway Safety)

56. When people take aspirin, $\frac{31}{50}$ of the time it is used to treat some type of pain. Approximately $\frac{7}{50}$ of all aspirin use is for treating headaches. What fraction of aspirin use is for treating pain other than headaches? (*Source:* Bayer Market Research)

The map of the world below shows the fraction of the world's surface land area taken up by each continent. In other words, the continent of Africa makes up $\frac{20}{100}$ of the land in the world. Use this map for Exercises 57 through 60.

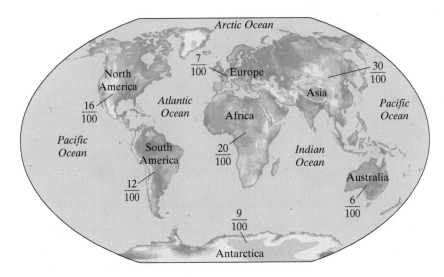

57. Find the fractional part of the world's land area within the continents of North America and South America.

58. Find the fractional part of the world's land area within the continents of Asia and Africa.

59. How much greater is the fractional part of the continent of Antarctica than the fractional part of the continent of Europe?

60. How much greater is the fractional part of the continent of Asia than the continent of Australia?

The theater industry is shifting toward theaters with multiple screens. Use the circle graph to answer Exercises 61 and 62. Write fraction answers in simplest form.

Fraction of U.S. Screens by Theater Type

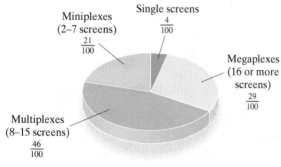

Miniplexes
(2–7 screens)
$\frac{21}{100}$

Single screens
$\frac{4}{100}$

Megaplexes
(16 or more
screens)
$\frac{29}{100}$

Multiplexes
(8–15 screens)
$\frac{46}{100}$

Source: Motion Picture Association of America

61. What fraction of U.S. theaters are single screens or miniplexes?

62. What fraction of U.S. theaters are multiplexes or megaplexes?

Review

Write the prime factorization of each number. See Section 2.2.

63. 10   **64.** 12   **65.** 8   **66.** 20   **67.** 55   **68.** 28

Concept Extensions

Perform each indicated operation.

69. $\dfrac{3}{8} + \dfrac{7}{8} - \dfrac{5}{8}$ **70.** $\dfrac{12}{20} - \dfrac{1}{20} - \dfrac{3}{20}$ **71.** $\dfrac{4}{11} + \dfrac{5}{11} - \dfrac{3}{11} + \dfrac{2}{11}$ **72.** $\dfrac{9}{12} + \dfrac{1}{12} - \dfrac{3}{12} - \dfrac{5}{12}$

Find and correct the error. See the Concept Check in this section.

73.
$$\dfrac{2}{7} + \dfrac{9}{7} = \dfrac{11}{14}$$

74.
$$\dfrac{3}{4} - \dfrac{1}{4} = \dfrac{2}{8} = \dfrac{1}{4}$$

Solve. Write each answer in simplest form.

75. In your own words, explain how to add like fractions.

76. In your own words, explain how to subtract like fractions.

77. Use the food pyramid for Exercises 49 through 52 and find the sum of all the daily servings' fractions. Explain your answer.

78. Use the map of the world for Exercises 57 through 60 and find the sum of all the continents' fractions. Explain your answer.

79. Mike Cannon jogged $\dfrac{3}{8}$ of a mile from home and then rested. Then he continued jogging farther from home for another $\dfrac{3}{8}$ of a mile until he discovered his watch had fallen off. He walked back along the same path for $\dfrac{4}{8}$ of a mile until he found his watch. Find how far he was from his home.

80. A trim carpenter needs the following lengths of boards: $\dfrac{5}{4}$ feet, $\dfrac{15}{4}$ feet, $\dfrac{9}{4}$ feet, and $\dfrac{13}{4}$ feet. Is a 10-foot board long enough for the carpenter to cut these lengths? If not, how much more length is needed?

2.7 LEAST COMMON MULTIPLES

Objectives

Ⓐ Find the Least Common Multiple (LCM) Using Multiples.

Ⓑ Find the LCM Using Prime Factorization.

Ⓒ Write Equivalent Fractions.

Objective Ⓐ Finding the Least Common Multiple Using Multiples

A multiple of a number is the product of that number and a natural number. For example, multiples of 5 are

$$5 \cdot 1 \quad 5 \cdot 2 \quad 5 \cdot 3 \quad 5 \cdot 4 \quad 5 \cdot 5 \quad 5 \cdot 6 \quad 5 \cdot 7 \quad 5 \cdot 8$$

$$\downarrow \quad \downarrow \quad \downarrow \quad \downarrow \quad \downarrow \quad \downarrow \quad \downarrow \quad \downarrow$$

$$5, \quad 10, \quad 15, \quad 20, \quad 25, \quad 30, \quad 35, \quad 40, \ldots$$

Multiples of 4 are

4, 8, 12, 16, 20, 24, 28, 32, 36, 40, 44, ...

Common multiples of both 4 and 5 are numbers that are found in both lists above. If we study the lists of multiples and extend them we have

Common multiples of 4 and 5: 20, 40, 60, 80, ...

We call the smallest number in the list of common multiples the **least common multiple (LCM).** From the list of common multiples of 4 and 5, we see that the LCM of 4 and 5 is 20.

Example 1 Find the LCM of 6 and 8.

Solution: Multiples of 6: 6, 12, 18, Ⓞ24, 30, 36, 42, Ⓞ48, ...

Multiples of 8: 8, 16, Ⓞ24, 32, 40, Ⓞ48, 56, ...

The common multiples are 24, 48, ... The least common multiple (LCM) is 24.

● Work Practice 1

Listing all the multiples of every number in a list can be cumbersome and tedious. We can condense the procedure shown in Example 1 with the following steps:

> ### Method 1: Finding the LCM of a List of Numbers Using Multiples of the Largest Number
>
> **Step 1:** Write the multiples of the largest number (starting with the number itself) until a multiple common to all numbers in the list is found.
>
> **Step 2:** The multiple found in Step 1 is the LCM.

Example 2 Find the LCM of 9 and 12.

Solution: We write the multiples of 12 until we find a number that is also a multiple of 9.

$12 \cdot 1 = 12$ Not a multiple of 9.

$12 \cdot 2 = 24$ Not a multiple of 9.

$12 \cdot 3 = 36$ A multiple of 9.

The LCM of 9 and 12 is 36.

● Work Practice 2

PRACTICE 1

Find the LCM of 15 and 50.

PRACTICE 2

Find the LCM of 8 and 10.

Answers

1. 150 **2.** 40

PRACTICE 3
Find the LCM of 8 and 16.

Example 3 Find the LCM of 7 and 14.

Solution: We write the multiples of 14 until we find one that is also a multiple of 7.

$14 \cdot 1 = 14$ A multiple of 7

The LCM of 7 and 14 is 14.

● Work Practice 3

PRACTICE 4
Find the LCM of 25 and 30.

Example 4 Find the LCM of 12 and 20.

Solution: We write the multiples of 20 until we find one that is also a multiple of 12.

$20 \cdot 1 = 20$ Not a multiple of 12
$20 \cdot 2 = 40$ Not a multiple of 12
$20 \cdot 3 = 60$ A multiple of 12

The LCM of 12 and 20 is 60.

● Work Practice 4

Objective Ⓑ Finding the LCM Using Prime Factorization

Method 1 for finding multiples works fine for smaller numbers, but may get tedious for larger numbers. A second method that uses prime factorization may be easier to use for larger numbers.

For example, to find the LCM of 270 and 84, let's look at the prime factorization of each.

$270 = 2 \cdot 3 \cdot 3 \cdot 3 \cdot 5$
$84 = 2 \cdot 2 \cdot 3 \cdot 7$

Recall that the LCM must be a multiple of both 270 and 84. Thus, to build the LCM, we will circle the greatest number of factors for each different prime number. The LCM is the product of the circled factors.

Prime Number Factors

270 =	2 ·	(3·3·3)·	(5)
84 =	(2·2)·	3·		(7)

Circle the greatest number of factors for each different prime number.

$LCM = 2 \cdot 2 \cdot 3 \cdot 3 \cdot 3 \cdot 5 \cdot 7 = 3780$

The number 3780 is the smallest number that both 270 and 84 divide into evenly.
This method 2 is summarized below:

Method 2: Finding the LCM of a List of Numbers Using Prime Factorization

Step 1: Write the prime factorization of each number.

Step 2: For each different prime factor in step 1, circle the greatest number of times that factor occurs in any one factorization.

Step 3: The LCM is the product of the circled factors.

Answers
3. 16 **4.** 150

Example 5 Find the LCM of 72 and 60.

Solution: First we write the prime factorization of each number.

$72 = 2 \cdot 2 \cdot 2 \cdot 3 \cdot 3$

$60 = 2 \cdot 2 \cdot 3 \cdot 5$

For the prime factors shown, we circle the greatest number of prime factors found in either factorization.

$72 = \boxed{2 \cdot 2 \cdot 2} \cdot \boxed{3 \cdot 3}$

$60 = 2 \cdot 2 \cdot 3 \cdot \boxed{5}$

The LCM is the product of the circled factors.

$LCM = 2 \cdot 2 \cdot 2 \cdot 3 \cdot 3 \cdot 5 = 360$

The LCM is 360.

🔵 **Work Practice 5**

PRACTICE 5

Find the LCM of 40 and 108.

Helpful Hint

If you prefer working with exponents, circle the factor with the greatest exponent.
Example 5:

$72 = \boxed{2^3} \cdot \boxed{3^2}$

$60 = 2^2 \cdot 3 \cdot \boxed{5}$

$LCD = 2^3 \cdot 3^2 \cdot 5 = 360$

Helpful Hint

If the number of factors of a prime number are equal, circle either one, but not both. For example,

$12 = \boxed{2 \cdot 2} \cdot \boxed{3}$

$15 = 3 \cdot \boxed{5}$ Circle either 3 but not both.

The LCM is $2 \cdot 2 \cdot 3 \cdot 5 = 60$.

Example 6 Find the LCM of 15, 18, and 54.

Solution:

$15 = 3 \cdot \boxed{5}$

$18 = \boxed{2} \cdot 3 \cdot 3$

$54 = 2 \cdot \boxed{3 \cdot 3 \cdot 3}$

The LCM is $2 \cdot 3 \cdot 3 \cdot 3 \cdot 5$ or 270.

🔵 **Work Practice 6**

PRACTICE 6

Find the LCM of 20, 24, and 45.

Example 7 Find the LCM of 11 and 33.

Solution:

$11 = \boxed{11}$ It makes no difference

$33 = \boxed{3} \cdot 11$ which 11 is circled.

The LCM is $3 \cdot 11$ or 33.

🔵 **Work Practice 7**

PRACTICE 7

Find the LCM of 7 and 21.

Answers

5. 1080   **6.** 360   **7.** 21

Objective ⓒ Writing Equivalent Fractions

To add or subtract unlike fractions in the next section, we first write equivalent fractions with the LCM as the denominator. Recall from Section 2.3 that fractions that represent the same portion of a whole are called "equivalent fractions."

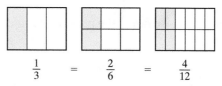

$$\frac{1}{3} \quad = \quad \frac{2}{6} \quad = \quad \frac{4}{12}$$

To write $\frac{1}{3}$ as an equivalent fraction with a denominator of 12, we multiply by 1 in the form of $\frac{4}{4}$.

$$\frac{1}{3} = \frac{1}{3} \cdot 1 = \frac{1}{3} \cdot \frac{4}{4} = \frac{1 \cdot 4}{3 \cdot 4} = \frac{4}{12}$$

$$\frac{4}{4} = 1$$

So $\dfrac{1}{3} = \dfrac{4}{12}$.

To write an equivalent fraction,

$$\frac{a}{b} = \frac{a}{b} \cdot \frac{c}{c} = \frac{a \cdot c}{b \cdot c}$$

where a, b, and c are nonzero numbers.

✔ **Concept Check** Which of the following is not equivalent to $\frac{3}{4}$?

a. $\dfrac{6}{8}$ **b.** $\dfrac{18}{24}$ **c.** $\dfrac{9}{14}$ **d.** $\dfrac{30}{40}$

PRACTICE 8

Write an equivalent fraction with the indicated denominator:

$$\frac{7}{8} = \frac{}{56}$$

Example 8 Write an equivalent fraction with the indicated denominator.

$$\frac{3}{4} = \frac{}{20}$$

Solution: In the denominators, since $4 \cdot 5 = 20$, we will multiply by 1 in the form of $\dfrac{5}{5}$.

$$\frac{3}{4} = \frac{3}{4} \cdot \frac{5}{5} = \frac{3 \cdot 5}{4 \cdot 5} = \frac{15}{20}$$

Thus, $\dfrac{3}{4} = \dfrac{15}{20}$.

● **Work Practice 8**

Answer

8. $\dfrac{49}{56}$

✔ **Concept Check Answer**

c

Helpful Hint

To check Example 8, write $\dfrac{15}{20}$ in simplest form.

$$\frac{15}{20} = \frac{3 \cdot \overset{1}{\cancel{5}}}{4 \cdot \underset{1}{\cancel{5}}} = \frac{3}{4}, \text{ the original fraction.}$$

If the original fraction is in lowest terms, we can check our work by writing the new equivalent fraction in simplest form. This form should be the original fraction.

✓**Concept Check** True or false? When the fraction $\dfrac{2}{9}$ is rewritten as an equivalent fraction with 27 as the denominator, the result is $\dfrac{2}{27}$.

Example 9 Write an equivalent fraction with the indicated denominator.

$$\frac{1}{2} = \frac{}{24}$$

Solution: Since $2 \cdot 12 = 24$, we multiply by 1 in the form of $\dfrac{12}{12}$.

$$\frac{1}{2} = \frac{1}{2} \cdot \frac{12}{12} = \frac{1 \cdot 12}{2 \cdot 12} = \frac{12}{24}$$

Thus, $\dfrac{1}{2} = \dfrac{12}{24}$.

● Work Practice 9

Example 10 Write an equivalent fraction with the given denominator.

$$3 = \frac{}{7}$$

Solution: Recall that $3 = \dfrac{3}{1}$. Since $1 \cdot 7 = 7$, multiply by 1 in the form $\dfrac{7}{7}$.

$$\frac{3}{1} = \frac{3}{1} \cdot \frac{7}{7} = \frac{3 \cdot 7}{1 \cdot 7} = \frac{21}{7}$$

● Work Practice 10

PRACTICE 9

Write an equivalent fraction with the indicated denominator.
$$\frac{3}{5} = \frac{}{15}$$

PRACTICE 10

Write an equivalent fraction with the given denominator.

$$4 = \frac{}{6}$$

Answers

9. $\dfrac{9}{15}$ 10. $\dfrac{24}{6}$

✓ **Concept Check Answer**

false; the correct result would be $\dfrac{6}{27}$

Vocabulary and Readiness Check

Use the choices below to fill in each blank.

least common multiple (LCM)   multiple   equivalent

1. Fractions that represent the same portion of a whole are called _____ fractions.
2. The smallest positive number that is a multiple of all numbers in a list is called the _____ .
3. A(n) _____ of a number is the product of that number and a natural number.

2.7 Exercise Set

FOR EXTRA HELP

MyMathLab   Math XL PRACTICE   WATCH   DOWNLOAD   READ   REVIEW

Objectives  **Mixed Practice** *Find the LCM of each list of numbers. See Examples 1 through 7.*

1. 3, 4

2. 4, 6

3. 9, 15

4. 15, 20

5. 12, 18

6. 10, 15

7. 24, 36

8. 42, 70

9. 18, 21

10. 24, 45

11. 15, 25

12. 21, 14

13. 8, 24

14. 15, 90

15. 6, 7

16. 13, 8

17. 8, 6, 27

18. 6, 25, 10

19. 25, 15, 6

20. 4, 14, 20

21. 34, 68

22. 25, 175

23. 84, 294

24. 48, 54

25. 30, 36, 50

26. 21, 28, 42

27. 50, 72, 120

28. 70, 98, 100

29. 11, 33, 121

30. 10, 15, 100

31. 4, 6, 10, 15

32. 25, 3, 15, 10

Objective *Write each fraction or whole number as an equivalent fraction with the given denominator. See Examples 8 through 10.*

33. $\dfrac{4}{7} = \dfrac{}{35}$

34. $\dfrac{3}{5} = \dfrac{}{20}$

35. $\dfrac{2}{3} = \dfrac{}{21}$

36. $6 = \dfrac{}{10}$

37. $5 = \dfrac{}{3}$

38. $\dfrac{9}{10} = \dfrac{}{70}$

39. $\dfrac{1}{2} = \dfrac{}{30}$

40. $\dfrac{1}{3} = \dfrac{}{30}$

41. $\dfrac{10}{7} = \dfrac{}{21}$

42. $\dfrac{5}{3} = \dfrac{}{21}$

43. $\dfrac{3}{4} = \dfrac{}{28}$ **44.** $\dfrac{4}{5} = \dfrac{}{45}$ **45.** $\dfrac{2}{3} = \dfrac{}{45}$ **46.** $\dfrac{2}{3} = \dfrac{}{75}$ **47.** $\dfrac{4}{9} = \dfrac{}{81}$

48. $\dfrac{5}{11} = \dfrac{}{88}$ **49.** $\dfrac{15}{13} = \dfrac{}{78}$ **50.** $\dfrac{9}{7} = \dfrac{}{84}$ **51.** $\dfrac{14}{17} = \dfrac{}{68}$ **52.** $\dfrac{19}{21} = \dfrac{}{126}$

The table shows the fraction of goods sold online by type of goods in a recent year. Use this table to answer Exercises 53 through 56.

53. Complete the table by writing each fraction as an equivalent fraction with a denominator of 100.

54. Which of these types of goods has the largest fraction sold online?

55. Which of these types of goods has the smallest fraction sold online?

56. Which of the types of goods has **more than** $\dfrac{3}{5}$ of the goods sold online? (*Hint:* write $\dfrac{3}{5}$ as an equivalent fraction with a denominator of 100.)

Type of Goods	Fraction of All Goods That Are Sold Online	Equivalent Fraction with a Denominator of 100
books and magazines	$\dfrac{27}{50}$	
clothing and accessories	$\dfrac{1}{2}$	
computer hardware	$\dfrac{23}{50}$	
computer software	$\dfrac{1}{2}$	
drugs, health and beauty aids	$\dfrac{3}{20}$	
electronics and appliances	$\dfrac{13}{20}$	
food, beer, and wine	$\dfrac{9}{20}$	
home furnishings	$\dfrac{13}{25}$	
music and videos	$\dfrac{3}{5}$	
office equipment and supplies	$\dfrac{61}{100}$	
sporting goods	$\dfrac{12}{25}$	
toys, hobbies, and games	$\dfrac{1}{2}$	

(*Source:* Fedstats.gov)

Review

Add or subtract as indicated. See Section 2.6.

57. $\dfrac{7}{10} - \dfrac{2}{10}$ **58.** $\dfrac{8}{13} - \dfrac{3}{13}$ **59.** $\dfrac{1}{5} + \dfrac{1}{5}$ **60.** $\dfrac{1}{8} + \dfrac{3}{8}$

61. $\dfrac{23}{18} - \dfrac{15}{18}$ **62.** $\dfrac{36}{30} - \dfrac{12}{30}$ **63.** $\dfrac{2}{9} + \dfrac{1}{9} + \dfrac{6}{9}$ **64.** $\dfrac{2}{12} + \dfrac{7}{12} + \dfrac{3}{12}$

Concept Extensions

Write each fraction as an equivalent fraction with the indicated denominator.

65. $\dfrac{37}{165} = \dfrac{}{3630}$

66. $\dfrac{108}{215} = \dfrac{}{4085}$

67. In your own words, explain how to find the LCM of two numbers.

68. In your own words, explain how to write a fraction as an equivalent fraction with a given denominator.

Solve. See the Concept Checks in this section.

69. Which of the following are equivalent to $\dfrac{2}{3}$?

   a. $\dfrac{10}{15}$ **b.** $\dfrac{40}{60}$

   c. $\dfrac{16}{20}$ **d.** $\dfrac{200}{300}$

70. True or False? When the fraction $\dfrac{7}{12}$ is rewritten with a denominator of 48, the result is $\dfrac{11}{48}$. If false, give the correct fraction.

2.8 ADDING AND SUBTRACTING UNLIKE FRACTIONS

Objectives

Ⓐ **Add Unlike Fractions.**

Ⓑ **Subtract Unlike Fractions.**

Ⓒ **Solve Problems by Adding or Subtracting Unlike Fractions.**

Objective Ⓐ Adding Unlike Fractions

In this section we add and subtract fractions with unlike denominators. To add or subtract these unlike fractions, we first write the fractions as equivalent fractions with a common denominator and then add or subtract the like fractions. The common denominator that we use is the least common multiple (LCM) of the denominators. This denominator is called the **least common denominator (LCD).**

To begin, let's add the unlike fractions $\frac{3}{4} + \frac{1}{6}$. The LCM of denominators 4 and 6 is 12. This means that the number 12 is also the LCD. So we write each fraction as an equivalent fraction with a denominator of 12, then add as usual. This addition process is shown next and also illustrated by figures.

Add: $\frac{3}{4} + \frac{1}{6}$	The LCD is 12.
Figures	**Algebra**
$\frac{3}{4}$ + $\frac{1}{6}$ $\frac{9}{12}$ + $\frac{2}{12}$ $\frac{9}{12} + \frac{2}{12} = \frac{11}{12}$	$\frac{3}{4} = \frac{3}{4} \cdot \frac{3}{3} = \frac{9}{12}$ and $\frac{1}{6} = \frac{1}{6} \cdot \frac{2}{2} = \frac{2}{12}$ Remember $\frac{3}{3} = 1$ and $\frac{2}{2} = 1$. Now we can add just as we did in Section 2.6. $\frac{3}{4} + \frac{1}{6} = \frac{9}{12} + \frac{2}{12} = \frac{11}{12}$
Thus, the sum is $\frac{11}{12}$.	

Adding or Subtracting Unlike Fractions

Step 1: Find the LCM of the denominators of the fractions. This number is the least common denominator (LCD).

Step 2: Write each fraction as an equivalent fraction whose denominator is the LCD.

Step 3: Add or subtract the like fractions.

Step 4: Write the sum or difference in simplest form.

PRACTICE 1

Add: $\dfrac{1}{6} + \dfrac{5}{18}$

Example 1 Add: $\dfrac{2}{5} + \dfrac{4}{15}$

Solution:

Step 1: The LCM of the denominators 5 and 15 is 15. Thus, the LCD is 15. In later examples, we shall simply say, for example, that the LCD of 5 and 15 is 15.

Step 2: $\dfrac{2}{5} = \dfrac{2}{5} \cdot \dfrac{3}{3} = \dfrac{6}{15}, \quad \dfrac{4}{15} = \dfrac{4}{15}$ ⟵ This fraction already has a denominator of 15.

⎿ Multiply by 1 in the form $\dfrac{3}{3}$

Step 3: $\dfrac{2}{5} + \dfrac{4}{15} = \dfrac{6}{15} + \dfrac{4}{15} = \dfrac{10}{15}$

Step 4: Write in simplest form.

$$\dfrac{10}{15} = \dfrac{2 \cdot \overset{1}{\cancel{5}}}{3 \cdot \underset{1}{\cancel{5}}} = \dfrac{2}{3}$$

● Work Practice 1

PRACTICE 2

Add: $\dfrac{5}{6} + \dfrac{2}{9}$

Example 2 Add: $\dfrac{11}{15} + \dfrac{3}{10}$

Solution:

Step 1: The LCD of 15 and 10 is 30.

Step 2: $\dfrac{11}{15} = \dfrac{11}{15} \cdot \dfrac{2}{2} = \dfrac{22}{30} \qquad \dfrac{3}{10} = \dfrac{3}{10} \cdot \dfrac{3}{3} = \dfrac{9}{30}$

Step 3: $\dfrac{11}{15} + \dfrac{3}{10} = \dfrac{22}{30} + \dfrac{9}{30} = \dfrac{31}{30}$

Step 4: $\dfrac{31}{30}$ is in simplest form. We can write the sum as $\dfrac{31}{30}$ or $1\dfrac{1}{30}$.

● Work Practice 2

PRACTICE 3

Add: $\dfrac{2}{5} + \dfrac{4}{9}$

Example 3 Add: $\dfrac{2}{3} + \dfrac{1}{7}$

Solution: The LCD of 3 and 7 is 21.

$$\dfrac{2}{3} + \dfrac{1}{7} = \dfrac{2}{3} \cdot \dfrac{7}{7} + \dfrac{1}{7} \cdot \dfrac{3}{3}$$

$$= \dfrac{14}{21} + \dfrac{3}{21}$$

$$= \dfrac{17}{21} \quad \text{Simplest form.}$$

● Work Practice 3

Answers

1. $\dfrac{4}{9}$ 2. $\dfrac{19}{18}$ or $1\dfrac{1}{18}$ 3. $\dfrac{38}{45}$

Example 4 Add: $\dfrac{1}{2} + \dfrac{2}{3} + \dfrac{5}{6}$

Solution: The LCD of 2, 3, and 6 is 6.

$$\dfrac{1}{2} + \dfrac{2}{3} + \dfrac{5}{6} = \dfrac{1}{2} \cdot \dfrac{3}{3} + \dfrac{2}{3} \cdot \dfrac{2}{2} + \dfrac{5}{6}$$

$$= \dfrac{3}{6} + \dfrac{4}{6} + \dfrac{5}{6}$$

$$= \dfrac{12}{6} = 2$$

● Work Practice 4

PRACTICE 4

Add: $\dfrac{1}{4} + \dfrac{4}{5} + \dfrac{9}{10}$

✓ **Concept Check** Find and correct the error in the following:

$$\dfrac{2}{9} + \dfrac{4}{11} = \dfrac{6}{20} = \dfrac{3}{10}$$

Objective ⓑ Subtracting Unlike Fractions

As indicated in the box on page 167, we follow the same steps when subtracting unlike fractions as when adding them.

Example 5 Subtract: $\dfrac{2}{5} - \dfrac{3}{20}$

Solution:

Step 1: The LCD of 5 and 20 is 20.

Step 2: $\dfrac{2}{5} = \dfrac{2}{5} \cdot \dfrac{4}{4} = \dfrac{8}{20}$ $\dfrac{3}{20} = \dfrac{3}{20}$ ⟵ The fraction already has a denominator of 20.

Step 3: $\dfrac{2}{5} - \dfrac{3}{20} = \dfrac{8}{20} - \dfrac{3}{20} = \dfrac{5}{20}$

Step 4: Write in simplest form.

$$\dfrac{5}{20} = \dfrac{\overset{1}{\cancel{5}}}{\underset{1}{\cancel{5}} \cdot 4} = \dfrac{1}{4}$$

● Work Practice 5

PRACTICE 5

Subtract: $\dfrac{7}{12} - \dfrac{5}{24}$

Example 6 Subtract: $\dfrac{10}{11} - \dfrac{2}{3}$

Solution:

Step 1: The LCD of 11 and 3 is 33.

Step 2: $\dfrac{10}{11} = \dfrac{10}{11} \cdot \dfrac{3}{3} = \dfrac{30}{33}$ $\dfrac{2}{3} = \dfrac{2}{3} \cdot \dfrac{11}{11} = \dfrac{22}{33}$

Step 3: $\dfrac{10}{11} - \dfrac{2}{3} = \dfrac{30}{33} - \dfrac{22}{33} = \dfrac{8}{33}$

Step 4: $\dfrac{8}{33}$ is in simplest form.

● Work Practice 6

PRACTICE 6

Subtract: $\dfrac{9}{10} - \dfrac{3}{7}$

Answers

4. $\dfrac{39}{20}$ or $1\dfrac{19}{20}$ 5. $\dfrac{3}{8}$ 6. $\dfrac{33}{70}$

✓ **Concept Check Answer**

When adding unlike fractions, we don't add the denominators. Correct solution:

$$\dfrac{2}{9} + \dfrac{4}{11} = \dfrac{22}{99} + \dfrac{36}{99} = \dfrac{58}{99}$$

PRACTICE 7

Subtract: $\dfrac{7}{8} - \dfrac{5}{6}$

Example 7 Subtract: $\dfrac{11}{12} - \dfrac{2}{9}$

Solution: The LCD of 12 and 9 is 36.

$$\dfrac{11}{12} - \dfrac{2}{9} = \dfrac{11}{12} \cdot \dfrac{3}{3} - \dfrac{2}{9} \cdot \dfrac{4}{4}$$

$$= \dfrac{33}{36} - \dfrac{8}{36}$$

$$= \dfrac{25}{36}$$

● Work Practice 7

✓**Concept Check** Find and correct the error in the following:

$$\dfrac{11}{12} - \dfrac{3}{4} = \dfrac{8}{8} = 1$$

Objective ⓒ Solving Problems by Adding or Subtracting Unlike Fractions

Very often, real-world problems involve adding or subtracting unlike fractions.

Example 8 Finding Total Weight

PRACTICE 8

To repair her sidewalk, a homeowner must pour small amounts of cement in three different locations. She needs $\dfrac{3}{5}$ of a cubic yard, $\dfrac{2}{10}$ of a cubic yard, and $\dfrac{2}{15}$ of a cubic yard for these locations. Find the total amount of cement the homeowner needs.

A freight truck has $\dfrac{1}{4}$ ton of computers, $\dfrac{1}{3}$ ton of televisions, and $\dfrac{3}{8}$ ton of small appliances. Find the total weight of its load.

Solution:

1. UNDERSTAND. Read and reread the problem. The phrase "total weight" tells us to add.

2. TRANSLATE.

In words:	total weight	is	weight of computers	plus	weight of televisions	plus	weight of appliances
	↓	↓	↓	↓	↓	↓	↓
Translate:	total weight	=	$\dfrac{1}{4}$	+	$\dfrac{1}{3}$	+	$\dfrac{3}{8}$

3. SOLVE: The LCD is 24.

$$\dfrac{1}{4} + \dfrac{1}{3} + \dfrac{3}{8} = \dfrac{1}{4} \cdot \dfrac{6}{6} + \dfrac{1}{3} \cdot \dfrac{8}{8} + \dfrac{3}{8} \cdot \dfrac{3}{3}$$

$$= \dfrac{6}{24} + \dfrac{8}{24} + \dfrac{9}{24}$$

$$= \dfrac{23}{24}$$

4. INTERPRET. *Check* the solution. *State* your conclusion: The total weight of the truck's load is $\dfrac{23}{24}$ ton.

● Work Practice 8

Answers

7. $\dfrac{1}{24}$ **8.** $\dfrac{14}{15}$ cu yd

✓**Concept Check Answer**

Correct solution:

$\dfrac{11}{12} - \dfrac{3}{4} = \dfrac{11}{12} - \dfrac{9}{12} = \dfrac{2}{12} = \dfrac{1}{6}$

Example 9 Calculating Flight Time

A flight from Tucson to Phoenix, Arizona, requires $\frac{5}{12}$ of an hour. If the plane has been flying $\frac{1}{4}$ of an hour, find how much time remains before landing.

Solution:

1. **UNDERSTAND.** Read and reread the problem. The phrase "how much time remains" tells us to subtract.

2. **TRANSLATE.**

In words:	time remaining	is	flight time from Tucson of Phoenix	minus	flight time already passed
	↓	↓	↓	↓	↓
Translate:	time remaining	=	$\frac{5}{12}$	−	$\frac{1}{4}$

3. **SOLVE:** The LCD is 12.

$$\frac{5}{12} - \frac{1}{4} = \frac{5}{12} - \frac{1}{4} \cdot \frac{3}{3}$$
$$= \frac{5}{12} - \frac{3}{12}$$
$$= \frac{2}{12}$$
$$= \frac{\overset{1}{\cancel{2}}}{\underset{1}{\cancel{2}} \cdot 6}$$
$$= \frac{1}{6}$$

4. **INTERPRET.** *Check* the solution. *State* your conclusion: The flight time remaining is $\frac{1}{6}$ of an hour.

● **Work Practice 9**

PRACTICE 9
Find the difference in length of two boards if one board is $\frac{4}{5}$ of a foot long and the other is $\frac{2}{3}$ of a foot long.

Answer

9. $\frac{2}{15}$ ft

Calculator Explorations   Performing Operations on Fractions

Scientific Calculator

Many calculators have a fraction key, such as $\boxed{a\ b/c}$, that allows you to enter fractions and perform operations on them, and then it gives the result as a fraction. If your calculator has a fraction key, use it to calculate

$$\frac{3}{5} + \frac{4}{7}$$

Enter the keystrokes

$$\boxed{3}\ \boxed{a\ b/c}\ \boxed{5}\ \boxed{+}\ \boxed{4}\ \boxed{a\ b/c}\ \boxed{7}\ \boxed{=}$$

The display should read $\boxed{1\_6\ \ 35}$, which represents the mixed number $1\frac{6}{35}$. Let's write the result as a fraction. To convert from mixed number notation to fractional notation, press

$$\boxed{2^{\text{nd}}}\ \boxed{d/c}$$

The display now reads $\boxed{41\ \ 35}$, which represents $\frac{41}{35}$, the sum in fractional notation.

Graphing Calculator

Graphing calculators also allow you to perform operations on fractions and will give exact fractional results. The fraction option on a graphing calculator may be found under the $\boxed{\text{MATH}}$ menu. To perform the addition to the left, try the keystrokes.

$$\boxed{3}\ \boxed{\div}\ \boxed{5}\ \boxed{+}\ \boxed{4}\ \boxed{\div}\ \boxed{7}\ \boxed{\text{MATH}}\ \boxed{\text{ENTER}}$$

$$\boxed{\text{ENTER}}$$

   The display should read
   $$\boxed{3/5 + 4/7 \blacktriangleright \text{Frac } 41/35}$$

Use a calculator to add the following fractions. Give each sum as a fraction.

1. $\dfrac{1}{16} + \dfrac{2}{5}$ **2.** $\dfrac{3}{20} + \dfrac{2}{25}$ **3.** $\dfrac{4}{9} + \dfrac{7}{8}$

4. $\dfrac{9}{11} + \dfrac{5}{12}$ **5.** $\dfrac{10}{17} + \dfrac{12}{19}$ **6.** $\dfrac{14}{31} + \dfrac{15}{21}$

Vocabulary and Readiness Check

Use the choices below to fill in each blank. Any numerical answers are not listed.

   least common denominator   equivalent

1. To add or subtract unlike fractions, we first write the fractions as _____ fractions with a common denominator. The common denominator we use is called the _____.

2. The LCD for $\dfrac{5}{8}$ and $\dfrac{1}{6}$ is _____.

3. $\dfrac{5}{8} + \dfrac{1}{6} = \dfrac{5}{8} \cdot \dfrac{3}{3} + \dfrac{1}{6} \cdot \dfrac{4}{4} = \underline{} + \underline{} = \underline{}.$

4. $\dfrac{5}{8} - \dfrac{1}{6} = \dfrac{5}{8} \cdot \dfrac{3}{3} - \dfrac{1}{6} \cdot \dfrac{4}{4} = \underline{} - \underline{} = \underline{}.$

2.8 Exercise Set

FOR EXTRA HELP
MyMathLab
PRACTICE   WATCH   DOWNLOAD   READ   REVIEW

Objective **A** *Add and simplify. See Examples 1 through 4.*

1. $\dfrac{2}{3} + \dfrac{1}{6}$

2. $\dfrac{5}{6} + \dfrac{1}{12}$

3. $\dfrac{1}{2} + \dfrac{1}{3}$

4. $\dfrac{2}{3} + \dfrac{1}{4}$

5. $\dfrac{2}{11} + \dfrac{2}{33}$

6. $\dfrac{5}{9} + \dfrac{1}{3}$

7. $\dfrac{3}{14} + \dfrac{3}{7}$

8. $\dfrac{2}{5} + \dfrac{2}{15}$

9. $\dfrac{11}{35} + \dfrac{2}{7}$

10. $\dfrac{4}{5} + \dfrac{3}{40}$

11. $\dfrac{8}{25} + \dfrac{7}{35}$

12. $\dfrac{5}{14} + \dfrac{10}{21}$

13. $\dfrac{7}{15} + \dfrac{5}{12}$

14. $\dfrac{5}{8} + \dfrac{3}{20}$

15. $\dfrac{2}{28} + \dfrac{2}{21}$

16. $\dfrac{6}{25} + \dfrac{7}{35}$

17. $\dfrac{9}{44} + \dfrac{17}{36}$

18. $\dfrac{2}{33} + \dfrac{2}{21}$

19. $\dfrac{5}{11} + \dfrac{3}{13}$

20. $\dfrac{3}{7} + \dfrac{9}{17}$

21. $\dfrac{1}{3} + \dfrac{1}{9} + \dfrac{1}{27}$

22. $\dfrac{1}{4} + \dfrac{1}{16} + \dfrac{1}{64}$

23. $\dfrac{5}{7} + \dfrac{1}{8} + \dfrac{1}{2}$

24. $\dfrac{10}{13} + \dfrac{7}{10} + \dfrac{1}{5}$

25. $\dfrac{5}{36} + \dfrac{3}{4} + \dfrac{1}{6}$

26. $\dfrac{7}{18} + \dfrac{2}{9} + \dfrac{5}{6}$

27. $\dfrac{13}{20} + \dfrac{3}{5} + \dfrac{1}{3}$

28. $\dfrac{2}{7} + \dfrac{13}{28} + \dfrac{2}{5}$

Objective **B** *Subtract and simplify. See Examples 5 through 7.*

29. $\dfrac{7}{8} - \dfrac{3}{16}$ **30.** $\dfrac{5}{13} - \dfrac{3}{26}$ **31.** $\dfrac{5}{6} - \dfrac{3}{7}$ **32.** $\dfrac{3}{4} - \dfrac{1}{7}$ **33.** $\dfrac{5}{7} - \dfrac{1}{8}$

34. $\dfrac{10}{13} - \dfrac{7}{10}$ **35.** $\dfrac{9}{11} - \dfrac{4}{9}$ **36.** $\dfrac{7}{18} - \dfrac{2}{9}$ **37.** $\dfrac{11}{35} - \dfrac{2}{7}$ **38.** $\dfrac{2}{5} - \dfrac{3}{25}$

39. $\dfrac{5}{12} - \dfrac{1}{9}$ **40.** $\dfrac{7}{12} - \dfrac{5}{18}$ **41.** $\dfrac{7}{15} - \dfrac{5}{12}$ **42.** $\dfrac{5}{8} - \dfrac{3}{20}$ **43.** $\dfrac{3}{28} - \dfrac{2}{21}$

44. $\dfrac{6}{25} - \dfrac{7}{35}$ **45.** $\dfrac{1}{100} - \dfrac{1}{1000}$ **46.** $\dfrac{1}{50} - \dfrac{1}{500}$ **47.** $\dfrac{21}{44} - \dfrac{11}{36}$ **48.** $\dfrac{7}{18} - \dfrac{2}{45}$

Objectives **A** **B** **Mixed Practice** *Perform the indicated operation. See Examples 1 through 7.*

49. $\dfrac{5}{12} + \dfrac{1}{9}$ **50.** $\dfrac{7}{12} + \dfrac{5}{18}$ **51.** $\dfrac{17}{35} - \dfrac{2}{7}$ **52.** $\dfrac{13}{24} - \dfrac{1}{6}$

53. $\dfrac{9}{28} - \dfrac{3}{40}$ **54.** $\dfrac{10}{26} - \dfrac{3}{8}$ **55.** $\dfrac{2}{3} + \dfrac{4}{45} + \dfrac{4}{5}$ **56.** $\dfrac{3}{16} + \dfrac{1}{4} + \dfrac{1}{16}$

Objective **C** *Find the perimeter of each geometric figure. (Hint: Recall that perimeter means distance around.)*

57.
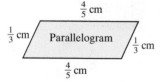

58.
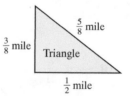

59.
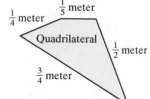

60.
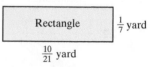

Solve. For Exercises 61 and 62, the solutions have been started for you. See Examples 8 and 9.

61. The slowest mammal is the three-toed sloth from South America. The sloth has an average ground speed of $\frac{1}{10}$ mph. In the trees, it can accelerate to $\frac{17}{100}$ mph. How much faster can a sloth travel in the trees? (*Source: The Guinness Book of World Records*)

Start the solution:

1. UNDERSTAND the problem. Reread it as many times as needed.
2. TRANSLATE into an equation. (Fill in the blanks.)

how much faster sloth travels in trees	is	sloth speed in trees	minus	sloth speed on ground
↓	↓	↓	↓	↓

how much faster sloth = _____ − _____
travels in trees

Finish with:

3. SOLVE. and
4. INTERPRET.

62. Killer bees have been known to chase people for up to $\frac{1}{4}$ of a mile, while domestic European honeybees will normally chase a person for no more than 100 feet, or $\frac{5}{264}$ of a mile. How much farther will a killer bee chase a person than a domestic honeybee? (*Source:* Coachella Valley Mosquito & Vector Control District)

Start the solution:

1. UNDERSTAND the problem. Reread it as many times as needed.
2. TRANSLATE into an equation. (Fill in the blanks.)

how much farther killer bee will chase than honeybee	is	distance killer bee chases	minus	distance honeybee chases
↓	↓	↓	↓	↓

how much farther killer = _____ − _____
bee will chase than honeybee

Finish with

3. SOLVE. and
4. INTERPRET.

63. Find the inner diameter of the washer. (*Hint:* Use the outer diameter and subtract the washer widths.)

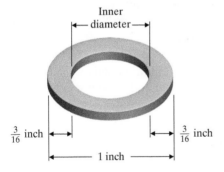

Inner diameter

$\frac{3}{16}$ inch $\frac{3}{16}$ inch

1 inch

64. Find the inner diameter of the tubing. (See the hint for Exercise 63.)

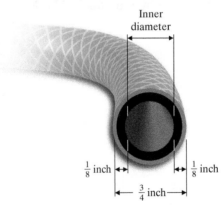

Inner diameter

$\frac{1}{8}$ inch $\frac{1}{8}$ inch

$\frac{3}{4}$ inch

65. Given the following diagram, find its total length. (*Hint:* Find the sum of the partial lengths.)

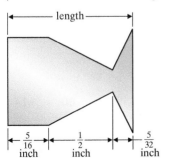

length

$\frac{5}{16}$ inch $\frac{1}{2}$ inch $\frac{5}{32}$ inch

66. Given the following diagram, find its total width. (*Hint:* Find the sum of the partial widths.)

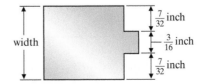

width

$\frac{7}{32}$ inch

$\frac{3}{16}$ inch

$\frac{7}{32}$ inch

67. Together, Thin Mints and Samoas account for $\frac{11}{25}$ of the Girl Scout cookies sold each year. Thin Mints alone account for $\frac{1}{4}$ of all Girl Scout cookie sales. What fraction of Girl Scout cookies sold are Samoas? (*Source:* Girl Scouts of the United States of America)

68. About $\frac{13}{20}$ of American students ages 10 to 17 name math, science, or art as their favorite subject in school. Art is the favorite subject for about $\frac{4}{25}$ of the American students ages 10 to 17. For what fraction of students this age is math or science their favorite subject? (*Source:* Peter D. Hart Research Associates for the National Science Foundation)

The table below shows the fraction of the Earth's water area taken up by each ocean. Use this table for Exercises 69 and 70.

Fraction of Earth's Water Area per Ocean	
Ocean	**Fraction**
Arctic	$\frac{1}{25}$
Atlantic	$\frac{13}{50}$
Pacific	$\frac{1}{2}$
Indian	$\frac{1}{5}$

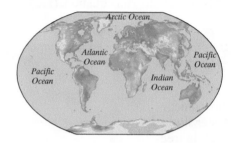

69. What fraction of the world's water surface area is accounted for by the Pacific and Atlantic Oceans?

70. What fraction of the world's water surface area is accounted for by the Arctic and Indian Oceans?

We first viewed this circle graph in Section 2.3. In this section we study it further. Use it to answer Exercises 71 through 74.

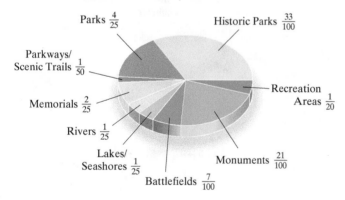

Areas Maintained by the National Park Service

Parks $\frac{4}{25}$ Historic Parks $\frac{33}{100}$
Parkways/ Scenic Trails $\frac{1}{50}$
Memorials $\frac{2}{25}$
Rivers $\frac{1}{25}$
Lakes/ Seashores $\frac{1}{25}$
Battlefields $\frac{7}{100}$
Monuments $\frac{21}{100}$
Recreation Areas $\frac{1}{20}$

Source: National Park Service

71. What fraction of areas maintained by the National Park Service are designated as National Lakes or National Seashores?

72. What fraction of areas maintained by the National Park Service are designated as National Recreation Areas?

73. What fraction of areas maintained by the National Park Service are NOT National Monuments?

74. What fraction of areas maintained by the National Park Service are NOT National Parkways or Scenic Trails?

Review

Multiply or divide as indicated. See Sections 2.4 and 2.5.

75. $1\frac{1}{2} \cdot 3\frac{1}{3}$ **76.** $2\frac{5}{6} \div 5$ **77.** $4 \div 7\frac{1}{4}$ **78.** $4\frac{3}{4} \cdot 5\frac{1}{5}$ **79.** $3 \cdot 2\frac{1}{9}$ **80.** $6\frac{2}{7} \cdot 14$

Concept Extensions

For Exercises 81 and 82 below, do the following:

a. *Draw three rectangles of the same size and represent each fraction in the sum or difference, one fraction per rectangle, by shading.*

b. *Using these rectangles as estimates, determine whether there is an error in the sum or difference.*

c. *If there is an error, correctly calculate the sum or difference.*

See the Concept Checks in this section.

81. $\dfrac{3}{5} + \dfrac{4}{5} \stackrel{?}{=} \dfrac{7}{10}$

82. $\dfrac{3}{4} - \dfrac{5}{8} \stackrel{?}{=} \dfrac{2}{4}$

Subtract from left to right.

83. $\dfrac{2}{3} - \dfrac{1}{4} - \dfrac{2}{540}$

84. $\dfrac{9}{10} - \dfrac{7}{200} - \dfrac{1}{3}$

Perform each indicated operation.

85. $\dfrac{30}{55} + \dfrac{1000}{1760}$

86. $\dfrac{19}{26} - \dfrac{968}{1352}$

87. In your own words, describe how to add or subtract two fractions with different denominators.

88. Find the sum of the fractions in the circle graph on page 176. Did the sum surprise you? Why or why not?

2.9 ADDING AND SUBTRACTING MIXED NUMBERS

Objective A Adding Mixed Numbers

Recall that a mixed number has a whole number part and a fraction part.

$$2\frac{3}{8} \text{ means } 2 + \frac{3}{8}$$

whole number

fraction

✓ **Concept Check** Which of the following are equivalent to 7?

a. $6\frac{5}{5}$

b. $6\frac{7}{7}$

c. $5\frac{8}{4}$

d. $6\frac{17}{17}$

e. all of these

Adding or Subtracting Mixed Numbers

To add or subtract mixed numbers, add or subtract the fraction parts and then add or subtract the whole number parts.

For example,

$$2\frac{2}{7}$$
$$+ 6\frac{3}{7}$$
$$\overline{\quad 8\frac{5}{7}} \longleftarrow \text{Add the fractions;}$$

then add the whole numbers

PRACTICE 1

Add: $4\frac{2}{5} + 5\frac{1}{6}$

Example 1 Add: $2\frac{1}{3} + 5\frac{3}{8}$. Check by estimating.

Solution: The LCD of 3 and 8 is 24.

$$2\frac{1 \cdot 8}{3 \cdot 8} = 2\frac{8}{24}$$
$$+ 5\frac{3 \cdot 3}{8 \cdot 3} = 5\frac{9}{24}$$
$$\overline{\qquad\qquad 7\frac{17}{24}} \longleftarrow \text{Add the fractions}$$

Add the whole numbers

To check by estimating, we round as usual. The fraction $2\frac{1}{3}$ rounds to 2, $5\frac{3}{8}$ rounds to 5, and $2 + 5 = 7$, our estimate.

Our exact answer is close to 7, so our answer is reasonable.

● **Work Practice 1**

Answer

1. $9\frac{17}{30}$

✓ **Concept Check Answer**

e

Helpful Hint

When adding or subtracting mixed numbers and whole numbers, it is a good idea to estimate to see if your answer is reasonable.

For the rest of this section, we leave most of the checking by estimating to you.

Example 2 Add: $3\frac{4}{5} + 1\frac{4}{15}$

Solution: The LCD of 5 and 15 is 15.

$$3\frac{4}{5} = 3\frac{12}{15}$$

$$+1\frac{4}{15} = 1\frac{4}{15} \qquad \text{Add the fractions; then add the whole numbers.}$$

$$\overline{\qquad\quad 4\frac{16}{15}} \qquad \text{Notice that the fraction part is improper.}$$

Since $\frac{16}{15}$ is $1\frac{1}{15}$ we can write the sum as

$$4\frac{16}{15} = 4 + 1\frac{1}{15} = 5\frac{1}{15}$$

● **Work Practice 2**

PRACTICE 2

Add: $2\frac{5}{14} + 5\frac{6}{7}$

✓**Concept Check** Explain how you could estimate the following sum:

$5\frac{1}{9} + 14\frac{10}{11}$.

Example 3 Add: $1\frac{4}{5} + 4 + 2\frac{1}{2}$

Solution: The LCD of 5 and 2 is 10.

$$1\frac{4}{5} = 1\frac{8}{10}$$

$$4 \quad = 4$$

$$+2\frac{1}{2} = 2\frac{5}{10}$$

$$\overline{\qquad\quad 7\frac{13}{10}} = 7 + 1\frac{3}{10} = 8\frac{3}{10}$$

● **Work Practice 3**

PRACTICE 3

Add: $10 + 2\frac{6}{7} + 3\frac{1}{5}$

Answers

2. $8\frac{3}{14}$ **3.** $16\frac{2}{35}$

✓ **Concept Check Answer**

Round each mixed number to the nearest whole number and add. $5\frac{1}{9}$ rounds to 5 and $14\frac{10}{11}$ rounds to 15, and the estimated sum is $5 + 15 = 20$.

Objective ⓑ Subtracting Mixed Numbers

PRACTICE 4

Subtract: $29\frac{7}{9} - 13\frac{5}{18}$

Example 4 Subtract: $9\frac{3}{7} - 5\frac{2}{21}$. Check by estimating.

Solution: The LCD of 7 and 21 is 21.

$$
\begin{aligned}
9\frac{3}{7} &= 9\frac{9}{21} \quad \leftarrow \text{The LCD of 7 and 21 is 21.}\\
-5\frac{2}{21} &= -5\frac{2}{21}\\
\hline
&\quad\; 4\frac{7}{21} \quad \leftarrow \text{Subtract the fractions.}
\end{aligned}
$$

Subtract the whole numbers.

Then $4\frac{7}{21}$ simplifies to $4\frac{1}{3}$. The difference is $4\frac{1}{3}$.

To check, $9\frac{3}{7}$ rounds to 9, $5\frac{2}{21}$ rounds to 5, and $9 - 5 = 4$, our estimate.

Our exact answer is close to 4, so our answer is reasonable.

● **Work Practice 4**

When subtracting mixed numbers, borrowing may be needed, as shown in the next example.

PRACTICE 5

Subtract: $9\frac{7}{15} - 5\frac{3}{5}$

Example 5 Subtract: $7\frac{3}{14} - 3\frac{6}{7}$

Solution: The LCD of 7 and 14 is 14.

$$
\begin{aligned}
7\frac{3}{14} &= 7\frac{3}{14}\\
-3\frac{6}{7} &= -3\frac{12}{14}
\end{aligned}
$$

Notice that we cannot subtract $\frac{12}{14}$ from $\frac{3}{14}$, so we borrow from the whole number 7.

borrow 1 from 7

$$7\frac{3}{14} = 6 + 1\frac{3}{14} = 6 + \frac{17}{14} \text{ or } 6\frac{17}{14}$$

Now subtract.

$$
\begin{aligned}
7\frac{3}{14} &= 7\frac{3}{14} = 6\frac{17}{14}\\
-3\frac{6}{7} &= -3\frac{12}{14} = -3\frac{12}{14}\\
\hline
&\qquad\qquad\qquad\quad 3\frac{5}{14} \quad \leftarrow \text{Subtract the fractions.}
\end{aligned}
$$

Subtract the whole numbers.

● **Work Practice 5**

Answers

4. $16\frac{1}{2}$ **5.** $3\frac{13}{15}$

✔ **Concept Check Answer**

Rewrite $5\frac{1}{4}$ as $4\frac{5}{4}$ by borrowing from the 5.

✔ **Concept Check** In the subtraction problem $5\frac{1}{4} - 3\frac{3}{4}$, $5\frac{1}{4}$ must be rewritten because $\frac{3}{4}$ cannot be subtracted from $\frac{1}{4}$. Why is it incorrect to rewrite $5\frac{1}{4}$ as $5\frac{5}{4}$?

Example 6 Subtract: $12 - 8\frac{3}{7}$

Solution:

$$12 \quad = \quad 11\frac{7}{7} \quad \text{Borrow 1 from 12 and write it as } \frac{7}{7}.$$

$$-8\frac{3}{7} = -8\frac{3}{7}$$

$$3\frac{4}{7} \leftarrow \text{Subtract the fractions.}$$

$$\uparrow$$

Subtract the whole numbers.

● Work Practice 6

PRACTICE 6

Subtract: $25 - 10\frac{2}{9}$

Objective C Solving Problems by Adding or Subtracting Mixed Numbers

Now that we know how to add and subtract mixed numbers, we can solve real-life problems.

Example 7 Calculating Total Weight

Two packages of ground round are purchased. One package weighs $2\frac{3}{8}$ pounds and the other $1\frac{4}{5}$ pounds. What is the combined weight of the ground round?

Solution:

1. UNDERSTAND. Read and reread the problem. The phrase "combined weight" tells us to add.
2. TRANSLATE.

In words:	combined weight	is	weight of one package	plus	weight of second package
	↓	↓	↓	↓	↓
Translate:	combined weight	=	$2\frac{3}{8}$	+	$1\frac{4}{5}$

3. SOLVE: Before we solve, let's estimate. The fraction $2\frac{3}{8}$ rounds to 2, $1\frac{4}{5}$ rounds to 2, and $2 + 2 = 4$. The combined weight should be close to 4.

$$2\frac{3}{8} = 2\frac{15}{40}$$

$$+1\frac{4}{5} = 1\frac{32}{40}$$

$$3\frac{47}{40} = 4\frac{7}{40}$$

4. INTERPRET. *Check* your work. Our estimate of 4 tells us that the exact answer of $4\frac{7}{40}$ is reasonable. *State* your conclusion: The combined weight of the ground round is $4\frac{7}{40}$ pounds.

PRACTICE 7

Two rainbow trout weigh $2\frac{1}{2}$ pounds and $3\frac{2}{3}$ pounds. What is the total weight of the two trout?

● Work Practice 7

Answers

6. $14\frac{7}{9}$ **7.** $6\frac{1}{6}$ lb

PRACTICE 8

The measurement around the trunk of a tree just below shoulder height is called its girth. The largest known American beech tree in the United States has a girth of $23\frac{1}{4}$ feet. The largest known sugar maple tree in the United States has a girth of $19\frac{5}{12}$ feet. How much larger is the girth of the largest known American beech tree than the girth of the largest known sugar maple tree? (*Source: American Forests*)

Girth

Example 8 Finding Legal Lobster Size

Lobster fishermen must measure the upper body shells of the lobsters they catch. Lobsters that are too small are thrown back into the ocean. Each state has its own size standard for lobsters to help control the breeding stock. Massachusetts divided its waters into four Lobster Conservation Management Areas, with a different minimum lobster size permitted in each area. In the off-shore area, the legal lobster size increased from $3\frac{13}{32}$ inches in 2006 to $3\frac{1}{2}$ inches in 2008.

How much of an increase was this? (*Source:* Massachusetts Division of Marine Fisheries)

Solution:

1. **UNDERSTAND.** Read and reread the problem carefully. The word "increase" found in the problem might make you think that we add to solve the problem. But the phrase "how much of an increase" tells us to subtract to find the increase.

2. **TRANSLATE.**

In words:	increase	is	new lobster size	minus	old lobster size
	↓	↓	↓	↓	↓
Translate:	increase	=	$3\frac{1}{2}$	−	$3\frac{13}{32}$

3. **SOLVE.** Before we solve, let's estimate. The fraction $3\frac{1}{2}$ can be rounded to 4, $3\frac{13}{32}$ can be rounded to 3, and $4 - 3 = 1$. The increase is not 1, but will be smaller since we rounded $3\frac{1}{2}$ up more than we rounded $3\frac{13}{32}$ down.

$$
\begin{array}{r}
3\frac{1}{2} = 3\frac{16}{32} \\
- \ 3\frac{13}{32} = 3\frac{13}{32} \\
\hline
\frac{3}{32}
\end{array}
$$

4. **INTERPRET.** *Check* your work. Our estimate tells us that the exact increase of $\frac{3}{32}$ is reasonable. *State* your conclusion: The increase in lobster size is $\frac{3}{32}$ of an inch.

● **Work Practice 8**

Answer

8. $3\frac{5}{6}$ ft

Vocabulary and Readiness Check

Use the choices below to fill in each blank.

round   fraction   whole number

improper   mixed number

1. The number $5\frac{3}{4}$ is called a(n) _____.

2. For $5\frac{3}{4}$, the 5 is called the _____ part and $\frac{3}{4}$ is called the _____ part.

3. To estimate operations on mixed numbers, we _____ mixed numbers to the nearest whole number.

4. The mixed number $2\frac{5}{8}$ written as a(n) _____ fraction is $\frac{21}{8}$.

Choose the best estimate for each sum or difference.

5. $3\frac{7}{8} + 2\frac{1}{5}$

   a. 6   **b.** 5   **c.** 1   **d.** 2

6. $3\frac{7}{8} - 2\frac{1}{5}$

   a. 6   **b.** 5   **c.** 1   **d.** 2

7. $8\frac{1}{3} - 1\frac{1}{2}$

   a. 4   **b.** 10   **c.** 6   **d.** 16

8. $8\frac{1}{3} + 1\frac{1}{2}$

   a. 4   **b.** 10   **c.** 6   **d.** 16

2.9 Exercise Set

 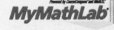

Objective Ⓐ *Add. For those exercises marked, find an exact sum and an estimated sum. See Examples 1 through 3.*

1. $4\frac{7}{10}$
$+2\frac{1}{10}$

2. $7\frac{4}{9}$
$+3\frac{2}{9}$

📱 3. $10\frac{3}{14}$
$+ 3\frac{4}{7}$

4. $12\frac{5}{12}$
$+ 4\frac{1}{6}$

5. $9\frac{1}{5}$
$+8\frac{2}{25}$

Exact: Exact: Exact: Exact:

Estimate: Estimate: Estimate: Estimate:

6. $6\frac{2}{13}$
$+8\frac{7}{26}$

7. $3\frac{1}{2}$
$+4\frac{1}{8}$

8. $9\frac{3}{4}$
$+2\frac{1}{8}$

📱 9. $1\frac{5}{6}$
$+5\frac{3}{8}$

10. $2\frac{5}{12}$
$+1\frac{5}{8}$

11. $8\frac{2}{5}$
$+11\frac{2}{3}$

12. $7\frac{3}{7}$
$+3\frac{3}{5}$

13. $11\frac{3}{5}$
$+7\frac{2}{5}$

14. $19\frac{7}{9}$
$+8\frac{2}{9}$

15. $40\frac{9}{10}$
$+15\frac{8}{27}$

16. $102\frac{5}{8}$
$+96\frac{21}{25}$

17. $3\frac{5}{8}$
$2\frac{1}{6}$
$+7\frac{3}{4}$

18. $4\frac{1}{3}$
$9\frac{2}{5}$
$+3\frac{1}{6}$

19. $12\frac{3}{14}$
10
$+25\frac{5}{12}$

20. $8\frac{2}{9}$
32
$+9\frac{10}{21}$

Objective Ⓑ *Subtract. For those exercises marked, find an exact difference and an estimated difference. See Examples 4 through 6.*

21. $4\frac{7}{10}$
$-2\frac{1}{10}$

Exact:

Estimate:

22. $7\frac{4}{9}$
$-3\frac{2}{9}$

Exact:

Estimate:

23. $10\frac{13}{14}$
$-3\frac{4}{7}$

Exact:

Estimate:

24. $12\frac{5}{12}$
$-4\frac{1}{6}$

Exact:

Estimate:

25. $9\frac{1}{5}$
$-8\frac{6}{25}$

26. $5\frac{2}{13}$
$-4\frac{7}{26}$

27. $5\frac{2}{3} - 3\frac{1}{5}$

28. $23\frac{3}{5}$
$-8\frac{8}{15}$

29. $15\frac{4}{7}$
$-9\frac{11}{14}$

30. $5\frac{3}{8} - 2\frac{13}{20}$

31. $47\frac{4}{18} - 23\frac{19}{24}$

32. $6\frac{1}{6} - 5\frac{11}{14}$

33. 10
$-8\frac{1}{5}$

34. 23
$-17\frac{3}{4}$

35. $11\frac{3}{5}$
$-9\frac{11}{15}$

36. $9\frac{1}{10}$
$-7\frac{2}{5}$

37. 6
$-2\frac{4}{9}$

38. 8
$-1\frac{7}{10}$

39. $63\frac{1}{6}$
$-47\frac{5}{12}$

40. $86\frac{2}{15}$
$-27\frac{3}{10}$

Objectives **A B** **Mixed Practice** *Perform the indicated operation. See Examples 1 through 6.*

41. $15\frac{1}{6}$
$+13\frac{5}{12}$

42. $21\frac{3}{10}$
$+11\frac{3}{5}$

43. $22\frac{7}{8}$
-7

44. $27\frac{3}{21}$
-9

45. $5\frac{8}{9} + 2\frac{1}{9}$

46. $12\frac{13}{16} + 7\frac{3}{16}$

47. $33\frac{11}{20} - 15\frac{19}{30}$

48. $54\frac{7}{30} - 38\frac{29}{50}$

Objective **C** *Solve. For Exercises 49 and 50, the solutions have been started for you. Write each answer in simplest form. See Examples 7 and 8.*

49. To prevent intruding birds, birdhouses built for Eastern Bluebirds should have an entrance hole measuring $1\frac{1}{2}$ inches in diameter. Entrance holes in birdhouses for Mountain Bluebirds should measure $1\frac{9}{16}$ inches in diameter. How much wider should entrance holes for Mountain Bluebirds be than for Eastern Bluebirds? (*Source:* North American Bluebird Society)

Start the solution:

1. UNDERSTAND the problem. Reread it as many times as needed.

2. TRANSLATE into an equation. (Fill in the blanks.)

how much wider	is	larger entrance hole	minus	smaller entrance hole
↓	↓	↓	↓	↓

how much wider $=$ _____ $-$ _____

Finish with:

3. SOLVE and

4. INTERPRET

50. If the total weight allowable without overweight charges is 50 pounds and the traveler's luggage weighs $60\frac{5}{8}$ pounds, on how many pounds will the traveler's overweight charges be based?

Start the solution:

1. UNDERSTAND the problem. Reread it as many times as needed.

2. TRANSLATE into an equation. (Fill in the blanks.)

overweight pounds	equals	luggage weight	minus	50 pounds
↓	↓	↓	↓	↓

overweight pounds $=$ _____ $-$ 50

Finish with:

3. SOLVE and

4. INTERPRET

51. Charlotte Dowlin has $15\frac{2}{3}$ feet of plastic pipe. She cuts off a $2\frac{1}{2}$-foot length and then a $3\frac{1}{4}$-foot length. If she now needs a 10-foot piece of pipe, will the remaining piece do? If not, by how much will the piece be short?

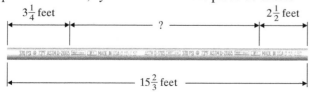

52. A trim carpenter cuts a board $3\frac{3}{8}$ feet long from one 6 feet long. How long is the remaining piece?

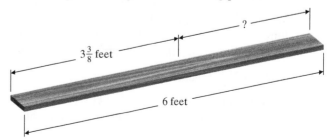

53. If Tucson's average annual rainfall is $11\frac{1}{4}$ inches and Yuma's is $3\frac{3}{5}$ inches, how much more rain, on average, does Tucson get than Yuma?

54. A pair of crutches needs adjustment. One crutch is 43 inches and the other is $41\frac{5}{8}$ inches. Find how much the short crutch should be lengthened to make both crutches the same length.

55. On four consecutive days, a concert pianist practiced for $2\frac{1}{2}$ hours, $1\frac{2}{3}$ hours, $2\frac{1}{4}$ hours, and $3\frac{5}{6}$ hours. Find his total practice time.

56. A tennis coach was preparing her team for a tennis tournament and enforced this practice schedule: Monday, $2\frac{1}{2}$ hours; Tuesday, $2\frac{2}{3}$ hours; Wednesday, $1\frac{3}{4}$ hours; and Thursday, $1\frac{9}{16}$ hours. How long did the team practice that week before Friday's tournament?

57. Jerald Divis, a tax consultant, takes $3\frac{1}{2}$ hours to prepare a personal tax return and $5\frac{7}{8}$ hours to prepare a small business return. How much longer does it take him to prepare the small business return?

58. Jessica Callac takes $2\frac{3}{4}$ hours to clean her room. Her brother Matthew takes $1\frac{1}{3}$ hours to clean his room. If they start at the same time, how long does Matthew have to wait for Jessica to finish?

59. Located on an island in New York City's harbor, the Statue of Liberty is one of the largest statues in the world. The copper figure is $46\frac{1}{20}$ meters tall from feet to tip of torch. The figure stands on a pedestal that is $46\frac{47}{50}$ meters tall. What is the overall height of the Statue of Liberty from the base of the pedestal to the tip of the torch? (*Source:* National Park Service)

60. The record for largest rainbow trout ever caught is $42\frac{1}{8}$ pounds and was set in Alaska in 1970. The record for largest tiger trout ever caught is $20\frac{13}{16}$ pounds and was set in Michigan in 1978. How much more did the record-setting rainbow trout weigh than the record-setting tiger trout? (*Source:* International Game Fish Association)

61. The longest floating pontoon bridge in the United States is the Evergreen Point Bridge in Seattle, Washington. It is 2526 yards long. The second-longest pontoon bridge in the United States is the Hood Canal Bridge in Point Gamble, Washington, which is $2173\frac{2}{3}$ yards long. How much longer is the Evergreen Point Bridge than the Hood Canal Bridge? (*Source:* Federal Highway Administration)

62. What is the difference between interest rates of $11\frac{1}{2}$ percent and $9\frac{3}{4}$ percent?

The following table lists some upcoming total eclipses of the Sun that will be visible in North America. The duration of each eclipse is listed in the table. Use the table to answer Exercises 63 through 66.

Total Solar Eclipses Visible from North America	
Date of Eclipse	**Duration (in Minutes)**
August 21, 2017	$2\frac{2}{3}$
April 8, 2024	$4\frac{7}{15}$
August 12, 2026	$2\frac{3}{10}$
(*Source:* NASA/Goddard Space Flight Center)	

63. What is the total duration for the three eclipses?

64. What is the total duration for the two eclipses occuring in even-numbered years?

65. How much longer will the April 8, 2024, eclipse be than the August 21, 2017, eclipse?

66. How much longer will the August 21, 2017, eclipse be than the August 12, 2026, eclipse?

Find the perimeter of each figure.

△ **67.**

$2\frac{1}{3}$ miles $2\frac{1}{3}$ miles

$2\frac{1}{3}$ miles

△ **68.**
7 inches $11\frac{1}{5}$ inches

$12\frac{1}{3}$ inches

△ **69.**
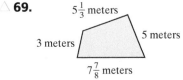
$5\frac{1}{3}$ meters

3 meters   5 meters

$7\frac{7}{8}$ meters

△ **70.**
$3\frac{1}{4}$ yards $3\frac{1}{4}$ yards

$3\frac{1}{4}$ yards $3\frac{1}{4}$ yards

$3\frac{1}{4}$ yards

Review

Evaluate each expression. See Section 1.9.

71. 2^3

72. 3^2

73. 5^2

74. 2^5

75. $20 \div 10 \cdot 2$

76. $36 - 5 \cdot 6 + 10$

77. $2 + 3(8 \cdot 7 - 1)$

78. $2(10 - 2 \cdot 5) + 13$

Simplify. Write any mixed number whose fraction part is not a proper fraction in simplest form. See Section 2.1.

79. $3\frac{5}{5}$

80. $10\frac{8}{7}$

81. $9\frac{10}{16}$

82. $6\frac{7}{14}$

Concept Extensions

Solve. See the Concept Checks in this section.

83. Which of the following are equivalent to 10?

   a. $9\dfrac{5}{5}$ **b.** $9\dfrac{100}{100}$ **c.** $6\dfrac{44}{11}$ **d.** $8\dfrac{13}{13}$

84. Which of the following are equivalent to $7\dfrac{3}{4}$?

   a. $6\dfrac{7}{4}$ **b.** $5\dfrac{11}{4}$ **c.** $7\dfrac{12}{16}$ **d.** all of them

Solve.

85. Explain in your own words why $9\dfrac{13}{9}$ is equal to $10\dfrac{4}{9}$.

86. In your own words, explain

   a. when to borrow when subtracting mixed numbers, and

   b. how to borrow when subtracting mixed numbers.

87. Carmen's Candy Clutch is famous for its "Nutstuff," a special blend of nuts and candy. A Supreme box of Nutstuff has $2\dfrac{1}{4}$ pounds of nuts and $3\dfrac{1}{2}$ pounds of candy. A Deluxe box has $1\dfrac{3}{8}$ pounds of nuts and $4\dfrac{1}{4}$ pounds of candy. Which box is heavier and by how much?

88. Willie Cassidie purchased three Supreme boxes and two Deluxe boxes of Nutstuff from Carmen's Candy Clutch. (See Exercise 87.) What is the total weight of his purchase?

2.10 ORDER, EXPONENTS, AND THE ORDER OF OPERATIONS

Objectives

A Compare Fractions.

B Evaluate Fractions Raised to Powers.

C Review Operations on Fractions.

D Use the Order of Operations.

Objective **A** Comparing Fractions

Recall that whole numbers can be shown on a number line using equally spaced distances.

From the number line, we can see the order of numbers. For example, we can see that 3 is less than 5 because 3 is to the left of 5.

For any two numbers on a number line, the number to the left is always the smaller number, and the number to the right is always the larger number.

We use the **inequality symbols** $<$ or $>$ to write the order of numbers.

Inequality Symbols

$<$ means *is less than.*

$>$ means *is greater than.*

For example,

3 is less than 5   or   5 is greater than 3

$3 < 5$ $5 > 3$

We can compare fractions the same way. To see fractions on a number line, divide the spaces between whole numbers into equal parts.

For example, let's compare $\frac{2}{5}$ and $\frac{4}{5}$.

$$\frac{5}{5} = 1$$

Since $\frac{4}{5}$ is to the right of $\frac{2}{5}$,

$$\frac{2}{5} < \frac{4}{5}$$ Notice that $2 < 4$ also.

Comparing Fractions

To determine which of two fractions is greater,

Step 1: Write the fractions as like fractions.

Step 2: The fraction with the greater numerator is the greater fraction.

Example 1 Insert $<$ or $>$ to form a true statement.

$$\frac{3}{10} \qquad \frac{2}{7}$$

Solution:

Step 1: The LCD of 10 and 7 is 70.

$$\frac{3}{10} = \frac{3}{10} \cdot \frac{7}{7} = \frac{21}{70}; \qquad \frac{2}{7} = \frac{2}{7} \cdot \frac{10}{10} = \frac{20}{70}$$

Continued on next page

PRACTICE 1

Insert $<$ or $>$ to form a true statement.

$$\frac{8}{9} \qquad \frac{10}{11}$$

Answer

1. $<$

189

Step 2: Since $21 > 20$, then $\dfrac{21}{70} > \dfrac{20}{70}$ or

$$\dfrac{3}{10} > \dfrac{2}{7}$$

Work Practice 1

PRACTICE 2

Insert $<$ or $>$ to form a true statement.

$$\dfrac{3}{5} \qquad \dfrac{2}{9}$$

Example 2 Insert $<$ or $>$ to form a true statement.

$$\dfrac{9}{10} \qquad \dfrac{11}{12}$$

Solution:

Step 1: The LCD of 10 and 12 is 60.

$$\dfrac{9}{10} = \dfrac{9}{10} \cdot \dfrac{6}{6} = \dfrac{54}{60} \qquad \dfrac{11}{12} = \dfrac{11}{12} \cdot \dfrac{5}{5} = \dfrac{55}{60}$$

Step 2: Since $54 < 55$, then $\dfrac{54}{60} < \dfrac{55}{60}$ or

$$\dfrac{9}{10} < \dfrac{11}{12}$$

Work Practice 2

Helpful Hint

If we think of $<$ and $>$ as arrowheads, a true statement is always formed when the arrow points to the smaller number.

$$\dfrac{2}{3} > \dfrac{1}{3} \qquad\qquad\qquad \dfrac{5}{6} < \dfrac{7}{6}$$
$$\uparrow \qquad\qquad\qquad\qquad\qquad \uparrow$$
points to smaller number   points to smaller number

Objective ⓑ Evaluating Fractions Raised to Powers

Recall from Section 1.9 that exponents indicate repeated multiplication.

exponent
$$\downarrow$$
$$5^3 = \underbrace{5 \cdot 5 \cdot 5} = 125$$
$$\uparrow$$
base   3 factors of 5

Exponents mean the same when the base is a fraction. For example,

$$\left(\dfrac{1}{3}\right)^4 = \underbrace{\dfrac{1}{3} \cdot \dfrac{1}{3} \cdot \dfrac{1}{3} \cdot \dfrac{1}{3}} = \dfrac{1}{81}$$
$$\uparrow$$
base   4 factors of $\dfrac{1}{3}$

PRACTICE 3–5

Evaluate each expression.

3. $\left(\dfrac{1}{5}\right)^2$ **4.** $\left(\dfrac{2}{3}\right)^3$

5. $\left(\dfrac{1}{4}\right)^2\left(\dfrac{2}{3}\right)^3$

Examples Evaluate each expression.

3. $\left(\dfrac{1}{4}\right)^2 = \dfrac{1}{4} \cdot \dfrac{1}{4} = \dfrac{1}{16}$

4. $\left(\dfrac{3}{5}\right)^3 = \dfrac{3}{5} \cdot \dfrac{3}{5} \cdot \dfrac{3}{5} = \dfrac{27}{125}$

5. $\left(\dfrac{1}{6}\right)^2 \cdot \left(\dfrac{3}{4}\right)^3 = \left(\dfrac{1}{6} \cdot \dfrac{1}{6}\right) \cdot \left(\dfrac{3}{4} \cdot \dfrac{3}{4} \cdot \dfrac{3}{4}\right) = \dfrac{1 \cdot 1 \cdot \overset{1}{\cancel{3}} \cdot \overset{1}{\cancel{3}} \cdot 3}{2 \cdot \underset{1}{\cancel{3}} \cdot 2 \cdot \underset{1}{\cancel{3}} \cdot 4 \cdot 4 \cdot 4} = \dfrac{3}{256}$

Work Practice 3–5

Answers

2. $>$ **3.** $\dfrac{1}{25}$ **4.** $\dfrac{8}{27}$ **5.** $\dfrac{1}{54}$

Objective ⓒ Reviewing Operations on Fractions

To get ready to use the order of operations with fractions, let's first review the operations on fractions that we have learned.

Review of Operations on Fractions		
Operation	**Procedure**	**Example**
Multiply	Multiply the numerators and multiply the denominators.	$\dfrac{5}{9} \cdot \dfrac{1}{2} = \dfrac{5 \cdot 1}{9 \cdot 2} = \dfrac{5}{18}$
Divide	Multiply the first fraction by the reciprocal of the second fraction.	$\dfrac{2}{3} \div \dfrac{11}{13} = \dfrac{2}{3} \cdot \dfrac{13}{11} = \dfrac{2 \cdot 13}{3 \cdot 11} = \dfrac{26}{33}$
Add or Subtract	**1.** Write each fraction as an equivalent fraction whose denominator is the LCD **2.** Add or subtract numerators and write the result over the common denominator.	$\dfrac{3}{4} + \dfrac{1}{8} = \dfrac{3}{4} \cdot \dfrac{2}{2} + \dfrac{1}{8} = \dfrac{6}{8} + \dfrac{1}{8} = \dfrac{7}{8}$

Examples Perform each indicated operation.

6. $\dfrac{1}{2} \div \dfrac{8}{7} = \dfrac{1}{2} \cdot \dfrac{7}{8} = \dfrac{1 \cdot 7}{2 \cdot 8} = \dfrac{7}{16}$ To divide: multiply by the reciprocal.

7. $\dfrac{6}{35} + \dfrac{3}{7} = \dfrac{6}{35} + \dfrac{3}{7} \cdot \dfrac{5}{5} = \dfrac{6}{35} + \dfrac{15}{35} = \dfrac{21}{35}$ To add: need the LCD. The LCD is 35.

$$= \dfrac{\overset{1}{\cancel{7}} \cdot 3}{\underset{1}{\cancel{7}} \cdot 5} = \dfrac{3}{5}$$

8. $\dfrac{2}{9} \cdot \dfrac{3}{11} = \dfrac{2 \cdot 3}{9 \cdot 11} = \dfrac{2 \cdot \overset{1}{\cancel{3}}}{\underset{1}{\cancel{3}} \cdot 3 \cdot 11} = \dfrac{2}{33}$ To multiply: multiply numerators and multiply denominators.

9. $\dfrac{6}{7} - \dfrac{1}{3} = \dfrac{6}{7} \cdot \dfrac{3}{3} - \dfrac{1}{3} \cdot \dfrac{7}{7} = \dfrac{18}{21} - \dfrac{7}{21} = \dfrac{11}{21}$ To subtract: need the LCD. The LCD is 21.

● Work Practice 6–9

PRACTICE 6–9

Perform each indicated operation.

6. $\dfrac{3}{7} \div \dfrac{10}{11}$ **7.** $\dfrac{4}{15} + \dfrac{2}{5}$

8. $\dfrac{2}{3} \cdot \dfrac{9}{10}$ **9.** $\dfrac{11}{12} - \dfrac{2}{5}$

Objective ⓓ Using the Order of Operations

The order of operations that we use on whole numbers applies to expressions containing fractions and mixed numbers also.

Order of Operations

1. Perform all operations within parentheses ( ), brackets [ ], or other grouping symbols such as square roots or fraction bars, starting with the innermost set.

2. Evaluate any expressions with exponents.

3. Multiply or divide in order from left to right.

4. Add or subtract in order from left to right.

Answers

6. $\dfrac{33}{70}$ **7.** $\dfrac{2}{3}$ **8.** $\dfrac{3}{5}$ **9.** $\dfrac{31}{60}$

PRACTICE 10

Simplify: $\dfrac{2}{9} \div \dfrac{4}{7} \cdot \dfrac{3}{10}$

Example 10 Simplify: $\dfrac{1}{5} \div \dfrac{2}{3} \cdot \dfrac{4}{5}$

Solution: Multiply or divide *in order* from left to right. We divide first.

$$\dfrac{1}{5} \div \dfrac{2}{3} \cdot \dfrac{4}{5} = \underbrace{\dfrac{1}{5} \cdot \dfrac{3}{2}}_{\uparrow} \cdot \dfrac{4}{5}$$

To divide, multiply by the reciprocal.

$$= \dfrac{3}{10} \cdot \dfrac{4}{5}$$

$$= \dfrac{3 \cdot 4}{10 \cdot 5}\qquad \text{Multiply.}$$

$$= \dfrac{3 \cdot 2 \cdot \overset{1}{\cancel{2}}}{\underset{1}{\cancel{2}} \cdot 5 \cdot 5}\qquad \text{Simplify.}$$

$$= \dfrac{6}{25}\qquad \text{Simplify.}$$

● **Work Practice 10**

PRACTICE 11

Simplify: $\left(\dfrac{2}{5}\right)^2 \div \left(\dfrac{3}{5} - \dfrac{11}{25}\right)$

Example 11 Simplify: $\left(\dfrac{2}{3}\right)^2 \div \left(\dfrac{8}{27} + \dfrac{2}{3}\right)$

Solution: Start within the right set of parentheses. We add.

$$\left(\dfrac{2}{3}\right)^2 \div \left(\dfrac{8}{27} + \dfrac{2}{3}\right) = \left(\dfrac{2}{3}\right)^2 \div \left(\dfrac{8}{27} + \dfrac{18}{27}\right)\quad \text{The LCD is 27. Write } \dfrac{2}{3} \text{ as } \dfrac{18}{27}.$$

$$= \left(\dfrac{2}{3}\right)^2 \div \dfrac{26}{27}\qquad \text{Simplify inside the parentheses.}$$

$$= \dfrac{4}{9} \div \dfrac{26}{27}\qquad \text{Write } \left(\dfrac{2}{3}\right)^2 \text{ as } \dfrac{4}{9}.$$

$$= \dfrac{4}{9} \cdot \dfrac{27}{26}$$

$$= \dfrac{\overset{1}{\cancel{2}} \cdot 2 \cdot 3 \cdot \overset{1}{\cancel{9}}}{\underset{1}{\cancel{9}} \cdot \underset{1}{\cancel{2}} \cdot 13}$$

$$= \dfrac{6}{13}$$

● **Work Practice 11**

✔ **Concept Check** What should be done first to simplify $3\left[\left(\dfrac{1}{4}\right)^2 + \dfrac{3}{2}\left(\dfrac{6}{7} - \dfrac{1}{3}\right)\right]$?

Recall from Section 1.7 that the average of a list of numbers is their sum divided by the number of numbers in the list.

PRACTICE 12

Find the average of $\dfrac{1}{2}, \dfrac{3}{8}$, and $\dfrac{7}{24}$.

Example 12 Find the average of $\dfrac{1}{3}, \dfrac{2}{5}$, and $\dfrac{2}{9}$.

Solution: The average is their sum, divided by 3.

$$\left(\dfrac{1}{3} + \dfrac{2}{5} + \dfrac{2}{9}\right) \div 3 = \left(\dfrac{15}{45} + \dfrac{18}{45} + \dfrac{10}{45}\right) \div 3\quad \text{The LCD is 45.}$$

$$= \dfrac{43}{45} \div 3\qquad \text{Add.}$$

$$= \dfrac{43}{45} \cdot \dfrac{1}{3}$$

$$= \dfrac{43}{135}\qquad \text{Multiply.}$$

● **Work Practice 12**

Answers

10. $\dfrac{7}{60}$ **11.** 1   **12.** $\dfrac{7}{18}$

✔ **Concept Check Answer**

 $\dfrac{6}{7} - \dfrac{1}{3}$

Vocabulary and Readiness Check

Use the choices below to fill in each blank. Not all choices will be used.

addition   multiplication   evaluate the exponential expression

subtraction   division

1. To simplify $\frac{1}{2} + \frac{2}{3} \cdot \frac{7}{8}$, which operation do we perform first? _____

2. To simplify $\frac{1}{2} \div \frac{2}{3} \cdot \frac{7}{8}$, which operation do we perform first? _____

3. To simplify $\frac{7}{8} \cdot \left(\frac{1}{2} - \frac{2}{3} \right)$, which operation do we perform first? _____

4. To simplify $9 - \left(\frac{3}{4} \right)^2$, which operation do we perform first? _____

2.10 Exercise Set

FOR EXTRA HELP

MyMathLab® · MathXL PRACTICE · WATCH · DOWNLOAD · READ · REVIEW

Objective A *Insert < or > to form a true statement. See Examples 1 and 2.*

1. $\frac{7}{9}$ $\frac{6}{9}$

2. $\frac{12}{17}$ $\frac{13}{17}$

3. $\frac{3}{3}$ $\frac{5}{3}$

4. $\frac{3}{23}$ $\frac{4}{23}$

5. $\frac{9}{42}$ $\frac{5}{21}$

6. $\frac{17}{32}$ $\frac{5}{16}$

7. $\frac{9}{8}$ $\frac{17}{16}$

8. $\frac{3}{8}$ $\frac{14}{40}$

9. $\frac{3}{4}$ $\frac{2}{3}$

10. $\frac{2}{5}$ $\frac{1}{3}$

11. $\frac{3}{5}$ $\frac{9}{14}$

12. $\frac{3}{10}$ $\frac{7}{25}$

13. $\frac{1}{10}$ $\frac{1}{11}$

14. $\frac{1}{13}$ $\frac{1}{14}$

15. $\frac{27}{100}$ $\frac{7}{25}$

16. $\frac{37}{120}$ $\frac{9}{30}$

Objective B *Evaluate each expression. See Examples 3 through 5.*

17. $\left(\frac{1}{2} \right)^4$

18. $\left(\frac{1}{7} \right)^2$

19. $\left(\frac{2}{5} \right)^3$

20. $\left(\frac{3}{4} \right)^3$

21. $\left(\frac{4}{7} \right)^3$

22. $\left(\frac{2}{3} \right)^4$

23. $\left(\frac{2}{9} \right)^2$

24. $\left(\frac{7}{11} \right)^2$

25. $\left(\dfrac{3}{4}\right)^2 \cdot \left(\dfrac{2}{3}\right)^3$ **26.** $\left(\dfrac{1}{6}\right)^2 \cdot \left(\dfrac{9}{10}\right)^2$ **27.** $\dfrac{9}{10}\left(\dfrac{2}{5}\right)^2$ **28.** $\dfrac{7}{11}\left(\dfrac{3}{10}\right)^2$

Objective Ⓒ *Perform each indicated operation. See Examples 6 through 9.*

29. $\dfrac{2}{15} + \dfrac{3}{5}$ **30.** $\dfrac{5}{12} + \dfrac{5}{6}$ **31.** $\dfrac{3}{7} \cdot \dfrac{1}{5}$ **32.** $\dfrac{9}{10} \div \dfrac{2}{3}$ **33.** $1 - \dfrac{4}{9}$

34. $5 - \dfrac{2}{3}$ **35.** $4\dfrac{2}{9} + 5\dfrac{9}{11}$ **36.** $7\dfrac{3}{7} + 6\dfrac{3}{5}$ **37.** $\dfrac{5}{6} - \dfrac{3}{4}$ **38.** $\dfrac{7}{10} - \dfrac{3}{25}$

39. $\dfrac{6}{11} \div \dfrac{2}{3}$ **40.** $\dfrac{3}{8} \cdot \dfrac{1}{11}$ **41.** $0 \cdot \dfrac{9}{10}$ **42.** $\dfrac{5}{6} \cdot 0$ **43.** $0 \div \dfrac{9}{10}$

44. $\dfrac{5}{6} \div 0$ **45.** $\dfrac{20}{35} \cdot \dfrac{7}{10}$ **46.** $\dfrac{18}{25} \div \dfrac{3}{5}$ **47.** $\dfrac{4}{7} - \dfrac{6}{11}$ **48.** $\dfrac{11}{20} + \dfrac{7}{15}$

Objective Ⓓ *Use the order of operations to simplify each expression. See Examples 10 and 11.*

49. $\dfrac{1}{5} + \dfrac{1}{3} \cdot \dfrac{1}{4}$ **50.** $\dfrac{1}{2} + \dfrac{1}{6} \cdot \dfrac{1}{3}$ **51.** $\dfrac{5}{6} \div \dfrac{1}{3} \cdot \dfrac{1}{4}$ **52.** $\dfrac{7}{8} \div \dfrac{1}{4} \cdot \dfrac{1}{7}$

53. $\dfrac{1}{5} \cdot \left(2\dfrac{5}{6} - \dfrac{1}{3}\right)$ **54.** $\dfrac{4}{7} \cdot \left(6 - 2\dfrac{1}{2}\right)$ **55.** $2 \cdot \left(\dfrac{1}{4} + \dfrac{1}{5}\right) + 2$ **56.** $\dfrac{2}{5} \cdot \left(5 - \dfrac{1}{2}\right) - 1$

57. $\left(\dfrac{3}{4}\right)^2 \div \left(\dfrac{3}{4} - \dfrac{1}{12}\right)$ **58.** $\left(\dfrac{8}{9}\right)^2 \div \left(2 - \dfrac{2}{3}\right)$ **59.** $\left(\dfrac{2}{3} - \dfrac{5}{9}\right)^2$ **60.** $\left(1 - \dfrac{2}{5}\right)^3$

61. $\dfrac{5}{9} \cdot \dfrac{1}{2} + \dfrac{2}{3} \cdot \dfrac{5}{6}$ **62.** $\dfrac{7}{10} \cdot \dfrac{1}{2} + \dfrac{3}{4} \cdot \dfrac{3}{5}$ **63.** $\dfrac{27}{16} \cdot \left(\dfrac{2}{3}\right)^2 - \dfrac{3}{20}$ **64.** $\dfrac{64}{27} \cdot \left(\dfrac{3}{4}\right)^2 - \dfrac{7}{10}$

65. $\dfrac{3}{13} \div \dfrac{9}{26} - \dfrac{7}{24} \cdot \dfrac{8}{14}$ **66.** $\dfrac{5}{11} \div \dfrac{15}{77} - \dfrac{7}{10} \cdot \dfrac{5}{14}$ **67.** $\dfrac{3}{14} + \dfrac{10}{21} \div \left(\dfrac{3}{7}\right)\left(\dfrac{9}{4}\right)$ **68.** $\dfrac{11}{15} + \dfrac{7}{9} \div \left(\dfrac{14}{3}\right)\left(\dfrac{2}{3}\right)$

69. $\left(\dfrac{3}{4} + \dfrac{1}{8}\right)^2 - \left(\dfrac{1}{2} + \dfrac{1}{8}\right)$ **70.** $\left(\dfrac{1}{6} + \dfrac{1}{3}\right)^3 + \left(\dfrac{2}{5} \cdot \dfrac{3}{4}\right)^2$

Find the average of each list of numbers. See Example 12.

71. $\dfrac{5}{6}$ and $\dfrac{2}{3}$ **72.** $\dfrac{1}{2}$ and $\dfrac{4}{7}$ **73.** $\dfrac{1}{5}, \dfrac{3}{10},$ and $\dfrac{3}{20}$ **74.** $\dfrac{1}{3}, \dfrac{1}{4},$ and $\dfrac{1}{6}$

Objectives **C** **D** **Mixed Practice**

75. The average fraction of online sales of computer hardware is $\dfrac{23}{50}$, of computer software is $\dfrac{1}{2}$, and of music and videos is $\dfrac{3}{5}$. Find the average of these fractions.

76. The average fraction of online sales of sporting goods is $\dfrac{12}{25}$, of toys and hobbies and games is $\dfrac{1}{2}$, and of computer hardware is $\dfrac{23}{50}$. Find the average of these fractions.

Review

Identify each key word with the operation it most likely translates to. After each word, write A for addition, S for subtraction, M for multiplication, and D for division. See Sections 1.3, 1.4, 1.6, and 1.7.

77. increased by   **78.** sum   **79.** triple   **80.** product

81. subtracted from   **82.** decreased by   **83.** quotient   **84.** divided by

85. times   **86.** difference   **87.** total   **88.** more than

Concept Extensions

Solve.

89. Calculate $\dfrac{2^3}{3}$ and $\left(\dfrac{2}{3}\right)^3$. Do both of these expressions simplify to the same number? Explain why or why not.

90. Calculate $\left(\dfrac{1}{2}\right)^2 \cdot \left(\dfrac{3}{4}\right)^2$ and $\left(\dfrac{1}{2} \cdot \dfrac{3}{4}\right)^2$. Do both of these expressions simplify to the same number? Explain why or why not.

Each expression contains one addition, one subtraction, one multiplication, and one division. Write the operations in the order that they should be performed. Do not actually simplify. See the Concept Check in this section.

91. $[9 + 3(4 - 2)] \div \dfrac{10}{21}$

92. $[30 - 4(3 + 2)] \div \dfrac{5}{2}$

93. $\dfrac{1}{3} \div \left(\dfrac{2}{3}\right)\left(\dfrac{4}{5}\right) - \dfrac{1}{4} + \dfrac{1}{2}$

94. $\left(\dfrac{5}{6} - \dfrac{1}{3}\right) \cdot \dfrac{1}{3} + \dfrac{1}{2} \div \dfrac{9}{8}$

Solve.

95. In 2008, about $\dfrac{114}{250}$ of the total weight of mail delivered by the United States Postal Service was first-class mail. That same year, about $\dfrac{49}{100}$ of the total weight of mail delivered by the United States Postal Service was standard mail. Which of these two categories account for a greater portion of the mail handled by weight? (*Source:* U.S. Postal Service)

96. The National Park System (NPS) in the United States includes a wide variety of park types. National military parks account for $\dfrac{3}{128}$ of all NPS parks, and $\dfrac{1}{24}$ of NPS parks are classified as national preserves. Which category, national military park or national preserve, is bigger? (*Source:* National Park Service)

97. As of this writing, there are several hundred individuals who are or have been United States astronauts. Of these, $\dfrac{11}{160}$ were born in Texas, while $\dfrac{5}{64}$ were born in New York. Which state is the birthplace of the greater number of astronauts, Texas or New York? (*Source:* NASA)

98. Approximately $\dfrac{7}{10}$ of U.S. adults have a savings account. About $\dfrac{11}{25}$ of U.S. adults have a non-interest-bearing checking account. Which type of banking service, savings account or non-interest-bearing checking account, do adults in the United States use more? (*Source:* Scarborough Research/ US Data.com, Inc.)

2.11 FRACTIONS AND PROBLEM SOLVING

Objective

Ⓐ Solve Problems by Performing Operations on Fractions or Mixed Numbers.

Objective Ⓐ Solving Problems Containing Fractions or Mixed Numbers

Now that we know how to add, subtract, multiply, and divide fractions and mixed numbers, we can solve problems containing these numbers.

Don't forget the key words and phrases listed below that help indicate which operation to use. Also included are several words and phrases that translate to the symbol "=".

Addition (+)	Subtraction (−)	Multiplication (·)	Division (÷)	Equality (=)
sum	difference	product	quotient	equals
plus	minus	times	divide	is equal to
added to	subtract	multiply	shared equally	is/was
more than	less than	multiply by	among	yields
increased by	decreased by	of	divided by	
total	less	double/triple	divided into	

Recall the following problem-solving steps introduced in Section 1.8. They may be helpful to you:

Problem-Solving Steps

1. UNDERSTAND the problem. Some ways of doing this are to read and reread the problem, construct a drawing, and look for key words to identify an operation.

2. TRANSLATE the problem. That is, write the problem in short form using words, and then translate to numbers and symbols.

3. SOLVE the problem. It is helpful to estimate the solution by rounding. Then carry out the indicated operation from step 2.

4. INTERPRET the results. *Check* the proposed solution in the stated problem and *state* your conclusions. Write your results with the correct units attached.

In the first example, we find the volume of a box. Volume measures the space enclosed by a region and is measured in cubic units. We study volume further in a later chapter.

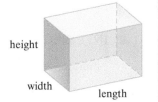

Volume of a box = length · width · height

Helpful Hint

Remember:

Perimeter measures the distance around a figure. It is measured in **units**.

$\boxed{}$ Perimeter

Area measures the amount of surface of a figure. It is measured in **square units**.

$\boxed{}$ Area

Volume measures the amount of space enclosed by a region. It is measured in **cubic units**.

 Volume

PRACTICE 1

Find the volume of a box that measures $4\frac{1}{3}$ feet by $1\frac{1}{2}$ feet by $3\frac{1}{3}$ feet.

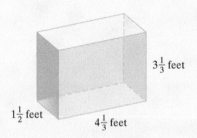

$3\frac{1}{3}$ feet

$1\frac{1}{2}$ feet $4\frac{1}{3}$ feet

Example 1 Finding Volume of a Camcorder Box

Sony recently produced a small camcorder. It measures 5 inches by $2\frac{1}{2}$ inches by $1\frac{3}{4}$ inches and can store 30 minutes of moving images. Find the volume of a box with these dimensions. (*Source: Guinness World Records*)

Solution:

1. **UNDERSTAND.** Read and reread the problem. The phrase "volume of a box" tells us what to do. The volume of a box is the product of its length, width, and height. Since we are multiplying, it makes no difference which measurement we call length, width, or height.

2. **TRANSLATE.**

In words:	volume of a box	is	length	·	width	·	height

$\downarrow \qquad\qquad \downarrow \quad \downarrow \qquad\qquad \downarrow \qquad\qquad \downarrow$

Translate: $\quad \text{volume of a box} = 5\text{ in.} \cdot 2\frac{1}{2}\text{ in.} \cdot 1\frac{3}{4}\text{ in.}$

3. **SOLVE:** Before we multiply, let's estimate by rounding each dimension to a whole number. The number 5 rounds to 5, $2\frac{1}{2}$ rounds to 3, and $1\frac{3}{4}$ rounds to 2, so our estimate is $5 \cdot 3 \cdot 2$ or 30 cubic inches.

$$5\text{ in.} \cdot 2\frac{1}{2}\text{ in.} \cdot 1\frac{3}{4}\text{ in.} = \frac{5}{1} \cdot \frac{5}{2} \cdot \frac{7}{4} \quad \text{cubic inches}$$

$$= \frac{5 \cdot 5 \cdot 7}{1 \cdot 2 \cdot 4} \quad \text{cubic inches}$$

$$= \frac{175}{8} \text{ or } 21\frac{7}{8} \quad \text{cubic inches}$$

4. **INTERPRET.** *Check* your work. The exact answer is somewhat close to our estimate. If you'd like, round $2\frac{1}{2}$ down to 2, and our estimate is $5 \cdot 2 \cdot 2$ or 20 cubic inches. This estimate is also appropriate and closer to our exact answer, so it is reasonable. *State* your conclusion: The volume of a box that measures 5 inches by $2\frac{1}{2}$ inches by $1\frac{3}{4}$ inches is $21\frac{7}{8}$ cubic inches.

● **Work Practice 1**

Answer

1. $21\frac{2}{3}$ cu ft

Example 2 Finding Unknown Length

Given the following diagram, find its total length.

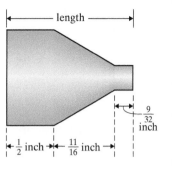

Given the following diagram, find its total width.

Solution:

1. UNDERSTAND. Read and reread the problem. Then study the diagram. The phrase "total length" tells us to add.

2. TRANSLATE. It makes no difference which length we call first, second, or third length.

In word:

total length	is	first length	+	second length	+	third length
↓	↓	↓		↓		↓

Translate: $\text{total length} = \frac{1}{2}\text{ in.} + \frac{11}{16}\text{ in.} + \frac{9}{32}\text{ in.}$

3. SOLVE:

$$\frac{1}{2} + \frac{11}{16} + \frac{9}{32} = \frac{1 \cdot 16}{2 \cdot 16} + \frac{11 \cdot 2}{16 \cdot 2} + \frac{9}{32}$$

$$= \frac{16}{32} + \frac{22}{32} + \frac{9}{32}$$

$$= \frac{47}{32} \text{ or } 1\frac{15}{32}$$

4. INTERPRET. *Check* your work. *State* your conclusion: The total length is $1\frac{15}{32}$ inches.

● **Work Practice 2**

Many problems require more than one operation to solve, as shown in the next application.

Example 3 Acreage for Single-Family Home Lots

A contractor is considering buying land to develop a subdivision for single-family homes. Suppose she buys 44 acres and calculates that $4\frac{1}{4}$ acres of this land will be used for roads and a retention pond. How many $\frac{3}{4}$-acre lots can she sell using the rest of the acreage?

Suppose that 25 acres of land are purchased, but because of roads and wetlands concerns, $6\frac{2}{3}$ acres cannot be developed into lots. How many $\frac{5}{6}$-acre lots can the rest of the land be divided into?

Solution:

1a. UNDERSTAND. Read and reread the problem. The phrase "using the rest of the acreage" tells is that initially we are to subtract.

Continued on next page

Answers
2. 2 in. **3.** 22 lots

2a. TRANSLATE. First, let's calculate the amount of acreage that can be used for lots.

In words:	acreage for lots	is	total acreage	minus	acreage for roads and a pond
	↓	↓	↓	↓	↓
Translate:	acreage for lots	=	44	−	$4\frac{1}{4}$

3a. SOLVE:

$$44 = 43\frac{4}{4}$$
$$-4\frac{1}{4} = -4\frac{1}{4}$$
$$\overline{\qquad\qquad 39\frac{3}{4}}$$

1b. UNDERSTAND. Now that we know $39\frac{3}{4}$ acres can be used for lots, we calculate how many $\frac{3}{4}$ acres are in $39\frac{3}{4}$. This means that we divide.

2b. TRANSLATE.

In words:	number of $\frac{3}{4}$-acre lots	is	acreage for lots	divided by	size of each lot
	↓	↓	↓	↓	↓
Translate:	number of $\frac{3}{4}$-acre lots	=	$39\frac{3}{4}$	÷	$\frac{3}{4}$

3b. SOLVE:

$$39\frac{3}{4} \div \frac{3}{4} = \frac{159}{4} \cdot \frac{4}{3} = \frac{\overset{53}{\cancel{159}} \cdot \overset{1}{\cancel{4}}}{\underset{1}{\cancel{4}} \cdot \underset{1}{\cancel{3}}} = \frac{53}{1} \text{ or } 53$$

4. INTERPRET. *Check* your work. *State* your conclusion: The contractor can sell $53\frac{3}{4}$-acre lots.

🔵 **Work Practice 3**

2.11 Exercise Set

FOR EXTRA HELP

MyMathLab
Powered by CourseCompass and MathXL

 Math XP
PRACTICE

WATCH

DOWNLOAD

READ

REVIEW

To prepare for problem-solving, translate each phrase to an expression. Do not simplify the expression.

1. The sum of $\frac{1}{2}$ and $\frac{1}{3}$.

2. The product of $\frac{1}{2}$ and $\frac{1}{3}$.

3. The quotient of 20 and $6\frac{2}{5}$.

4. The difference of 20 and $6\frac{2}{5}$.

5. Subtract $\frac{5}{8}$ from $\frac{15}{16}$.

6. The total of $\frac{15}{36}$ and $\frac{18}{30}$.

7. $\frac{21}{68}$ increased by $\frac{7}{34}$.

8. $\frac{21}{68}$ decreased by $\frac{7}{34}$.

9. The product of $8\frac{1}{3}$ and $\frac{7}{9}$.

10. $37\frac{1}{2}$ divided by $9\frac{1}{2}$.

Objective Ⓐ *Solve. Write any improper-fraction answers as mixed numbers. For Exercises 11 and 12, the solutions have been started for you. Write each answer in simplest form. See Examples 1 through 3.*

11. A recipe for brownies calls for $1\frac{2}{3}$ cups of sugar. If you are doubling the recipe, how much sugar do you need?

Start the solution:
1. UNDERSTAND the problem. Reread it as many times as needed.
2. TRANSLATE into an equation. (Fill in the blanks below.)

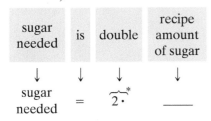

Finish with:
3. SOLVE
4. INTERPRET
*Note: Another way to double a number is to add the number to the same number.

12. A nacho recipe calls for $\frac{1}{3}$ cup cheddar cheese and $\frac{1}{2}$ cup jalapeño cheese. Find the total amount of cheese in the recipe.

Start the solution:
1. UNDERSTAND the problem. Reread it as many times as needed.
2. TRANSLATE into an equation. (Fill in the blanks below.)

total cheese	is	how much cheddar	added to	how much jalapeño cheese
↓	↓	↓	↓	↓
total cheese	=	___	+	___

Finish with:
3. SOLVE
4. INTERPRET

13. A decorative wall in a garden is to be built using bricks that are $2\frac{3}{4}$ inches wide and mortar joints that are $\frac{1}{2}$ inch wide. Use the diagram to find the height of the wall.

height — Mortar joint

14. Suppose that the contractor building the wall in Exercise 13 decides that he wants one more layer of bricks with a mortar joint below and above that layer. Find the new height of the wall.

15. Doug and Claudia Scaggs recently drove $290\frac{1}{4}$ miles on $13\frac{1}{2}$ gallons of gas. Calculate how many miles per gallon they get in their vehicle.

16. A contractor is using 18 acres of his land to sell $\frac{3}{4}$-acre lots. How many lots can he sell?

17. The life expectancy of a circulating coin is 30 years. The life expectancy of a circulating dollar bill is only $\frac{1}{20}$ as long. Find the life expectancy of circulating paper money. (*Source:* The U.S. Mint)

18. The Indian head one-cent coin of 1859–1864 was made of copper and nickel only. If $\frac{3}{25}$ of the coin was nickel, what part of the whole coin was copper? (*Source:* The U.S. Mint)

19. The Gauge Act of 1846 set the standard gauge for U.S. railroads at $56\frac{1}{2}$ inches. (See figure.) If the standard gauge in Spain is $65\frac{9}{10}$ inches, how much wider is Spain's standard gauge than the U.S. standard gauge? (*Source:* San Diego Railroad Museum)

Track gauge (U.S. $56\frac{1}{2}$ inches)

$\frac{5}{8}$ inch

Point of measurement of gauge

20. The standard railroad track gauge (see figure) in Spain is $65\frac{9}{10}$ inches, while in neighboring Portugal it is $65\frac{11}{20}$ inches. Which gauge is wider and by how much? (*Source:* San Diego Railroad Museum)

21. Mark Nguyen is a tailor making costumes for a play. He needs enough material for 1 large shirt that requires $1\frac{1}{2}$ yards of material and 5 small shirts that each require $\frac{3}{4}$ yard of material. He finds a 5-yard remnant of material on sale. Is 5 yards of material enough to make all 6 shirts? If not, how much more material does he need?

22. A beanbag manufacturer makes a large beanbag requiring $4\frac{1}{3}$ yards of vinyl fabric and a smaller size requiring $3\frac{1}{4}$ yards. A 100-yard roll of fabric is to be used to make 12 large beanbags. How many smaller beanbags can be made from the remaining piece?

23. A plumber has a 10-foot piece of PVC pipe. How many $\frac{9}{5}$-foot pieces can be cut from the 10-foot piece?

24. A carpenter has a 12-foot board to be used to make windowsills. If each sill requires $2\frac{5}{16}$ feet, how many sills can be made from the 12-foot board?

25. Suppose that the cross section of a piece of pipe looks like the diagram shown. Find the total outer diameter.

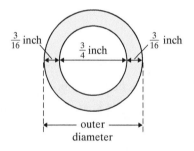

$\frac{3}{16}$ inch $\frac{3}{4}$ inch $\frac{3}{16}$ inch

outer diameter

26. Suppose that the cross section of a piece of pipe looks like the diagram shown. Find the total inner diameter.

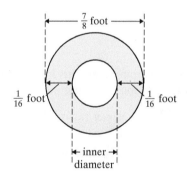

$\frac{7}{8}$ foot

$\frac{1}{16}$ foot $\frac{1}{16}$ foot

inner diameter

27. A recipe for chocolate chip cookies calls for $2\frac{1}{2}$ cups of flour. If you are making $1\frac{1}{2}$ recipes, how many cups of flour are needed?

28. A recipe for a homemade cleaning solution calls for $1\frac{3}{4}$ cups of vinegar. If you are tripling the recipe, how much vinegar is needed?

29. The Polaroid Pop Shot, the world's first disposable instant camera, can take color photographs measuring $4\frac{1}{2}$ inches by $2\frac{1}{2}$ inches. Find the area of a photograph. (*Source: Guinness World Records*)

30. A model for a proposed computer chip measures $\frac{3}{4}$ inch by $1\frac{1}{4}$ inches. Find its area.

31. A total solar eclipse on July 11, 2010, will last $5\frac{1}{3}$ minutes and can be viewed from the South Pacific, Easter Island, Chile, and Argentina. The next total solar eclipse on November 13, 2012, will last $4\frac{1}{30}$ minutes and can be viewed in the South Pacific and Australia. How much longer is the 2010 eclipse? (*Source:* NASA/Goddard Space Flight Center)

32. The pole vault record for the 1908 Summer Olympics was $12\frac{1}{6}$ feet. The record for the 2008 Summer Olympics was a little over $19\frac{1}{2}$ feet. Find the difference in the heights. (*Source:* International Olympic Committee)

△ **33.** A small cell phone measures $3\frac{1}{5}$ inches by $1\frac{7}{10}$ inches by 1 inch. Find the volume of a box with those dimensions. (*Source: Guinness World Records*)

△ **34.** Early cell phones were large and heavy. One early model measured approximately 8 inches by $2\frac{1}{2}$ inches by $2\frac{1}{2}$ inches. Find the volume of a box with those dimensions.

35. A stack of $\frac{5}{8}$-inch-wide sheetrock has a height of $41\frac{7}{8}$ inches. How many sheets of sheetrock are in the stack?

36. A stack of $\frac{5}{4}$-inch-thick books has a height of $28\frac{3}{4}$ inches. How many books are in the stack?

37. William Arcencio is remodeling his home. In order to save money, he is upgrading the plumbing himself. He needs 12 pieces of copper tubing, each $\frac{3}{4}$ of a foot long.
   a. If he has a 10-foot piece of tubing, will that be enough?
   b. How much more does he need or how much tubing will he have left over?

38. Trishelle Dallam is building a bookcase. Each shelf will be $2\frac{3}{8}$ feet long, and she needs wood for 7 shelves.
   a. How many shelves can she cut from an 8-foot board?
   b. Based on your answer for part a, how many 8-foot boards will she need?

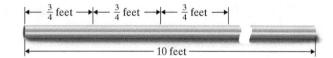

$\frac{3}{4}$ feet $\frac{3}{4}$ feet $\frac{3}{4}$ feet

10 feet

Recall that the average of a list of numbers is their sum divided by the number of numbers in the list. Use this procedure for Exercises 39 and 40.

39. A female lion had 4 cubs. They weighed $2\frac{1}{8}$, $2\frac{7}{8}$, $3\frac{1}{4}$, and $3\frac{1}{2}$ pounds. What is the average cub weight?

40. Three brook trout were caught, tagged, and then released. They weighed $1\frac{1}{2}$, $1\frac{3}{8}$, and $1\frac{7}{8}$ pounds. Find their average weight.

Find the area and perimeter of each figure.

△ **41.**

Rectangle | $\frac{3}{16}$ inch

$\frac{3}{8}$ inch

△ **42.**

Square | $1\frac{7}{10}$ mile

△ **43.**

Square | $\frac{5}{9}$ meter

△ **44.**

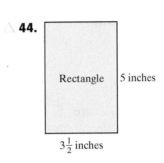

Rectangle | 5 inches

$3\frac{1}{2}$ inches

For Exercises 45 through 48, see the diagram. (Source: www.usflag.org)

45. The length of the U.S. flag is $1\frac{9}{10}$ its width. If a flag is being designed with a width of $2\frac{1}{2}$ feet, find its length.

46. The width of the Union portion of the U.S. flag is $\frac{7}{13}$ of the width of the flag. If a flag is being designed with a width of $2\frac{1}{2}$ feet, find the width of the Union portion.

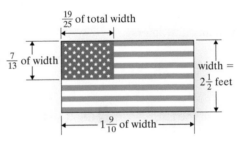

$\frac{19}{25}$ of total width

$\frac{7}{13}$ of width

width = $2\frac{1}{2}$ feet

$1\frac{9}{10}$ of width

47. There are 13 stripes of equal width in the flag. If the width of a flag is $2\frac{1}{2}$ feet, find the width of each stripe.

48. The length of the Union portion of the flag is $\frac{19}{25}$ of the total width. If the width of a flag is $2\frac{1}{2}$ feet, find the length of the Union portion.

Review

Simplify. See Section 1.9.

49. $\sqrt{9}$

50. $\sqrt{4}$

51. 9^2

52. 4^2

53. $8 \div 4 \cdot 2$

54. $20 \div 5 \cdot 2$

55. $3^2 - 2^2 + 5^2$

56. $8^2 - 6^2 + 7^2$

57. $5 + 3[14 - (12 \div 3)]$

58. $7 + 2[20 - (35 \div 5)]$

Concept Extensions

59. Suppose you are finding the average of $7\frac{1}{9}$ and $12\frac{19}{20}$. Can the average be $1\frac{1}{2}$? Can the average be $15\frac{1}{2}$? Why or why not?

60. Suppose that you are finding the average of $1\frac{3}{4}$, $1\frac{1}{8}$, and $1\frac{9}{10}$. Can the average be $2\frac{1}{4}$? Can the average be $\frac{15}{16}$? Why or why not?

The figure shown is for Exercises 61 and 62.

61. Find the area of the figure. (*Hint:* The area of the figure can be found by finding the sum of the areas of the rectangles shown in the figure.)

62. Find the perimeter of the figure.

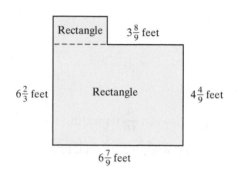

63. On a particular day, 240 customers ate lunch at a local restaurant. If $\frac{3}{10}$ of them ordered a $7 lunch, $\frac{5}{12}$ of them ordered a $5 lunch, and the remaining customers ordered a $9 lunch, how many customers ordered a $9 lunch?

64. Scott purchased a case of 24 apples. He used $\frac{1}{3}$ of them to make an apple pie, $\frac{1}{4}$ of them to make apple crisp, and kept the rest for after-school snacks for his children. How many apples did Scott keep for snacks?

65. Coins were practically made by hand in the late 1700s. Back then, it took 3 years to produce our nation's first million coins. Today, it takes only $\frac{11}{13,140}$ as long to produce the same amount. Calculate how long it takes today in hours to produce one million coins. (*Hint:* First convert 3 years to equivalent hours.) (*Source:* The U.S. Mint)

66. The largest suitcase measures $13\frac{1}{3}$ feet by $8\frac{3}{4}$ feet by $4\frac{4}{25}$ feet. Find its volume. (*Source: Guinness World Records*)

Helpful Hint

Are you preparing for your test? Use the Test Prep Videos to see the fully worked-out solutions to any of the exercises you want to review.

2 Chapter Highlights

Definitions and Concepts	Examples
Section 2.1 Introduction to Fractions and Mixed Numbers	

<table>
<tr>
<td>A fraction is of the form.

$\dfrac{\text{numerator}}{\text{denominator}}$ ← number of parts being considered
← number of equal parts in the whole</td>
<td>Write a fraction to represent the shaded part of the figure.

$\dfrac{3}{8}$ ← number of parts shaded
← number of equal parts</td>
</tr>
<tr>
<td>A fraction is called a proper fraction if its numerator is less than its denominator.

A fraction is called an improper fraction if its numerator is greater than or equal to its denominator.

A mixed number contains a whole number and a fraction.</td>
<td>$\dfrac{1}{3}, \dfrac{2}{5}, \dfrac{7}{8}, \dfrac{100}{101}$

$\dfrac{5}{4}, \dfrac{2}{2}, \dfrac{9}{7}, \dfrac{101}{100}$

$1\dfrac{1}{2}, 5\dfrac{7}{8}, 25\dfrac{9}{10}$</td>
</tr>
<tr>
<td>To Write a Mixed Number as an Improper Fraction
<ol>
<li>Multiply the denominator of the fraction by the whole number.</li>
<li>Add the numerator of the fraction to the product from step 1.</li>
<li>Write this sum from step 2 as the numerator of the improper fraction over the original denominator.</li>
</ol></td>
<td>$$5\dfrac{2}{7} = \dfrac{7 \cdot 5 + 2}{7} = \dfrac{35 + 2}{7} = \dfrac{37}{7}$$</td>
</tr>
<tr>
<td>To Write an Improper Fraction as a Mixed Number or a Whole Number
<ol>
<li>Divide the denominator into the numerator.</li>
<li>The whole number part of the mixed number is the quotient. The fraction is the remainder over the original denominator.</li>
</ol>
$\text{quotient}\dfrac{\text{remainder}}{\text{original denominator}}$</td>
<td>$\dfrac{17}{3} = 5\dfrac{2}{3}$

$\begin{array}{r} 5 \\ 3\overline{)17} \\ \underline{15} \\ 2 \end{array}$</td>
</tr>
<tr>
<td colspan="2" align="center">Section 2.2   Factors and Prime Factorization</td>
</tr>
<tr>
<td>A prime number is a natural number that has exactly two different factors, 1 and itself.

A composite number is any natural number other than 1 that is not prime.

The prime factorization of a number is the factorization in which all the factors are prime numbers.</td>
<td>$2, 3, 5, 7, 11, 13, 17, \ldots$

$4, 6, 8, 9, 10, 12, 14, 15, 16, \ldots$

Write the prime factorization of 60.

$\quad 60 = 6 \cdot 10$
$\qquad = 2 \cdot 3 \cdot 2 \cdot 5 \quad$ or $\quad 2^2 \cdot 3 \cdot 5$</td>
</tr>
</table>

Definitions and Concepts	**Examples**

Section 2.3   Simplest Form of a Fraction

Fractions that represent the same portion of a whole are called **equivalent fractions.**

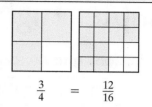

$$\frac{3}{4} = \frac{12}{16}$$

A fraction is in **simplest form** or **lowest terms** when the numerator and the denominator have no common factors other than 1.

The fraction $\frac{2}{3}$ is in simplest form.

To write a fraction in simplest form, write the prime factorizations of the numerator and the denominator and then divide both by all common factors.

Write in simplest form: $\frac{30}{36}$

$$\frac{30}{36} = \frac{2 \cdot 3 \cdot 5}{2 \cdot 2 \cdot 3 \cdot 3} = \frac{2}{2} \cdot \frac{3}{3} \cdot \frac{5}{2 \cdot 3} = 1 \cdot 1 \cdot \frac{5}{6} = \frac{5}{6}$$

or $\frac{30}{36} = \frac{\overset{1}{\cancel{2}} \cdot \overset{1}{\cancel{3}} \cdot 5}{\underset{1}{\cancel{2}} \cdot 2 \cdot \underset{1}{\cancel{3}} \cdot 3} = \frac{5}{6}$

Two fractions are equivalent if

Method 1.   They simplify to the same fraction.

Determine whether $\frac{7}{8}$ and $\frac{21}{24}$ are equivalent.

Method 1. $\frac{7}{8}$ is in simplest form; $\frac{21}{24} = \frac{\overset{1}{\cancel{3}} \cdot 7}{\underset{1}{\cancel{3}} \cdot 8} = \frac{7}{8}$

Since both simplify to $\frac{7}{8}$, then $\frac{7}{8} = \frac{21}{24}$.

Method 2.   Their cross products are equal.

Method 2.

$$\begin{matrix} 24 \cdot 7 \\ = 168 \end{matrix} \qquad \frac{7}{8} \enspace \diagdown\!\!\!\!\diagup \enspace \frac{21}{24} \qquad \begin{matrix} 8 \cdot 21 \\ = 168 \end{matrix}$$

Since $168 = 168, \frac{7}{8} = \frac{21}{24}$.

Section 2.4   Multiplying Fractions and Mixed Numbers

To multiply two fractions, multiply the numerators and multiply the denominators.

Multiply.

$$\frac{7}{8} \cdot \frac{3}{5} = \frac{7 \cdot 3}{8 \cdot 5} = \frac{21}{40}$$

$$\frac{3}{4} \cdot \frac{1}{6} = \frac{3 \cdot 1}{4 \cdot 6} = \frac{\overset{1}{\cancel{3}} \cdot 1}{4 \cdot \underset{1}{\cancel{3}} \cdot 2} = \frac{1}{8}$$

To multiply with mixed numbers or whole numbers, first write any mixed or whole numbers as fractions and then multiply as usual.

$$2\frac{1}{3} \cdot \frac{1}{9} = \frac{7}{3} \cdot \frac{1}{9} = \frac{7 \cdot 1}{3 \cdot 9} = \frac{7}{27}$$

Definitions and Concepts	**Examples**

Section 2.5   Dividing Fractions and Mixed Numbers

To find the **reciprocal** of a fraction, interchange its numerator and denominator.

To divide two fractions, multiply the first fraction by the reciprocal of the second fraction.

To divide with mixed numbers or whole numbers, first write any mixed or whole numbers as fractions and then divide as usual.

The reciprocal of $\frac{3}{5}$ is $\frac{5}{3}$.

Divide.

$$\frac{3}{10} \div \frac{7}{9} = \frac{3}{10} \cdot \frac{9}{7} = \frac{3 \cdot 9}{10 \cdot 7} = \frac{27}{70}$$

$$2\frac{5}{8} \div 3\frac{7}{16} = \frac{21}{8} \div \frac{55}{16} = \frac{21}{8} \cdot \frac{16}{55} = \frac{21 \cdot 16}{8 \cdot 55}$$

$$= \frac{21 \cdot 2 \cdot \overset{1}{\cancel{8}}}{\underset{1}{\cancel{8}} \cdot 55} = \frac{42}{55}$$

Section 2.6   Adding and Subtracting like Fractions

Fractions that have the same denominator are called **like fractions.**

To add or subtract like fractions, combine the numerators and place the sum or difference over the common denominator.

$\frac{1}{3}$ and $\frac{2}{3}$; $\frac{5}{7}$ and $\frac{6}{7}$

$\frac{2}{7} + \frac{3}{7} = \frac{5}{7}$ ← Add the numerators.
              ← Keep the common denominator.

$\frac{7}{8} - \frac{4}{8} = \frac{3}{8}$ ← Subtract the numerators.
              ← Keep the common denominator.

Section 2.7   Least Common Multiples

The **least common multiple (LCM)** is the smallest number that is a multiple of all numbers in a list of numbers.

METHOD 1 FOR FINDING THE LCM OF A LIST OF NUMBERS USING MULTIPLES

Step 1: Write the multiples of the largest number (starting with the number itself) until a multiple common to all numbers in the list is found.

Step 2: The multiple found in step 1 is the LCM.

The LCM of 2 and 6 is 6 because 6 is the smallest number that is a multiple of both 2 and 6.

Find the LCM of 4 and 6 using Method 1.

$6 \cdot 1 = 6$ Not a multiple of 4
$6 \cdot 2 = 12$ A multiple of 4

The LCM is 12.

(continued)

Definitions and Concepts	**Examples**

Section 2.7   Least Common Multiples (*continued*)

METHOD 2 FOR FINDING THE LCM OF A LIST OF NUMBERS USING PRIME FACTORIZATION	Find the LCM of 6 and 20 using Method 2.
Step 1: Write the prime factorization of each number.	$6 = 2 \cdot \boxed{3}$
Step 2: For each different prime factor in step 1, circle the greatest number of times that factor occurs in any one factorization.	$20 = \boxed{2 \cdot 2} \cdot \boxed{5}$ The LCM is
Step 3: The LCM is the product of the circled factors.	$2 \cdot 2 \cdot 3 \cdot 5 = 60$
Equivalent fractions represent the same portion of a whole.	Write an equivalent fraction with the indicated denominator. $\dfrac{2}{8} = \dfrac{}{16}$ $\dfrac{2 \cdot 2}{8 \cdot 2} = \dfrac{4}{16}$

Section 2.8   Adding and Subtracting Unlike Fractions

TO ADD OR SUBTRACT FRACTIONS WITH UNLIKE DENOMINATORS	Add: $\dfrac{3}{20} + \dfrac{2}{5}$
Step 1: Find the LCD.	**Step 1:** The LCD of 20 and 5 is 20.
Step 2: Write each fraction as an equivalent fraction whose denominator is the LCD.	**Step 2:** $\dfrac{3}{20} = \dfrac{3}{20}; \dfrac{2}{5} = \dfrac{2}{5} \cdot \dfrac{4}{4} = \dfrac{8}{20}$
Step 3: Add or subtract the like fractions.	**Step 3:** $\dfrac{3}{20} + \dfrac{2}{5} = \dfrac{3}{20} + \dfrac{8}{20} = \dfrac{11}{20}$
Step 4: Write the sum or difference in simplest form.	**Step 4:** $\dfrac{11}{20}$ is in simplest form.

Section 2.9   Adding and Subtracting Mixed Numbers

To add or subtract with mixed numbers, add or subtract the fractions and then add or subtract the whole numbers.	Add: $2\dfrac{1}{2} + 5\dfrac{7}{8}$ $2\dfrac{1}{2} = 2\dfrac{4}{8}$ $+5\dfrac{7}{8} = 5\dfrac{7}{8}$ $\rule{3cm}{0.4pt}$ $7\dfrac{11}{8} = 7 + 1\dfrac{3}{8} = 8\dfrac{3}{8}$

Section 2.10   Order, Exponents, and the Order of Operations

To compare like fractions, compare the numerators. The order of the fractions is the same as the order of the numerators.	Compare $\dfrac{3}{10}$ and $\dfrac{4}{10}$. $\dfrac{3}{10} < \dfrac{4}{10}$ since $3 < 4$

Definitions and Concepts	**Examples**

Section 2.10   Order, Exponents, and the Order of Operations (*continued*)

To compare unlike fractions, first write the fractions as like fractions. Then the fraction with the greater numerator is the greater fraction.

Compare $\dfrac{2}{5}$ and $\dfrac{3}{7}$.

$$\frac{2}{5} = \frac{2}{5} \cdot \frac{7}{7} = \frac{14}{35} \qquad \frac{3}{7} = \frac{3}{7} \cdot \frac{5}{5} = \frac{15}{35}$$

Since $14 < 15$, then

$$\frac{14}{35} < \frac{15}{35} \quad \text{or} \quad \frac{2}{5} < \frac{3}{7}$$

Exponents mean repeated multiplication whether the base is a whole number or a fraction.

$$\left(\frac{1}{2}\right)^3 = \frac{1}{2} \cdot \frac{1}{2} \cdot \frac{1}{2} = \frac{1}{8}$$

ORDER OF OPERATIONS

1. Perform all operations within parentheses ( ), brackets [ ], or other grouping symbols such as square roots or fraction bars.

Perform each indicated operation.

$$\frac{1}{2} + \frac{2}{3} \cdot \frac{1}{5} = \frac{1}{2} + \frac{2}{15} \qquad \text{Multiply.}$$

2. Evaluate any expressions with exponents.

$$= \frac{1}{2} \cdot \frac{15}{15} + \frac{2}{15} \cdot \frac{2}{2} \qquad \text{The LCD is 30.}$$

3. Multiply or divide in order from left to right.

$$= \frac{15}{30} + \frac{4}{30}$$

4. Add or subtract in order from left to right.

$$= \frac{19}{30} \qquad \text{Add.}$$

Section 2.11   Fractions and Problem Solving

PROBLEM-SOLVING STEPS

A stack of $\dfrac{3}{4}$-inch plywood has a height of $50\dfrac{1}{4}$ inches. How many sheets of plywood are in the stack?

1. UNDERSTAND the problem.

1. UNDERSTAND. Read and reread the problem. We want to know how many $\dfrac{3}{4}$'s are in $50\dfrac{1}{4}$, so we divide.

2. TRANSLATE the problem.

2. TRANSLATE.

number of sheets in stack	is	height of stack	÷	height of a sheet

$$\begin{array}{ccc} \text{number of sheets in stack} & = & 50\dfrac{1}{4} \quad \div \quad \dfrac{3}{4} \end{array}$$

3. SOLVE the problem.

3. SOLVE. $50\dfrac{1}{4} \div \dfrac{3}{4} = \dfrac{201}{4} \cdot \dfrac{4}{3}$

$$= \frac{\overset{67}{\cancel{201}} \cdot \overset{1}{\cancel{4}}}{\underset{1}{\cancel{4}} \cdot \underset{1}{\cancel{3}}}$$

$$= 67$$

4. INTERPRET the results.

4. INTERPRET. *Check* your work and *state* your conclusion: There are 67 sheets of plywood in the stack.

Chapter 2 Review

(2.1) *Determine whether each number is an improper fraction, a proper fraction, or a mixed number.*

1. $\frac{11}{23}$ **2.** $\frac{9}{8}$ **3.** $\frac{1}{2}$ **4.** $2\frac{1}{4}$

Write a fraction to represent the shaded area.

5.
6.
7.
8.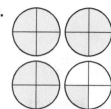

9. A basketball player made 11 free throws out of 12 during a game. What fraction of free throws did the player make?

10. A new car lot contained 23 blue cars out of a total of 131 cars.
   a. How many cars on the lot are not blue?
   b. What fraction of cars on the lot are not blue?

Write each improper fraction as a mixed number or a whole number.

11. $\frac{15}{4}$ **12.** $\frac{275}{6}$ **13.** $\frac{39}{13}$ **14.** $\frac{60}{12}$

Write each mixed number as an improper fraction.

15. $1\frac{1}{5}$ **16.** $1\frac{1}{21}$ **17.** $2\frac{8}{9}$ **18.** $3\frac{11}{12}$

(2.2) *Identify each number as prime or composite.*

19. 51 **20.** 17

List all factors of each number.

21. 42 **22.** 20

Find the prime factorization of each number.

23. 68 **24.** 90 **25.** 785 **26.** 255

(2.3) *Write each fraction in simplest form.*

27. $\frac{12}{28}$ **28.** $\frac{15}{27}$ **29.** $\frac{25}{75}$ **30.** $\frac{36}{72}$

31. $\frac{29}{32}$ **32.** $\frac{18}{23}$ **33.** $\frac{48}{6}$ **34.** $\frac{54}{9}$

Solve.

35. There are 12 inches in a foot. What fractional part of a foot does 8 inches represent?

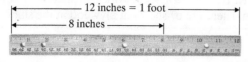

36. Six out of 15 cars are white. What fraction of the cars are *not* white?

212

Determine whether each two fractions are equivalent.

37. $\dfrac{10}{34}$ and $\dfrac{4}{14}$

38. $\dfrac{30}{50}$ and $\dfrac{9}{15}$

(2.4) *Multiply. Write each answer in simplest form. Estimate where noted.*

39. $\dfrac{3}{5} \cdot \dfrac{1}{2}$

40. $\dfrac{6}{7} \cdot \dfrac{5}{12}$

41. $\dfrac{24}{5} \cdot \dfrac{15}{8}$

42. $\dfrac{27}{21} \cdot \dfrac{7}{18}$

43. $5 \cdot \dfrac{7}{8}$

44. $6 \cdot \dfrac{5}{12}$

45. $\dfrac{39}{3} \cdot \dfrac{7}{13} \cdot \dfrac{5}{21}$

46. $\dfrac{42}{5} \cdot \dfrac{15}{6} \cdot \dfrac{7}{9}$

47. $1\dfrac{5}{8} \cdot 3\dfrac{1}{5}$

48. $3\dfrac{6}{11} \cdot 1\dfrac{7}{13}$

49. $\dfrac{3}{4} \cdot 8 \cdot 4\dfrac{1}{8}$

50. $2\dfrac{1}{9} \cdot 3 \cdot \dfrac{1}{38}$

Exact: Exact:

Estimate: Estimate:

51. There are $7\dfrac{1}{3}$ grams of fat in each ounce of hamburger. How many grams of fat are in a 5-ounce hamburger patty?

52. An art teacher needs 45 pieces of PVC piping for an art project. If each piece needs to be $\dfrac{3}{4}$ inch long, find the total length of piping she needs.

△ **53.** Find the area of each rectangle.

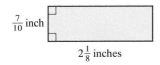

△ **54.**

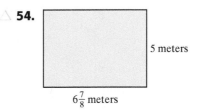

(2.5) *Find the reciprocal of each number.*

55. 7

56. $\dfrac{1}{8}$

57. $\dfrac{14}{23}$

58. $\dfrac{17}{5}$

Divide. Write each answer in simplest form.

59. $\dfrac{3}{4} \div \dfrac{3}{8}$

60. $\dfrac{21}{4} \div \dfrac{7}{5}$

61. $\dfrac{5}{3} \div 2$

62. $5 \div \dfrac{15}{8}$

63. $6\dfrac{3}{4} \div 1\dfrac{2}{7}$

64. $5\dfrac{1}{2} \div 2\dfrac{1}{11}$

65. A truck traveled 341 miles on $15\dfrac{1}{2}$ gallons of gas. How many miles might we expect the truck to travel on 1 gallon of gas?

66. Herman Heltznutt walks 5 days a week for a total distance of $5\dfrac{1}{4}$ miles per week. If he walks the same distance each day, find the distance he walks each day.

(2.6) *Add or subtract as indicated. Simplify your answers.*

67. $\dfrac{7}{11} + \dfrac{3}{11}$ **68.** $\dfrac{4}{50} + \dfrac{2}{50}$ **69.** $\dfrac{11}{15} - \dfrac{1}{15}$ **70.** $\dfrac{4}{21} - \dfrac{1}{21}$ **71.** $\dfrac{4}{15} + \dfrac{3}{15} + \dfrac{2}{15}$

72. $\dfrac{3}{20} + \dfrac{7}{20} + \dfrac{2}{20}$ **73.** $\dfrac{1}{12} + \dfrac{11}{12}$ **74.** $\dfrac{3}{4} + \dfrac{1}{4}$ **75.** $\dfrac{11}{25} + \dfrac{6}{25} + \dfrac{2}{25}$ **76.** $\dfrac{4}{21} + \dfrac{1}{21} + \dfrac{11}{21}$

Solve.

77. One evening Mark Alorenzo did $\dfrac{3}{8}$ of his homework before supper, another $\dfrac{2}{8}$ of it while his children did their homework, and $\dfrac{1}{8}$ after his children went to bed. What part of his homework did he do that evening?

△ **78.** The Simpsons will be fencing in their land, which is in the shape of a rectangle. In order to do this, they need to find its perimeter. Find the perimeter of their land.

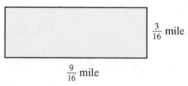

$\frac{3}{16}$ mile

$\frac{9}{16}$ mile

(2.7) *Find the LCM of each list of numbers.*

79. 5, 11   **80.** 20, 30   **81.** 20, 24   **82.** 16, 5   **83.** 12, 21, 63   **84.** 6, 8, 18

Write each fraction as an equivalent fraction with the given denominator.

85. $\dfrac{7}{8} = \dfrac{}{64}$ **86.** $\dfrac{2}{3} = \dfrac{}{30}$ **87.** $\dfrac{7}{11} = \dfrac{}{33}$ **88.** $\dfrac{10}{13} = \dfrac{}{26}$ **89.** $\dfrac{4}{15} = \dfrac{}{60}$ **90.** $\dfrac{5}{12} = \dfrac{}{60}$

(2.8) *Add or subtract as indicated. Simplify your answers.*

91. $\dfrac{7}{18} + \dfrac{2}{9}$ **92.** $\dfrac{4}{15} + \dfrac{1}{5}$ **93.** $\dfrac{4}{13} - \dfrac{1}{26}$ **94.** $\dfrac{7}{12} - \dfrac{1}{9}$

95. $\dfrac{1}{3} + \dfrac{9}{14}$ **96.** $\dfrac{7}{18} + \dfrac{5}{24}$ **97.** $\dfrac{11}{15} - \dfrac{4}{9}$ **98.** $\dfrac{9}{14} - \dfrac{3}{35}$

Find the perimeter of each figure.

△ **99.**

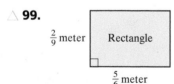

$\frac{2}{9}$ meter   Rectangle

$\frac{5}{6}$ meter

△ **100.**

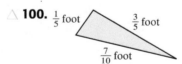

$\frac{1}{5}$ foot $\frac{3}{5}$ foot

$\frac{7}{10}$ foot

101. Find the difference in length of two scarves if one scarf is $\dfrac{5}{12}$ of a yard long and the other is $\dfrac{2}{3}$ of a yard long.

102. Truman Kalzote cleaned $\dfrac{3}{5}$ of his house yesterday and $\dfrac{1}{10}$ of it today. How much of the house has been cleaned?

(2.9) *Add or subtract as indicated. Simplify your answers.*

103. $31\dfrac{2}{7} + 14\dfrac{10}{21}$ **104.** $24\dfrac{4}{5} + 35\dfrac{1}{5}$ **105.** $69\dfrac{5}{22} - 36\dfrac{7}{11}$ **106.** $36\dfrac{3}{20} - 32\dfrac{5}{6}$

107. $29\dfrac{2}{9}$

$27\dfrac{7}{18}$

$+54\dfrac{2}{3}$

108. $7\dfrac{3}{8}$

$9\dfrac{5}{6}$

$+3\dfrac{1}{12}$

109. $9\dfrac{3}{5}$

$-4\dfrac{1}{7}$

110. $8\dfrac{3}{11}$

$-5\dfrac{1}{5}$

Solve.

111. The average annual snowfall at a certain ski resort is $62\dfrac{3}{10}$ inches. Last year it had $54\dfrac{1}{2}$ inches. How many inches below average was last year's snowfall?

112. Dinah's homemade canned peaches contain $15\dfrac{3}{5}$ ounces per can. A can of Amy's brand contains $15\dfrac{5}{8}$ ounces per can. Amy's brand weighs how much more than Dinah's?

△**113.** Find the perimeter of a sheet of shelf paper needed to fit exactly a square drawer $1\dfrac{1}{4}$ feet long on each side.

$1\frac{1}{4}$ feet

△**114.** Find the perimeter of a rectangular sheet of gift wrap that is $2\dfrac{1}{4}$ feet by $3\dfrac{1}{3}$ feet.

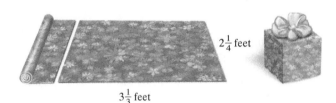

$2\frac{1}{4}$ feet

$3\frac{1}{3}$ feet

(2.10) *Insert < or > to form a true statement.*

115. $\dfrac{5}{11}$ $\quad$ $\dfrac{6}{11}$

116. $\dfrac{4}{35}$ $\quad$ $\dfrac{3}{35}$

117. $\dfrac{5}{14}$ $\quad$ $\dfrac{16}{42}$

118. $\dfrac{6}{35}$ $\quad$ $\dfrac{17}{105}$

119. $\dfrac{7}{8}$ $\quad$ $\dfrac{6}{7}$

120. $\dfrac{7}{10}$ $\quad$ $\dfrac{2}{3}$

Evaluate each expression. Use the order of operations to simplify.

121. $\left(\dfrac{3}{7}\right)^2$

122. $\left(\dfrac{4}{5}\right)^3$

123. $\left(\dfrac{1}{2}\right)^4 \cdot \left(\dfrac{3}{5}\right)^2$

124. $\left(\dfrac{1}{3}\right)^2 \cdot \left(\dfrac{9}{10}\right)^2$

125. $\dfrac{5}{13} \div \dfrac{1}{2} \cdot \dfrac{4}{5}$

126. $\dfrac{8}{11} \div \dfrac{1}{3} \cdot \dfrac{11}{12}$

127. $\left(\dfrac{6}{7} - \dfrac{3}{14}\right)^2$

128. $\left(\dfrac{1}{3}\right)^2 - \dfrac{2}{27}$

129. $\dfrac{8}{9} - \dfrac{1}{8} \div \dfrac{3}{4}$

130. $\dfrac{9}{10} - \dfrac{1}{9} \div \dfrac{2}{3}$

131. $\dfrac{2}{7} \cdot \left(\dfrac{1}{5} + \dfrac{3}{10} \right)$

132. $\dfrac{9}{10} \div \left(\dfrac{1}{5} + \dfrac{1}{20} \right)$

133. $\left(\dfrac{3}{4} + \dfrac{1}{2} \right) \div \left(\dfrac{4}{9} + \dfrac{1}{3} \right)$

134. $\left(\dfrac{3}{8} - \dfrac{1}{16} \right) \div \left(\dfrac{1}{2} - \dfrac{1}{8} \right)$

135. $\dfrac{6}{7} \cdot \dfrac{5}{2} - \dfrac{3}{4} \cdot \dfrac{1}{2}$

136. $\dfrac{9}{10} \cdot \dfrac{1}{3} - \dfrac{2}{5} \cdot \dfrac{1}{11}$

Find the average of each list of fractions.

137. $\dfrac{2}{3}, \dfrac{5}{6}, \dfrac{1}{9}$

138. $\dfrac{4}{5}, \dfrac{9}{10}, \dfrac{3}{20}$

(2.11)

139. Saturn has 28 moons. The planet Uranus has only $\dfrac{3}{4}$ as many. Find the number of moons for Uranus. (*Source:* NASA)

140. James Hardaway just bought $5\dfrac{7}{8}$ acres of land adjacent to the $9\dfrac{3}{4}$ acres he already owned. How much land does he now own?

Find the unknown measurements.

△**141.**

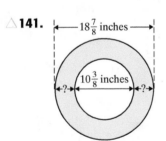

△**142.**

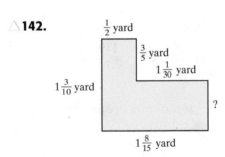

Find the perimeter and area of each rectangle. Attach the proper units to each. Remember that perimeter is measured in units and area is measured in square units.

△**143.** $\frac{1}{2}$ mile

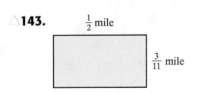

$\frac{3}{11}$ mile

△**144.** $\frac{5}{12}$ meter

$\frac{3}{4}$ meter

Answers to Selected Exercises

Chapter 2 Fractions

Section 2.1

Vocabulary and Readiness Check **1.** fraction; denominator; numerator **3.** improper; proper; mixed number

Exercise Set 2.1 1. numerator: 1; denominator: 2; proper **3.** numerator: 10; denominator: 3; improper **5.** numerator: 15; denominator: 15; improper

7. 1 **9.** undefined **11.** 13 **13.** 0 **15.** undefined **17.** 16 **19.** $\frac{5}{6}$ **21.** $\frac{7}{12}$ **23.** $\frac{3}{7}$ **25.** $\frac{4}{9}$ **27.** $\frac{1}{6}$ **29.** $\frac{5}{8}$ **31.**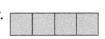

33.  **35.** ⊘⊘⊘⊘⊘⊘◯ **37.** ▦▦▦▦ **39.** $\frac{42}{131}$ **41. a.** 89 **b.** $\frac{89}{131}$ **43.** $\frac{7}{44}$

45. $\frac{15}{28}$ of the tropical storms **47.** $\frac{11}{31}$ of the month **49.** $\frac{10}{31}$ of the class **51. a.** $\frac{33}{50}$ of the states **b.** 17 states **c.** $\frac{17}{50}$ of the states

53. a. $\frac{21}{50}$ **b.** 29 **c.** $\frac{29}{50}$ **55. a.** $\frac{11}{4}$ **b.** $2\frac{3}{4}$ **57. a.** $\frac{23}{6}$ **b.** $3\frac{5}{6}$ **59. a.** $\frac{4}{3}$ **b.** $1\frac{1}{3}$ **61. a.** $\frac{11}{2}$ **b.** $5\frac{1}{2}$ **63.** $\frac{7}{3}$ **65.** $\frac{18}{5}$ **67.** $\frac{53}{8}$ **69.** $\frac{41}{15}$

71. $\frac{83}{7}$ **73.** $\frac{84}{13}$ **75.** $\frac{109}{24}$ **77.** $\frac{211}{12}$ **79.** $\frac{187}{20}$ **81.** $\frac{265}{107}$ **83.** $\frac{500}{3}$ **85.** $3\frac{2}{5}$ **87.** $4\frac{5}{8}$ **89.** $3\frac{2}{15}$ **91.** $2\frac{4}{21}$ **93.** 33 **95.** 15

97. $66\frac{2}{3}$ **99.** $10\frac{17}{23}$ **101.** $17\frac{13}{18}$ **103.** $1\frac{7}{175}$ **105.** $6\frac{65}{112}$ **107.** 9 **109.** 125 **111.** 7^5 **113.** $2^3 \cdot 3$ **115.** answers may vary **117.** $\frac{2}{3}$

119. ◯◯◯◯◯◯◯◯◯ **121.** $\frac{576}{3167}$ of the stores **123.** $\frac{1700}{2250}$ of the affiliates

Section 2.2

Vocabulary and Readiness Check **1.** prime factorization **3.** prime **5.** factors

Exercise Set 2.2 1. 1, 2, 4, 8 **3.** 1, 5, 25 **5.** 1, 2, 4 **7.** 1, 2, 3, 6, 9, 18 **9.** 1, 29 **11.** 1, 2, 4, 5, 8, 10, 16, 20, 40, 80 **13.** 1, 2, 3, 4, 6, 12 **15.** 1, 2, 17, 34
17. prime **19.** composite **21.** prime **23.** composite **25.** prime **27.** composite **29.** prime **31.** composite **33.** composite **35.** 2^5 **37.** $3 \cdot 5$
39. $2^3 \cdot 5$ **41.** $2^2 \cdot 3^2$ **43.** $3 \cdot 13$ **45.** $2^2 \cdot 3 \cdot 5$ **47.** $2 \cdot 5 \cdot 11$ **49.** $5 \cdot 17$ **51.** 2^7 **53.** $2 \cdot 7 \cdot 11$ **55.** $2^2 \cdot 3 \cdot 5^2$ **57.** $2^4 \cdot 3 \cdot 5$ **59.** $2^2 \cdot 3^2 \cdot 23$ **61.** $2 \cdot 3^2 \cdot 7^2$
63. $7^2 \cdot 13$ **65.** $3 \cdot 11$ **67.** $2 \cdot 7^2$ **69.** prime **71.** $3^3 \cdot 17$ **73.** prime **75.** $2^2 \cdot 5^2 \cdot 7$ **77.** 4300 **79.** 7,660,000 **81.** 20,000 **83.** 159 **85.** $\frac{27}{159}$
87. $2^2 \cdot 3^5 \cdot 5 \cdot 7$ **89.** answers may vary **91.** answers may vary

Section 2.3

Calculator Explorations **1.** $\frac{4}{7}$ **3.** $\frac{20}{27}$ **5.** $\frac{15}{8}$ **7.** $\frac{9}{2}$

Vocabulary and Readiness Check **1.** simplest form **3.** cross products **5.** 0

Exercise Set 2.3 1. $\frac{1}{4}$ **3.** $\frac{2}{21}$ **5.** $\frac{7}{8}$ **7.** $\frac{2}{3}$ **9.** $\frac{7}{10}$ **11.** $\frac{7}{9}$ **13.** $\frac{3}{5}$ **15.** $\frac{27}{64}$ **17.** $\frac{5}{8}$ **19.** $\frac{5}{8}$ **21.** $\frac{14}{17}$ **23.** $\frac{3}{2}$ or $1\frac{1}{2}$ **25.** $\frac{3}{4}$ **27.** $\frac{5}{14}$ **29.** $\frac{3}{14}$
31. $\frac{11}{17}$ **33.** $\frac{3}{14}$ **35.** $\frac{7}{8}$ **37.** $\frac{3}{5}$ **39.** 14 **41.** equivalent **43.** not equivalent **45.** equivalent **47.** equivalent **49.** not equivalent
51. not equivalent **53.** $\frac{1}{4}$ of a shift **55.** $\frac{1}{2}$ mi **57. a.** $\frac{8}{25}$ **b.** 34 states **c.** $\frac{17}{25}$ **59.** $\frac{5}{12}$ of the wall **61. a.** 18 **b.** $\frac{9}{25}$ **63.** $\frac{11}{160}$ of U.S. astronauts
65. 364 **67.** 2322 **69.** 2520 **71.** answers may vary **73.** $\frac{3}{5}$ **75.** $\frac{9}{25}$ **77.** $\frac{1}{25}$ **79.** $\frac{1}{10}$ **81.** answers may vary **83.** $\frac{2}{25}$ **85.** answers may vary
87. 786, 222, 900, 1470 **89.** 6; answers may vary

Section 2.4

Vocabulary and Readiness Check **1.** $\frac{a \cdot c}{b \cdot d}$ **3.** multiplication

Exercise Set 2.4 1. $\frac{2}{15}$ **3.** $\frac{6}{35}$ **5.** $\frac{9}{80}$ **7.** $\frac{5}{28}$ **9.** $\frac{12}{5}$ or $2\frac{2}{5}$ **11.** $\frac{1}{70}$ **13.** 0 **15.** $\frac{1}{110}$ **17.** $\frac{18}{55}$ **19.** $\frac{27}{80}$ **21.** $\frac{1}{56}$ **23.** $\frac{2}{105}$ **25.** 0 **27.** $\frac{1}{90}$
29. 8 **31.** 6 **33.** 20 **35.** 3 **37.** $\frac{5}{2}$ or $2\frac{1}{2}$ **39.** $\frac{1}{5}$ **41.** $\frac{5}{3}$ or $1\frac{2}{3}$ **43.** $\frac{2}{3}$ **45.** Exact: $\frac{77}{10}$ or $7\frac{7}{10}$; Estimate: 8 **47.** Exact: $\frac{836}{35}$ or $23\frac{31}{35}$; Estimate: 24
49. $\frac{25}{2}$ or $21\frac{1}{2}$ **51.** 15 **53.** 6 **55.** $\frac{45}{4}$ or $11\frac{1}{4}$ **57.** $\frac{49}{3}$ or $16\frac{1}{3}$ **59.** $\frac{1}{30}$ **61.** 0 **63.** $\frac{16}{5}$ or $3\frac{1}{5}$ **65.** $\frac{7}{2}$ or $3\frac{1}{2}$ **67.** $\frac{1}{8}$ **69.** $\frac{1}{56}$ **71.** $\frac{55}{3}$ or $18\frac{1}{3}$

73. 0 **75.** $\frac{208}{7}$ or $29\frac{5}{7}$ **77.** 50 **79.** 20 **81.** 128 **83.** 49 million **85.** 868 mi **87.** $\frac{3}{16}$ in. **89.** 30 gal **91.** $\frac{17}{2}$ or $8\frac{1}{2}$ in. **93.** $\frac{39}{2}$ or $19\frac{1}{2}$ in.

95. $\frac{2242}{625}$ or $3\frac{367}{625}$ sq in. **97.** $\frac{1}{14}$ sq ft **99.** $\frac{7}{2}$ or $3\frac{1}{2}$ sq yd **101.** 3840 mi **103.** 2400 mi **105.** 206 **107.** 56 R 12 **109.** answers may vary

111. $3\frac{2}{3} \cdot 1\frac{1}{7} = \frac{11}{3} \cdot \frac{8}{7} = \frac{11 \cdot 8}{3 \cdot 7} = \frac{88}{21}$ or $4\frac{4}{21}$ **113.** b **115.** a **117.** 37 **119.** $87\frac{3}{5}$ million households

Section 2.5

Vocabulary and Readiness Check **1.** reciprocals **3.** $\frac{a \cdot d}{b \cdot c}$

Exercise Set 2.5 **1.** $\frac{7}{4}$ **3.** 11 **5.** $\frac{1}{15}$ **7.** $\frac{7}{12}$ **9.** $\frac{4}{5}$ **11.** $\frac{16}{9}$ or $1\frac{7}{9}$ **13.** $\frac{18}{35}$ **15.** $\frac{3}{4}$ **17.** $\frac{1}{100}$ **19.** $\frac{1}{3}$ **21.** $\frac{5}{3}$ or $1\frac{2}{3}$ **23.** $\frac{35}{36}$ **25.** $\frac{14}{37}$ **27.** $\frac{8}{45}$ **29.** 1

31. undefined **33.** 0 **35.** $\frac{7}{10}$ **37.** $\frac{1}{6}$ **39.** $\frac{40}{3}$ or $13\frac{1}{3}$ **41.** 5 **43.** $\frac{5}{28}$ **45.** $\frac{36}{35}$ or $1\frac{1}{35}$ **47.** $\frac{26}{51}$ **49.** 0 **51.** $\frac{17}{13}$ or $1\frac{4}{13}$ **53.** $\frac{35}{18}$ or $1\frac{17}{18}$ **55.** $\frac{19}{30}$

57. $\frac{1}{6}$ **59.** $\frac{121}{60}$ or $2\frac{1}{60}$ **61.** 96 **63.** $\frac{3}{4}$ **65.** undefined **67.** $\frac{11}{119}$ **69.** $\frac{35}{11}$ or $3\frac{2}{11}$ **71.** $\frac{9}{5}$ or $1\frac{4}{5}$ **73.** $3\frac{3}{16}$ miles **75.** $\frac{5}{6}$ Tbsp **77.** $\frac{19}{30}$ in. **79.** 14 lb

81. $4\frac{2}{3}$ m **83.** $\frac{8}{35}$ **85.** $\frac{128}{51}$ or $2\frac{26}{51}$ **87.** $\frac{16}{15}$ or $1\frac{1}{15}$ **89.** $\frac{121}{400}$ **91.** 201 **93.** 196 **95.** 1569 **97.** $20\frac{2}{3} \div 10\frac{1}{2} = \frac{62}{3} \div \frac{21}{2} = \frac{62}{3} \cdot \frac{2}{21} = \frac{124}{63}$ or $1\frac{61}{63}$

99. c **101.** d **103.** 5 **105.** 654 aircraft **107.** answers may vary

Section 2.6

Vocabulary and Readiness Check **1.** like; unlike **3.** $\frac{a - c}{b}$ **5.** unlike **7.** like **9.** like **11.** unlike

Exercise Set 2.6 **1.** $\frac{3}{7}$ **3.** $\frac{1}{5}$ **5.** $\frac{2}{3}$ **7.** $\frac{7}{20}$ **9.** $\frac{1}{2}$ **11.** $\frac{13}{11}$ or $1\frac{2}{11}$ **13.** $\frac{7}{13}$ **15.** $\frac{2}{3}$ **17.** $\frac{6}{11}$ **19.** $\frac{3}{5}$ **21.** 1 **23.** $\frac{3}{4}$ **25.** $\frac{5}{6}$ **27.** $\frac{4}{5}$ **29.** $\frac{1}{90}$ **31.** $\frac{19}{33}$

33. $\frac{13}{21}$ **35.** $\frac{9}{10}$ **37.** 0 **39.** $\frac{3}{4}$ **41.** 1 in. **43.** 2 m **45.** $\frac{7}{10}$ mi **47.** $\frac{3}{2}$ or $1\frac{1}{2}$ h **49.** $\frac{9}{24} = \frac{3}{8}$ **51.** $\frac{2}{24} = \frac{1}{12}$ **53.** $\frac{13}{100}$ **55.** $\frac{2}{5}$ **57.** $\frac{7}{25}$ **59.** $\frac{1}{50}$

61. $\frac{1}{4}$ **63.** $2 \cdot 5$ **65.** 2^3 **67.** $5 \cdot 11$ **69.** $\frac{5}{8}$ **71.** $\frac{8}{11}$ **73.** $\frac{2}{7} + \frac{9}{7} = \frac{11}{7}$ or $1\frac{4}{7}$ **75.** answers may vary **77.** 1; answers may vary **79.** $\frac{1}{4}$ of a mi

Section 2.7

Vocabulary and Readiness Check **1.** equivalent **3.** multiple

Exercise Set 2.7 **1.** 12 **3.** 45 **5.** 36 **7.** 72 **9.** 126 **11.** 75 **13.** 24 **15.** 42 **17.** 216 **19.** 150 **21.** 68 **23.** 588 **25.** 900 **27.** 1800

29. 363 **31.** 60 **33.** $\frac{20}{35}$ **35.** $\frac{14}{21}$ **37.** $\frac{15}{3}$ **39.** $\frac{15}{30}$ **41.** $\frac{30}{21}$ **43.** $\frac{21}{28}$ **45.** $\frac{30}{45}$ **47.** $\frac{36}{81}$ **49.** $\frac{90}{78}$ **51.** $\frac{56}{68}$ **53.** $\frac{54}{100}, \frac{50}{100}, \frac{46}{100}, \frac{50}{100}, \frac{15}{100}, \frac{65}{100}, \frac{45}{100},$

$\frac{52}{100}, \frac{60}{100}, \frac{61}{100}, \frac{48}{100}, \frac{50}{100}$ **55.** drugs, health and beauty aids **57.** $\frac{1}{2}$ **59.** $\frac{2}{5}$ **61.** $\frac{4}{9}$ **63.** 1 **65.** $\frac{814}{3630}$ **67.** answers may vary **69.** a, b, and d

Section 2.8

Calculator Explorations **1.** $\frac{37}{80}$ **3.** $\frac{95}{72}$ **5.** $\frac{394}{323}$

Vocabulary and Readiness Check **1.** equivalent; least common denominator **3.** $\frac{15}{24} + \frac{4}{24} + \frac{19}{24}$

Exercise Set 2.8 **1.** $\frac{5}{6}$ **3.** $\frac{5}{6}$ **5.** $\frac{8}{33}$ **7.** $\frac{9}{14}$ **9.** $\frac{3}{5}$ **11.** $\frac{13}{25}$ **13.** $\frac{53}{60}$ **15.** $\frac{1}{6}$ **17.** $\frac{67}{99}$ **19.** $\frac{98}{143}$ **21.** $\frac{13}{27}$ **23.** $\frac{75}{56}$ or $1\frac{19}{56}$ **25.** $\frac{19}{18}$ or $1\frac{1}{18}$

27. $\frac{19}{12}$ or $1\frac{7}{12}$ **29.** $\frac{11}{16}$ **31.** $\frac{17}{42}$ **33.** $\frac{33}{56}$ **35.** $\frac{37}{99}$ **37.** $\frac{1}{35}$ **39.** $\frac{11}{36}$ **41.** $\frac{1}{20}$ **43.** $\frac{1}{84}$ **45.** $\frac{9}{1000}$ **47.** $\frac{17}{99}$ **49.** $\frac{19}{36}$ **51.** $\frac{1}{5}$ **53.** $\frac{69}{280}$

55. $\frac{14}{9}$ or $1\frac{5}{9}$ **57.** $\frac{34}{15}$ or $2\frac{4}{15}$ cm **59.** $\frac{17}{10}$ or $1\frac{7}{10}$ m **61.** $\frac{7}{100}$ mph **63.** $\frac{5}{8}$ in. **65.** $\frac{31}{32}$ in. **67.** $\frac{19}{100}$ of Girl Scout cookies **69.** $\frac{19}{25}$ **71.** $\frac{1}{25}$

73. $\frac{79}{100}$ **75.** 5 **77.** $\frac{16}{29}$ **79.** $\frac{19}{3}$ or $6\frac{1}{3}$ **81.** $\frac{3}{5} + \frac{4}{5} = \frac{7}{5}$ or $1\frac{2}{5}$ **83.** $\frac{223}{540}$ **85.** $\frac{49}{44}$ or $1\frac{5}{44}$ **87.** answers may vary

Section 2.9

Vocabulary and Readiness Check **1.** mixed number **3.** round **5.** a **7.** c

Exercise Set 2.9 **1.** Exact: $6\frac{4}{5}$; Estimate: 7 **3.** Exact: $13\frac{11}{14}$; Estimate: 14 **5.** $17\frac{7}{25}$ **7.** $7\frac{5}{8}$ **9.** $7\frac{5}{24}$ **11.** $20\frac{1}{15}$ **13.** 19 **15.** $56\frac{53}{270}$ **17.** $13\frac{13}{24}$

19. $47\frac{53}{84}$ **21.** Exact: $2\frac{3}{5}$; Estimate: 3 **23.** Exact: $7\frac{5}{14}$; Estimate: 7 **25.** $\frac{24}{25}$ **27.** $2\frac{7}{15}$ **29.** $5\frac{11}{14}$ **31.** $23\frac{31}{72}$ **33.** $1\frac{4}{5}$ **35.** $1\frac{13}{15}$ **37.** $3\frac{5}{9}$

39. $15\frac{3}{4}$ **41.** $28\frac{7}{12}$ **43.** $15\frac{7}{8}$ **45.** 8 **47.** $17\frac{11}{12}$ **49.** $\frac{1}{16}$ in. **51.** no; she will be $\frac{1}{12}$ of a foot short **53.** $7\frac{13}{20}$ in. **55.** $10\frac{1}{4}$ hr **57.** $2\frac{3}{8}$ hr **59.** $92\frac{99}{100}$ m **61.** $352\frac{1}{3}$ yd **63.** $9\frac{13}{30}$ min **65.** $1\frac{4}{5}$ min **67.** 7 mi **69.** $21\frac{5}{24}$ m **71.** 8 **73.** 25 **75.** 4 **77.** 167 **79.** 4 **81.** $9\frac{5}{8}$ **83.** a, b, c **85.** answers may vary **87.** Supreme is heavier by $\frac{1}{8}$ lb

Section 2.10

Vocabulary and Readiness Check **1.** multiplication **3.** subtraction

Exercise Set 2.10 **1.** > **3.** < **5.** < **7.** > **9.** > **11.** < **13.** > **15.** < **17.** $\frac{1}{16}$ **19.** $\frac{8}{125}$ **21.** $\frac{64}{343}$ **23.** $\frac{4}{81}$ **25.** $\frac{1}{6}$ **27.** $\frac{18}{125}$ **29.** $\frac{11}{15}$ **31.** $\frac{3}{35}$ **33.** $\frac{5}{9}$ **35.** $10\frac{4}{99}$ **37.** $\frac{1}{12}$ **39.** $\frac{9}{11}$ **41.** 0 **43.** 0 **45.** $\frac{2}{5}$ **47.** $\frac{2}{77}$ **49.** $\frac{17}{60}$ **51.** $\frac{5}{8}$ **53.** $\frac{1}{2}$ **55.** $\frac{29}{10}$ or $2\frac{9}{10}$ **57.** $\frac{27}{32}$ **59.** $\frac{1}{81}$ **61.** $\frac{5}{6}$ **63.** $\frac{3}{5}$ **65.** $\frac{1}{2}$ **67.** $\frac{19}{7}$ or $2\frac{5}{7}$ **69.** $\frac{9}{64}$ **71.** $\frac{3}{4}$ **73.** $\frac{13}{60}$ **75.** $\frac{13}{25}$ **77.** A **79.** M **81.** S **83.** D **85.** M **87.** A **89.** no; answers may vary **91.** subtraction, multiplication, addition, division **93.** division, multiplication, subtraction, addition **95.** standard mail **97.** New York

Section 2.11

Exercise Set 2.11 **1.** $\frac{1}{2} + \frac{1}{3}$ **3.** $20 \div 6\frac{2}{5}$ **5.** $\frac{15}{16} - \frac{5}{8}$ **7.** $\frac{21}{68} + \frac{7}{34}$ **9.** $8\frac{1}{3} \cdot \frac{7}{9}$ **11.** $3\frac{1}{3}$ c **13.** $12\frac{1}{2}$ in. **15.** $21\frac{1}{2}$ mi per gal **17.** $1\frac{1}{2}$ yr **19.** $9\frac{2}{5}$ in. **21.** no; $\frac{1}{4}$ yd **23.** 5 pieces **25.** $\frac{9}{8}$ or $1\frac{1}{8}$ in. **27.** $3\frac{3}{4}$ c **29.** $11\frac{1}{4}$ sq in. **31.** $1\frac{3}{10}$ min **33.** $5\frac{11}{25}$ cu in. **35.** 67 sheets **37.** a. yes b. 1 ft left over **39.** $2\frac{15}{16}$ lb **41.** area: $\frac{9}{128}$ sq in.; perimeter: $1\frac{1}{8}$ in. **43.** area: $\frac{25}{81}$ sq m; perimeter: $2\frac{2}{9}$ m **45.** $4\frac{3}{4}$ ft **47.** $\frac{5}{26}$ ft **49.** 3 **51.** 81 **53.** 4 **55.** 30 **57.** 35 **59.** no; no; answers may vary **61.** $36\frac{44}{81}$ sq ft **63.** 68 customers **65.** 22 hr

Chapter 2 Review **1.** proper **2.** improper **3.** proper **4.** mixed number **5.** $\frac{2}{6}$ **6.** $\frac{4}{7}$ **7.** $\frac{7}{3}$ **8.** $\frac{13}{4}$ **9.** $\frac{11}{12}$ **10.** a. 108 b. $\frac{108}{131}$ **11.** $3\frac{3}{4}$ **12.** $45\frac{5}{6}$ **13.** 3 **14.** 5 **15.** $\frac{6}{5}$ **16.** $\frac{22}{21}$ **17.** $\frac{26}{9}$ **18.** $\frac{47}{12}$ **19.** composite **20.** prime **21.** 1, 2, 3, 6, 7, 14, 21, 42 **22.** 1, 2, 4, 5, 10, 20 **23.** $2^2 \cdot 17$ **24.** $2 \cdot 3^2 \cdot 5$ **25.** $5 \cdot 157$ **26.** $3 \cdot 5 \cdot 17$ **27.** $\frac{3}{7}$ **28.** $\frac{5}{9}$ **29.** $\frac{1}{3}$ **30.** $\frac{1}{2}$ **31.** $\frac{29}{32}$ **32.** $\frac{18}{23}$ **33.** 8 **34.** 6 **35.** $\frac{2}{3}$ of a foot **36.** $\frac{3}{5}$ of the cars **37.** no **38.** yes **39.** $\frac{3}{10}$ **40.** $\frac{5}{14}$ **41.** 9 **42.** $\frac{1}{2}$ **43.** $\frac{35}{8}$ or $4\frac{3}{8}$ **44.** $\frac{5}{2}$ or $2\frac{1}{2}$ **45.** $\frac{5}{3}$ or $1\frac{2}{3}$ **46.** $\frac{49}{3}$ or $16\frac{1}{3}$ **47.** Exact: $\frac{26}{5}$ or $5\frac{1}{5}$; Estimate: 6 **48.** Exact: $\frac{60}{11}$ or $5\frac{5}{11}$; Estimate: 8 **49.** $\frac{99}{4}$ or $24\frac{3}{4}$ **50.** $\frac{1}{6}$ **51.** $\frac{110}{3}$ or $36\frac{2}{3}$ g **52.** $\frac{135}{4}$ or $33\frac{3}{4}$ in. **53.** $\frac{119}{80}$ or $1\frac{39}{80}$ sq in. **54.** $\frac{275}{8}$ or $34\frac{3}{8}$ sq m **55.** $\frac{1}{7}$ **56.** 8 **57.** $\frac{23}{14}$ **58.** $\frac{5}{17}$ **59.** 2 **60.** $\frac{15}{4}$ or $3\frac{3}{4}$ **61.** $\frac{5}{6}$ **62.** $\frac{8}{3}$ or $2\frac{2}{3}$ **63.** $\frac{21}{4}$ or $5\frac{1}{4}$ **64.** $\frac{121}{46}$ or $2\frac{29}{46}$ **65.** 22 mi **66.** $\frac{21}{20}$ or $1\frac{1}{20}$ mi **67.** $\frac{10}{11}$ **68.** $\frac{3}{25}$ **69.** $\frac{2}{3}$ **70.** $\frac{1}{7}$ **71.** $\frac{3}{5}$ **72.** $\frac{3}{5}$ **73.** 1 **74.** 1 **75.** $\frac{19}{25}$ **76.** $\frac{16}{21}$ **77.** $\frac{3}{4}$ of his homework **78.** $\frac{3}{2}$ or $1\frac{1}{2}$ mi **79.** 55 **80.** 60 **81.** 120 **82.** 80 **83.** 252 **84.** 72 **85.** $\frac{56}{64}$ **86.** $\frac{20}{30}$ **87.** $\frac{21}{33}$ **88.** $\frac{20}{26}$ **89.** $\frac{16}{60}$ **90.** $\frac{25}{60}$ **91.** $\frac{11}{18}$ **92.** $\frac{7}{15}$ **93.** $\frac{7}{26}$ **94.** $\frac{17}{36}$ **95.** $\frac{41}{42}$ **96.** $\frac{43}{72}$ **97.** $\frac{13}{45}$ **98.** $\frac{39}{70}$ **99.** $\frac{19}{9}$ or $2\frac{1}{9}$ m **100.** $\frac{3}{2}$ or $1\frac{1}{2}$ ft **101.** $\frac{1}{4}$ of a yd **102.** $\frac{7}{10}$ has been cleaned **103.** $45\frac{16}{21}$ **104.** 60 **105.** $32\frac{13}{22}$ **106.** $3\frac{19}{60}$ **107.** $111\frac{5}{18}$ **108.** $20\frac{7}{24}$ **109.** $5\frac{16}{35}$ **110.** $3\frac{4}{55}$ **111.** $7\frac{4}{5}$ in. **112.** $11\frac{1}{6}$ ft **113.** 5 ft **114.** $\frac{1}{40}$ oz **115.** < **116.** > **117.** < **118.** < **119.** > **120.** > **121.** $\frac{9}{49}$ **122.** $\frac{64}{125}$ **123.** $\frac{9}{400}$ **124.** $\frac{9}{100}$ **125.** $\frac{8}{13}$ **126.** 2 **127.** $\frac{81}{196}$ **128.** $\frac{1}{7}$ **129.** $\frac{13}{18}$ **130.** $\frac{11}{15}$ **131.** $\frac{1}{7}$ **132.** $\frac{18}{5}$ or $3\frac{3}{5}$ **133.** $\frac{45}{28}$ or $1\frac{17}{28}$ **134.** $\frac{5}{6}$ **135.** $\frac{99}{56}$ or $1\frac{43}{56}$ **136.** $\frac{29}{110}$ **137.** $\frac{29}{54}$ **138.** $\frac{37}{60}$ **139.** 21 moons **140.** $15\frac{5}{8}$ acres **141.** each measurement is $4\frac{1}{4}$ in. **142.** $\frac{7}{10}$ yd **143.** perimeter: $1\frac{6}{11}$ mi; area: $\frac{3}{22}$ sq mi **144.** perimeter: $2\frac{1}{3}$ m; area: $\frac{5}{16}$ sq m

Decimals

3

Objectives

Helpful Hint   Notice that place values to the left of the decimal point end in "s." Place values to the right of the decimal point end in "ths."

3.1 INTRODUCTION TO DECIMALS

Objective Ⓐ Decimal Notation and Writing Decimals in Words

Like fractional notation, decimal notation is used to denote a part of a whole. Numbers written in decimal notation are called **decimal numbers,** or simply **decimals.** The decimal 17.758 has three parts.

$$1\ 7\ .\ 7\ 5\ 8$$

Whole number part   ↑ Decimal part

Decimal point

In Section 1.2, we introduced place value for whole numbers. Place names and place values for the whole number part of a decimal number are exactly the same, as shown next. Place names and place values for the decimal part are also shown.

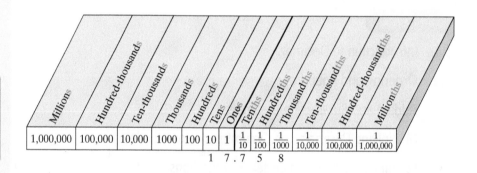

Millions	Hundred-thousands	Ten-thousands	Thousands	Hundreds	Tens	Ones	Tenths	Hundredths	Thousandths	Ten-thousandths	Hundred-thousandths	Millionths
1,000,000	100,000	10,000	1000	100	10	1	$\frac{1}{10}$	$\frac{1}{100}$	$\frac{1}{1000}$	$\frac{1}{10,000}$	$\frac{1}{100,000}$	$\frac{1}{1,000,000}$

$$1\ 7\ .\ 7\ \ 5\ \ 8$$

Notice that the value of each place is $\frac{1}{10}$ of the value of the place to its left. For example,

$$1 \cdot \frac{1}{10} = \frac{1}{10}$$
↑ ones   ↑ tenths

$$\frac{1}{10} \cdot \frac{1}{10} = \frac{1}{100}$$
↑ tenths   ↑ hundredths

The decimal number 17.758 means

1 ten	+	7 ones	+	7 tenths	+	5 hundredths	+	8 thousandths
↓	↓	↓	↓	↓	↓	↓	↓	↓
or $1 \cdot 10$ +		$7 \cdot 1$ +		$7 \cdot \frac{1}{10}$ +		$5 \cdot \frac{1}{100}$ +		$8 \cdot \frac{1}{1000}$
or 10 +		7 +		$\frac{7}{10}$ +		$\frac{5}{100}$ +		$\frac{8}{1000}$

Writing (or Reading) a Decimal in Words

Step 1: Write the whole number part in words.

Step 2: Write "and" for the decimal point.

Step 3: Write the decimal part in words as though it were a whole number, followed by the place value of the last digit.

Example 1 Write the decimal 1.3 in words.

Solution: one and three tenths

Work Practice 1

PRACTICE 1

Write the decimal 8.7 in words.

Example 2

Write the decimal in the following sentence in words: The Golden Jubilee Diamond is a 545.67-carat cut diamond. (*Source: The Guinness Book of Records*)

Solution: five hundred forty-five and sixty-seven hundredths

Work Practice 2

PRACTICE 2

Write the decimal 97.28 in words.

Example 3 Write the decimal 19.5023 in words.

Solution: nineteen and five thousand, twenty-three ten-thousandths

Work Practice 3

PRACTICE 3

Write the decimal 302.105 in words.

Example 4

Write the decimal in the following sentence in words: The oldest known fragments of the Earth's crust are zircon crystals; they were discovered in Australia and are thought to be 4.276 billion years old. (*Source: The Guinness Book of Records*)

Solution: four and two hundred seventy-six thousandths

Work Practice 4

PRACTICE 4

Write the decimal 72.1085 in words.

Suppose that you are paying $368.42 for an automotive repair job at Jake's Body Shop by writing a check. Checks are usually written using the following format.

Answers

1. eight and seven tenths
2. ninety-seven and twenty-eight hundredths **3.** three hundred two and one hundred five thousandths
4. seventy-two and one thousand eighty-five ten-thousandths

PRACTICE 5

Fill in the check to CLECO (Central Louisiana Electric Company) to pay for your monthly electric bill of $207.40.

Example 5 Fill in the check to Camelot Music to pay for your purchase of $92.98.

Solution:

● Work Practice 5

PRACTICE 6–7

Write each decimal in standard form.
6. Three hundred and ninety-six hundredths
7. Thirty-nine and forty-two thousandths

Objective ⓑ Writing Decimals in Standard Form

A decimal written in words can be written in standard form by reversing the preceding procedure.

Examples Write each decimal in standard form.

6. Forty-eight and twenty-six hundredths is

48.26

hundredths place

7. Six and ninety-five thousandths is

6.095

thousandths place

● Work Practice 6–7

Helpful Hint

When converting a decimal from words to decimal notation, make sure the last digit is in the correct place by inserting 0s if necessary. For example,

Two and thirty-eight thousandths is 2.038

thousandths place

Objective ⓒ Writing Decimals as Fractions

Once you master reading and writing decimals, writing a decimal as a fraction follows naturally.

Decimal	In Words	Fraction
0.7	seven tenths	$\dfrac{7}{10}$
0.51	fifty-one hundredths	$\dfrac{51}{100}$
0.009	nine thousandths	$\dfrac{9}{1000}$
0.05	five hundredths	$\dfrac{5}{100} = \dfrac{1}{20}$

Answers

5. CLECO; 207.40; Two hundred seven and $\dfrac{40}{100}$ **6.** 300.96   **7.** 39.042

Notice that the number of decimal places in a decimal number is the same as the number of zeros in the denominator of the equivalent fraction. We can use this fact to write decimals as fractions.

$$0.51 = \frac{51}{100} \qquad 0.009 = \frac{9}{1000}$$

2 decimal places   2 zeros   3 decimal places   3 zeros

Example 8 Write 0.43 as a fraction.

Solution: $0.43 = \frac{43}{100}$

2 decimal places   2 zeros

● Work Practice 8

Example 9 Write 5.7 as a mixed number.

Solution: $5.7 = 5\frac{7}{10}$

1 decimal place   1 zero

● Work Practice 9

Examples Write each decimal as a fraction or a mixed number. Write your answer in simplest form.

10. $0.125 = \frac{125}{1000} = \frac{\overset{1}{\cancel{125}}}{8 \cdot \cancel{125}} = \frac{1}{8}$

11. $23.5 = 23\frac{5}{10} = 23\frac{\overset{1}{\cancel{5}}}{2 \cdot \cancel{5}} = 23\frac{1}{2 \cdot 1} = 23\frac{1}{2}$

12. $105.083 = 105\frac{83}{1000}$

● Work Practice 10–12

Objective ⓓ Writing Fractions as Decimals

If the denominator of a fraction is a power of 10, we can write it as a decimal by reversing the procedure above.

Examples Write each fraction as a decimal.

13. $\frac{8}{10} = 0.8$

1 zero   1 decimal place

14. $\frac{87}{10} = 8.7$

1 zero   1 decimal place

15. $\frac{18}{1000} = 0.018$

3 zeros   3 decimal places

16. $\frac{507}{100} = 5.07$

2 zeros   2 decimal places

● Work Practice 13–16

PRACTICE 8

Write 0.037 as a fraction.

PRACTICE 9

Write 14.97 as a mixed number.

PRACTICE 10–12

Write each decimal as a fraction or mixed number. Write your answer in simplest form.
10. 0.12
11. 57.8
12. 209.986

PRACTICE 13–16

Write each fraction as a decimal.
13. $\frac{58}{100}$ **14.** $\frac{59}{100}$
15. $\frac{6}{1000}$ **16.** $\frac{172}{10}$

Answers

8. $\frac{37}{1000}$ **9.** $14\frac{97}{100}$ **10.** $\frac{3}{25}$
11. $57\frac{4}{5}$ **12.** $209\frac{493}{500}$ **13.** 0.58
14. 0.59   **15.** 0.006   **16.** 17.2

Vocabulary and Readiness Check

Use the choices below to fill in each blank.

words   decimals   and

tens   tenths   standard form

1. The number "twenty and eight hundredths" is written in _____ and "20.08" is written in _____.
2. Like fractions, _____ are used to denote parts of a whole.
3. When writing a decimal number in words, the decimal point is written as _____.
4. The place value _____ is to the right of the decimal point while _____ is to the left of the decimal point.

Determine the place value for the digit 7 in each number.

5. 70   **6.** 700   **7.** 0.7   **8.** 0.07

3.1 Exercise Set

FOR EXTRA HELP

MyMathLab  PRACTICE   WATCH   DOWNLOAD   READ   REVIEW

Objective A *Write each decimal number in words. See Examples 1 through 4.*

1. 6.52   **2.** 7.59   **3.** 16.23   **4.** 47.65

5. 0.205   **6.** 0.495   **7.** 167.009   **8.** 233.056

9. 200.005   **10.** 5000.02   **11.** 105.6   **12.** 410.30

13. The Akashi Kaikyo Bridge, between Kobe and Awaji-Shima, Japan, is approximately 2.43 miles long.

14. The English Channel Tunnel is 31.04 miles long. (*Source: Railway Directory & Year Book*)

15. Mercury makes a complete orbit of the Sun every 87.97 days. (*Source:* National Space Science Data Center)

16. Saturn makes a complete orbit of the Sun every 29.48 years. (*Source:* National Space Science Data Center)

17. The total number of television households within the United States for the 2008–2009 season was 114.5 million. (*Source:* Nielsen Media Research)

18. In 2009, it took the United States Postal Service an average of 3.9 days to deliver a book rate parcel. (*Source:* USPS)

Fill in each check for the described purchase. See Example 5.

19. Your monthly car loan of $321.42 to R. W. Financial.

Your Preprinted Name Your Preprinted Address	60–8124/7233 1000613331	1407
DATE		
PAYTO THE ORDER OF	$	
	DOLLARS	
FIRST STATE BANK OF FARTHINGTON FARTHINGTON, IL 64422		
MEMO		
⑈621497260⑈ 1000613331⑈ 1407		

20. Your part of the monthly apartment rent, which is $213.70. You pay this to Amanda Dupre.

Your Preprinted Name Your Preprinted Address	60–8124/7233 1000613331	1408
DATE		
PAYTO THE ORDER OF	$	
	DOLLARS	
FIRST STATE BANK OF FARTHINGTON FARTHINGTON, IL 64422		
MEMO		
⑈621497260⑈ 1000613331⑈ 1408		

21. Your cell phone bill of $59.68 to Bell South.

Your Preprinted Name Your Preprinted Address	60–8124/7233 1000613331	1409
DATE		
PAYTO THE ORDER OF	$	
	DOLLARS	
FIRST STATE BANK OF FARTHINGTON FARTHINGTON, IL 64422		
MEMO		
⑈621497260⑈ 1000613331⑈ 1409		

22. Your grocery bill of $87.49 to Albertsons.

Your Preprinted Name Your Preprinted Address	60–8124/7233 1000613331	1410
DATE		
PAYTO THE ORDER OF	$	
	DOLLARS	
FIRST STATE BANK OF FARTHINGTON FARTHINGTON, IL 64422		
MEMO		
⑈621497260⑈ 1000613331⑈ 1410		

Objective B *Write each decimal number in standard form. See Examples 6 and 7.*

23. Six and five tenths

24. Three and nine tenths

25. Nine and eight hundredths

26. Twelve and six hundredths

27. Seven hundred five and six hundred twenty-five thousandths

28. Eight hundred four and three hundred ninety-nine thousandths

29. Forty-six ten-thousandths

30. Thirty-eight ten-thousandths

31. The record rainfall amount for a 24-hour period in Alabama is thirty-two and fifty-two hundredths inches. This record was set at Dauphin Island Sea Lab in 1997. (*Source:* National Climatic Data Center)

32. In June, 2009, MySpace.com blogs had a twelve and sixty-four hundredths market share, the most of any blog or personal website. (*Source:* Marketingcharts.com)

33. The average IndyCar burns one and three-tenths gallons of fuel per lap at the Indianapolis Motor Speedway. (*Source:* INDY500.com)

34. Dario Franchitti posted the fastest lap speed in the 2009 Indianapolis 500 of two hundred twenty-two and forty-four thousandths miles per hour on lap 187. (*Source:* INDY500.com)

Objective Ⓒ *Write each decimal as a fraction or a mixed number. Write your answer in simplest form. See Examples 8 through 12.*

35. 0.3　　　　**36.** 0.9　　　　🖩 **37.** 0.27　　　　**38.** 0.39　　　　**39.** 0.8

40. 0.4　　　　**41.** 0.15　　　　**42.** 0.64　　　　**43.** 5.47　　　　**44.** 6.3

45. 0.048　　　**46.** 0.082　　　🖩 **47.** 7.008　　　**48.** 9.005　　　**49.** 15.802

50. 11.406　　　**51.** 0.3005　　　**52.** 0.2006　　　**53.** 487.32　　　**54.** 298.62

Objective Ⓓ *Write each fraction as a decimal. See Examples 13 through 16.*

🖩 **55.** $\dfrac{6}{10}$　　　**56.** $\dfrac{3}{10}$　　　🖩 **57.** $\dfrac{45}{100}$　　　**58.** $\dfrac{75}{100}$

59. $\dfrac{37}{10}$　　　**60.** $\dfrac{28}{10}$　　　**61.** $\dfrac{268}{1000}$　　　**62.** $\dfrac{709}{1000}$

63. $\dfrac{9}{100}$　　　**64.** $\dfrac{7}{100}$　　　**65.** $\dfrac{4026}{1000}$　　　**66.** $\dfrac{3601}{1000}$

🖩 **67.** $\dfrac{28}{1000}$　　　**68.** $\dfrac{63}{1000}$　　　**69.** $\dfrac{563}{10}$　　　**70.** $\dfrac{206}{10}$

Objectives Ⓐ Ⓑ Ⓒ Ⓓ **Mixed Practice** *Fill in the chart. The first row is completed for you. See Examples 1 through 16.*

	Decimal Number in Standard Form	In Words	Fraction
	0.37	thirty-seven hundredths	$\dfrac{37}{100}$
71.			$\dfrac{43}{100}$
72.			$\dfrac{89}{100}$
73.		eight tenths	
74.		five tenths	
75.	0.077		
76.	0.019		

Review

Round 47,261 to the indicated place value. See Section 1.5.

77. tens

78. hundreds

79. thousands

80. ten-thousands

Concept Extensions

81. In your own words, describe how to write a decimal as a fraction or a mixed number.

82. In your own words, describe how to write a fraction as a decimal.

83. Write 0.00026849576 in words.

84. Write 0.00026849576 as a fraction. Do not simplify the resulting fraction.

85. Write $17\frac{268}{1000}$ as a decimal.

86. Write $7\frac{12}{100}$ as a decimal.

A Compare Decimals.

B Round a Decimal Number to a Given Place Value.

3.2 ORDERING AND ROUNDING

Objective **A** Comparing Decimals

One way to compare decimals is to compare their graphs on a number line. Recall from Section 2.10 that for any two numbers on a number line, the number to the left is smaller and the number to the right is larger. The decimals 0.5 and 0.8 are graphed as follows:

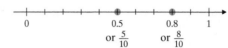

0   0.5   0.8   1
or $\frac{5}{10}$ or $\frac{8}{10}$

Comparing decimals by comparing their graphs on a number line can be time consuming. Another way to compare the size of decimals is to compare digits in corresponding places.

> ### Comparing Two Decimals
>
> Compare digits in the same places from left to right. When two digits are not equal, the number with the larger digit is the larger decimal. If necessary, insert 0s after the last digit to the right of the decimal point to continue comparing.
>
> Compare hundredths-place digits
>
> 28.253   28.263
>
>   ↑   ↑
>
>   5   <   6
>
> so 28.253   <   28.263

Before we continue, let's take a moment and convince ourselves that inserting a zero after the last digit to the right of a decimal point does not change the value of the number.

For example, let's show that

$$0.7 = 0.70$$

If we write 0.7 as a fraction, we have

$$0.7 = \frac{7}{10}$$

Let's now multiply by 1. Recall that multiplying a number by 1 does not change the value of the number.

$$0.7 = \frac{7}{10} = \frac{7}{10} \cdot 1 = \frac{7}{10} \cdot \frac{10}{10} = \frac{7 \cdot 10}{10 \cdot 10} = \frac{70}{100} = 0.70$$

Thus $0.7 = 0.70$ and so on.

Helpful Hint

For any decimal, inserting 0s after the last digit to the right of the decimal point does not change the value of the number.

$$7.6 = 7.60 = 7.600, \text{ and so on}$$

When a whole number is written as a decimal, the decimal point is placed to the right of the ones digit.

$$25 = 25.0 = 25.00, \text{ and so on}$$

Example 1 Insert <, >, or = to form a true statement.

0.378   0.368

Solution:

0. 3 78   0. 3 68   The tenths places are the same.

0.3 7 8   0.3 6 8   The hundredths places are different.

Since 7 > 6, then 0.378 > 0.368.

● Work Practice 1

PRACTICE 1

Insert <, >, or = to form a true statement.

13.208   13.281

Example 2 Insert <, >, or = to form a true statement.

0.052   0.236

Solution: 0. 0 52 < 0. 2 36   0 is smaller than 2 in the tenths place.
               ↑   ↑

● Work Practice 2

PRACTICE 2

Insert <, >, or = to form a true statement.

0.124   0.086

Example 3 Insert <, >, or = to form a true statement.

0.52   0.063

Solution: 0. 5 2 > 0. 0 63   0 is smaller than 5 in the tenths place.
               ↑   ↑

● Work Practice 3

PRACTICE 3

Insert <, >, or = to form a true statement.

0.61   0.076

Example 4 Write the decimals in order from smallest to largest.

7.035, 8.12, 7.03, 7.1

Solution: By comparing the ones digits, the decimal 8.12 is the largest number. To write the rest of the decimals in order, we compare digits to the right of the decimal point. We will insert zeros to help us compare.

7.035   7.030   7.100

Helpful Hint

You may also immediately notice that 7.1 is larger than both 7.035 and 7.03.

By comparing digits to the right of the decimal point, we can now arrange the decimals from smallest to largest.

7.030,   7.035,   7.100,   8.12   or

7.03,   7.035,   7.1,   8.12

● Work Practice 4

PRACTICE 4

Write the decimals in order from smallest to largest.

14.605, 14.65, 13.9, 14.006

Objective B Rounding Decimals

We **round the decimal part** of a decimal number in nearly the same way as we round whole numbers. The only difference is that we delete digits to the right of the rounding place, instead of replacing these digits by 0s. For example,

24.954   rounded to the nearest hundredth is   24.95
  ↑
hundredths place

Answers

1. <   **2.** >   **3.** >

4. 13.9, 14.006, 14.605, 14.65

Rounding Decimals to a Place Value to the Right of the Decimal Point

Step 1: Locate the digit to the right of the given place value.

Step 2: If this digit is 5 or greater, add 1 to the digit in the given place value and delete all digits to its right. If this digit is less than 5, delete all digits to the right of the given place value.

PRACTICE 5

Round 123.7814 to the nearest thousandth.

Example 5 Round 736.2359 to the nearest tenth.

Solution:

Step 1: We locate the digit to the right of the tenths place.

tenths place

736.2③59

digit to the right

Step 2: Since the digit to the right is less than 5, we delete it and all digits to its right.

Thus, 736.2359 rounded to the nearest tenth is 736.2.

● Work Practice 5

PRACTICE 6

Round 123.7817 to the nearest tenth.

Example 6 Round 736.2359 to the nearest hundredth.

Solution:

Step 1: We locate the digit to the right of the hundredths place.

hundredths place

736.23⑤9

digit to the right

Step 2: Since the digit to the right is 5, we add 1 to the digit in the hundredths place and delete all digits to the right of the hundredths place.

736.23⑤9

Delete these digits.
Add 1.

Thus, 736.2359 rounded to the nearest hundredth is 736.24.

● Work Practice 6

Rounding often occurs with money amounts. Since there are 100 cents in a dollar, each cent is $\frac{1}{100}$ of a dollar. This means that if we want to round to the nearest cent, we round to the nearest hundredth of a dollar.

PRACTICE 7

In Sandersville, the price of a gallon of premium gasoline is $3.1589. Round this to the nearest cent.

Example 7 The price of a gallon of premium gasoline in Cross City is currently $3.1779. Round this to the nearest cent.

Solution:

hundredths place ——   —— 7 is greater than 5

$3.17⑦9

Add 1. —— Delete these digits.

Since the digit to the right is greater than 5, we add 1 to the hundredths digit and delete all digits to the right of the hundredths digit.

Thus, $3.1779 rounded to the nearest cent is $3.18.

● Work Practice 7

Answers

5. 123.781   **6.** 123.8   **7.** $3.16

Example 8 Round $0.098 to the nearest cent.

Solution:

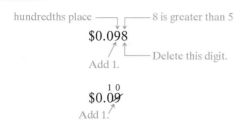

hundredths place ———┐ ┌——— 8 is greater than 5
$0.098
Add 1. └——— Delete this digit.

$$ \overset{1\ 0}{\$0.09} $$
Add 1.

9 + 1 = 10, so replace the digit 9 by 0 and carry the 1 to the place value to the left. Thus, $0.098 rounded to the nearest cent is $0.10.

● **Work Practice 8**

✓ **Concept Check** 1756.0894 rounded to the nearest ten is

a. 1756.1   **b.** 1760.0894

c. 1760   **d.** 1750

Example 9 Determining State Taxable Income

A high school teacher's taxable income is $41,567.72. The tax tables in the teacher's state use amounts to the nearest dollar. Round the teacher's income to the nearest whole dollar.

Solution: Rounding to the nearest whole dollar means rounding to the ones place.

ones place ———┐ ┌——— 7 is greater than 5
$41,567.72
Add 1. └——— Delete these digits.

Thus, the teacher's income rounded to the nearest dollar is $41,568.

● **Work Practice 9**

In Section 3.4, we will introduce a formula for the distance around a circle. The distance around a circle is given the special name **circumference.**

The symbol π is the Greek letter pi, pronounced "pie." We use π to denote the following constant:

$$ \pi = \frac{\text{circumference of a circle}}{\text{diameter of a circle}} $$

The value π is an **irrational number.** This means if we try to write it as a decimal, it neither ends nor repeats in a pattern.

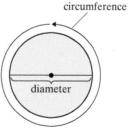

circumference

diameter

Example 10 $\pi \approx 3.14159265$. Round π to the nearest hundredth.

Solution:

hundredths place ———┐ ┌——— 1 is less than 5.
3.14159265
└——— Delete these digits.

Thus, 3.14159265 rounded to the nearest hundredth is 3.14. In other words, $\pi \approx 3.14$.

● **Work Practice 10**

Vocabulary and Readiness Check

Use the choices below to fill in each blank. Some choices may be used more than once or not at all.

before	7.0	diameter
after	0.7	circumference

1. Another name for the distance around a circle is its _____.

2. $\pi = \dfrac{\rule{2cm}{0.4pt}\ \text{of a circle}}{\rule{2cm}{0.4pt}\ \text{of a circle}}$

3. The decimal point in a whole number is _____ the last digit.

4. The whole number 7 = _____.

3.2 Exercise Set

FOR EXTRA HELP

MyMathLab

 PRACTICE WATCH DOWNLOAD READ REVIEW

Objective A *Insert* $<$, $>$, *or* $=$ *to form a true statement. See Examples 1 through 3.*

1. 0.15   0.16

2. 0.12   0.15

3. 0.57   0.54

4. 0.59   0.52

5. 0.098   0.1

6. 0.0756   0.2

7. 0.54900   0.549

8. 0.98400   0.984

9. 167.908   167.980

10. 519.3405   519.3054

11. 420,000   0.000042

12. 0.000987   987,000

Write the decimals in order from smallest to largest. See Example 4.

13. 0.006, 0.06, 0.0061

14. 0.082, 0.008, 0.080

15. 0.042, 0.36, 0.03

16. 0.21, 0.056, 0.065

17. 1.1, 1.16, 1.01, 1.09

18. 3.6, 3.069, 3.09, 3.06

19. 21.001, 20.905, 21.03, 21.12

20. 36.050, 35.72, 35.702, 35.072

Objective B *Round each decimal to the given place value. See Examples 5 through 10.*

21. 0.57, to the nearest tenth

22. 0.54, to the nearest tenth

23. 0.234, to the nearest hundredth

24. 0.452, to the nearest hundredth

25. 0.5942, to the nearest thousandth

26. 63.4523, to the nearest thousandth

27. 98,207.23, to the nearest ten

28. 68,934.543, to the nearest ten

29. 12.342, to the nearest tenth

30. 42.9878, to the nearest thousandth

31. 17.667, to the nearest hundredth

32. 0.766, to the nearest hundredth

33. 0.501, to the nearest tenth

34. 0.602, to the nearest tenth

35. 0.1295, to the nearest thousandth

36. 0.8295, to the nearest thousandth

37. 3829.34, to the nearest ten

38. 4520.876, to the nearest hundred

Round each monetary amount to the nearest cent or dollar as indicated. See Examples 7 through 9.

39. $0.067, to the nearest cent

40. $0.025, to the nearest cent

41. $42,650.14, to the nearest dollar

42. $768.45, to the nearest dollar

43. $26.95, to the nearest dollar

44. $14,769.52, to the nearest dollar

45. $0.1992, to the nearest cent

46. $0.7633, to the nearest cent

Round each number to the given place value. See Examples 5 through 10.

47. The Apple MacBook Air, at its thinnest point, measures 0.4064 cm. Round this number to the nearest tenth. (*Source:* Apple, Inc.)

48. A large tropical cockroach of the family Dictyoptera is the fastest-moving insect. This insect was clocked at a speed of 3.36 miles per hour. Round this number to the nearest tenth. (*Source:* University of California, Berkeley)

49. During the 2009 Boston Marathon, Ernst Van Dyk of South Africa was the first wheelchair competitor to cross the finish line. His time was 1.5581 hours. Round this time to the nearest hundredth. (*Source:* Boston Athletic Association)

50. The population density of the state of Louisiana is 102.5794 people per square mile. Round this population density to the nearest tenth. (*Source:* U.S. Census Bureau)

51. A used biology textbook is priced at $47.89. Round this price to the nearest dollar.

52. A used office desk is advertised at $49.95 by Drawley's Office Furniture. Round this price to the nearest dollar.

53. Lindsey Vonn of the United States won the gold medal for the women's downhill in the 2010 Winter Olympics. Her winning time was 1.736 minutes. Round this time to the nearest hundredth of a minute. (*Source:* International Olympic Committee)

54. The population density of the state of Arkansas is 54.444 people per square mile. Round this population density to the nearest tenth. (*Source:* U.S. Census Bureau)

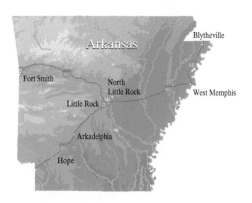

55. The length of a day on Mars is 24.6229 hours. Round this figure to the nearest thousandth. (*Source:* National Space Science Data Center)

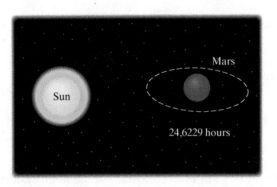

24.6229 hours

56. Venus makes a complete orbit around the Sun every 224.695 days. Round this figure to the nearest whole day. (*Source:* National Space Science Data Center)

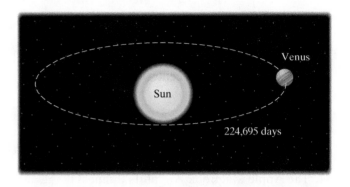

224.695 days

57. Millennium Force is a roller coaster at Cedar Point, an amusement park in Sandusky, Ohio. At the time of its debut, Millennium Force was the world's tallest and fastest roller coaster. A ride on the Millennium Force lasts about 2.75 minutes. Round this figure to the nearest tenth. (*Source:* Cedar Fair, L.P.)

58. During the 2008 NFL season, the average length of an Oakland Raiders' punt was 48.78 yards. Round this figure to the nearest whole yard. (*Source:* National Football League)

Review

Perform each indicated operation. See Sections 1.3 and 1.4.

59. 3452 + 2314

60. 8945 + 4536

61. 94 − 23

62. 82 − 47

63. 482 − 239

64. 4002 − 3897

Concept Extensions

Solve. See the Concept Check in this section.

65. 2849.1738 rounded to the nearest hundred is
   a. 2849.17
   b. 2800
   c. 2850
   d. 2849.174

66. 146.059 rounded to the nearest ten is
   a. 146.0
   b. 146.1
   c. 140
   d. 150

67. 2849.1738 rounded to the nearest hundredth is
   a. 2849.17
   b. 2800
   c. 2850
   d. 2849.174

68. 146.059 rounded to the nearest tenth is
   a. 146.0
   b. 146.1
   c. 140
   d. 150

Mixed Practice (Sections 3.1, 3.2) *The table gives the average speed, in kilometers per hour, for the winners of the Tour de France for each of the years listed. Use the table to answer Exercises 69 through 72. (Source: letour.fr/us)*

Year	Cyclist/Nationality	Average Speed (in kph)
2002	Lance Armstrong/USA	39.982
2003	Lance Armstrong/USA	40.030
2004	Lance Armstrong/USA	41.016
2005	Lance Armstrong/USA	41.654
2006	Oscar Pereiro/Spain	40.789
2007	Alberto Contador/Spain	39.233
2008	Carlos Sastre/Spain	40.413
2009	Alberto Contador/Spain	40.788

69. What is the fastest average speed on the list? Write this speed as a mixed number. Which cyclist achieved this average speed?

70. What is the slowest average speed on the list? Write this speed as a mixed number. Which cyclist achieved this speed?

71. Make a list of the average winning speeds in order from fastest to slowest for the years 2006 through 2009.

72. Make a list of the average winning speeds in order from fastest to slowest for the years 2002 through 2005.

73. Write a 5-digit number that rounds to 1.7.

74. Write a 4-digit number that rounds to 26.3.

75. Write a decimal number that is greater than 8 but less than 9.

76. Write a decimal number that is greater than 48.1, but less than 48.2.

77. Which number(s) rounds to 0.26?
0.26559   0.26499   0.25786   0.25186

78. Which number(s) rounds to 0.06?
0.0612   0.066   0.0586   0.0506

Write these numbers from smallest to largest.

79. 0.9
0.1038
0.10299
0.1037

80. 0.01
0.0839
0.09
0.1

81. The all-time top six movies* (those that earned the most money in the United States) along with the approximate amount of money they have earned are listed in the table. Estimate the total amount of money that these movies have earned by first rounding each earning to the nearest hundred million. (*Source:* The Internet Movie Database)

Top All-Time American Movies	
Movie	**Gross Domestic Earnings**
Avatar (2009)	$737.6 million
Titanic (1997)	$600.8 million
The Dark Knight (2008)	$533.3 million
Star Wars: A New Hope (1977)	$460.9 million
Shrek 2 (2004)	$436.5 million
E.T. (1982)	$434.9 million
*Note: Many of these movies are still earning substantial amounts of money.	

82. In a recent year, American manufacturers shipped approximately 27.5 million music videos to retailers. The value of these shipments was approximately $484.9 million. Estimate the value of an individual music video by rounding 484.9 and 27.5 to the nearest ten, then dividing. (*Source:* Recording Industry Association of America)

3.3 ADDING AND SUBTRACTING DECIMALS

Objective Ⓐ Adding Decimals

Adding decimals is similar to adding whole numbers. We add digits in corresponding place values from right to left, carrying if necessary. To make sure that digits in corresponding place values are added, we line up the decimal points vertically.

> ### Adding or Subtracting Decimals
>
> **Step 1:** Write the decimals so that the decimal points line up vertically.
>
> **Step 2:** Add or subtract as with whole numbers.
>
> **Step 3:** Place the decimal point in the sum or difference so that it lines up vertically with the decimal points in the problem.

In this section, we will insert zeros in decimal numbers so that place value digits line up neatly. For instance, see Example 1.

Example 1 Add: $23.85 + 1.604$

Solution: First we line up the decimal points vertically.

$$
\begin{array}{r}
23.85\textcolor{gray}{0} \quad \text{\small Insert one 0 so that digits line up neatly.}\\
+\ 1.604\\
\uparrow\\
\text{\small line up decimal points}
\end{array}
$$

Then we add the digits from right to left as for whole numbers.

$$
\begin{array}{r}
\overset{1}{2}3.850\\
+\ 1.604\\
\hline
25.454
\end{array}
$$

Place the decimal point in the sum so that all decimal points line up.

● **Work Practice 1**

> ### Helpful Hint
>
> Recall that 0's may be placed after the last digit to the right of the decimal point without changing the value of the decimal. This may be used to help line up place values when adding decimals.
>
> $$
> \begin{array}{r}
> 3.2\\
> 15.567\\
> +\ 0.11\\
> \end{array}
> \qquad \text{becomes} \qquad
> \begin{array}{r}
> 3.2\textcolor{gray}{00} \quad \text{\small Insert two 0s.}\\
> 15.567\\
> +\ 0.11\textcolor{gray}{0} \quad \text{\small Insert one 0.}\\
> \hline
> 18.877 \quad \text{\small Add.}
> \end{array}
> $$

Example 2 Add: 763.7651 + 22.001 + 43.89

Solution: First we line up the decimal points.

$$
\begin{array}{r}
\overset{1\ \ 1\ \ 1}{763.7651} \\
22.0010 \quad \text{Insert one 0.} \\
+\ 43.8900 \quad \text{Insert two 0s.} \\
\hline
829.6561 \quad \text{Add.}
\end{array}
$$

● Work Practice 2

Helpful Hint

Don't forget that the decimal point in a whole number is after the last digit.

Example 3 Add: 45 + 2.06

Solution:
$$
\begin{array}{r}
45.00 \quad \text{Insert a decimal point and two 0s.} \\
+\ 2.06 \quad \text{Line up decimal points.} \\
\hline
47.06 \quad \text{Add.}
\end{array}
$$

● Work Practice 3

✔**Concept Check** What is wrong with the following calculation of the sum of 7.03, 2.008, 19.16, and 3.1415?

$$
\begin{array}{r}
7.03 \\
2.008 \\
19.16 \\
+\ 3.1415 \\
\hline
3.6042
\end{array}
$$

Objective ⓑ Subtracting Decimals

Subtracting decimals is similar to subtracting whole numbers. We line up digits and subtract from right to left, borrowing when needed.

Example 4 Subtract: 35.218 − 23.65. Check your answer.

Solution: First we line up the decimal points.

$$
\begin{array}{r}
\overset{4\ \ 1111}{3\cancel{5}.2\cancel{1}8} \\
-\ 23.650 \quad \text{Insert one 0.} \\
\hline
11.568 \quad \text{Subtract.}
\end{array}
$$

Recall that we can check a subtraction problem by adding.

$$
\begin{array}{r}
\overset{1\ \ 1}{11.568} \quad \text{Difference} \\
+\ 23.650 \quad \text{Subtrahend} \\
\hline
35.218 \quad \text{Minuend}
\end{array}
$$

● Work Practice 4

PRACTICE 2

Add.
a. 34.567 + 129.43 + 2.8903
b. 11.21 + 46.013 + 362.526

PRACTICE 3

Add: 26.072 + 119

PRACTICE 4

Subtract. Check your answers.
a. 82.75 − 15.9
b. 126.032 − 95.71

Answers
2. a. 166.8873 **b.** 419.749
3. 145.072 **4. a.** 66.85 **b.** 30.322

✔**Concept Check Answer**
The decimal points and places are not lined up properly.

PRACTICE 5

Subtract. Check your answers.
a. $5.8 - 3.92$
b. $9.72 - 4.068$

Example 5 Subtract: $3.5 - 0.068$. Check your answer.

Solution:

$$
\begin{array}{r}
\overset{9}{}\overset{4\;\cancel{10}\;10}{} \\
3.\cancel{5}\cancel{0}\cancel{0} \\
-\;0.0\,6\,8 \\
\hline
3.4\,3\,2
\end{array}
$$

Insert two 0s.
Line up decimal points.
Subtract.

Check:

$$
\begin{array}{r}
3.432 \\
+\,0.068 \\
\hline
3.500
\end{array}
$$

Difference
Subtrahend
Minuend

● Work Practice 5

PRACTICE 6

Subtract. Check your answers.
a. $53 - 29.31$
b. $120 - 68.22$

Example 6 Subtract: $85 - 17.31$. Check your answer.

Solution:

$$
\begin{array}{r}
\overset{9}{} \\
\overset{7\;14\;\cancel{10}\;10}{} \\
\cancel{8}\cancel{5}.\cancel{0}\cancel{0} \\
-1\,7.3\,1 \\
\hline
6\,7.6\,9
\end{array}
$$

Check:

$$
\begin{array}{r}
67.69 \\
+17.31 \\
\hline
85.00
\end{array}
$$

Difference
Subtrahend
Minuend

● Work Practice 6

Objective ⒸⒸ Estimating When Adding or Subtracting Decimals

To help avoid errors, we can also estimate to see if our answer is reasonable when adding or subtracting decimals. Although only one estimate is needed per operation, we show two to show variety.

PRACTICE 7

Add or subtract as indicated. Then estimate to see if the answer is reasonable by rounding the given numbers and adding or subtracting the rounded numbers.
a. $48.1 + 326.97$
b. $18.09 - 0.746$

Example 7 Add or subtract as indicated. Then estimate to see if the answer is reasonable by rounding the given numbers and adding or subtracting the rounded numbers.

a. $27.6 + 519.25$

Solution:

Exact		Estimate 1		Estimate 2
$\overset{1}{}27.60$	rounds to	30		30
$+519.25$	rounds to	$+500$	or	$+520$
546.85		530		550

Since the exact answer is close to either estimate, it is reasonable. (In the first estimate, each number is rounded to the place value of the leftmost digit. In the second estimate, each number is rounded to the nearest ten.)

b. $11.01 - 0.862$

Solution:

Exact		Estimate 1		Estimate 2
$\overset{0\;\;9\;10\,10}{1\cancel{1}.\cancel{0}\cancel{1}\cancel{0}}$	rounds to	10		11
-0.862	rounds to	$-\;1$	or	$-\;1$
10.148		9		10

In the first estimate, we rounded the first number to the nearest ten and the second number to the nearest one. In the second estimate, we rounded both numbers to the nearest one. Both estimates show us that our answer is reasonable.

● Work Practice 7

Helpful Hint Remember that estimates are for our convenience to quickly check the reasonableness of an answer.

Answers
5. a. 1.88 **b.** 5.652
6. a. 23.69 **b.** 51.78
7. a. 375.07 **b.** 17.344

✓Concept Check Why shouldn't the sum $21.98 + 42.36$ be estimated as $30 + 50 = 80$?

Objective ⓓ Solving Problems by Adding or Subtracting Decimals

Decimals are very common in real-life problems.

Example 8   Calculating the Cost of Owning an Automobile

Find the total monthly cost of owning and operating a certain automobile given the expenses shown.

Monthly car payment:	$256.63
Monthly insurance cost:	$47.52
Average gasoline bill per month:	$95.33

Solution:

1. **UNDERSTAND.** Read and reread the problem. The phrase "total monthly cost" tells us to add.

2. **TRANSLATE.**

In words:	total monthly cost	is	car payment	plus	insurance cost	plus	gasoline bill
	↓	↓	↓	↓	↓	↓	↓
Translate:	total monthly cost	=	$256.63	+	$47.52	+	$95.33

3. **SOLVE:** Let's also estimate by rounding each number to the nearest ten.

$$
\begin{array}{ll}
\overset{111}{256.63} & \text{rounds to} \quad 260 \\
47.52 & \text{rounds to} \quad 50 \\
+ \ 95.33 & \text{rounds to} \ \underline{100} \\
\hline
\$399.48 & \text{Exact.} \qquad 410 \quad \text{Estimate.}
\end{array}
$$

4. **INTERPRET.** *Check* your work. Since our estimate is close to our exact answer, our answer is reasonable. *State* your conclusion: The total monthly cost is $399.48.

● Work Practice 8

The next bar graph has horizontal bars. To visualize the value represented by a bar, see how far it extends to the right. The value of each bar is labeled and we will study bar graphs further in a later chapter.

Example 9   Comparing Average Heights

The bar graph shows the current average heights for adults in various countries. How much greater is the average height in Denmark than the average height in the United States?

Continued on next page

PRACTICE 8

Find the total monthly cost of owning and operating a certain automobile given the expenses shown.

Monthly car payment:	$536.52
Monthly insurance cost:	$52.68
Average gasoline bill per month:	$87.50

Answer
8. $676.70

✓ **Concept Check Answer**

Each number is rounded incorrectly. The estimate is too high.

PRACTICE 9

Use the bar graph in Example 9. How much greater is the average height in the Netherlands than the average height in Israel?

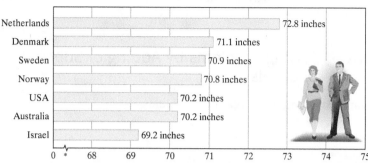

Average Adult Height

Netherlands	72.8 inches
Denmark	71.1 inches
Sweden	70.9 inches
Norway	70.8 inches
USA	70.2 inches
Australia	70.2 inches
Israel	69.2 inches

0   *   68   69   70   71   72   73   74   75

Source: *Disabled World*, October 2008

* The ⌁ means that some numbers are purposefully missing on the axis.

Solution:

1. UNDERSTAND. Read and reread the problem. Since we want to know "how much greater," we subtract.

2. TRANSLATE.

In words:	How much greater	is	Denmark's average height	minus	U. S. average height
	↓	↓	↓	↓	↓
Translate:	How much greater	=	71.1	−	70.2

3. SOLVE: We estimate by rounding each number to the nearest whole.

$$\begin{array}{r} \overset{0\;11}{7\cancel{1}.\cancel{1}} \\ -\;70.2 \\ \hline 0.9 \end{array}$$ rounds to   71
   rounds to   − 70
   Exact.   1   Estimate.

4. INTERPRET. *Check* your work. Since our estimate is close to our exact answer, 0.9 inches is reasonable. *State* your conclusion: The average height in Denmark is 0.9 inch greater than the average U.S. height.

Work Practice 9

Answer

9. 3.6 in.

Calculator Explorations

Entering Decimal Numbers

To enter a decimal number, find the key marked ⟨ · ⟩. To enter the number 2.56, for example, press the keys ⟨ 2 ⟩⟨ · ⟩⟨ 5 ⟩⟨ 6 ⟩.

The display will read ⟨   2.56 ⟩.

Operations on Decimal Numbers

Operations on decimal numbers are performed in the same way as operations on whole or signed numbers. For example, to find 8.625 − 4.29, press the keys ⟨ 8.625 ⟩⟨ − ⟩⟨ 4.29 ⟩⟨ = ⟩ or ⟨ ENTER ⟩.

The display will read ⟨   4.335 ⟩. (Although entering 8.625, for example, requires pressing more than one key, we group numbers together here for easier reading.)

Use a calculator to perform each indicated operation.

1. 315.782 + 12.96

2. 29.68 + 85.902

3. 6.249 − 1.0076

4. 5.238 − 0.682

5.   12.555
     224.987
     5.2
   + 622.65

6.   47.006
     0.17
     313.259
   + 139.088

Vocabulary and Readiness Check

Use the choices below to fill in each blank. Not all choices will be used.

minuend	vertically	first	true	37.0	horizontally
difference	subtrahend	last	false	0.37	

1. The number 37 equals _____.

2. The decimal point in a whole number is positioned after the _____ digit.

3. In $89.2 - 14.9 = 74.3$, the number 74.3 is called the _____, 89.2 is the _____, and 14.9 is the _____.

4. To add or subtract decimals, we line up the decimal points _____.

5. True or false: The number 5.6 is closer to 5 than 6 on a number line. _____.

6. True or false: The number 10.48 is closer to 10 than 11 on a number line. _____.

3.3 Exercise Set

FOR EXTRA HELP

MyMathLab® Powered by CourseCompass™ and MathXL® | Math XL PRACTICE | WATCH | DOWNLOAD | READ | REVIEW

Objectives Ⓐ Ⓒ **Mixed Practice** *Add. See Examples 1 through 3, and 7. For those exercises marked, also estimate to see if the answer is reasonable.*

 1. $1.3 + 2.2$

2. $2.5 + 4.1$

3. $5.7 + 1.13$

4. $2.31 + 6.4$

5. $0.003 + 0.091$

6. $0.004 + 0.085$

7. $19.23 + 602.782$

8. $47.14 + 409.567$

9. $490 + 93.09$

10. $600 + 83.0062$

11.
$$234.89$$
$$+ 230.67$$
Exact: Estimate:

12.
$$734.89$$
$$+ 640.56$$
Exact: Estimate:

13.
$$100.009$$
$$6.08$$
$$+ \quad 9.034$$
Exact: Estimate:

14.
$$200.89$$
$$7.49$$
$$+ \quad 62.83$$
Exact: Estimate:

 **15.** $24.6 + 2.39 + 0.0678$

16. $32.4 + 1.58 + 0.0934$

17. Find the sum of 45.023, 3.006, and 8.403

18. Find the sum of 65.0028, 5.0903, and 6.9003

Objectives Ⓑ Ⓒ **Mixed Practice** *Subtract and check. See Examples 4 through 7. For those exercises marked, also estimate to see if the answer is reasonable.*

19. $8.8 - 2.3$

20. $7.6 - 2.1$

 21. $18 - 2.7$

22. $28 - 3.3$

23.
$$654.9$$
$$- \quad 56.67$$

24.
$$863.23$$
$$- \quad 39.453$$

25. $5.9 - 4.07$
Exact:
Estimate:

26. $6.4 - 3.04$
Exact:
Estimate:

239

27. $923.5 - 61.9$ **28.** $845.93 - 45.8$ **29.** $500.34 - 123.45$ **30.** $600.74 - 463.98$

31.
$$\begin{array}{r} 1000 \\ -\ 123.4 \\ \hline \end{array}$$

Exact:

Estimate:

32.
$$\begin{array}{r} 2000 \\ -\ 327.47 \\ \hline \end{array}$$

Exact:

Estimate:

33. $200 - 5.6$

34. $800 - 8.9$

35. $3 - 0.0012$ **36.** $7 - 0.097$ **37.** Subtract 6.7 from 23.   **38.** Subtract 9.2 from 45.

Objectives Ⓐ Ⓑ **Mixed Practice** *Perform the indicated operation. See Examples 1 through 6.*

39. $86.05 + 1.978$ **40.** $95.07 + 4.216$ **41.** $86.05 - 1.978$ **42.** $95.07 - 4.216$

43. Add 150 and 93.17.   **44.** Add 250 and 86.07.   **45.** $150 - 93.17$ **46.** $250 - 86.07$

47. Subtract 8.94 from 12.1.

48. Subtract 6.73 from 20.2.

Objective Ⓓ *Solve. For Exercises 49 and 50, the solutions have been started for you. See Examples 8 and 9.*

49. Ann-Margaret Tober bought a book for $32.48. If she paid with two $20 bills, what was her change?

Start the solution:

1. UNDERSTAND the problem. Reread it as many times as needed.
2. TRANSLATE into an equation. (Fill in the blank.)

change	is	two $20 bills	minus	cost of book
↓	↓	↓	↓	↓
change	=	40	−	_____

Finish with
3. SOLVE and 4. INTERPRET

50. Phillip Guillot bought a car part for $18.26. If he paid with two $10 bills, what was his change?

Start the solution:

1. UNDERSTAND the problem. Reread it as many times as needed.
2. TRANSLATE into an equation. (Fill in the blank.)

change	is	two $10 bills	minus	cost of car part
↓	↓	↓	↓	↓
change	=	20	−	_____

Finish with
3. SOLVE and 4. INTERPRET

51. Find the total monthly cost of owning and maintaining a car given the information shown.

Monthly car payment:	$275.36
Monthly insurance cost:	$ 83.00
Average cost of gasoline per month:	$ 81.60
Average maintenance cost per month:	$ 14.75

52. Find the total monthly cost of owning and maintaining a car given the information shown.

Monthly car payment:	$306.42
Monthly insurance cost:	$ 53.50
Average cost of gasoline per month:	$123.00
Average maintenance cost per month:	$ 23.50

53. Gasoline was $2.839 per gallon one week and $2.979 per gallon the next. By how much did the price change?

54. A pair of eyeglasses costs a total of $347.89. The frames of the glasses are $97.23. How much do the lenses of the eyeglasses cost?

55. Find the perimeter.

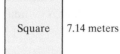

Square | 7.14 meters

56. Find the perimeter.

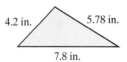

4.2 in.   5.78 in.
7.8 in.

The iPod nano is a miniature version of Apple Computer's popular iPod audio player. The nano was first introduced in 2005 with a storage capacity of 16 gigabytes. (This is about 4000 3-minute or 3-megabyte songs.)

57. The top face of the iPod nano measures 3.6 inches by 1.5 inches. Find the perimeter of the rectangular face.

58. The face of the larger Apple iPod measures 4.1 inches by 2.4 inches. Find the perimeter of this rectangular face.

59. The long-term mean average U.S. temperature (the average of all U.S. average temperatures) is 52.85 degrees Fahrenheit. The average temperature in 1998, the warmest annual average, was 55.08 degrees Fahrenheit. How much warmer was the average U.S. temperature in 1998 than the mean of all U.S. average temperatures?

60. In 2008, the U.S. minimum wage was $6.65 per hour. One year later, in 2009, the U.S. minimum wage was raised to $7.25 per hour. How much of an increase was this? (*Source:* U.S. Department of Labor)

61. The average wind speed at the weather station on Mt. Washington in New Hampshire is 35.2 miles per hour. The highest speed ever recorded at the station is 321.0 miles per hour. How much faster is the highest speed than the average wind speed? (*Source:* National Climatic Data Center)

62. The average annual rainfall in Omaha, Nebraska, is 30.22 inches. The average annual rainfall in New Orleans, Louisiana, is 61.88 inches. On average, how much more rain does New Orleans receive annually than Omaha? (*Source:* National Climatic Data Center)

63. Andy Green still holds the record for one-mile land speed. This record was 129.567 miles per hour faster than a previous record of 633.468 set in 1983. What was Green's record-setting speed? (*Source:* United States Auto Club; this record was made in October 1997)

64. It costs $4.90 to send a 2-pound package locally via parcel post at a U.S. Post Office. To send the same package as Express Mail, it costs $16.30. How much more does it cost to send a package as Express Mail? (*Source:* USPS)

65. The Apple iPhone was a revolutionary touch screen phone when it was introduced in 2007. It measured 4.5 inches by 2.4 inches. Find the perimeter of this phone. (*Source: New York Times*)

66. The Google phone, G1, which was introduced in October 2008 to rival the Apple iPhone, measures 4.6 inches by 2.16 inches. Find the perimeter of the phone. (*Source: New York Times*)

67. The average U.S. movie theater ticket price in 2009 was $7.50. In 2008, it was $7.18. Find the increase in average movie theater ticket price from 2008 to 2009. (*Source:* MPAA)

68. The average U.S. movie theater ticket price in 2000 was $5.39. For 2010, it is predicted to be $7.80. Find the increase in average movie theater ticket price for this 10-year period. (*Source:* MPAA and Internet)

This bar graph shows the predicted increase in the total number of text messaging users in the United States. Use this graph for Exercises 69 and 70. (Source: CellSigns, Inc.) Note: Some of these values are projections.

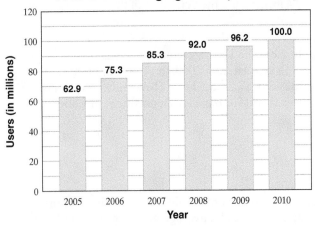

Total U.S. Messaging Users (in millions)

69. Find the increase in U.S. messaging users from 2005 to 2006.

70. Find the increase in U.S. messaging users from 2007 to 2009.

71. The snowiest city in the United States is Blue Canyon, California, which receives an average of 111.6 more inches of snow than the second snowiest city. The second snowiest city in the United States is Marquette, Michigan. Marquette receives an average of 129.2 inches of snow annually. How much snow does Blue Canyon receive on average each year? (*Source:* National Climatic Data Center)

72. The driest city in the world is Aswan, Egypt, which receives an average of only 0.02 inch of rain per year. Yuma, Arizona, is the driest city in the United States. Yuma receives an average of 2.63 more inches of rain each year than Aswan. What is the average annual rainfall in Yuma? (*Source:* National Climatic Data Center)

73. A landscape architect is planning a border for a flower garden shaped like a triangle. The sides of the garden measure 12.4 feet, 29.34 feet, and 25.7 feet. Find the amount of border material needed.

74. A contractor purchased enough railing to completely enclose the newly built deck shown below. Find the amount of railing purchased.

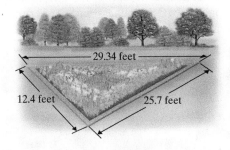

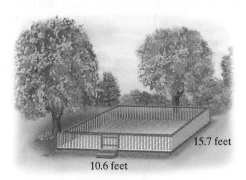

The table shows the average retail price of a gallon of gasoline (all grades and formulations) in the United States in May of each of the years shown. Use this table to answer Exercises 75 and 76. (Source: Energy Information Administration)

Year	Gasoline Price (dollars per gallon)
2005	2.338
2006	2.752
2007	3.176
2008	3.813
2009	2.314

75. How much more was the average cost of a gallon of gasoline in 2008 than in 2005?

76. How much less was the average cost of a gallon of gasoline in 2009 than in 2007?

The following table shows spaceflight information for astronaut James A. Lovell. Use this table to answer Exercises 77 and 78.

Spaceflights of James A. Lovell		
Year	Mission	Duration (in hours)
1965	Gemini 6	330.583
1966	Gemini 12	94.567
1968	Apollo 8	147.0
1970	Apollo 13	142.9
(*Source:* NASA)		

77. Find the total time spent in spaceflight by astronaut James A. Lovell.

78. Find the total time James A. Lovell spent in spaceflight on all Apollo missions.

The bar graph shows the top five chocolate-consuming nations in the world. Use this table to answer Exercises 79 through 84.

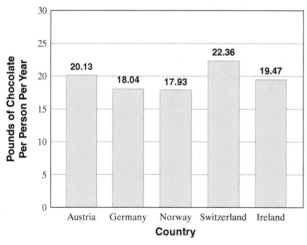

Source: Chocolate Manufacturers Association

79. Which country in the table has the greatest chocolate consumption per person?

80. Which country in the table has the least chocolate consumption per person?

81. How much more is the greatest chocolate consumption than the least chocolate consumption shown in the table?

82. How much more chocolate does the average Austrian consume than the average German?

83. Make a new chart listing the countries and their corresponding chocolate consumptions in order from greatest to least.

84. Find the sum of the five bar heights shown in the graph. What type of company might be interested in this sum?

Review

Multiply. See Sections 1.6 and 2.10.

85. $23 \cdot 2$

86. $46 \cdot 3$

87. $43 \cdot 90$

88. $30 \cdot 32$

89. $\left(\dfrac{2}{3}\right)^2$

90. $\left(\dfrac{1}{5}\right)^3$

Concept Extensions

A friend asks you to check his calculations for Exercises 91 and 92. Are they correct? If not, explain your friend's errors and correct the calculations. See the first Concept Check in this section.

91.
$$\begin{array}{r} \overset{1}{9}.2 \\ \overset{1}{8}.63 \\ +\,4.005 \\ \hline 4.960 \end{array}$$

92.
$$\begin{array}{r} \overset{8\,9\,9\,9}{9\cancel{0}\cancel{0}.\cancel{0}} \\ -\ 96.4 \\ \hline 803.5 \end{array}$$

Find the unknown length in each figure.

△ **93.**

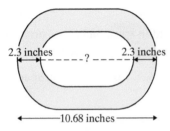

2.3 inches   ?   2.3 inches

—10.68 inches—

△ **94.**

←5.26→|←— 7.82 —→|← ? →
meters   meters   meters

←————17.67 meters————→

Let's review the values of these common U.S. coins in order to answer the following exercises.

     Penny   Nickel   Dime   Quarter

    $0.01 $0.05 $0.10 $0.25

For Exercises 95 and 96, write the value of each group of coins. To do so, it is usually easiest to start with the coin(s) of greatest value and end with the coin(s) of least value.

95.

96.

97. Name the different ways that coins can have a value of $0.17 given that you may use no more than 10 coins.

98. Name the different ways that coin(s) can have a value of $0.25 given that there are no pennies.

99. Why shouldn't the sum
$$82.95 + 51.26$$
be estimated as $90 + 60 = 150$?
See the second Concept Check in this section.

100. Laser beams can be used to measure the distance to the moon. One measurement showed the distance to the moon to be 256,435.235 miles. A later measurement showed that the distance is 256,436.012 miles. Find how much farther away the moon is in the second measurement as compared to the first.

101. Explain how adding or subtracting decimals is similar to adding or subtracting whole numbers.

102. Explain how adding or subtracting decimals is different from adding or subtracting whole numbers.

3.4 MULTIPLYING DECIMALS AND CIRCUMFERENCE OF A CIRCLE

Objectives

A Multiply Decimals.

B Estimate When Multiplying Decimals.

C Multiply by Powers of 10.

D Find the Circumference of a Circle.

E Solve Problems by Multiplying Decimals.

Objective **A** Multiplying Decimals

Multiplying decimals is similar to multiplying whole numbers. The only difference is that we place a decimal point in the product. To discover where a decimal point is placed in the product, let's multiply 0.6×0.03. We first write each decimal as an equivalent fraction and then multiply.

$$0.6 \quad \times \quad 0.03 \quad = \frac{6}{10} \times \frac{3}{100} = \frac{18}{1000} = 0.018$$

1 decimal place   2 decimal places   3 decimal places

Notice that $1 + 2 = 3$, the number of decimal places in the product. Now let's multiply 0.03×0.002.

$$0.03 \quad \times \quad 0.002 \quad = \frac{3}{100} \times \frac{2}{1000} = \frac{6}{100,000} = 0.00006$$

2 decimal places   3 decimal places   5 decimal places

Again, we see that $2 + 3 = 5$, the number of decimal places in the product.

Instead of writing decimals as fractions each time we want to multiply, we notice a pattern from these examples and state a rule that we can use:

Multiplying Decimals

Step 1: Multiply the decimals as though they are whole numbers.

Step 2: The decimal point in the product is placed so that the number of decimal places in the product is equal to the *sum* of the number of decimal places in the factors.

Example 1 Multiply: 23.6×0.78

Solution:

$$
\begin{array}{r}
23.6 \\
\times\, 0.78 \\
\hline
1888 \\
16520 \\
\hline
18.408
\end{array}
$$

     23.6   1 decimal place
    × 0.78   2 decimal places

Since $1 + 2 = 3$, insert the decimal point in the product so that there are 3 decimal places.

● **Work Practice 1**

PRACTICE 1

Multiply: 45.9×0.42

Example 2 Multiply: 0.283×0.3

Solution:

    0.283   3 decimal places
   ×   0.3   1 decimal place
  0.0849   Since $3 + 1 = 4$, insert the decimal point in the product so that there are 4 decimal places.

Insert one 0 since the product must have 4 decimal places.

● **Work Practice 2**

PRACTICE 2

Multiply: 0.112×0.6

Answers
1. 19.278   **2.** 0.0672

PRACTICE 3

Multiply: 0.0721×48

Example 3 Multiply: 0.0531×16

Solution:

$$
\begin{array}{r}
0.0531 \quad \text{4 decimal places} \\
\times \quad 16 \quad \text{0 decimal places} \\
\hline
3186 \\
5310 \\
\hline
0.8496 \\
\end{array}
$$

4 decimal places $(4 + 0 = 4)$

● **Work Practice 3**

✔**Concept Check** True or false? The number of decimal places in the product of 0.261 and 0.78 is 6. Explain.

Objective Ⓑ Estimating When Multiplying Decimals

Just as for addition and subtraction, we can estimate when multiplying decimals to check the reasonableness of our answer.

PRACTICE 4

Multiply: 30.26×2.98. Then estimate to see whether the answer is reasonable.

Example 4 Multiply: 28.06×1.95. Then estimate to see whether the answer is reasonable by rounding each factor, then multiplying the rounded numbers.

Solution:

Exact:	**Estimate 1**	**Estimate 2**
28.06	28 Rounded to ones	30 Rounded to tens
$\times$ 1.95	$\times$ 2	$\times$ 2
14030	56	60
252540		
280600		
54.7170		

The answer 54.7170 is reasonable.

● **Work Practice 4**

As shown in Example 4, estimated results will vary depending on what estimates are used. Notice that estimating results is a good way to see whether the decimal point has been correctly placed.

Objective Ⓒ Multiplying by Powers of 10

There are some patterns that occur when we multiply a number by a power of 10 such as 10, 100, 1000, 10,000, and so on.

$23.6951 \times 10 = 236.951$ Move the decimal point *1 place* to the *right*.

1 zero

$23.6951 \times 100 = 2369.51$ Move the decimal point *2 places* to the *right*.

2 zeros

$23.6951 \times 100,000 = 2,369,510.$ Move the decimal point *5 places* to the *right* (insert a 0).

5 zeros

Answers

3. 3.4608   **4.** 90.1748

✔ **Concept Check Answer**

false: 3 decimal places and 2 decimal places means 5 decimal places in the product

Notice that we move the decimal point the same number of places as there are zeros in the power of 10.

Multiplying Decimals by Powers of 10 such as 10, 100, 1000, 10,000...

Move the decimal point to the *right* the same number of places as there are *zeros* in the power of 10.

Examples Multiply.

5. $7.68 \times 10 = 76.8$ 7.68
6. $23.702 \times 100 = 2370.2$ 23.702
7. $76.3 \times 1000 = 76{,}300$ 76.300

● Work Practice 5–7

PRACTICE 5–7

Multiply.
5. 23.7×10
6. 203.004×100
7. 1.15×1000

There are also powers of 10 that are less than 1. The decimals 0.1, 0.01, 0.001, 0.0001, and so on are examples of powers of 10 less than 1. Notice the pattern when we multiply by these powers of 10:

$569.2 \times 0.1 = 56.92$ Move the decimal point *1 place* to the *left*.
1 decimal place

$569.2 \times 0.01 = 5.692$ Move the decimal point *2 places* to the *left*.
2 decimal places

$569.2 \times 0.0001 = 0.05692$ Move the decimal point *4 places* to the *left* (insert one 0).
4 decimal places

Multiplying Decimals by Powers of 10 such as 0.1, 0.01, 0.001, 0.0001...

Move the decimal point to the *left* the same number of places as there are *decimal places* in the power of 10.

Examples Multiply.

8. $42.1 \times 0.1 = 4.21$ 42.1
9. $76{,}805 \times 0.01 = 768.05$ 76,805.
10. $9.2 \times 0.001 = 0.0092$ 0009.2

● Work Practice 8–10

PRACTICE 8–10

Multiply.
8. 7.62×0.1
9. 1.9×0.01
10. 7682×0.001

Many times we see large numbers written, for example, in the form 451.8 million rather than in the longer standard notation. The next example shows us how to interpret these numbers.

Answers
5. 237   **6.** 20,300.4   **7.** 1150
8. 0.762   **9.** 0.019   **10.** 7.682

PRACTICE 11

In 2015, the population of the United States is projected to be 321.2 million. Write this number in standard notation. (*Source:* United Nations Population Division)

Example 11 In 2050, the population of the United States is projected to be 451.8 million. Write this number in standard notation. (*Source:* U.S. Census Bureau)

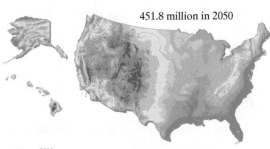

451.8 million in 2050

Solution: 451.8 million = 451.8 × 1 million
= 451.8 × 1,000,000 = 451,800,000

● Work Practice 11

Objective ⓓ Finding the Circumference of a Circle

Recall from Section 1.3 that the distance around a polygon is called its perimeter. The distance around a circle is given the special name **circumference,** and this distance depends on the radius or the diameter of the circle.

> ### *Circumference of a Circle*
>
>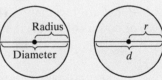
>
> Radius
> Diameter
> r
> d
>
> Circumference = $2 \cdot \pi \cdot$ **r**adius or Circumference = $\pi \cdot$ **d**iameter

In Section 3.2, we learned about the symbol π as the Greek letter pi, pronounced "pie." It is a constant between 3 and 4.

> ### *Approximations for π*
>
> Two common approximations for π are:
>
> $$\pi \approx 3.14 \qquad \text{or} \qquad \pi \approx \frac{22}{7}$$
>
> a decimal approximation   a fraction approximation

PRACTICE 12

Find the circumference of a circle whose radius is 11 meters. Then use the approximation 3.14 for π to approximate this circumference.

△ **Example 12** Circumference of a Circle

Find the circumference of a circle whose radius is 5 inches. Then use the approximation 3.14 for π to approximate the circumference.

Solution: Circumference = $2 \cdot \pi \cdot$ radius
= $2 \cdot \pi \cdot 5$ inches
= 10π inches

Next, we replace π with the approximation 3.14.

Circumference = 10π inches
("is approximately") → $\approx 10(3.14)$ inches
= 31.4 inches

5 inches

The *exact* circumference or distance around the circle is 10π inches, which is *approximately* 31.4 inches.

● Work Practice 12

Answers

11. 321,200,000   **12.** 22π m; 69.08 m

Objective ⒠ Solving Problems by Multiplying Decimals

The solutions to many real-life problems are found by multiplying decimals. We continue using our four problem-solving steps to solve such problems.

Example 13 Finding the Total Cost of Materials for a Job

A college student is hired to paint a billboard with paint costing $2.49 per quart. If the job requires 3 quarts of paint, what is the total cost of the paint?

Solution:

1. UNDERSTAND. Read and reread the problem. The phrase "total cost" might make us think addition, but since this problem requires repeated addition, let's multiply.

2. TRANSLATE.

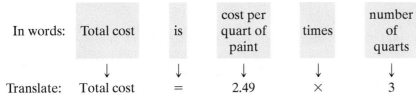

In words: | Total cost | is | cost per quart of paint | times | number of quarts |

Translate: Total cost = 2.49 × 3

3. SOLVE. We can estimate to check our calculations. The number 2.49 rounds to 2 and 2 × 3 = 6.

$$\begin{array}{r} \overset{1\ 2}{2.49} \\ \times\quad 3 \\ \hline 7.47 \end{array}$$

4. INTERPRET. *Check* your work. Since 7.47 is close to our estimate of 6, our answer is reasonable. *State* your conclusion: The total cost of the paint is $7.47.

● Work Practice 13

PRACTICE 13

A biology major is fertilizing her garden. She uses 5.6 ounces of fertilizer per square yard. The garden measures 60.5 square yards. How much fertilizer does she need?

Answer
13. 338.8 oz

Vocabulary and Readiness Check

Use the choices below to fill in each blank.

circumference	left	sum	zeros
decimal places	right	product	factor

1. When multiplying decimals, the number of decimal places in the product is equal to the _____ of the number of decimal places in the factors.
2. In $8.6 \times 5 = 43$, the number 43 is called the _____, while 8.6 and 5 are each called a(n) _____.
3. When multiplying a decimal number by powers of 10, such as 10, 100, 1000, and so on, we move the decimal point in the number to the _____ the same number of places as there are _____ in the power of 10.
4. When multiplying a decimal number by powers of 10, such as 0.1, 0.01, and so on, we move the decimal point in the number to the _____ the same number of places as there are _____ in the power of 10.
5. The distance around a circle is called its _____.

Do not multiply. Just give the number of decimal places in the product. See the Concept Check in this section.

6.
$$\begin{array}{r} 0.46 \\ \times\ 0.81 \\ \hline \end{array}$$

7.
$$\begin{array}{r} 57.9 \\ \times\ 0.36 \\ \hline \end{array}$$

8.
$$\begin{array}{r} 0.428 \\ \times\ \ \ 0.2 \\ \hline \end{array}$$

9.
$$\begin{array}{r} 0.0073 \\ \times\ \ \ \ 21 \\ \hline \end{array}$$

10.
$$\begin{array}{r} 0.028 \\ \times\ 1.36 \\ \hline \end{array}$$

11.
$$\begin{array}{r} 5.1296 \\ \times\ 7.3987 \\ \hline \end{array}$$

3.4 Exercise Set

FOR EXTRA HELP

MyMathLab   Math XL PRACTICE   WATCH   DOWNLOAD   READ   REVIEW

Objectives Ⓐ Ⓑ **Mixed Practice** *Multiply. See Examples 1 through 4. For those exercises marked, also estimate to see if the answer is reasonable.*

1.
$$\begin{array}{r} 0.2 \\ \times\ 0.6 \\ \hline \end{array}$$

2.
$$\begin{array}{r} 0.7 \\ \times\ 0.9 \\ \hline \end{array}$$

3.
$$\begin{array}{r} 1.2 \\ \times\ 0.5 \\ \hline \end{array}$$

4.
$$\begin{array}{r} 6.8 \\ \times\ 0.3 \\ \hline \end{array}$$

5. 0.26×5

6. 0.19×6

7. 5.3×4.2
Exact:
Estimate:

8. 6.2×3.8
Exact:
Estimate:

9.
$$\begin{array}{r} 0.576 \\ \times\ \ \ 0.7 \\ \hline \end{array}$$

10.
$$\begin{array}{r} 0.971 \\ \times\ \ \ 0.5 \\ \hline \end{array}$$

11.
$$\begin{array}{r} 1.0047 \\ \times\ \ \ \ \ 8.2 \\ \hline \end{array}$$
Exact: Estimate:

12.
$$\begin{array}{r} 2.0005 \\ \times\ \ \ \ \ 5.5 \\ \hline \end{array}$$
Exact: Estimate:

13.
$$\begin{array}{r} 490.2 \\ \times\ 0.023 \\ \hline \end{array}$$

14.
$$\begin{array}{r} 300.9 \\ \times\ 0.032 \\ \hline \end{array}$$

15. Multiply 16.003 and 5.31

16. Multiply 31.006 and 3.71

Objective Ⓒ *Multiply. See Examples 5 through 10.*

17. 6.5×10

18. 7.2×100

19. 6.5×0.1

20. 4.7×0.1

21. 7.2×0.01

22. 0.06×0.01

23. 7.093×100

24. 0.5×100

25. 6.046×1000 **26.** 9.1×1000 📱 **27.** 37.62×0.001 **28.** 14.3×0.001

Objectives Ⓐ Ⓑ Ⓒ **Mixed Practice** *Multiply. See Examples 1 through 10.*

29. 0.123×0.4 **30.** 0.216×0.3 **31.** 0.123×100 **32.** 0.216×100

33. 8.6×0.15 **34.** 0.42×5.7 **35.** 9.6×0.01 **36.** 5.7×0.01

37. 562.3×0.001 **38.** 993.5×0.001 **39.** $\begin{array}{r} 5.62 \\ \times\ 7.7 \\ \hline \end{array}$ **40.** $\begin{array}{r} 8.03 \\ \times\ 5.5 \\ \hline \end{array}$

Write each number in standard notation. See Example 11.

41. The storage silos at the main Hershey chocolate factory in Hershey, Pennsylvania, can hold enough cocoa beans to make 5.5 billion Hershey's milk chocolate bars. (*Source:* Hershey Foods Corporation)

42. The total forecasted amount of money spent in the United States on online advertising in 2010 is $26.1 billion. (*Source:* ClickZ)

43. The Blue Streak is the oldest roller coaster at Cedar Point, an amusement park in Sandusky, Ohio. Since 1964, it has given more than 49.8 million rides. (*Source:* Cedar Fair, L.P.)

44. About 45.6 million American households own at least one dog. (*Source:* American Pet Products Association)

45. The most-visited national park in the United States in the Blue Ridge Parkway in Viriginia and North Carolina. An estimated 314 thousand people visit the park each week. (*Source:* National Park Service)

46. In a recent year, approximately 21.4 thousand vessels passed through the Suez Canal. (*Source:* suezcanal.gov)

Objective Ⓓ *Find the circumference of each circle. Then use the approximation 3.14 for π and approximate each circumference. See Example 12.*

📱 **47.**

4 meters

△ **48.**
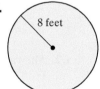
8 feet

△ **49.**

10 centimeters

△ **50.**

22 inches

△ **51.**
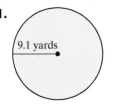
9.1 yards

△ **52.**

5.9 kilometers

Objectives Ⓓ Ⓔ **Mixed Practice** *Solve. For Exercises 53 and 54, the solutions have been started for you. See Examples 12 and 13. For circumference applications, find the exact circumference and then use 3.14 for π to approximate the circumference.*

53. An electrician for Central Power and Light worked 40 hours last week. Calculate his pay before taxes for last week if his hourly wage is $17.88.

Start the solution:

1. UNDERSTAND the problem. Reread it as many times as needed.

2. TRANSLATE into an equation. (Fill in the blanks.)

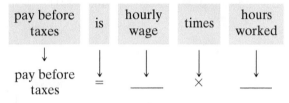

Finish with:

3. SOLVE and **4.** INTERPRET.

54. An assembly line worker worked 20 hours last week. Her hourly rate is $19.52 per hour. Calculate her pay before taxes.

Start the solution:

1. UNDERSTAND the problem. Reread it as many times as needed.

2. TRANSLATE into an equation. (Fill in the blanks.)

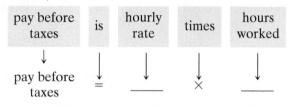

Finish with:

3. SOLVE and **4.** INTERPRET.

55. Under certain conditions, the average cost of driving a medium sedan in 2009 was $0.54 per mile. How much would it have cost to drive a car 8750 miles in 2009? (*Source:* American Automobile Association)

56. At the beginning of 2010, a U.S. airline passenger paid $0.1433, on average, to fly 1 mile. Use this number to calculate the cost to fly from Atlanta, Georgia, to Minneapolis, Minnesota, a distance of 905 miles. Round to the nearest cent. (*Source:* Air Transport Association of America)

57. A 1-ounce serving of cream cheese contains 6.2 grams of saturated fat. How much saturated fat is in 4 ounces of cream cheese? (*Source: Home and Garden Bulletin No. 72;* U.S. Department of Agriculture)

58. A 3.5-ounce serving of lobster meat contains 0.1 gram of saturated fat. How much saturated fat do 3 servings of lobster meat contain? (*Source:* The National Institute of Health)

59. Recall that the face of the Apple iPhone (see Section 3.3) measures 4.5 inches by 2.4 inches. Find the area of the face of the Apple iPhone.

60. Recall that the face of the Google G1 phone (see Section 3.3) measures 4.6 inches by 2.16 inches. Find the area of the face of the Google G1 phone.

61. In 1893, the first ride called a Ferris wheel was constructed by Washington Gale Ferris. Its diameter was 250 feet. Find its circumference. Give an exact answer and an approximation using 3.14 for π. (*Source: The Handy Science Answer Book,* Visible Ink Press, 1994)

62. The radius of Earth is approximately 3950 miles. Find the distance around Earth at the equator. Give an exact answer and an approximation using 3.14 for π. (*Hint:* Find the circumference of a circle with radius 3950 miles.)

63. The London Eye, built for the Millennium celebration in London, resembles a gigantic ferris wheel with a diameter of 135 meters. If Adam Hawn rides the Eye for one revolution, find how far he travels. Give an exact answer and an approximation using 3.14 for π. (*Source:* Londoneye.com)

64. The world's longest suspension bridge is the Akashi Kaikyo Bridge in Japan. This bridge has two circular caissons, which are underwater foundations. If the diameter of a caisson is 80 meters, find its circumference. Give an exact answer and an approximation using 3.14 for π. (*Source: Scientific American; How Things Work Today*)

80 meters
Caisson

65. A meter is a unit of length in the metric system that is approximately equal to 39.37 inches. Sophia Wagner is 1.65 meters tall. Find her approximate height in inches.

66. The doorway to a room is 2.15 meters tall. Approximate this height in inches. (*Hint:* See Exercise 65.)

67. a. Approximate the circumference of each circle.

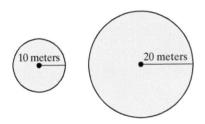

10 meters   20 meters

b. If the radius of a circle is doubled, is its corresponding circumference doubled?

68. a. Approximate the circumference of each circle.

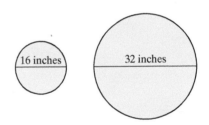

16 inches   32 inches

b. If the diameter of a circle is doubled, is its corresponding circumference doubled?

69. Recall that the top face of the Apple iPod nano (see Section 3.3) measures 3.6 inches by 1.5 inches. Find the area of the face of the iPod nano.

70. Recall that the face of the regular Apple iPod (see Section 3.3) measures 4.1 inches by 2.4 inches. Find the area of the face of this iPod.

Review

Divide. See Sections 1.7 and 2.5.

71. $130 \div 5$

72. $486 \div 27$

73. $2016 \div 56$

74. $1863 \div 69$

75. $2920 \div 365$

76. $2916 \div 6$

77. $\dfrac{24}{7} \div \dfrac{8}{21}$

78. $\dfrac{162}{25} \div \dfrac{9}{75}$

Concept Extensions

Mixed Practice (Sections 3.3, 3.4) *Perform the indicated operations.*

79. $3.6 + 0.04$

80. $7.2 + 0.14 + 98.6$

81. $3.6 - 0.04$

82. $100 - 48.6$

83. 0.221×0.5

84. 3.6×0.04

85. Find how far radio waves travel in 20.6 seconds. (Radio waves travel at a speed of $1.86 \times 100,000$ miles per second.)

86. If it takes radio waves approximately 8.3 minutes to travel from the Sun to the Earth, find approximately how far it is from the Sun to the Earth. (*Hint:* See Exercise 85.)

87. In your own words, explain how to find the number of decimal places in a product of decimal numbers.

88. In your own words, explain how to multiply by a power of 10.

89. Write down two decimal numbers whose product will contain 5 decimal places. Without multiplying, explain how you know your answer is correct.

90. Explain the process for multiplying a decimal number by a power of 10.

3.5 DIVIDING DECIMALS AND ORDER OF OPERATIONS

Objectives

(A) Divide Decimals.

(B) Estimate When Dividing Decimals.

(C) Divide Decimals by Powers of 10.

(D) Solve Problems by Dividing Decimals.

(E) Review Order of Operations to Simplify Expressions Containing Decimals.

Objective (A) Dividing Decimals

Dividing decimal numbers is similar to dividing whole numbers. The only difference is that we place a decimal point in the quotient. If the divisor is a whole number, we place the decimal point in the quotient directly above the decimal point in the dividend, and then divide as with whole numbers. Recall that division can be checked by multiplication.

Dividing by a Whole Number

Step 1: Place the decimal point in the quotient directly above the decimal point in the dividend.

Step 2: Divide as with whole numbers.

Example 1 Divide: $270.2 \div 7$. Check your answer.

Solution: We divide as usual. The decimal point in the quotient is directly above the decimal point in the dividend.

```
        ┌── Write the decimal point.
                38.6  ← quotient
divisor → 7)270.2  ← dividend
          −21↓
            60
          −56↓
            4 2
           −4 2
              0
```

Check:
```
          6 4
          38.6  ← quotient
        ×   7  ← divisor
        270.2  ← dividend
```

The quotient is 38.6.

● Work Practice 1

PRACTICE 1

Divide: $370.4 \div 8$. Check your answer.

Example 2 Divide: $32\overline{)8.32}$

Solution: We divide as usual. The decimal point in the quotient is directly above the decimal point in the dividend.

```
           0.26  ← quotient
divisor → 32)8.32  ← dividend
          −64
           192
          −192
             0
```

Check:
```
          0.26    quotient
        ×  32    divisor
           52
         7 80
         8.32    dividend
```

● Work Practice 2

PRACTICE 2

Divide: $48\overline{)34.08}$. Check your answer.

Sometimes to continue dividing we need to insert zeros after the last digit in the dividend.

Answers
1. 46.3 **2.** 0.71

255

PRACTICE 3

Divide and check.
a. $0.4 \div 8$
b. $13.62 \div 12$

Example 3 Divide and check: $0.5 \div 4$.

Solution:

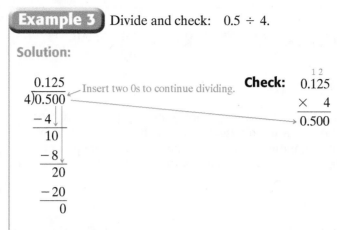

Insert two 0s to continue dividing.

```
    0.125
4)0.500
   -4
    10
    -8
    20
   -20
     0
```

Check:
```
  1 2
  0.125
×     4
  0.500
```

● **Work Practice 3**

If the divisor is not a whole number, before we divide we need to move the decimal point to the right until the divisor is a whole number.

$$1.5\overline{)64.85}$$

divisor ⌐   ⌐ dividend

To understand how this works, let's rewrite

$$1.5\overline{)64.85} \quad \text{as} \quad \frac{64.85}{1.5}$$

and then multiply by 1 in the form of $\frac{10}{10}$. We use the form $\frac{10}{10}$ so that the denominator (divisor) becomes a whole number.

$$\frac{64.85}{1.5} = \frac{64.85}{1.5} \cdot 1 = \frac{64.85}{1.5} \cdot \frac{10}{10} = \frac{64.85 \cdot 10}{1.5 \cdot 10} = \frac{648.5}{15},$$

which can be written as $15.\overline{)648.5}$. Notice that

$$1.5\overline{)64.85} \text{ is equivalent to } 15.\overline{)648.5}$$

The decimal points in the dividend and the divisor were both moved one place to the right, and the divisor is now a whole number. This procedure is summarized next:

Dividing by a Decimal

Step 1: Move the decimal point in the divisor to the right until the divisor is a whole number.

Step 2: Move the decimal point in the dividend to the right the *same number of places* as the decimal point was moved in Step 1.

Step 3: Divide. Place the decimal point in the quotient directly over the moved decimal point in the dividend.

Answers

3. a. 0.05 **b.** 1.135

Example 4 Divide: $10.764 \div 2.3$

Solution: We move the decimal points in the divisor and the dividend one place to the right so that the divisor is a whole number.

$$2.3\overline{)10.764} \qquad \text{becomes} \qquad \begin{array}{r} 4.68 \\ 23.\overline{)107.64} \\ -92 \\ \hline 15\ 6 \\ -13\ 8 \\ \hline 1\ 84 \\ -1\ 84 \\ \hline 0 \end{array}$$

● Work Practice 4

Example 5 Divide: $5.264 \div 0.32$

Solution:

$$0.32\overline{)5.264} \qquad \text{becomes} \qquad \begin{array}{r} 16.45 \\ 32.\overline{)526.40} \quad \text{Insert one 0.} \\ -32 \\ \hline 206 \\ -192 \\ \hline 14\ 4 \\ -12\ 8 \\ \hline 1\ 60 \\ -1\ 60 \\ \hline 0 \end{array}$$

● Work Practice 5

✔**Concept Check** Is it always true that the number of decimal places in a quotient equals the sum of the decimal places in the dividend and divisor?

Example 6 Divide: $17.5 \div 0.48$. Round the quotient to the nearest hundredth.

Solution: First we move the decimal points in the divisor and the dividend two places. Then we divide and round the quotient to the nearest hundredth.

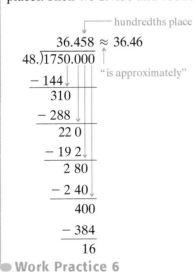

$$\underset{\uparrow}{36.458} \approx 36.46$$

"is approximately"

When rounding to the nearest hundredth, carry the division process out to one more decimal place, the thousandths place.

● Work Practice 6

Objective B Estimating When Dividing Decimals

Just as for addition, subtraction, and multiplication of decimals, we can estimate when dividing decimals to check the reasonableness of our answer.

PRACTICE 7

Divide: 713.7 ÷ 91.5. Then estimate to see whether the proposed answer is reasonable.

Example 7 Divide: 272.356 ÷ 28.4. Then estimate to see whether the proposed result is reasonable.

Solution:

Exact:	Estimate 1		Estimate 2

$$
\begin{array}{r}
9.59 \\
284.\overline{)2723.56} \\
-2556 \\
\hline
167\ 5 \\
-142\ 0 \\
\hline
25\ 56 \\
-25\ 56 \\
\hline
0
\end{array}
$$

Estimate 1:
$$
\begin{array}{r}
9 \\
30\overline{)270}
\end{array}
$$
or
Estimate 2:
$$
\begin{array}{r}
10 \\
30\overline{)300}
\end{array}
$$

The estimate is 9 or 10, so 9.59 is reasonable.

● **Work Practice 7**

✓**Concept Check** If a quotient is to be rounded to the nearest thousandth, to what place should the division be carried out? (Assume that the division carries out to your answer.)

Objective C Dividing Decimals by Powers of 10

As with multiplication, there are patterns that occur when we divide decimals by powers of 10 such as 10, 100, 1000, and so on.

$$\frac{569.2}{10} = 56.92$$ Move the decimal point *1 place* to the *left*.
— 1 zero

$$\frac{569.2}{10,000} = 0.05692$$ Move the decimal point *4 places* to the *left*.
— 4 zeros

This pattern suggests the following rule:

> ### Dividing Decimals by Powers of 10 such as 10, 100, or 1000
> Move the decimal point of the dividend to the *left* the same number of places as there are *zeros* in the power of 10.

PRACTICE 8–9

Divide.

8. $\frac{128.3}{1000}$ **9.** $\frac{0.56}{10}$

Answers
7. 7.8 **8.** 0.1283 **9.** 0.056

✓**Concept Check Answer**
ten-thousandths place

Examples Divide.

8. $\frac{786.1}{1000} = 0.7861$ Move the decimal point *3 places* to the *left*.
— 3 zeros

9. $\frac{0.12}{10} = 0.012$ Move the decimal point *1 place* to the *left*.
— 1 zero

● **Work Practice 8–9**

Objective ⓓ Solving Problems by Dividing Decimals

Many real-life problems involve dividing decimals.

Example 10 Calculating Materials Needed for a Job

A gallon of paint covers a 250-square-foot area. If Betty Adkins wishes to paint a wall that measures 1450 square feet, how many gallons of paint does she need? If she can buy only gallon containers of paint, how many gallon containers does she need?

Solution:

1. UNDERSTAND. Read and reread the problem. We need to know how many 250s are in 1450, so we divide.

2. TRANSLATE.

In words:	number of gallons	is	square feet	divided by	square feet per gallon
	↓	↓	↓	↓	↓
Translate:	number of gallons	=	1450	÷	250

3. SOLVE. Let's see if our answer is reasonable by estimating. The dividend 1450 rounds to 1500 and divisor 250 rounds to 300. Then $1500 \div 300 = 5$.

$$
\begin{array}{r}
5.8 \\
250\overline{)1450.0} \\
-1250 \\
\hline
200\,0 \\
-200\,0 \\
\hline
0
\end{array}
$$

4. INTERPRET. *Check* your work. Since our estimate is close to our answer of 5, our answer is reasonable. *State* your conclusion: Betty needs 5.8 gallons of paint. If she can buy only gallon containers of paint, she needs 6 gallon containers of paint to complete the job.

● Work Practice 10

Objective ⓔ Simplifying Expressions with Decimals

In the remaining examples, we will review the order of operations by simplifying expressions that contain decimals.

Order of Operations

1. Perform all operations within parentheses ( ), brackets [ ], or other grouping symbols such as square roots or fraction bars, starting with the innermost set.

2. Evaluate any expressions with exponents.

3. Multiply or divide in order from left to right.

4. Add or subtract in order from left to right.

PRACTICE 10

A bag of fertilizer covers 1250 square feet of lawn. Tim Parker's lawn measures 14,800 square feet. How many bags of fertilizer does he need? If he can buy only whole bags of fertilizer, how many whole bags does he need?

Answer
10. 11.84 bags; 12 bags

PRACTICE 11

Simplify: $897.8 \div 100 \times 10$

Example 11 Simplify: $723.6 \div 1000 \times 10$

Solution: Multiply or divide in order from left to right.

$$723.6 \div 1000 \times 10 = 0.7236 \times 10 \quad \text{Divide.}$$
$$= 7.236 \quad \text{Multiply.}$$

● Work Practice 11

PRACTICE 12

Simplify: $8.69(3.2 - 1.8)$

Example 12 Simplify: $0.5(8.6 - 1.2)$

Solution: According to the order of operations, we simplify inside the parentheses first.

$$0.5(8.6 - 1.2) = 0.5(7.4) \quad \text{Subtract.}$$
$$= 3.7 \quad \text{Multiply.}$$

● Work Practice 12

PRACTICE 13

Simplify: $\dfrac{20.06 - (1.2)^2 \div 10}{0.02}$

Example 13 Simplify: $\dfrac{5.68 + (0.9)^2 \div 100}{0.2}$

Solution: First we simplify the numerator of the fraction. Then we divide.

$$\frac{5.68 + (0.9)^2 \div 100}{0.2} = \frac{5.68 + 0.81 \div 100}{0.2} \quad \text{Simplify } (0.9)^2.$$
$$= \frac{5.68 + 0.0081}{0.2} \quad \text{Divide.}$$
$$= \frac{5.6881}{0.2} \quad \text{Add.}$$
$$= 28.4405 \quad \text{Divide.}$$

● Work Practice 13

Answers

11. 89.78   **12.** 12.166   **13.** 995.8

 Calculator Explorations

Calculator errors can easily be made by pressing an incorrect key or by not pressing a correct key hard enough. Estimation is a valuable tool that can be used to check calculator results.

Example Use estimation to determine whether the calculator result is reasonable or not. (For example, a result that is not reasonable can occur if proper keys are not pressed.)

Simplify: $82.064 \div 23$

Calculator display: $\boxed{35.68}$

Solution: Round each number to the nearest 10. Since $80 \div 20 = 4$, the calculator display 35.68 is not reasonable.

Use estimation to determine whether each result is reasonable or not.

1. 102.62×41.8 Result: 428.9516

2. $174.835 \div 47.9$ Result: 3.65

3. $1025.68 - 125.42$ Result: 900.26

4. $562.781 + 2.96$ Result: 858.781

Vocabulary and Readiness Check

Use the choices below to fill in each blank. Some choices may be used more than once, and some not used at all.

dividend   divisor   quotient   true

zeros   left   right   false

1. In $6.5 \div 5 = 1.3$, the number 1.3 is called the _____, 5 is the _____, and 6.5 is the _____.
2. To check a division exercise, we can perform the following multiplication: quotient · _____ = _____.
3. To divide a decimal number by a power of 10, such as 10, 100, 1000, and so on, we move the decimal point in the number to the _____ the same number of places as there are _____ in the power of 10.
4. True or false: If $1.058 \div 0.46 = 2.3$, then $2.3 \times 0.46 = 1.058$ _____.

Recall properties of division and simplify.

5. $\dfrac{5.9}{1}$

6. $\dfrac{0.7}{0.7}$

7. $\dfrac{0}{9.86}$

8. $\dfrac{2.36}{0}$

9. $\dfrac{7.261}{7.261}$

10. $\dfrac{8.25}{1}$

11. $\dfrac{11.1}{0}$

12. $\dfrac{0}{89.96}$

3.5 Exercise Set

FOR EXTRA HELP

MyMathLab®   Math XP PRACTICE   WATCH   DOWNLOAD   READ   REVIEW

Objectives A B Mixed Practice *Divide. See Examples 1 through 5 and 7. For those exercises marked, also estimate to see if the answer is reasonable.*

1. $3\overline{)13.8}$

2. $2\overline{)11.8}$

 3. $5\overline{)0.47}$

4. $6\overline{)0.51}$

5. $0.06\overline{)18}$

6. $0.04\overline{)20}$

 7. $0.82\overline{)4.756}$

8. $0.92\overline{)3.312}$

 9. $5.5\overline{)36.3}$
Exact:
Estimate:

10. $2.2\overline{)21.78}$
Exact:
Estimate:

11. $6.195 \div 15$

12. $8.823 \div 17$

13. $0.54 \div 12$

14. $1.35 \div 18$

15. Divide 4.2 by 0.6.

16. Divide 3.6 by 0.9.

17. $0.27\overline{)1.296}$

18. $0.34\overline{)2.176}$

19. $0.02\overline{)42}$

20. $0.03\overline{)24}$

21. $0.6\overline{)18}$

22. $0.4\overline{)20}$

23. $0.005\overline{)35}$

24. $0.0007\overline{)35}$

25. $7.2\overline{)70.56}$
Exact:
Estimate:

26. $6.3\overline{)54.18}$
Exact:
Estimate:

27. $5.4\overline{)51.84}$

28. $7.7\overline{)33.88}$

29. $\dfrac{1.215}{0.027}$

30. $\dfrac{3.213}{0.051}$

31. $0.25\overline{)13.648}$

32. $0.75\overline{)49.866}$

33. $3.78\overline{)0.02079}$

34. $2.96\overline{)0.01332}$

Divide. Round the quotients as indicated. See Example 6.

35. Divide 429.34 by 2.4 and round the quotient to the nearest whole number.

36. Divide 54.8 by 2.6 and round the quotient to the nearest whole number.

37. Divide 0.549 by 0.023 and round the quotient to the nearest hundredth.

38. Divide 0.0453 by 0.98 and round the quotient to the nearest thousandth.

39. Divide 45.23 by 0.4 and round the quotient to the nearest tenth.

40. Divide 83.32 by 0.6 and round the quotient to the nearest tenth.

Objective Ⓒ *Divide. See Examples 8 and 9.*

41. $\dfrac{54.982}{100}$ **42.** $\dfrac{342.54}{100}$ **43.** $\dfrac{26.87}{10}$ **44.** $\dfrac{13.49}{10}$ **45.** $\dfrac{12.9}{1000}$ **46.** $\dfrac{0.27}{1000}$

Objectives Ⓐ Ⓒ **Mixed Practice** *Divide. See Examples 1, 5, 8, and 9.*

47. $7\overline{)88.2}$ **48.** $9\overline{)130.5}$ **49.** $\dfrac{13.1}{10}$ **50.** $\dfrac{17.7}{10}$

51. $6.8\overline{)83.13}$ **52.** $4.8\overline{)123.72}$ **53.** $\dfrac{456.25}{10,000}$ **54.** $\dfrac{986.11}{10,000}$

Objective Ⓓ *Solve. For Exercises 55 and 56, the solutions have been started for you. See Example 10.*

55. Josef Jones is painting the walls of a room. The walls have a total area of 546 square feet. A quart of paint covers 52 square feet. If he must buy paint in whole quarts, how many quarts does he need?

Start the solution:

1. UNDERSTAND the problem. Reread it as many times as needed.

2. TRANSLATE into an equation. (Fill in the blanks.)

number of quarts	is	square feet	divided by	square feet per quart
↓	↓	↓	↓	↓
number of quarts	=	_____	÷	_____

3. SOLVE. Don't forget to round up your quotient.
4. INTERPRET.

56. A shipping box can hold 36 books. If 486 books must be shipped, how many boxes are needed?

Start the solution:

1. UNDERSTAND the problem. Reread it as many times as needed.

2. TRANSLATE into an equation. (Fill in the blanks.)

number of boxes	is	number of books	divided by	books per box
↓	↓	↓	↓	↓
number of boxes	=	_____	÷	_____

3. SOLVE. Don't forget to round up your quotient.
4. INTERPRET.

57. A pound of fertilizer covers 39 square feet of lawn. Vivian Bulgakov's lawn measures 7883.5 square feet. How much fertilizer, to the nearest tenth of a pound, does she need to buy?

58. A page of a book contains about 1.5 kilobytes of information. If a computer disk can hold 740 kilobytes of information, how many pages of a book can be stored on one computer disk? Round to the nearest tenth of a page.

59. There are approximately 39.37 inches in 1 meter. How many meters, to the nearest tenth of a meter, are there in 200 inches?

←———1 meter———→
←—≈39.37 inches—→

60. There are 2.54 centimeters in 1 inch. How many inches are there in 50 centimeters? Round to the nearest tenth.

←———1 inch———→
←——2.54 cm——→

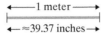 **61.** In the United States, an average child will wear down 730 crayons by his or her tenth birthday. Find the number of boxes of 64 crayons this is equivalent to. Round to the nearest tenth. (*Source:* Binney & Smith Inc.)

62. During a recent year, American farmers received an average of $47.20 per hundred pounds of turkey. What was the average price per pound for turkeys? Round to the nearest cent. (*Source:* National Agricultural Statistics Service)

A child is to receive a dose of 0.5 teaspoon of cough medicine every 4 hours. If the bottle contains 4 fluid ounces, answer Exercises 63 through 66.

63. A fluid ounce equals 6 teaspoons. How many teaspoons are in 4 fluid ounces?

64. The bottle of medicine contains how many doses for the child? (*Hint:* See Exercise 63.)

65. If the child takes a dose every four hours, how many days will the medicine last?

66. If the child takes a dose every six hours, how many days will the medicine last?

67. Americans ages 18–22 drive, on average, 12,900 miles per year. About how many miles each week is that? Round to the nearest tenth. (*Note:* There are 52 weeks in a year.) (*Source:* U.S. Department of Energy)

68. Drake Saucier was interested in the gas mileage on his "new" used car. He filled the tank, drove 423.8 miles, and filled the tank again. When he refilled the tank, it took 19.35 gallons of gas. Calculate the miles per gallon for Drake's car. Round to the nearest tenth.

69. During the 24 hours of the Le Mans endurance auto race in 2009, the winning team of Marc Gene, Alexander Wurz, and David Brabham drove a total of 3230.4 miles in 24 hours. What was their average speed in miles per hour? (*Source:* Automobile Club de l'Ouest)

70. In 2008, Ethiopian runner Tirunesh Dibaba set a new world record for the women's 5000-meter event. Her time for the event was 851.15 seconds. What was her average speed in meters per second? Round to the nearest tenth. (*Source:* USA Today)

71. Candace Parker of the Los Angeles Sparks was the WNBA's Rookie of the Year for 2008. She scored a total of 610 points in the 33 games she played in the 2008 regular season. What was the average number of points she scored per game? Round to the nearest hundredth. (*Source:* Women's National Basketball Association)

72. During the 2008 National Football League regular season, the New Orleans Saints was the top-scoring team with a total of 463 points throughout the season. The Saints played 16 games. What was the average number of points the team scored per game? Round to the nearest hundredth. (*Source:* National Football League)

Objective Ⓔ *Simplify each expression. See Examples 11 through 13.*

73. $0.7(6 - 2.5)$

74. $1.4(2 - 1.8)$

75. $\dfrac{0.29 + 1.69}{3}$

76. $\dfrac{1.697 - 0.29}{0.7}$

77. $30.03 + 5.1 \times 9.9$

78. $60 - 6.02 \times 8.97$

79. $7.8 - 4.83 \div 2.1 + 9.2$

80. $90 - 62.1 \div 2.7 + 8.6$

81. $93.07 \div 10 \times 100$ **82.** $35.04 \div 100 \times 10$ 📱 **83.** $\dfrac{7.8 + 1.1 \times 100 - 3.6}{0.2}$ **84.** $\dfrac{9.6 - 7.8 \div 10 + 1.2}{0.02}$

85. $5(20.6 - 2.06) - (0.8)^2$ **86.** $(10.6 - 9.8)^2 \div 0.01 + 8.6$

87. $6 \div 0.1 + 8.9 \times 10 - 4.6$ **88.** $8 \div 10 + 7.6 \times 0.1 - (0.1)^2$

Review

Write each decimal as a fraction. See Section 3.1.

89. 0.9 **90.** 0.7 **91.** 0.05 **92.** 0.08

Concept Extensions

Mixed Practice (*Sections 3.3, 3.4, 3.5*) *Perform the indicated operation.*

93. $1.278 \div 0.3$ **94.** 1.278×0.3 **95.** $1.278 + 0.3$ **96.** $1.278 - 0.3$

97. $\begin{array}{r} 8.6 \\ \times\, 3.1 \\ \hline \end{array}$ **98.** $7.2 + 0.05 + 49.1$ **99.** $\begin{array}{r} 1000 \\ -\ 95.71 \\ \hline \end{array}$ **100.** $\dfrac{87.2}{10{,}000}$

Choose the best estimate.

101. 8.62×41.7
    a. 36
    b. 32
    c. 360
    d. 3.6

102. $1.437 + 20.69$
    a. 34
    b. 22
    c. 3.4
    d. 2.2

103. $78.6 \div 97$
    a. 7.86
    b. 0.786
    c. 786
    d. 7860

104. $302.729 - 28.697$
    a. 270
    b. 20
    c. 27
    d. 300

Recall from Section 1.7 that the average of a list of numbers is their total divided by how many numbers there are in the list. Use this procedure to find the average of the test scores listed in Exercises 105 and 106. If necessary, round to the nearest tenth.

105. $86, 78, 91, 87$ **106.** $56, 75, 80$

△ **107.** The area of a rectangle is 38.7 square feet. If its width is 4.5 feet, find its length.

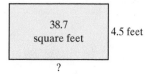

△ **108.** The perimeter of a square is 180.8 centimeters. Find the length of a side.

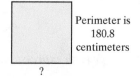

✏ **109.** When dividing decimals, describe the process you use to place the decimal point in the quotient.

✏ **110.** In your own words, describe how to quickly divide a number by a power of 10 such as 10, 100, 1000, etc.

To convert wind speeds in miles per hour to knots, divide by 1.15. Use this information and the Saffir-Simpson Hurricane Intensity chart below to answer Exercises 111 and 112. Round to the nearest tenth.

		Saffir-Simpson Hurricane Intensity Scale		
Category	**Wind Speed**	**Barometric Pressure [inches of mercury (Hg)]**	**Storm Surge**	**Damage Potential**
1 (Weak)	75–95 mph	≥28.94 in.	4–5 ft	Minimal damage to vegetation
2 (Moderate)	96–110 mph	28.50–28.93 in.	6–8 ft	Moderate damage to houses
3 (Strong)	111–130 mph	27.91–28.49 in.	9–12 ft	Extensive damage to small buildings
4 (Very Strong)	131–155 mph	27.17–27.90 in.	13–18 ft	Extreme structural damage
5 (Devastating)	>155 mph	<27.17 in.	>18 ft	Catastrophic building failures possible

111. The chart gives wind speeds in miles per hour. What is the range of wind speeds for a Category 1 hurricane in knots?

112. What is the range of wind speeds for a Category 4 hurricane in knots?

113. A rancher is building a horse corral that's shaped like a rectangle with dimensions of 24.28 meters by 15.675 meters. He plans to make a four-wire fence; that is, he will string four wires around the corral. How much wire will he need?

114. A college student signed up for a new credit card that guarantees her no interest charges on transferred balances for a year. She transferred over a $2523.86 balance from her old credit card. Her minimum payment is $185.35 per month. If she only pays the minimum, will she pay off her balance before interest charges start again?

3.6 FRACTIONS AND DECIMALS

Objective **A** Writing Fractions as Decimals

To write a fraction as a decimal, we interpret the fraction bar to mean division and find the quotient.

Writing Fractions as Decimals

To write a fraction as a decimal, divide the numerator by the denominator.

PRACTICE 1

a. Write $\frac{2}{5}$ as a decimal.

b. Write $\frac{9}{40}$ as a decimal.

Example 1 Write $\frac{1}{4}$ as a decimal.

Solution: $\frac{1}{4} = 1 \div 4$

$$
\begin{array}{r}
0.25 \\
4\overline{)1.00} \\
-\ 8 \\
\hline
20 \\
-20 \\
\hline
0
\end{array}
$$

Thus, $\frac{1}{4}$ written as a decimal is 0.25.

● Work Practice 1

PRACTICE 2

a. Write $\frac{5}{6}$ as a decimal.

b. Write $\frac{2}{9}$ as a decimal.

Example 2 Write $\frac{2}{3}$ as a decimal.

Solution:

$$
\begin{array}{r}
0.666\ldots \\
3\overline{)2.000} \\
-1\,8 \\
\hline
20 \\
-18 \\
\hline
20 \\
-18 \\
\hline
2
\end{array}
$$

This pattern will continue because $\frac{2}{3} = 0.6666\ldots$

Remainder is 2, then 0 is brought down.

Remainder is 2, then 0 is brought down.

Remainder is 2.

Notice the digit 2 keeps occurring as the remainder. This will continue so that the digit 6 will keep repeating in the quotient. We place a bar over the digit 6 to indicate that it repeats.

$$\frac{2}{3} = 0.666\ldots = 0.\overline{6}$$

We can also write a decimal approximation for $\frac{2}{3}$. For example, $\frac{2}{3}$ rounded to the nearest hundredth is 0.67. This can be written as $\frac{2}{3} \approx 0.67$.

● Work Practice 2

Answers

1. **a.** 0.4 **b.** 0.225

2. **a.** $0.8\overline{3}$ **b.** $0.\overline{2}$

Example 3 Write $\frac{22}{7}$ as a decimal. (The fraction $\frac{22}{7}$ is an approximation for π.)
Round to the nearest hundredth.

Solution:

$$
\begin{array}{r}
3.142 \approx 3.14 \\
7\overline{)22.000} \\
-21 \\
\hline
1\,0 \\
-\,7 \\
\hline
30 \\
-28 \\
\hline
20 \\
-14 \\
\hline
6
\end{array}
$$

Carry the division out to the thousandths place.

The fraction $\frac{22}{7}$ in decimal form is approximately 3.14. Thus, $\pi \approx \frac{22}{7}$ (a fraction approximation for π) and $\pi \approx 3.14$ (a decimal approximation for π).

● **Work Practice 3**

PRACTICE 3

Write $\frac{28}{13}$ as a decimal. Round to the nearest thousandth.

Example 4 Write $2\frac{3}{16}$ as a decimal.

Solution:

Option 1. Write the fractional part only as a decimal.

$$
\frac{3}{16} \longrightarrow
\begin{array}{r}
0.1875 \\
16\overline{)3.0000} \\
-1\,6 \\
\hline
1\,40 \\
-1\,28 \\
\hline
120 \\
-112 \\
\hline
80 \\
-80 \\
\hline
0
\end{array}
$$

Thus $2\frac{3}{16} = 2.1875$

Option 2. Write $2\frac{3}{16}$ as an improper fraction, and divide.

$$
2\frac{3}{16} = \frac{35}{16} \longrightarrow
\begin{array}{r}
2.1875 \\
16\overline{)35.0000} \\
-32 \\
\hline
3\,0 \\
-1\,6 \\
\hline
1\,40 \\
-1\,28 \\
\hline
120 \\
-112 \\
\hline
80 \\
-80 \\
\hline
0
\end{array}
$$

Thus $2\frac{3}{16} = 2.1875$

● **Work Practice 4**

PRACTICE 4

Write $3\frac{5}{16}$ as a decimal.

Some fractions may be written as decimals using our knowledge of decimals. From Section 3.1, we know that if the denominator of a fraction is 10, 100, 1000, or so on, we can immediately write the fraction as a decimal. For example,

$$\frac{4}{10} = 0.4, \qquad \frac{12}{100} = 0.12, \text{ and so on.}$$

Answers
3. 2.154   **4.** 3.3125

PRACTICE 5

Write $\dfrac{3}{5}$ as a decimal.

Example 5 Write $\dfrac{4}{5}$ as a decimal.

Solution: Let's write $\dfrac{4}{5}$ as an equivalent fraction with a denominator of 10.

$$\frac{4}{5} = \frac{4}{5} \cdot \frac{2}{2} = \frac{8}{10} = 0.8$$

● **Work Practice 5**

PRACTICE 6

Write $\dfrac{3}{50}$ as a decimal.

Example 6 Write $\dfrac{1}{25}$ as a decimal.

Solution: $\dfrac{1}{25} = \dfrac{1}{25} \cdot \dfrac{4}{4} = \dfrac{4}{100} = 0.04$

● **Work Practice 6**

✓**Concept Check** Suppose you are writing the fraction $\dfrac{9}{16}$ as a decimal. How do you know you have made a mistake if your answer is 1.735?

Objective ⓑ Comparing Fractions and Decimals

Now we can compare decimals and fractions by writing fractions as equivalent decimals.

PRACTICE 7

Insert $<$, $>$, or $=$ to form a true statement.

$\dfrac{1}{5}$ ___ 0.25

Example 7 Insert $<$, $>$, or $=$ to form a true statement.

$\dfrac{1}{8}$ ___ 0.12

Solution: First we write $\dfrac{1}{8}$ as an equivalent decimal. Then we compare decimal places.

$$\begin{array}{r} 0.125 \\ 8)\overline{1.000} \\ -8 \\ \hline 20 \\ -16 \\ \hline 40 \\ -40 \\ \hline 0 \end{array}$$

Original numbers	$\dfrac{1}{8}$	0.12
Decimals	0.125	0.120
Compare	0.125 > 0.12	

Thus, $\dfrac{1}{8} > 0.12$

● **Work Practice 7**

PRACTICE 8

Insert $<$, $>$, or $=$ to form a true statement.

a. $\dfrac{1}{2}$ ___ 0.54 **b.** $0.\overline{4}$ ___ $\dfrac{4}{9}$

c. $\dfrac{5}{7}$ ___ 0.72

Example 8 Insert $<$, $>$, or $=$ to form a true statement.

$0.\overline{7}$ ___ $\dfrac{7}{9}$

Solution: We write $\dfrac{7}{9}$ as a decimal and then compare.

$$\begin{array}{r} 0.77\ldots = 0.\overline{7} \\ 9)\overline{7.00} \\ -63 \\ \hline 70 \\ -63 \\ \hline 7 \end{array}$$

Original numbers	$0.\overline{7}$	$\dfrac{7}{9}$
Decimals	$0.\overline{7}$	$0.\overline{7}$
Compare	$0.\overline{7} = 0.\overline{7}$	

Thus, $0.\overline{7} = \dfrac{7}{9}$

● **Work Practice 8**

Answers

5. 0.6 **6.** 0.06 **7.** $<$
8. a. $<$ **b.** $=$ **c.** $<$

✓ **Concept Check Answer**

$\dfrac{9}{16}$ is less than 1 while 1.735 is greater than 1.

Example 9 Write the numbers in order from smallest to largest.

$$\frac{9}{20}, \frac{4}{9}, 0.456$$

Solution:

Original numbers	$\frac{9}{20}$	$\frac{4}{9}$	0.456
Decimals	0.450	0.444 …	0.456
Compare in order	2nd	1st	3rd

Written in order, we have

1st 2nd 3rd
↓   ↓   ↓
$$\frac{4}{9}, \frac{9}{20}, 0.456$$

● Work Practice 9

Objective ◉ Solving Area Problems Containing Fractions and Decimals

Sometimes real-life problems contain both fractions and decimals. In this section, we solve such problems concerning area. In the next example, we review the area of a triangle. This concept will be studied more in depth in a later chapter.

△ **Example 10** The area of a triangle is Area = $\frac{1}{2}$ · base · height. Find the area of the triangle shown.

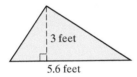

3 feet

5.6 feet

Solution:

$$\text{Area} = \frac{1}{2} \cdot \text{base} \cdot \text{height}$$

$$= \frac{1}{2} \cdot 5.6 \cdot 3$$

$$= 0.5 \cdot 5.6 \cdot 3 \qquad \text{Write } \frac{1}{2} \text{ as the decimal } 0.5.$$

$$= 8.4$$

The area of the triangle is 8.4 square feet.

● Work Practice 10

PRACTICE 9
Write the numbers in order from smallest to largest.

a. $\frac{1}{3}, 0.302, \frac{3}{8}$ **b.** $1.26, 1\frac{1}{4}, 1\frac{2}{5}$

c. $0.4, 0.41, \frac{5}{7}$

PRACTICE 10
Find the area of the triangle.

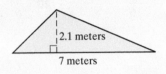

2.1 meters

7 meters

Answers

9. a. $0.302, \frac{1}{3}, \frac{3}{8}$ **b.** $1\frac{1}{4}, 1.26, 1\frac{2}{5}$

c. $0.4, 0.41, \frac{5}{7}$ **10.** 7.35 sq m

Vocabulary and Readiness Check

Answer each exercise "true" or "false."

1. The number $0.\overline{5}$ means 0.555.
2. To write $\dfrac{9}{19}$ as a decimal, perform the division $9\overline{)19}$.
3. $(1.2)^2$ means $(1.2)(1.2)$ or 1.44.
4. To simplify $8.6(9.6 - 4.8)$, we first subtract.

3.6 Exercise Set

FOR EXTRA HELP   PRACTICE WATCH DOWNLOAD READ REVIEW

Objective Ⓐ *Write each number as a decimal. See Examples 1 through 6.*

1. $\dfrac{1}{5}$ 2. $\dfrac{1}{20}$ 3. $\dfrac{17}{25}$ 4. $\dfrac{13}{25}$ 5. $\dfrac{3}{4}$ 6. $\dfrac{3}{8}$

7. $\dfrac{2}{25}$ 8. $\dfrac{3}{25}$ 9. $\dfrac{6}{5}$ 10. $\dfrac{5}{4}$ 11. $\dfrac{11}{12}$ 12. $\dfrac{5}{12}$

13. $\dfrac{17}{40}$ 14. $\dfrac{19}{25}$ 15. $\dfrac{9}{20}$ 16. $\dfrac{31}{40}$ 17. $\dfrac{1}{3}$ 18. $\dfrac{7}{9}$

19. $\dfrac{7}{16}$ 20. $\dfrac{9}{16}$ 21. $\dfrac{7}{11}$ 22. $\dfrac{9}{11}$ 23. $5\dfrac{17}{20}$ 24. $4\dfrac{7}{8}$

25. $\dfrac{78}{125}$ 26. $\dfrac{159}{375}$

Round each number as indicated.

27. Round your decimal answer to Exercise 17 to the nearest hundredth.

28. Round your decimal answer to Exercise 18 to the nearest hundredth.

29. Round your decimal answer to Exercise 19 to the nearest hundredth.

30. Round your decimal answer to Exercise 20 to the nearest hundredth.

31. Round your decimal answer to Exercise 21 to the nearest tenth.

32. Round your decimal answer to Exercise 22 to the nearest tenth.

Write each fraction as a decimal. If necessary, round to the nearest hundredth.

33. Of the U.S. mountains that are over 14,000 feet in elevation, $\dfrac{56}{91}$ are located in Colorado. (*Source:* U.S. Geological Survey)

34. About $\dfrac{21}{50}$ of all blood donors have type A blood. (*Source:* American Red Cross Biomedical Services)

35. The United States contains the greatest fraction of people who use the Internet, with about $\frac{71}{97}$ people using it. (*Source:* UCLA Center for Communication Policy)

36. By 2008, $\frac{39}{62}$ of all individuals who had flown in space were citizens of the United States. (*Source:* World Spaceflight)

37. When first launched, the Hubble Space Telescope's primary mirror was out of shape on the edges by $\frac{1}{50}$ of a human hair. This very small defect made it difficult to focus on faint objects being viewed. Because the HST was in low Earth orbit, it was serviced by a shuttle and the defect was corrected.

38. The two mirrors currently in use in the Hubble Space Telescope were ground so that they do not deviate from a perfect curve by more than $\frac{1}{800,000}$ of an inch. Do not round this number.

Objective Ⓑ *Insert $<$, $>$, or $=$ to form a true statement. See Examples 7 and 8.*

39. 0.562   0.569

40. 0.983   0.988

41. 0.215 $\frac{43}{200}$

42. $\frac{29}{40}$ 0.725

43. $\frac{9}{100}$ 0.0932

44. $\frac{1}{200}$ 0.00563

45. $0.\overline{6}$ $\frac{5}{6}$

46. $0.\overline{1}$ $\frac{2}{17}$

47. $\frac{51}{91}$ $0.56\overline{4}$

48. $0.58\overline{3}$ $\frac{6}{11}$

49. $\frac{1}{9}$ 0.1

50. 0.6 $\frac{2}{3}$

51. 1.38 $\frac{18}{13}$

52. 0.372 $\frac{22}{59}$

53. 7.123 $\frac{456}{64}$

54. 12.713 $\frac{89}{7}$

Write the numbers in order from smallest to largest. See Example 9.

55. 0.34, 0.35, 0.32

56. 0.47, 0.42, 0.40

57. 0.49, 0.491, 0.498

58. 0.72, 0.727, 0.728

59. $\frac{3}{4}$, 0.78, 0.73

60. $\frac{2}{5}$, 0.49, 0.42

61. $\frac{4}{7}$, 0.453, 0.412

62. $\frac{6}{9}$, 0.663, 0.668

63. 5.23, $\frac{42}{8}$, 5.34

64. 7.56, $\frac{67}{9}$, 7.562

65. $\frac{12}{5}$, 2.37, $\frac{17}{8}$

66. $\frac{29}{16}$, 1.75, $\frac{59}{32}$

Objective **C** *Find the area of each triangle or rectangle. See Example 10.*

△ **67.**

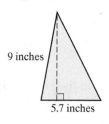

9 inches

5.7 inches

△ **68.**

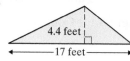

4.4 feet

17 feet

△ **69.**

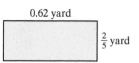

3.6 centimeters

5.2 centimeters

△ **70.**

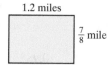

10 meters

25.6 meters

71.

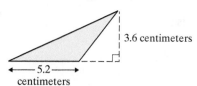

0.62 yard

$\frac{2}{5}$ yard

△

△ **72.**

1.2 miles

$\frac{7}{8}$ mile

Review

Simplify. See Sections 1.9 and 2.10.

73. 2^3

74. 5^4

75. $6^2 \cdot 2$

76. $4 \cdot 3^4$

77. $\left(\frac{1}{3}\right)^4$

78. $\left(\frac{4}{5}\right)^3$

79. $\left(\frac{3}{5}\right)^2$

80. $\left(\frac{7}{2}\right)^2$

81. $\left(\frac{2}{5}\right)\left(\frac{5}{2}\right)^2$

82. $\left(\frac{2}{3}\right)^2\left(\frac{3}{2}\right)^3$

Concept Extensions

Without calculating, describe each number as $< 1, = 1,$ *or* > 1*. See the Concept Check in this section.*

83. 1.0

84. 1.0000

85. 1.00001

86. $\frac{101}{99}$

87. $\frac{99}{100}$

88. $\frac{99}{99}$

In 2009, there were 13,750 commercial radio stations in the United States. The most popular formats are listed in the table along with their counts. Use this graph to answer Exercises 89–92.

89. Write the fraction of radio stations with a country music format as a decimal. Round to the nearest thousandth.

90. Write the fraction of radio stations with a news/talk format as a decimal. Round to the nearest hundredth.

91. Estimate, by rounding each number in the table to the nearest hundred, the total number of stations with the top six formats in 2009.

92. Use your estimate from Exercise 91 to write the fraction of radio stations accounted for by the top six formats as a decimal. Round to the nearest hundredth.

Top Commercial Radio Station Formats in 2009

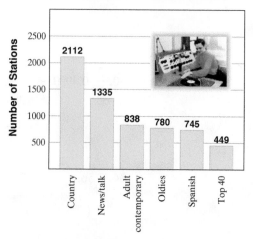

Number of Stations

2500
2000
1500
1000
500

2112
1335
838
780
745
449

Country
News/talk
Adult contemporary
Oldies
Spanish
Top 40

Format (Total stations: 13,750)

93. Describe two ways to determine the larger of two fractions.

94. Describe two ways to write fractions as decimals.

95. Describe two ways to write mixed numbers as decimals.

96. Do you prefer performing operations on decimals or fractions? Why?

Find the value of each expression. Give the result as a decimal.

97. $(9.6)(5) - \dfrac{3}{4}$

98. $2(7.8) - \dfrac{1}{5}$

99. $\left(\dfrac{1}{10}\right)^2 + (1.6)(2.1)$

100. $8.25 - \left(\dfrac{1}{2}\right)^2$

101. $\dfrac{3}{8}(5.9 - 4.7)$

102. $\dfrac{1}{4}(9.6 + 5.2)$

3.7 MEAN, MEDIAN, AND MODE

Objective **A** Finding the Mean

Sometimes we want to summarize data by displaying them in a graph, but sometimes it is also desirable to be able to describe a set of data, or a set of numbers, by a single "middle" number. Three such **measures of central tendency** are the **mean,** the **median,** and the **mode.**

The most common measure of central tendency is the mean (sometimes called the "arithmetic mean" or the "average"). Recall that we first introduced finding the average of a list of numbers in Section 1.7.

> The **mean (average)** of a set of number items is the sum of the items divided by the number of items.
>
> $$\text{mean} = \frac{\text{sum of items}}{\text{number of items}}$$

Example 1 Finding the Mean Time in an Experiment

Seven students in a psychology class conducted an experiment on mazes. Each student was given a pencil and asked to successfully complete the same maze. The timed results are below:

Student	Ann	Thanh	Carlos	Jesse	Melinda	Ramzi	Dayni
Time (Seconds)	13.2	11.8	10.7	16.2	15.9	13.8	18.5

a. Who completed the maze in the shortest time? Who completed the maze in the longest time?

b. Find the mean time.

c. How many students took longer than the mean time? How many students took shorter than the mean time?

Solution:

a. Carlos completed the maze in 10.7 seconds, the shortest time. Dayni completed the maze in 18.5 seconds, the longest time.

b. To find the mean (or average), we find the sum of the items and divide by 7, the number of items.

$$\text{mean} = \frac{13.2 + 11.8 + 10.7 + 16.2 + 15.9 + 13.8 + 18.5}{7}$$

$$= \frac{100.1}{7} = 14.3$$

c. Three students, Jesse, Melinda, and Dayni, had times longer than the mean time. Four students, Ann, Thanh, Carlos, and Ramzi, had times shorter than the mean time.

● **Work Practice 1**

✓**Concept Check** Estimate the mean of the following set of data:

5, 10, 10, 10, 10, 15

Often in college, the calculation of a **grade point average** (GPA) is a **weighted mean** and is calculated as shown in Example 2.

PRACTICE 1

Find the mean of the following test scores: 87, 75, 96, 91, and 78.

Example 2 Calculating Grade Point Average (GPA)

The following grades were earned by a student during one semester. Find the student's grade point average.

Course	Grade	Credit Hours
College mathematics	A	3
Biology	B	3
English	A	3
PE	C	1
Social studies	D	2

Solution: To calculate the grade point average, we need to know the point values for the different possible grades. The point values of grades commonly used in colleges and universities are given below:

A: 4, B: 3, C: 2, D: 1, F: 0

Now, to find the grade point average, we multiply the number of credit hours for each course by the point value of each grade. The grade point average is the sum of these products divided by the sum of the credit hours.

Course	Grade	Point Value of Grade	Credit Hours	Point Value × Credit Hours
College mathematics	A	4	3	12
Biology	B	3	3	9
English	A	4	3	12
PE	C	2	1	2
Social studies	D	1	2	2
		Totals:	12	37

$$\text{grade point average} = \frac{37}{12} \approx 3.08 \text{ rounded to two decimal places}$$

The student earned a grade point average of 3.08.

● **Work Practice 2**

Objective ⓑ Finding the Median

You may have noticed that a very low number or a very high number can affect the mean of a list of numbers. Because of this, you may sometimes want to use another measure of central tendency. A second measure of central tendency is called the **median.** The median of a list of numbers is not affected by a low or high number in the list.

> The **median** of a set of numbers in numerical order is the middle number. If the number of items is odd, the median is the middle number. If the number of items is even, the median is the mean of the two middle numbers.

Example 3 Find the median of the following list of numbers:

25, 54, 56, 57, 60, 71, 98

Solution: Because this list is in numerical order, the median is the middle number, 57.

● **Work Practice 3**

PRACTICE 2

Find the grade point average if the following grades were earned in one semester.

Grade	Credit Hours
A	2
B	4
C	5
D	2
A	2

PRACTICE 3

Find the median of the list of numbers: 5, 11, 14, 23, 24, 35, 38, 41, 43

Answers
2. 2.67 **3.** 24

PRACTICE 4

Find the median of the list of scores:

36, 91, 78, 65, 95, 95, 88, 71

Example 4 Find the median of the following list of scores: 67, 91, 75, 86, 55, 91

Solution: First we list the scores in numerical order and then find the middle number.

55, 67, 75, 86, 91, 91

Since there is an even number of scores, there are two middle numbers, 75 and 86. The median is the mean of the two middle numbers.

$$\text{median} = \frac{75 + 86}{2} = 80.5$$

The median is 80.5.

Helpful Hint Don't forget to write the numbers in order from smallest to largest before finding the median.

● Work Practice 4

Objective C Finding the Mode

The last common measure of central tendency is called the **mode.**

The **mode** of a set of numbers is the number that occurs most often. (It is possible for a set of numbers to have more than one mode or to have no mode.)

PRACTICE 5

Find the mode of the list of numbers:

14, 10, 10, 13, 15, 15, 15, 17, 18, 18, 20

Example 5 Find the mode of the list of numbers:

11, 14, 14, 16, 31, 56, 65, 77, 77, 78, 79

Solution: There are two numbers that occur the most often. They are 14 and 77. This list of numbers has two modes, 14 and 77.

● Work Practice 5

PRACTICE 6

Find the median and the mode of the list of numbers:

26, 31, 15, 15, 26, 30, 16, 18, 15, 35

Example 6 Find the median and the mode of the following set of numbers. These numbers were high temperatures for 14 consecutive days in a city in Montana.

76, 80, 85, 86, 89, 87, 82, 77, 76, 79, 82, 89, 89, 92

Solution: First we write the numbers in numerical order.

76, 76, 77, 79, 80, 82, 82, 85, 86, 87, 89, 89, 89, 92

Since there is an even number of items, the median is the mean of the two middle numbers, 82 and 85.

$$\text{median} = \frac{82 + 85}{2} = 83.5$$

The mode is 89, since 89 occurs most often.

● Work Practice 6

✔**Concept Check** True or false? Every set of numbers *must* have a mean, median, and mode. Explain your answer.

Helpful Hint

Don't forget that it is possible for a list of numbers to have no mode. For example, the list

2, 4, 5, 6, 8, 9

has no mode. There is no number or numbers that occur more often than the others

Answers

4. 83 **5.** 15 **6.** median: 22; mode: 15

✔**Concept Check Answer**

false; a set of numbers may have no mode

Vocabulary and Readiness Check

Use the choices below to fill in each blank. Some choices may be used more than once.

mean	mode	grade point average
median	average	

1. Another word for "mean" is _____.

2. The number that occurs most often in a set of numbers is called the _____.

3. The _____ of a set of number items is $\dfrac{\text{sum of items}}{\text{number of items}}$.

4. The _____ of a set of numbers is the middle number. If the number of numbers is even, it is the _____ of the two middle numbers.

5. An example of weighted mean is a calculation of _____.

3.7 Exercise Set

FOR EXTRA HELP

MyMathLab *Powered by CourseCompass™ and MathXL®*

 Math XP
PRACTICE

 WATCH

 DOWNLOAD

 READ

 REVIEW

Objectives A B C Mixed Practice *For each set of numbers, find the mean, median, and mode. If necessary, round the mean to one decimal place. See Examples 1 and 3 through 6.*

1. 15, 23, 24, 18, 25

2. 45, 36, 28, 46, 52

3. 7.6, 8.2, 8.2, 9.6, 5.7, 9.1

4. 4.9, 7.1, 6.8, 6.8, 5.3, 4.9

5. 0.5, 0.2, 0.2, 0.6, 0.3, 1.3, 0.8, 0.1, 0.5

6. 0.6, 0.6, 0.8, 0.4, 0.5, 0.3, 0.7, 0.8, 0.1

7. 231, 543, 601, 293, 588, 109, 334, 268

8. 451, 356, 478, 776, 892, 500, 467, 780

The ten tallest buildings in the world, completed as of the start of 2009, are listed in the following table. Use this table to answer Exercises 9 through 14. If necessary, round results to one decimal place. See Examples 1 and 3 through 6.

9. Find the mean height of the five tallest buildings.

10. Find the median height of the five tallest buildings.

11. Find the median height of the eight tallest buildings.

12. Find the mean height of the eight tallest buildings.

Building	Height (in Feet)
Taipei 101	1670
Shanghai World Financial Center	1614
Petronas Tower 1, Kuala Lumpur	1483
Petronas Tower 2, Kuala Lumpur	1483
Willis Tower, Chicago	1451
Jin Mao Building, Shanghai	1381
Two International Finance Centre, Hong Kong	1362
CITIC Plaza, Guangzhou	1283
Shun Hing Square, Shenzhen	1260
Empire State Building, New York	1250
(*Source:* Council on Tall Buildings and Urban Habitat)	

13. Given the building heights, explain how you know, without calculating, that the answer to Exercise 10 is greater than the answer to Exercise 11.

14. Given the building heights, explain how you know, without calculating, that the answer to Exercise 12 is less than the answer to Exercise 9.

For Exercises 15 through 18, the grades are given for a student for a particular semester. Find the grade point average. If necessary, round the grade point average to the nearest hundredth. See Example 2.

15.

Grade	Credit Hours
B	3
C	3
A	4
C	4

16.

Grade	Credit Hours
D	1
F	1
C	4
B	5

17.

Grade	Credit Hours
A	3
A	3
A	4
B	3
C	1

18.

Grade	Credit Hours
B	2
B	2
C	3
A	3
B	3

For Exercises 19 through 27, find the mean, median, and mode, as requested. See Examples 1 and 3 through 6. During an experiment, the following times (in seconds) were recorded:

7.8, 6.9, 7.5, 4.7, 6.9, 7.0.

19. Find the mean.   **20.** Find the median.   **21.** Find the mode.

In a mathematics class, the following test scores were recorded for a student:

93, 85, 89, 79, 88, 91.

22. Find the mean.   **23.** Find the median.   **24.** Find the mode.

The following pulse rates were recorded for a group of 15 students:

78, 80, 66, 68, 71, 64, 82, 71, 70, 65, 70, 75, 77, 86, 72.

25. Find the mean.   **26.** Find the median.   **27.** Find the mode.

28. How many pulse rates were higher than the mean?   **29.** How many pulse rates were lower than the mean?

Review

Write each fraction in simplest form. See Section 2.3.

30. $\dfrac{12}{20}$ **31.** $\dfrac{6}{18}$ **32.** $\dfrac{4}{36}$ **33.** $\dfrac{18}{30}$ **34.** $\dfrac{35}{100}$ **35.** $\dfrac{55}{75}$

Concept Extensions

Find the missing numbers in each set of numbers.

36. 16, 18, _____, _____, _____. The mode is 21. The median is 20.

37. _____, _____, _____, 40, _____. The mode is 35. The median is 37. The mean is 38.

38. Write a list of numbers for which you feel the median would be a better measure of central tendency than the mean.

39. Without making any computations, decide whether the median of the following list of numbers will be a whole number. Explain your reasoning.

36, 77, 29, 58, 43

3 Chapter Highlights

Helpful Hint Are you preparing for your test? Use the Test Prep Videos to see the fully worked-out solutions to any of the exercises you want to review.

Definitions and Concepts	Examples
Section 3.1 Introduction to Decimals	

PLACE-VALUE CHART

hundreds	tens	ones	decimal point	tenths	hundredths	thousandths	ten-thousandths	hundred-thousandths
		4	↑	2	6	5		
100	10	1	decimal point	$\frac{1}{10}$	$\frac{1}{100}$	$\frac{1}{1000}$	$\frac{1}{10,000}$	$\frac{1}{100,000}$

4.265 means

$$4 \cdot 1 + 2 \cdot \frac{1}{10} + 6 \cdot \frac{1}{100} + 5 \cdot \frac{1}{1000}$$

or

$$4 + \frac{2}{10} + \frac{6}{100} + \frac{5}{1000}$$

Definitions and Concepts	Examples
WRITING (OR READING) A DECIMAL IN WORDS	Write 3.08 in words. Three and eight hundredths
Step 1: Write the whole number part in words.	
Step 2: Write "and" for the decimal point.	
Step 3: Write the decimal part in words as though it were a whole number, followed by the place value of the last digit.	
A decimal written in words can be written in standard form by reversing the above procedure.	Write "four and twenty-one thousandths" in standard form. 4.021

Section 3.2 Ordering and Rounding	

To **compare decimals,** compare digits in the same place from left to right. When two digits are not equal, the number with the larger digit is the larger decimal.

3.0261 > 3.0186 because

    ↑   ↑

    2 > 1

TO ROUND DECIMALS TO A PLACE VALUE TO THE RIGHT OF THE DECIMAL POINT

Round 86.1256 to the nearest hundredth.

Step 1: Locate the digit to the right of the given place value.

Step 1: 86.12⑤6 — hundredths place / digit to the right

Step 2: If this digit is 5 or greater, add 1 to the digit in the given place value and delete all digits to its right. If this digit is less than 5, delete all digits to the right of the given place value.

Step 2: Since the digit to the right is 5 or greater, we add 1 to the digit in the hundredths place and delete all digits to its right.

86.1256 rounded to the nearest hundredth is 86.13.

Definitions and Concepts	**Examples**

Section 3.3   Adding and Subtracting Decimals

TO ADD OR SUBTRACT DECIMALS

Step 1: Write the decimals so that the decimal points line up vertically.

Step 2: Add or subtract as with whole numbers.

Step 3: Place the decimal point in the sum or difference so that it lines up vertically with the decimal points in the problem.

Add: $4.6 + 0.28$

$$\begin{array}{r} 4.60 \\ +0.28 \\ \hline 4.88 \end{array}$$

Subtract: $2.8 - 1.04$

$$\begin{array}{r} {\overset{7\ 10}{2.8\!\!\!/0}} \\ -1.04 \\ \hline 1.76 \end{array}$$

Section 3.4   Multiplying Decimals and Circumference of a Circle

TO MULTIPLY DECIMALS

Step 1: Multiply the decimals as though they are whole numbers.

Step 2: The decimal point in the product is placed so that the number of decimal places in the product is equal to the *sum* of the number of decimal places in the factors.

The **circumference** of a circle is the distance around the circe.

$C = 2 \cdot \pi \cdot \text{radius}$ or
$C = \pi \cdot \text{diameter}$,

where $\pi \approx 3.14$ or $\dfrac{22}{7}$.

Multiply: 1.48×5.9

$$\begin{array}{r} 1.4\,8 \quad \leftarrow \text{2 decimal places}\\ \times\ \ 5.9 \quad \leftarrow \text{1 decimal place}\\ \hline 1\,3\,3\,2 \\ 7\,4\,0\,0 \\ \hline 8.7\,3\,2 \quad \leftarrow \text{3 decimal places} \end{array}$$

Find the exact circumference of a circle with radius 5 miles and an approximation by using 3.14 for π.

$$\begin{aligned} C &= 2 \cdot \pi \cdot \text{radius}\\ &= 2 \cdot \pi \cdot 5\\ &= 10\pi\\ &\approx 10(3.14)\\ &= 31.4 \end{aligned}$$

The circumference is exactly 10π miles and *approximately* 31.4 miles.

Section 3.5   Dividing Decimals and Order of Operations

TO DIVIDE DECIMALS

Step 1: If the divisor is not a whole number, move the decimal point in the divisor to the right until the divisor is a whole number.

Step 2: Move the decimal point in the dividend to the right the *same number of places* as the decimal point was moved in step 1.

Step 3: Divide. The decimal point in the quotient is directly over the moved decimal point in the dividend.

Divide: $1.118 \div 2.6$

$$\begin{array}{r} 0.43 \\ 2.6\overline{)1.1\,18} \\ -1\,0\,4 \\ \hline 78 \\ -78 \\ \hline 0 \end{array}$$

ORDER OF OPERATIONS

1. Perform all operations within parentheses ( ), brackets [ ], or grouping symbols such as square roots or fraction bars.

2. Evaluate any expressions with exponents.

3. Multiply or divide in order from left to right.

4. Add or subtract in order from left to right.

Simplify.

$$\begin{aligned} 1.9(12.8 - 4.1) &= 1.9(8.7) \quad \text{Subtract.}\\ &= 16.53 \quad \text{Multiply.} \end{aligned}$$

Definitions and Concepts	**Examples**

Section 3.6   Fractions and Decimals

To **write fractions as decimals,** divide the numerator by the denominator.	Write $\dfrac{3}{8}$ as a decimal. $$\begin{array}{r} 0.375 \\ 8\overline{)3.000} \\ -2\,4 \\ \hline 60 \\ -56 \\ \hline 40 \\ -40 \\ \hline 0 \end{array}$$

Section 3.7   Mean, Median, and Mode

The **mean** (or **average**) of a set of number items is $$\text{mean} = \dfrac{\text{sum of items}}{\text{number of items}}$$ The **median** of a set of numbers in numerical order is the middle number. If the number of items is even, the median is the mean of the two middle numbers. The **mode** of a set of numbers is the number that occurs most often. (A set of numbers may have no mode or more than one mode.)	Find the mean, median, and mode of the following set of numbers: 33, 35, 35, 43, 68, 68 $$\text{mean} = \dfrac{33 + 35 + 35 + 43 + 68 + 68}{6} = 47$$ The median is the mean of the two middle numbers, 35 and 43 $$\text{median} = \dfrac{35 + 43}{2} = 39$$ There are two modes because there are two numbers that occur twice: 35 and 68

Chapter 3 Review

(3.1) *Determine the place value of the digit 4 in each decimal.*

1. 23.45

2. 0.000345

Write each decimal in words.

3. 0.45

4. 0.00345

5. 109.23

6. 46.007

Write each decimal in standard form.

7. Two and fifteen hundredths

8. Five hundred three and one hundred two thousandths

Write the decimal as a fraction or a mixed number. Write your answer in simplest form.

9. 0.16

10. 12.023

11. 1.0045

12. 25.25

Write each fraction as a decimal.

13. $\dfrac{9}{10}$

14. $\dfrac{25}{100}$

15. $\dfrac{45}{1000}$

16. $\dfrac{261}{10}$

(3.2) *Insert* $<, >,$ *or* $=$ *to make a true statement.*

17. 0.49   0.43

18. 0.973   0.9730

Write the decimals in order from smallest to largest.

19. 8.6, 8.09, 0.92

20. 0.09, 0.1, 0.091

Round each decimal to the given place value.

21. 0.623, nearest tenth

22. 0.9384, nearest hundredth

Round each money amount to the nearest cent.

23. $0.259

24. $12.461

Solve.

25. In a recent year, engaged couples in the United States spent an average of $31,304.35 on their wedding. Round this number to the nearest whole dollar.

26. A certain kind of chocolate candy bar contains 10.75 teaspoons of sugar. Write this number as a mixed number.

(3.3) *Add or subtract as indicated.*

27. 2.4 + 7.12

28. 3.9 − 1.2

29. 6.4 + 0.88

30. 19.02 + 6.98 + 0.007

31. 892.1 − 432.4

32. 100.342 − 0.064

33. Subtract 34.98 from 100.

34. Subtract 10.02 from 200.

35. Find the total distance between Grove City and Jerome.

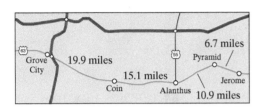

36. The price of oil was $49.02 per barrel on October 23. It was $51.46 on October 24. Find by how much the price of oil increased from the 23rd to the 24th.

△ **37.** Find the perimeter.

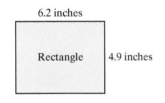

△ **38.** Find the perimeter.

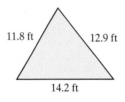

(3.4) *Multiply.*

39. 3.7
     × 5

40. 9.1
     × 6

41. 7.2 × 10

42. 9.345 × 1000

43. 4.02
     × 2.3

44. 39.02
     × 87.3

Solve.

△ **45.** Find the exact circumference of the circle. Then use the approximation 3.14 for π and approximate the circumference.

46. A kilometer is approximately 0.625 mile. It is 102 kilometers from Hays to Colby. Write 102 kilometers in miles to the nearest tenth of a mile.

Write each number in standard notation.

47. Saturn is a distance of about 887 million miles from the Sun.

48. The tail of a comet can be over 600 thousand miles long.

(3.5) *Divide. Round the quotient to the nearest thousandth if necessary.*

49. 3)0.2631

50. 20)316.5

51. 21 ÷ 0.3

52. 0.0063 ÷ 0.03

53. $0.34\overline{)2.74}$

54. $19.8\overline{)601.92}$

55. $\dfrac{2.67}{100}$

56. $\dfrac{93}{10}$

57. There are approximately 3.28 feet in 1 meter. Find how many meters are in 24 feet to the nearest tenth of a meter.

      ←——1 meter——→
      ←— ≈3.28 feet —→

58. George Strait pays $69.71 per month to pay back a loan of $3136.95. In how many months will the loan be paid off?

Simplify each expression.

59. $7.6 \times 1.9 + 2.5$

60. $(2.3)^2 - 1.4$

61. $\dfrac{7 + 0.74}{0.06}$

62. $\dfrac{(1.5)^2 + 0.5}{0.05}$

63. $0.9(6.5 - 5.6)$

64. $0.0726 \div 10 \times 1000$

(3.6) *Write each fraction as a decimal. Round to the nearest thousandth if necessary.*

65. $\dfrac{4}{5}$

66. $\dfrac{12}{13}$

67. $2\dfrac{1}{3}$

68. $\dfrac{13}{60}$

Insert <, >, or = to make a true statement.

69. $0.392 \quad 0.3920$

70. $0.\overline{4} \quad \dfrac{4}{9}$

71. $0.293 \quad \dfrac{5}{17}$

72. $\dfrac{4}{7} \quad 0.625$

Write the numbers in order from smallest to largest.

73. $0.839, \dfrac{17}{20}, 0.837$

74. $\dfrac{18}{11}, 1.63, \dfrac{19}{12}$

Find each area.

△ **75.**

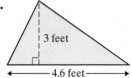

3 feet

←——4.6 feet——→

△ **76.**

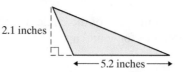

2.1 inches

←——5.2 inches——→

(3.7) *Find the mean, median, and any mode(s) for each list of numbers. If necessary, round to the nearest tenth.*

77. 13, 23, 33, 14, 6

78. 45, 86, 21, 60, 86, 64, 45

79. 14,000, 20,000, 12,000, 20,000, 36,000, 45,000

80. 560, 620, 123, 400, 410, 300, 400, 780, 430, 450

For Exercises 39 and 40, the grades are given for a student for a particular semester. Find each grade point average. If necessary, round the grade point average to the nearest hundredth.

81.

Grade	Credit Hours
A	3
A	3
C	2
B	3
C	1

82.

Grade	Credit Hours
B	3
B	4
C	2
D	2
B	3

Answers to Selected Exercises

Answers to Selected Exercises

Chapter 3 Decimals

Section 3.1

Vocabulary and Readiness Check   **1.** words; standard form   **3.** and   **5.** tens   **7.** tenths

Exercise Set 3.1   **1.** six and fifty-two hundredths   **3.** sixteen and twenty-three hundredths   **5.** two hundred five thousandths   **7.** one hundred sixty-seven and nine thousandths   **9.** two hundred and five thousandths   **11.** one hundred five and six tenths   **13.** two and forty-three hundredths   **15.** eighty-seven and ninety-seven hundredths   **17.** one hundred fourteen and five tenths   **19.** R. W. Financial; 321.42; Three hundred twenty-one and 42/100   **21.** Bell South; 59.68; Fifty-nine and 68/100   **23.** 6.5   **25.** 9.08   **27.** 705.625   **29.** 0.0046   **31.** 32.52   **33.** 1.3   **35.** $\frac{3}{10}$ **37.** $\frac{27}{100}$ **39.** $\frac{4}{5}$ **41.** $\frac{3}{20}$ **43.** $5\frac{47}{100}$ **45.** $\frac{6}{125}$ **47.** $7\frac{1}{125}$ **49.** $15\frac{401}{500}$ **51.** $\frac{601}{2000}$ **53.** $487\frac{8}{25}$ **55.** 0.6   **57.** 0.45   **59.** 3.7   **61.** 0.268   **63.** 0.09   **65.** 4.026   **67.** 0.028   **69.** 56.3   **71.** 0.43; forty-three hundredths   **73.** 0.8; $\frac{8}{10}$ or $\frac{4}{5}$ **75.** seventy-seven thousandths; $\frac{77}{1000}$ **77.** 47,260   **79.** 47,000   **81.** answers may vary   **83.** twenty-six million, eight hundred forty-nine thousand, five hundred seventy-six hundred-billionths   **85.** 17.268

Section 3.2

Vocabulary and Readiness Check   **1.** circumference   **3.** after

Exercise Set 3.2   **1.** <   **3.** >   **5.** <   **7.** =   **9.** <   **11.** >   **13.** 0.006, 0.0061, 0.06   **15.** 0.03, 0.042, 0.36   **17.** 1.01, 1.09, 1.1, 1.16   **19.** 20.905, 21.001, 21.03, 21.12   **21.** 0.6   **23.** 0.23   **25.** 0.594   **27.** 98,210   **29.** 12.3   **31.** 17.67   **33.** 0.5   **35.** 0.130   **37.** 3830   **39.** $0.07   **41.** $42,650   **43.** $27   **45.** $0.20   **47.** 0.4 cm   **49.** 1.56 hr   **51.** $48   **53.** 1.74 min   **55.** 24.623 hr   **57.** 2.8 min   **59.** 5766   **61.** 71   **63.** 243   **65.** b   **67.** a   **69.** 41.654; $41\frac{327}{500}$; Lance Armstrong   **71.** 40.789, 40.788, 40.413, 39.233   **73.** answers may vary   **75.** answers may vary   **77.** 0.26499, 0.25786   **79.** 0.10299, 0.1037, 0.1038, 0.9   **81.** $3100 million

Section 3.3

Calculator Explorations   **1.** 328.742   **3.** 5.2414   **5.** 865.392

Vocabulary and Readiness Check   **1.** 37.0   **3.** difference; minuend; subtrahend   **5.** false

Exercise Set 3.3   **1.** 3.5   **3.** 6.83   **5.** 0.094   **7.** 622.012   **9.** 583.09   **11.** Exact: 465.56; Estimate:
$$\begin{array}{r} 230 \\ +\,230 \\ \hline 460 \end{array}$$
  13. Exact: 115.123; Estimate:
$$\begin{array}{r} 100 \\ 6 \\ +\quad9 \\ \hline 115 \end{array}$$
15. 27.0578   **17.** 56.432   **19.** 6.5   **21.** 15.3   **23.** 598.23   **25.** Exact: 1.83; Estimate: $6 - 4 = 2$ **27.** 861.6   **29.** 376.89   **31.** Exact: 876.6; Estimate: 1000
$$\begin{array}{r} -\,100 \\ \hline 900 \end{array}$$
33. 194.4   **35.** 2.9988   **37.** 16.3   **39.** 88.028   **41.** 84.072   **43.** 243.17   **45.** 56.83   **47.** 3.16   **49.** $7.52   **51.** $454.71   **53.** $0.14   **55.** 28.56 m   **57.** 10.2 in.   **59.** 2.23 degrees Fahrenheit   **61.** 285.8 mph   **63.** 763.035 mph   **65.** 13.8 in.   **67.** $0.32   **69.** 12.4 million (12,400,000)   **71.** 240.8 in.   **73.** 67.44 ft   **75.** $1.475   **77.** 715.05 hr   **79.** Switzerland   **81.** 4.43 lb   **83.**

Country	Pounds of Chocolate per Person
Switzerland	22.36
Austria	20.13
Ireland	19.47
Germany	18.04
Norway	17.93

85. 46   **87.** 3870   **89.** $\frac{4}{9}$ **91.** incorrect;
$$\begin{array}{r} 9.200 \\ 8.630 \\ +\,4.005 \\ \hline 21.835 \end{array}$$
  93. 6.08 in.   **95.** $1.20   **97.** 1 nickel, 1 dime, and 2 pennies; 3 nickels and 2 pennies; 1 dime and 7 pennies; 2 nickels and 7 pennies   **99.** answers may vary   **101.** answers may vary

Section 3.4

Vocabulary and Readiness Check   **1.** sum   **3.** right; zeros   **5.** circumference   **7.** 3   **9.** 4   **11.** 8

Exercise Set 3.4   **1.** 0.12   **3.** 0.6   **5.** 1.3   **7.** Exact: 22.26; Estimate: $5 \times 4 = 20$ **9.** 0.4032   **11.** Exact: 8.23854; Estimate:
$$\begin{array}{r} 1 \\ \times\,8 \\ \hline 8 \end{array}$$
  13. 11.2746   **15.** 84.97593   **17.** 65   **19.** 0.65   **21.** 0.072   **23.** 709.3   **25.** 6046   **27.** 0.03762   **29.** 0.0492   **31.** 12.3   **33.** 1.29   **35.** 0.096   **37.** 0.5623   **39.** 43.274   **41.** 5,500,000,000   **43.** 49,800,000   **45.** 314,000   **47.** $8\pi \approx 25.12$ m   **49.** $10\pi \approx 31.4$ cm   **51.** $18.2\pi \approx 57.148$ yd   **53.** $715.20   **55.** $4725   **57.** 24.8 g   **59.** 10.8 sq in.   **61.** 250π ft ≈ 785 ft   **63.** 135π m ≈ 423.9 m   **65.** 64.9605 in.   **67. a.** 62.8 m and 125.6 m   **b.** yes   **69.** 5.4 sq in.   **71.** 26   **73.** 36   **75.** 8   **77.** 9   **79.** 3.64   **81.** 3.56   **83.** 0.1105   **85.** 3,831,600 mi   **87.** answers may vary   **89.** answers may vary

Section 3.5

Calculator Explorations **1.** not reasonable **3.** reasonable

Vocabulary and Readiness Check **1.** quotient; divisor; dividend **3.** left; zeros **5.** 5.9 **7.** 0 **9.** 1 **11.** undefined

Exercise Set 3.5 **1.** 4.6 **3.** 0.094 **5.** 300 **7.** 5.8 **9.** Exact: 6.6; Estimate: $6\overline{)36}$ **11.** 0.413 **13.** 0.045 **15.** 7 **17.** 4.8 **19.** 2100 **21.** 30
23. 7000 **25.** Exact: 9.8; Estimate: $7\overline{)70}$ **27.** 9.6 **29.** 45 **31.** 54.592 **33.** 0.0055 **35.** 179 **37.** 23.87 **39.** 113.1 **41.** 0.54982 **43.** 2.687
45. 0.0129 **47.** 12.6 **49.** 1.31 **51.** 12.225 **53.** 0.045625 **55.** 11 qt **57.** 202.1 lb **59.** 5.1 m **61.** 11.4 boxes **63.** 24 tsp **65.** 8 days
67. 248.1 mi **69.** 134.6 mph **71.** 18.48 points per game **73.** 2.45 **75.** 0.66 **77.** 80.52 **79.** 14.7 **81.** 930.7 **83.** 571 **85.** 92.06
87. 144.4 **89.** $\frac{9}{10}$ **91.** $\frac{1}{20}$ **93.** 4.26 **95.** 1.578 **97.** 26.66 **99.** 904.29 **101.** c **103.** b **105.** 85.5 **107.** 8.6 ft **109.** answers may vary
111. 65.2–82.6 knots **113.** 319.64 m

Section 3.6

Vocabulary and Readiness Check **1.** false **3.** true

Exercise Set 3.6 **1.** 0.2 **3.** 0.68 **5.** 0.75 **7.** 0.08 **9.** 1.2 **11.** $0.91\overline{6}$ **13.** 0.425 **15.** 0.45 **17.** $0.\overline{3}$ **19.** 0.4375 **21.** $0.\overline{63}$ **23.** 5.85 **25.** 0.624
27. 0.33 **29.** 0.44 **31.** 0.6 **33.** 0.62 **35.** 0.73 **37.** 0.02 **39.** < **41.** = **43.** < **45.** < **47.** < **49.** > **51.** < **53.** < **55.** 0.32, 0.34, 0.35
57. 0.49, 0.491, 0.498 **59.** $0.73, \frac{3}{4}, 0.78$ **61.** $0.412, 0.453, \frac{4}{7}$ **63.** $5.23, \frac{42}{8}, 5.34$ **65.** $\frac{17}{8}, 2.37, \frac{12}{5}$ **67.** 25.65 sq in. **69.** 9.36 sq cm **71.** 0.248 sq yd
73. 8 **75.** 72 **77.** $\frac{1}{81}$ **79.** $\frac{9}{25}$ **81.** $\frac{5}{2}$ **83.** = 1 **85.** > 1 **87.** < 1 **89.** 0.154 **91.** 6100 stations **93.** answers may vary **95.** answers may vary
97. 47.25 **99.** 3.37 **101.** 0.45

Section 3.7

Vocabulary and Readiness Check **1.** average **3.** mean (or average) **5.** grade point average

Exercise Set 3.7 **1.** mean: 21; median: 23; no mode **3.** mean: 8.1; median: 8.2; mode: 8.2 **5.** mean: 0.5; median: 0.5; mode: 0.2 and 0.5
7. mean: 370.9; median: 313.5; no mode **9.** 1540.2 ft **11.** 1467 ft **13.** answers may vary **15.** 2.79 **17.** 3.64 **19.** 6.8 **21.** 6.9 **23.** 88.5 **25.** 73
27. 70 and 71 **29.** 9 rates **31.** $\frac{1}{3}$ **33.** $\frac{3}{5}$ **35.** $\frac{11}{15}$ **37.** 35, 35, 37, 43 **39.** yes; answers may vary

Chapter 3 Review

1. tenths **2.** hundred-thousandths **3.** forty-five hundredths **4.** three hundred forty-five hundred-thousandths
5. one hundred nine and twenty-three hundredths **6.** forty-six and seven thousandths **7.** 2.15 **8.** 503.102 **9.** $\frac{4}{25}$ **10.** $12\frac{23}{1000}$ **11.** $1\frac{9}{2000}$
12. $25\frac{1}{4}$ **13.** 0.9 **14.** 0.25 **15.** 0.045 **16.** 26.1 **17.** > **18.** = **19.** 0.92, 8.09, 8.6 **20.** 0.09, 0.091, 0.1 **21.** 0.6 **22.** 0.94 **23.** $0.26 **24.** $12.46
25. $31,304 **26.** $10\frac{3}{4}$ **27.** 9.52 **28.** 2.7 **29.** 7.28 **30.** 26.007 **31.** 459.7 **32.** 100.278 **33.** 65.02 **34.** 189.98 **35.** 52.6 mi **36.** $2.44 **37.** 22.2 in.
38. 38.9 ft **39.** 18.5 **40.** 54.6 **41.** 72 **42.** 9345 **43.** 9.246 **44.** 3406.446 **45.** 14π m, 43.96 m **46.** 63.8 mi **47.** 887,000,000 **48.** 600,000
49. 0.0877 **50.** 15.825 **51.** 70 **52.** 0.21 **53.** 8.059 **54.** 30.4 **55.** 0.0267 **56.** 9.3 **57.** 7.3 m **58.** 45 mo **59.** 16.94 **60.** 3.89 **61.** 129 **62.** 55
63. 0.81 **64.** 7.26 **65.** 0.8 **66.** 0.923 **67.** $2.\overline{3}$ or 2.333 **68.** $0.21\overline{6}$ or 0.217 **69.** = **70.** = **71.** < **72.** < **73.** $0.837, 0.839, \frac{17}{20}$ **74.** $\frac{19}{12}, 1.63, \frac{18}{11}$
75. 6.9 sq ft **76.** 5.46 sq in. **77.** mean: 17.8; median: 14; no mode **78.** mean: 58.1; median: 60; mode: 45 and 86
79. mean: 24,500; median: 20,000; mode: 20,000 **80.** mean: 447.3; median: 420; mode: 400 **81.** 3.25 **82.** 2.57

4

Ratio, Proportion, Percent, and Unit Conversion

4.1 RATIO AND PROPORTION

Objectives

- **A** Write Ratios as Fractions.
- **B** Write Rates as Fractions.
- **C** Determine Whether Proportions Are True.
- **D** Find an Unknown Number in a Proportion.
- **E** Solve Problems by Writing Proportions.

Objective **A** Writing Ratios as Fractions

A **ratio** is the quotient of two quantities. A ratio, in fact, is no different from a fraction, except that a ratio is sometimes written using notation other than fractional notation. For example, the ratio of 1 to 2 can be written as

$$1 \text{ to } 2 \quad \text{or} \quad \frac{1}{2} \quad \text{or} \quad 1:2$$

fractional notation   colon notation

These ratios are all read as, "the ratio of 1 to 2."

✓**Concept Check** How should each ratio be read aloud?

a. $\frac{8}{5}$ **b.** $\frac{5}{8}$

In this section, we write ratios using fractional notation. If the fraction happens to be an improper fraction, do not write the fraction as a mixed number. Why? The mixed number form is not a ratio or quotient of two quantities.

Writing a Ratio as a Fraction

The order of the quantities is important when writing ratios. To write a ratio as a fraction, write the *first number* of the ratio as the *numerator* of the fraction and the *second number* as the *denominator*.

Helpful Hint

The ratio of 6 to 11 is $\frac{6}{11}$, *not* $\frac{11}{6}$.

Example 1 Write the ratio of 12 to 17 using fractional notation.

Solution: The ratio is $\frac{12}{17}$.

Helpful Hint Don't forget that order is important when writing ratios. The ratio $\frac{17}{12}$ is *not* the same as the ratio $\frac{12}{17}$.

● Work Practice 1

To simplify a ratio, we just write the fraction in simplest form. Common factors as well as common units can be divided out.

PRACTICE 1

Write the ratio of 20 to 23 using fractional notation.

Answer

1. $\frac{20}{23}$

✓ **Concept Check Answers**
a. "the ratio of eight to five"
b. "the ratio of five to eight"

287

PRACTICE 2

Write the ratio of $8 to $6 as a fraction in simplest form.

PRACTICE 3

Write the ratio of 1.71 to 4.56 as a fraction in simplest form.

PRACTICE 4

Use the circle graph below to write the ratio of work miles to total miles as a fraction in simplest form.

Work
4800 miles

Medical
150 miles

Vacation/
other
900 miles

Visit friends
1800 miles

Shopping
1800 miles

School/
church
600 miles

Social/
recreational
1950 miles

Family business
3000 miles

Total yearly mileage: 15,000

Sources: The American Automobile Manufacturers Association and The National Automobile Dealers Association.

△ PRACTICE 5

Given the triangle shown:

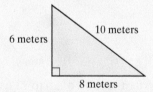

10 meters

6 meters

8 meters

a. Find the ratio of the length of the shortest side to the length of the longest side.

b. Find the ratio of the length of the longest side to the perimeter of the triangle.

Answers

2. $\frac{4}{3}$ 3. $\frac{3}{8}$ 4. $\frac{8}{25}$ 5. a. $\frac{3}{5}$ b. $\frac{5}{12}$

✓ **Concept Check Answer**

$\frac{7}{5}$ would be the ratio of the rectangle's length to its width.

Example 2 Write the ratio of $15 to $10 as a fraction in simplest form.

Solution:

$$\frac{\$15}{\$10} = \frac{15}{10} = \frac{3 \cdot \overset{1}{\cancel{5}}}{2 \cdot \cancel{5}_{1}} = \frac{3}{2}$$

● Work Practice 2

> **Helpful Hint**
>
> In this example, although $\frac{3}{2} = 1\frac{1}{2}$, a ratio is a quotient of *two* quantities. For that reason, ratios are not written as mixed numbers.

If a ratio contains decimal numbers or mixed numbers, we simplify by writing the ratio as a ratio of whole numbers.

Example 3 Write the ratio of 2.6 to 3.1 as a fraction in simplest form.

Solution: The ratio in fraction form is

$$\frac{2.6}{3.1}$$

Now let's clear the ratio of decimals.

$$\frac{2.6}{3.1} = \frac{2.6}{3.1} \cdot 1 = \frac{2.6}{3.1} \cdot \frac{10}{10} = \frac{2.6 \cdot 10}{3.1 \cdot 10} = \frac{26}{31} \quad \text{Simplest form}$$

● Work Practice 3

Example 4 Writing a Ratio from a Circle Graph

The circle graph in the margin shows the part of a car's total mileage that falls into a particular category. Write the ratio of medical miles to total miles as a fraction in simplest form.

Solution: $\dfrac{\text{medical miles}}{\text{total miles}} = \dfrac{150 \cancel{\text{ miles}}}{15,000 \cancel{\text{ miles}}} = \dfrac{150}{15,000} = \dfrac{\overset{1}{\cancel{150}}}{\underset{1}{\cancel{150}} \cdot 100} = \dfrac{1}{100}$

● Work Practice 4

Example 5 Given the rectangle shown:

a. Find the ratio of its width to its length.

b. Find the ratio of its length to its perimeter.

7 feet

5 feet

Solution:

a. The ratio of its width to its length is

$$\frac{\text{width}}{\text{length}} = \frac{5 \ \cancel{\text{feet}}}{7 \ \cancel{\text{feet}}} = \frac{5}{7}$$

b. Recall that the perimeter of the rectangle is the distance around the rectangle: $7 + 5 + 7 + 5 = 24$ feet. The ratio of its length to its perimeter is

$$\frac{\text{length}}{\text{perimeter}} = \frac{7 \ \cancel{\text{feet}}}{24 \ \cancel{\text{feet}}} = \frac{7}{24}$$

● Work Practice 5

✓ **Concept Check**   Explain why the answer $\frac{7}{5}$ would be incorrect for part (a) of Example 5.

Objective Ⓑ Writing Rates as Fractions

A special type of ratio is a rate. **Rates** are used to compare *different* kinds of quantities. For example, suppose that a recreational runner can run 3 miles in 33 minutes. If we write this rate as a fraction, we have

$$\frac{3 \text{ miles}}{33 \text{ minutes}} = \frac{1 \text{ mile}}{11 \text{ minutes}} \quad \text{In simplest form}$$

Helpful Hint

When comparing quantities with different units, write the units as part of the comparison. They do not divide out.

Same Units: $\dfrac{3 \cancel{\text{ inches}}}{12 \cancel{\text{ inches}}} = \dfrac{1}{4}$

Different Units: $\dfrac{2 \text{ miles}}{20 \text{ minutes}} = \dfrac{1 \text{ mile}}{10 \text{ minutes}}$ Units are still written.

Example 6 Write the rate as a fraction in simplest form: 10 nails every 6 feet

Solution: $\dfrac{10 \text{ nails}}{6 \text{ feet}} = \dfrac{5 \text{ nails}}{3 \text{ feet}}$

● Work Practice 6

PRACTICE 6

Write the rate as a fraction in simplest form: 12 commercials every 45 minutes

Examples Write each rate as a fraction in simplest form.

7. \$2160 for 12 weeks is $\dfrac{2160 \text{ dollars}}{12 \text{ weeks}} = \dfrac{180 \text{ dollars}}{1 \text{ week}}$

8. 360 miles on 16 gallons of gasoline is $\dfrac{360 \text{ miles}}{16 \text{ gallons}} = \dfrac{45 \text{ miles}}{2 \text{ gallons}}$

● Work Practice 7–8

PRACTICE 7–8

Write each rate as a fraction in simplest form.
7. \$1680 for 8 weeks
8. 236 miles on 12 gallons of gasoline

Note: A **unit rate** is a rate with a denominator of 1. A familiar example of a unit rate is mph, read as **"miles per hour."** For example, 55 mph means 55 miles per 1 hour or $\dfrac{55 \text{ miles}}{1 \text{ hour}}$.

If we write the rate in Example 8 as a unit rate, we have

Helpful Hint
In this context, the word "per" translates to division.

$$\frac{45 \text{ miles}}{2 \text{ gallons}} = \frac{22.5 \text{ miles}}{1 \text{ gallon}} \text{ or } 22.5 \text{ miles/gallon}$$

Objective Ⓒ Determining Whether Proportions Are True

A **proportion** is a statement that 2 ratios or rates are equal. For example,

$$\frac{5}{6} = \frac{10}{12}$$

is a proportion. We can read this as, "5 is to 6 as 10 is to 12."

Let's write each sentence as a proportion.
"12 diamonds is to 15 rubies as 4 diamonds is to 5 rubies" translates to

$$\begin{array}{ccc} \text{diamonds} \rightarrow & \dfrac{12}{15} = \dfrac{4}{5} & \leftarrow \text{diamonds} \\ \text{rubies} \rightarrow & & \leftarrow \text{rubies} \end{array}$$

Answers
6. $\dfrac{4 \text{ commercials}}{15 \text{ min}}$ 7. $\dfrac{\$210}{1 \text{ wk}}$
8. $\dfrac{59 \text{ mi}}{3 \text{ gal}}$

"5 hits is to 9 at bats as 20 hits is to 36 at bats" translates to

hits $\rightarrow$ $\dfrac{5}{9} = \dfrac{20}{36}$ $\leftarrow$ hits
at bats $\rightarrow$ $\leftarrow$ at bats

Helpful Hint

Notice in the previous proportions that the numerators contain the same units and the denominators contain the same units. In this text, proportions will be written so that this is the case.

Like other mathematical statements, a proportion may be either true or false. A proportion is true if its ratios are equal. Since ratios are fractions, one way to determine whether a proportion is true is to write both fractions in simplest form and compare them.

Another way is to compare cross products as we did in Section 2.3.

Using Cross Products to Determine Whether Proportions Are True or False

Cross products

$a \cdot d$ $b \cdot c$

$$\frac{a}{b} = \frac{c}{d}$$

If cross products are *equal*, the proportion is *true*.
If $ad = bc$, then the proportion is true.

If cross products are *not equal*, the proportion is *false*.
If $ad \neq bc$, then the proportion is false.

PRACTICE 9

Is $\dfrac{3}{6} = \dfrac{4}{8}$ a true proportion?

Example 9 Is $\dfrac{2}{3} = \dfrac{4}{6}$ a true proportion?

Solution:

Cross products

$2 \cdot 6$ $3 \cdot 4$

$$\frac{2}{3} = \frac{4}{6}$$

$2 \cdot 6 \overset{?}{=} 3 \cdot 4$ Are cross products equal?
$12 = 12$ Equal, so proportion is true.

Since the cross products are equal, the proportion is true.

● **Work Practice 9**

PRACTICE 10

Is $\dfrac{3.6}{6} = \dfrac{5.4}{8}$ a true proportion?

Example 10 Is $\dfrac{4.1}{7} = \dfrac{2.9}{5}$ a true proportion?

Solution:

Cross products

$4.1 \cdot 5$ $7 \cdot 2.9$

$$\frac{4.1}{7} = \frac{2.9}{5}$$

$4.1 \cdot 5 \overset{?}{=} 7 \cdot 2.9$ Are cross products equal?
$20.5 \neq 20.3$ Not equal, so proportion is false.

Since the cross products are not equal, $\dfrac{4.1}{7} \neq \dfrac{2.9}{5}$. The proportion is false.

● **Work Practice 10**

Answers

9. yes   **10.** no

Objective ⒟ Finding Unknown Numbers in Proportions

When one number of a proportion is unknown, we can use cross products to find the unknown number. For example, to find the unknown number n in the proportion $\frac{n}{30} = \frac{2}{3}$, we first find the cross products.

$n \cdot 3$ $30 \cdot 2$ Find the cross products.

$$\frac{n}{30} = \frac{2}{3}$$

If the proportion is true, then cross products are equal.

$n \cdot 3 = 30 \cdot 2$ Set the cross products equal to each other.

$n \cdot 3 = 60$ Write $2 \cdot 30$ as 60.

To find the unknown number n, we ask ourselves, "What number times 3 is 60?" The number is 20 and can be found by dividing 60 by 3.

$n = \dfrac{60}{3}$ Divide 60 by the number multiplied by n.

$n = 20$ Simplify.

Thus, the unknown number is 20.

To *check*, replace n with this value, 20, and verify that a true proportion results.

Finding an Unknown Value n in a Proportion

Step 1: Set the cross products equal to each other.

Step 2: Divide the number not multiplied by n by the number multiplied by n.

Example 11 Find the value of the unknown number n.

$$\frac{51}{34} = \frac{3}{n}$$

Solution:

Step 1:

$$\frac{51}{34} = \frac{3}{n}$$

$51 \cdot n = 34 \cdot 3$ Set cross products equal.

$51 \cdot n = 102$ Multiply.

Step 2:

$n = \dfrac{102}{51}$ Divide 102 by 51, the number multiplied by n.

$n = 2$ Simplify.

Check to see that 2 is the unknown number n.

● Work Practice 11

PRACTICE 11

Find the value of the unknown number n.

$$\frac{15}{2} = \frac{60}{n}$$

Answer

11. $n = 8$

PRACTICE 12

Find the unknown number n.

$$\frac{8}{n} = \frac{5}{9}$$

Example 12 Find the unknown number n.

$$\frac{7}{n} = \frac{6}{5}$$

Solution:

Step 1:

$$\frac{7}{n} = \frac{6}{5}$$

$7 \cdot 5 = n \cdot 6$ Set the cross products equal to each other.

$35 = n \cdot 6$ Multiply.

Step 2:

$$\frac{35}{6} = n$$ Divide 35 by 6, the number multiplied by n.

$$5\frac{5}{6} = n$$

Check to see that $5\frac{5}{6}$ is the unknown number.

● **Work Practice 12**

PRACTICE 13

Find the unknown number n.

$$\frac{n}{6} = \frac{0.7}{1.2}$$

Example 13 Find the unknown number n.

$$\frac{n}{3} = \frac{0.8}{1.5}$$

Solution:

Step 1:

$$\frac{n}{3} = \frac{0.8}{1.5}$$

$n \cdot 1.5 = 3 \cdot 0.8$ Set the cross products equal to each other.

$n \cdot 1.5 = 2.4$ Multiply.

Step 2:

$$n = \frac{2.4}{1.5}$$ Divide 2.4 by 1.5, the number multiplied by n.

$n = 1.6$ Simplify.

Check to see that 1.6 is the unknown number.

● **Work Practice 13**

Objective ⓔ Solving Problems by Writing Proportions

Writing proportions is a powerful tool for solving problems in almost every field, including business, chemistry, biology, health sciences, and engineering, as well as in daily life. Given a specified ratio (or rate) of two quantities, a proportion can be used to determine an unknown quantity.

In this section, we use the same problem-solving steps that we have used earlier in this text.

Answers

12. $n = 14\frac{2}{5}$ **13.** $n = 3.5$

Example 14 Determining Distances from a Map

On a chamber of commerce map of Abita Springs, 5 miles corresponds to 2 inches. How many miles correspond to 7 inches?

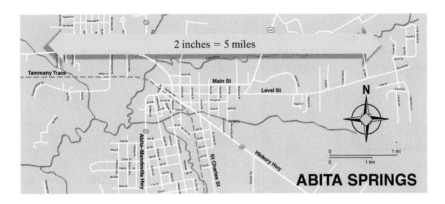

Solution:

1. UNDERSTAND. Read and reread the problem. You may want to draw a diagram.

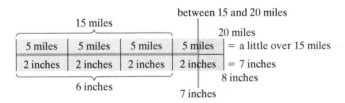

    From the diagram we can see that a reasonable solution should be between 15 and 20 miles.

2. TRANSLATE. We will let n represent our unknown number. Since 5 miles corresponds to 2 inches as n miles corresponds to 7 inches, we have the proportion

    $$\begin{array}{l} \text{miles} \quad \rightarrow \\ \text{inches} \quad \rightarrow \end{array} \frac{5}{2} = \frac{n}{7} \begin{array}{l} \leftarrow \quad \text{miles} \\ \leftarrow \quad \text{inches} \end{array}$$

3. SOLVE: In earlier sections, we estimated to obtain a reasonable answer. Notice we did this in Step 1 above.

    $$\frac{5}{2} = \frac{n}{7}$$

    $5 \cdot 7 = 2 \cdot n$　　　Set the cross products equal to each other.

    $35 = 2 \cdot n$　　　Multiply.

    $\dfrac{35}{2} = n$　　　Divide 35 by 2, the number multiplied by n.

    $n = 17\dfrac{1}{2}$ or 17.5　　　Simplify.

4. INTERPRET. *Check* your work. This result is reasonable since it is between 15 and 20 miles. *State* your conclusion: 7 inches corresponds to 17.5 miles.

● **Work Practice 14**

PRACTICE 14

On an architect's blueprint, 1 inch corresponds to 4 feet. How long is a wall represented by a $4\dfrac{1}{4}$-inch line on the blueprint?

Answer
14. 17 ft

Helpful Hint

We can also solve Example 14 by writing the proportion

$$\frac{2 \text{ inches}}{5 \text{ miles}} = \frac{7 \text{ inches}}{n \text{ miles}}$$

Although other proportions may be used to solve Example 14, we will solve by writing proportions so that the numerators have the same unit measures and the denominators have the same unit measures.

PRACTICE 15

An auto mechanic recommends that 3 ounces of isopropyl alcohol be mixed with a tankful of gas (14 gallons) to increase the octane of the gasoline for better engine performance. At this rate, how many gallons of gas can be treated with a 16-ounce bottle of alcohol?

Example 15 Finding Medicine Dosage

The standard dose of an antibiotic is 4 cc (cubic centimeters) for every 25 pounds (lb) of body weight. At this rate, find the standard dose for a 140-lb woman.

Solution:

1. UNDERSTAND. Read and reread the problem. You may want to draw a diagram to estimate a reasonable solution.

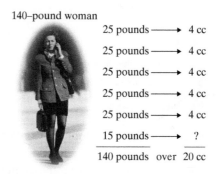

140–pound woman

25 pounds ⟶	4 cc
25 pounds ⟶	4 cc
25 pounds ⟶	4 cc
25 pounds ⟶	4 cc
25 pounds ⟶	4 cc
15 pounds ⟶	?
140 pounds over	20 cc

From the diagram, we can see that a reasonable solution is a little over 20 cc.

2. TRANSLATE. We will let n represent the unknown number. From the problem, we know that 4 cc is to 25 pounds as n cc is to 140 pounds, or

$$\begin{array}{c} \text{cubic centimeters} \rightarrow \\ \text{pounds} \rightarrow \end{array} \quad \frac{4}{25} = \frac{n}{140} \quad \begin{array}{c} \leftarrow \text{cubic centimeters} \\ \leftarrow \text{pounds} \end{array}$$

3. SOLVE:

$$\frac{4}{25} = \frac{n}{140}$$

$$4 \cdot 140 = 25 \cdot n \qquad \text{Set the cross products equal to each other.}$$

$$560 = 25 \cdot n \qquad \text{Multiply.}$$

$$\frac{560}{25} = n \qquad \text{Divide 560 by 25, the number multiplied by } n.$$

$$n = 22\frac{2}{5} \text{ or } 22.4 \qquad \text{Simplify.}$$

4. INTERPRET. *Check* your work. This result is reasonable since it is a little over 20 cc. *State* your conclusion: The standard dose for a 140-lb woman is 22.4 cc.

● **Work Practice 15**

Answer

15. $74\frac{2}{3}$ or $74.\overline{6}$ gal

Vocabulary and Readiness Check

Use the choices below to fill in each blank. Some choices may be used more than once, some not at all.

rate	unit	ratio	different
numerator	true	cross products	denominator
division	false	proportion	

Answer each statement true or false.

1. The quotient of two quantities is called a ratio. _____

2. The ratio $\frac{7}{5}$ means the same as the ratio $\frac{5}{7}$. _____

3. The ratio $\frac{7.2}{8.1}$ is in simplest form. _____

4. The ratio $\frac{10 \text{ feet}}{30 \text{ feet}}$ is in simplest form. _____

5. The ratio $\frac{9}{10}$ is in simplest form. _____

6. The ratio 2 to 5 equals $\frac{5}{2}$ in fractional notation. _____

7. The ratio 30 : 41 equals $\frac{30}{41}$ in fractional notation. _____

8. The ratio 15 to 45 equals $\frac{3}{1}$ in fractional notation. _____

9. A rate with a denominator of 1 is called a(n) _____ rate.

10. A(n) _____ is the quotient of two quantities.

11. The word *per* translates to "_____."

12. To write a rate as a unit rate, divide the _____ of the rate by the _____.

13. $\frac{4.2}{8.4} = \frac{1}{2}$ is called a(n) _____ while $\frac{7}{8}$ is called a(n) _____.

14. In $\frac{a}{b} = \frac{c}{d}$, $a \cdot d$ and $b \cdot c$ are called _____.

15. In a proportion, if cross products are equal, the proportion is _____.

16. In a proportion, if cross products are not equal, the proportion is _____.

4.1 Exercise Set

FOR EXTRA HELP

Objective Ⓐ *Write each ratio using fractional notation. Do not simplify. See Examples 1 through 3.*

1. 23 to 10

2. 14 to 5

3. $3\frac{3}{4}$ to $1\frac{2}{3}$

4. $2\frac{2}{5}$ to $6\frac{1}{2}$

Write each ratio as a ratio of whole numbers using fractional notation. Write the fraction in simplest form. See Examples 1 through 3.

5. 16 to 24

6. 25 to 150

7. 7.7 to 10

8. 8.1 to 10

9. 10 hours to 24 hours

10. 18 quarts to 30 quarts

11. $32 to $100

12. $46 to $102

13. 24 days to 14 days

14. 80 miles to 120 miles

15. 32,000 bytes to 46,000 bytes

16. 600 copies to 150 copies

17. 8 inches to 20 inches

18. 9 yards to 2 yards

Find the ratio described in each exercise as a fraction in simplest form. See Examples 4 and 5.

19. Find the ratio of the longest side to the perimeter of the right-triangular-shaped billboard.

8 feet, 15 feet, 17 feet

20. Find the ratio of the width to the perimeter of the rectangular vegetable garden.

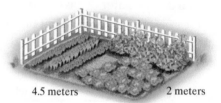

4.5 meters   2 meters

In 2009, 558 films by U.S. production companies were released. Use this information for Exercises 21 and 22.

21. In 2009, 20 digital 3-D films were released by U.S. production companies. Find the ratio of digital films to total films for 2009.

22. In 2009, 400 independent films were released by U.S. production companies. Find the ratio of independent films to total films for 2009.

23. Of the U.S. mountains that are over 14,000 feet in elevation, 57 are located in Colorado and 19 are located in Alaska. Find the ratio of the number of mountains over 14,000 feet found in Alaska to the number of mountains over 14,000 feet found in Colorado. (*Source:* U.S. Geological Survey)

24. Citizens of the United States eat an average of 25 pints of ice cream per year. Residents of the New England states eat an average of 39 pints of ice cream per year. Find the ratio of the amount of ice cream eaten by New Englanders to the amount eaten by the average U.S. citizen. (*Source:* International Dairy Foods Association)

Objective **B** *Write each rate as a fraction in simplest form. See Examples 6 through 8.*

25. 5 shrubs every 15 feet

26. 14 lab tables for 28 students

27. 15 returns for 100 sales

28. 150 graduate students for 8 advisors

29. 8 phone lines for 36 employees

30. 6 laser printers for 28 computers

31. 18 gallons of pesticide for 4 acres of crops

32. 4 inches of rain in 18 hours

33. 6 flight attendants for 200 passengers

34. 240 pounds of grass seed for 9 lawns

35. 355 calories in a 10-fluid-ounce chocolate milkshake (*Source: Home and Garden Bulletin No. 72,* U.S. Department of Agriculture)

36. 160 calories in an 8-fluid-ounce serving of cream of tomato soup (*Source: Home and Garden Bulletin No. 72,* U.S. Department of Agriculture)

Write each rate as a unit rate.

37. 330 calories in a 3-ounce serving

38. 275 miles in 11 hours

39. A hummingbird moves its wings at a rate of 5400 wingbeats a minute. Write this rate in wingbeats per second.

40. A bat moves its wings at a rate of 1200 wingbeats a minute. Write this rate in wingbeats per second.

Objective **C** *Determine whether each proportion is a true proportion. See Examples 9 and 10.*

41. $\dfrac{8}{6} = \dfrac{9}{7}$

42. $\dfrac{7}{12} = \dfrac{4}{7}$

43. $\dfrac{9}{36} = \dfrac{2}{8}$

44. $\dfrac{8}{24} = \dfrac{3}{9}$

Write each sentence as a proportion. Then determine whether the proportion is a true proportion. See Examples 9 and 10.

45. one and eight tenths is to two as four and five tenths is to five

46. fifteen hundredths is to three as thirty-five hundredths is to seven

47. two thirds is to one fifth as two fifths is to one ninth

48. ten elevenths is to three fourths as one fourth is to one half

Objective **D** *For each proportion, find the unknown number n. See Examples 11 through 13.*

49. $\dfrac{n}{5} = \dfrac{6}{10}$

50. $\dfrac{n}{3} = \dfrac{12}{9}$

51. $\dfrac{18}{54} = \dfrac{3}{n}$

52. $\dfrac{25}{100} = \dfrac{7}{n}$

53. $\dfrac{n}{8} = \dfrac{50}{100}$

54. $\dfrac{n}{21} = \dfrac{12}{18}$

55. $\dfrac{8}{15} = \dfrac{n}{6}$

56. $\dfrac{12}{10} = \dfrac{n}{16}$

57. $\dfrac{0.05}{12} = \dfrac{n}{0.6}$

58. $\dfrac{7.8}{13} = \dfrac{n}{2.6}$

59. $\dfrac{8}{\frac{1}{3}} = \dfrac{24}{n}$

60. $\dfrac{12}{\frac{3}{4}} = \dfrac{48}{n}$

61. $\dfrac{n}{1\frac{1}{5}} = \dfrac{4\frac{1}{6}}{6\frac{2}{3}}$

62. $\dfrac{n}{3\frac{1}{8}} = \dfrac{7\frac{3}{5}}{2\frac{3}{8}}$

63. $\dfrac{25}{n} = \dfrac{3}{\frac{7}{30}}$

64. $\dfrac{9}{n} = \dfrac{5}{\frac{11}{15}}$

Objective **E** *Solve. For Exercises 65 and 66, the solutions have been started for you. See Examples 14 and 15.*
An NBA basketball player averages 45 baskets for every 100 attempts.

65. If he attempted 800 field goals, how many baskets did he make?

Start the solution:

1. UNDERSTAND the problem. Reread it as many times as needed. Let's let

   n = how many field goals he made

2. TRANSLATE into an equation.

   baskets (field goals) → $\dfrac{45}{100} = \dfrac{n}{800}$ ← baskets (field goals)
   attempts → ← attempts

3. SOLVE the equation. Set cross products equal to each other and solve.

   $$\dfrac{45}{100} \diagup\!\!\!\!\diagdown \dfrac{n}{800}$$

   Finish by SOLVING and **4.** INTERPRET.

66. If he made 225 baskets, how many did he attempt?

Start the solution:

1. UNDERSTAND the problem. Reread it as many times as needed. Let's let

   n = how many baskets attempted

2. TRANSLATE into an equation.

   baskets → $\dfrac{45}{100} = \dfrac{225}{n}$ ← baskets
   attempts → ← attempts

3. SOLVE the equation. Set cross products equal to each other and solve.

   $$\dfrac{45}{100} \diagup\!\!\!\!\diagdown \dfrac{225}{n}$$

   Finish by SOLVING and **4.** INTERPRET.

It takes a word processor 30 minutes to word process and spell check 4 pages.

67. Find how long it takes her to word process and spell check 22 pages.

68. Find how many pages she can word process and spell check in 4.5 hours.

On an architect's blueprint, 1 inch corresponds to 8 feet.

69. Find the length of a wall represented by a line $2\dfrac{7}{8}$ inches long on the blueprint.

70. Find the length of a wall represented by a line $5\dfrac{1}{4}$ inches long on the blueprint.

A Honda Civic Hybrid car averages 627 miles on a 12.3-gallon tank of gas.

71. Manuel Lopez is planning a 1250-mile vacation trip in his Honda Civic Hybrid. Find how many gallons of gas he can expect to burn. Round to the nearest gallon.

72. Ramona Hatch has enough money to put 6.9 gallons of gas in her Honda Civic Hybrid. She is planning on driving home from college for the weekend. If her home is 290 miles away, should she make it home before she runs out of gas?

The scale on an Italian map states that 1 centimeter corresponds to 30 kilometers.

73. Find how far apart Milan and Rome are if their corresponding points on the map are 15 centimeters apart.

74. On the map, a small Italian village is located 0.4 centimeter from the Mediterranean Sea. Find the actual distance.

A bag of Scott fertilizer covers 3000 square feet of lawn.

△ **75.** Find how many bags of fertilizer should be purchased to cover a rectangular lawn 260 feet by 180 feet.

△ **76.** Find how many bags of fertilizer should be purchased to cover a square lawn measuring 160 feet on each side.

A self-tanning lotion advertises that a 3-oz bottle will provide four applications.

77. Jen Haddad found a great deal on a 14-oz bottle of the self-tanning lotion she had been using. Based on the advertising claims, how many applications of the self-tanner should Jen expect? Round down to the smaller whole number.

78. The Community College thespians need fake tans for a play they are doing. If the play has a cast of 35, how many ounces of self-tanning lotion should the cast purchase? Round up to the next whole number of ounces.

The school's computer lab goes through 5 reams of printer paper every 3 weeks.

79. Find out how long a case of printer paper is likely to last (a case of paper holds 8 reams of paper). Round to the nearest week.

80. How many cases of printer paper should be purchased to last the entire semester of 15 weeks? Round up to the next case.

81. In the Seattle Space Needle, the elevators whisk you to the revolving restaurant at a speed of 800 feet in 60 seconds. If the revolving restaurant is 500 feet up, how long will it take you to reach the restaurant by elevator? (*Source:* Seattle Space Needle)

82. A 16-oz grande Tazo Black Iced Tea at Starbucks has 80 calories. How many calories are there in a 24-oz venti Tazo Black Iced Tea? (*Source:* Starbucks Coffee Company)

83. Mosquitos are annoying insects. To eliminate mosquito larvae, a certain granular substance can be applied to standing water in a ratio of 1 tsp per 25 sq ft of standing water.

   a. At this rate, find how many teaspoons of granules must be used for 450 square feet.

   b. If 3 tsp = 1 tbsp, how many tablespoons of granules must be used?

84. Another type of mosquito control is liquid, where 3 oz of pesticide is mixed with 100 oz of water. This mixture is sprayed on roadsides to control mosquito breeding grounds hidden by tall grass.

   a. If one mixture of water with this pesticide can treat 150 feet of roadway, how many ounces of pesticide are needed to treat one mile? (*Hint:* 1 mile = 5280 feet)

   b. If 8 liquid ounces equals one cup, write your answer to part **a** in cups. Round to the nearest cup.

85. The daily supply of oxygen for one person is provided by 625 square feet of lawn. A total of 3750 square feet of lawn would provide the daily supply of oxygen for how many people? (*Source:* Professional Lawn Care Association of America)

86. In a recent year, approximately $16 billion of the $40 billion Americans spent on their pets was spent on pet food. Petsmart had $4,672,656 in net sales that year. How much of Petsmart's net sales would you expect to have been spent on pet food? (*Source:* American Pet Products Manufacturers Association and Petsmart)

87. A student would like to estimate the height of the Statue of Liberty in New York City's harbor. The length of the Statue of Liberty's right arm is 42 feet. The student's right arm is 2 feet long and her height is $5\frac{1}{3}$ feet. Use this information to estimate the height of the Statue of Liberty. How close is your estimate to the statue's actual height of 111 feet, 1 inch from heel to top of head? (*Source:* National Park Service)

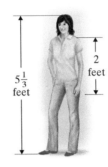

88. The length of the Statue of Liberty's index finger is 8 feet while the height to the top of the head is about 111 feet. Suppose your measurements are proportionally the same as this statue and your height is 5 feet.

  a. Use this information to find the proposed length of your index finger. Give an exact measurement and then a decimal rounded to the nearest hundredth.

  b. Measure your index finger and write it as a decimal in feet rounded to the nearest hundredth. How close is the length of your index finger to the answer to part **a**? Explain why.

89. There are 72 milligrams of cholesterol in a 3.5-ounce serving of lobster. How much cholesterol is in 5 ounces of lobster? Round to the nearest tenth of a milligram. (*Source:* The National Institute of Health)

90. There are 76 milligrams of cholesterol in a 3-ounce serving of skinless chicken. How much cholesterol is in 8 ounces of chicken? (*Source:* USDA)

91. The adult daily dosage for a certain medicine is 150 mg (milligrams) of medicine for every 20 pounds of body weight.

  a. At this rate, find the daily dose for a man who weighs 275 pounds.

  b. If the man is to receive 500 mg of this medicine every 8 hours, is he receiving the proper dosage?

92. The adult daily dosage for a certain medicine is 80 mg (milligrams) for every 25 pounds of body weight.

  a. At this rate, find the daily dose for a woman who weighs 190 pounds.

  b. If she is to receive this medicine every 6 hours, find the amount to be given every 6 hours.

93. The gas/oil ratio for a certain chainsaw is 50 to 1.

  a. How much oil (in gallons) should be mixed with 5 gallons of gasoline?

  b. If 1 gallon equals 128 fluid ounces, write the answer to part **a** in fluid ounces. Round to the nearest whole ounce.

94. The gas/oil ratio for a certain tractor mower is 20 to 1.

  a. How much oil (in gallons) should be mixed with 10 gallons of gas?

  b. If 1 gallon equals 4 quarts, write the answer to part **a** in quarts.

Review

Find the prime factorization of each number. See Section 2.2.

95. 20   **96.** 24   **97.** 200   **98.** 300   **99.** 32   **100.** 81

Concept Extensions

As we have seen earlier, proportions are often used in medicine dosage calculations. The exercises below have to do with liquid drug preparations, where the weight of the drug is contained in a volume of solution. The description of mg and ml below will help.

mg *means milligrams (A paper clip weighs about a gram. A milligram is about the weight of* $\dfrac{1}{1000}$ *of a paper clip.)*

ml *means milliliter (A liter is about a quart. A milliliter is about the amount of liquid in* $\dfrac{1}{1000}$ *of a quart.)*

One way to solve the applications below is to set up the proportion $\dfrac{\text{mg}}{\text{ml}} = \dfrac{\text{mg}}{\text{ml}}$.

A solution strength of 15 mg of medicine in 1 ml of solution is available.

101. If a patient needs 12 mg of medicine, how many ml do you administer?

102. If a patient need 33 mg of medicine, how many ml do you administer?

A solution strength of 8 mg of medicine in 1 ml of solution is available.

103. If a patient needs 10 mg of medicine, how many ml do you administer?

104. If a patient needs 6 mg of medicine, how many ml do you administer?

105. Is the ratio $\dfrac{11}{15}$ the same as the ratio of $\dfrac{15}{11}$? Explain your answer.

106. Explain why the ratio $\dfrac{40}{17}$ is incorrect for Exercise 19.

107. Explain the difference between a ratio and a proportion.

108. Explain how to find the unknown number in a proportion such as $\dfrac{n}{18} = \dfrac{12}{8}$.

For each proportion, find the unknown number n.

109. $\dfrac{n}{1150} = \dfrac{588}{483}$

110. $\dfrac{222}{1515} = \dfrac{37}{n}$

4.2 SIMILAR TRIANGLES

Objectives

A Decide Whether Two Triangles Are Congruent.

B Find the Ratio of Corresponding Sides in Similar Triangles.

C Find Unknown Lengths of Sides in Similar Triangles.

Objective A Deciding Whether Two Triangles Are Congruent

Two triangles are **congruent** when they have the same shape and the same size. In congruent triangles, the measures of corresponding angles are equal and the lengths of corresponding sides are equal. The following triangles are congruent:

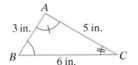 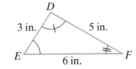

Since these triangles are congruent, the measures of corresponding angles are equal.

Angles with equal measure: $\angle A$ and $\angle D$, $\angle B$ and $\angle E$, $\angle C$ and $\angle F$. Also, the lengths of corresponding sides are equal.

Equal corresponding sides: $\overline{AB}$ and $\overline{DE}$, $\overline{BC}$ and $\overline{EF}$, $\overline{CA}$ and $\overline{FD}$

Any one of the following may be used to determine whether two triangles are congruent:

Congruent Triangles

Angle-Side-Angle (ASA)

If the measures of two angles of a triangle equal the measures of two angles of another triangle, and the lengths of the sides between each pair of angles are equal, the triangles are congruent.

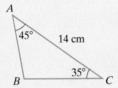 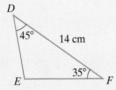

For example, these two triangles are congruent by Angle-Side-Angle.

Side-Side-Side (SSS)

If the lengths of the three sides of a triangle equal the lengths of the corresponding sides of another triangle, the triangles are congruent.

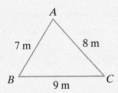 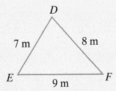

For example, these two triangles are congruent by Side-Side-Side.

Side-Angle-Side (SAS)

If the lengths of two sides of a triangle equal the lengths of corresponding sides of another triangle, and the measures of the angles between each pair of sides are equal, the triangles are congruent.

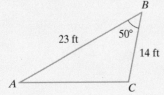 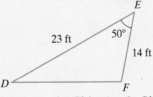

For example, these two triangles are congruent by Side-Angle-Side.

303

PRACTICE 1

a. Determine whether triangle *MNO* is congruent to triangle *RQS*.

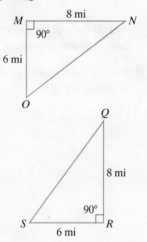

b. Determine whether triangle *GHI* is congruent to triangle *JKL*.

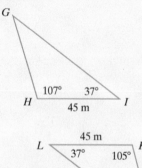

 Example 1 Determine whether triangle *ABC* is congruent to triangle *DEF*.

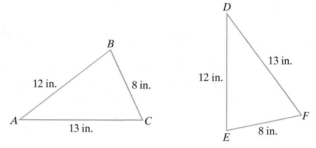

Solution: Since the lengths of all three sides of triangle *ABC* equal the lengths of all three sides of triangle *DEF*, the triangles are congruent.

● **Work Practice 1**

In Example 1, notice that as soon as we know that the two triangles are congruent, we know that all three corresponding angles are congruent.

Objective Ⓑ Finding the Ratios of Corresponding Sides in Similar Triangles

Two triangles are **similar** when they have the same shape but not necessarily the same size. In similar triangles, the measures of corresponding angles are equal and corresponding sides are in proportion. The following triangles are similar:

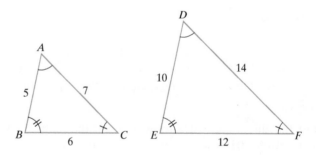

Since these triangles are similar, the measures of corresponding angles are equal.

Angles with equal measure: $\angle A$ and $\angle D$, $\angle B$ and $\angle E$, $\angle C$ and $\angle F$. Also, the lengths of corresponding sides are in proportion.

Sides in proportion: $\dfrac{AB}{DE} = \dfrac{BC}{EF} = \dfrac{CA}{FD}$ or, in this particular case,

$$\frac{AB}{DE} = \frac{5}{10} = \frac{1}{2},\ \frac{BC}{EF} = \frac{6}{12} = \frac{1}{2},\ \frac{CA}{FD} = \frac{7}{14} = \frac{1}{2}$$

The ratio of corresponding sides is $\dfrac{1}{2}$.

Answers

1. a. congruent   **b.** not congruent

Example 2 Find the ratio of corresponding sides for the similar triangles *ABC* and *DEF*.

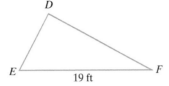

PRACTICE 2

Find the ratio of corresponding sides for the similar triangles *QRS* and *XYZ*.

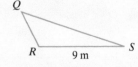

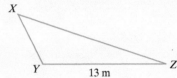

Solution: We are given the lengths of two corresponding sides. Their ratio is

$$\frac{12 \text{ feet}}{19 \text{ feet}} = \frac{12}{19}$$

● **Work Practice 2**

Objective ⓒ Finding Unknown Lengths of Sides in Similar Triangles

Because the ratios of lengths of corresponding sides are equal, we can use proportions to find unknown lengths in similar triangles.

Example 3 Given that the triangles are similar, find the missing length *n*.

Solution: Since the triangles are similar, corresponding sides are in proportion. Thus, the ratio of 2 to 3 is the same as the ratio of 10 to *n*, or

$$\frac{2}{3} = \frac{10}{n}$$

To find the unknown length *n*, we set cross products equal.

$$\frac{2}{3} = \frac{10}{n}$$

$2 \cdot n = 3 \cdot 10$ Set cross products equal.
$2 \cdot n = 30$ Multiply.
$n = \dfrac{30}{2}$ Divide 30 by 2, the number multiplied by *n*.
$n = 15$

The missing length is 15 units.

● **Work Practice 3**

PRACTICE 3

Given that the triangles are similar, find the missing length *n*.

a.

b.

Answers

2. $\dfrac{9}{13}$ **3. a.** $n = 8$ **b.** $n = \dfrac{10}{3}$ or $3\dfrac{1}{3}$

✓**Concept Check** The following two triangles are similar. Which vertices of the first triangle appear to correspond to which vertices of the second triangle?

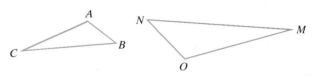

Many applications involve diagrams containing similar triangles. Surveyors, astronomers, and many other professionals continually use similar triangles in their work.

PRACTICE 4

Tammy Shultz, a firefighter, needs to estimate the height of a burning building. She estimates the length of her shadow to be 8 feet long and the length of the building's shadow to be 60 feet long. Find the approximate height of the building if she is 5 feet tall.

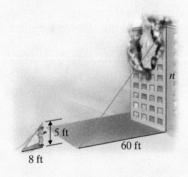

Answer
4. approximately 37.5 ft

✓**Concept Check Answer**
A corresponds to O; B corresponds to N; C corresponds to M

Example 4 Finding the Height of a Tree

Mel Rose is a 6-foot-tall park ranger who needs to know the height of a particular tree. He measures the shadow of the tree to be 69 feet long when his own shadow is 9 feet long. Find the height of the tree.

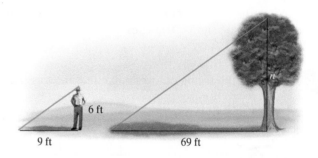

Solution:

1. UNDERSTAND. Read and reread the problem. Notice that the triangle formed by the Sun's rays, Mel, and his shadow is similar to the triangle formed by the Sun's rays, the tree, and its shadow.

2. TRANSLATE. Write a proportion from the similar triangles formed.

$$\frac{\text{Mel's height}}{\text{height of tree}} \rightarrow \frac{6}{n} = \frac{9}{69} \leftarrow \frac{\text{length of Mel's shadow}}{\text{length of tree's shadow}}$$

$$\text{or } \frac{6}{n} = \frac{3}{23} \quad \text{Simplify } \tfrac{9}{69}. \text{ (ratio in lowest terms)}$$

3. SOLVE for n:

$$\frac{6}{n} = \frac{3}{23}$$

$$6 \cdot 23 = n \cdot 3 \quad \text{Set cross products equal.}$$
$$138 = n \cdot 3 \quad \text{Multiply.}$$
$$\frac{138}{3} = n \quad \text{Divide 138 by 3, the number multiplied by } n.$$
$$46 = n$$

4. INTERPRET. *Check* to see that replacing n with 46 in the proportion makes the proportion true. *State* your conclusion: The height of the tree is 46 feet.

● **Work Practice 4**

Vocabulary and Readiness Check

Answer each question true or false.

1. Two triangles that have the same shape but not necessarily the same size are congruent.
2. Two triangles are congruent if they have the same shape and size.
3. Congruent triangles are also similar.
4. Similar triangles are also congruent.
5. For the two similar triangles, the ratio of corresponding sides is $\frac{5}{6}$.

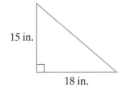

Each pair of triangles is similar. Name the congruent angles and the corresponding sides that are proportional.

6.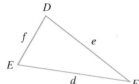

7.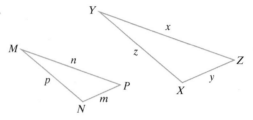

4.2 Exercise Set

Objective **A** *Determine whether each pair of triangles is congruent. If congruent, state the reason why, such as SSS, SAS, or ASA. See Example 1.*

1.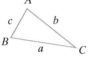

2.

3.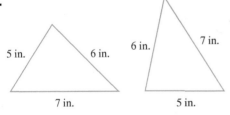

4.

5.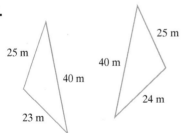

6.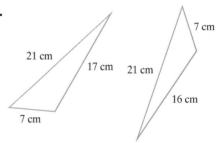

7.
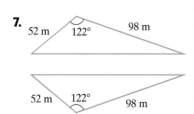
52 m   122°   98 m

52 m   122°   98 m

8.
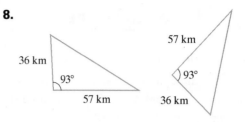
36 km   93°   57 km
57 km   93°   36 km

Objective **B** *Find each ratio of the corresponding sides of the given similar triangles. See Example 2.*

9.
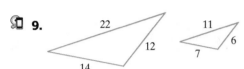
22   11
12   6
14   7

10.
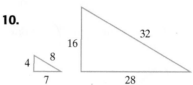
16   32
4   8
7   28

11.
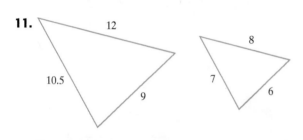
12
10.5   8
9   7   6

12.
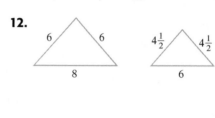
6   6 $4\frac{1}{2}$ $4\frac{1}{2}$
8   6

Objective **C** *Given that the pairs of triangles are similar, find the unknown length of the side labeled n. See Example 3.*

13.

3   6 n 9

14.

5   60
3   n

15.
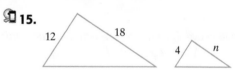
12   18   4 n

16.
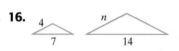
4   n
7   14

17.
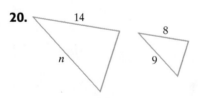
n 12   3.75   9

18.
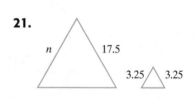
9   15 n 22.5

19.
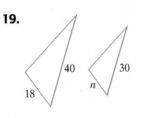
40   30
18   n

20.
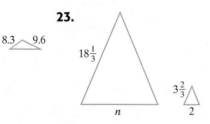
14   8
n 9

21.
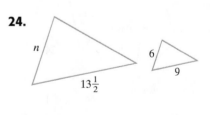
n 17.5
3.25   3.25

22.

33.2 n 8.3   9.6

23.
$18\frac{1}{3}$ $3\frac{2}{3}$
n 2

24.
n 6
$13\frac{1}{2}$ 9

25.
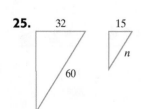
32   15
60   n

26.
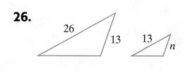
26   13   13 n

27.

28.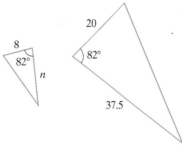

Solve. For Exercises 29 and 30, the solutions have been started for you. See Example 4.

29. Given the following diagram, approximate the height of the observation deck in the Seattle Space Needle in Seattle, Washington. (*Source:* Seattle Space Needle)

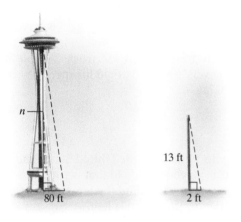

Start the solution:

1. UNDERSTAND the problem. Reread it as many times as needed.

2. TRANSLATE into a proportion using the similar triangles formed. (Fill in the blanks.)

height of
observation deck → $\dfrac{n}{13} = \dfrac{}{}$ ← length of Space
Needle shadow
height of pole → ← length of pole shadow

3. SOLVE by setting cross products equal.

4. INTERPRET.

30. Fountain Hills, Arizona, boasts the tallest fountain in the world. The fountain sits in a 28-acre lake and shoots up a column of water every hour. Based on the diagram below, what is the height of the fountain?

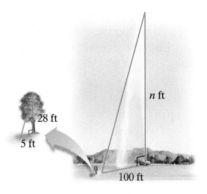

Start the solution:

1. UNDERSTAND the problem. Reread it as many times as needed.

2. TRANSLATE into a proportion using the similar triangles formed. (Fill in the blanks.)

height of tree → $\dfrac{28}{n} = \dfrac{}{}$ ← length of tree
shadow
height of fountain → ← length of fountain shadow

3. SOLVE by setting cross products equal.

4. INTERPRET.

31. Given the following diagram, approximate the height of the Bank One Tower in Oklahoma City, Oklahoma. Here, we use *x* to represent the unknown number. (*Source: The World Almanac*)

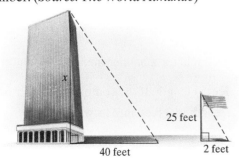

32. The tallest tree standing today is a redwood located in the Humboldt Redwoods State Park near Ukiah, California. Given the following diagram, approximate its height. Here, we use *x* to represent the unknown number. (*Source: Guinness World Records*)

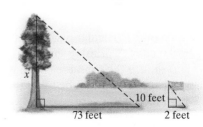

33. Samantha Black, a 5-foot-tall park ranger, needs to know the height of a tree. She notices that when the shadow of the tree is 48 feet long, her shadow is 4 feet long. Find the height of the tree.

34. Lloyd White, a firefighter, needs to estimate the height of a burning building. He estimates the length of his shadow to be 9 feet long and the length of the building's shadow to be 75 feet long. Find the approximate height of the building if he is 6 feet tall.

35. If a 30-foot tree casts an 18-foot shadow, find the length of the shadow cast by a 24-foot tree.

36. If a 24-foot flagpole casts a 32-foot shadow, find the length of the shadow cast by a 44-foot antenna. Round to the nearest tenth.

Review

Solve. See Section 4.1.

37. For the health of his fish, Pete's Sea World uses the standard that a 20-gallon tank should house only 19 neon tetras. Find the number of neon tetras that Pete would place into a 55-gallon tank.

38. A local package express deliveryman is traveling the city expressway at 45 mph when he is forced to slow down due to traffic ahead. His truck slows at the rate of 3 mph every 5 seconds. Find his speed 8 seconds after braking.

Solve. See Section 5.1.

39. Launch Umbilical Tower 1 is the name of the gantry used for the *Apollo* launch that took Neil Armstrong and Buzz Aldrin to the moon. Find the height of the gantry to the nearest whole number.

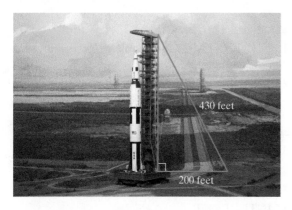

430 feet

200 feet

40. Arena polo, popular in the United States and England, is played on a field that is 100 yards long and usually 50 yards wide. Find the length, to the nearest yard, of the diagonal of this field.

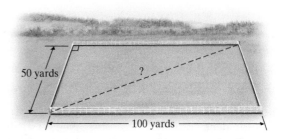

50 yards

?

100 yards

Perform the indicated operation. See Sections 3.3 through 3.5.

41. $3.6 + 0.41$

42. $3.6 - 0.41$

43. $(0.41)(3)$

44. $0.48 \div 3$

Concept Extensions

45. The print area on a particular page measures 7 inches by 9 inches. A printing shop is to copy the page and reduce the print area so that its length is 5 inches. What will its width be? Will the print now fit on a 3-by-5-inch index card?

46. The art sample for a banner measures $\frac{1}{3}$ foot in width by $1\frac{1}{2}$ feet in length. If the completed banner is to have a length of 9 feet, find its width.

Given that the pairs of triangles are similar, find the length of the side labeled n. Round your results to 1 decimal place.

47.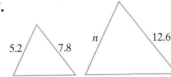

48.

49. In your own words, describe any differences in similar triangles and congruent triangles.

50. Describe a situation where similar triangles would be useful for a contractor building a house.

51. A triangular park is planned and waiting to be approved by the city zoning commission. A drawing of the park shows sides of length 5 inches, $7\frac{1}{2}$ inches, and $10\frac{5}{8}$ inches. If the scale on the drawing is $\frac{1}{4}$ in. = 10 ft, find the actual proposed dimensions of the park.

52. John and Robyn Costello draw a triangular deck on their house plans. Robyn measures sides of the deck drawing on the plans to be 3 inches, $4\frac{1}{2}$ inches, and 6 inches. If the scale on the drawing is $\frac{1}{4}$ in. = 1 foot, find the lengths of the sides of the deck they want built.

Objectives

A Understand Percent.

B Write Percents as Decimals.

C Write Decimals as Percents.

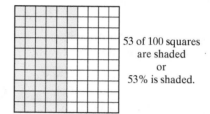 **INTRODUCTION TO PERCENT**

Objective **A** Understanding Percent

The word **percent** comes from the Latin phrase *per centum*, which means **"per 100."** For example, 53% (percent) means 53 per 100. In the square below, 53 of the 100 squares are shaded. Thus, 53% of the figure is shaded.

53 of 100 squares
are shaded
or
53% is shaded.

Since 53% means 53 per 100, 53% is the ratio of 53 to 100, or $\frac{53}{100}$.

$$53\% = \frac{53}{100}$$

Also,

$$7\% = \frac{7}{100} \quad \text{7 parts per 100 parts}$$

$$73\% = \frac{73}{100} \quad \text{73 parts per 100 parts}$$

$$109\% = \frac{109}{100} \quad \text{109 parts per 100 parts}$$

> **Percent**
>
> **Percent** means **per one hundred.** The "%" symbol is used to denote percent.

Percent is used in a variety of everyday situations. For example,

- 77.6% of the U.S. population uses the Internet.
- The store is having a 25%-off sale.
- 78% of us trust our local fire department.
- The enrollment in community colleges is predicted to increase 1.3% each year.
- The South is the home of 49% of all frequent paint-ball participants.

PRACTICE 1

Of 100 students in a club, 23 are freshmen. What percent of the students are freshmen?

Example 1 Silver (gray) has been the most popular color for cars in the United States the past nine years.

Out of 100 people, 25 people drive silver cars. What percent of people drive silver cars? (*Source*: *U.S. News & World Report*)

Solution: Since 25 people out of 100 drive silver cars, the fraction is $\frac{25}{100}$. Then

$$\frac{25}{100} = 25\%$$

● **Work Practice 1**

Answer

1. 23%

312

rightCopyright 2011 Pearson Education, Inc.

Example 2 46 out of every 100 college students live at home. What percent of students live at home? (*Source:* Independent Insurance Agents of America)

Solution:

$$\frac{46}{100} = 46\%$$

● Work Practice 2

PRACTICE 2

29 out of 100 executives are in their forties. What percent of executives are in their forties?

Objective ⓑ Writing Percents as Decimals

Since percent means "per hundred," we have that

$$1\% = \frac{1}{100} = 0.01$$

In other words, the percent symbol means "per hundred" or, equivalently, "$\frac{1}{100}$" or "0.01." Thus

$$87\% = 87 \times \frac{1}{100} = \frac{87}{100}$$

or

$$87\% = 87 \times (0.01) = 0.87$$

> Results are the same.

Of course, we know that the end results are the same, that is,

$$\frac{87}{100} = 0.87$$

The above gives us two options for converting percents. We can replace the percent symbol, %, by $\frac{1}{100}$ or 0.01 and then multiply.

For consistency, when we
- convert from a percent to a *decimal,* we will drop the % symbol and multiply by 0.01 (this section).
- convert from a percent to a *fraction,* we will drop the % symbol and multiply by $\frac{1}{100}$ (next section).

Thus, to write 53% as a decimal,

$$53\% = 53(0.01) = 0.53$$ Replace the percent symbol with 0.01. Then multiply.

Writing a Percent as a Decimal

Replace the percent symbol with its decimal equivalent, 0.01; then multiply.

$$43\% = 43(0.01) = 0.43$$

Helpful Hint

If it helps, think of writing a percent as a decimal by

Percent → | Remove the % symbol and move decimal point 2 places to the left | → Decimal

Answer

2. 29%

PRACTICE 3

Write 89% as a decimal.

PRACTICE 4–7

Write each percent as a decimal.
4. 2.7%   **5.** 150%
6. 0.69%   **7.** 800%

Example 3 Write 23% as a decimal.

Solution:

$$23\% = 23(0.01) \qquad \text{Replace the percent symbol with 0.01.}$$
$$= 0.23 \qquad\qquad \text{Multiply.}$$

Work Practice 3

Examples Write each percent as a decimal.

4. $4.6\% = 4.6(0.01) = 0.046$ Replace the percent symbol with 0.01. Then multiply.

5. $190\% = 190(0.01) = 1.90$ or 1.9

6. $0.74\% = 0.74(0.01) = 0.0074$

7. $100\% = 100(0.01) = 1.00$ or 1

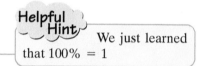
Helpful Hint
We just learned that 100% = 1

Work Practice 4–7

✓**Concept Check** Why is it incorrect to write the percent 0.033% as 3.3 in decimal form?

Objective ◉ Writing Decimals as Percents

To write a decimal as a percent, we use the result of Example 7 above. In this example, we found that 1 = 100%.

$$0.38 = 0.38(1) = 0.38(100\%) = 38\%$$

Notice that the result is

$$0.38 = 0.38(100\%) = 38.\% \qquad \text{Multiply by 1 in the form of 100\%.}$$

Writing a Decimal as a Percent

Multiply by 1 in the form of 100%.

$$0.27 = 0.27(100\%) = 27.\%$$

Answers

3. 0.89 **4.** 0.027 **5.** 1.5
6. 0.0069 **7.** 8.00 or 8

✓**Concept Check Answer**

To write a percent as a decimal, the decimal point should be moved two places to the left, not to the right. So the correct answer is 0.00033.

Helpful Hint

If it helps, think of writing a decimal as a percent by reversing the steps in the Helpful Hint on the previous page.

Percent ← | Move the decimal point 2 places to the right and attach a % symbol. | ← Decimal

Example 8 Write 0.65 as a percent.

Solution:

$$0.65 = 0.65(100\%) = 65.\%$$ Multiply by 100%.
$$= 65\%$$

● **Work Practice 8**

PRACTICE 8
Write 0.19 as a percent.

Examples Write each decimal as a percent.

9. $1.25 = 1.25(100\%) = 125.\%$ or 125%

10. $0.012 = 0.012(100\%) = 001.2\%$ or 1.2%

11. $0.6 = 0.6(100\%) = 060.\%$ or 60%

Helpful Hint A zero was inserted as a placeholder.

● **Work Practice 9–11**

PRACTICE 9–11
Write each decimal as a percent.
9. 1.75 **10.** 0.044 **11.** 0.7

✓**Concept Check** Why is it incorrect to write the decimal 0.0345 as 34.5% in percent form?

Answers
8. 19% **9.** 175% **10.** 4.4%
11. 70%

✓ **Concept Check Answer**
To change a decimal to a percent, multiply by 100%, or move the decimal point *only* two places to the right. So the correct answer is 3.45%.

Vocabulary and Readiness Check

Use the choices below to fill in each blank. Some choices may be used more than once, some not at all.

$\dfrac{1}{100}$ 0.01 100% percent

1. _____ means "per hundred."
2. _____ = 1.
3. The % symbol is read as _____.
4. To write a decimal as a *percent*, multiply by 1 in the form of _____.
5. To write a percent as a *decimal*, drop the % symbol and multiply by _____.

4.3 Exercise Set

Objective A *Solve. See Examples 1 and 2.*

1. In a survey of 100 college students, 96 use the Internet. What percent use the Internet?

2. A basketball player makes 81 out of 100 attempted free throws. What percent of free throws are made?

3. Michigan leads the United States in tart cherry production, producing 75 out of every 100 tart cherries each year.

   a. What percent of tart cherries are produced in Michigan?

   b. What percent of tart cherries are *not* produced in Michigan? (*Source:* Cherry Marketing Institute)

4. The United States is the world's second-largest producer of apples. Four out of every 100 apples harvested in the United States are exported (shipped to other countries). (*Source:* U.S. Apple Association)

   a. What percent of U.S.–grown apples are exported?

   b. What percent of U.S.–grown apples are not exported?

One hundred adults were asked to name their favorite sport, and the results are shown in the circle graph.

5. What sport was preferred by most adults? What percent preferred this sport?

6. What sport was preferred by the least number of adults? What percent preferred this sport?

7. What percent of adults preferred football or soccer?

8. What percent of adults preferred basketball or baseball?

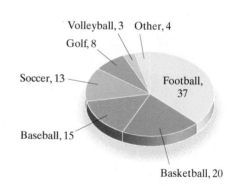

Objective B *Write each percent as a decimal. See Examples 3 through 7.*

9. 41%   **10.** 62%   **11.** 6%   **12.** 3%

13. 100%   **14.** 136%   **15.** 73.6%   **16.** 45.7%

17. 2.8%   **18.** 1.4%   **19.** 0.6%   **20.** 0.9%

21. 300%   **22.** 500%   **23.** 32.58%   **24.** 72.18%

Write each percent as a decimal. See Examples 3 through 7.

25. People take aspirin for a variety of reasons. The most common use of aspirin is to prevent heart disease, accounting for 38% of all aspirin use. (*Source:* Bayer Market Research)

26. Japan exports 73.2% of all motorcycles manufactured there. (*Source:* Japan Automobile Manufacturers Association)

27. In the United States recently, 20.2% of households had no landlines, just cell phones. (*Source:* CTIA—The Wireless Association)

28. In the United States recently, 17.4% of households had no cell phones, just landlines. (*Source:* CTIA—The Wireless Association)

29. Women make up 46.5% of the total U.S. labor force. (*Source:* U.S. Department of Labor)

30. In 2008, 57.4% of the paper used in the United States was recovered for recycling. (*Source:* American Forest & Paper Association)

Objective Ⓒ *Write each decimal as a percent. See Examples 8 through 11.*

31. 0.98   **32.** 0.75   **33.** 3.1   **34.** 4.8   **35.** 29.00

36. 56.00   **37.** 0.003   **38.** 0.006   **39.** 0.22   **40.** 0.45

41. 5.3   **42.** 1.6   **43.** 0.056   **44.** 0.027   **45.** 0.3328

46. 0.1115   **47.** 3.00   **48.** 5.00   **49.** 0.7   **50.** 0.8

Write each decimal as a percent. See Examples 8 through 11.

51. About 0.68 of homes with televisions were tuned into Super Bowl XLIV.

52. The cost of an item on sale is 0.7 of the regular price.

53. In the 2009 Tour de France, 0.039 of the riders participating were Americans. (*Source:* Versus.com)

54. In the second quarter of 2009, retail sales of new Harley-Davidson motorcycles were down about 0.301. (*Source:* Harley-Davidson)

55. Nearly 0.093 of people in the United States are affected by pollen allergies. (*Source:* National Institute of Allergy and Infectious Diseases)

56. According to the 2000 census, 0.491 of the American population is male. (*Source:* U.S. Census Bureau)

Review

Write each fraction as a decimal. See Section 3.6.

57. $\dfrac{1}{4}$ **58.** $\dfrac{3}{5}$ **59.** $\dfrac{13}{20}$ **60.** $\dfrac{11}{40}$ **61.** $\dfrac{9}{10}$ **62.** $\dfrac{7}{10}$

Concept Extensions

Solve. See the Concept Checks in this section.

63. Which of the following are correct?
 a. 6.5% = 0.65 **b.** 7.8% = 0.078
 c. 120% = 0.12 **d.** 0.35% = 0.0035

64. Which of the following are correct?
 a. 0.231 = 23.1% **b.** 5.12 = 0.0512%
 c. 3.2 = 320% **d.** 0.0175 = 0.175%

Recall that 1 = 100%. This means that 1 whole is 100%. Use this for Exercises 65 and 66. (Source: Some Body by Dr. Pete Rowen)

65. The four blood types are A, B, O, and AB. (Each blood type can also be further classified as Rh-positive or Rh-negative depending upon whether your blood contains protein or not.) Given the percent blood types for the United States below, calculate the percent of United States population with AB blood type.

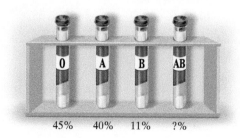

66. The top four components of bone are below. Find the missing percent.
 1. Minerals—45%
 2. Living tissue—30%
 3. Water—20%
 4. Other—?

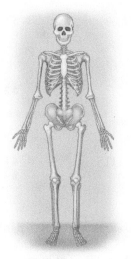

The bar graph shows the predicted fastest-growing occupations. Use the graph for Exercises 67 through 70. (Source: Bureau of Labor Statistics)

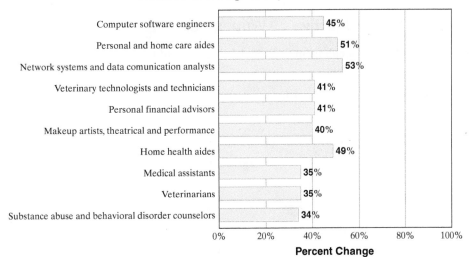

Fastest-Growing Occupations 2006–2016

Source: Bureau of Labor Statistics

67. What occupation is predicted to be the fastest growing?

68. What occupation is predicted to be the second fastest growing?

69. Write the percent change for veterinarians as a decimal.

70. Write the percent change for makeup artists as a decimal.

71. In your own words, explain how to write a percent as a decimal.

72. In your own words, explain how to write a decimal as a percent.

4.4 PERCENTS AND FRACTIONS

Objective (A) Writing Percents as Fractions

Recall from Section 4.3 that percent means per hundred. Thus

$$1\% = \frac{1}{100} = 0.01$$

For example,

$$87\% = 87 \times \frac{1}{100} = \frac{87}{100} \quad \text{Writing } 87\% \text{ as a fraction.}$$

or

$$87\% = 87 \times 0.01 = 0.87 \quad \text{Writing } 87\% \text{ as a decimal.}$$

In this section we are writing percents as fractions, so we do the following.

> ### Writing a Percent as a Fraction
>
> Replace the percent symbol with its fraction equivalent, $\frac{1}{100}$; then multiply. Don't forget to simplify the fraction if possible.
>
> $$7\% = 7 \cdot \frac{1}{100} = \frac{7}{100}$$

PRACTICE 1–5

Write each percent as a fraction or mixed number in simplest form.

1. 25%

2. 2.3%

3. 225%

4. $66\frac{2}{3}\%$

5. 8%

Examples Write each percent as a fraction or mixed number in simplest form.

1. $40\% = 40 \cdot \frac{1}{100} = \frac{40}{100} = \frac{2 \cdot \overset{1}{\cancel{20}}}{5 \cdot \underset{1}{\cancel{20}}} = \frac{2}{5}$

2. $1.9\% = 1.9 \cdot \frac{1}{100} = \frac{1.9}{100}$. We don't want the numerator of the fraction to contain a decimal, so we multiply by 1 in the form of $\frac{10}{10}$.

$$= \frac{1.9}{100} \cdot \frac{10}{10} = \frac{1.9 \cdot 10}{100 \cdot 10} = \frac{19}{1000}$$

3. $125\% = 125 \cdot \frac{1}{100} = \frac{125}{100} = \frac{5 \cdot \overset{1}{\cancel{25}}}{4 \cdot \underset{1}{\cancel{25}}} = \frac{5}{4} \text{ or } 1\frac{1}{4}$

4. $33\frac{1}{3}\% = 33\frac{1}{3} \cdot \frac{1}{100} = \frac{100}{3} \cdot \frac{1}{100} = \frac{\overset{1}{\cancel{100}} \cdot 1}{3 \cdot \underset{1}{\cancel{100}}} = \frac{1}{3}$

$\underbrace{\hspace{1.2cm}}_{} \to$ Write as an improper fraction. $\uparrow$

5. $100\% = 100 \cdot \frac{1}{100} = \frac{100}{100} = 1$

> **Helpful Hint** Just as in the previous section, we confirm that 100% = 1.

● **Work Practice 1–5**

Objective Ⓑ Writing Fractions as Percents

Recall that to write a percent as a fraction, we replace the percent symbol by its fraction equivalent, $\frac{1}{100}$. We reverse these steps to write a fraction as a percent.

Writing a Fraction as a Percent

Multiply by 1 in the form of 100%.

$$\frac{1}{8} = \frac{1}{8} \cdot 100\% = \frac{1}{8} \cdot \frac{100}{1}\% = \frac{100}{8}\% = 12\frac{1}{2}\% \quad \text{or} \quad 12.5\%$$

Helpful Hint

From Example 5, we know that

$$100\% = 1$$

Recall that when we multiply a number by 1, we are not changing the value of that number. This means that when we multiply a number by 100%, we are not changing its value but rather writing the number as an equivalent percent.

Examples Write each fraction or mixed number as a percent.

6. $\frac{9}{20} = \frac{9}{20} \cdot 100\% = \frac{9}{20} \cdot \frac{100}{1}\% = \frac{900}{20}\% = 45\%$

7. $\frac{2}{3} = \frac{2}{3} \cdot 100\% = \frac{2}{3} \cdot \frac{100}{1}\% = \frac{200}{3}\% = 66\frac{2}{3}\%$

8. $1\frac{1}{2} = \frac{3}{2} \cdot 100\% = \frac{3}{2} \cdot \frac{100}{1}\% = \frac{300}{2}\% = 150\%$

Helpful Hint

$\frac{200}{3} = 66.\overline{6}$. Thus, another way to write $\frac{200}{3}\%$ is $66.\overline{6}\%$.

● Work Practice 6–8

✓**Concept Check** Which digit in the percent 76.4582% represents

a. A tenth percent?

b. A thousandth percent?

c. A hundredth percent?

d. A whole percent?

PRACTICE 6–8

Write each fraction or mixed number as a percent.

6. $\frac{1}{2}$ **7.** $\frac{7}{40}$ **8.** $2\frac{1}{4}$

Answers

6. 50%   **7.** $17\frac{1}{2}\%$ **8.** 225%

✓ **Concept Check Answers**

a. 4 **b.** 8 **c.** 5 **d.** 6

PRACTICE 9

Write $\dfrac{3}{17}$ as a percent. Round to the nearest hundredth percent.

Example 9 Write $\dfrac{1}{12}$ as a percent. Round to the nearest hundredth percent.

Solution:

$$\frac{1}{12} = \frac{1}{12} \cdot 100\% = \frac{1}{12} \cdot \frac{100}{1}\% = \frac{100}{12}\% \approx 8.33\%$$

"approximately"

$$\begin{array}{r} 8.333 \approx 8.33 \\ 12\overline{)100.000} \\ -96 \\ \hline 4\,0 \\ -3\,6 \\ \hline 40 \\ -36 \\ \hline 40 \\ -36 \\ \hline 4 \end{array}$$

Thus, $\dfrac{1}{12}$ is approximately 8.33%.

Work Practice 9

Objective C Converting Percents, Decimals, and Fractions

Let's summarize what we have learned so far about percents, decimals, and fractions:

> **Summary of Converting Percents, Decimals, and Fractions**
>
> - *To write a percent as a decimal,* replace the % symbol with its decimal equivalent, 0.01; then multiply.
>
> - *To write a percent as a fraction,* replace the % symbol with its fraction equivalent, $\dfrac{1}{100}$; then multiply.
>
> - *To write a decimal or fraction as a percent,* multiply by 100%.

If we let p represent a number, below we summarize using symbols.

Write a percent as a decimal:	Write a percent as a fraction:	Write a number as a percent:
$p\% = p(0.01)$	$p\% = p \cdot \dfrac{1}{100}$	$p = p \cdot 100\%$

Answer

9. 17.65%

Example 10 36.4% of automobile thefts in the continental United States occur in the South. Write this percent as a decimal and as a fraction. (*Source:* National Insurance Crime Bureau)

Solution:

As a decimal: $36.4\% = 36.4(0.01) = 0.364$

As a fraction: $36.4\% = 36.4 \cdot \dfrac{1}{100} = \dfrac{36.4}{100} = \dfrac{36.4}{100} \cdot \dfrac{10}{10} = \dfrac{364}{1000} = \dfrac{\overset{1}{\cancel{4}} \cdot 91}{\underset{1}{\cancel{4}} \cdot 250} = \dfrac{91}{250}$

Thus, 36.4% written as a decimal is 0.364, and written as a fraction is $\dfrac{91}{250}$.

● **Work Practice 10**

Example 11 An advertisement for a stereo system reads "$\dfrac{1}{4}$ off." What percent off is this?

Solution: Write $\dfrac{1}{4}$ as a percent.

$$\frac{1}{4} = \frac{1}{4} \cdot 100\% = \frac{1}{4} \cdot \frac{100}{1}\% = \frac{100}{4}\% = 25\%$$

Thus, "$\dfrac{1}{4}$ off" is the same as "25% off."

● **Work Practice 11**

Note: It is helpful to know a few basic percent conversions.

PRACTICE 10

A family decides to spend no more than 22.5% of its monthly income on rent. Write 22.5% as a decimal and as a fraction.

PRACTICE 11

Provincetown's budget for waste disposal increased by $1\dfrac{1}{4}$ times over the budget from last year. What percent increase is this?

PRACTICE 10

A family decides to spend no more than 22.5% of its monthly income on rent. Write 22.5% as a decimal and as a fraction.

PRACTICE 11

Provincetown's budget for waste disposal increased by $1\dfrac{1}{4}$ times over the budget from last year. What percent increase is this?

Answer

10. $0.225, \dfrac{9}{40}$ **11.** 1.25%

Vocabulary and Readiness Check

Use the choices below to fill in each blank. Some choices may be used more than once.

$\dfrac{1}{100}$ 100%   percent

1. _____ means "per hundred."

2. _____ = 1.

3. To write a decimal or a fraction as a *percent*, multiply by 1 in the form of _____.

4. To write a percent as a *fraction*, drop the % symbol and multiply by _____.

Write each fraction as a percent.

5. $\dfrac{13}{100}$ **6.** $\dfrac{92}{100}$ **7.** $\dfrac{87}{100}$ **8.** $\dfrac{71}{100}$ **9.** $\dfrac{1}{100}$ **10.** $\dfrac{2}{100}$

4.4 Exercise Set

FOR EXTRA HELP

MyMathLab   Math XP PRACTICE   WATCH   DOWNLOAD   READ   REVIEW

Objective A *Write each percent as a fraction or mixed number in simplest form. See Examples 1 through 5.*

1. 12%   **2.** 24%   **3.** 4%   **4.** 2%   **5.** 4.5%

6. 7.5%   **7.** 175%   **8.** 250%   **9.** 73%   **10.** 86%

11. 12.5%   **12.** 62.5%   **13.** 6.25%   **14.** 3.75%   **15.** 6%

16. 16%   **17.** $10\dfrac{1}{3}$%   **18.** $7\dfrac{3}{4}$%   **19.** $22\dfrac{3}{8}$%   **20.** $15\dfrac{5}{8}$%

Objective B *Write each fraction or mixed number as a percent. See Examples 6 through 8.*

21. $\dfrac{3}{4}$ **22.** $\dfrac{1}{4}$ **23.** $\dfrac{7}{10}$ **24.** $\dfrac{3}{10}$ **25.** $\dfrac{2}{5}$ **26.** $\dfrac{4}{5}$

27. $\dfrac{59}{100}$ **28.** $\dfrac{73}{100}$ **29.** $\dfrac{17}{50}$ **30.** $\dfrac{47}{50}$ **31.** $\dfrac{3}{8}$ **32.** $\dfrac{5}{8}$

33. $\frac{5}{16}$ **34.** $\frac{7}{16}$ **35.** $1\frac{3}{5}$ **36.** $1\frac{3}{4}$ **37.** $\frac{7}{9}$ **38.** $\frac{1}{3}$

39. $\frac{13}{20}$ **40.** $\frac{3}{20}$ **41.** $2\frac{1}{2}$ **42.** $2\frac{1}{5}$ **43.** $1\frac{9}{10}$ **44.** $2\frac{7}{10}$

Write each fraction as a percent. Round to the nearest hundredth percent. See Example 9.

45. $\frac{7}{11}$ **46.** $\frac{5}{12}$ **47.** $\frac{4}{15}$ **48.** $\frac{10}{11}$

49. $\frac{1}{7}$ **50.** $\frac{1}{9}$ **51.** $\frac{11}{12}$ **52.** $\frac{5}{6}$

Objective C *Complete each table. See Examples 10 and 11.*

53.

Percent	Decimal	Fraction
35%		
		$\frac{1}{5}$
	0.5	
70%		
		$\frac{3}{8}$

54.

Percent	Decimal	Fraction
	0.6	
		$\frac{2}{5}$
	0.25	
12.5%		
		$\frac{5}{8}$
		$\frac{7}{50}$

55.

Percent	Decimal	Fraction
40%		
	0.235	
		$\frac{4}{5}$
$33\frac{1}{3}\%$		
		$\frac{7}{8}$
7.5%		

56.

Percent	Decimal	Fraction
	0.525	
		$\frac{3}{4}$
$66\frac{2}{3}\%$		
		$\frac{5}{6}$
100%		

57.

Percent	Decimal	Fraction
200%		
	2.8	
705%		
		$4\frac{27}{50}$

58.

Percent	Decimal	Fraction
800%		
	3.2	
608%		
		$9\frac{13}{50}$

Solve. See Examples 10 and 11.

59. China produces 26.2% of the world's aluminum products. Write this percent as a decimal and a fraction. (*Source:* U.S. Geological Survey, *Minerals Yearbook*)

60. In 2008, 46.5% of all veterinarians in private practice were female. Write this percent as a decimal and a fraction. (*Source:* American Veterinary Medical Association)

61. At this writing, 23% of Americans surveyed are in favor of abolishing the penny. Write this percent as a decimal and a fraction.

62. One version of the quarter is made of an alloy of copper, nickel, and strengthening impurities. About 8% is nickel. Write this percent as a decimal and a fraction. (*Source:* Gallup)

63. Mali has a very young population. It is estimated that $\frac{483}{1000}$ of its population is under the age of 12. Write this fraction as a percent. (*Source:* The Top 10 of Everything, 2009)

64. In 2008, approximately $\frac{2}{5}$ of the total money that Americans spent on their pets was spent on pet food. Write this fraction as a percent. (*Source:* American Pet Products Manufacturers Association)

65. The sales tax in Slidell, Louisiana, is 8.75%. Write this percent as a decimal.

66. A real estate agent receives a commission of 3% of the sale price of a house. Write this percent as a decimal.

67. Canada produces $\frac{1}{4}$ of the uranium produced in the world. Write this fraction as a percent. (*Source:* World Nuclear Association)

68. In 2008, the U.S. Postal Service handled $\frac{23}{50}$ of the world's card and letter mail volume. Write this decimal as a percent. (*Source:* U.S. Postal Service)

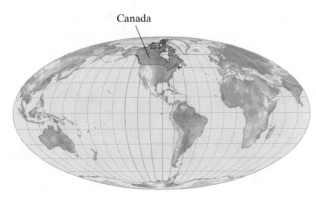

Canada

In Exercises 69 through 74, write the percent from the circle graph as a decimal and a fraction.

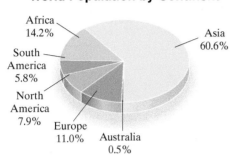

World Population by Continent

Africa 14.2%
South America 5.8%
North America 7.9%
Europe 11.0%
Australia 0.5%
Asia 60.6%

69. Australia: 0.5%   **70.** Europe: 11%

71. Africa: 14.2%   **72.** Asia: 60.6%

73. North America: 7.9%   **74.** South America: 5.8%

Review

Find the value of n. See Section 4.1.

75. $3 \cdot n = 45$ **76.** $7 \cdot n = 48$ **77.** $8 \cdot n = 80$

78. $2 \cdot n = 16$ **79.** $6 \cdot n = 72$ **80.** $5 \cdot n = 35$

Concept Extensions

Solve. See the Concept Check in this section.

81. Given the percent 52.8647%, round as indicated.

  a. Round to a tenth of a percent.
  b. Round to a hundredth of a percent.

82. Given the percent 0.5269%, round as indicated.

  a. Round to a tenth of a percent.
  b. Round to a hundredth of a percent.

83. Write 1.07835 as a percent rounded to the nearest tenth of a percent.

84. Write 1.25348 as a percent rounded to the nearest tenth of a percent.

85. Write 0.65794 as a percent rounded to the nearest hundredth of a percent.

86. Write 0.92571 as a percent rounded to the nearest hundredth of a percent.

87. Write 0.7682 as a percent rounded to the nearest percent.

88. Write 0.2371 as a percent rounded to the nearest percent.

What percent of the figure is shaded?

89.

90.

91.

92.

Fill in the blanks.

93. A fraction written as a percent is greater than 100% when the numerator is _____ than the denominator. (greater/less)

94. A decimal written as a percent is less than 100% when the decimal is _____ than 1. (greater/less)

95. In your own words, explain how to write a percent as a fraction.

96. In your own words, explain how to write a fraction as a decimal.

Write each fraction as a decimal and then write each decimal as a percent. Round the decimal to three decimal places (nearest thousandth) and the percent to the nearest tenth of a percent.

97. $\dfrac{21}{79}$

98. $\dfrac{56}{102}$

99. $\dfrac{850}{736}$

100. $\dfrac{506}{248}$

4.5 SOLVING PERCENT PROBLEMS USING EQUATIONS

Objectives

Ⓐ Write Percent Problems as Equations.

Ⓑ Solve Percent Problems

Note: Sections 4.5 and 4.6 introduce two methods for solving percent problems. It is not necessary that you study both sections. You may want to check with your instructor for further advice.

Throughout this text, we have written mathematical statements such as $3 + 10 = 13$, or area = length · width. These statements are called "equations." An **equation** is a mathematical statement that contains an equal sign. To solve percent problems in this section, we translate the problems into such mathematical statements, or equations.

Objective Ⓐ Writing Percent Problems as Equations

Recognizing key words in a percent problem is helpful in writing the problem as an equation. Three key words in the statement of a percent problem and their meanings are as follows:

of means **multiplication** (·)
is means **equals** (=)
what (or some equivalent) means **the unknown number**

In our examples, we let the letter *n* stand for the unknown number.

> **Helpful Hint**
>
> Any letter of the alphabet can be used to represent the unknown number. In this section, we use the letter *n*.

Example 1 Translate to an equation.

Solution: 5 is what percent of 20?

$$5 = \quad n \quad \cdot 20$$

● Work Practice 1

PRACTICE 1

Translate: 6 is what percent of 24?

> **Helpful Hint**
>
> Remember that an equation is simply a mathematical statement that contains an equal sign (=).
>
> $$5 = n \cdot 20$$
>
> ↑
> equal sign

Example 2 Translate to an equation.

1.2 is 30% of what number?

Solution: 1.2 is 30% of what number?

$$1.2 = 30\% \quad \cdot \quad n$$

● Work Practice 2

PRACTICE 2

Translate: 1.8 is 20% of what number?

Answers
1. $6 = n \cdot 24$ 2. $1.8 = 20\% \cdot n$

329

PRACTICE 3

Translate: What number is 40% of 3.6?

Example 3 Translate to an equation.

What number is 25% of 0.008?

Solution: What number is 25% of 0.008?

$$n = 25\% \cdot 0.008$$

● Work Practice 3

PRACTICE 4–6

Translate each to an equation.
4. 42% of 50 is what number?
5. 15% of what number is 9?
6. What percent of 150 is 90?

Examples Translate each of the following to an equation:

4. 38% of 200 is what number?

$$38\% \cdot 200 = n$$

5. 40% of what number is 80?

$$40\% \cdot n = 80$$

6. What percent of 85 is 34?

$$n \cdot 85 = 34$$

● Work Practice 4–6

✓**Concept Check** In the equation $2 \cdot n = 10$, what step should be taken to solve the equation for n?

Objective Ⓑ Solving Percent Problems

You may have noticed by now that each percent problem has contained three numbers—in our examples, two are known and one is unknown. Each of these numbers is given a special name.

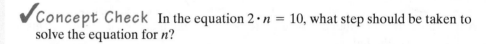

15%	of	60	is	9
15% percent	·	60 base	=	9 amount

We call this equation the **percent equation.**

Percent Equation

percent · base = amount

Helpful Hint

Notice that the percent equation given above is a true statement. To see this, simplify the left side as shown:

$$15\% \cdot 60 = 9$$
$$0.15 \cdot 60 = 9 \quad \text{Write 15\% as 0.15.}$$
$$9 = 9 \quad \text{Multiply.}$$

The statement $9 = 9$ is true.

Answers

3. $n = 40\% \cdot 3.6$ **4.** $42\% \cdot 50 = n$
5. $15\% \cdot n = 9$ **6.** $n \cdot 150 = 90$

✓ **Concept Check Answer**

If $2 \cdot n = 10$, then $n = \dfrac{10}{2}$, or $n = 5$.

After a percent problem has been written as a percent equation, we can use the equation to find the unknown number. This is called **solving** the equation.

Example 7 Solving Percent Equation for the Amount

What number is 35% of 40?

    ↓   ↓   ↓   ↓ ↓

Solution: n $= 35\% \cdot 40$ Translate to an equation.

             n $= 0.35 \cdot 40$ Write 35% as 0.35.

             n $= 14$ Multiply $0.35 \cdot 40 = 14$.

Thus, 14 is 35% of 40.

Is this reasonable? To see, round 35% to 40%. Then 40% of 40 or 0.40(40) is 16. Our result is reasonable since 16 is close to 14.

● **Work Practice 7**

Helpful Hint

When solving a percent equation, write the percent as a decimal (or fraction).

Example 8 Solving Percent Equation for the Amount

85% of 300 is what number?

   ↓   ↓ ↓ ↓   ↓

Solution: $85\% \cdot 300 =$ n Translate to an equation.

        $0.85 \cdot 300 =$ n Write 85% as 0.85.

              $255 =$ n Multiply $0.85 \cdot 300 = 255$.

Thus, 85% of 300 is 255.

Is this result reasonable? To see, round 85% to 90%. Then 90% of 300 or 0.90(300) = 270, which is close to 255.

● **Work Practice 8**

Example 9 Solving Percent Equation for the Base

12% of what number is 0.6?

   ↓   ↓   ↓   ↓ ↓

Solution: $12\% \cdot$ n $= 0.6$ Translate to an equation.

       $0.12 \cdot$ n $= 0.6$ Write 12% as 0.12.

Recall from Section 4.1 that if "0.12 times some number is 0.6," then the number is 0.6 divided by 0.12.

    $n = \dfrac{0.6}{0.12}$ Divide 0.6 by 0.12, the number multiplied by n.

    $n = 5$

Thus, 12% of 5 is 0.6.

Is this reasonable? To see, round 12% to 10%. Then 10% of 5 or 0.10(5) = 0.5, which is close to 0.6.

● **Work Practice 9**

PRACTICE 7

What number is 20% of 85?

PRACTICE 8

90% of 150 is what number?

PRACTICE 9

15% of what number is 1.2?

Answers

7. 17   **8.** 135   **9.** 8

PRACTICE 10

27 is $4\frac{1}{2}$ % of what number?

Example 10 Solving Percent Equation for the Base

$$13 \quad \text{is} \quad 6\frac{1}{2}\% \quad \text{of} \quad \underbrace{\text{what number?}}$$
$$\downarrow \quad \downarrow \quad \downarrow \quad \downarrow \quad \quad \downarrow$$

Solution:
$$13 = 6\frac{1}{2}\% \cdot n \quad \text{Translate to an equation.}$$
$$13 = 0.065 \cdot n \quad 6\frac{1}{2}\% = 6.5\% = 0.065.$$
$$\frac{13}{0.065} = n \quad \text{Divide 13 by 0.065, the number multiplied by } n.$$
$$200 = n$$

Thus, 13 is $6\frac{1}{2}\%$ of 200.

Check to see if this result is reasonable.

● Work Practice 10

PRACTICE 11

What percent of 80 is 8?

Example 11 Solving Percent Equation for the Percent

$$\underbrace{\text{What percent}} \text{ of } 12 \text{ is } 9?$$
$$\downarrow \quad \quad \downarrow \quad \downarrow \quad \downarrow$$

Solution:
$$n \quad \cdot 12 = 9 \quad \text{Translate to an equation.}$$
$$n = \frac{9}{12} \quad \text{Divide 9 by 12, the number multiplied by } n.$$
$$n = 0.75$$

Next, since we are looking for percent, we write 0.75 as a percent.

$$n = 75\%$$

So, 75% of 12 is 9.

To check, see that $75\% \cdot 12 = 9$.

● Work Practice 11

> **Helpful Hint**
>
> If your unknown in the percent equation is the percent, don't forget to convert your answer to a percent.

PRACTICE 12

35 is what percent of 25?

Example 12 Solving Percent Equation for the Percent

$$78 \text{ is } \underbrace{\text{what percent}} \text{ of } 65?$$
$$\downarrow \quad \downarrow \quad \quad \downarrow \quad \quad \downarrow \quad \downarrow$$

Solution:
$$78 = n \quad \cdot 65 \quad \text{Translate to an equation.}$$
$$\frac{78}{65} = n \quad \text{Divide 78 by 65, the number multiplied by } n.$$
$$1.2 = n$$
$$120\% = n \quad \text{Write 1.2 as a percent.}$$

So, 78 is 120% of 65.

Check this result.

● Work Practice 12

Answers

10. 600 **11.** 10% **12.** 140%

✓Concept Check   Consider these problems.

1. 75% of 50 =
   a. 50   **b.** a number greater than 50   **c.** a number less than 50

2. 40% of a number is 10. Is the number
   a. 10?   **b.** less than 10?   **c.** greater than 10?

3. 800 is 120% of what number? Is the number
   a. 800?   **b.** less than 800?   **c.** greater than 800?

Helpful Hint

Use the following to see if your answers are reasonable.

$$(100\%) \text{ of a number } = \text{ the number}$$

$$\left(\begin{array}{c}\text{a percent}\\\text{greater than}\\100\%\end{array}\right) \text{of a number} = \begin{array}{c}\text{a number greater}\\\text{than the original number}\end{array}$$

$$\left(\begin{array}{c}\text{a percent}\\\text{less than } 100\%\end{array}\right) \text{of a number} = \begin{array}{c}\text{a number less}\\\text{than the original number}\end{array}$$

Vocabulary and Readiness Check

Use the choices below to fill in each blank.

percent	amount	of	less
base	the number	is	greater

1. The word _____ translates to "=."

2. The word _____ usually translates to "multiplication."

3. In the statement "10% of 90 is 9," the number 9 is called the _____ , 90 is called the _____ , and 10 is called the _____ .

4. 100% of a number = _____ .

5. Any "percent greater than 100%" of "a number" = "a number _____ than the original number."

6. Any "percent less than 100%" of "a number" = "a number _____ than the original number."

Identify the percent, the base, and the amount in each equation. Recall that percent · base = amount.

7. 42% · 50 = 21

8. 30% · 65 = 19.5

9. 107.5 = 125% · 86

10. 99 = 110% · 90

4.5 Exercise Set

Objective A Translating *Translate each to an equation. Do not solve. See Examples 1 through 6.*

 **1.** 18% of 81 is what number?

2. 36% of 72 is what number?

3. 20% of what number is 105?

4. 40% of what number is 6?

5. 0.6 is 40% of what number?

6. 0.7 is 20% of what number?

 7. What percent of 80 is 3.8?

8. 9.2 is what percent of 92?

9. What number is 9% of 43?

10. What number is 25% of 55?

11. What percent of 250 is 150?

12. What percent of 375 is 300?

Objective B *Solve. See Examples 7 and 8.*

 13. 10% of 35 is what number?

14. 25% of 68 is what number?

15. What number is 14% of 205?

16. What number is 18% of 425?

Solve. See Examples 9 and 10.

 17. 1.2 is 12% of what number?

18. 0.22 is 44% of what number?

19. $8\frac{1}{2}$% of what number is 51?

20. $4\frac{1}{2}$% of what number is 45?

Solve. See Examples 11 and 12.

21. What percent of 80 is 88?

22. What percent of 40 is 60?

23. 17 is what percent of 50?

24. 48 is what percent of 50?

Objectives Ⓐ Ⓑ **Mixed Practice** *Solve. See Examples 1 through 12.*

25. 0.1 is 10% of what number?

26. 0.5 is 5% of what number?

27. 150% of 430 is what number?

28. 300% of 56 is what number?

29. 82.5 is $16\frac{1}{2}$% of what number?

30. 7.2 is $6\frac{1}{4}$% of what number?

31. 2.58 is what percent of 50?

32. 2.64 is what percent of 25?

33. What number is 42% of 60?

34. What number is 36% of 80?

35. What percent of 184 is 64.4?

36. What percent of 120 is 76.8?

37. 120% of what number is 42?

38. 160% of what number is 40?

39. 2.4% of 26 is what number?

40. 4.8% of 32 is what number?

41. What percent of 600 is 3?

42. What percent of 500 is 2?

43. 6.67 is 4.6% of what number?

44. 9.75 is 7.5% of what number?

45. 1575 is what percent of 2500?

46. 2520 is what percent of 3500?

47. 2 is what percent of 50?

48. 2 is what percent of 40?

Review

Find the value of n in each proportion. See Section 4.1.

49. $\dfrac{27}{n} = \dfrac{9}{10}$

50. $\dfrac{35}{n} = \dfrac{7}{5}$

51. $\dfrac{n}{5} = \dfrac{8}{11}$

52. $\dfrac{n}{3} = \dfrac{6}{13}$

Write each phrase as a proportion.

53. 17 is to 12 as n is to 20

54. 20 is to 25 as n is to 10

55. 8 is to 9 as 14 is to n

56. 5 is to 6 as 15 is to n

Concept Extensions

For each equation, determine the next step taken to find the value of n. See the first Concept Check in this section.

57. $5 \cdot n = 32$

    a. $n = 5 \cdot 32$ **b.** $n = \dfrac{5}{32}$ **c.** $n = \dfrac{32}{5}$ **d.** none of these

58. $n = 0.7 \cdot 12$

    a. $n = 8.4$ **b.** $n = \dfrac{12}{0.7}$ **c.** $n = \dfrac{0.7}{12}$ **d.** none of these

59. $0.06 = n \cdot 7$

    a. $n = 0.06 \cdot 7$ **b.** $n = \dfrac{0.06}{7}$ **c.** $n = \dfrac{7}{0.06}$ **d.** none of these

60. $0.01 = n \cdot 8$

    a. $n = 0.01 \cdot 8$ **b.** $n = \dfrac{8}{0.01}$ **c.** $n = \dfrac{0.01}{8}$ **d.** none of these

61. Write a word statement for the equation $20\% \cdot n = 18.6$. Use the phrase "some number" for "n".

62. Write a word statement for the equation $n = 33\frac{1}{3}\% \cdot 24$. Use the phrase "some number" for "n".

For each exercise, determine whether the percent, n, is (a) 100%, (b) greater than 100%, or (c) less than 100%. See the last Concept Check in this section.

63. $n\%$ of 20 is 30   **64.** $n\%$ of 98 is 98   **65.** $n\%$ of 120 is 85   **66.** $n\%$ of 35 is 50

For each exercise, determine whether the number, n, is (a) equal to 45, (b) greater than 45, or (c) less than 45.

    67. 55% of 45 is n **68.** 230% of 45 is n **69.** 100% of 45 is n

    70. 30% of n is 45   **71.** 100% of n is 45   **72.** 180% of n is 45

    73. In your own words, explain how to solve a percent equation.

    74. Write a percent problem that uses the percent 50%.

Solve.

75. 1.5% of 45,775 is what number?

76. What percent of 75,528 is 27,945.36?

77. 22,113 is 180% of what number?

4.6 SOLVING PERCENT PROBLEMS USING PROPORTIONS

There is more than one method that can be used to solve percent problems. (See the note at the beginning of Section 4.5.) In the last section, we used the percent equation. In this section, we will use proportions.

Objective **A** Writing Percent Problems as Proportions

To understand the proportion method, recall that 70% means the ratio of 70 to 100, or $\frac{70}{100}$.

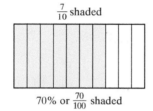

$$70\% = \frac{70}{100} = \frac{7}{10}$$

$\frac{7}{10}$ shaded

70% or $\frac{70}{100}$ shaded

Since the ratio $\frac{70}{100}$ is equal to the ratio $\frac{7}{10}$, we have the proportion

$$\frac{7}{10} = \frac{70}{100}.$$

We call this proportion the "percent proportion." In general, we can name the parts of this proportion as follows:

Percent Proportion

$$\frac{amount}{base} = \frac{percent}{100} \quad \leftarrow \text{always 100}$$

or

$$\text{amount} \rightarrow \frac{a}{b} = \frac{p}{100} \leftarrow \text{percent}$$
$$\text{base} \rightarrow$$

When we translate percent problems to proportions, the **percent,** p, can be identified by looking for the symbol % or the word *percent*. The **base,** b, usually follows the word *of*. The **amount,** a, is the part compared to the whole.

Helpful Hint

Part of Proportion	How It's Identified
Percent	% or percent
Base	Appears after *of*
Amount	Part compared to whole

PRACTICE 1

Translate to a proportion.
15% of what number is 55?

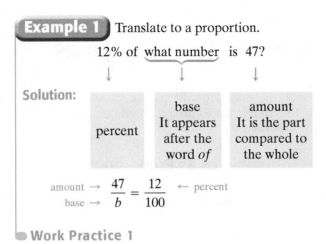

Example 1 Translate to a proportion.

12% of what number is 47?

Solution:

| percent | base
It appears
after the
word *of* | amount
It is the part
compared to
the whole |

amount → $\dfrac{47}{b} = \dfrac{12}{100}$ ← percent
base →

● **Work Practice 1**

PRACTICE 2

Translate to a proportion. 35 is
what percent of 70?

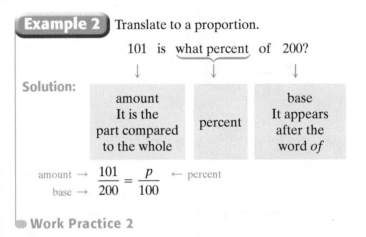

Example 2 Translate to a proportion.

101 is what percent of 200?

Solution:

| amount
It is the
part compared
to the whole | percent | base
It appears
after the
word *of* |

amount → $\dfrac{101}{200} = \dfrac{p}{100}$ ← percent
base →

● **Work Practice 2**

PRACTICE 3

Translate to a proportion. What
number is 25% of 68?

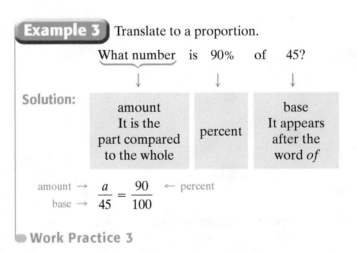

Example 3 Translate to a proportion.

What number is 90% of 45?

Solution:

| amount
It is the
part compared
to the whole | percent | base
It appears
after the
word *of* |

amount → $\dfrac{a}{45} = \dfrac{90}{100}$ ← percent
base →

● **Work Practice 3**

PRACTICE 4

Translate to a proportion. 520 is
65% of what number?

Example 4 Translate to a proportion.

238 is 40% of what number?

Solution: | amount | percent | base |

$$\dfrac{238}{b} = \dfrac{40}{100}$$

● **Work Practice 4**

Answers

1. $\dfrac{55}{b} = \dfrac{15}{100}$ 2. $\dfrac{35}{70} = \dfrac{p}{100}$

3. $\dfrac{a}{68} = \dfrac{25}{100}$ 4. $\dfrac{520}{b} = \dfrac{65}{100}$

Example 5 Translate to a proportion.

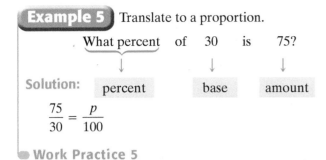

What percent of 30 is 75?

Solution: percent   base   amount

$$\frac{75}{30} = \frac{p}{100}$$

● Work Practice 5

PRACTICE 5

Translate to a proportion. What percent of 50 is 65?

Example 6 Translate to a proportion.

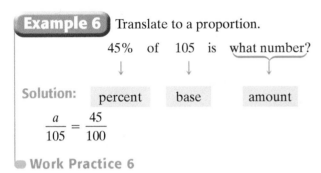

45% of 105 is what number?

Solution: percent   base   amount

$$\frac{a}{105} = \frac{45}{100}$$

● Work Practice 6

PRACTICE 6

Translate to a proportion. 36% of 80 is what number?

Objective B Solving Percent Problems

The proportions that we have written in this section contain three values that can change: the percent, the base, and the amount. If any two of these values are known, we can find the third (the unknown value). To do this, we write a percent proportion and find the unknown value as we did in Section 4.1.

Example 7 Solving Percent Proportion for the Amount

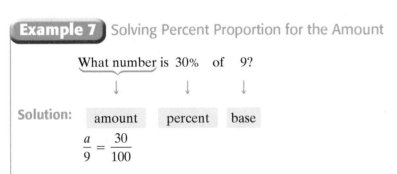

What number is 30% of 9?

Solution: amount   percent   base

$$\frac{a}{9} = \frac{30}{100}$$

To solve, we set cross products equal to each other.

$$\frac{a}{9} = \frac{30}{100}$$

$a \cdot 100 = 9 \cdot 30$ Set cross products equal.

$a \cdot 100 = 270$ Multiply.

Recall from Section 4.1 that if "some number times 100 is 270," then the number is 270 divided by 100.

$a = \frac{270}{100}$ Divide 270 by 100, the number multiplied by a.

$a = 2.7$ Simplify.

Thus, 2.7 is 30% of 9.

● Work Practice 7

PRACTICE 7

What number is 8% of 120?

> **Helpful Hint** The proportion in Example 7 contains the ratio $\frac{30}{100}$. A ratio in a proportion may be simplified before solving the proportion. The unknown number in both
>
> $\frac{a}{9} = \frac{30}{100}$ and $\frac{a}{9} = \frac{3}{10}$ is 2.7

Answers

5. $\frac{65}{50} = \frac{p}{100}$ 6. $\frac{a}{80} = \frac{36}{100}$

7. 9.6

✔**Concept Check** Consider the statement: "78 is what percent of 350?"
Which part of the percent proportion is unknown?

a. the amount   **b.** the base   **c.** the percent

Consider another statement: "14 is 10% of some number."
Which part of the percent proportion is unknown?

a. the amount   **b.** the base   **c.** the percent

PRACTICE 8

75% of what number is 60?

Example 8 Solving Percent Proportion for the Base

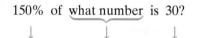

150% of <u>what number</u> is 30?

Solution: percent   base   amount

$$\frac{30}{b} = \frac{150}{100} \text{ Write the proportion.}$$

$$\frac{30}{b} = \frac{3}{2} \qquad \text{Write } \frac{150}{100} \text{ as } \frac{3}{2}.$$

$$30 \cdot 2 = b \cdot 3 \qquad \text{Set cross products equal.}$$

$$60 = b \cdot 3 \qquad \text{Multiply.}$$

$$\frac{60}{3} = b \qquad \text{Divide 60 by 3, the number multiplied by } b.$$

$$20 = b \qquad \text{Simplify.}$$

Thus, 150% of 20 is 30.

● **Work Practice 8**

✔**Concept Check** When solving a percent problem by using a proportion,
describe how you can check the result.

PRACTICE 9

15.2 is 5% of what number?

Example 9 Solving Percent Proportion for the Base

20.8 is 40% of <u>what number</u>?

Solution: amount   percent   base

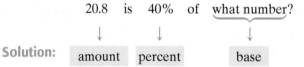

$$\frac{20.8}{b} = \frac{40}{100} \quad \text{or} \quad \frac{20.8}{b} = \frac{2}{5} \text{ Write the proportion and simplify } \frac{40}{100}.$$

$$20.8 \cdot 5 = b \cdot 2 \qquad \text{Set cross products equal.}$$

$$104 = b \cdot 2 \qquad \text{Multiply.}$$

$$\frac{104}{2} = b \qquad \text{Divide 104 by 2, the number multiplied by } b.$$

$$52 = b \qquad \text{Simplify.}$$

So, 20.8 is 40% of 52.

● **Work Practice 9**

Answers
8. 80 **9.** 304

✔ **Concept Check Answers**
c, b; by putting the result into the
proportion and checking that the
proportion is true

Example 10 Solving Percent Proportion for the Percent

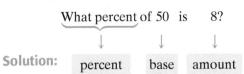

What percent of 50 is 8?

Solution: percent   base   amount

$$\frac{8}{50} = \frac{p}{100} \quad \text{or} \quad \frac{4}{25} = \frac{p}{100}$$ Write the proportion and simplify $\frac{8}{50}$.

$$4 \cdot 100 = 25 \cdot p$$ Set cross products equal.

$$400 = 25 \cdot p$$ Multiply.

$$\frac{400}{25} = p$$ Divide 400 by 25, the number multiplied by p.

$$16 = p$$ Simplify.

So, 16% of 50 is 8.

● Work Practice 10

PRACTICE 10

What percent of 40 is 6?

Helpful Hint

Recall from our percent proportion that this number already is a percent. Just keep the number as is and attach a % symbol.

Example 11 Solving Percent Proportion for the Percent

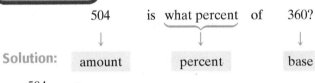

504   is what percent of   360?

Solution: amount   percent   base

$$\frac{504}{360} = \frac{p}{100}$$

Let's choose not to simplify the ratio $\frac{504}{360}$.

$$504 \cdot 100 = 360 \cdot p$$ Set cross products equal.

$$50{,}400 = 360 \cdot p$$ Multiply.

$$\frac{50{,}400}{360} = p$$ Divide 50,400 by 360, the number multiplied by p.

$$140 = p$$ Simplify.

Notice that by choosing not to simplify $\frac{504}{360}$, we had larger numbers in our equation. Either way, we find that 504 is 140% of 360.

● Work Practice 11

PRACTICE 11

336 is what percent of 160?

You may have noticed the following while working examples.

Helpful Hint

Use the following to see whether your answers are reasonable.

100% of a number = the number

$\left(\begin{array}{c} \text{a percent} \\ \text{greater than} \\ 100\% \end{array} \right)$ of a number = $\begin{array}{c} \text{a number larger} \\ \text{than the original number} \end{array}$

$\left(\begin{array}{c} \text{a percent} \\ \text{less than } 100\% \end{array} \right)$ of a number = $\begin{array}{c} \text{a number less} \\ \text{than the original number} \end{array}$

Answers
10. 15%   **11.** 210%

Vocabulary and Readiness Check

Use the choices below to fill in each blank. These choices will be used more than once.

amount   base   percent

1. When translating the statement "20% of 15 is 3" to a proportion, the number 3 is called the _____, 15 is the _____, and 20 is the _____.
2. In the question "50% of what number is 28?", which part of the percent proportion is unknown? _____
3. In the question "What number is 25% of 200?", which part of the percent proportion is unknown? _____
4. In the question "38 is what percent of 380?", which part of the percent proportion is unknown? _____

Identify the amount, the base, and the percent in each equation. Recall that $\dfrac{\text{amount}}{\text{base}} = \dfrac{\text{percent}}{100}$.

5. $\dfrac{12.6}{42} = \dfrac{30}{100}$

6. $\dfrac{201}{300} = \dfrac{67}{100}$

7. $\dfrac{20}{100} = \dfrac{102}{510}$

8. $\dfrac{40}{100} = \dfrac{248}{620}$

4.6 Exercise Set

FOR EXTRA HELP

MyMathLab®
PRACTICE   WATCH   DOWNLOAD   READ   REVIEW

Objective Ⓐ **Translating** *Translate each to a proportion. Do not solve. See Examples 1 through 6.*

1. 98% of 45 is what number?

2. 92% of 30 is what number?

3. What number is 4% of 150?

4. What number is 7% of 175?

5. 14.3 is 26% of what number?

6. 1.2 is 47% of what number?

7. 35% of what number is 84?

8. 85% of what number is 520?

9. What percent of 400 is 70?

10. What percent of 900 is 216?

11. 8.2 is what percent of 82?

12. 9.6 is what percent of 96?

Objective Ⓑ *Solve. See Example 7.*

13. 40% of 65 is what number?

14. 25% of 84 is what number?

15. What number is 18% of 105?

16. What number is 60% of 29?

Solve. See Examples 8 and 9.

17. 15% of what number is 90?

18. 55% of what number is 55?

19. 7.8 is 78% of what number?

20. 1.1 is 44% of what number?

Solve. See Examples 10 and 11.

21. What percent of 35 is 42?

22. What percent of 98 is 147?

23. 14 is what percent of 50?

24. 24 is what percent of 50?

Objectives Ⓐ Ⓑ **Mixed Practice** *Solve. See Examples 1 through 11.*

25. 3.7 is 10% of what number?

26. 7.4 is 5% of what number?

27. 2.4% of 70 is what number?

28. 2.5% of 90 is what number?

29. 160 is 16% of what number?

30. 30 is 6% of what number?

31. 394.8 is what percent of 188?

32. 550.4 is what percent of 172?

33. What number is 89% of 62?

34. What number is 53% of 130?

35. What percent of 6 is 2.7?

36. What percent of 5 is 1.6?

37. 140% of what number is 105?

38. 170% of what number is 221?

39. 1.8% of 48 is what number?

40. 7.8% of 24 is what number?

41. What percent of 800 is 4?

42. What percent of 500 is 3?

43. 3.5 is 2.5% of what number?

44. 9.18 is 6.8% of what number?

45. 20% of 48 is what number?

46. 75% of 14 is what number?

47. 2486 is what percent of 2200?

48. 9310 is what percent of 3800?

Review

Add or subtract as indicated. See Sections 2.6, 2.8, and 2.9.

49. $\dfrac{11}{16} + \dfrac{3}{16}$

50. $\dfrac{5}{8} - \dfrac{7}{12}$

51. $3\dfrac{1}{2} - \dfrac{11}{30}$

52. $2\dfrac{2}{3} + 4\dfrac{1}{2}$

Add or subtract the decimals. See Section 3.3.

53. 0.41
     $+ 0.29$

54. 10.78
      4.3
     $+ \ 0.21$

55. 2.38
     $- 0.19$

56. 16.37
     $- \ 2.61$

Concept Extensions

57. Write a word statement for the proportion $\frac{n}{28} = \frac{25}{100}$. Use the phrase "what number" for "n."

58. Write a percent statement that translates to $\frac{16}{80} = \frac{20}{100}$.

Suppose you have finished solving four percent problems using proportions that you set up correctly. Check each answer to see if each makes the proportion a true proportion. If any proportion is not true, solve it to find the correct solution. See the Concept Checks in this section.

59. $\frac{a}{64} = \frac{25}{100}$

Is the amount equal to 17?

60. $\frac{520}{b} = \frac{65}{100}$

Is the base equal to 800?

61. $\frac{p}{100} = \frac{13}{52}$

Is the percent equal to 25 (25%)?

62. $\frac{36}{12} = \frac{p}{100}$

Is the percent equal to 50 (50%)?

63. In your own words, describe how to identify the percent, the base, and the amount in a percent problem.

64. In your own words, explain how to use a proportion to solve a percent problem.

Solve. Round to the nearest tenth, if necessary.

65. What number is 22.3% of 53,862?

66. What percent of 110,736 is 88,542?

67. 8652 is 119% of what number?

4.7 APPLICATIONS OF PERCENT

Objective Ⓐ Solving Applications Involving Percent

Percent is used in a variety of everyday situations. The next examples show just a few ways that percent occurs in real-life settings. (Each of these examples shows two ways of solving these problems. If you studied Section 4.5 only, see *Method 1*. If you studied Section 4.6 only, see *Method 2*.)

The first example has to do with the Appalachian Trail, a hiking trail conceived by a forester in 1921 and diagrammed to the right.

Mount Katahdin, Maine

The Appalachian Trail

Springer Mountain, Georgia

Example 1 The circle graph in the margin shows the Appalachian Trail mileage by state. If the total mileage of the trail is 2174, use the circle graph to determine the number of miles in the state of New York. Round to the nearest whole mile.

Solution: *Method 1.* First, we state the problem in words.

In words: What number is 4% of 2174?

Translate: n = 4% · 2174

To solve for n, we find $4\% \cdot 2174$.

$n = 0.04 \cdot 2174$ Write 4% as a decimal.

$n = 86.96$ Multiply.

$n \approx 87$ Round to the nearest whole.

Rounded to the nearest whole mile, we have that approximately 87 miles of the Appalachian Trail are in New York state.

Method 2. State the problem in words; then translate.

In words: What number is 4% of 2174?

amount   percent   base

Translate:
$$\text{amount} \rightarrow \frac{a}{2174} = \frac{4}{100} \leftarrow \text{percent}$$
base →

Next, we solve for a.

$a \cdot 100 = 2174 \cdot 4$ Set cross products equal.

$a \cdot 100 = 8696$ Multiply.

$\dfrac{a \cdot 100}{100} = \dfrac{8696}{100}$ Divide both sides by 100.

$a = 86.96$ Simplify.

$a \approx 87$ Round to the nearest whole.

Rounded to the nearest whole mile, we have that approximately 87 miles of the Appalachian Trail are in New York state.

● **Work Practice 1**

PRACTICE 1

If the total mileage of the Appalachian Trail is 2174, use the circle graph to determine the number of miles in the state of Virginia.

Appalachian Trail Mileage by State Percent

Georgia 4%
Maine 13%   North Carolina 4%
Tennessee 14%
New Hampshire 7%
Vermont 7%
Virginia 25%
Massachusetts 4%
Connecticut 2%
New York 4%
New Jersey 3%
Pennsylvania 11%
West Virginia 0.2%
Maryland 2%

Total miles: 2174
Source: purebound.com

Answer

1. 543.5 mi

PRACTICE 2

In Florida, about 34,000 new nurses were recently needed and hired. If there are now 130,000 nurses, what percent of new nurses were needed in Florida? Round to the nearest whole percent. (*Source: St. Petersburg Times* and *The Registered Nurse Population*)

Example 2 Finding Percent of Nursing Schools with Increases in Enrollment

There is a worldwide shortage of nurses, with numbers of nurses projected to be 20% below requirements by 2020. Until 2001, there has also been a continual decline in enrollment in nursing schools. That has recently changed.

In 2003, 2178 of the total 2593 nursing schools in the United States had an increase in applications or enrollment. What percent of nursing schools had an increase? Round to the nearest whole percent. (*Source:* CNN and *Nurse Week*)

Solution: *Method 1.* First, we state the problem in words.

In words: 2178   is   what percent   of   2593?

Translate: 2178   = n ·   2593

Next, solve for n.

$\dfrac{2178}{2593} = n$ Divide 2178 by 2593, the number multiplied by n.

$0.84 \approx n$ Divide and round to the nearest hundredth.

$84\% \approx n$ Write as a percent.

In 2003, about 84% of nursing schools had an increase in applications or enrollment.

Method 2.

In words: 2178   is   what percent   of   2593?

           amount   percent   base

Translate: amount → $\dfrac{2178}{2593}$ = $\dfrac{p}{100}$ ← percent
           base →

Next, solve for p.

$2178 \cdot 100 = 2593 \cdot p$ Set cross products equal.

$217{,}800 = 2593 \cdot p$ Multiply.

$\dfrac{217{,}800}{2593} = p$ Divide 217,800 by 2593, the number multiplied by p.

$84 \approx p$

In 2003, about 84% of nursing schools had an increase in applications or enrollment.

◉ **Work Practice 2**

PRACTICE 3

The freshmen class of 775 students is 31% of all students at Euclid University. How many students go to Euclid University?

Example 3 Finding the Base Number of Absences

Mr. Buccaran, the principal at Slidell High School, counted 31 freshmen absent during a particular day. If this is 4% of the total number of freshmen, how many freshmen are there at Slidell High School?

Solution: *Method 1.* First we state the problem in words; then we translate.

In words: 31   is   4%   of   what number?

Translate: 31   =   4%   · n

Answers

2. 26%   **3.** 2500

Next, we solve for n.

$$31 = 0.04 \cdot n \quad \text{Write 4\% as a decimal.}$$

$$\frac{31}{0.04} = n \quad \text{Divide 31 by 0.04, the number multiplied by } n.$$

$$775 = n \quad \text{Simplify.}$$

There are 775 freshmen at Slidell High School.

Method 2. First we state the problem in words; then we translate.

In words: 31   is   4%   of   what number?

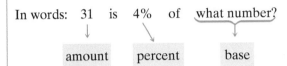

amount   percent   base

Translate: $\underset{\text{base} \rightarrow}{\overset{\text{amount} \rightarrow}{}} \dfrac{31}{b} = \dfrac{4}{100} \leftarrow \text{percent}$

Next, we solve for b.

$$31 \cdot 100 = b \cdot 4 \quad \text{Set cross products equal.}$$

$$3100 = b \cdot 4 \quad \text{Multiply.}$$

$$\frac{3100}{4} = b \quad \text{Divide 3100 by 4, the number multiplied by } b.$$

$$775 = b \quad \text{Simplify.}$$

There are 775 freshmen at Slidell High School.

⬤ **Work Practice 3**

Example 4   Finding the Base Increase in Licensed Drivers

From 2000 to 2007, the number of licensed drivers on the road in the United States increased by 6.5%. In 2000, there were 190 million licensed drivers on the road.

a. Find the increase in licensed drivers from 2000 to 2007.
b. Find the number of licensed drivers on the road in 2007.
    (*Source:* Federal Highway Administration)

Solution: *Method 1.*   First we find the increase in licensed drivers.

In words: What number   is   6.5%   of   190?

Translate: n =   6.5%   ·   190

Continued on next page

PRACTICE 4

From 2000 to 2007, the number of registered vehicles on the road in the United States increased by 3%. In 2000, the number of vehicles on the road was 240 million.
a. Find the increase in the number of vehicles on the road in 2007.
b. Find the total number of registered vehicles on the road in 2007.
(*Source:* Federal Highway Administration)

Answer
4. a. 7.2 million   **b.** 247.2 million

Next, we solve for *n*.

$n = 0.065 \cdot 190$ Write 6.5% as a decimal.

$n = 12.35$ Multiply.

a. The increase in licensed drivers was 12.35 million.

b. This means that the number of licensed drivers in 2007 was

| Number of licensed drivers in 2007 | = | Number of licensed drivers in 2000 | + | Increase in number of licensed drivers |

$$= 190 \text{ million} + 12.35 \text{ million}$$
$$= 202.35 \text{ million}$$

Method 2.   First we find the increase in licensed drivers.

In words: What number is   6.5%   of   190?

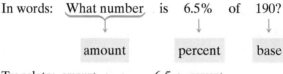

amount   percent   base

Translate: amount → $\dfrac{a}{190} = \dfrac{6.5}{100}$ ← percent
base →

Next, we solve for *a*.

$a \cdot 100 = 190 \cdot 6.5$ Set cross products equal.

$a \cdot 100 = 1235$ Multiply.

$\dfrac{a \cdot 100}{100} = \dfrac{1235}{100}$ Divide both sides by 100.

$a = 12.35$ Simplify.

a. The increase in licensed drivers was 12.35 million.

b. This means that the number of licensed drivers in 2007 was

| Number of licensed drivers in 2007 | = | Number of licensed drivers in 2000 | + | Increase in number of licensed drivers |

$$= 190 \text{ million} + 12.35 \text{ million}$$
$$= 202.35 \text{ million}$$

● **Work Practice 4**

Objective Ⓑ Finding Percent Increase and Percent Decrease

We often use percents to show how much an amount has increased or decreased.

Suppose that the population of a town is 10,000 people and then it increases by 2000 people. The **percent of increase** is

amount of increase → $\dfrac{2000}{10,000} = 0.2 = 20\%$
original amount →

In general, we have the following.

Percent of Increase

$$\text{percent of increase} = \frac{\text{amount of increase}}{\text{original amount}}$$

Then write the quotient as a percent.

Example 5 Finding Percent Increase

The number of applications for a mathematics scholarship at Yale increased from 34 to 45 in one year. What is the percent increase? Round to the nearest whole percent.

Solution: First we find the amount of increase by subtracting the original number of applicants from the new number of applicants.

amount of increase = 45 − 34 = 11

The amount of increase is 11 applicants. To find the percent of increase,

$$\text{percent of increase} = \frac{\text{amount of increase}}{\text{original amount}} = \frac{11}{34} \approx 0.32 = 32\%$$

The number of applications increased by about 32%.

● **Work Practice 5**

✓ **Concept Check** A student is calculating the percent increase in enrollment from 180 students one year to 200 students the next year. Explain what is wrong with the following calculations:

Amount of increase = 200 − 180 = 20

Percent of increase $= \dfrac{20}{200} = 0.1 = 10\%$

Suppose that your income was $300 a week and then it decreased by $30. The **percent of decrease** is

amount of decrease → $\dfrac{\$30}{\$300} = 0.1 = 10\%$
original amount →

Percent of Decrease

$$\text{percent of decrease} = \frac{\text{amount of decrease}}{\text{original amount}}$$

Then write the quotient as a percent.

Example 6 Finding Percent Decrease

In response to a decrease in sales, a company with 1500 employees reduces the number of employees to 1230. What is the percent decrease?

Solution: First we find the amount of decrease by subtracting 1230 from 1500.

amount of decrease = 1500 − 1230 = 270

The amount of decrease is 270. To find the percent of decrease,

$$\text{percent of decrease} = \frac{\text{amount of decrease}}{\text{original amount}} = \frac{270}{1500} = 0.18 = 18\%$$

The number of employees decreased by 18%.

● **Work Practice 6**

✓ **Concept Check** An ice cream stand sold 6000 ice cream cones last summer. This year the same stand sold 5400 cones. Was there a 10% increase, a 10% decrease, or neither? Explain.

PRACTICE 5

The number of people attending the local play, *Peter Pan,* increased from 285 on Friday to 333 on Saturday. Find the percent increase in attendance. Round to the nearest tenth percent.

Helpful Hint Make sure that this number is the original number and not the new number.

PRACTICE 6

A town with a population of 20,200 in 1995 decreased to 18,483 in 2005. What was the percent decrease?

Answers

5. 16.8%   **6.** 8.5%

✓ **Concept Check Answers**

To find the percent of increase, you have to divide the amount of increase (20) by the original amount (180); 10% decrease.

Objective Ⓐ *Solve. For Exercises 1 and 2, the solutions have been started for you. See Examples 1 through 4. If necessary, round percents to the nearest tenth and all other answers to the nearest whole.*

1. An inspector found 24 defective bolts during an inspection. If this is 1.5% of the total number of bolts inspected, how many bolts were inspected?

Start the solution:

1. UNDERSTAND the problem. Reread it as many times as needed.

Go to Method 1 or Method 2.

Method 1.

2. TRANSLATE into an equation. (Fill in the boxes.)

24   is   1.5%   of   what number?

24 ☐ 1.5% ☐ n

3. SOLVE for n. (See Example 3, Method 1, for help.)

4. INTERPRET. The total number of bolts inspected was _____.

Method 2.

2. TRANSLATE into a proportion. (Fill in the blanks with "amount" or "base.")

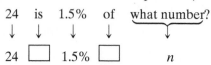

24   is   1.5%   of   what number?

_____   percent   _____

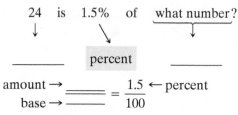

amount → $\dfrac{}{}$ = $\dfrac{1.5}{100}$ ← percent

base →

3. SOLVE the proportion. (See Example 3, Method 2, for help.)

4. INTERPRET. The total number of bolts inspected was _____.

3. The Total Gym® provides weight resistance through adjustments of incline. The minimum weight resistance is 4% of the weight of the person using the Total Gym. Find the minimum weight resistance possible for a 220-pound man. (*Source:* Total Gym)

5. A student's cost for last semester at her community college was $2700. She spent $378 of that on books. What percent of last semester's college costs was spent on books?

2. A day care worker found 28 children absent one day during an epidemic of chicken pox. If this was 35% of the total number of children attending the day care center, how many children attend this day care center?

Start the solution:

1. UNDERSTAND the problem. Reread it as many times as needed.

Go to Method 1 or Method 2.

Method 1.

2. TRANSLATE into an equation. (Fill in the boxes.)

28   is   35%   of   what number?

28 ☐ 35% ☐ n

3. SOLVE for n. (See Example 3, Method 1, for help.)

4. INTERPRET. The total number of children attending the day care center was _____.

Method 2.

2. TRANSLATE into a proportion. (Fill in the blanks with "amount" or "base.")

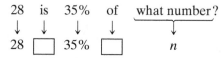

28   is   35%   of   what number?

_____   percent   _____

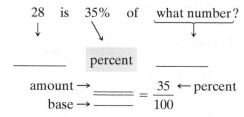

amount → $\dfrac{}{}$ = $\dfrac{35}{100}$ ← percent

base →

3. SOLVE the proportion. (See Example 3, Method 2, for help.)

4. INTERPRET. The total number of children attending the day care center was _____.

4. The maximum weight resistance for the Total Gym is 60% of the weight of the person using it. Find the maximum weight resistance possible for a 220-pound man. (See Exercise 3 if needed.)

6. Pierre Sampeau belongs to his local food cooperative, where he receives a percentage of what he spends each year as a dividend. He spent $3850 last year at the food cooperative store and received a dividend of $154. What percent of his total spending at the food cooperative did he receive as a dividend?

7. In a recent year, approximately 32% of films were rated R. If 725 films were rated, how many were rated R? (*Source:* Motion Picture Association of America)

8. In a recent year, approximately 8% of films were rated PG. If 725 films were rated, how many were rated PG? (*Source:* Motion Picture Association of America)

9. Approximately 160,650 of America's 945,000 restaurants are pizza restaurants. Determine the percent of restaurants in America that are pizza restaurants. (*Source:* Pizza Marketplace, National Restaurant Association)

10. Of the 58,200 veterinarians in private practice in the United States, approximately 27,354 are female. Determine the percent of female veterinarians in private practice in the United States. (*Source:* American Veterinary Medical Association)

11. A furniture company currently produces 6200 chairs per month. If production decreases by 8%, find the decrease and the new number of chairs produced each month.

12. The enrollment at a local college decreased by 5% over last year's enrollment of 7640. Find the decrease in enrollment and the current enrollment.

13. From 2006 to 2016, the number of people employed as physician assistants in the United States is expected to increase by 27%. The number of people employed as physician assistants in 2006 was 66,000. Find the predicted number of physician assistants in 2016. (*Source:* Bureau of Labor Statistics)

14. From 2001 to 2007, the number of households owning dogs increased by 13.5%. The number of households owning dogs in 2001 was 37,900,000. Find the number of households owning dogs in 2007. (*Source:* American Veterinary Medical Association)

Let's look at the populations of two states, North Dakota and Louisiana. Their locations are shown on the partial U.S. map below. Round each answer to the nearest thousand. (*Source:* U.S. Dept. of Commerce)

15. In 2000, the population of North Dakota was approximately 642 thousand. If the population decreased by 0.8% between 2000 and 2009, find the population of North Dakota in 2009.

16. In 2000, the population in Louisiana was approximately 4470 thousand. If the population increased about 0.5% between 2000 and 2009, find the population of Louisiana in 2009.

North Dakota

Louisiana

A popular extreme sport is snowboarding. Ski trails are marked with difficulty levels of easy ●, intermediate ■, difficult ◆, expert ◆◆, and other variations. Use this information for Exercises 17 and 18. Round each percent to the nearest whole. See Example 2.

17. At Keystone ski area in Colorado, approximately 41 of the 135 total ski runs are rated intermediate. What percent of the runs are intermediate?

18. At Telluride ski area in Colorado, about 28 of the 115 total ski runs are rated easy. What percent of the runs are easy?

For each food described, find the percent of total calories from fat. If necessary, round to the nearest tenth percent. See Example 2.

19. Ranch dressing serving size of 2 tablespoons

	Calories
Total	40
From fat	20

20. Unsweetened cocoa powder serving size of 1 tablespoon

	Calories
Total	20
From fat	5

21.

Nutrition Facts
Serving Size 1 pouch (20g)
Servings Per Container 6

Amount Per Serving

Calories	80
Calories from fat	10

	% Daily Value*
Total Fat 1g	2%
Sodium 45mg	2%
Total Carbohydrate 17g	6%
Sugars 9g	
Protein 0g	
Vitamin C	25%

Not a significant source of saturated fat, cholesterol, dietary fiber, vitamin A, calcium and iron.

*Percent Daily Values are based on a 2,000 calorie diet.

Artificial Fruit Snacks

22.

Nutrition Facts
Serving Size $\frac{1}{4}$ cup (33g)
Servings Per Container About 9

Amount Per Serving

Calories 190	Calories from Fat 130

	% Daily Value
Total Fat 16g	24%
Saturated Fat 3g	16%
Cholesterol 0mg	0%
Sodium 135mg	6%
Total Carbohydrate 9g	3%
Dietary Fiber 1g	5%
Sugars 2g	
Protein 5g	

Vitamin A 0% • Vitamin C 0%
Calcium 0% • Iron 8%

Peanut Mixture

23.

Nutrition Facts
Serving Size 18 crackers (29g)
Servings Per Container About 9

Amount Per Serving

Calories 120	Calories from Fat 35

	% Daily Value*
Total Fat 4g	6%
Saturated Fat 0.5g	3%
Polyunsaturated Fat 0g	
Monounsaturated Fat 1.5g	
Cholesterol 0mg	0%
Sodium 220mg	9%
Total Carbohydrate 21g	7%
Dietary Fiber 2g	7%
Sugars 3g	
Protein 2g	

Vitamin A 0% • Vitamin C 0%
Calcium 2% • Iron 4%
Phosphorus 10%

Snack Crackers

24.

Nutrition Facts
Serving Size 28 crackers (31g)
Servings Per Container About 6

Amount Per Serving

Calories 130	Calories from Fat 35

	% Daily Value*
Total Fat 4g	6%
Saturated Fat 2g	10%
Polyunsaturated Fat 1g	
Monounsaturated Fat 1g	
Cholesterol 0mg	0%
Sodium 470mg	20%
Total Carbohydrate 23g	8%
Dietary Fiber 1g	4%
Sugars 4g	
Protein 2g	

Vitamin A 0% • Vitamin C 0%
Calcium 0% • Iron 2%

Snack Crackers

Solve. If necessary, round money amounts to the nearest cent and all other amounts to the nearest tenth. See Examples 1 through 4.

25. A family paid $26,250 as a down payment for a home. If this represents 15% of the price of the home, find the price of the home.

26. A banker learned that $842.40 is withheld from his monthly check for taxes and insurance. If this represents 18% of his total pay, find the total pay.

27. An owner of a repair service company estimates that for every 40 hours a repairperson is on the job, he can bill for only 78% of the hours. The remaining hours, the repairperson is idle or driving to or from a job. Determine the number of hours per 40-hour week the owner can bill for a repairperson.

28. A manufacturer of electronic components expects 1.04% of its products to be defective. Determine the number of defective components expected in a batch of 28,350 components. Round to the nearest whole component.

29. A car manufacturer announced that next year the price of a certain model of car will increase by 4.5%. This year the price is $19,286. Find the increase in price and the new price.

30. A union contract calls for a 6.5% salary increase for all employees. Determine the increase and the new salary that a worker currently making $58,500 under this contract can expect.

A popular extreme sport is artificial wall climbing. The photo shown is an artificial climbing wall. Exercises 31 and 32 are about the Footsloggers Climbing Tower in Boone, North Carolina.

31. A climber is resting at a height of 21 feet while on the Footsloggers Climbing Tower. If this is 60% of the tower's total height, find the height of the tower.

32. A group plans to climb the Footsloggers Climbing Tower at the group rate, once they save enough money. Thus far, $126 has been saved. If this is 70% of the total amount needed for the group, find the total price.

33. Tuition for an Ohio resident at the Columbus campus of Ohio State University was $4761 in 2001. The tuition increased by 82.3% during the period from 2001 to 2009. Find the increase, and the tuition for the 2009–2010 school year. Round the increase to the nearest whole dollar. (*Source:* Ohio State University)

34. The population of Americans aged 65 and older was 38 million in 2007. That population is projected to increase by 90% by 2030. Find the increase and the projected 2030 population. (*Source:* Bureau of the Census)

35. From 2008–2009 to 2017–2018, the number of associate degrees awarded is projected to increase by 5.7%. If the number of associate degrees awarded in 2008–2009 was 731,000, find the increase and the projected number of associate degrees awarded in the 2017–2018 school year. (*Source:* National Center for Education Statistics)

36. From 2008–2009 to 2017–2018, the number of bachelor degrees awarded is projected to increase by 8%. If the number of bachelor degrees awarded in 2008–2009 was 1,603,000, find the increase and the projected number of bachelor degrees awarded in the 2017–2018 school year. (*Source:* National Center for Education Statistics)

Objective **B** *Find the amount of increase and the percent increase. See Example 5.*

	Original Amount	New Amount	Amount of Increase	Percent Increase
37.	50	80		
38.	8	12		
39.	65	117		
40.	68	170		

Find the amount of decrease and the percent decrease. See Example 6.

	Original Amount	New Amount	Amount of Decrease	Percent Decrease
41.	8	6		
42.	25	20		
43.	160	40		
44.	200	162		

Solve. Round percents to the nearest tenth, if necessary. See Examples 5 and 6.

45. There are 150 calories in a cup of whole milk and only 84 in a cup of skim milk. In switching to skim milk, find the percent decrease in number of calories per cup.

46. In reaction to a slow economy, the number of employees at a soup company decreased from 530 to 477. What was the percent decrease in the number of employees?

47. The number of cable TV systems recently decreased from 10,845 to 10,700. Find the percent decrease.

48. Before taking a typing course, Geoffry Landers could type 32 words per minute. By the end of the course, he was able to type 76 words per minute. Find the percent increase.

49. In 1940, the average size of a privately owned farm in the United States was 174 acres. In a recent year, the average size of a privately owned farm in the United States had increased to 449 acres. What is this percent increase? (*Source:* National Agricultural Statistics Service)

50. In 2003, 5.5 million digital television sets were sold in the United States. By 2007, this number had increased to 27.1 million. What was the percent increase? Round to the nearest percent. (*Source:* Motion Picture Association of America)

51. When music CDs were first introduced in 1983, the average suggested list price was $21.50. By 2007, the average suggested list price was $14.88. What was the percent decrease in the average suggested list price for music CDs from 1983 to 2007? (*Source:* Recording Industry Association of America)

52. In 1994, there were 784 deaths from boating accidents in the United States. By 2008, the number of deaths from boating accidents had decreased to 655. What was the percent decrease? (*Source:* U.S. Coast Guard)

53. In 2006, there were 3570 thousand elementary and secondary teachers employed in the United States. This number is expected to increase to 3769 thousand teachers in 2012. What is the percent increase? (*Source:* National Center for Education Statistics)

54. In 2006, approximately 500,000 correctional officers were employed in the United States. By 2016, this number is expected to increase to 580,000 correctional officers. What is the percent increase? (*Source:* Bureau of Labor Statistics)

55. In a recent 10-year period, the number of indoor cinema sites in the United States decreased from 6903 to 5545. What is this percent decrease? (*Source:* National Association of Theater Owners)

56. As the largest health care occupation, registered nurses held about 2.5 million jobs in 2006. The number of registered nurses is expected to be 3.075 million by 2016. What is the percent increase? (*Source:* Bureau of Labor Statistics)

57. In 2006, approximately 504,000 computer systems analysts were employed in the United States. By 2016, this is expected to increase to 650,000. What is the percent increase? (*Source:* Bureau of Labor Statistics)

58. In 1999, there were 10.9 million total restaurant employees in the United States. By 2019, this number is expected to increase to 14.8 million. What is the percent increase? (*Source:* National Restaurant Association)

59. The number of cell phone tower sites in the United States was 178,025 in 2005. By 2010, the number of cell sites had increased to 247,081. What was the percent increase? Round to the nearest percent. (*Source:* CTIA—The Wireless Association)

60. The population of Tokyo is expected to decrease from 127,400 thousand in 2005 to 99,900 thousand in 2050. Find the percent decrease. (*Source:* International Programs Center, Bureau of the Census, U.S. Dept. of Commerce)

Review

Perform each indicated operation. See Sections 3.3 and 3.4.

61.
$$\begin{array}{r} 0.12 \\ \times\ 38 \\ \hline \end{array}$$

62.
$$\begin{array}{r} 42 \\ \times\ 0.7 \\ \hline \end{array}$$

63. $9.20 + 1.98$

64. $46 + 7.89$

65. $78 - 19.46$

66. $64.80 - 10.72$

Concept Extensions

67. If a number is increased by 100%, how does the increased number compare with the original number? Explain your answer.

68. In your own words, explain what is wrong with the following statement. "Last year we had 80 students attend. This year we have a 50% increase or a total of 160 students attending."

Explain what errors were made by each student when solving percent of increase or decrease problems and then correct the errors. See the Concept Checks in this section.

The population of a certain rural town was 150 in 1980, 180 in 1990, and 150 in 2000.

69. Find the percent of increase in population from 1980 to 1990.

Miranda's solution: Percent of increase $= \dfrac{30}{180} = 0.1\overline{6} \approx 16.7\%$

70. Find the percent of decrease in population from 1990 to 2000.

Jeremy's solution: Percent of decrease $= \dfrac{30}{150} = 0.20 = 20\%$

71. The percent of increase from 1980 to 1990 is the same as the percent of decrease from 1990 to 2000. True or false.

Chris's answer: True because they had the same amount of increase as the amount of decrease.

4.8 PERCENT AND PROBLEM-SOLVING: SALES TAX, COMMISSION, AND DISCOUNT

Objective (A) Calculating Sales Tax and Total Price

Percents are frequently used in the retail trade. For example, most states charge a tax on certain items when purchased. This tax is called a **sales tax,** and retail stores collect it for the state. Sales tax is almost always stated as a percent of the purchase price.

A 9% sales tax rate on a purchase of a $10 calculator gives a sales tax of

$$\text{sales tax} = 9\% \text{ of } \$10 = 0.09 \cdot \$10.00 = \$0.90$$

The total price to the customer would be

$$\underbrace{\text{purchase price}} \quad \text{plus} \quad \underbrace{\text{sales tax}}$$

$$\$10.00 \qquad + \qquad \$0.90 = \$10.90$$

This example suggests the following equations:

> ### Sales Tax and Total Price
>
> $$\text{sales tax} = \text{tax rate} \cdot \text{purchase price}$$
>
> $$\text{total price} = \text{purchase price} + \text{sales tax}$$

In this section we round dollar amounts to the nearest cent.

Example 1 Finding Sales Tax and Purchase Price

Find the sales tax and the total price on the purchase of an $85.50 atlas in a city where the sales tax rate is 7.5%.

Solution: The purchase price is $85.50 and the tax rate is 7.5%.

$$\boxed{\text{sales tax}} = \boxed{\text{tax rate}} \cdot \boxed{\text{purchase price}}$$

$$\text{sales tax} = 7.5\% \cdot \$85.50$$
$$= 0.075 \cdot \$85.5 \qquad \text{Write 7.5\% as a decimal.}$$
$$\approx \$6.41 \qquad \text{Rounded to the nearest cent}$$

Thus, the sales tax is $6.41. Next find the total price.

$$\boxed{\text{total price}} = \boxed{\text{purchase price}} + \boxed{\text{sales tax}}$$

$$\text{total price} = \$85.50 + \$6.41$$
$$= \$91.91$$

The sales tax on $85.50 is $6.41, and the total price is $91.91.

● **Work Practice 1**

PRACTICE 1

If the sales tax rate is 8.5%, what is the sales tax and the total amount due on a $59.90 Goodgrip tire? (Round the sales tax to the nearest cent.)

Answer

1. tax: $5.09; total: $64.99

✓**Concept Check** The purchase price of a textbook is $50 and sales tax is 10%. If you are told by the cashier that the total price is $75, how can you tell that a mistake has been made?

Example 2 Finding a Sales Tax Rate

The sales tax on a $406 Sony flat-screen digital 27-inch television is $34.51. Find the sales tax rate.

Solution: Let r represent the unknown sales tax rate. Then

$$\underbrace{\text{sales tax}}_{\downarrow} = \underbrace{\text{tax rate}}_{\downarrow} \cdot \underbrace{\text{purchase price}}_{\swarrow}$$

$$\$34.51 = r \cdot \$406$$

$$\frac{34.51}{406} = \frac{r \cdot 406}{406} \quad \text{Divide both sides by 406.}$$

$$0.085 = r \quad \text{Simplify.}$$

$$8.5\% = r \quad \text{Write 0.085 as a percent.}$$

The sales tax rate is 8.5%.

● Work Practice 2

PRACTICE 2

The sales tax on an $18,500 automobile is $1665. Find the sales tax rate.

Objective ⑧ Calculating Commissions

A **wage** is payment for performing work. Hourly wage, commissions, and salary are some of the ways wages can be paid. Many people who work in sales are paid a commission. An employee who is paid a **commission** is paid a percent of his or her total sales.

> **Commission**
>
> commission = commission rate · sales

Example 3 Finding the Amount of Commission

Sherry Souter, a real estate broker for Wealth Investments, sold a house for $214,000 last week. If her commission is 1.5% of the selling price of the home, find the amount of her commission.

Solution:

$$\underbrace{\text{commission}}_{\downarrow} = \underbrace{\text{commission rate}}_{\downarrow} \cdot \underbrace{\text{sales}}_{\downarrow}$$

$$\text{commission} = 1.5\% \cdot \$214{,}000$$

$$= 0.015 \cdot \$214{,}000 \quad \text{Write 1.5\% as 0.015.}$$

$$= \$3210 \quad \text{Multiply.}$$

Continued on next page

PRACTICE 3

A sales representative for Office Product Copiers sold $47,632 worth of copy equipment and supplies last month. What is his commission for the month if he is paid a commission of 6.6% of his total sales for the month?

Answers
2. 9% **3.** $3143.71

✓**Concept Check Answer**

Since $10\% = \frac{1}{10}$, the sales tax is $\frac{\$50}{10} = \$5$. The total price should have been $55.

Her commission on the house is $3210.

● **Work Practice 3**

Example 4 Finding a Commission Rate

A salesperson earned $1560 for selling $13,000 worth of electronics equipment. Find the commission rate.

Solution: Let r stand for the unknown commission rate. Then

commission	=	commission rate	·	sales
↓		↓		↓

$$\$1560 = r \cdot \$13,000$$

$$\frac{1560}{13,000} = r \qquad \text{Divide 1560 by 13,000, the number multiplied by } r.$$

$$0.12 = r \qquad \text{Simplify.}$$

$$12\% = r \qquad \text{Write 0.12 as a percent.}$$

The commission rate is 12%.

● **Work Practice 4**

Objective ⓒ Calculating Discount and Sale Price

Suppose that an item that normally sells for $40 is on sale for 25% off. This means that the **original price** of $40 is reduced, or **discounted,** by 25% of $40, or $10. The **discount rate** is 25%, the **amount of discount** is $10, and the **sale price** is $40 − $10, or $30. Study the diagram below to visualize these terms.

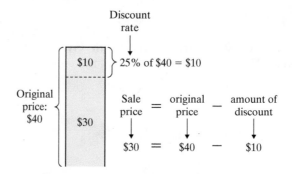

To calculate discounts and sale prices, we can use the following equations:

Discount and Sale Price

amount of discount = discount rate · original price

sale price = original price − amount of discount

Example 5 Finding a Discount and a Sale Price

An electric rice cooker that normally sells for $65 is on sale for 25% off. What is the amount of discount and what is the sale price?

Solution: First we find the amount of discount, or simply the discount.

amount of discount = discount rate · original price
        ↓   ↓   ↓
amount of discount =   25%   · $65
                    = 0.25 · $65   Write 25% as 0.25.
                    = $16.25   Multiply.

The discount is $16.25. Next, find the sale price.

sale price = original price − discount
     ↓   ↓   ↓
sale price = $65   − $16.25
            = $48.75   Subtract.

The sale price is $48.75.

● **Work Practice 5**

PRACTICE 5

A discontinued washer and dryer combo is advertised on sale for 35% off the regular price of $700. Find the amount of discount and the sale price.

Vocabulary and Readiness Check

Use the choices below to fill in each blank. Some choices may be used more than once.

amount of discount   sale price   sales tax

commission   total price

1. _____ = tax rate $\cdot$ purchase price.
2. _____ = purchase price + sales tax.
3. _____ = commission rate $\cdot$ sales.
4. _____ = discount rate $\cdot$ original price.
5. _____ = original price − amount of discount.
6. sale price = original price − _____.

4.8 Exercise Set

FOR EXTRA HELP

MyMathLab

Powered by CourseCompass™ and MathXL®

MathXL PRACTICE   WATCH   DOWNLOAD   READ   REVIEW

Objective Ⓐ *Solve. See Examples 1 and 2.*

1. What is the sales tax on a jacket priced at $150 if the sales tax rate is 5%?

2. If the sales tax rate is 6%, find the sales tax on a microwave oven priced at $188.

3. The purchase price of a camcorder is $799. What is the total price if the sales tax rate is 7.5%?

4. A stereo system has a purchase price of $426. What is the total price if the sales tax rate is 8%?

5. A new large-screen television has a purchase price of $4790. If the sales tax on this purchase is $335.30, find the sales tax rate.

6. The sales tax on the purchase of a $6800 used car is $374. Find the sales tax rate.

7. The sales tax on a table saw is $10.20.

   a. What is the purchase price of the table saw (before tax) if the sales tax rate is 8.5%? (*Hint:* Use the sales tax equation and insert the replacement values.)

   b. Find the total price of the table saw.

8. The sales tax on a one-half-carat diamond ring is $76.

   a. Find the purchase price of the ring (before tax) if the sales tax rate is 9.5%. (See the hint for Exercise 7a.)

   b. Find the total price of the ring.

9. A gold and diamond bracelet sells for $1800. Find the sales tax and the total price if the sales tax rate is 6.5%.

10. The purchase price of a personal computer is $1890. If the sales tax rate is 8%, what is the sales tax and the total price?

11. The sales tax on the purchase of a futon is $24.25. If the tax rate is 5%, find the purchase price of the futon.

12. The sales tax on the purchase of a TV-DVD combination is $32.85. If the tax rate is 9%, find the purchase price of the TV-DVD.

13. The sales tax is $98.70 on a stereo sound system purchase of $1645. Find the sales tax rate.

14. The sales tax is $103.50 on a necklace purchase of $1150. Find the sales tax rate.

15. A cell phone costs $210, a battery recharger costs $15, and batteries cost $5. What is the sales tax and total price for purchasing these items if the sales tax rate is 7%?

16. Ms. Warner bought a blouse for $35, a skirt for $55, and a blazer for $95. Find the sales tax and the total price she paid, given a sales tax rate of 6.5%.

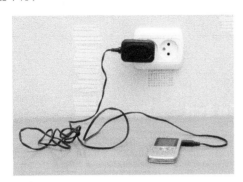

Objective **B** *Solve. See Examples 3 and 4.*

17. A sales representative for a large furniture warehouse is paid a commission rate of 4%. Find her commission if she sold $1,329,401 worth of furniture last year.

18. Rosie Davis-Smith is a beauty consultant for a home cosmetic business. She is paid a commission rate of 12.8%. Find her commission if she sold $1638 in cosmetics last month.

19. A salesperson earned a commission of $1380.40 for selling $9860 worth of paper products. Find the commission rate.

20. A salesperson earned a commission of $3575 for selling $32,500 worth of books to various bookstores. Find the commission rate.

21. How much commission will Jack Pruet make on the sale of a $325,900 house if he receives 1.5% of the selling price?

22. Frankie Lopez sold $9638 of jewelry this week. Find her commission for the week if she receives a commission rate of 5.6%.

23. A real estate agent earned a commission of $5565 for selling a house. If his rate is 3%, find the selling price of the house. (*Hint:* Use the commission equation and insert the replacement values.)

24. A salesperson earned $1750 for selling fertilizer. If her commission rate is 7%, find the selling price of the fertilizer. (See the hint for Exercise 23.)

Objective **C** *Find the amount of discount and the sale price. See Example 5.*

	Original Price	Discount Rate	Amount of Discount	Sale Price
25.	$89	10%		
26.	$74	20%		
27.	$196.50	50%		
28.	$110.60	40%		
29.	$410	35%		
30.	$370	25%		
31.	$21,700	15%		
32.	$17,800	12%		

33. A $300 fax machine is on sale for 15% off. Find the amount of discount and the sale price.

34. A $4295 designer dress is on sale for 30% off. Find the amount of discount and the sale price.

Objectives Ⓐ Ⓑ **Mixed Practice** *Complete each table.*

	Purchase Price	Tax Rate	Sales Tax	Total Price
35.	$305	9%		
36.	$243	8%		
37.	$56	5.5%		
38.	$65	8.4%		

	Sale	Commission Rate	Commission
39.	$235,800	3%	
40.	$195,450	5%	
41.	$17,900		$1432
42.	$25,600		$2304

Review

Multiply. See Sections 3.4 and 3.6.

43. $2000 \cdot \dfrac{3}{10} \cdot 2$

44. $500 \cdot \dfrac{2}{25} \cdot 3$

45. $400 \cdot \dfrac{3}{100} \cdot 11$

46. $1000 \cdot \dfrac{1}{20} \cdot 5$

47. $600 \cdot 0.04 \cdot \dfrac{2}{3}$

48. $6000 \cdot 0.06 \cdot \dfrac{3}{4}$

Concept Extensions

Solve. See the Concept Check in this section.

49. Your purchase price is $68 and the sales tax rate is 9.5%. Round each amount and use the rounded amounts to estimate the total price. Choose the best estimate.

  a. $105   **b.** $58   **c.** $93   **d.** $77

50. Your purchase price is $200 and the tax rate is 10%. Choose the best estimate of the total price.

  a. $190   **b.** $210   **c.** $220   **d.** $300

Tipping

One very useful application of percent is mentally calculating a tip. Recall that to find 10% of a number, simply move the decimal point one place to the left. To find 20% of a number, just double 10% of the number. To find 15% of a number, find 10% and then add to that number half of the 10% amount. Mentally fill in the chart below. To do so, start by rounding the bill amount to the nearest dollar.

Tipping Chart			
Bill Amount	**10%**	**15%**	**20%**
51. $40.21			
52. $15.89			
53. $72.17			
54. $9.33			

55. Suppose that the original price of a shirt is $50. Which is better, a 60% discount or a discount of 30% followed by a discount of 35% of the reduced price? Explain your answer.

56. Which is better, a 30% discount followed by an additional 25% off or a 20% discount followed by an additional 40% off? To see, suppose an item costs $100 and calculate each discounted price. Explain your answer.

57. A diamond necklace sells for $24,966. If the tax rate is 7.5%, find the total price.

58. A house recently sold for $562,560. The commission rate on the sale is 5.5%. If the real estate agent is to receive 60% of the commission, find the amount received by the agent.

4.9 PERCENT AND PROBLEM-SOLVING: INTEREST

Objectives

Ⓐ Calculate Simple Interest.

Ⓑ Calculate Compound Interest.

Ⓒ Calculate Monthly Payments.

Objective Ⓐ Calculating Simple Interest

Interest is money charged for using other people's money. When you borrow money, you pay interest. When you loan or invest money, you earn interest. The money borrowed, loaned, or invested is called the **principal amount,** or simply **principal.** Interest is normally stated in terms of a percent of the principal for a given period of time. The **interest rate** is the percent used in computing the interest. Unless stated otherwise, *the rate is understood to be per year.* When the interest is computed on the original principal, it is called **simple interest.** Simple interest is calculated using the following equation:

> ### Simple Interest
>
> Simple Interest = Principal · Rate · Time
>
> $$I = P \cdot R \cdot T$$
>
> where the rate is understood to be per year and time is in years.

Example 1 Finding Simple Interest

Find the simple interest after 2 years on $500 at an interest rate of 12%.

Solution: In this example, $P = \$500$, $R = 12\%$, and $T = 2$ years. Replace the variables with values in the formula $I = PRT$.

$$I = P \cdot R \cdot T$$
$$I = \$500 \cdot 12\% \cdot 2 \quad \text{Let } P = \$500, R = 12\%, \text{ and } T = 2.$$
$$= \$500 \cdot (0.12) \cdot 2 \quad \text{Write 12\% as a decimal.}$$
$$= \$120 \quad \text{Multiply.}$$

The simple interest is $120.

● Work Practice 1

If time is not given in years, we need to convert the given time to years.

Example 2 Finding Simple Interest

Ivan Borski borrowed $2400 at 10% simple interest for 8 months to buy a used Toyota Corolla. Find the simple interest he paid.

Solution: Since there are 12 months in a year, we first find what part of a year 8 months is.

$$8 \text{ months} = \frac{8}{12} \text{ year} = \frac{2}{3} \text{ year}$$

Now we find the simple interest.

simple interest	=	principal	·	rate	·	time
↓		↓		↓		↓
simple interest	=	$2400	·	10% ·		$\frac{2}{3}$

Continued on next page

PRACTICE 1

Find the simple interest after 5 years on $875 at an interest rate of 7%.

PRACTICE 2

A student borrowed $1500 for 9 months on her credit card at a simple interest rate of 20%. How much interest did she pay?

Answers
1. $306.25 **2.** $225

363

$$= \$2400 \cdot 0.10 \cdot \frac{2}{3}$$

$$= \$160$$

The interest on Ivan's loan is $160.

● **Work Practice 2**

✓**Concept Check** Suppose in Example 2 you had obtained an answer of $16,000. How would you know that you had made a mistake in this problem?

When money is borrowed, the borrower pays the original amount borrowed, or the principal, as well as the interest. When money is invested, the investor receives the original amount invested, or the principal, as well as the interest. In either case, the **total amount** is the sum of the principal and the interest.

Finding the Total Amount of a Loan or Investment

total amount (paid or received) = principal + interest

Example 3 Finding the Total Amount of an Investment

An accountant invested $2000 at a simple interest rate of 10% for 2 years. What total amount of money will she have from her investment in 2 years?

Solution: First we find her interest.

$$I = P \cdot R \cdot T$$

$$= \$2000 \cdot (0.10) \cdot 2 \quad \text{Let } P = \$2000, R = 10\% \text{ or } 0.10, \text{ and } T = 2.$$

$$= \$400$$

The interest is $400.

Next, we add the interest to the principal.

total amount	=	principal	+	interest
↓		↓		↓
total amount	=	$2000	+	$400
	=	$2400		

After 2 years, she will have a total amount of $2400.

● **Work Practice 3**

✓**Concept Check** Which investment would earn more interest: an amount of money invested at 8% interest for 2 years, or the same amount of money invested at 8% for 3 years? Explain.

Objective Ⓑ Calculating Compound Interest

Recall that simple interest depends on the original principal only. Another type of interest is compound interest. **Compound interest** is computed on not only the principal, but also on the interest already earned in previous compounding periods. Compound interest is used more often than simple interest.

Let's see how compound interest differs from simple interest. Suppose that $2000 is invested at 7% interest **compounded annually** for 3 years. This means that interest is added to the principal at the end of each year and that next year's interest is computed on this new amount. In this section, we round dollar amounts to the nearest cent.

	Amount at Beginning of Year	Principal	·	Rate	·	Time	= Interest	Amount at End of Year
1st year	$2000	$2000	·	0.07	·	1	= $140	$2000 + 140 = $2140
2nd year	$2140	$2140	·	0.07	·	1	= $149.80	$2140 + 149.80 = $2289.80
3rd year	$2289.80	$2289.80	·	0.07	·	1	= $160.29	$2289.80 + 160.29 = $2450.09

The compound interest earned can be found by

$$\text{total amount} \quad - \quad \text{original principal} \quad = \quad \text{compound interest}$$
$$\downarrow \qquad\qquad\qquad \downarrow \qquad\qquad\qquad\qquad \downarrow$$
$$\$2450.09 \quad - \quad \$2000 \quad = \quad \$450.09$$

The simple interest earned would have been

$$\text{principal} \quad \cdot \quad \text{rate} \quad \cdot \quad \text{time} \quad = \quad \text{interest}$$
$$\downarrow \qquad\quad \downarrow \qquad\quad \downarrow \qquad\quad \downarrow$$
$$\$2000 \quad \cdot \quad 0.07 \quad \cdot \quad 3 \quad = \quad \$420$$

Since compound interest earns "interest on interest," compound interest earns more than simple interest.

Computing compound interest using the method above can be tedious. We can use a calculator and the compound interest formula below to compute compound interest more quickly.

Compound Interest Formula

The total amount A in an account is given by

$$A = P\left(1 + \frac{r}{n}\right)^{n \cdot t}$$

where P is the principal, r is the interest rate written as a decimal, t is the length of time in years, and n is the number of times compounded per year.

Example 4 $1800 is invested at 2% interest compounded annually. Find the total amount after 3 years.

Solution: "Compounded annually" means 1 time a year, so $n = 1$. Also, $P = \$1800$, $r = 2\% = 0.02$, and $t = 3$ years.

$$A = P\left(1 + \frac{r}{n}\right)^{n \cdot t}$$
$$= 1800\left(1 + \frac{0.02}{1}\right)^{1 \cdot 3}$$
$$= 1800(1.02)^3$$
$$\approx 1910.17 \qquad \text{Round to 2 decimal places.}$$

Helpful Hint Remember order of operations. **First** evaluate $(1.02)^3$, then multiply by 1800

The total amount at the end of 3 years is $1910.17.

● Work Practice 4

PRACTICE 4

$3000 is invested at 4% interest compounded annually. Find the total amount after 6 years.

Answer
4. $3795.96

PRACTICE 5

$5500 is invested at $6\frac{1}{4}\%$ compounded *daily* for 5 years. Find the total amount at the end of 5 years. (Use 1 year = 365 days.)

Example 5 Finding Total Amount Received from an Investment

$4000 is invested at 5.3% compounded quarterly for 10 years. Find the total amount at the end of 10 years.

Solution: "Compounded quarterly" means 4 times a year, so $n = 4$. Also, $P = \$4000$, $r = 5.3\% = 0.053$, and $t = 10$ years.

$$A = P\left(1 + \frac{r}{n}\right)^{n \cdot t}$$

$$= 4000\left(1 + \frac{0.053}{4}\right)^{4 \cdot 10}$$

$$= 4000(1.01325)^{40}$$

$$\approx 6772.12$$

The total amount after 10 years is $6772.12.

● **Work Practice 5**

Note: Part of the compound interest formula, $\left(1 + \frac{r}{n}\right)^{n \cdot t}$ is called the **compound interest factor.** Another way to calculate the total amount, A, in the compound interest formula is to multiply the principal, P, by the appropriate compound interest factor.

The Calculator Explorations box on page 367 shows how compound interest factors are calculated.

Objective ● Calculating a Monthly Payment

We conclude this section with a method to find the monthly payment on a loan.

Finding the Monthly Payment of a Loan

$$\text{monthly payment} = \frac{\text{principal} + \text{interest}}{\text{total number of payments}}$$

PRACTICE 6

Find the monthly payment on a $3000 3-year loan if the interest on the loan is $1123.58.

Example 6 Finding a Monthly Payment

Find the monthly payment on a $2000 loan for 2 years. The interest on the 2-year loan is $435.88.

Solution: First we determine the total number of monthly payments. The loan is for 2 years. Since there are 12 months per year, the number of payments is $2 \cdot 12$, or 24. Now we calculate the monthly payment.

$$\text{monthly payment} = \frac{\text{principal} + \text{interest}}{\text{total number of payments}}$$

$$\text{monthly payment} = \frac{\$2000 + \$435.88}{24}$$

$$\approx \$101.50$$

The monthly payment is about $101.50.

● **Work Practice 6**

Answers

5. $7517.41

6. $114.54

Calculator Explorations   Compound Interest Formula

For a review of using your calculator to evaluate compound interest, see this box.

Let's review the calculator keys pressed to evaluate the expression in Example 5,

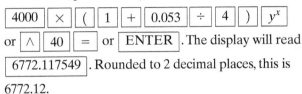

$$4000\left(1 + \frac{0.053}{4}\right)^{40}$$

To evaluate, press the keys

| 4000 | × | (| 1 | + | 0.053 | ÷ | 4 |) | y^x |

or | ∧ | 40 | = | or | ENTER |. The display will read

| 6772.117549 |. Rounded to 2 decimal places, this is 6772.12.

Find the compound interest.

1. $600, 5 years, 9%, compounded quarterly

2. $10,000, 15 years, 4%, compounded daily

3. $1200, 20 years, 11%, compounded annually

4. $5800, 1 year, 7%, compounded semiannually

5. $500, 4 years, 6%, compounded quarterly.

6. $2500, 19 years, 5%, compounded daily.

 Calculator Explorations   Compound Interest Factor

A compound interest factor may be found by using your calculator and evaluating the formula

$$\textbf{compound interest factor} = \left(1 + \frac{r}{n}\right)^{n \cdot t}$$

where r is the interest rate, t is the time in years, and n is the number of times compounded per year. For example, the compound interest factor for 10 years at 8% compounded semiannually is 2.19112. Let's find this factor by evaluating the compound interest factor formula when $r = 8\%$ or 0.08, $t = 10$, and $n = 2$ (compounded semiannually means 2 times per year). Thus,

$$\text{compound interest factor} = \left(1 + \frac{0.08}{2}\right)^{2 \cdot 10}$$

or $\left(1 + \dfrac{0.08}{2}\right)^{20}$

To evaluate, press the keys

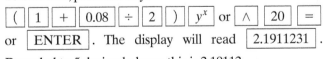

| (| 1 | + | 0.08 | ÷ | 2 |) | y^x | or | ∧ | 20 | = |

or | ENTER |. The display will read | 2.1911231 |. Rounded to 5 decimal places, this is 2.19112.

Find the compound interest factors.

7. 5 years, 9%, compounded quarterly

8. 15 years, 14%, compounded daily

9. 20 years, 11%, compounded annually

10. 1 year, 7%, compounded semiannually

11. Find the total amount after 4 years when $500 is invested at 6% compounded quarterly. (Multiply the appropriate compound interest factor by $500.)

12. Find the total amount after 19 years when $2500 is invested at 5% compounded daily.

Vocabulary and Readiness Check

Use the choices below to fill in each blank. Choices may be used more than once.

| total amount | simple | principal amount | compound |

1. To calculate _____ interest, use $I = P \cdot R \cdot T$.

2. To calculate _____ interest, use $A = P\left(1 + \dfrac{r}{n}\right)^{n \cdot t}$.

3. _____ interest is computed not only on the original principal, but also on interest already earned in previous compounding periods.

4. When interest is computed on the original principal only, it is called _____ interest.

5. _____ (paid or received) = principal + interest.

6. The _____ is the money borrowed, loaned, or invested.

4.9 Exercise Set

FOR EXTRA HELP

  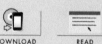

PRACTICE　WATCH　DOWNLOAD　READ　REVIEW

Objective Ⓐ *Find the simple interest. See Examples 1 and 2.*

	Principal	Rate	Time
1.	$200	8%	2 years
3.	$160	11.5%	4 years
5.	$5000	10%	$1\frac{1}{2}$ years
7.	$375	18%	6 months
9.	$2500	16%	21 months

	Principal	Rate	Time
2.	$800	9%	3 years
4.	$950	12.5%	5 years
6.	$1500	14%	$2\frac{1}{4}$ years
8.	$775	15%	8 months
10.	$1000	10%	18 months

Solve. See Examples 1 through 3.

11. A company borrows $162,500 for 5 years at a simple interest rate of 12.5%. Find the interest paid on the loan and the total amount paid back.

12. $265,000 is borrowed to buy a house. If the simple interest rate on the 30-year loan is 8.25%, find the interest paid on the loan and the total amount paid back.

13. A money market fund advertises a simple interest rate of 9%. Find the total amount received on an investment of $5000 for 15 months.

14. The Real Service Company takes out a 270-day (9-month) short-term, simple interest loan of $4500 to finance the purchase of some new equipment. If the interest rate is 14%, find the total amount that the company pays back.

15. Marsha borrows $8500 and agrees to pay it back in 4 years. If the simple interest rate is 17%, find the total amount she pays back.

16. An 18-year-old is given a high school graduation gift of $2000. If this money is invested at 8% simple interest for 5 years, find the total amount.

Objective Ⓑ *Find the total amount in each compound interest account. See Examples 4 and 5.*

17. $6150 is compounded semiannually at a rate of 14% for 15 years.

18. $2060 is compounded annually at a rate of 15% for 10 years.

19. $1560 is compounded daily at a rate of 8% for 5 years.

20. $1450 is compounded quarterly at a rate of 10% for 15 years.

21. $10,000 is compounded semiannually at a rate of 9% for 20 years.

22. $3500 is compounded daily at a rate of 8% for 10 years.

23. $2675 is compounded annually at a rate of 9% for 1 year.

24. $6375 is compounded semiannually at a rate of 10% for 1 year.

25. $2000 is compounded annually at a rate of 8% for 5 years.

26. $2000 is compounded semiannually at a rate of 8% for 5 years.

27. $2000 is compounded quarterly at a rate of 8% for 5 years.

28. $2000 is compounded daily at a rate of 8% for 5 years.

Objective ⓒ *Solve. See Example 6.*

29. A college student borrows $1500 for 6 months to pay for a semester of school. If the interest is $61.88, find the monthly payment.

30. Jim Tillman borrows $1800 for 9 months. If the interest is $148.90, find his monthly payment.

31. $20,000 is borrowed for 4 years. If the interest on the loan is $10,588.70, find the monthly payment.

32. $105,000 is borrowed for 15 years. If the interest on the loan is $181,125, find the monthly payment.

Review

Find the perimeter of each figure. See Section 1.3.

△ **33.**

Rectangle 6 yards
10 yards

△ **34.**

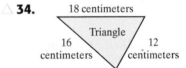
18 centimeters
Triangle
16 centimeters   12 centimeters

△ **35.**

Regular pentagon— All sides are same length 7 meters

△ **36.**

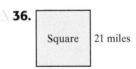
Square 21 miles

Concept Extensions

37. Explain how to look up a compound interest factor in the compound interest table.

38. Explain how to find the amount of interest in a compounded account.

39. Compare the following accounts: Account 1: $1000 is invested for 10 years at a simple interest rate of 6%. Account 2: $1000 is compounded semiannually at a rate of 6% for 10 years. Discuss how the interest is computed for each account. Determine which account earns more interest. Why?

A Define U.S. Units of Length and Convert from One Unit to Another.

B Use Mixed Units of Length.

C Perform Arithmetic Operations on U.S. Units of Length.

D Define Metric Units of Length and Convert from One Unit to Another.

E Perform Arithmetic Operations on Metric Units of Length.

4.10 LENGTH: US AND METRIC SYSTEMS

Objective **A** Defining and Converting U.S. System Units of Length

In the United States, two systems of measurement are commonly used. They are the **United States (U.S.), or English, measurement system** and the **metric system.** The U.S. measurement system is familiar to most Americans. Units such as feet, miles, ounces, and gallons are used. However, the metric system is also commonly used in fields such as medicine, sports, international marketing, and certain physical sciences. We are accustomed to buying 2-liter bottles of soft drinks, watching televised coverage of the 100-meter dash at the Olympic Games, or taking a 200-milligram dose of pain reliever.

The U.S. system of measurement uses the **inch, foot, yard,** and **mile** to measure length. The following is a summary of equivalencies between units of length:

U.S. Units of Length

$$12 \text{ inches (in.)} = 1 \text{ foot (ft)}$$
$$3 \text{ feet} = 1 \text{ yard (yd)}$$
$$36 \text{ inches} = 1 \text{ yard}$$
$$5280 \text{ feet} = 1 \text{ mile (mi)}$$

To convert from one unit of length to another, we will use **unit fractions.** We define a unit fraction to be a fraction that is equivalent to 1. Examples of unit fractions are as follows:

Unit Fractions

$$\frac{12 \text{ in.}}{1 \text{ ft}} = 1 \text{ or } \frac{1 \text{ ft}}{12 \text{ in.}} = 1 \text{ (since 12 in.} = 1 \text{ ft)}$$

$$\frac{3 \text{ ft}}{1 \text{ yd}} = 1 \text{ or } \frac{1 \text{ yd}}{3 \text{ ft}} = 1 \text{ (since 3 ft} = 1 \text{ yd)}$$

$$\frac{5280 \text{ ft}}{1 \text{ mi}} = 1 \text{ or } \frac{1 \text{ mi}}{5280 \text{ ft}} = 1 \text{ (since 5280 ft} = 1 \text{ mi)}$$

Remember that multiplying a number by 1 does not change the value of the number.

Example 1 Convert 8 feet to inches.

Solution: We multiply 8 feet by a unit fraction that uses the equality 12 inches = 1 foot. The unit fraction should be in the form $\dfrac{\text{units to convert to}}{\text{original units}}$ or in this case $\dfrac{12 \text{ inches}}{1 \text{ foot}}$. We do this so that like units divide out, as shown.

$$8 \text{ ft} = \frac{8 \text{ ft}}{1} \cdot 1 \qquad \text{Multiply by 1 in the form of } \tfrac{12 \text{ in.}}{1 \text{ ft}}.$$
$$= \frac{8 \text{ ft}}{1} \cdot \frac{12 \text{ in.}}{1 \text{ ft}}$$
$$= 8 \cdot 12 \text{ in.}$$
$$= 96 \text{ in.} \qquad \text{Multiply.}$$

Thus, 8 ft = 96 in., as shown in the diagram:

8 feet = 96 inches

|←1 foot→|←1 foot→|←1 foot→|←1 foot→|←1 foot→|←1 foot→|←1 foot→|←1 foot→|

|←12 in.→|←12 in.→|←12 in.→|←12 in.→|←12 in.→|←12 in.→|←12 in.→|←12 in.→|

● **Work Practice Problem 1**

Example 2 Convert 7 feet to yards.

Solution: We multiply by a unit fraction that compares 1 yard to 3 feet.

$$7 \text{ ft} = \frac{7 \text{ ft}}{1} \cdot 1$$
$$= \frac{7 \text{ ft}}{1} \cdot \frac{1 \text{ yd}}{3 \text{ ft}} \begin{array}{l} \leftarrow \text{ Units to convert to} \\ \leftarrow \text{ Original units} \end{array}$$
$$= \frac{7}{3} \text{ yd}$$
$$= 2\frac{1}{3} \text{ yd} \qquad \text{Divide.}$$

Thus, 7 ft = $2\frac{1}{3}$ yd, as shown in the diagram.

7 feet = $2\frac{1}{3}$ yards

|←1 foot→|←1 foot→|←1 foot→|←1 foot→|←1 foot→|←1 foot→|←1 foot→|

|←———— 1 yard ————→|←———— 1 yard ————→|←$\frac{1}{3}$ yard→|

● **Work Practice Problem 2**

PRACTICE PROBLEM 1
Convert 5 feet to inches.

PRACTICE PROBLEM 2
Convert 7 yards to feet.

Answers
1. 60 in **2.** 21 ft

PRACTICE PROBLEM 3

Suppose the bill in the photo measures 18 inches. Convert 18 inches to feet, using decimals.

Example 3 Finding Length of Pelican's Bill

The Australian pelican has the longest bill, measuring from 13 to 18.5 inches long. The pelican in the photo has a 15-inch bill. Convert 15 inches to feet, using decimals.

Solution:

$$15 \text{ in.} = \frac{15 \text{ in.}}{1} \cdot \frac{1 \text{ ft}}{12 \text{ in.}} \quad \leftarrow \text{Units to convert to} \atop \leftarrow \text{Original units}$$

$$= \frac{15}{12} \text{ ft}$$

$$= \frac{5}{4} \text{ ft} \qquad \text{Simplify } \frac{15}{12}.$$

$$= 1.25 \text{ ft} \qquad \text{Divide.}$$

Thus, 15 in. = 1.25 ft, as shown in the diagram.

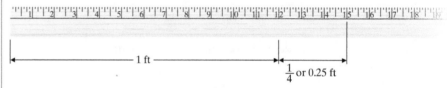

15 inches = 1.25 ft

1 ft

$\frac{1}{4}$ or 0.25 ft

● **Work Practice Problem 3**

Helpful Hint

When converting from one unit to another, select a unit fraction with the properties below:

$$\frac{\text{units you are converting to}}{\text{original units}}$$

By using this unit fraction, the original units will divide out, as wanted.

Objective Ⓑ Using Mixed U.S. System Units of Length

Sometimes it is more meaningful to express a measurement of length with mixed units such as 1 ft and 5 in. We usually condense this and write 1 ft 5 in.

In Example 2, we found that 7 feet was the same as $2\frac{1}{3}$ yards. The measurement can also be written as a mixture of yards and feet. That is,

7 ft = _____ yd _____ ft

Because 3 ft = 1 yd, we divide 3 into 7 to see how many whole yards are in 7 feet. The quotient is the number of yards, and the remainder is the number of feet.

$$\begin{array}{r} 2 \text{ yd } 1 \text{ ft} \\ 3\overline{)7} \\ -6 \\ \hline 1 \end{array}$$

Thus, 7 ft = 2 yd 1 ft, as seen in the diagram:

7 ft

1 yd   1 yd   1 ft

Answer

3. 1.5 ft

Example 4 Convert: 134 in. = _____ ft _____ in.

Solution: Because 12 in. = 1 ft, we divide 12 into 134. The quotient is the number of feet. The remainder is the number of inches. To see why we divide 12 into 134, notice that

$$134 \text{ in.} = \frac{134 \text{ in.}}{1} \cdot \frac{1 \text{ ft}}{12 \text{ in.}} = \frac{134}{12} \text{ ft}$$

$$
\begin{array}{r}
11 \text{ ft } 2 \text{ in.} \\
12\overline{)134} \\
-\ 12 \\
\hline
14 \\
-\ 12 \\
\hline
2
\end{array}
$$

Thus, 134 in. = 11 ft 2 in.

● **Work Practice Problem 4**

Example 5 Convert 3 feet 7 inches to inches.

Solution: First, we convert 3 feet to inches. Then we add 7 inches.

$$3 \text{ ft} = \frac{3 \text{ ft}}{1} \cdot \frac{12 \text{ in.}}{1 \text{ ft}} = 36 \text{ in.}$$

Then

$$3 \text{ ft } 7 \text{ in.} = 36 \text{ in.} + 7 \text{ in.} = 43 \text{ in.}$$

● **Work Practice Problem 5**

Objective ⊙ Performing Operations on U.S. System Units of Length

Finding sums or differences of measurements often involves converting units, as shown in the next example. Just remember that, as usual, only like units can be added or subtracted.

Example 6 Add 3 ft 2 in. and 5 ft 11 in.

Solution: To add, we line up the similar units.

$$
\begin{array}{r}
3 \text{ ft } \ 2 \text{ in.} \\
+\ 5 \text{ ft } 11 \text{ in.} \\
\hline
8 \text{ ft } 13 \text{ in.}
\end{array}
$$

Since 13 inches is the same as 1 ft 1 in., we have

$$8 \text{ ft } 13 \text{ in.} = 8 \text{ ft} + 1 \text{ ft } 1 \text{ in.}$$
$$= 9 \text{ ft } 1 \text{ in.}$$

● **Work Practice Problem 6**

✔ **Concept Check** How could you estimate the following sum?

$$
\begin{array}{r}
7 \text{ yd } \ 4 \text{ in.} \\
+\ 3 \text{ yd } 27 \text{ in.} \\
\hline
\end{array}
$$

PRACTICE PROBLEM 4

Convert:
68 in. = _____ ft _____ in.

PRACTICE PROBLEM 5

Convert 5 yards 2 feet to feet.

PRACTICE PROBLEM 6

Add 4 ft 8 in. to 8 ft 11 in.

Answers
4. 5 ft 8 in **5.** 17 ft **6.** 13 ft 7 in

✔ **Concept Check Answer**
round each to the nearest yard:
7 yd + 4 yd = 11 yd

PRACTICE PROBLEM 7

A carpenter cuts 1 ft 9 in. from a board of length 5 ft 8 in. Find the remaining length of the board.

Example 7 Finding the Length of a Piece of Rope

A rope of length 6 yd 1 ft has 2 yd 2 ft cut from one end. Find the length of the remaining rope.

Solution: Subtract 2 yd 2 ft from 6 yd 1 ft.

$$
\begin{aligned}
\text{beginning length} &\rightarrow & 6 \text{ yd } 1 \text{ ft} \\
-\qquad\text{amount cut} &\rightarrow & -2 \text{ yd } 2 \text{ ft} \\
\hline
\text{remaining length} & &
\end{aligned}
$$

We cannot subtract 2 ft from 1 ft, so we borrow 1 yd from the 6 yd. One yard is converted to 3 ft and combined with the 1 ft already there.

Borrow 1 yd = 3 ft

5 yd + (1 yd) (3 ft)

$$
\begin{array}{rclr}
6\text{ yd } 1 \text{ ft} & = & 5 \text{ yd } 4 \text{ ft} \\
-2 \text{ yd } 2 \text{ ft} & = & -2 \text{ yd } 2 \text{ ft} \\
\hline
& & 3 \text{ yd } 2 \text{ ft}
\end{array}
$$

The remaining rope is 3 yd 2 ft long.

● **Work Practice Problem 7**

Objective ⓓ Defining and Converting Metric System Units of Length

The basic unit of length in the metric system is the **meter.** A meter is slightly longer than a yard. It is approximately 39.37 inches long. Recall that a yard is 36 inches long.

1 yard = 36 inches

1 meter ≈ 39.37 inches

All units of length in the metric system are based on the meter. The following is a summary of the prefixes used in the metric system. Also shown are equivalencies between units of length. Like the decimal system, the metric system uses powers of 10 to define units.

Metric Unit of Length
1 kilometer (km) = 1000 meters (m)
1 hectometer (hm) = 100 m
1 dekameter (dam) = 10 m
1 meter (m) = 1 m
1 decimeter (dm) = 1/10 m or 0.1 m
1 centimeter (cm) = 1/100 m or 0.01 m
1 millimeter (mm) = 1/1000 m or 0.001 m

Answer

7. 3 ft 11 in.

The figure below will help you with decimeters, centimeters, and millimeters.

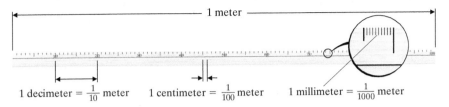

1 decimeter = $\frac{1}{10}$ meter   1 centimeter = $\frac{1}{100}$ meter   1 millimeter = $\frac{1}{1000}$ meter

> **Helpful Hint**
>
> Study the figure above for other equivalencies between metric units of length.
>
> 10 decimeters = 1 meter   10 millimeters = 1 centimeter
> 100 centimeters = 1 meter   10 centimeters = 1 decimeter
> 1000 millimeters = 1 meter

These same prefixes are used in the metric system for mass and capacity. The most commonly used measurements of length in the metric system are the **meter, millimeter, centimeter,** and **kilometer.**

Being comfortable with the metric units of length means gaining a "feeling" for metric lengths, just as you have a "feeling" for the length of an inch, a foot, and a mile. To help you accomplish this, study the following examples:

A millimeter is about the thickness of a large paper clip.

A centimeter is about the width of a large paper clip.

A meter is slightly longer than a yard.

A kilometer is about two-thirds of a mile.

The length of this book is approximately 27.5 centimeters.

The width of this book is approximately 21.5 centimeters.

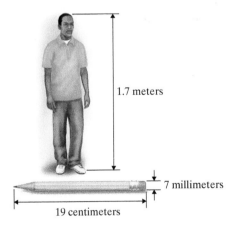

As with the U.S. system of measurement, unit fractions may be used to convert from one unit of length to another. For example, let's convert 1200 meters to kilometers. To do so, we will multiply by 1 in the form of the unit fraction

$$\frac{1 \text{ km}}{1000 \text{ m}} \quad \begin{array}{l} \leftarrow \text{ Units to convert to} \\ \leftarrow \text{ Original units} \end{array}$$

$$1200 \text{ m} = \frac{1200 \text{ m}}{1} \cdot 1 = \frac{1200 \text{ m}}{1} \cdot \overbrace{\frac{1 \text{ km}}{1000 \text{ m}}}^{\text{Unit fraction}} = \frac{1200 \text{ km}}{1000} = 1.2 \text{ km}$$

Thus, 1200 m = 1.2 km as shown in the diagram.

1200 m = 1.200 km	1000 m	200 m
3 places to the left	← 1 km →	← 0.2 km →

The metric system does, however, have a distinct advantage over the U.S. system of measurement: The ease of converting from one unit of length to another. Since all units of length are powers of 10 of the meter, converting from one unit of length to another is as simple as moving the decimal point. Listing units of length in order from largest to smallest helps to keep track of how many places to move the decimal point when converting.

Let's again convert 1200 meters to kilometers. This time, to convert from meters to kilometers, we move along the chart shown 3 units to the left, from meters to kilometers. This means that we move the decimal point 3 places to the left.

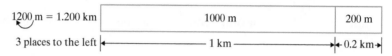

km hm dam **m** dm cm mm
3 units to the left

PRACTICE PROBLEM 8

Convert 2.5 m to millimeters.

Example 8 Convert 2.3 m to centimeters.

Solution: First we will convert by using a unit fraction.

$$2.3 \text{ m} = \frac{2.3 \text{ m}}{1} \cdot \overbrace{\frac{100 \text{ cm}}{1 \text{ m}}}^{\text{Unit fraction}} = 230 \text{ cm}$$

Now we will convert by listing the units of length in order from left to right and moving from meters to centimeters.

km hm dam m dm cm mm
2 units to the right

2.30 m = 230. cm
2 places to the right

With either method, we get 230 cm.
● **Work Practice Problem 8**

PRACTICE PROBLEM 9

Convert 3500 m to kilometers.

Example 9 Convert 450,000 mm to meters.

Solution: We list the units of length in order from left to right and move from millimeters to meters.

km hm dam m dm cm mm
3 units to the left

450,000 mm = 450.000 m or 450 m

● **Work Practice Problem 9**

Answers
8. 2500 mm   **9.** 3.5 km

✔ **Concept Check** What is wrong with the following conversion of 150 cm to meters?

$$150.00 \text{ cm} = 15,000 \text{ m}$$

Objective ⓔ Performing Operations on Metric System Units of Length

To add, subtract, multiply, or divide with metric measurements of length, we write all numbers using the same unit of length and then add, subtract, multiply, or divide as with decimals.

Example 10 Subtract 430 m from 1.3 km.

Solution: First we convert both measurements to kilometers or both to meters.

$$430 \text{ m} = 0.43 \text{ km} \qquad \text{or} \qquad 1.3 \text{ km} = 1300 \text{ m}$$

$$\begin{array}{r} 1.30 \text{ km} \\ - 0.43 \text{ km} \\ \hline 0.87 \text{ km} \end{array} \qquad\qquad \begin{array}{r} 1300 \text{ m} \\ - 430 \text{ m} \\ \hline 870 \text{ m} \end{array}$$

The difference is 0.87 km or 870 m.

● **Work Practice Problem 10**

PRACTICE PROBLEM 10

Subtract 640 m from 2.1 km.

Answer

10. 1.46 km or 1460 m

✔ **Concept Check Answer**

decimal should be moved to the left: 1.5 m

Mental Math

Convert as indicated.

1. 12 inches to feet

2. 6 feet to yards

3. 24 inches to feet

4. 36 inches to feet

5. 36 inches to yards

6. 2 yards to inches

Determine whether the measurement in each statement is reasonable.

7. The screen of a home television set has a 30-meter diagonal.

8. A window measures 1 meter by 0.5 meter.

9. A drinking glass is made of glass 2 millimeters thick.

10. A paper clip is 4 kilometers long.

11. The distance across the Colorado River is 50 kilometers.

12. A model's hair is 30 centimeters long.

4.10 Exercise Set

Objective A *Convert each measurement as indicated. See Examples 1 through 3.*

1. 60 in. to feet

2. 84 in. to feet

3. 12 yd to feet

4. 18 yd to feet

5. 42,240 ft to miles

6. 36,960 ft to miles

7. 102 in. to feet

8. 150 in. to feet

9. 10 ft to yards

10. 25 ft to yards

11. 6.4 mi to feet

12. 3.8 mi to feet

13. 162 in. to yd (Write answer as a decimal.)

14. 7216 yd to mi (Write answer as a decimal.)

15. 3 in. to ft (Write answer as a decimal.)

16. 129 in. to ft (Write answer as a decimal.)

Objective B *Convert each measurement as indicated. See Examples 4 and 5.*

17. 40 ft = _____ yd _____ ft

18. 100 ft = _____ yd _____ ft

19. 41 in. = _____ ft _____ in.

20. 75 in. = _____ ft _____ in.   **21.** 10,000 ft = _____ mi _____ ft   **22.** 25,000 ft = _____ mi _____ ft

23. 5 ft 2 in. = _____ in.   **24.** 4 ft 11 in. = _____ in.   **25.** 7 yd 2 ft = _____ ft

26. 7 yd 1 ft = _____ ft   **27.** 2 yd 1 ft = _____ in.   **28.** 1 yd 2 ft = _____ in.

Objective C *Perform each indicated operation. Simplify the result if possible. See Examples 6 and 7.*

29. 5 ft 8 in. + 6 ft 7 in.   **30.** 9 ft 10 in. + 8 ft 4 in.   **31.** 12 yd 2 ft + 9 yd 2 ft

32. 16 yd 2 ft + 8 yd 1 ft   **33.** 24 ft 8 in. − 16 ft 3 in.   **34.** 15 ft 5 in. − 8 ft 2 in.

35. 16 ft 3 in. − 10 ft 9 in.   **36.** 14 ft 8 in. − 3 ft 11 in.   **37.** 6 ft 8 in. ÷ 2

38. 26 ft 10 in. ÷ 2   **39.** 12 yd 2 ft × 4   **40.** 15 yd 1 ft × 8

Objective D *Convert as indicated. See Examples 8 and 9.*

41. 40 m to centimeters   **42.** 18 m to centimeters   **43.** 40 mm to centimeters

44. 18 mm to centimeters   **45.** 300 m to kilometers   **46.** 400 m to kilometers

47. 1400 mm to meters   **48.** 6400 mm to meters   **49.** 1500 cm to meters

50. 6400 cm to meters   **51.** 0.42 km to centimeters   **52.** 0.95 km to centimeters

53. 7 km to meters   **54.** 5 km to meters   **55.** 8.3 cm to millimeters

56. 4.6 cm to millimeters

57. 20.1 mm to decimeters

58. 140.2 mm to decimeters

59. 0.04 m to millimeters

60. 0.2 m to millimeters

Objective **E** *Perform each indicated operation. See Example 10.*

61. 8.6 m + 0.34 m

62. 14.1 cm + 3.96 cm

63. 2.9 m + 40 mm

64. 30 cm + 8.9 m

65. 24.8 mm − 1.19 cm

66. 45.3 m − 2.16 dam

67. 15 km − 2360 m

68. 14 cm − 15 mm

69. 18.3 m × 3

70. 14.1 m × 4

71. 6.2 km ÷ 4

72. 9.6 m ÷ 5

Objectives **A** **C** **D** **E** **Mixed Practice** *Solve. Remember to insert units when writing your answers. For Exercises 73 through 82, complete the charts.*

		Yards	Feet	Inches
73.	Crysler Building in New York City		1046	
74.	4-story building			792
75.	Python length		35	
76.	Ostrich height			108

Complete the chart.

		Meters	Millimeters	Kilometers	Centimeters
77.	Length of elephant	5			
78.	Height of grizzly bear	3			
79.	Tennis ball diameter				6.5
80.	Golf ball diameter				4.6
81.	Distance from London to Paris			342	
82.	Distance from Houston to Dallas			396	

83. The National Zoo maintains a small patch of bamboo, which it grows as a food supply for its pandas. Two weeks ago, the bamboo was 6 ft 10 in. tall. Since then, the bamboo has grown 3 ft 8 in. How tall is the bamboo now?

84. While exploring in the Marianas Trench, a submarine probe was lowered to a point 1 mile 1400 feet below the ocean's surface. Later it was lowered an additional 1 mile 4000 feet below this point. How far is the probe below the surface of the Pacific?

85. The length of one of the Statue of Liberty's hands is 16 ft 5 in. One of the Statue's eyes is 2 ft 6 in. across. How much longer is a hand than the width of an eye? (*Source:* National Park Service)

86. The width of the Statue of Liberty's head from ear to ear is 10 ft. The height of the Statue's head from chin to cranium is 17 ft 3 in. How much taller is the Statue's head than its width? (*Source:* National Park Service)

87. A 3.4-m rope is attached to a 5.8-m rope. However, when the ropes are tied, 8 cm of length is lost to form the knot. What is the length of the tied ropes?

88. A 2.15-m-long sash cord has become frayed at both ends so that 1 cm is trimmed from each end. How long is the remaining cord?

89. The ice on a pond is 5.33 cm thick. For safe skating, the owner of the pond insists that it must be 80 mm thick. How much thicker must the ice be before skating is allowed?

90. The sediment on the bottom of the Towamencin Creek is normally 14 cm thick, but the recent flood washed away 22 mm of sediment. How thick is it now?

91. The Amana Corporation stacks up its microwave ovens in a distribution warehouse. Each stack is 1 ft 9 in. wide. How far from the wall would 9 of these stacks extend?

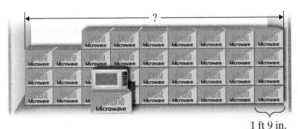

92. The highway commission is installing concrete sound barriers along a highway. Each barrier is 1 yd 2 ft long. Find the total length of 25 barriers placed end to end.

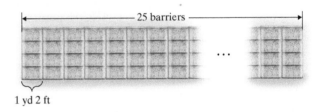

93. A logging firm needs to cut a 67-m-long redwood log into 20 equal pieces before loading it onto a truck for shipment. How long will each piece be?

94. An 18.3-m-tall flagpole is mounted on a 65-cm-high pedestal. How far is the top of the flagpole from the ground?

Estimate each sum or difference. See the Concept Check in this section.

95.   5 yd 2 in.
        + 7 yd 30 in.

96.   45 ft 1 in.
        − 10 ft 11 in.

97. Using a unit other than the foot, write a length that is equivalent to 4 feet. (*Hint:* There are many possibilities.)

98. Using a unit other than the meter, write a length that is equivalent to 7 meters. (*Hint:* There are many possibilities.)

99. To convert from meters to centimeters, the decimal point is moved two places to the right. Explain how this relates to the fact that the prefix *centi* means $\frac{1}{100}$.

100. Explain why conversions in the metric system are easier to make than conversions in the U.S. system of measurement.

Objectives

A Define U.S. Units of Weight and Convert from One Unit to Another.

B Perform Arithmetic Operations on Units of Weight.

C Define Metric Units of Mass and Convert from One Unit to Another.

D Perform Arithmetic Operations on Units of Mass.

4.11 WEIGHT AND MASS: US AND METRIC SYSTEMS

Objective A Defining and Converting U.S. System Units of Weight

Whenever we talk about how heavy an object is, we are concerned with the object's **weight.** We discuss weight when we refer to a 12-ounce box of Rice Krispies, a 15-pound tabby cat, or a barge hauling 24 tons of garbage.

12 ounces

15 pounds

24 tons of garbage

The most common units of weight in the U.S. measurement system are the **ounce,** the **pound,** and the **ton.** The following is a summary of equivalencies between units of weight:

U.S. Units of Weight	Unit Fractions
16 ounces (oz) = 1 pound (lb)	$\dfrac{16\ oz}{1\ lb} = \dfrac{1\ lb}{16\ oz} = 1$
2000 pounds = 1 ton	$\dfrac{2000\ lb}{1\ ton} = \dfrac{1\ ton}{2000\ lb} = 1$

✔**Concept Check** If you were describing the weight of a fully-loaded semi-trailer, which type of unit would you use: ounce, pound, or ton? Why?

Unit fractions that equal 1 are used to convert between units of weight in the U.S. system. When converting using unit fractions, recall that the numerator of a unit fraction should contain the units we are converting to and the denominator should contain the original units.

Example 1 Convert 9000 pounds to tons.

Solution: We multiply 9000 lb by a unit fraction that uses the equality

2000 pounds = 1 ton.

Remember, the unit fraction should be $\dfrac{\text{units to convert to}}{\text{original units}}$ or $\dfrac{1\ ton}{2000\ lb}$.

PRACTICE PROBLEM 1

Convert 4500 pounds to tons.

Answer

1. $2\dfrac{1}{4}$ tons

✔ **Concept Check Answer**

ton

382

Copyright 2007 Pearson Education, Inc.

$$9000 \text{ lb} = \frac{9000 \text{ lb}}{1} \cdot 1 = \frac{9000 \text{ lb}}{1} \cdot \frac{1 \text{ ton}}{2000 \text{ lb}} = \frac{9000 \text{ tons}}{2000} = \frac{9}{2} \text{ tons or } 4\frac{1}{2} \text{ tons}$$

2000 lb	2000 lb	2000 lb	2000 lb	1000 lb

$$9000 \text{ lb} = 4\frac{1}{2} \text{ tons}$$

1 ton	1 ton	1 ton	1 ton	$\frac{1}{2}$ ton

● **Work Practice Problem 1**

Example 2 Convert 3 pounds to ounces.

PRACTICE PROBLEM 2

Convert 56 ounces to pounds.

Solution: We multiply by the unit fraction $\frac{16 \text{ oz}}{1 \text{ lb}}$ to convert from pounds to ounces.

$$3 \text{ lb} = \frac{3 \text{ lb}}{1} \cdot 1 = \frac{3 \text{ lb}}{1} \cdot \frac{16 \text{ oz}}{1 \text{ lb}} = 3 \cdot 16 \text{ oz} = 48 \text{ oz}$$

1 pound	1 pound	1 pound

$$3 \text{ lb} = 48 \text{ oz}$$

16 ounces	16 ounces	16 ounces

● **Work Practice Problem 2**

As with length, it is sometimes useful to simplify a measurement of weight by writing it in terms of mixed units.

Example 3 Convert: 33 ounces = _____ lb _____ oz

PRACTICE PROBLEM 3

Convert:
45 ounces = _____ lb _____ oz

Solution: Because 16 oz = 1 lb, divide 16 into 33 to see how many pounds are in 33 ounces. The quotient is the number of pounds, and the remainder is the number of ounces. To see why we divide 16 into 33, notice that

$$33 \text{ oz} = 33 \text{ oz} \cdot \frac{1 \text{ lb}}{16 \text{ oz}} = \frac{33}{16} \text{ lb}$$

$$\begin{array}{r} 2 \text{ lb } 1 \text{ oz} \\ 16 \overline{)33} \\ -32 \\ \hline 1 \end{array}$$

Thus, 33 ounces is the same as 2 lb 1 oz.

16 ounces	16 ounces	1 ounce

$$33 \text{ oz} = 2 \text{ lb } 1 \text{ oz}$$

1 pound	1 pound	1 ounce

● **Work Practice Problem 3**

Objective B Performing Operations on U.S. System Units of Weight

Performing arithmetic operations on units of weight works the same way as performing arithmetic operations on units of length.

PRACTICE PROBLEM 4

Subtract 5 tons 1200 lb from 8 tons 100 lb.

Example 4 Subtract 3 tons 1350 lb from 8 tons 1000 lb.

Solution: To subtract, we line up similar units.

$$\begin{array}{r} 8 \text{ tons } 1000 \text{ lb} \\ -\,3 \text{ tons } 1350 \text{ lb} \end{array}$$

Since we cannot subtract 1350 lb from 1000 lb, we borrow 1 ton from the 8 tons. To do so, we write 1 ton as 2000 lb and combine it with the 1000 lb.

7 tons + (1 ton) 2000 lb

$$\begin{array}{rcl} 8 \text{ tons } 1000 \text{ lb} & = & 7 \text{ tons } 3000 \text{ lb} \\ -\,3 \text{ tons } 1350 \text{ lb} & = & -\,3 \text{ tons } 1350 \text{ lb} \\ \hline & & 4 \text{ tons } 1650 \text{ lb} \end{array}$$

To check, see that the sum of 4 tons 1650 lb and 3 tons 1350 lb is 8 tons 1000 lb.

● Work Practice Problem 4

PRACTICE PROBLEM 5

A 5-lb 14-oz batch of cookies is packed into a 6-oz container before it is mailed. Find the total weight.

Example 5 Finding the Weight of a Child

Bryan weighed 8 lb 8 oz at birth. By the time he was 1 year old, he had gained 11 lb 14 oz. Find his weight at age 1 year.

Solution:

$$\begin{array}{lcl} \text{birth weight} & \rightarrow & 8 \text{ lb } 8 \text{ oz} \\ +\text{ weight gained} & \rightarrow & +11 \text{ lb } 14 \text{ oz} \\ \hline \text{total weight} & \rightarrow & 19 \text{ lb } 22 \text{ oz} \end{array}$$

Since 22 oz equals 1 lb 6 oz,

$$19 \text{ lb } 22 \text{ oz} = 19 \text{ lb} + 1 \text{ lb } 6 \text{ oz}$$
$$= 20 \text{ lb } 6 \text{ oz}$$

Bryan weighed 20 lb 6 oz on his first birthday.

● Work Practice Problem 5

Objective C Defining and Converting Metric System Units of Mass

In scientific and technical areas, a careful distinction is made between **weight** and **mass**. **Weight** is really a measure of the pull of gravity. The farther from Earth an object gets, the less it weighs. However, **mass** is a measure of the amount of substance in the object and does not change. Astronauts orbiting Earth weigh much less than they weigh on Earth, but they have the same mass in orbit as they do on Earth. Here on Earth weight and mass are the same, so either term may be used.

The basic unit of mass in the metric system is the **gram.** It is defined as the mass of water contained in a cube 1 centimeter (cm) on each side.

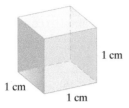

1 cm

1 cm

1 cm

The following examples may help you get a feeling for metric masses:

A tablet contains 200 milligrams of ibuprofen.

A large paper clip weighs approximately 1 gram.

A box of crackers weighs 453 grams.

A kilogram is slightly over 2 pounds. An adult woman may weigh 60 kilograms.

The prefixes for units of mass in the metric system are the same as for units of length, as shown in the following table:

Metric Unit of Mass
1 **kilo**gram (kg) = 1000 grams (g)
1 **hecto**gram (hg) = 100 g
1 **deka**gram (dag) = 10 g
1 gram (g) = 1 g
1 **deci**gram (dg) = 1/10 g or 0.1 g
1 **centi**gram (cg) = 1/100 g or 0.01 g
1 **milli**gram (mg) = 1/1000 g or 0.001 g

✔ Concept Check   True or false? A decigram is larger than a dekagram. Explain.

The **milligram,** the **gram,** and the **kilogram** are the three most commonly used units of mass in the metric system.

As with lengths, all units of mass are powers of 10 of the gram, so converting from one unit of mass to another involves moving only the decimal point. To convert from one unit of mass to another in the metric system, list the units of mass in order from largest to smallest.

Let's convert 4300 milligrams to grams. To convert from milligrams to grams, we move along the table 3 units to the left.

kg   hg   dag   **g**   dg   cg   **mg**

3 units to the left

This means that we move the decimal point 3 places to the left to convert from milligrams to grams.

$$4300 \text{ mg} = 4.3 \text{ g}$$

Don't forget, the same conversion can be done with unit fractions.

$$4300 \text{ mg} = \frac{4300 \text{ mg}}{1} \cdot 1 = \frac{4300 \text{ mg}}{1} \cdot \frac{0.001 \text{ g}}{1 \text{ mg}}$$
$$= 4300 \cdot 0.001 \text{ g}$$
$$= 4.3 \text{ g} \quad \text{To multiply by 0.001, move the decimal point 3 places to the left.}$$

To see that this is reasonable, study the diagram:

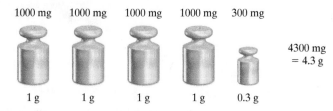

|1000 mg | 1000 mg | 1000 mg | 1000 mg | 300 mg |
| 1 g | 1 g | 1 g | 1 g | 0.3 g |

4300 mg
= 4.3 g

Thus, 4300 mg = 4.3 g

PRACTICE PROBLEM 6

Convert 3.41 g to milligrams.

Example 6 Convert 3.2 kg to grams.

Solution: First we convert by using a unit fraction.

Unit fraction

$$3.2 \text{ kg} = 3.2 \text{ kg} \cdot 1 = 3.2 \text{ kg} \cdot \frac{1000 \text{ g}}{1 \text{ kg}} = 3200 \text{ g}$$

Now let's list the units of mass in order from left to right and move from kilograms to grams.

kg   hg   dag   g   dg   cg   mg

3 units to the right

$$3.200 \text{ kg} = 3200. \text{ g}$$

3 places to the right

| 1 kg | 1 kg | 1 kg | 0.2 kg |
| 1000 g | 1000 g | 1000 g | 200 g |

3.2 kg
= 3200 g

● **Work Practice Problem 6**

Convert 2.35 cg to grams.

Solution: We list the units of mass in a chart and move from centigrams to grams.

kg   hg   dag   g   dg   cg   mg

2 units to the left

02.35 cg = 0.0235 g

2 places to the left

● **Work Practice Problem 7**

PRACTICE PROBLEM 7

Convert 56.2 cg to grams.

Objective ⓓ Performing Operations on Metric System Units of Mass

Arithmetic operations can be performed with metric units of mass just as we performed operations with metric units of length. We convert each number to the same unit of mass and add, subtract, multiply, or divide as with decimals.

Example 8 Subtract 5.4 dg from 1.6 g.

Solution: We convert both numbers to decigrams or to grams before subtracting.

$$5.4 \text{ dg} = 0.54 \text{ g}$$ or $$1.6 \text{ g} = 16 \text{ dg}$$

$$\begin{array}{r} 1.60 \text{ g} \\ -\ 0.54 \text{ g} \\ \hline 1.06 \text{ g} \end{array}$$ $$\begin{array}{r} 16.0 \text{ dg} \\ -\ 5.4 \text{ dg} \\ \hline 10.6 \text{ dg} \end{array}$$

The difference is 1.06 g or 10.6 dg.

● **Work Practice Problem 8**

PRACTICE PROBLEM 8

Subtract 3.1 dg from 2.5 g.

Answers

7. 0.562 g,   **8.** 2.19 g or 21.9 dg

Mental Math

Convert.

1. 16 ounces to pounds

2. 32 ounces to pounds

3. 1 ton to pounds

4. 3 tons to pounds

5. 1 pound to ounces

6. 3 pounds to ounces

7. 2000 pounds to tons

8. 4000 pounds to tons

Determine whether the measurement in each statement is reasonable.

9. The doctor prescribed a pill containing 2 kg of medication.

10. A full-grown cat weighs approximately 15 g.

11. A bag of flour weighs 4.5 kg.

12. A staple weighs 15 mg.

13. A professor weighs less than 150 g.

14. A car weighs 2000 mg.

4.11 Exercise Set

FOR EXTRA HELP

PRACTICE   WATCH   DOWNLOAD   READ   REVIEW

Objective (A) *Convert as indicated. See Examples 1 through 3.*

1. 2 pounds to ounces

2. 5 pounds to ounces

3. 5 tons to pounds

4. 7 tons to pounds

5. 12,000 pounds to tons

6. 32,000 pounds to tons

7. 60 ounces to pounds

8. 90 ounces to pounds

9. 3500 pounds to tons

10. 11,000 pounds to tons

11. 16.25 pounds to ounces

12. 14.5 pounds to ounces

13. 4.9 tons to pounds

14. 8.3 tons to pounds

15. $4\frac{3}{4}$ pounds to ounces

16. $9\frac{1}{8}$ pounds to ounces

17. 2950 pounds to the nearest tenth of a ton

18. 51 ounces to the nearest tenth of a pound

19. $\frac{4}{5}$ oz to pounds

20. $\frac{1}{4}$ oz to pounds

21. $5\frac{3}{4}$ lb to ounces

22. $2\frac{1}{4}$ lb to ounces

23. 10 lb 1 oz to ounces

24. 7 lb 6 oz to ounces

25. 89 oz to _____ lb _____ oz

26. 100 oz = _____ lb _____ oz

Objective Ⓑ *Perform each indicated operation. See Examples 4 and 5.*

27. 34 lb 12 oz + 18 lb 14 oz

28. 6 lb 10 oz + 10 lb 8 oz

29. 6 tons 1540 lb + 2 tons 850 lb

30. 2 tons 1575 lb + 1 ton 480 lb

31. 5 tons 1050 lb − 2 tons 875 lb

32. 4 tons 850 lb − 1 ton 260 lb

33. 12 lb 4 oz − 3 lb 9 oz

34. 45 lb 6 oz − 26 lb 10 oz

35. 5 lb 3 oz × 6

36. 2 lb 5 oz × 5

37. 6 tons 1500 lb ÷ 5

38. 5 tons 400 lb ÷ 4

Objective Ⓒ *Convert as indicated. See Examples 6 and 7.*

39. 500 g to kilograms

40. 650 g to kilograms

41. 4 g to milligrams

42. 9 g to milligrams

43. 25 kg to grams

44. 18 kg to grams

45. 48 mg to grams

46. 112 mg to grams

47. 6.3 g to kilograms

48. 4.9 g to kilograms

49. 15.14 g to milligrams

50. 16.23 g to milligrams

51. 4.01 kg to grams

52. 3.16 kg to grams

53. 35 hg to centigrams

54. 4.26 cg to dekagrams

Objective Ⓓ *Perform each indicated operation. See Example 8.*

55. 3.8 mg + 9.7 mg

56. 41.6 g + 9.8 g

57. 205 mg + 5.61 g

58. 2.1 g + 153 mg

59. 9 g − 7150 mg

60. 4 kg − 2410 g

61. 1.61 kg − 250 g

62. 6.13 g − 418 mg

63. 5.2 kg × 2.6   **64.** 4.8 kg × 9.3   **65.** 17 kg ÷ 8   **66.** 8.25 g ÷ 6

Objectives Ⓐ Ⓑ Ⓒ Ⓓ **Mixed Practice** *Solve. Remember to insert units when writing your answers.*

	Object	Tons	Pounds	Ounces
67.	Statue of Liberty—weight of copper sheeting	100		
68.	Statue of Liberty—weight of steel	125		
69.	A 12-inch cube of osmium (heaviest metal)		1,345	
70.	A 12-inch cube of lithium (lightest metal)		32	

	Object	Grams	Kilograms	Milligrams	Centigrams
71.	Capsule of Amoxicillin (Antibiotic)			500	
72.	Tablet of Topamax (Epilepsy and Migraine uses)			25	
73.	A six-year-old boy		21		
74.	A golf ball	45			

75. A can of 7-Up weighs 336 grams. Find the weight in kilograms of 24 cans.

76. Guy Green normally weighs 73 kg, but he lost 2800 grams after being sick with the flu. Find Guy's new weight.

77. Sudafed is a decongestant that comes in two strengths. Regular strength contains 60 mg of medication. Extra strength contains 0.09 g of medication. How much extra medication is in the extra-strength tablet?

78. A small can of Planters sunflower seeds weighs 177 g. If each can contains 6 servings, find the weight of one serving.

79. Doris Johnson has two open containers of Uncle Ben's rice. If she combines 1 lb 10 oz from one container with 3 lb 14 oz from the other container, how much total rice does she have?

80. Dru Mizel maintains the records of the amount of coal delivered to his department in the steel mill. In January, 3 tons 1500 lb were delivered. In February, 2 tons 1200 lb were delivered. Find the total amount delivered in these two months.

81. Carla Hamtini was amazed when she grew a 28 lb 10 oz zucchini in her garden, but later she learned that the heaviest zucchini ever grown weighed 64 lb 8 oz in Llanharry, Wales, by B. Lavery in 1990. How far below the record weight was Carla's zucchini? (*Source: The Guinness Book of Records*)

82. The heaviest baby born in good health weighed an incredible 22 lb 8 oz. He was born in Italy in September, 1955. How much heavier is this than a 7 lb 12 oz baby? (*Source: The Guinness Book of Records*)

83. Tim Caucutt's doctor recommends that Tim limit his daily intake of sodium to 0.6 gram. A one-ounce serving of Cheerios with $\frac{1}{2}$ cup of fortified skim milk contains 350 mg of sodium. How much more sodium can Tim have after he eats a bowl of Cheerios for breakfast, assuming he intends to follow the doctor's orders?

84. A large bottle of Hire's Root Beer weighs 1900 grams. If a carton contains 6 large bottles of root beer, find the weight in kilograms of 5 cartons.

85. Three milligrams of preservatives are added to a 0.5-kg box of dried fruit. How many milligrams of preservatives are in 3 cartons of dried fruit if each carton contains 16 boxes?

86. One box of Swiss Miss Cocoa Mix weighs 0.385 kg, but 39 grams of this weight is the packaging. Find the actual weight of the cocoa in 8 boxes.

87. A carton of 12 boxes of Quaker Oats Oatmeal weighs 6.432 kg. Each box includes 26 grams of packaging material. What is the actual weight of the oatmeal in the carton?

88. The supermarket prepares hamburger in 85-gram market packages. When Leo Gonzalas gets home, he divides the package in half before refrigerating the meat. How much will each package weigh?

89. The Shop 'n Bag supermarket chain ships hamburger meat by placing 10 packages of hamburger in a box, with each package weighing 3 lb 4 oz. How much will 4 boxes of hamburger weigh?

90. The Quaker Oats Company ships its 1-lb 2-oz boxes of oatmeal in cartons containing 12 boxes of oatmeal. How much will 3 such cartons weigh?

91. A carton of Del Monte Pineapple weighs 55 lb 4 oz, but 2 lb 8 oz of this weight is due to packaging. Subtract the weight of the packaging to find the actual weight of the pineapple in 4 cartons.

92. The Hormel Corporation ships cartons of canned ham weighing 43 lb 2 oz each. Of this weight, 3 lb 4 oz is due to packaging. Find the actual weight of the ham found in 3 cartons.

93. A package of Trailway's Gorp, a high-energy hiking trail mix, contains 0.3 kg of nuts, 0.15 kg of chocolate bits, and 400 grams of raisins. Find the total weight of the package.

94. The manufacturer of Anacin wants to reduce the caffeine content of its aspirin by $\frac{1}{4}$. Currently, each regular tablet contains 32 mg of caffeine. How much caffeine should be removed from each tablet?

95. Use a unit other than centigram and write a mass that is equivalent to 25 centigrams. (*Hint:* There are many possibilities.)

96. Use a unit other than pound and write a weight that is equivalent to 4000 pounds. (*Hint:* There are many possibilities.)

True or False? See the Concept Check in the section.

97. A kilogram is larger than a gram.

98. A decigram is larger than a milligram.

99. Why is the decimal point moved to the right when grams are converted to milligrams?

100. To change 8 pounds to ounces, multiply by 16. Why is this the correct procedure?

A Define U.S. Units of Capacity and Convert from One Unit to Another.

B Perform Arithmetic Operations on U.S. Units of Capacity.

C Define Metric Units of Capacity and Convert from One Unit to Another.

D Perform Arithmetic Operations on Metric Units of Capacity.

4.12 CAPACITY: US AND METRIC SYSTEMS

Objective **A** Defining and Converting U.S. System Units of Capacity

Units of **capacity** are generally used to measure liquids. The number of gallons of gasoline needed to fill a gas tank in a car, the number of cups of water needed in a bread recipe, and the number of quarts of milk sold each day at a supermarket are all examples of using units of capacity. The following summary shows equivalencies between units of capacity:

U.S. Units of Capacity

$$8 \text{ fluid ounces (fl oz)} = 1 \text{ cup (c)}$$
$$2 \text{ cups} = 1 \text{ pint (pt)}$$
$$2 \text{ pints} = 1 \text{ quart (qt)}$$
$$4 \text{ quarts} = 1 \text{ gallon (gal)}$$

Just as with units of length and weight, we can form unit fractions to convert between different units of capacity. For instance,

$$\frac{2 \text{ c}}{1 \text{ pt}} = \frac{1 \text{ pt}}{2 \text{ c}} = 1 \quad \text{and} \quad \frac{2 \text{ pt}}{1 \text{ qt}} = \frac{1 \text{ qt}}{2 \text{ pt}} = 1$$

PRACTICE PROBLEM 1

Convert 43 pints to quarts.

Example 1 Convert 9 quarts to gallons.

Solution: We multiply by the unit fraction $\frac{1 \text{ gal}}{4 \text{ qt}}$.

$$9 \text{ qt} = \frac{9 \text{ qt}}{1} \cdot 1$$

$$= \frac{9 \text{ qt}}{1} \cdot \frac{1 \text{ gal}}{4 \text{ qt}}$$

$$= \frac{9 \text{ gal}}{4}$$

$$= 2\frac{1}{4} \text{ gal}$$

Thus, 9 quarts is the same as $2\frac{1}{4}$ gallons, as shown in the diagram:

1 gallon + 1 gallon + $\frac{1}{4}$ gallon

9 quarts = $2\frac{1}{4}$ gal

● **Work Practice Problem 1**

Answer

1. $21\frac{1}{2}$ qt

Example 2   Convert 14 cups to quarts.

Solution: Our equivalency table contains no direct conversion from cups to quarts. However, from this table we know that

$$1 \text{ qt} = 2 \text{ pt} = \frac{2 \text{ pt}}{1} \cdot 1 = \frac{2 \text{ pt}}{1} \cdot \frac{2 \text{ c}}{1 \text{ pt}} = 4 \text{ c}$$

so 1 qt = 4 c. Now we have the unit fraction $\dfrac{1 \text{ qt}}{4 \text{ c}}$. Thus,

$$14 \text{ c} = \frac{14 \text{ c}}{1} \cdot 1 = \frac{14 \text{ c}}{1} \cdot \frac{1 \text{ qt}}{4 \text{ c}} = \frac{14 \text{ qt}}{4} = \frac{7}{2} \text{ qt} \quad \text{or} \quad 3\frac{1}{2} \text{ qt}$$

1 quart + 1 quart + 1 quart + $\frac{1}{2}$ quart

14 cups = $3\frac{1}{2}$qt

● **Work Practice Problem 2**

✔ **Concept Check**   If 50 cups are converted to quarts, will the equivalent number of quarts be less than or greater than 50? Explain.

Objective Ⓑ Performing Operations on U.S. System Units of Capacity

As is true of units of length and weight, units of capacity can be added, subtracted, multiplied, and divided.

Example 3   Subtract 3 qt from 4 gal 2 qt.

Solution: To subtract, we line up similar units.

$$\begin{array}{r} 4 \text{ gal } 2 \text{ qt} \\ -\phantom{4 \text{ gal }} 3 \text{ qt} \end{array}$$

We cannot subtract 3 qt from 2 qt. We need to borrow 1 gallon from the 4 gallons, convert it to 4 quarts, and then combine it with the 2 quarts.

3 gal + (1 gal) 4 qt

$$\begin{array}{rcl} 4 \text{ gal } 2 \text{ qt} & = & 3 \text{ gal } 6 \text{ qt} \\ -\phantom{4 \text{ gal }} 3 \text{ qt} & = & -\phantom{3 \text{ gal }} 3 \text{ qt} \\ \hline & & 3 \text{ gal } 3 \text{ qt} \end{array}$$

To check, see that the sum of 3 gal 3 qt and 3 qt is 4 gal 2 qt.

● **Work Practice Problem 3**

Example 4   **Finding the Amount of Water in an Aquarium**

An aquarium contains 6 gal 3 qt of water. If 2 gal 2 qt of water is added, what is the total amount of water in the aquarium?

Solution:

beginning water	→	6 gal 3 qt
+ water added	→	+ 2 gal 2 qt
total water	→	8 gal 5 qt

Continued on next page

PRACTICE PROBLEM 2

Convert 26 quarts to cups.

PRACTICE PROBLEM 3

Subtract 2 qt from 1 gal 1 qt.

PRACTICE PROBLEM 4

A large oil drum contains 15 gal 3 qt of oil. How much will be in the drum if an additional 4 gal 3 qt of oil is poured into it?

Answers

2. 104 c   **3.** 3 qt   **4.** 20 gal 2 qt

✔ **Concept Check Answer**

less than 50

Since 5 qt = 1 gal 1 qt, we have

$$= \overbrace{8 \text{ gal}}^{8 \text{ gal}} + \overbrace{1 \text{ gal 1 qt}}^{5 \text{ qt}}$$
$$= 9 \text{ gal 1 qt}$$

The total amount of water is 9 gal 1 qt.

● **Work Practice Problem 4**

Objective ⓒ Defining and Converting Metric System Units of Capacity

Thus far, we know that the basic unit of length in the metric system is the meter and that the basic unit of mass in the metric system is the gram. What is the basic unit of capacity? The **liter.** By definition, a **liter** is the capacity or volume of a cube measuring 10 centimeters on each side.

The following examples may help you get a feeling for metric capacities:
    One liter of liquid is slightly more than one quart.

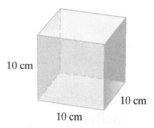

1 quart   1 liter

Many soft drinks are packaged in 2-liter bottles.

The metric system was designed to be a consistent system. Once again, the prefixes for metric units of capacity are the same as for metric units of length and mass, as summarized in the following table:

Metric Unit of Capacity
1 **kilo**liter (kl) = 1000 liters (L)
1 **hecto**liter (hl) = 100 L
1 **deka**liter (dal) = 10 L
1 liter (L) = 1 L
1 **deci**liter (dl) = 1/10 L or 0.1 L
1 **centi**liter (cl) = 1/100 L or 0.01 L
1 **milli**liter (ml) = 1/1000 L or 0.001 L

The **milliliter** and the **liter** are the two most commonly used metric units of capacity.

Converting from one unit of capacity to another involves multiplying by powers of 10 or moving the decimal point to the left or to the right. Listing units of capacity in order from largest to smallest helps to keep track of how many places to move the decimal point when converting.

Let's convert 2.6 liters to milliliters. To convert from liters to milliliters, we move along the chart 3 units to the right.

kl   hl   dal   **L**   dl   cl   **ml**

3 units to the right

This means that we move the decimal point 3 places to the right to convert from liters to milliliters.

2.600 L = 2600. ml

This same conversion can be done with unit fractions.

$$2.6 \text{ L} = \frac{2.6 \text{ L}}{1} \cdot 1$$
$$= \frac{2.6 \text{ L}}{1} \cdot \frac{1000 \text{ ml}}{1 \text{ L}}$$
$$= 2.6 \cdot 1000 \text{ ml}$$
$$= 2600 \text{ ml} \quad \text{To multiply by 1000, move the decimal point 3 places to the right.}$$

To visualize the result, study the diagram below:

MILK   MILK   MILK   2.6 L

1000 ml   1000 ml   600 ml = 2600 ml

Thus, 2.6 L = 2600 ml.

Example 5 Convert 3210 ml to liters.

Solution: Let's use the unit fraction method first.

Unit fraction

$$3210 \text{ ml} = \frac{3210 \text{ ml}}{1} \cdot 1 = 3210 \text{ ml} \cdot \frac{1 \text{ L}}{1000 \text{ ml}} = 3.21 \text{ L}$$

Now let's list the unit measures in order from left to right and move from milliliters to liters.

kl   hl   dal   L   dl   cl   ml

3 units to the left

3210 ml = 3.210 L, the same results as before and
3 places to the left   shown below in the diagram.

1000 ml   1000 ml   1000 ml

MILK   MILK   MILK   210 ml

                                    3210 ml

1 L   1 L   1 L   0.210 L = 3.210 L

● **Work Practice Problem 5**

PRACTICE PROBLEM 5

Convert 2100 ml to liters.

Answer
5. 2.1 L

Copyright 2007 Pearson Education, Inc.

PRACTICE PROBLEM 6

Convert 2.13 dal to liters.

Example 6   Convert 0.185 dl to milliliters.

Solution: We list the unit measures in order from left to right and move from deciliters to milliliters.

kl   hl   dal   L   dl   cl   ml

2 units to the right

0.185 dl = 18.5 ml

2 places to the right

● Work Practice Problem 6

Objective ⓓ Performing Operations on Metric System Units of Capacity

As was true for length and weight, arithmetic operations involving metric units of capacity can also be performed. Make sure that the metric units of capacity are the same before adding, subtracting, multiplying, or dividing.

PRACTICE PROBLEM 7

Add 1250 ml to 2.9 L.

Example 7   Add 2400 ml to 8.9 L.

Solution: We must convert both to liters or both to milliliters before adding the capacities together.

$$
\begin{array}{r}
2400 \text{ ml} = 2.4 \text{ L} \\
2.4 \text{ L} \\
+ \ 8.9 \text{ L} \\
\hline
11.3 \text{ L}
\end{array}
\qquad \text{or} \qquad
\begin{array}{r}
8.9 \text{ L} = 8900 \text{ ml} \\
2400 \text{ ml} \\
+ \ 8900 \text{ ml} \\
\hline
11{,}300 \text{ ml}
\end{array}
$$

The total is 11.3 L or 11,300 ml. They both represent the same capacity.

● Work Practice Problem 7

✔ **Concept Check**   How could you estimate the following operation? Subtract 950 ml from 7.5 L.

PRACTICE PROBLEM 8

If 28.6 L of water can be pumped every minute, how much water can be pumped in 85 minutes?

Example 8   **Finding the Amount of Medication a Person Has Received**

A patient hooked up to an IV unit in the hospital is to receive 12.5 ml of medication every hour. How much medication does the patient receive in 3.5 hours?

Solution: We multiply 12.5 ml by 3.5.

$$
\begin{array}{r}
\text{medication per hour} \quad \rightarrow \quad 12.5 \text{ ml} \\
\times \quad\quad\quad \text{hours} \quad \rightarrow \quad \times \ 3.5 \\
\hline
\text{total medication} \quad\quad\quad 625 \\
3750 \\
\hline
43.75 \text{ ml}
\end{array}
$$

The patient receives 43.75 ml of medication.

● Work Practice Problem 8

Answers

6. 21.3 L   **7.** 4150 ml or 4.15 L
  8. 2431 L

✔ **Concept Check Answer**

950 ml = 0.95 L; round 0.95 to 1;
7.5 − 1 = 6.5 L

Mental Math

Convert as indicated.

1. 2 c to pints

2. 4 c to pints

3. 4 qt to gallons

4. 8 qt to gallons

5. 2 pt to quarts

6. 6 pt to quarts

7. 8 fl oz to cups

8. 24 fl oz to cups

9. 1 pt to cups

10. 3 pt to cups

11. 1 gal to quarts

12. 2 gal to quarts

Determine whether the measurement in each statement is reasonable.

13. Clair took a dose of 2 L of cough medicine to cure her cough.

14. John drank 250 ml of milk for lunch.

15. Jeannie likes to relax in a tub filled with 3000 ml of hot water.

16. Sarah pumped 20 L of gasoline into her car yesterday.

4.12 Exercise Set

FOR EXTRA HELP

MyMathLab · Powered by CourseCompass and MathXL

 PRACTICE   WATCH   DOWNLOAD   READ   REVIEW

Objective (A) *Convert each measurement as indicated. See Examples 1 and 2.*

1. 32 fluid ounces to cups

2. 16 quarts to gallons

3. 8 quarts to pints

4. 9 pints to quarts

5. 10 quarts to gallons

6. 15 cups to pints

7. 80 fluid ounces to pints

8. 18 pints to gallons

9. 2 quarts to cups

10. 3 pints to fluid ounces

11. 120 fluid ounces to quarts

12. 20 cups to gallons

13. 6 gallons to fluid ounces

14. 5 quarts to cups

15. $4\frac{1}{2}$ pints to cups

16. $6\frac{1}{2}$ gallons to quarts

17. 5 gal 3 qt to quarts

18. 4 gal 1 qt to quarts

19. $\frac{1}{2}$ cup to pint

20. $\frac{1}{2}$ pint to quarts

21. 58 qt = _____ gal _____ qt

22. 70 qt = _____ gal _____ qt

23. 39 pt = _____ gal _____ qt _____ pt

24. 29 pt = _____ gal _____ qt _____ pt

25. $2\frac{3}{4}$ gallons to pints

26. $3\frac{1}{4}$ quarts to cups

Objective Ⓑ *Perform each indicated operation. See Examples 3 and 4.*

27. 4 gal 3 qt + 5 gal 2 qt

28. 2 gal 3 qt + 8 gal 3 qt

29. 1 c 5 fl oz + 2 c 7 fl oz

30. 2 c 3 fl oz + 2 c 6 fl oz

31. 3 gal − 1 gal 3 qt

32. 2 pt − 1 pt 1 c

33. 3 gal 1 qt − 1 qt 1 pt

34. 3 qt 1 c − 1 c 4 fl oz

35. 1 pt 1 c × 3

36. 1 qt 1 pt × 2

37. 8 gal 2 qt × 2

38. 6 gal 1 pt × 2

39. 9 gal 2 qt ÷ 2

40. 5 gal 6 fl oz ÷ 2

Objective Ⓒ *Convert as indicated. See Examples 5 and 6.*

41. 5 L to milliliters

42. 8 L to milliliters

43. 4500 ml to liters

44. 3100 ml to liters

45. 3.2 L to centiliters

46. 1.7 L to centiliters

47. 410 L to kiloliters

48. 250 L to kiloliters

49. 64 ml to liters

50. 39 ml to liters

51. 0.16 kl to liters

52. 0.48 kl to liters

53. 3.6 L to milliliters

54. 1.9 L to milliliters

55. 0.16 L to kiloliters

56. 0.127 L to kiloliters

Objective **D** *Perform each indicated operation. See Examples 7 and 8.*

57. 2.9 L + 19.6 L   **58.** 18.5 L + 4.6 L   **59.** 2700 ml + 1.8 L   **60.** 4.6 L + 1600 ml

61. 8.6 L − 190 ml   **62.** 4.8 L − 283 ml   **63.** 11,400 ml − 0.8 L   **64.** 6850 ml − 0.3 L

65. 480 ml × 8   **66.** 290 ml × 6   **67.** 81.2 L ÷ 0.5   **68.** 5.4 L ÷ 3.6

Objectives **A** **B** **C** **D** Mixed Practice *Solve. Remember to insert units when writing your answers.*

	Capacity	Cups	Gallons	Quarts	Pints
69.	An average-size bath of water		21		
70.	A dairy cow's daily milk yield				38
71.	Your kidneys filter about this amount of blood every minute	4			
72.	The amount of water needed in a punch recipe	2			

73. Many diet experts advise individuals to drink 64 ounces of water each day. How many quarts of water is this?

74. A recipe for walnut fudge cake calls for $1\frac{1}{4}$ cups of water. How many fluid ounces is this?

75. Margie Phitts added 354 ml of Prestone dry gas to the 18.6 L of gasoline in her car's tank. Find the total amount of gasoline in the tank.

76. Chris Peckaitis wishes to share a 2-L bottle of Coca Cola equally with 7 of his friends. How much will each person get?

77. Can 5 pt 1 c of fruit punch and 2 pt 1 c of ginger ale be poured into a 1-gal container without it overflowing?

78. Three cups of prepared Jell-O are poured into 6 dessert dishes. How many fluid ounces of Jell-O are in each dish?

Solve. See the Concept Checks in the section.

79. If 70 pints are converted to gallons, will the equivalent number of gallons be less than or greater than 70? Explain why.

80. If 30 gallons are converted to quarts, will the equivalent number of quarts be less than or greater than 30? Explain why.

81. Explain how to estimate the following operation: Add 986 ml to 6.9 L.

82. Find the number of fluid ounces in 1 gallon.

A cubic centimeter (cc) is the amount of space that a volume of 1 mL occupies. Because of this, we will say that 1 cc = 1 mL.

A common syringe is one with a capacity of 3 cc. Use the diagram and give the measurement indicated by each arrow.

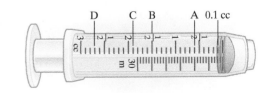

83. A   **84.** B   **85.** C   **86.** D

Helpful Hint Are you preparing for your test? Use the Chapter Test Prep Videos to see the fully worked-out solutions to any of the exercises you want to review.

4 Chapter Highlights

Definitions and Concepts	Examples
Section 4.1 Ratio and Proportion	

A **ratio** is the quotient of two quantities.	The ratio of 3 to 4 can be written as $\dfrac{3}{4}$ or $3:4$ ↑ fraction notation ↑ colon notation
Rates are used to compare different kinds of quantities.	Write the rate 12 spikes every 8 inches as a fraction in simplest form. $\dfrac{12 \text{ spikes}}{8 \text{ inches}} = \dfrac{3 \text{ spikes}}{2 \text{ inches}}$
A **unit rate** is a rate with a denominator of 1.	Write as a unit rate: 117 miles on 5 gallons of gas $\dfrac{117 \text{ miles}}{5 \text{ gallons}} = \dfrac{23.4 \text{ miles}}{1 \text{ gallon}}$ or 23.4 miles per gallon or 23.4 miles/gallon
A **proportion** is a statement that two ratios or rates are equal.	$\dfrac{1}{2} = \dfrac{4}{8}$ is a proportion.
USING CROSS PRODUCTS TO DETERMINE WHETHER PROPORTIONS ARE TRUE OR FALSE	Is $\dfrac{6}{10} = \dfrac{9}{15}$ a true proportion?

Cross products

$a \cdot d$ $b \cdot c$

$$\dfrac{a}{b} = \dfrac{c}{d}$$

If cross products are equal, the proportion is true.
If $ad = bc$, then the proportion is true.
If cross products are not equal, the proportion is false.
If $ad \neq bc$, then the proportion is false.

Cross products

$6 \cdot 15$ $10 \cdot 9$

$$\dfrac{6}{10} = \dfrac{9}{15}$$

$6 \cdot 15 \overset{?}{=} 10 \cdot 9$ Are cross products equal?
$90 = 90$

Since cross products are equal, the proportion is a true proportion.

FINDING AN UNKNOWN VALUE *n* IN A PROPORTION

Step 1. Set the cross products equal to each other.

Find *n*: $\dfrac{n}{7} = \dfrac{5}{8}$

Step 1.

$$\dfrac{n}{7} = \dfrac{5}{8}$$

$n \cdot 8 = 7 \cdot 5$ Set the cross products equal to each other.
$n \cdot 8 = 35$ Multiply.

Definitions and Concepts	**Examples**

Section 4.1　Ratio and Proportion (*continued*)

Step 2. Divide the number not multiplied by n by the number multiplied by n.

Step 2.

$$n = \frac{35}{8} \quad \text{Divide 35 by 8, the number multiplied by } n.$$

$$n = 4\frac{3}{8}$$

Section 4.2　Similar Triangles

Congruent triangles have the same shape and the same size. Corresponding angles are equal, and corresponding sides are equal.

Congruent triangles

Similar triangles have exactly the same shape but not necessarily the same size. Corresponding angles are equal, and the ratios of the lengths of corresponding sides are equal.

Similar triangles

$$\frac{AB}{DE} = \frac{3}{9} = \frac{1}{3}, \frac{BC}{EF} = \frac{6}{18} = \frac{1}{3},$$

$$\frac{CA}{FD} = \frac{4}{12} = \frac{1}{3}$$

Section 4.3　Introduction to Percent

Percent means "per hundred." The % symbol denotes percent.

$$51\% = \frac{51}{100} \quad 51 \text{ per } 100$$

$$7\% = \frac{7}{100} \quad 7 \text{ per } 100$$

To write a percent as a decimal, replace the % symbol with its decimal equivalent, 0.01, and multiply.

To write a decimal as a percent, multiply by 100%.

$$32\% = 32(0.01) = 0.32$$

$$0.08 = 0.08(100\%) = 08.\% = 8\%$$

Section 4.4　Percents and Fractions

To write a percent as a fraction, replace the % symbol with its fraction equivalent, $\frac{1}{100}$, and multiply.

$$25\% = \frac{25}{100} = \frac{\overset{1}{\cancel{25}}}{4 \cdot \cancel{25}} = \frac{1}{4}$$

To write a fraction as a percent, multiply by 100%.

$$\frac{1}{6} = \frac{1}{6} \cdot 100\% = \frac{1}{6} \cdot \frac{100}{1}\% = \frac{100}{6}\% = 16\frac{2}{3}\%$$

Definitions and Concepts	Examples
Section 4.5 Solving Percent Problems Using Equations	

Three key words in the statement of a percent problem are
  of, which means **multiplication** ($\cdot$)
  is, which means **equals** ($=$)
  what (or some equivalent word or phrase), which stands for **the unknown number**
	Solve:
	  6 is 12% of what number?
	  ↓ ↓ ↓ ↓ ↓
	  $6 = 12\% \cdot n$
	  $6 = 0.12 \cdot n$ Write 12% as a decimal.
	  $\dfrac{6}{0.12} = n$ Divide 6 by 0.12, the number multiplied by n.
	  $50 = n$
	Thus, 6 is 12% of 50.

Definitions and Concepts	Examples
Section 4.6 Solving Percent Problems Using Proportions	

PERCENT PROPORTION $$\frac{\text{amount}}{\text{base}} = \frac{\text{percent}}{100} \leftarrow \text{always } 100$$ or $$\text{amount} \rightarrow \frac{a}{b} = \frac{p}{100} \leftarrow \text{percent}$$ $$\text{base} \rightarrow$$	Solve: 20.4 is what percent of 85? 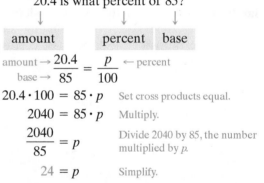 $20.4 \cdot 100 = 85 \cdot p$ Set cross products equal. $2040 = 85 \cdot p$ Multiply. $\dfrac{2040}{85} = p$ Divide 2040 by 85, the number multiplied by p. $24 = p$ Simplify. Thus, 20.4 is 24% of 85.

Definitions and Concepts	Examples
Section 4.7 Applications of Percent	

PERCENT OF INCREASE $$\text{percent of increase} = \frac{\text{amount of increase}}{\text{original amount}}$$ **PERCENT OF DECREASE** $$\text{percent of decrease} = \frac{\text{amount of decrease}}{\text{original amount}}$$	A town with a population of 16,480 decreased to 13,870 over a 12-year period. Find the percent decrease. Round to the nearest whole percent. $\text{amount of decrease} = 16{,}480 - 13{,}870$ $= 2610$ $\text{percent of decrease} = \dfrac{\text{amount of decrease}}{\text{original amount}}$ $= \dfrac{2610}{16{,}480} \approx 0.16$ $= 16\%$ The town's population decreased by 16%.

Definitions and Concepts	Examples
Section 4.8 Percent and Problem-Solving: Sales Tax, Commission, and Discount	

SALES TAX AND TOTAL PRICE
 	
  sales tax = sales tax rate $\cdot$ purchase price
  total price = purchase price + sales tax
	Find the sales tax and the total price of a purchase of $42 if the sales tax rate is 9%.
	
	sales tax = sales tax rate $\cdot$ purchase price
	↓ ↓ ↓
	sales tax = 9% $\cdot$ $42
	$= 0.09 \cdot \$42$
	$= \$3.78$

Definitions and Concepts	Examples

Section 4.8 Percent and Problem-Solving: Sales Tax, Commission, and Discount (*continued*)

The total price is

total price = purchase price + sales tax

total price = $42 + $3.78

= $45.78

COMMISSION

commission = commission rate · total sales

A salesperson earns a commission of 3%. Find the commission from sales of $12,500 worth of appliances.

commission = commission rate · sales

commission = 3% · $12,500

= 0.03 · 12,500

= $375

DISCOUNT AND SALE PRICE

amount of discount = discount rate · original price

sale price = original price − amount of discount

A suit is priced at $320 and is on sale today for 25% off. What is the sale price?

amount of discount = discount rate · original price

amount of discount = 25% · $320

= 0.25 · 320

= $80

sale price = original price − amount of discount

sale price = $320 − $80

= $240

The sale price is $240.

Section 4.9 Percent and Problem-Solving: Interest

SIMPLE INTEREST

interest = principal · rate · time

where the rate is understood to be per year.

Find the simple interest after 3 years on $800 at an interest rate of 5%.

interest = principal · rate · time

interest = $800 · 5% · 3

= $800 · 0.05 · 3   Write 5% as 0.05.

= $120   Multiply.

The interest is $120.

Compound interest is computed not only on the principal, but also on interest already earned in previous compounding periods.

$$A = P\left(1 + \frac{r}{n}\right)^{n \cdot t}$$

where n is the number of times compounded per year.

$800 is invested at 5% compounded quarterly for 10 years. Find the total amount at the end of 10 years.

$$A = \$800\left(1 + \frac{0.05}{4}\right)^{4 \cdot 10}$$

$$= \$800\,(1.0125)^{40}$$

$$\approx \$1314.90$$

Chapter 4 Review

(4.1) *Write each ratio as a fraction in simplest form.*

1. 23 to 37

2. 6000 people to 4800 people

3. $121 to $143

4. 4.25 yards to 8.75 yards

The circle graph below shows how the top 25 movies (or films) of 2009 were rated. Use this graph to answer the questions.

Top 25 Movies of 2009

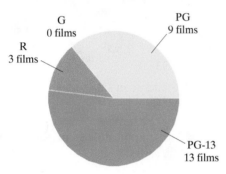

G
0 films

R
3 films

PG
9 films

PG-13
13 films

Source: MPAA

Note: There were no G-rated films in the top 25 for 2009

5. a. How many top 25 movies were rated PG?

   b. Find the ratio of top 25 PG-rated movies to total top movies for that year.

6. a. How many top 25 movies were rated R?

   b. Find the ratio of top 25 R-rated movies to total top movies for that year.

Write each rate as a fraction in simplest form.

7. 6 professors for 20 graduate research assistants

8. 15 word processing pages printed in 6 minutes

Write each rate as a unit rate.

9. 468 miles in 9 hours

10. 180 feet in 12 seconds

Determine whether each proportion is true.

11. $\dfrac{21}{8} = \dfrac{14}{6}$

12. $\dfrac{3.75}{3} = \dfrac{7.5}{6}$

Find the unknown number n in each proportion.

13. $\dfrac{n}{9} = \dfrac{5}{3}$

14. $\dfrac{4}{13} = \dfrac{10}{n}$

15. $\dfrac{27}{\frac{9}{4}} = \dfrac{n}{5}$

16. $\dfrac{0.4}{n} = \dfrac{2}{4.7}$

Solve. An owner of a Ford Escort can drive 420 miles on 11 gallons of gas.

17. If Tom Aloiso runs out of gas in an Escort and AAA comes to his rescue with $1\frac{1}{2}$ gallons of gas, determine whether Tom can then drive to a gas station 65 miles away.

18. Find how many gallons of gas Tom can expect to burn on a 3000-mile trip. Round to the nearest gallon.

Yearly homeowner property taxes are figured at a rate of $1.15 tax for every $100 of house value.

19. If a homeowner pays $627.90 in property taxes, find the value of his home.

20. Find the property taxes on a town house valued at $89,000.

(4.2) *Given that the pairs of triangles are similar, find the unknown length n.*

21.
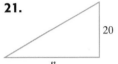

22.

23.

Solve.

24. A housepainter needs to estimate the height of a condominium. He estimates the length of his shadow to be 7 feet long and the length of the building's shadow to be 42 feet long. Find the approximate height of the building if the housepainter is $5\frac{1}{2}$ feet tall.

25. A toy company is making a triangular sail for a toy sailboat. The toy sail is to be the same shape as a real sailboat's sail. Use the following diagram to find the unknown lengths *x* and *y*.

(4.3) *Solve.*

26. In a survey of 100 adults, 37 preferred pepperoni on their pizzas. What percent preferred pepperoni?

27. A basketball player made 77 out of 100 attempted free throws. What percent of free throws was made?

Write each percent as a decimal.

28. 83%

29. 75%

30. 0.5%

31. 0.7%

32. 200%

33. 400%

34. 26.25%

35. 85.34%

Write each decimal as a percent.

36. 2.6

37. 0.055

38. 0.35

39. 1.02

40. 0.71

41. 0.65

42. 4

43. 9

(4.4) *Write each percent as a fraction or mixed number in simplest form.*

44. 1%   **45.** 10%   **46.** 25%   **47.** 8.5%

48. 10.2%   **49.** $16\frac{2}{3}$%   **50.** $33\frac{1}{3}$%   **51.** 110%

Write each fraction or mixed number as a percent.

52. $\frac{1}{5}$ **53.** $\frac{7}{10}$ **54.** $\frac{5}{6}$ **55.** $1\frac{2}{3}$

56. $1\frac{1}{4}$ **57.** $\frac{3}{5}$ **58.** $\frac{1}{16}$ **59.** $\frac{5}{8}$

(4.5) *Translate each to an equation and solve.*

60. 1250 is 1.25% of what number?

61. What number is $33\frac{1}{3}$% of 24,000?

62. 124.2 is what percent of 540?

63. 22.9 is 20% of what number?

64. What number is 40% of 7500?

65. 693 is what percent of 462?

(4.6) *Translate each to a proportion and solve.*

66. 104.5 is 25% of what number?

67. 16.5 is 5.5% of what number?

68. What number is 36% of 180?

69. 63 is what percent of 35?

70. 93.5 is what percent of 85?

71. What number is 33% of 500?

(4.7) *Solve.*

72. In a survey of 2000 people, it was found that 1320 have a microwave oven. Find the percent of people who own microwaves.

73. Of the 12,360 freshmen entering County College, 2000 are enrolled in basic college mathematics. Find the percent of entering freshmen who are enrolled in basic college mathematics. Round to the nearest whole percent.

74. The number of violent crimes in a city decreased from 675 to 534. Find the percent decrease. Round to the nearest tenth of a percent.

75. The current charge for dumping waste in a local land-fill is $16 per cubic foot. To cover new environmental costs, the charge will increase to $33 per cubic foot. Find the percent increase.

76. This year the fund drive for a charity collected $215,000. Next year, a 4% decrease is expected. Find how much is expected to be collected in next year's drive.

77. A local union negotiated a new contract that increases the hourly pay 15% over last year's pay. The old hourly rate was $11.50. Find the new hourly rate rounded to the nearest cent.

(4.8) *Solve.*

78. If the sales tax rate is 5.5%, what is the total amount charged for a $250 coat?

79. Find the sales tax paid on a $25.50 purchase if the sales tax rate is 4.5%.

80. Russ James is a sales representative for a chemical company and is paid a commission rate of 5% on all sales. Find his commission if he sold $100,000 worth of chemicals last month.

81. Carol Sell is a sales clerk in a clothing store. She receives a commission of 7.5% on all sales. Find her commission for the week if her sales for the week were $4005. Round to the nearest cent.

82. A $3000 mink coat is on sale for 30% off. Find the discount and the sale price.

83. A $90 calculator is on sale for 10% off. Find the discount and the sale price.

(4.9) *Solve.*

84. Find the simple interest due on $4000 loaned for 4 months at 12% interest.

85. Find the simple interest due on $6500 loaned for 3 months at 20%.

86. Find the total amount in an account if $5500 is compounded annually at 12% for 15 years.

87. Find the total amount in an account if $6000 is compounded semiannually at 11% for 10 years.

88. Find the compound interest earned if $100 is compounded quarterly at 12% for 5 years.

89. Find the compound interest earned if $1000 is compounded quarterly at 18% for 20 years.

Answers to Selected Exercises

Chapter 4 Ratio, Proportion, Percent, and Unit Conversion

Section 4.1

Vocabulary and Readiness Check **1.** true **3.** false **5.** true **7.** true **9.** unit **11.** division **13.** proportion; ratio **15.** true

Exercise Set 4.1 **1.** $\frac{23}{10}$ **3.** $\frac{3\frac{3}{4}}{1\frac{2}{3}}$ **5.** $\frac{2}{3}$ **7.** $\frac{77}{100}$ **9.** $\frac{5}{12}$ **11.** $\frac{8}{25}$ **13.** $\frac{12}{7}$ **15.** $\frac{16}{23}$ **17.** $\frac{2}{5}$ **19.** $\frac{17}{40}$ **21.** $\frac{10}{279}$ **23.** $\frac{1}{3}$ **25.** $\frac{1 \text{ shrub}}{3 \text{ ft}}$ **27.** $\frac{3 \text{ returns}}{20 \text{ sales}}$

29. $\frac{2 \text{ phone lines}}{9 \text{ employees}}$ **31.** $\frac{9 \text{ gal}}{2 \text{ acres}}$ **33.** $\frac{3 \text{ flight attendants}}{100 \text{ passengers}}$ **35.** $\frac{71 \text{ cal}}{2 \text{ fl oz}}$ **37.** 110 cal/oz **39.** 90 wingbeats/sec **41.** false **43.** true **45.** $\frac{1.8}{2} = \frac{4.5}{5}$; true

47. $\frac{\frac{2}{3}}{\frac{1}{5}} = \frac{\frac{2}{5}}{\frac{1}{9}}$; false **49.** 3 **51.** 9 **53.** 4 **55.** 3.2 **57.** 0.0025 **59.** 1 **61.** $\frac{3}{4}$ **63.** $\frac{35}{18}$ **65.** 360 baskets **67.** 165 min **69.** 23 ft **71.** 25 gal **73.** 450 km

75. 16 bags **77.** 18 applications **79.** 5 weeks **81.** 37.5 sec **83. a.** 18 tsp **b.** 6 tbsp **85.** 6 people **87.** 112 ft; 11-in. difference **89.** 102.9 mg **91. a.** 2062.5 mg **b.** no **93. a.** 0.1 gal **b.** 13 fl oz **95.** $2^2 \cdot 5$ **97.** $2^3 \cdot 5^2$ **99.** 2^5 **101.** 0.8 ml **103.** 1.25 ml **105.** no; answers may vary **107.** answers may vary **109.** 1400

Section 4.2

Vocabulary and Readiness Check **1.** false **3.** true **5.** false **7.** $\angle M$ and $\angle Y$, $\angle N$ and $\angle X$, $\angle P$ and $\angle Z$; $\frac{p}{z} = \frac{m}{y} = \frac{n}{x}$

Exercise Set 4.2 **1.** congruent; SSS **3.** not congruent **5.** congruent; ASA **7.** congruent; SAS **9.** $\frac{2}{1}$ **11.** $\frac{3}{2}$ **13.** 4.5 **15.** 6 **17.** 5 **19.** 13.5

21. 17.5 **23.** 10 **25.** 28.125 **27.** 10 **29.** 520 ft **31.** 500 ft **33.** 60 ft **35.** 14.4 ft **37.** 52 neon tetras **39.** 381 ft **41.** 4.01 **43.** 1.23 **45.** $3\frac{8}{9}$ in.; no
47. 8.4 **49.** answers may vary **51.** 200 ft, 300 ft, 425 ft

Section 4.3

Vocabulary and Readiness Check **1.** Percent **3.** percent **5.** 0.01

Exercise Set 4.3 **1.** 96% **3. a.** 75% **b.** 25% **5.** football; 37% **7.** 50% **9.** 0.41 **11.** 0.06 **13.** 1.00 or 1 **15.** 0.736 **17.** 0.028 **19.** 0.006
21. 3.00 or 3 **23.** 0.3258 **25.** 0.38 **27.** 0.202 **29.** 0.465 **31.** 98% **33.** 310% **35.** 2900% **37.** 0.3% **39.** 22% **41.** 530% **43.** 5.6%
45. 33.28% **47.** 300% **49.** 70% **51.** 68% **53.** 3.9% **55.** 9.3% **57.** 0.25 **59.** 0.65 **61.** 0.9 **63.** b, d **65.** 4% **67.** network systems and data communication analysts **69.** 0.35 **71.** answers may vary

Section 4.4

Vocabulary and Readiness Check **1.** Percent **3.** 100% **5.** 13% **7.** 87% **9.** 1%

Exercise Set 4.4 **1.** $\frac{3}{25}$ **3.** $\frac{1}{25}$ **5.** $\frac{9}{200}$ **7.** $\frac{7}{4}$ or $1\frac{3}{4}$ **9.** $\frac{73}{100}$ **11.** $\frac{1}{8}$ **13.** $\frac{1}{16}$ **15.** $\frac{3}{50}$ **17.** $\frac{31}{300}$ **19.** $\frac{179}{800}$ **21.** 75% **23.** 70%

25. 40% **27.** 59% **29.** 34% **31.** $37\frac{1}{2}$% **33.** $31\frac{1}{4}$% **35.** 160% **37.** $77\frac{7}{9}$% **39.** 65% **41.** 250% **43.** 190% **45.** 63.64% **47.** 26.67%

49. 14.29% **51.** 91.67% **53.** $0.35, \frac{7}{20}$; $20\%, 0.2$; $50\%, \frac{1}{2}$; $0.7, \frac{7}{10}$; $37.5\%, 0.375$ **55.** $0.4, \frac{2}{5}$; $23\frac{1}{2}\%, \frac{47}{200}$; $80\%, 0.8$; $0.333\overline{3}, \frac{1}{3}$; $87.5\%, 0.875$; $0.075, \frac{3}{40}$

57. $2, 2$; $280\%, 2\frac{4}{5}$; $7.05, 7\frac{1}{20}$; $454\%, 4.54$ **59.** $0.262; \frac{131}{500}$ **61.** $0.23; \frac{23}{100}$ **63.** 48.3% **65.** 0.0875 **67.** 25% **69.** $0.005; \frac{1}{200}$ **71.** $0.142; \frac{71}{500}$

73. $0.079; \frac{79}{1000}$ **75.** $n = 15$ **77.** $n = 10$ **79.** $n = 12$ **81. a.** 52.9% **b.** 52.86% **83.** 107.8% **85.** 65.79% **87.** 77% **89.** 75% **91.** 80%
93. greater **95.** answers may vary **97.** 0.266; 26.6% **99.** 1.155; 115.5%

Section 4.5

Vocabulary and Readiness Check **1.** is **3.** amount; base; percent **5.** greater **7.** percent: 42%; base: 50; amount: 21
9. percent: 125%; base: 86; amount: 107.5

Exercise Set 4.5 **1.** $18\% \cdot 81 = x$ **3.** $20\% \cdot x = 105$ **5.** $0.6 = 40\% \cdot x$ **7.** $x \cdot 80 = 3.8$ **9.** $x = 9\% \cdot 43$ **11.** $x \cdot 250 = 150$ **13.** 3.5 **15.** 28.7
17. 10 **19.** 600 **21.** 110% **23.** 34% **25.** 1 **27.** 645 **29.** 500 **31.** 5.16% **33.** 25.2 **35.** 35% **37.** 35 **39.** 0.624 **41.** 0.5% **43.** 145

45. 63% **47.** 4% **49.** $n = 30$ **51.** $n = 3\frac{7}{11}$ **53.** $\frac{17}{12} = \frac{n}{20}$ **55.** $\frac{8}{9} = \frac{14}{n}$ **57.** c **59.** b **61.** Twenty percent of some number is eighteen and

six tenths. **63.** b **65.** c **67.** c **69.** a **71.** a **73.** answers may vary **75.** 686.625 **77.** 12,285

Section 4.6

Vocabulary and Readiness Check **1.** amount; base; percent **3.** amount **5.** amount: 12.6; base: 42; percent: 30 **7.** amount: 102; base: 510; percent: 20

Exercise Set 4.6 **1.** $\dfrac{a}{45} = \dfrac{98}{100}$ **3.** $\dfrac{a}{150} = \dfrac{4}{100}$ **5.** $\dfrac{14.3}{b} = \dfrac{26}{100}$ **7.** $\dfrac{84}{b} = \dfrac{35}{100}$ **9.** $\dfrac{70}{400} = \dfrac{p}{100}$ **11.** $\dfrac{8.2}{82} = \dfrac{p}{100}$ **13.** 26 **15.** 18.9 **17.** 600 **19.** 10 **21.** 120% **23.** 28% **25.** 37 **27.** 1.68 **29.** 1000 **31.** 210% **33.** 55.18 **35.** 45% **37.** 75 **39.** 0.864 **41.** 0.5% **43.** 140 **45.** 9.6 **47.** 113% **49.** $\dfrac{7}{8}$ **51.** $3\dfrac{2}{15}$ **53.** 0.7 **55.** 2.19 **57.** answers may vary **59.** no; $a = 16$ **61.** yes **63.** answers may vary **65.** 12,011.2 **67.** 7270.6

Section 4.7

Exercise Set 4.7 **1.** 1600 bolts **3.** 8.8 lb **5.** 14% **7.** 232 films **9.** 17% **11.** 496 chairs; 5704 chairs **13.** 83,820 physician assistants **15.** 636.864 thousand or approximately 637 thousand **17.** 30% **19.** 50% **21.** 12.5% **23.** 29.2% **25.** $175.000 **27.** 31.2 hr **29.** increase: $867.87; new price: $20,153.87 **31.** 35 ft **33.** increase: $3918; tuition in 2009–2010: $8679 **35.** increase: 41,667 associate degrees; 2017–2018: 772,667 associate degrees **37.** 30; 60% **39.** 52; 80% **41.** 2; 25% **43.** 120; 75% **45.** 44% **47.** 1.3% **49.** 158.0% **51.** 30.8% **53.** 5.6% **55.** 19.7% **57.** 29.0% **59.** 38.8% **61.** 4.56 **63.** 11.18 **65.** 58.54 **67.** The increased number is double the original number. **69.** percent increase $= \dfrac{30}{150} = 20\%$ **71.** False; the percents are different.

Section 4.8

Vocabulary and Readiness Check **1.** sales tax **3.** commission **5.** sale price

Exercise Set 4.8 **1.** $7.50 **3.** $858.93 **5.** 7% **7. a.** $120 **b.** $130.20 **9.** $117; $1917 **11.** $485 **13.** 6% **15.** $16.10; $246.10 **17.** $53,176.04 **19.** 14% **21.** $4888.50 **23.** $185,500 **25.** $8.90; $80.10 **27.** $98.25; $98.25 **29.** $143.50; $266.50 **31.** $3255; $18,445 **33.** $45; $255 **35.** $27.45; $332.45 **37.** $3.08; $59.08 **39.** $7074 **41.** 8% **43.** 1200 **45.** 132 **47.** 16 **49.** d **51.** $4.00; $6.00; $8.00 **53.** $7.20; $10.80; $14.40 **55.** a discount of 60% is better; answers may vary **57.** $26,838.45

Section 4.9

Calculator Explorations **1.** $936.31 **3.** $9674.77 **5.** $634.49 **7.** 1.56051 **9.** 8.06231 **11.** $634.49

Vocabulary and Readiness Check **1.** simple **3.** Compound **5.** Total amount

Exercise Set 4.9 **1.** $32 **3.** $73.60 **5.** $750 **7.** $33.75 **9.** $700 **11.** $101,562.50; $264,062.50 **13.** $5562.50 **15.** $14,280 **17.** $46,815.37 **19.** $2327.14 **21.** $58,163.64 **23.** $2915.75 **25.** $2938.66 **27.** $2971.89 **29.** $260.31 **31.** $637.26 **33.** 32 yd **35.** 35 m **37.** answers may vary **39.** answers may vary

Section 4.10

Exercise Set 4.10 **1.** 5 ft **3.** 36 ft **5.** 8 mi **7.** $8\dfrac{1}{2}$ ft **9.** $3\dfrac{1}{3}$ yd **11.** 33,792 ft **13.** 4.5 yd **15.** 0.25 ft **17.** 13 yd 1 ft **19.** 3 ft 5 in. **21.** 1 mi 4720 ft **23.** 62 in. **25.** 23 ft **27.** 84 in. **29.** 12 ft 3 in. **31.** 22 yd 1 ft **33.** 8 ft 5 in. **35.** 5 ft 6 in. **37.** 3 ft 4 in. **39.** 50 yd 2 ft **41.** 4000 cm **43.** 4.0 cm **45.** 0.3 km **47.** 1.4 m **49.** 15 m **51.** 42,000 cm **53.** 7000 m **55.** 83 mm **57.** 0.201 dm **59.** 40 mm **61.** 8.94 m **63.** 2.94 m or 2940 mm **65.** 1.29 cm or 12.9 mm **67.** 12.640 km or 12,640 m **69.** 54.9 m **71.** 1.55 km **73.** $348\dfrac{2}{3}$ yd; 12,552 in. **75.** $11\dfrac{2}{3}$ yd; 140 in. **77.** 5000 mm; 0.005 km; 500 cm **79.** 0.065 m; 65 mm; 0.000065 km **81.** 342,000 m; 342,000,000 mm; 34,200,000 cm **83.** 10 ft 6 in. **85.** 13 ft 11 in. **87.** 9.12 m **89.** 26.7 mm **91.** 15 ft 9 in. **93.** 3.35 m **95.** Estimate: 13 yd **97.** answers may vary: for example, $1\dfrac{1}{3}$ yd or 48 in. **99.** answers may vary

Mental Math **1.** 1 lb **3.** 2000 lb **5.** 16 oz **7.** 1 ton **9.** no **11.** yes **13.** no

Section 4.11

Exercise Set 4.11 **1.** 32 oz **3.** 10,000 lb **5.** 6 tons **7.** $3\dfrac{3}{4}$ lb **9.** $1\dfrac{3}{4}$ tons **11.** 260 oz **13.** 9800 lb **15.** 76 oz **17.** 1.5 tons **19.** $\dfrac{1}{20}$ lb **21.** 92 oz **23.** 161 oz **25.** 5 lb 9 oz **27.** 53 lb 10 oz **29.** 9 tons 390 lb **31.** 3 tons 175 lb **33.** 8 lb 11 oz **35.** 31 lb 2 oz **37.** 1 ton 700 lb **39.** 0.5 kg **41.** 4000 mg **43.** 25,000 g **45.** 0.048 g **47.** 0.0063 kg **49.** 15,140 mg **51.** 4010 g **53.** 350,000 cg **55.** 13.5 mg **57.** 5.815 g or 5815 mg **59.** 1850 mg or 1.850 g **61.** 1360 g or 1.360 kg **63.** 13.52 kg **65.** 2.125 kg **67.** 200,000 lb; 3,200,000 oz **69.** $\dfrac{269}{400}$ or 0.6725 ton; 21,520 oz **71.** 0.5 g; 0.0005 kg; 50 cg **73.** 21,000 g; 21,000,000 mg; 2,100,000 cg **75.** 8.064 kg **77.** 30 mg **79.** 5 lb 8 oz **81.** 35 lb 14 oz **83.** 250 mg **85.** 144 mg **87.** 6.12 kg **89.** 130 lb **91.** 211 lb **93.** 850 g or 0.85 kg **95.** answers may vary **97.** true **99.** answers may vary

Mental Math **1.** 1 pt **3.** 1 gal **5.** 1 qt **7.** 1 c **9.** 2 c **11.** 4 qt **13.** no **15.** no

Section 4.12

Exercise Set 4.12 **1.** 4 c **3.** 16 pt **5.** $2\frac{1}{2}$ gal **7.** 5 pt **9.** 8 c **11.** $3\frac{3}{4}$ qt **13.** 768 fl oz **15.** 9 c **17.** 23 qt **19.** $\frac{1}{4}$ pt
21. 14 gal 2 qt **23.** 4 gal 3 qt 1 pt **25.** 22 pt **27.** 10 gal 1 qt **29.** 4 c 4 fl oz **31.** 1 gal 1 qt **33.** 2 gal 3 qt 1 pt **35.** 2 qt 1 c
37. 17 gal **39.** 4 gal 3 qt **41.** 5000 ml **43.** 4.5 L **45.** 320 cl **47.** 0.41 kl **49.** 0.064 L **51.** 160 L **53.** 3600 ml
55. 0.00016 kl **57.** 22.5 L **59.** 4.5 L or 4500 ml **61.** 8410 ml or 8.41 L **63.** 10,600 ml or 10.6 L **65.** 3840 ml **67.** 162.4 L
69. 336 c; 84 qt; 168 pt **71.** $\frac{1}{4}$ gal; 1 qt; 2 pt **73.** 2 qt **75.** 18.954 L **77.** yes **79.** answers may vary **81.** answers may vary
83. 0.6 cc **85.** 1.9 cc

Chapter 4 Review **1.** $\frac{23}{37}$ **2.** $\frac{5}{4}$ **3.** $\frac{11}{13}$ **4.** $\frac{17}{35}$ **5. a.** 9 **b.** $\frac{9}{25}$ **6. a.** 3 **b.** $\frac{3}{25}$ **7.** $\frac{3 \text{ professors}}{10 \text{ assistants}}$ **8.** $\frac{5 \text{ pages}}{2 \text{ min}}$ **9.** 52 mi/hr **10.** 15 ft/sec **11.** no
12. yes **13.** 15 **14.** 32.5 **15.** 60 **16.** 0.94 **17.** no **18.** 79 gal **19.** $54,600 **20.** $1023.50 **21.** $37\frac{1}{2}$ **22.** $13\frac{1}{3}$ **23.** 17.4
24. 33 ft **25.** $x = \frac{5}{6}$ in.; $y = 2\frac{1}{6}$ in. **26.** 37% **27.** 77% **28.** 0.83 **29.** 0.75 **30.** 0.005 **31.** 0.007 **32.** 2.00 or 2 **33.** 4.00 or 4 **34.** 0.2625
35. 0.8534 **36.** 260% **37.** 5.5% **38.** 35% **39.** 102% **40.** 71% **41.** 65% **42.** 400% **43.** 900% **44.** $\frac{1}{100}$ **45.** $\frac{1}{10}$ **46.** $\frac{1}{4}$ **47.** $\frac{17}{200}$
48. $\frac{51}{500}$ **49.** $\frac{1}{6}$ **50.** $\frac{1}{3}$ **51.** $1\frac{1}{10}$ **52.** 20% **53.** 70% **54.** $83\frac{1}{3}$% **55.** $166\frac{2}{3}$% **56.** 125% **57.** 60% **58.** 6.25% **59.** 62.5%
60. 100,000 **61.** 8000 **62.** 23% **63.** 114.5 **64.** 3000 **65.** 150% **66.** 418 **67.** 300 **68.** 64.8 **69.** 180% **70.** 110% **71.** 165
72. 66% **73.** 16% **74.** 20.9% **75.** 106.25% **76.** $206,400 **77.** $13.23 **78.** $263.75 **79.** $1.15 **80.** $5000 **81.** $300.38
82. discount: $900; sale price: $2100 **83.** discount: $9; sale price: $81 **84.** $160 **85.** $325 **86.** $30,104.61 **87.** $17,506.54 **88.** $80.61
89. $32,830.10

5

Real Numbers and Introduction to Algebra

Objective Ⓐ Finding Square Roots

The square of a number is the number times itself. For example:

The square of 5 is 25 because 5^2 or $5 \cdot 5 = 25$.
The square of 4 is 16 because 4^2 or $4 \cdot 4 = 16$.
The square of 10 is 100 because 10^2 or $10 \cdot 10 = 100$.

Recall from Chapter 1 that the reverse process of squaring is finding a **square root.** For example:

A square root of 16 is 4 because $4^2 = 16$.
A square root of 25 is 5 because $5^2 = 25$.
A square root of 100 is 10 because $10^2 = 100$.

We use the symbol $\sqrt{}$, called a **radical sign,** to name square roots. For example:

$\sqrt{16} = 4$ because $4^2 = 16$
$\sqrt{25} = 5$ because $5^2 = 25$

Square Root of a Number

A square root of a number a is a number b whose square is a. We use the radical sign $\sqrt{}$ to name square roots. In symbols,

$\sqrt{a} = b$ if $b^2 = a$

Also,

$\sqrt{0} = 0$

Example 1 Find each square root.

a. $\sqrt{49}$ **b.** $\sqrt{1}$ **c.** $\sqrt{81}$

Solution:

a. $\sqrt{49} = 7$ because $7^2 = 49$
b. $\sqrt{1} = 1$ because $1^2 = 1$
c. $\sqrt{81} = 9$ because $9^2 = 81$

● Work Practice 1

Example 2 Find: $\sqrt{\dfrac{1}{36}}$

Solution: $\sqrt{\dfrac{1}{36}} = \dfrac{1}{6}$ because $\dfrac{1}{6} \cdot \dfrac{1}{6} = \dfrac{1}{36}$

● Work Practice 2

Example 3 Find: $\sqrt{\dfrac{4}{25}}$

Solution: $\sqrt{\dfrac{4}{25}} = \dfrac{2}{5}$ because $\dfrac{2}{5} \cdot \dfrac{2}{5} = \dfrac{4}{25}$

● Work Practice 3

PRACTICE 1

Find each square root.
a. $\sqrt{100}$ **b.** $\sqrt{64}$
c. $\sqrt{121}$ **d.** $\sqrt{0}$

PRACTICE 2

Find: $\sqrt{\dfrac{1}{4}}$

PRACTICE 3

Find: $\sqrt{\dfrac{9}{16}}$

Answers
1. a. 10 **b.** 8 **c.** 11 **d.** 0
2. $\dfrac{1}{2}$ **3.** $\dfrac{3}{4}$

Objective ⓑ Approximating Square Roots

Thus far, we have found square roots of perfect squares. Numbers like $\frac{1}{4}$, 36, $\frac{4}{25}$, and 1 are called **perfect squares** because their square root is a whole number or a fraction. A square root such as $\sqrt{5}$ cannot be written as a whole number or a fraction since 5 is not a perfect square.

Although $\sqrt{5}$ cannot be written as a whole number or a fraction, it can be approximated by estimating, by using a table (as in Appendix E), or by using a calculator.

PRACTICE 4

Use Appendix E or a calculator to approximate each square root to the nearest thousandth.

a. $\sqrt{10}$ **b.** $\sqrt{72}$

Example 4 Use Appendix E or a calculator to approximate each square root to the nearest thousandth.

a. $\sqrt{43} \approx 6.557$ is approximately
b. $\sqrt{80} \approx 8.944$

⬤ Work Practice 4

Helpful Hint

$\sqrt{80}$, above, is *approximately* 8.944. This means that if we multiply 8.944 by 8.944, the product is *close* to 80.

$$8.944 \times 8.944 \approx 79.995$$

It is possible to approximate a square root to the nearest whole number without the use of a calculator or table. To do so, study the number line below and look for patterns.

Above the number line, notice that as the numbers under the radical signs increase, their value, and thus their placement on the number line, increase also.

PRACTICE 5

Without a calculator or table, approximate $\sqrt{62}$ to the nearest whole.

Example 5 Without a calculator or table:

a. Determine which two whole numbers $\sqrt{78}$ is between.
b. Use part **a** to approximate $\sqrt{78}$ to the nearest whole.

Solution:

a. Review perfect squares and recall that $\sqrt{64} = 8$ and $\sqrt{81} = 9$. Since 78 is between 64 and 81, $\sqrt{78}$ is between $\sqrt{64}$ (or 8) and $\sqrt{81}$ (or 9).

Thus, $\sqrt{78}$ is between 8 and 9.

b. Since 78 is closer to 81, then (as our number line shows) $\sqrt{78}$ is closer to $\sqrt{81}$, or 9.

⬤ Work Practice 5

Objective ⓒ Using the Pythagorean Theorem

One important application of square roots has to do with right triangles. Recall that a **right triangle** is a triangle in which one of the angles is a right angle, or measures 90° (degrees). The **hypotenuse** of a right triangle is the side opposite the right angle.

Answers
4. a. 3.162   **b.** 8.426
5. 8

The **legs** of a right triangle are the other two sides. These are shown in the following figure. The right angle in the triangle is indicated by the small square drawn in that angle.

The following theorem is true for all right triangles:

Pythagorean Theorem

In any **right triangle,**

$$(\text{leg})^2 + (\text{other leg})^2 = (\text{hypotenuse})^2$$

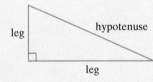

Using the Pythagorean theorem, we can use one of the following formulas to find an unknown length of a right triangle:

Finding an Unknown Length of a Right Triangle

$$\text{hypotenuse} = \sqrt{(\text{leg})^2 + (\text{other leg})^2}$$

or

$$\text{leg} = \sqrt{(\text{hypotenuse})^2 - (\text{other leg})^2}$$

Example 6 Find the length of the hypotenuse of the given right triangle.

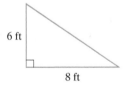

Solution:　Since we are finding the hypotenuse, we use the formula

$$\text{hypotenuse} = \sqrt{(\text{leg})^2 + (\text{other leg})^2}$$

Putting the known values into the formula, we have

$$\text{hypotenuse} = \sqrt{(6)^2 + (8)^2}$$　The legs are 6 feet and 8 feet.

$$= \sqrt{36 + 64}$$

$$= \sqrt{100}$$

$$= 10$$

The hypotenuse is 10 feet long.

🔊 **Work Practice 6**

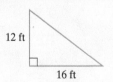

PRACTICE 7

Approximate the length of the hypotenuse of the given right triangle. Round to the nearest whole unit.

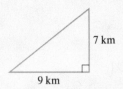

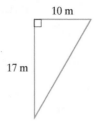 **Example 7** Approximate the length of the hypotenuse of the given right triangle. Round the length to the nearest whole unit.

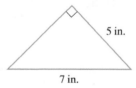

Solution:

$$\text{hypotenuse} = \sqrt{(\text{leg})^2 + (\text{other leg})^2}$$

$$= \sqrt{(17)^2 + (10)^2} \quad \text{The legs are 10 meters and 17 meters.}$$

$$= \sqrt{289 + 100}$$

$$= \sqrt{389}$$

$$\approx 20 \quad \text{From Appendix E or a calculator}$$

The hypotenuse is exactly $\sqrt{389}$ meters, which is approximately 20 meters.

● **Work Practice 7**

PRACTICE 8

Find the length of the leg in the given right triangle. Give the exact length and a two-decimal-place approximation.

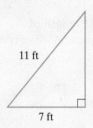

Example 8 Find the length of the leg in the given right triangle. Give the exact length and a two-decimal-place approximation.

Solution: Notice that the hypotenuse measures 7 inches and the length of one leg measures 5 inches. Since we are looking for the length of the other leg, we use the formula

$$\text{leg} = \sqrt{(\text{hypotenuse})^2 - (\text{other leg})^2}$$

Putting the known values into the formula, we have

$$\text{leg} = \sqrt{(7)^2 - (5)^2} \quad \text{The hypotenuse is 7 inches, and the other leg is 5 inches.}$$

$$= \sqrt{49 - 25}$$

$$= \sqrt{24} \quad \text{Exact answer}$$

$$\approx 4.90 \quad \text{From Appendix E or a calculator}$$

The length of the leg is exactly $\sqrt{24}$ inches, which is approximately 4.90 inches.

● **Work Practice 8**

✔**Concept Check** The following lists are the lengths of the sides of two triangles. Which set forms a right triangle? Explain.

a. 8, 15, 17 **b.** 24, 30, 40

Answers

7. 11 km **8.** $\sqrt{72}$ ft ≈ 8.49 ft

✔ **Concept Check Answers**

set (a) forms a right triangle

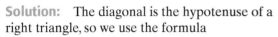 **Example 9** Finding the Length of a Sidewalk

An inner-city park is in the shape of a square that measures 300 feet on a side. A sidewalk is to be constructed along the diagonal of the park. Find the length of the sidewalk rounded to the nearest whole foot.

Solution: The diagonal is the hypotenuse of a right triangle, so we use the formula

$$\text{hypotenuse} = \sqrt{(\text{leg})^2 + (\text{other leg})^2}$$

Putting the known values into the formula we have

$$\text{hypotenuse} = \sqrt{(300)^2 + (300)^2} \quad \text{The legs are both 300 feet.}$$
$$= \sqrt{90{,}000 + 90{,}000}$$
$$= \sqrt{180{,}000}$$
$$\approx 424 \quad \text{From Appendix E or a calculator}$$

The length of the sidewalk is approximately 424 feet.

🖙 **Work Practice 9**

PRACTICE 9

A football field is a rectangle measuring 100 yards by 53 yards. Draw a diagram and find the length of the diagonal of a football field to the nearest yard.

Answer
9. 113 yd

🖩 **Calculator Explorations** **Finding Square Roots**

To simplify or approximate square roots using a calculator, locate the key marked $\boxed{\sqrt{\ }}$.

To simplify $\sqrt{64}$, for example, press the keys

$\boxed{64}$ $\boxed{\sqrt{\ }}$ or $\boxed{\sqrt{\ }}$ $\boxed{64}$

The display should read $\boxed{\quad 8\quad}$. Then

$$\sqrt{64} = 8$$

To *approximate* $\sqrt{10}$, press the keys

$\boxed{10}$ $\boxed{\sqrt{\ }}$ or $\boxed{\sqrt{\ }}$ $\boxed{10}$

The display should read $\boxed{3.16227766}$. This is an *approximation* for $\sqrt{10}$. A three-decimal-place approximation is

$$\sqrt{10} \approx 3.162$$

Is this answer reasonable? Since 10 is between perfect squares 9 and 16, $\sqrt{10}$ is between $\sqrt{9} = 3$ and $\sqrt{16} = 4$. Our answer is reasonable since 3.162 is between 3 and 4.

Simplify.

1. $\sqrt{1024}$
2. $\sqrt{676}$

Approximate each square root. Round each answer to the nearest thousandth.

3. $\sqrt{31}$
4. $\sqrt{19}$
5. $\sqrt{97}$
6. $\sqrt{56}$

Vocabulary and Readiness Check

Use the choices below to fill in each blank. Some choices may be used more than once.

squaring   Pythagorean theorem   radical   leg

hypotenuse   perfect squares   10

1. $\sqrt{100} =$ _____ because $10 \cdot 10 = 100$.

2. The _____ sign is used to denote the square root of a number.

3. The reverse process of _____ a number is finding a square root of a number.

4. The numbers $9, 1$, and $\dfrac{1}{25}$ are called _____.

5. Label the parts of the right triangle. ———

6. The _____ can be used for right triangles.

5.1 Exercise Set

FOR EXTRA HELP

MyMathLab | Math XL PRACTICE | WATCH | DOWNLOAD | READ | REVIEW

Objective Ⓐ *Find each square root. See Examples 1 through 3.*

 **1.** $\sqrt{4}$

2. $\sqrt{9}$

 3. $\sqrt{121}$

4. $\sqrt{144}$

 5. $\sqrt{\dfrac{1}{81}}$

6. $\sqrt{\dfrac{1}{64}}$

7. $\sqrt{\dfrac{16}{64}}$

8. $\sqrt{\dfrac{36}{81}}$

Objective Ⓑ *Use Appendix E or a calculator to approximate each square root. Round the square root to the nearest thousandth. See Examples 4 and 5.*

9. $\sqrt{3}$

10. $\sqrt{5}$

 11. $\sqrt{15}$

12. $\sqrt{17}$

13. $\sqrt{47}$

14. $\sqrt{65}$

15. $\sqrt{26}$

16. $\sqrt{35}$

Determine what two whole numbers each square root is between without using a calculator or table. Then use a calculator or Appendix E to check. See Example 5.

 17. $\sqrt{38}$

18. $\sqrt{27}$

19. $\sqrt{101}$

20. $\sqrt{85}$

Objectives Ⓐ Ⓑ **Mixed Practice** *Find each square root. If necessary, round the square root to the nearest thousandth. See Examples 1 through 5.*

21. $\sqrt{256}$

22. $\sqrt{625}$

23. $\sqrt{92}$

24. $\sqrt{18}$

25. $\sqrt{\dfrac{49}{144}}$

26. $\sqrt{\dfrac{121}{169}}$

27. $\sqrt{71}$

28. $\sqrt{27}$

Objectives ⊙ *Find the unknown length in each right triangle. If necessary, approximate the length to the nearest thousandth. See Examples 6 through 8.*

29.
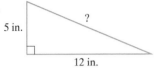

30.
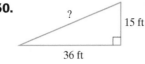

31.
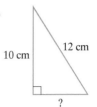

32.
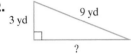

33.
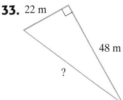

34.
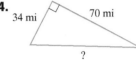

35.

36.
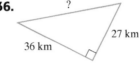

Sketch each right triangle and find the length of the side not given. If necessary, approximate the length to the nearest thousandth. (Each length is in units.) See Examples 6 through 8.

37. leg = 3, leg = 4

38. leg = 9, leg = 12

39. leg = 5, hypotenuse = 13

40. leg = 6, hypotenuse = 10

41. leg = 10, leg = 14

42. leg = 2, leg = 16

43. leg = 35, leg = 28

44. leg = 30, leg = 15

45. leg = 30, leg = 30

46. leg = 21, leg = 21

47. hypotenuse = 2, leg = 1

48. hypotenuse = 9, leg = 8

49. leg = 7.5, leg = 4

50. leg = 12, leg = 22.5

Solve. See Example 9.

51. A standard city block is a square with each side measuring 100 yards. Find the length of the diagonal of a city block to the nearest hundredth yard.

52. A section of land is a square with each side measuring 1 mile. Find the length of the diagonal of the section of land to the nearest thousandth mile.

53. Find the height of the tree. Round the height to one decimal place.

54. Find the height of the antenna. Round the height to one decimal place.

55. The playing field for football is a rectangle that is 300 feet long by 160 feet wide. Find, to the nearest foot, the length of a straight-line run that started at one corner and went diagonally to end at the opposite corner.

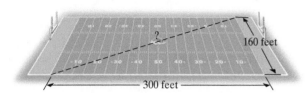

56. A soccer field is in the shape of a rectangle and its dimensions depend on the age of the players. The dimensions of the soccer field below are the minimum dimensions for international play. Find the length of the diagonal of this rectangle. Round the answer to the nearest tenth of a yard.

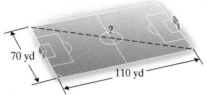

Review

Find the value of n in each proportion. See Section 4.1.

57. $\dfrac{n}{6} = \dfrac{2}{3}$

58. $\dfrac{8}{n} = \dfrac{4}{8}$

59. $\dfrac{9}{11} = \dfrac{n}{55}$

60. $\dfrac{5}{6} = \dfrac{35}{n}$

61. $\dfrac{3}{n} = \dfrac{7}{14}$

62. $\dfrac{n}{9} = \dfrac{4}{6}$

Concept Extensions

Use the results of Exercises 17–20 and approximate each square root to the nearest whole without using a calculator or table. Then use a calculator or Appendix E to check. See Example 5.

63. $\sqrt{38}$

64. $\sqrt{27}$

65. $\sqrt{101}$

66. $\sqrt{85}$

67. Without using a calculator, explain how you know that $\sqrt{105}$ is *not* approximately 9.875.

68. Without using a calculator, explain how you know that $\sqrt{27}$ is *not* approximately 3.296.

Does the set form the lengths of the sides of a right triangle? See the Concept Check in this section.

69. 25, 60, 65

70. 20, 45, 50

71. Find the exact length of *x*. Then give a two-decimal-place approximation.

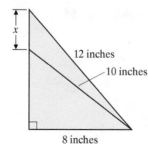

5.2 SYMBOLS AND SETS OF NUMBERS

Objectives

Ⓐ Define the Meaning of the Symbols $=, \neq, <, >, \leq,$ and $\geq$.

Ⓑ Translate Sentences into Mathematical Statements.

Ⓒ Identify Integers, Rational Numbers, Irrational Numbers, and Real Numbers.

Ⓓ Find the Absolute Value of a Real number.

Throughout the previous chapters, we have studied different sets of numbers. In this section, we review these sets of numbers. We also introduce a few new sets of numbers in order to show the relationships among these common sets of real numbers. We begin with a review of the set of natural numbers and the set of whole numbers and how we use symbols to compare these numbers. A **set** is a collection of objects, each of which is called a **member** or **element** of the set. A pair of brace symbols { } encloses the list of elements and is translated as "the set of" or "the set containing."

Natural Numbers

$$\{1, 2, 3, 4, 5, 6, \ldots\}$$

Whole Numbers

$$\{0, 1, 2, 3, 4, 5, 6, \ldots\}$$

> **Helpful Hint**
>
> The three dots (an ellipsis) at the end of the list of elements of a set means that the list continues in the same manner indefinitely.

Objective Ⓐ Equality and Inequality Symbols

Picturing natural numbers and whole numbers on a number line helps us to see the order of the numbers. Symbols can be used to describe in writing the order of two quantities. We will use equality symbols and inequality symbols to compare quantities.

Below is a review of these symbols. The letters a and b are used to represent quantities. Letters such as a and b that are used to represent numbers or quantities are called **variables.**

Equality and Inequality Symbols

		Meaning
Equality symbol:	$a = b$	a is equal to b.
Inequality symbols:	$a \neq b$	a is not equal to b.
	$a < b$	a is less than b.
	$a > b$	a is greater than b.
	$a \leq b$	a is less than or equal to b.
	$a \geq b$	a is greater than or equal to b.

These symbols may be used to form **mathematical statements** such as

$$2 = 2 \quad \text{and} \quad 2 \neq 6$$

Recall that on a number line, we see that a number **to the right of** another number is **larger.** Similarly, a number **to the left of** another number is **smaller.** For example, 3 is to the left of 5 on the number line, which means that 3 is less than 5, or $3 < 5$. Similarly, 2 is to the right of 0 on the number line, which means that 2 is greater than 0, or $2 > 0$. Since 0 is to the left of 2, we can also say that 0 is less than 2, or $0 < 2$.

$3 < 5$

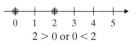

$2 > 0$ or $0 < 2$

> ### Helpful Hint
>
> Recall that $2 > 0$ has exactly the same meaning as $0 < 2$. Switching the order of the numbers and reversing the direction of the inequality symbol does not change the meaning of the statement.
>
> $6 > 4$ has the same meaning as $4 < 6$.
>
> Also notice that when the statement is true, the inequality arrow points to the smaller number.

Our discussion above can be generalized in the order property below.

> ### Order Property for Real Numbers
>
> For any two real numbers a and b, a is less than b if a is to the left of b on a number line.
>
> $a < b$ or also $b > a$

PRACTICE 1–6

Determine whether each statement is true or false.

1. $8 < 6$ **2.** $100 > 10$
3. $21 \leq 21$ **4.** $21 \geq 21$
5. $0 \geq 5$ **6.** $25 \geq 22$

Examples Determine whether each statement is true or false.

1. $2 < 3$ True.   Since 2 is to the left of 3 on a number line
2. $72 < 27$ False.   72 is to the right of 27 on a number line, so $72 > 27$.
3. $8 \geq 8$ True.   Since $8 = 8$ is true
4. $8 \leq 8$ True.   Since $8 = 8$ is true
5. $23 \leq 0$ False.   Since neither $23 < 0$ nor $23 = 0$ is true
6. $0 \leq 23$ True.   Since $0 < 23$ is true

● Work Practice 1–6

> ### Helpful Hint
>
> If either $3 < 3$ or $3 = 3$ is true, then $3 \leq 3$ is true.

Objective B Translating Sentences into Mathematical Statements

Now, let's use the symbols discussed on the previous page to translate sentences into mathematical statements.

Example 7 Translate each sentence into a mathematical statement.

a. Nine is less than or equal to eleven.   **b.** Eight is greater than one.
c. Three is not equal to four.

PRACTICE 7

Translate each sentence into a mathematical statement.

a. Fourteen is greater than or equal to fourteen.
b. Zero is less than five.
c. Nine is not equal to ten.

Solution:

a.

nine	is less than or equal to	eleven
↓	↓	↓
9	$\leq$	11

b.

eight	is greater than	one
↓	↓	↓
8	$>$	1

c.

three	is not equal to	four
↓	↓	↓
3	$\neq$	4

● Work Practice 7

Answers

1. false   **2.** true   **3.** true
4. true   **5.** false   **6.** true
7. a. $14 \geq 14$ **b.** $0 < 5$ **c.** $9 \neq 10$

Objective C Identifying Common Sets of Numbers

Whole numbers are not sufficient to describe many situations in the real world. For example, quantities smaller than zero must sometimes be represented, such as temperatures less than 0 degrees.

Recall that we can place numbers less than zero on a number line as follows: Numbers less than 0 are to the left of 0 and are labeled −1, −2, −3, and so on. The numbers we have labeled on the number line below are called the set of **integers.**

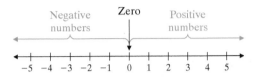

Integers to the left of 0 are called **negative integers;** integers to the right of 0 are called **positive integers.** The integer 0 is neither positive nor negative.

> ### Integers
>
> {..., −3, −2, −1, 0, 1, 2, 3, ...}

Helpful Hint

A − sign, such as the one in −2, tells us that the number is to the left of 0 on a number line.

   −2 is read "negative two."

A + sign or no sign tells us that the number lies to the right of 0 on a number line. For example, 3 and +3 both mean positive three.

Example 8 Use an integer to express the number in the following. "The lowest temperature ever recorded at South Pole Station, Antarctica, occurred during the month of June. The record-low temperature was 117 degrees below zero." (*Source:* The National Oceanic and Atmospheric Administration)

Solution: The integer −117 represents 117 degrees below zero.

● **Work Practice 8**

PRACTICE 8

Use an integer to express the number in the following. The elevation of New Orleans, Louisiana, is an average of 8 feet below sea level. (*Source: The World Almanac*)

Answer

8. −8

A problem with integers in real-life settings arises when quantities are smaller than some integer but greater than the next smallest integer. On a number line, these quantities may be visualized by points between integers. Some of these quantities between integers can be represented as quotients of integers. For example,

The point on the number line halfway between 0 and 1 can be represented by $\frac{1}{2}$, a quotient of integers.

The point on the number line halfway between 0 and -1 can be represented by $-\frac{1}{2}$. Other quotients of integers and their graphs are shown below.

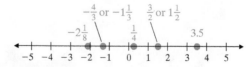

These numbers, each of which can be represented as a quotient of integers, are examples of **rational numbers.** It's not possible to list the set of rational numbers using the notation that we have been using. For this reason, we will use a different notation.

Rational Numbers

$$\left\{ \frac{a}{b} \,\middle|\, a \text{ and } b \text{ are integers and } b \neq 0 \right\}$$

We read this set as "the set of numbers $\frac{a}{b}$ such that a and b are integers and b **is not equal to 0.**"

Helpful Hint

We commonly refer to rational numbers as fractions.

Notice that every integer is also a rational number since each integer can be written as a quotient of integers. For example, the integer 5 is also a rational number since $5 = \frac{5}{1}$. For the rational number $\frac{5}{1}$, recall that the top number, 5, is called the numerator and the bottom number, 1, is called the denominator.

Let's practice **graphing** numbers on a number line.

PRACTICE 9

Graph the numbers on the number line.

$$-2\frac{1}{2}, \quad -\frac{2}{3}, \quad \frac{1}{5}, \quad \frac{5}{4}, \quad 2.25$$

-5 -4 -3 -2 -1 0 1 2 3 4 5

Example 9 Graph the numbers on a number line.

$$-\frac{4}{3}, \quad \frac{1}{4}, \quad \frac{3}{2}, \quad -2\frac{1}{8}, \quad 3.5$$

Solution: To help graph the improper fractions in the list, we first write them as mixed numbers.

$-\frac{4}{3}$ or $-1\frac{1}{3}$ $\frac{3}{2}$ or $1\frac{1}{2}$

$-2\frac{1}{8}$ $\frac{1}{4}$ 3.5

-5 -4 -3 -2 -1 0 1 2 3 4 5

● **Work Practice 9**

Every rational number has a point on the number line that corresponds to it. But not every point on the number line corresponds to a rational number. Those points that do not correspond to rational numbers correspond instead to **irrational numbers.**

Answer

9.

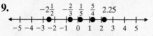

$-2\frac{1}{2}$ $-\frac{2}{3}$ $\frac{1}{5}$ $\frac{5}{4}$ 2.25

-5 -4 -3 -2 -1 0 1 2 3 4 5

Irrational Numbers

{Nonrational numbers that correspond to points on a number line}

An irrational number that you have probably seen is π. Also, $\sqrt{2}$, the length of the diagonal of the square shown below, is an irrational number.

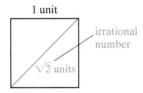

1 unit

irrational number

$\sqrt{2}$ units

Both rational and irrational numbers can be written as decimal numbers. The decimal equivalent of a rational number will either terminate or repeat in a pattern. For example, upon dividing we find that

$$\frac{3}{4} = 0.75 \qquad \text{(Decimal number terminates or ends.)}$$

$$\frac{2}{3} = 0.66666\ldots \qquad \text{(Decimal number repeats in a pattern.)}$$

The decimal representation of an irrational number will neither terminate nor repeat. (For further review of decimals, see Chapter 3.)

The set of numbers, each of which corresponds to a point on a number line, is called the set of **real numbers.** One and only one point on a number line corresponds to each real number.

Real Numbers

{All numbers that correspond to points on a number line}

Several different sets of numbers have been discussed in this section. The following diagram shows the relationships among these sets of real numbers. Notice that, together, the rational numbers and the irrational numbers make up the real numbers.

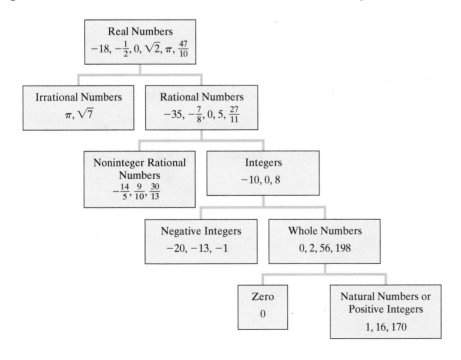

Now that other sets of numbers have been reviewed, let's continue our practice of comparing numbers.

PRACTICE 10

Insert $<, >,$ or $=$ between the pairs of numbers to form true statements.

a. -11 -9

b. 4.511 4.151

c. $\dfrac{7}{8}$ $\dfrac{2}{3}$

Example 10 Insert $<, >,$ or $=$ between the pairs of numbers to form true statements.

a. -5 -6 **b.** 3.195 3.2 **c.** $\dfrac{1}{4}$ $\dfrac{1}{3}$

Solution:

a. $-5 > -6$ since -5 lies to the right of -6 on a number line.

b. By comparing digits in the same place values, we find that $3.195 < 3.2$, since $0.1 < 0.2$.

c. By dividing, we find that $\dfrac{1}{4} = 0.25$ and $\dfrac{1}{3} = 0.33\ldots.$ Since $0.25 < 0.33\ldots, \dfrac{1}{4} < \dfrac{1}{3}.$

● **Work Practice 10**

PRACTICE 11

Given the set $\left\{-100, -\dfrac{2}{5}, 0, \pi, 6, 913\right\}$, list the numbers in this set that belong to the set of:

a. Natural numbers
b. Whole numbers
c. Integers
d. Rational numbers
e. Irrational numbers
f. Real numbers

Example 11 Given the set $\left\{-2, 0, \dfrac{1}{4}, 112, -3, 11, \sqrt{2}\right\}$, list the numbers in this set that belong to the set of:

a. Natural numbers   **b.** Whole numbers   **c.** Integers
d. Rational numbers   **e.** Irrational numbers   **f.** Real numbers

Solution:

a. The natural numbers are 11 and 112.

b. The whole numbers are $0, 11,$ and 112.

c. The integers are $-3, -2, 0, 11,$ and 112.

d. Recall that integers are rational numbers also. The rational numbers are
$-3, -2, 0, \dfrac{1}{4}, 11,$ and 112.

e. The only irrational number is $\sqrt{2}$.

f. All numbers in the given set are real numbers.

● **Work Practice 11**

Objective ⓓ Finding the Absolute Value of a Number

A number line not only gives us a picture of the real numbers, it also helps us visualize the distance between numbers. The distance between a real number a and 0 is given a special name called the **absolute value** of a. "The absolute value of a" is written in symbols as $|a|$.

Answers

10. a. $<$ **b.** $>$ **c.** $>$

11. a. $6, 913$ **b.** $0, 6, 913$

c. $-100, 0, 6, 913$

d. $-100, -\dfrac{2}{5}, 0, 6, 913$ **e.** π

f. all numbers in the given set

Absolute Value

The **absolute value** of a real number a, denoted by $|a|$, is the distance between a and 0 on a number line.

For example, $|3| = 3$ and $|-3| = 3$ since both 3 and -3 are a distance of 3 units from 0 on a number line.

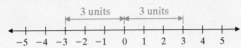

Example 12 Find the absolute value of each number.

a. $|4|$ **b.** $|-5|$ **c.** $|0|$

d. $\left|-\dfrac{2}{9}\right|$ **e.** $|4.93|$

Solution:

a. $|4| = 4$ since 4 is 4 units from 0 on the number line.
b. $|-5| = 5$ since -5 is 5 units from 0 on the number line.
c. $|0| = 0$ since 0 is 0 units from 0 on the number line.

d. $\left|-\dfrac{2}{9}\right| = \dfrac{2}{9}$

e. $|4.93| = 4.93$

Work Practice 12

PRACTICE 12

Find the absolute value of each number.

a. $|7|$ **b.** $|-8|$ **c.** $\left|\dfrac{2}{3}\right|$

d. $|0|$ **e.** $|-3.06|$

Example 13 Insert $<$, $>$, or $=$ in the appropriate space to make each statement true.

a. $|0|$ ___ 2 **b.** $|-5|$ ___ 5 **c.** $|-3|$ ___ $|-2|$

d. $|-9|$ ___ $|-9.7|$ **e.** $\left|-7\dfrac{1}{6}\right|$ ___ $|7|$

Solution:

a. $|0| < 2$ since $|0| = 0$ and $0 < 2$.
b. $|-5| = 5$.
c. $|-3| > |-2|$ since $3 > 2$.
d. $|-9| < |-9.7|$ since $9 < 9.7$.

e. $\left|-7\dfrac{1}{6}\right| > |7|$ since $7\dfrac{1}{6} > 7$.

Work Practice 13

PRACTICE 13

Insert $<$, $>$, or $=$ in the appropriate space to make each statement true.

a. $|-4|$ ___ 4
b. -3 ___ $|0|$
c. $|-2.7|$ ___ $|-2|$
d. $|-6|$ ___ $|-16|$

e. $|10|$ ___ $\left|-10\dfrac{1}{3}\right|$

Answers

12. a. 7 **b.** 8 **c.** $\dfrac{2}{3}$ **d.** 0 **e.** 3.06

13. a. $=$ **b.** $<$ **c.** $>$ **d.** $<$ **e.** $<$

Vocabulary and Readiness Check

Use the choices below to fill in each blank. Not all choices will be used.

real	natural	absolute value	$\frac{1}{2}$	$\frac{1}{4}$	$|a|$	whole

rational	inequality	integers	0	1	$|-1|$

1. The _____ numbers are {0, 1, 2, 3, 4, …}.
2. The _____ numbers are {1, 2, 3, 4, 5, …}.
3. The symbols ≠, ≤, and > are called _____ symbols.
4. The _____ are {…,−3,−2,−1, 0, 1, 2, 3, …}.
5. The _____ numbers are {all numbers that correspond to points on a number line}.
6. The _____ numbers are $\left\{ \dfrac{a}{b} \mid a \text{ and } b \text{ are integers}, b \neq 0 \right\}$.
7. The integer _____ is neither positive nor negative.
8. The point on the number line halfway between 0 and $\frac{1}{2}$ can be represented by _____.
9. The distance between a real number a and 0 is called the _____ of a.
10. The absolute value of a is written in symbols as _____.

5.2 Exercise Set

Objectives **A** **C** **Mixed Practice** *Insert <, >, or = in the space between the paired numbers to make each statement true. See Examples 1 through 6 and 10.*

1. 4 ___ 10   **2.** 8 ___ 5   **3.** 7 ___ 3   **4.** 9 ___ 15

5. 6.26 ___ 6.26   **6.** 1.13 ___ 1.13   **7.** 0 ___ 7   **8.** 20 ___ 0

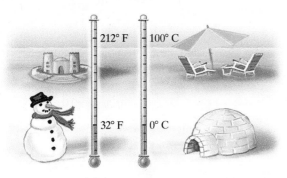

9. The freezing point of water is 32° Fahrenheit. The boiling point of water is 212° Fahrenheit. Write an inequality statement using < or > comparing the numbers 32 and 212.

10. The freezing point of water is 0° Celsius. The boiling point of water is 100° Celsius. Write an inequality statement using < or > comparing the numbers 0 and 100.

△ **11.** An angle measuring 30° and an angle measuring 45° are shown. Write an inequality statement using ≤ or ≥ comparing the numbers 30 and 45.

△ **12.** The sum of the measures of the angles of a parallelogram is 360°. The sum of the measures of the angles of a triangle is 180°. Write an inequality statement using ≤ or ≥ comparing the numbers 360 and 180.

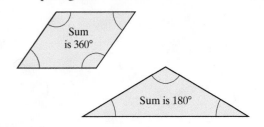

Determine whether each statement is true or false. See Examples 1 through 6 and 10.

13. $11 \leq 11$

14. $8 \geq 9$

15. $-11 > -10$

16. $-16 > -17$

17. $5.092 < 5.902$

18. $1.02 > 1.021$

19. $\frac{9}{10} \leq \frac{8}{9}$

20. $\frac{4}{5} \leq \frac{9}{11}$

Rewrite each inequality so that the inequality symbol points in the opposite direction and the resulting statement has the same meaning as the given one. See Examples 1 through 6 and 10.

21. $25 \geq 20$

22. $-13 \leq 13$

23. $0 < 6$

24. $5 > 3$

25. $-10 > -12$

26. $-4 < -2$

Objectives **B** **C** **Mixed Practice–Translating** *Write each sentence as a mathematical statement.*
See Examples 7 and 10.

27. Seven is less than eleven.

28. Twenty is greater than two.

29. Five is greater than or equal to four.

30. Negative ten is less than or equal to thirty-seven.

31. Fifteen is not equal to negative two.

32. Negative seven is not equal to seven.

Use integers to represent the values in each statement. See Example 8.

33. The highest elevation in California is Mt. Whitney, with an altitude of 14,494 feet. The lowest elevation in California is Death Valley, with an altitude of 282 feet below sea level. (*Source:* U.S. Geological Survey)

34. Driskill Mountain, in Louisiana, has an altitude of 535 feet. New Orleans, Louisiana, lies 8 feet below sea level. (*Source:* U.S. Geological Survey)

35. The number of graduate students at the University of Texas at Austin is 28,000 fewer than the number of undergraduate students. (*Source:* University of Texas at Austin)

36. The number of students admitted to the class of 2011 at UCLA is 38,792 fewer students than the number that had applied. (*Source:* UCLA)

37. Gretchen Bertani deposited $475 in her savings account. She later withdrew $195.

38. David Lopez was deep-sea diving. During his dive, he ascended 17 feet and later descended 15 feet.

Graph each set of numbers on the number line. See Example 9.

39. $-4, 0, 2, -2$

40. $-3, 0, 1, -5$

41. $-2, 4, \frac{1}{3}, -\frac{1}{4}$

42. $-5, 3, -\frac{1}{3}, \frac{7}{8}$

43. $-4.5, \frac{7}{4}, 3.25, -\frac{3}{2}$

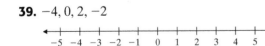

44. $4.5, -\frac{9}{4}, 1.75, -\frac{7}{2}$

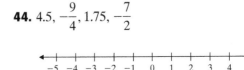

Tell which set or sets each number belongs to: natural numbers, whole numbers, integers, rational numbers, irrational numbers, or real numbers. See Example 11.

45. 0

46. $\dfrac{1}{4}$

47. -7

48. $-\dfrac{1}{7}$

49. 265

50. 7941

51. $\dfrac{2}{3}$

52. $\sqrt{3}$

Determine whether each statement is true or false.

53. Every rational number is also an integer.

54. Every natural number is positive.

55. 0 is a real number.

56. $\dfrac{1}{2}$ is an integer.

57. Every negative number is also a rational number.

58. Every rational number is also a real number.

59. Every real number is also a rational number.

60. Every whole number is an integer.

Objective **D** *Find each absolute value. See Example 12.*

61. $|8.9|$

62. $|11.2|$

63. $|-20|$

64. $|-17|$

65. $\left|\dfrac{9}{2}\right|$

66. $\left|\dfrac{10}{7}\right|$

67. $\left|-\dfrac{12}{13}\right|$

68. $\left|-\dfrac{1}{15}\right|$

Insert $<$, $>$, or $=$ in the appropriate space to make each statement true. See Examples 12 and 13.

69. $|-5|$ -4

70. $|-12|$ $|0|$

71. $\left|-\dfrac{5}{8}\right|$ $\left|\dfrac{5}{8}\right|$

72. $\left|\dfrac{2}{5}\right|$ $\left|-\dfrac{2}{5}\right|$

73. $|-2|$ $|-2.7|$

74. $|-5.01|$ $|-5|$

75. $|0|$ $|-8|$

76. $|-12|$ $\dfrac{-24}{2}$

Review

Perform each indicated operation. See Section 1.9.

77. $90 + 12^2 - 5^3$

78. $3 \cdot (7 - 4) + 2 \cdot 5^2$

79. $12 \div 4 - 2 + 7$

80. $12 \div (4 - 2) + 7$

Concept Extensions

The bar graph shows apple production in Massachusetts from 2003 through 2009. Each bar represents a different year, and the height of each bar represents the apple production for that year in thousands of bushels. (The federal standard for bushel is 48 lb, although 42 lb is also commonly used.)

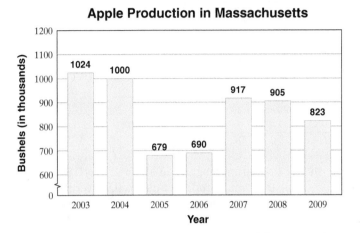

Apple Production in Massachusetts

(Source: New England Agriculture Statistical Service and Agricultural Statistics Board.)

81. Write an inequality comparing the apple production in 2008 with the apple production in 2009.

82. Write an inequality comparing the apple production in 2006 with the apple production in 2007.

83. Determine the change in apple production between 2003 and 2004.

84. According to the bar graph, which year shown produced the largest crop?

The bar graph shows cranberry production from the top five cranberry-producing states. (Source: National Agricultural Statistics Service)

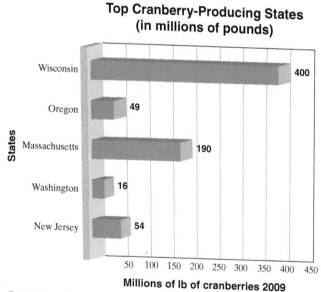

Top Cranberry-Producing States (in millions of pounds)

Source: National Agricultural Statistics Service

85. Write an inequality comparing the 2009 cranberry production in Oregon with the 2009 cranberry production in Washington.

86. Write an inequality comparing the 2009 cranberry production in Massachusetts with the 2009 cranberry production in Wisconsin.

87. Determine the difference between the 2009 cranberry production in Washington and the 2009 cranberry production in New Jersey.

88. According to the bar graph, which two states had almost equal 2009 cranberry crops?

The apparent magnitude of a star is the measure of its brightness as seen by someone on Earth. The smaller the apparent magnitude, the brighter the star. Below, the apparent magnitudes of some stars are listed. Use this table to answer Exercises 89 through 94.

Star	Apparent Magnitude	Star	Apparent Magnitude
Arcturus	−0.04	Spica	0.98
Sirius	−1.46	Rigel	0.12
Vega	0.03	Regulus	1.35
Antares	0.96	Canopus	−0.72
Sun	−26.7	Hadar	0.61

(Source: Norton's 2000.0: Star Atlas and Reference Handbook, 18th ed., Longman Group, UK, 1989)

89. The apparent magnitude of the sun is −26.7. The apparent magnitude of the star Arcturus is −0.04. Write an inequality statement comparing the numbers −0.04 and −26.7.

90. The apparent magnitude of Antares is 0.96. The apparent magnitude of Spica is 0.98. Write an inequality statement comparing the numbers 0.96 and 0.98.

91. Which is brighter, the sun or Arcturus?

92. Which is dimmer, Antares or Spica?

93. Which star listed is the brightest?

94. Which star listed is the dimmest?

95. In your own words, explain how to find the absolute value of a number.

96. Give an example of a real-life situation that can be described with integers but not with whole numbers.

5.3 EXPONENTS, ORDER OF OPERATIONS, AND VARIABLE EXPRESSIONS

Objectives

Ⓐ Define and Use Exponents and the Order of Operations.

Ⓑ Evaluate Algebraic Expressions, Given Replacement Values for Variables.

Ⓒ Determine Whether a Number Is a Solution of a Given Equation.

Ⓓ Translate Phrases into Expressions and Sentences into Equations.

Objective Ⓐ Exponents and the Order of Operations

Frequently in algebra, products occur that contain repeated multiplication of the same factor. For example, the volume of a cube whose sides each measure 2 centimeters is $(2 \cdot 2 \cdot 2)$ cubic centimeters. We may use **exponential notation** to write such products in a more compact form. For example,

$2 \cdot 2 \cdot 2$ may be written as 2^3.

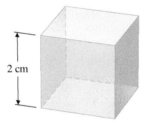

2 cm

Volume is $(2 \cdot 2 \cdot 2)$
cubic centimeters.

The 2 in 2^3 is called the **base;** it is the repeated factor. The 3 in 2^3 is called the **exponent** and is the number of times the base is used as a factor. The expression 2^3 is called an **exponential expression.**

$$2^{\overset{\text{exponent}}{3}} = 2 \cdot 2 \cdot 2 = 8$$

base —————↑ $\quad 2$ is a factor 3 times.

Example 1 Evaluate (find the value of) each expression.

a. 3^2 [read as "3 squared" or as "3 to the second power"]
b. 5^3 [read as "5 cubed" or as "5 to the third power"]
c. 2^4 [read as "2 to the fourth power"]
d. 7^1
e. $\left(\dfrac{3}{7}\right)^2$
f. $(0.6)^2$

Solution:

a. $3^2 = 3 \cdot 3 = 9$
b. $5^3 = 5 \cdot 5 \cdot 5 = 125$
c. $2^4 = 2 \cdot 2 \cdot 2 \cdot 2 = 16$
d. $7^1 = 7$
e. $\left(\dfrac{3}{7}\right)^2 = \left(\dfrac{3}{7}\right)\left(\dfrac{3}{7}\right) = \dfrac{3 \cdot 3}{7 \cdot 7} = \dfrac{9}{49}$
f. $(0.6)^2 = (0.6)(0.6) = 0.36$

● Work Practice 1

PRACTICE 1

Evaluate each expression.
a. 4^2
b. 2^2
c. 3^4
d. 9^1
e. $\left(\dfrac{2}{5}\right)^3$
f. $(0.8)^2$

Helpful Hint

$2^3 \neq 2 \cdot 3$ since 2^3 indicates **repeated multiplication of the same factor.**

$2^3 = 2 \cdot 2 \cdot 2 = 8$, whereas $2 \cdot 3 = 6$

Answers

1. a. 16   b. 4   c. 81   d. 9
e. $\dfrac{8}{125}$ f. 0.64

Using symbols for mathematical operations is a great convenience. The more operation symbols presented in an expression, the more careful we must be when performing the indicated operation. For example, in the expression $2 + 3 \cdot 7$, do we add first or multiply first? To eliminate confusion, **grouping symbols** are used. Examples of grouping symbols are parentheses ( ), brackets [ ], braces { }, absolute value bars | |, and the fraction bar. If we wish $2 + 3 \cdot 7$ to be simplified by adding first, we enclose $2 + 3$ in parentheses.

$$(2 + 3) \cdot 7 = 5 \cdot 7 = 35$$

If we wish to multiply first, $3 \cdot 7$ may be enclosed in parentheses.

$$2 + (3 \cdot 7) = 2 + 21 = 23$$

To eliminate confusion when no grouping symbols are present, we use the following agreed-upon order of operations.

Order of Operations

1. Perform all operations within grouping symbols first, starting with the innermost set.
2. Evaluate exponential expressions.
3. Multiply or divide in order from left to right.
4. Add or subtract in order from left to right.

Using this order of operations, we now simplify $2 + 3 \cdot 7$. There are no grouping symbols and no exponents, so we multiply and then add.

$$2 + 3 \cdot 7 = 2 + 21 \quad \text{Multiply.}$$
$$= 23 \quad \text{Add.}$$

PRACTICE 2–5

Simplify each expression.
2. $3 \cdot 2 + 4^2$
3. $28 \div 7 \cdot 2$
4. $\dfrac{9}{5} \cdot \dfrac{1}{3} - \dfrac{1}{3}$
5. $5 + 3[2(3 \cdot 4 + 1) - 20]$

Examples Simplify each expression.

2. $6 \div 3 + 5^2 = 6 \div 3 + 25$ Evaluate 5^2
$$= 2 + 25 \quad \text{Divide.}$$
$$= 27 \quad \text{Add.}$$

3. $20 \div 5 \cdot 4 = 4 \cdot 4$
$$= 16$$

Helpful Hint Remember to multiply or divide in order from left to right.

4. $\dfrac{3}{2} \cdot \dfrac{1}{2} - \dfrac{1}{2} = \dfrac{3}{4} - \dfrac{1}{2}$ Multiply.
$$= \dfrac{3}{4} - \dfrac{2}{4} \quad \text{The least common denominator is 4.}$$
$$= \dfrac{1}{4} \quad \text{Subtract.}$$

5. $1 + 2[5(2 \cdot 3 + 1) - 10] = 1 + 2[5(7) - 10]$ Simplify the expression in the innermost set of parentheses. $2 \cdot 3 + 1 = 6 + 1 = 7$.
$$= 1 + 2[35 - 10] \quad \text{Multiply 5 and 7.}$$
$$= 1 + 2[25] \quad \text{Subtract inside the brackets.}$$
$$= 1 + 50 \quad \text{Multiply 2 and 25.}$$
$$= 51 \quad \text{Add.}$$

● **Work Practice 2–5**

In the next example, the fraction bar serves as a grouping symbol and separates the numerator and denominator. Simplify each separately.

Answers
2. 22   3. 8   4. $\dfrac{4}{15}$ 5. 23

Example 6 Simplify: $\dfrac{3 + |4 - 3| + 2^2}{6 - 3}$

Solution:

$\dfrac{3 + |4 - 3| + 2^2}{6 - 3} = \dfrac{3 + |1| + 2^2}{6 - 3}$ Simplify the expression inside the absolute value bars.

$= \dfrac{3 + 1 + 2^2}{3}$ Find the absolute value and simplify the denominator.

$= \dfrac{3 + 1 + 4}{3}$ Evaluate the exponential expression.

$= \dfrac{8}{3}$ Simplify the numerator.

● Work Practice 6

PRACTICE 6

Simplify: $\dfrac{1 + |7 - 4| + 3^2}{8 - 5}$

Helpful Hint

Be careful when evaluating an exponential expression.

$3 \cdot 4^2 = 3 \cdot 16 = 48$ $\qquad$ $(3 \cdot 4)^2 = (12)^2 = 144$

$\uparrow$ $\qquad\qquad\qquad\qquad$ $\uparrow$

Base is 4. $\qquad\qquad\qquad$ Base is $3 \cdot 4$.

Objective Ⓑ Evaluating Algebraic Expressions

Recall that letters used to represent quantities are called **variables.** An **algebraic expression** is a collection of numbers, variables, operation symbols, and grouping symbols. For example,

$$2x, \quad -3, \quad 2x - 10, \quad 5(p^2 + 1), \quad xy, \quad \text{and} \quad \dfrac{3y^2 - 6y + 1}{5}$$

are algebraic expressions.

Expressions	Meaning
$2x$	$2 \cdot x$
$5(p^2 + 1)$	$5 \cdot (p^2 + 1)$
$3y^2$	$3 \cdot y^2$
xy	$x \cdot y$

If we give a specific value to a variable, we can **evaluate an algebraic expression.** To evaluate an algebraic expression means to find its numerical value once we know the values of the variables.

Algebraic expressions are often used in problem solving. For example, the expression

$$16t^2$$

gives the distance in feet (neglecting air resistance) that an object will fall in t seconds.

Answer

6. $\dfrac{13}{3}$

PRACTICE 7

Evaluate each expression
when $x = 1$ and $y = 4$.

a. $3y^2$

b. $2y - x$

c. $\dfrac{11x}{3y}$

d. $\dfrac{x}{y} + \dfrac{6}{y}$

e. $y^2 - x^2$

Example 7 Evaluate each expression when $x = 3$ and $y = 2$.

a. $5x^2$ **b.** $2x - y$ **c.** $\dfrac{3x}{2y}$ **d.** $\dfrac{x}{y} + \dfrac{y}{2}$ **e.** $x^2 - y^2$

Solution:

a. Replace x with 3. Then simplify.

$$5x^2 = 5 \cdot (3)^2 = 5 \cdot 9 = 45$$

b. Replace x with 3 and y with 2. Then simplify.

$$2x - y = 2(3) - 2 \quad \text{Let } x = 3 \text{ and } y = 2.$$
$$= 6 - 2 \qquad \text{Multiply.}$$
$$= 4 \qquad \text{Subtract.}$$

c. Replace x with 3 and y with 2. Then simplify.

$$\frac{3x}{2y} = \frac{3 \cdot 3}{2 \cdot 2} = \frac{9}{4} \quad \text{Let } x = 3 \text{ and } y = 2.$$

d. Replace x with 3 and y with 2. Then simplify.

$$\frac{x}{y} + \frac{y}{2} = \frac{3}{2} + \frac{2}{2} = \frac{5}{2}$$

e. Replace x with 3 and y with 2. Then simplify.

$$x^2 - y^2 = 3^2 - 2^2 = 9 - 4 = 5$$

● **Work Practice 7**

Objective ⓒ Solutions of Equations

Many times a problem-solving situation is modeled by an equation. An **equation** is a mathematical statement that two expressions have equal value. The equal symbol "=" is used to equate the two expressions. For example,

$$3 + 2 = 5, 7x = 35, \frac{2(x - 1)}{3} = 0, \text{ and } I = PRT \text{ are all equations.}$$

Helpful Hint

An equation contains the equal symbol "=". An algebraic expression does not.

✓**Concept Check** Which of the following are equations? Which are expressions?

a. $5x = 8$ **b.** $5x - 8$ **c.** $12y + 3x$ **d.** $12y = 3x$

When an equation contains a variable, deciding which value(s) of the variable make the equation a true statement is called **solving** the equation for the variable. A **solution** of an equation is a value for the variable that makes the equation a true statement. For example, 3 is a solution of the equation $x + 4 = 7$, because if x is replaced with 3 the statement is true.

$$x + 4 = 7$$
$$\downarrow$$
$$3 + 4 \overset{?}{=} 7 \quad \text{Replace } x \text{ with 3.}$$
$$7 = 7 \quad \text{True}$$

Similarly, 1 is not a solution of the equation $x + 4 = 7$, because $1 + 4 = 7$ is **not** a true statement.

Answers

7. **a.** 48 **b.** 7 **c.** $\dfrac{11}{12}$ **d.** $\dfrac{7}{4}$ **e.** 15

✓**Concept Check Answer**

equations: **a, d**; expressions: **b, c**

Example 8 Decide whether 2 is a solution of $3x + 10 = 8x$.

Solution: Replace x with 2 and see if a true statement results.

$$3x + 10 = 8x \quad \text{Original equation}$$
$$3(2) + 10 \stackrel{?}{=} 8(2) \quad \text{Replace } x \text{ with 2.}$$
$$6 + 10 \stackrel{?}{=} 16 \quad \text{Simplify each side.}$$
$$16 = 16 \quad \text{True}$$

Since we arrived at a true statement after replacing x with 2 and simplifying both sides of the equation, 2 is a solution of the equation.

● **Work Practice 8**

Objective ⒟ Translating Words to Symbols

Now that we know how to represent an unknown number by a variable, let's practice translating phrases into algebraic expressions (no "=" symbol) and sentences into equations (with "=" symbol). Oftentimes solving problems involves the ability to translate word phrases and sentences into symbols. Below is a list of key words and phrases to help us translate.

Helpful Hint

Order matters when subtracting and also dividing, so be especially careful with these translations.

Addition (+)	Subtraction (−)	Multiplication (·)	Division (÷)	Equality (=)
Sum	Difference of	Product	Quotient	Equals
Plus	Minus	Times	Divide	Gives
Added to	Subtracted from	Multiply	Into	Is/was/should be
More than	Less than	Twice	Ratio	Yields
Increased by	Decreased by	Of	Divided by	Amounts to
Total	Less			Represents
				Is the same as

Example 9 Write an algebraic expression that represents each phrase. Let the variable x represent the unknown number.

a. The sum of a number and 3

b. The product of 3 and a number

c. The quotient of 7.3 and a number

d. 10 decreased by a number

e. 5 times a number, increased by 7

Solution:

a. $x + 3$ since "sum" means to add

b. $3 \cdot x$ and $3x$ are both ways to denote the product of 3 and x

c. $7.3 \div x$ or $\dfrac{7.3}{x}$

d. $10 - x$ because "decreased by" means to subtract

e. $\underbrace{5x}_{\substack{5 \text{ times} \\ \text{a number}}} + 7$

● **Work Practice 9**

Helpful Hint

Make sure you understand the difference when translating phrases containing "decreased by," "subtracted from," and "less than."

Phrase	Translation	
A number decreased by 10	$x - 10$	
A number subtracted from 10	$10 - x$	Notice the order.
10 less than a number	$x - 10$	
A number less 10	$x - 10$	

Now let's practice translating sentences into equations.

PRACTICE 10

Write each sentence as an equation. Let x represent the unknown number.

a. The ratio of a number and 6 is 24.

b. The difference of 10 and a number is 18.

c. One less than twice a number is 99.

Example 10 Write each sentence as an equation. Let x represent the unknown number.

a. The quotient of 15 and a number is 4.

b. Three subtracted from 12 is a number.

c. 17 added to four times a number is 21.

Solution:

a. In words:

the quotient of 15 and a number	is	4
↓	↓	↓

Translate: $\dfrac{15}{x}$ $=$ 4

b. In words:

three subtracted **from** 12	is	a number
↓	↓	↓

Translate: $12 - 3$ $=$ x

Care must be taken when the operation is subtraction. The expression $3 - 12$ would be incorrect. Notice that $3 - 12 \neq 12 - 3$.

c. In words:

17	added to	four times a number	is	21
↓	↓	↓	↓	↓

Translate: 17 $+$ $4x$ $=$ 21

● **Work Practice 10**

Answers

10. a. $\dfrac{x}{6} = 24$ **b.** $10 - x = 18$

c. $2x - 1 = 99$

Calculator Explorations

Exponents

To evaluate exponential expressions on a calculator, find the key marked $\boxed{y^x}$ or $\boxed{\wedge}$. To evaluate, for example, 6^5, press the following keys: $\boxed{6}\ \boxed{y^x}\ \boxed{5}\ \boxed{=}$ or $\boxed{6}\ \boxed{\wedge}\ \boxed{5}\ \boxed{=}$.

$\updownarrow$ or

$\boxed{\text{ENTER}}$

The display should read $\boxed{\quad 7776\quad}$.

Order of Operations

Some calculators follow the order of operations, and others do not. To see whether or not your calculator has the order of operations built in, use your calculator to find $2 + 3 \cdot 4$. To do this, press the following sequence of keys:

$\boxed{2}\ \boxed{+}\ \boxed{3}\ \boxed{\times}\ \boxed{4}\ \boxed{=}$

$\updownarrow$ or

$\boxed{\text{ENTER}}$

The correct answer is 14 because the order of operations is to multiply before we add. If the calculator displays $\boxed{\quad 14\quad}$, then it has the order of operations built in.

Even if the order of operations is built in, parentheses must sometimes be inserted. For example, to simplify $\dfrac{5}{12 - 7}$, press the keys

$\boxed{5}\ \boxed{\div}\ \boxed{(}\ \boxed{1}\ \boxed{2}\ \boxed{-}\ \boxed{7}\ \boxed{)}\ \boxed{=}$.

$\updownarrow$ or

$\boxed{\text{ENTER}}$

The display should read $\boxed{\quad 1\quad}$.

Use a calculator to evaluate each expression.

1. 5^3

2. 7^4

3. 9^5

4. 8^6

5. $2(20 - 5)$

6. $3(14 - 7) + 21$

7. $24(862 - 455) + 89$

8. $99 + (401 + 962)$

9. $\dfrac{4623 + 129}{36 - 34}$

10. $\dfrac{956 - 452}{89 - 86}$

Vocabulary and Readiness Check

Use the choices below to fill in each blank. Some choices may be used more than once.

addition   multiplication   exponent   expression   solution   evaluating the expression

subtraction   division   base   equation   variable(s)

1. In 2^5, the 2 is called the _____ and the 5 is called the _____.

2. True or false: 2^5 means 2.5. _____

3. To simplify $8 + 2 \cdot 6$, which operation should be performed first? _____

4. To simplify $(8 + 2) \cdot 6$, which operation should be performed first? _____

5. To simplify $9(3 - 2) \div 3 + 6$, which operation should be performed first? _____

6. To simplify $8 \div 2 \cdot 6$, which operation should be performed first? _____

7. A combination of operations on letters (variables) and numbers is a(n) _____.

8. A letter that represents a number is a(n) _____.

9. $3x - 2y$ is called a(n) _____ and the letters x and y are _____.

10. Replacing a variable in an expression by a number and then finding the value of the expression is called _____.

11. A statement of the form "expression = expression" is called a(n) _____.

12. A value for the variable that makes the equation a true statement is called a(n) _____.

5.3 Exercise Set

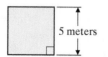

FOR EXTRA HELP

MyMathLab   MathXP PRACTICE   WATCH   DOWNLOAD   READ   REVIEW

Objective A *Evaluate. See Example 1.*

1. 3^5

2. 5^4

 3. 3^3

4. 4^4

5. 1^5

6. 1^8

7. 5^1

8. 8^1

9. 7^2

10. 9^2

 11. $\left(\dfrac{2}{3}\right)^4$

12. $\left(\dfrac{6}{11}\right)^2$

13. $\left(\dfrac{1}{5}\right)^3$

14. $\left(\dfrac{1}{2}\right)^5$

15. $(1.2)^2$

16. $(1.5)^2$

17. $(0.7)^3$

18. $(0.4)^3$

△ **19.** The area of a square whose sides each measure 5 meters is $(5 \cdot 5)$ square meters. Write this area using exponential notation.

5 meters

△ **20.** The area of a circle whose radius is 9 meters is $(9 \cdot 9 \cdot \pi)$ square meters. Write this area using exponential notation.

9 m

Simplify each expression. See Examples 2 through 6.

21. $5 + 6 \cdot 2$

22. $8 + 5 \cdot 3$

23. $4 \cdot 8 - 6 \cdot 2$

24. $12 \cdot 5 - 3 \cdot 6$

25. $18 \div 3 \cdot 2$

26. $48 \div 6 \cdot 2$

27. $2 + (5 - 2) + 4^2$

28. $6 - 2 \cdot 2 + 2^5$

29. $5 \cdot 3^2$

30. $2 \cdot 5^2$

31. $\frac{1}{4} \cdot \frac{2}{3} - \frac{1}{6}$

32. $\frac{3}{4} \cdot \frac{1}{2} + \frac{2}{3}$

33. $\frac{6 - 4}{9 - 2}$

34. $\frac{8 - 5}{24 - 20}$

35. $2[5 + 2(8 - 3)]$

36. $3[4 + 3(6 - 4)]$

37. $\frac{19 - 3 \cdot 5}{6 - 4}$

38. $\frac{14 - 2 \cdot 3}{12 - 8}$

39. $\frac{|6 - 2| + 3}{8 + 2 \cdot 5}$

40. $\frac{15 - |3 - 1|}{12 - 3 \cdot 2}$

41. $\frac{3 + 3(5 + 3)}{3^2 + 1}$

42. $\frac{3 + 6(8 - 5)}{4^2 + 2}$

43. $\frac{6 + |8 - 2| + 3^2}{18 - 3}$

44. $\frac{16 + |13 - 5| + 4^2}{17 - 5}$

45. $2 + 3[10(4 \cdot 5 - 16) - 30]$

46. $3 + 4[8(5 \cdot 5 - 20) - 41]$

47. $\left(\frac{2}{3}\right)^3 + \frac{1}{9} + \frac{1}{3} \cdot \frac{4}{3}$

48. $\left(\frac{3}{8}\right)^2 + \frac{1}{4} + \frac{1}{8} \cdot \frac{3}{2}$

Objective Ⓑ *Evaluate each expression when* $x = 1$, $y = 3$, *and* $z = 5$. *See Example 7.*

49. $3y$

50. $4x$

51. $\frac{z}{5x}$

52. $\frac{y}{2z}$

53. $3x - 2$

54. $6y - 8$

55. $|2x + 3y|$

56. $|5z - 2y|$

57. $xy + z$

58. $yz - x$

59. $5y^2$

60. $2z^2$

Evaluate each expression when $x = 12$, $y = 8$, *and* $z = 4$. *See Example 7.*

61. $\frac{x}{z} + 3y$

62. $\frac{y}{z} + 8x$

63. $x^2 - 3y + x$

64. $y^2 - 3x + y$

65. $\frac{x^2 + z}{y^2 + 2z}$

66. $\frac{y^2 + x}{x^2 + 3y}$

Objective Ⓒ *Decide whether the given number is a solution of the given equation. See Example 8.*

67. $3x - 6 = 9; 5$

68. $2x + 7 = 3x; 6$

69. $2x + 6 = 5x - 1; 0$

70. $4x + 2 = x + 8; 2$

71. $2x - 5 = 5; 8$

72. $3x - 10 = 8; 6$

73. $x + 6 = x + 6; 2$

74. $x + 6 = x + 6; 10$

75. $x = 5x + 15; 0$ **76.** $4 = 1 - x; 1$ **77.** $\frac{1}{3}x = 9; 27$ **78.** $\frac{2}{7}x = \frac{3}{14}; 6$

Objective **D** *Write each phrase as an algebraic expression. Let x represent the unknown number. See Example 9.*

79. Fifteen more than a number

80. A number increased by 9

81. Five subtracted from a number

82. Five decreased by a number

83. The ratio of a number and 4

84. The quotient of a number and 9

85. Three times a number, increased by 22

86. Twice a number, decreased by 72

Write each sentence as an equation or inequality. Use x to represent any unknown number. See Example 10.

87. One increased by two equals the quotient of nine and three.

88. Four subtracted from eight is equal to two squared.

89. Three is not equal to four divided by two.

90. The difference of sixteen and four is greater than ten.

91. The sum of 5 and a number is 20.

92. Seven subtracted from a number is 0.

93. The product of 7.6 and a number is 17.

94. 9.1 times a number equals 4

95. Thirteen minus three times a number is 13.

96. Eight added to twice a number is 42.

Review

Add. See Section 1.3.

97. $15 + 20$

98. $20 + 15$

99. $47 + 236 + 77$

100. $362 + 37 + 90$

Concept Extensions

101. Are parentheses necessary in the expression $2 + (3 \cdot 5)$? Explain your answer.

102. Are parentheses necessary in the expression $(2 + 3) \cdot 5$? Explain your answer.

For Exercises 103 and 104, match each expression in the first column with its value in the second column.

103. **a.** $(6 + 2) \cdot (5 + 3)$ 19
    b. $(6 + 2) \cdot 5 + 3$ 22
    c. $6 + 2 \cdot 5 + 3$ 64
    d. $6 + 2 \cdot (5 + 3)$ 43

104. **a.** $(1 + 4) \cdot 6 - 3$ 15
    b. $1 + 4 \cdot (6 - 3)$ 13
    c. $1 + 4 \cdot 6 - 3$ 27
    d. $(1 + 4) \cdot (6 - 3)$ 22

Recall that perimeter measures the distance around a plane figure and area measures the amount of surface of a plane figure. The expression $2l + 2w$ gives the perimeter of the rectangle below (measured in units), and the expression lw gives its area (measured in square units). Complete the chart below for the given lengths and widths. Be sure to include units.

	Length: l	Width: w	Perimeter of Rectangle: $2l + 2w$	Area of Rectangle: lw
105.	4 in.	3 in.		
106.	6 in.	1 in.		
107.	5.3 in.	1.7 in.		
108.	4.6 in.	2.4 in.		

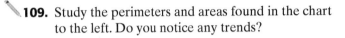 **109.** Study the perimeters and areas found in the chart to the left. Do you notice any trends?

110. In your own words, explain the difference between an expression and an equation.

111. Insert one set of parentheses so that the following expression simplifies to 32.

$$20 - 4 \cdot 4 \div 2$$

112. Insert parentheses so that the following expression simplifies to 28.

$$2 \cdot 5 + 3^2$$

Determine whether each is an expression or an equation. See the Concept Check in this section.

113. **a.** $5x + 6$
    b. $2a = 7$
    c. $3a + 2 = 9$
    d. $4x + 3y - 8z$
    e. $5^2 - 2(6 - 2)$

114. **a.** $3x^2 - 26$
    b. $3x^2 - 26 = 1$
    c. $2x - 5 = 7x - 5$
    d. $9y + x - 8$
    e. $3^2 - 4(5 - 3)$

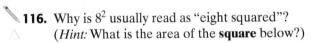 **115.** Why is 4^3 usually read as "four cubed"? (*Hint:* What is the volume of the **cube** below?)

116. Why is 8^2 usually read as "eight squared"? (*Hint:* What is the area of the **square** below?)

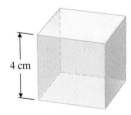

4 cm

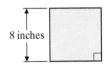

8 inches

117. Write any expression, using 3 or more numbers, that simplifies to 11.

118. Write any expression, using 4 or more numbers, that simplifies to 7.

5.4 ADDING REAL NUMBERS

Real numbers can be added, subtracted, multiplied, divided, and raised to powers, just as whole numbers can.

Objective Ⓐ Adding Real Numbers

Adding real numbers can be visualized by using a number line. A positive number can be represented on the number line by an arrow of appropriate length pointing to the right, and a negative number by an arrow of appropriate length pointing to the left.

Both arrows represent 2 or +2.

They both point to the right, and they are both 2 units long.

Both arrows represent −3.

They both point to the left, and they are both 3 units long.

To add signed numbers such as $5 + (-2)$ on a number line, we start at 0 on the number line and draw an arrow representing 5. From the tip of this arrow, we draw another arrow representing −2. The tip of the second arrow ends at their sum, 3.

$$5 + (-2) = 3$$

To add $-1 + (-4)$ on the number line, we start at 0 and draw an arrow representing −1. From the tip of this arrow, we draw another arrow representing −4. The tip of the second arrow ends at their sum, −5.

$$-1 + (-4) = -5$$

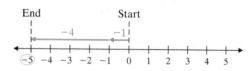

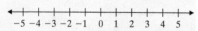
Example 1 Add: $-1 + (-2)$

Solution:

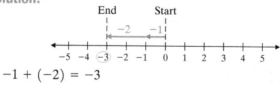

$$-1 + (-2) = -3$$

● Work Practice 1

Thinking of integers as money earned or lost might help make addition more meaningful. Earnings can be thought of as positive numbers. If \$1 is earned and later another \$3 is earned, the total amount earned is \$4. In other words, $1 + 3 = 4$.

On the other hand, losses can be thought of as negative numbers. If \$1 is lost and later another \$3 is lost, a total of \$4 is lost. In other words, $(-1) + (-3) = -4$.

In Example 1, we added numbers with the same sign. Adding numbers whose signs are not the same can be pictured on a number line also.

Example 2 Add: $-4 + 6$

Solution:

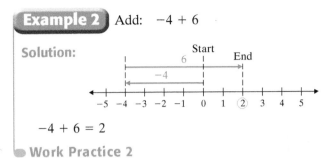

$-4 + 6 = 2$

● Work Practice 2

Add using a number line:
$-5 + 8$

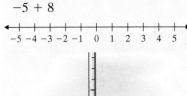

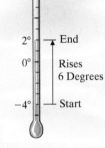

Let's use temperature as an example. If the thermometer registers 4 degrees below 0 degrees and then rises 6 degrees, the new temperature is 2 degrees above 0 degrees. Thus, it is reasonable that $-4 + 6 = 2$. (See the diagram in the margin.)

Example 3 Add: $4 + (-6)$

Solution:

$4 + (-6) = -2$

● Work Practice 3

Add using a number line:
$5 + (-4)$

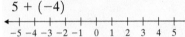

Using a number line each time we add two numbers can be time consuming. Instead, we can notice patterns in the previous examples and write rules for adding real numbers.

Adding Real Numbers

To add two real numbers

1. with the *same sign,* add their absolute values. Use their common sign as the sign of the answer.

2. with *different signs,* subtract their absolute values. Give the answer the same sign as the number with the larger absolute value.

Example 4 Add without using a number line: $(-7) + (-6)$

Solution: Here, we are adding two numbers with the same sign.

$(-7) + (-6) = -13$

↑ ↖ sum of absolute values ($|-7| = 7, |-6| = 6, 7 + 6 = 13$)
same sign

● Work Practice 4

Add without using a number line: $(-8) + (-5)$

Example 5 Add without using a number line: $(-10) + 4$

Solution: Here, we are adding two numbers with different signs.

$(-10) + 4 = -6$

↑ ↖ difference of absolute values ($|-10| = 10, |4| = 4, 10 - 4 = 6$)
sign of number with larger absolute value, -10

● Work Practice 5

Add without using a number line: $(-14) + 6$

Answers
2. 3 **3.** 1 **4.** -13 **5.** -8

PRACTICE 6–11

Add without using a number line.

6. $(-17) + (-10)$
7. $(-4) + 12$
8. $1.5 + (-3.2)$
9. $-\dfrac{5}{12} + \left(-\dfrac{1}{12}\right)$
10. $12.1 + (-3.6)$
11. $-\dfrac{4}{5} + \dfrac{2}{3}$

Examples Add without using a number line.

6. $(-8) + (-11) = -19$
7. $(-2) + 10 = 8$
8. $0.2 + (-0.5) = -0.3$
9. $-\dfrac{7}{10} + \left(-\dfrac{1}{10}\right) = -\dfrac{8}{10} = -\dfrac{\overset{1}{\cancel{2}} \cdot 4}{\underset{1}{\cancel{2}} \cdot 5} = -\dfrac{4}{5}$
10. $11.4 + (-4.7) = 6.7$
11. $-\dfrac{3}{8} + \dfrac{2}{5} = -\dfrac{15}{40} + \dfrac{16}{40} = \dfrac{1}{40}$

● **Work Practice 6–11**

In Example 12a, we add three numbers. Remember that by the associative and commutative properties for addition, we may add numbers in any order that we wish. For Example 12a, let's add the numbers from left to right.

PRACTICE 12

Find each sum.

a. $16 + (-9) + (-9)$
b. $[3 + (-13)] + [-4 + (-7)]$

Example 12 Find each sum.

a. $3 + (-7) + (-8)$
b. $[7 + (-10)] + [-2 + (-4)]$

Solution:

a. Perform the additions from left to right.

$3 + (-7) + (-8) = -4 + (-8)$ Adding numbers with different signs
$= -12$ Adding numbers with like signs

b. Simplify inside the brackets first.

$[7 + (-10)] + [-2 + (-4)] = [-3] + [-6]$
$= -9$ Add.

● **Work Practice 12**

Helpful Hint Don't forget that brackets are grouping symbols. We simplify within them first.

Objective Ⓑ Finding Opposites

To help us subtract real numbers in the next section, we first review what we mean by opposites. The graphs of 4 and -4 are shown on the number line below.

Notice that the graphs of 4 and -4 lie on opposite sides of 0, and each is 4 units away from 0. Such numbers are known as **opposites** or **additive inverses** of each other.

Opposite or Additive Inverse

Two numbers that are the same distance from 0 but lie on opposite sides of 0 are called **opposites** or **additive inverses** of each other.

Answers

6. -27 7. 8 8. -1.7 9. $-\dfrac{1}{2}$ 10. 8.5

11. $-\dfrac{2}{15}$ 12. a. -2 b. -21

Examples Find the opposite of each number.

13. 10   The opposite of 10 is −10.

14. −3   The opposite of −3 is 3.

15. $\dfrac{1}{2}$ The opposite of $\dfrac{1}{2}$ is $-\dfrac{1}{2}$.

16. −4.5   The opposite of −4.5 is 4.5.

● Work Practice 13–16

PRACTICE 13–16

Find the opposite of each number.

13. −35   **14.** 12

15. $-\dfrac{3}{11}$ **16.** 1.9

We use the symbol "−" to represent the phrase "the opposite of" or "the additive inverse of." In general, if a is a number, we write the opposite or additive inverse of a as $-a$. We know that the opposite of −3 is 3. Notice that this translates as

the opposite of   −3   is   3

     ↓   ↓   ↓   ↓

     −   (−3)   =   3

This is true in general.

If a is a number, then $-(-a) = a$.

Example 17 Simplify each expression.

a. $-(-10)$ **b.** $-\left(-\dfrac{1}{2}\right)$ **c.** $-(-2x)$

d. $-|-6|$ **e.** $-|4.1|$

Solution:

a. $-(-10) = 10$ **b.** $-\left(-\dfrac{1}{2}\right) = \dfrac{1}{2}$

c. $-(-2x) = 2x$

d. $-|-6| = -6$ Since $|-6| = 6$.

e. $-|4.1| = -4.1$ Since $|4.1| = 4.1$.

● Work Practice 17

PRACTICE 17

Simplify each expression.

a. $-(-22)$

b. $-\left(-\dfrac{2}{7}\right)$

c. $-(-x)$

d. $-|-14|$

e. $-|2.3|$

Let's discover another characteristic about opposites. Notice that the sum of a number and its opposite is always 0.

$$10 + (-10) = 0 \qquad -3 + 3 = 0$$

     opposites   opposites

$$\dfrac{1}{2} + \left(-\dfrac{1}{2}\right) = 0$$

     opposites

In general, we can write the following:

The sum of a number a and its opposite $-a$ is 0.

$$a + (-a) = 0 \qquad \text{Also,} \qquad -a + a = 0.$$

Notice that this means that the opposite of 0 is then 0 since $0 + 0 = 0$.

Answers

13. 35   **14.** −12   **15.** $\dfrac{3}{11}$ **16.** −1.9

17. a. 22   **b.** $\dfrac{2}{7}$ **c.** x **d.** −14

e. −2.3

PRACTICE 18–19

Add.

18. $30 + (-30)$

19. $-81 + 81$

Examples Add.

18. $-56 + 56 = 0$
19. $17 + (-17) = 0$

● Work Practice 18–19

✔**Concept Check** What is wrong with the following calculation?

$$5 + (-22) = 17$$

Objective Ⓒ Evaluating Algebraic Expressions

We can continue our work with algebraic expressions by evaluating expressions given real-number replacement values.

PRACTICE 20

Evaluate $x + 3y$ for $x = -6$ and $y = 2$.

Example 20 Evaluate $2x + y$ for $x = 3$ and $y = -5$.

Solution: Replace x with 3 and y with -5 in $2x + y$.

$$2x + y = 2 \cdot 3 + (-5)$$
$$= 6 + (-5)$$
$$= 1$$

● Work Practice 20

PRACTICE 21

Evaluate $x + y$ for $x = -13$ and $y = -9$.

Example 21 Evaluate $x + y$ for $x = -2$ and $y = -10$.

Solution:

$$x + y = (-2) + (-10) \quad \text{Replace } x \text{ with } -2 \text{ and } y \text{ with } -10.$$
$$= -12$$

● Work Practice 21

Objective Ⓓ Solving Applications That Involve Addition

Positive and negative numbers are used in everyday life. Stock market returns show gains and losses as positive and negative numbers. Temperatures in cold climates often dip into the negative range, commonly referred to as "below zero" temperatures. Bank statements report deposits and withdrawals as positive and negative numbers.

Although problem-solving steps were introduced in Chapter 1, in this chapter, we will concentrate on the translating only. Then, in Section 6.4, we will review and use the same problem-solving steps as in Chapter 1.

Answers

18. 0 **19.** 0 **20.** 0 **21.** -22

✔**Concept Check Answer**

$5 + (-22) = -17$

Example 22 Calculating Temperature

In Philadelphia, Pennsylvania, the record extreme high temperature is 104°F. Decrease this temperature by 111 degrees, and the result is the record extreme low temperature. Find this temperature. (*Source:* National Climatic Data Center)

Solution:

In words:

extreme low temperature	=	extreme high temperature	+	decrease of 111°
↓		↓		↓

Translate: extreme low temperature   =   104   +   (−111)

= −7

The record extreme low temperature in Philadelphia, Pennsylvania, is −7°F.

● **Work Practice 22**

PRACTICE 22

If the temperature was −7° Fahrenheit at 6 a.m., and it rose 4 degrees by 7 a.m. and then rose another 7 degrees in the hour from 7 a.m. to 8 a.m., what was the temperature at 8 a.m.?

Answer
22. 4°F

Vocabulary and Readiness Check

Use the choices below to fill in each blank. Not all choices will be used.

$-a$ a 0 commutative   associative

1. If n is a number, then $-n + n = $ _____.
2. Since $x + n = n + x$, we say that addition is _____.
3. If a is a number, then $-(-a) = $ _____.
4. Since $n + (x + a) = (n + x) + a$, we say that addition is _____.

5.4 Exercise Set

FOR EXTRA HELP

MyMathLab *Powered by CourseCompass™ and MathXL*

 PRACTICE   WATCH   DOWNLOAD   READ   REVIEW

Objectives Ⓐ Ⓑ Mixed Practice *Add. See Examples 1 through 12, 18, and 19.*

1. $6 + (-3)$

2. $9 + (-12)$

3. $-6 + (-8)$

4. $-6 + (-14)$

5. $8 + (-7)$

6. $16 + (-4)$

7. $-14 + 2$

8. $-10 + 5$

9. $-2 + (-3)$

10. $-7 + (-4)$

11. $-9 + (-3)$

12. $-11 + (-5)$

13. $-7 + 3$

14. $-5 + 9$

15. $10 + (-3)$

16. $8 + (-6)$

17. $5 + (-7)$

18. $3 + (-6)$

19. $-16 + 16$

20. $23 + (-23)$

21. $27 + (-46)$

22. $53 + (-37)$

23. $-18 + 49$

24. $-26 + 14$

25. $-33 + (-14)$

26. $-18 + (-26)$

27. $6.3 + (-8.4)$

28. $9.2 + (-11.4)$

29. $117 + (-79)$

30. $144 + (-88)$

31. $-9.6 + (-3.5)$

32. $-6.7 + (-7.6)$

33. $-\dfrac{3}{8} + \dfrac{5}{8}$

34. $-\dfrac{5}{12} + \dfrac{7}{12}$

35. $-\dfrac{7}{16} + \dfrac{1}{4}$

36. $-\dfrac{5}{9} + \dfrac{1}{3}$

37. $-\dfrac{7}{10} + \left(-\dfrac{3}{5}\right)$

38. $-\dfrac{5}{6} + \left(-\dfrac{2}{3}\right)$

39. $|-8| + (-16)$

40. $|-6| + (-61)$

41. $-15 + 9 + (-2)$

42. $-9 + 15 + (-5)$

43. $-21 + (-16) + (-22)$

44. $-18 + (-6) + (-40)$

45. $-23 + 16 + (-2)$

46. $-14 + (-3) + 11$

47. $|5 + (-10)|$

48. $|7 + (-17)|$

49. $6 + (-4) + 9$

50. $8 + (-2) + 7$

51. $[-17 + (-4)] + [-12 + 15]$

52. $[-2 + (-7)] + [-11 + 22]$

53. $|9 + (-12)| + |-16|$

54. $|43 + (-73)| + |-20|$

55. $-13 + [5 + (-3) + 4]$

56. $-30 + [1 + (-6) + 8]$

57. Find the sum of -38 and 12.

58. Find the sum of -44 and 16.

Objective Ⓑ *Find each additive inverse or opposite. See Examples 13 through 17.*

59. 6

60. 4

61. -2

62. -8

63. 0

64. $-\dfrac{1}{4}$

65. $|-6|$

66. $|-11|$

Simplify each of the following. See Example 17.

67. $-|-2|$

68. $-|-5|$

69. $-(-7)$

70. $-(-14)$

71. $-(-7.9)$

72. $-(-8.4)$

73. $-(-5z)$

74. $-(-7m)$

75. $\left|-\dfrac{2}{3}\right|$

76. $-\left|-\dfrac{2}{3}\right|$

Objective Ⓒ *Evaluate $x + y$ for the given replacement values. See Examples 20 and 21.*

77. $x = -20$ and $y = -50$

78. $x = -1$ and $y = -29$

Evaluate $3x + y$ for the given replacement values. See Examples 20 and 21.

79. $x = 2$ and $y = -3$

80. $x = 7$ and $y = -11$

Objective Ⓓ **Translating** *Translate each phrase; then simplify. See Example 22.*

81. Find the sum of -6 and 25.

82. Find the sum of -30 and 15.

83. Find the sum of -31, -9, and 30.

84. Find the sum of -49, -2, and 40.

Solve. See Example 22.

85. Suppose a deep-sea diver dives from the surface to 215 feet below the surface. He then dives down 16 more feet. Use positive and negative numbers to represent this situation. Then find the diver's present depth.

86. Suppose a diver dives from the surface to 248 meters below the surface and then swims up 8 meters, down 16 meters, down another 28 meters, and then up 32 meters. Use positive and negative numbers to represent this situation. Then find the diver's depth after these movements.

87. The lowest temperature ever recorded in Massachusetts was $-35°F$. The highest recorded temperature in Massachusetts was $142°$ higher than the record low temperature. Find Massachusetts' highest recorded temperature. (*Source:* National Climatic Data Center)

88. On January 2, 1943, the temperature was $-4°$ at 7:30 a.m. in Spearfish, South Dakota. Incredibly, it got $49°$ warmer in the next 2 minutes. To what temperature did it rise by 7:32?

89. The lowest elevation on Earth is −411 meters (that is, 411 meters below sea level) at the Dead Sea. If you are standing 316 meters above the Dead Sea, what is your elevation? (*Source:* National Geographic Society)

90. The lowest elevation in Australia is −52 feet at Lake Eyre. If you are standing at a point 439 feet above Lake Eyre, what is your elevation? (*Source:* National Geographic Society)

91. During the PGA 2008 Wyndham Championship tournament, the winner, Carl Pettersson, had scores of −6, −9, −4, and −2. What was his total score for the tournament? (*Source:* Professional Golfer's Association)

92. Catriona Matthew won the HSBC LPGA Brasil Cup 2009 Tournament with the following hole scores for round 1: −2, +2, −2, −2, −2. What was her final score for round 1? (*Source:* LPGA of America)

93. A negative net income results when a company spends more money than it brings in. Johnson Outdoors Inc. had the following quarterly net incomes during its 2009 fiscal year. (*Source:* Yahoo Finance)

Quarter of Fiscal 2009	Net Income (in millions)
First	2.5
Second	9
Third	−14.2
Fourth	−4.2

What was the total net income for fiscal year 2009?

94. LeapFrog Enterprises Inc. had the following quarterly net incomes during its 2009 fiscal year. (*Source:* Yahoo Finance)

Quarter of Fiscal 2009	Net Income (in millions)
First	−27.1
Second	−12.2
Third	7.2
Fourth	29.4

What was the total net income for fiscal year 2009?

Review

Subtract. See Sections 1.4 and 3.3.

95. $76.1 - 4.09$　　　　**96.** $93.7 - 10.08$　　　　**97.** $200 - 59$　　　　**98.** $400 - 18$

Concept Extensions

The following bar graph shows each month's average daily low temperature in degrees Fahrenheit for Barrow, Alaska. Use this graph to answer Exercises 99 through 104.

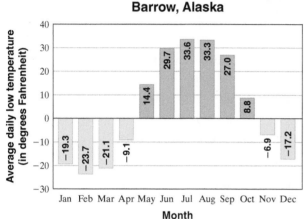

Source: National Climatic Data Center

99. For what month is the graphed temperature the highest?

100. For what month is the graphed temperature the lowest?

101. For what month is the graphed temperature positive *and* closest to 0°?

102. For what month is the graphed temperature negative *and* closest to 0°?

103. Find the average (mean) of the temperatures shown for the months of April, May, and October.

104. Find the average (mean) of the temperatures shown for the months of January, September, and October.

105. Name 2 numbers whose sum is -17.

106. Name 2 numbers whose sum is -30.

Each calculation below is incorrect. Find the error and correct it. See the Concept Check in this section.

107. $7 + (-10) \stackrel{?}{=} 17$

108. $-4 + 14 \stackrel{?}{=} -18$

109. $-10 + (-12) \stackrel{?}{=} -120$

110. $-15 + (-17) \stackrel{?}{=} 32$

For Exercises 111 through 114, determine whether each statement is true or false.

111. The sum of two negative numbers is always a negative number.

112. The sum of two positive numbers is always a positive number.

113. The sum of a positive number and a negative number is always a negative number.

114. The sum of zero and a negative number is always a negative number.

115. In your own words, explain how to add two negative numbers.

116. In your own words, explain how to add a positive number and a negative number.

A Subtract Real Numbers.

B Evaluate Algebraic Expressions Using Real Numbers.

C Determine Whether a Number Is a Solution of a Given Equation.

D Solve Applications That Involve Subtraction of Real Numbers.

E Find Complementary and Supplementary Angles.

5.5 SUBTRACTING REAL NUMBERS

Objective A Subtracting Real Numbers

Now that addition of real numbers has been discussed, we can explore subtraction. We know that $9 - 7 = 2$. Notice that $9 + (-7) = 2$, also. This means that

$$9 - 7 = 9 + (-7)$$

Notice that the *difference* of 9 and 7 is the same as the *sum* of 9 and the opposite of 7. This is how we can subtract real numbers.

> **Subtracting Real Numbers**
>
> If a and b are real numbers, then $a - b = a + (-b)$.

In other words, to find the difference of two numbers, we add the opposite of the number being subtracted.

> **Example 1** Subtract.
>
> **a.** $-13 - 4$ **b.** $5 - (-6)$ **c.** $3 - 6$ **d.** $-1 - (-7)$
>
> **Solution:**
>
> **a.** $-13 - 4 = -13 + (-4)$ Add -13 to the opposite of 4, which is -4.
>
> $\quad\quad\quad = -17$
>
> **b.** $5 - (-6) = 5 + (6)$ Add 5 to the opposite of -6, which is 6.
>
> $\quad\quad\quad = 11$
>
> **c.** $3 - 6 = 3 + (-6)$ Add 3 to the opposite of 6, which is -6.
>
> $\quad\quad\quad = -3$
>
> **d.** $-1 - (-7) = -1 + (7) = 6$

● **Work Practice 1**

Helpful Hint

Study the patterns indicated.

No change — Change to addition.
Change to opposite.

$5 - 11 = 5 + (-11) = -6$
$-3 - 4 = -3 + (-4) = -7$
$7 - (-1) = 7 + (1) = 8$

> **Examples** Subtract.
>
> **2.** $5.3 - (-4.6) = 5.3 + (4.6) = 9.9$
>
> **3.** $-\dfrac{3}{10} - \dfrac{5}{10} = -\dfrac{3}{10} + \left(-\dfrac{5}{10}\right) = -\dfrac{8}{10} = -\dfrac{4}{5}$
>
> **4.** $-\dfrac{2}{3} - \left(-\dfrac{4}{5}\right) = -\dfrac{2}{3} + \left(\dfrac{4}{5}\right) = -\dfrac{10}{15} + \dfrac{12}{15} = \dfrac{2}{15}$

● **Work Practice 2–4**

Subtract.
a. $-20 - 6$
b. $3 - (-5)$
c. $7 - 17$
d. $-4 - (-9)$

Subtract.
2. $9.6 - (-5.7)$

3. $-\dfrac{4}{9} - \dfrac{2}{9}$

4. $-\dfrac{1}{4} - \left(-\dfrac{2}{5}\right)$

Answers
1. a. -26 **b.** 8 **c.** -10 **d.** 5
2. 15.3 **3.** $-\dfrac{2}{3}$ **4.** $\dfrac{3}{20}$

Example 5 Write each phrase as an expression and simplify.

a. Subtract 8 from −4.   **b.** Decrease 10 by −20.

Solution: Be careful when interpreting these. The order of numbers in subtraction is important.

a. 8 is to be subtracted **from** −4.

$$-4 - 8 = -4 + (-8) = -12$$

b. To decrease 10 by −20, we find 10 **minus** −20.

$$10 - (-20) = 10 + 20 = 30$$

● Work Practice 5

PRACTICE 5

Write each phrase as an expression and simplify.

a. Subtract 7 from −11.
b. Decrease 35 by −25.

If an expression contains additions and subtractions, just write the subtractions as equivalent additions. Then simplify from left to right.

Example 6 Simplify each expression.

a. $-14 - 8 + 10 - (-6)$ **b.** $1.6 - (-10.3) + (-5.6)$

Solution:

a. $-14 - 8 + 10 - (-6) = -14 + (-8) + 10 + 6 = -6$

b. $1.6 - (-10.3) + (-5.6) = 1.6 + 10.3 + (-5.6) = 6.3$

● Work Practice 6

PRACTICE 6

Simplify each expression.
a. $-20 - 5 + 12 - (-3)$
b. $5.2 - (-4.4) + (-8.8)$

When an expression contains parentheses and brackets, remember the order of operations. Start with the innermost set of parentheses or brackets and work your way outward.

Example 7 Simplify each expression.

a. $-3 + [(-2 - 5) - 2]$ **b.** $2^3 - 10 + [-6 - (-5)]$

Solution:

a. Start with the innermost set of parentheses. Rewrite $-2 - 5$ as an addition.

$$
\begin{aligned}
-3 + [(-2 - 5) - 2] &= -3 + [(-2 + (-5)) - 2] \\
&= -3 + [(-7) - 2] \quad &\text{Add: } -2 + (-5). \\
&= -3 + [-7 + (-2)] \quad &\text{Write } -7 - 2 \text{ as an addition.} \\
&= -3 + [-9] \quad &\text{Add.} \\
&= -12 \quad &\text{Add.}
\end{aligned}
$$

b. Start simplifying the expression inside the brackets by writing $-6 - (-5)$ as an addition.

$$
\begin{aligned}
2^3 - 10 + [-6 - (-5)] &= 2^3 - 10 + [-6 + 5] \\
&= 2^3 - 10 + [-1] \quad &\text{Add.} \\
&= 8 - 10 + (-1) \quad &\text{Evaluate } 2^3. \\
&= 8 + (-10) + (-1) \quad &\text{Write } 8 - 10 \text{ as an addition.} \\
&= -2 + (-1) \quad &\text{Add.} \\
&= -3 \quad &\text{Add.}
\end{aligned}
$$

● Work Practice 7

PRACTICE 7

Simplify each expression.
a. $-9 + [(-4 - 1) - 10]$
b. $5^2 - 20 + [-11 - (-3)]$

Answers
5. a. −18 **b.** 60 **6. a.** −10
b. 0.8 **7. a.** −24 **b.** −3

Objective Ⓑ Evaluating Algebraic Expressions

It is important to be able to evaluate expressions for given replacement values. This helps, for example, when checking solutions of equations.

PRACTICE 8

Find the value of each expression when $x = 1$ and $y = -4$.

a. $\dfrac{x - y}{14 + x}$

b. $x^2 - y$

Example 8 Find the value of each expression when $x = 2$ and $y = -5$.

a. $\dfrac{x - y}{12 + x}$ b. $x^2 - y$

Solution:

a. Replace x with 2 and y with -5. Be sure to put parentheses around -5 to separate signs. Then simplify the resulting expression.

$$\frac{x - y}{12 + x} = \frac{2 - (-5)}{12 + 2} = \frac{2 + 5}{14} = \frac{7}{14} = \frac{1}{2}$$

b. Replace x with 2 and y with -5 and simplify.

$$x^2 - y = 2^2 - (-5) = 4 - (-5) = 4 + 5 = 9$$

● **Work Practice 8**

Helpful Hint

For additional help when replacing variables with replacement values, first place parentheses about any variables.

For Example 8b above, we have

$$x^2 - y = (x)^2 - (y) = (2)^2 - (-5) = 4 - (-5) = 4 + 5 = 9$$

Place parentheses about variables   Replace variables with values

Objective Ⓒ Solutions of Equations

Recall from Section 5.3 that a solution of an equation is a value for the variable that makes the equation true.

PRACTICE 9

Determine whether -2 is a solution of $-1 + x = 1$.

Example 9 Determine whether -4 is a solution of $x - 5 = -9$.

Solution: Replace x with -4 and see if a true statement results.

$$x - 5 = -9 \quad \text{Original equation}$$
$$-4 - 5 \overset{?}{=} -9 \quad \text{Replace } x \text{ with } -4.$$
$$-4 + (-5) \overset{?}{=} -9$$
$$-9 = -9 \quad \text{True}$$

Thus -4 is a solution of $x - 5 = -9$.

● **Work Practice 9**

Answers

8. a. $\dfrac{1}{3}$ b. 5   9. -2 is not a solution.

Objective ⓓ Solving Applications that Involve Subtraction

Another use of real numbers is in recording altitudes above and below sea level, as shown in the next example.

Example 10 Finding a Change in Elevation

The highest point in the United States is the top of Mount McKinley, at a height of 20,320 feet above sea level. The lowest point is Death Valley, California, which is 282 feet below sea level. How much higher is Mount McKinley than Death Valley? (*Source:* U.S. Geological Survey)

Solution: UNDERSTAND. Read and reread the problem. To find "how much higher," we subtract. Don't forget that since Death Valley is 282 feet *below* sea level, we represent its height by −282. Draw a diagram to help visualize the problem.

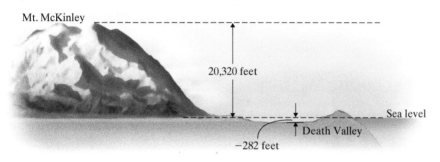

In words:

how much higher is Mt. McKinley	=	height of Mt. McKinley	minus	height of Death Valley
↓	↓	↓	↓	↓

Translate:

$$\text{how much higher is Mt. McKinley} = 20{,}320 - (-282)$$
$$= 20{,}320 + 282$$
$$= 20{,}602$$

Thus, Mount McKinley is 20,602 feet higher than Death Valley.

● **Work Practice 10**

Objective ⓔ Finding Complementary and Supplementary Angles

A knowledge of geometric concepts is needed by many professionals, such as doctors, carpenters, electronic technicians, gardeners, machinists, and pilots, just to name a few. With this in mind, we review the geometric concepts of **complementary** and **supplementary angles.**

Complementary and Supplementary Angles

Two angles are **complementary** if the sum of their measures is 90°.

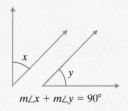

$m\angle x + m\angle y = 90°$

Two angles are **supplementary** if the sum of their measures is 180°.

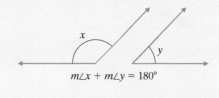

$m\angle x + m\angle y = 180°$

PRACTICE 10

The highest point in Asia is the top of Mount Everest, at a height of 29,028 feet above sea level. The lowest point is the Dead Sea, which is 1312 feet below sea level. How much higher is Mount Everest than the Dead Sea? (*Source:* National Geographic Society)

Answer
10. 30,340 ft

PRACTICE 11

Find the measure of each unknown complementary or supplementary angle.

a.

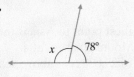

b.

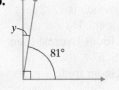

Example 11 Find the measure of each unknown complementary or supplementary angle.

a.

b.

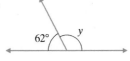

Solution:

a. These angles are complementary, so their sum is $90°$. This means that the measure of angle x, $m\angle x$, is $90° - 38°$.

$$m\angle x = 90° - 38° = 52°$$

b. These angles are supplementary, so their sum is $180°$. This means that $m\angle y$ is $180° - 62°$.

$$m\angle y = 180° - 62° = 118°$$

● **Work Practice 11**

Answers

11. a. $102°$ **b.** $9°$

Vocabulary and Readiness Check

Multiple choice: Select the correct lettered response following each exercise.

1. It is true that $a - b = $ _____ .
   a. $b - a$ **b.** $a + (-b)$ **c.** $a + b$

2. The opposite of n is _____ .
   a. $-n$ **b.** $-(-n)$ **c.** n

3. To evaluate $x - y$ for $x = -10$ and $y = -14$, we replace x with -10 and y with -14 and evaluate _____ .
   a. $10 - 14$ **b.** $-10 - 14$ **c.** $-14 - 10$ **d.** $-10 - (-14)$

4. The expression $-5 - 10$ equals _____ .
   a. $5 - 10$ **b.** $5 + 10$ **c.** $-5 + (-10)$ **d.** $10 - 5$

5.5 Exercise Set

FOR EXTRA HELP

MyMathLab

 PRACTICE   WATCH   DOWNLOAD   READ   REVIEW

Objective A *Subtract. See Examples 1 through 4.*

1. $-6 - 4$ 2. $-12 - 8$ 3. $4 - 9$ 4. $8 - 11$ 5. $16 - (-3)$

6. $12 - (-5)$ 7. $7 - (-4)$ 8. $3 - (-6)$ 9. $-26 - (-18)$ 10. $-60 - (-48)$

11. $-6 - 5$ 12. $-8 - 4$ 13. $16 - (-21)$ 14. $15 - (-33)$ 15. $-6 - (-11)$

16. $-4 - (-16)$ 17. $-44 - 27$ 18. $-36 - 51$ 19. $-21 - (-21)$ 20. $-17 - (-17)$

21. $-\dfrac{3}{11} - \left(-\dfrac{5}{11}\right)$ 22. $-\dfrac{4}{7} - \left(-\dfrac{1}{7}\right)$ 23. $9.7 - 16.1$ 24. $8.3 - 11.2$ 25. $-2.6 - (-6.7)$

26. $-6.1 - (-5.3)$ 27. $\dfrac{1}{2} - \dfrac{2}{3}$ 28. $\dfrac{3}{4} - \dfrac{7}{8}$ 29. $-\dfrac{1}{6} - \dfrac{3}{4}$ 30. $-\dfrac{1}{10} - \dfrac{7}{8}$

31. $8.3 - (-0.62)$ 32. $4.3 - (-0.87)$ 33. $0 - 8.92$ 34. $0 - (-4.21)$

Translating *Translate each phrase to an expression and simplify. See Example 5.*

35. Subtract −5 from 8.

36. Subtract −2 from 3.

37. Find the difference between −6 and −1.

38. Find the difference between −17 and −1.

39. Subtract 8 from 7.

40. Subtract 9 from −4.

41. Decrease −8 by 15.

42. Decrease 11 by −14.

Mixed Practice (Sections 5.3, 5.4, 5.5) *Simplify each expression. (Remember the order of operations.) See Examples 6 and 7.*

43. $-10 - (-8) + (-4) - 20$

44. $-16 - (-3) + (-11) - 14$

45. $5 - 9 + (-4) - 8 - 8$

46. $7 - 12 + (-5) - 2 + (-2)$

47. $-6 - (2 - 11)$

48. $-9 - (3 - 8)$

49. $3^3 - 8 \cdot 9$

50. $2^3 - 6 \cdot 3$

51. $2 - 3(8 - 6)$

52. $4 - 6(7 - 3)$

53. $(3 - 6) + 4^2$

54. $(2 - 3) + 5^2$

55. $-2 + [(8 - 11) - (-2 - 9)]$

56. $-5 + [(4 - 15) - (-6) - 8]$

57. $|-3| + 2^2 + [-4 - (-6)]$

58. $|-2| + 6^2 + (-3 - 8)$

Objective B *Evaluate each expression when $x = -5$, $y = 4$, and $t = 10$. See Example 8.*

59. $x - y$

60. $y - x$

61. $\dfrac{9 - x}{y + 6}$

62. $\dfrac{15 - x}{y + 2}$

63. $|x| + 2t - 8y$

64. $|y| + 3x - 2t$

65. $y^2 - x$

66. $t^2 - x$

67. $\dfrac{|x - (-10)|}{2t}$

68. $\dfrac{|5y - x|}{6t}$

Objective C *Decide whether the given number is a solution of the given equation. See Example 9.*

69. $x - 9 = 5$; −4

70. $x - 10 = -7$; 3

71. $-x + 6 = -x - 1$; −2

72. $-x - 6 = -x - 1$; −10

73. $-x - 13 = -15$; 2

74. $4 = 1 - x$; 5

Objectives (D) (E) **Mixed Practice** *Solve. See Examples 10 and 11.*

75. The coldest temperature ever recorded on Earth was −129°F in Antarctica. The warmest temperature ever recorded was 136°F in the Sahara Desert. How many degrees warmer is 136°F than −129°F? (*Source: Questions Kids Ask,* Grolier Limited, 1991, and *The World Almanac*)

76. The coldest temperature ever recorded in the United States was −80°F in Alaska. The warmest temperature ever recorded was 134°F in California. How many degrees warmer is 134°F than −80°F? (*Source: The World Almanac,* 2005)

77. Mauna Kea in Hawaii has an elevation of 13,796 feet above sea level. The Mid-America Trench in the Pacific Ocean has an elevation of 21,857 feet below sea level. Find the difference in elevation between those two points. (*Source:* National Geographic Society and Defense Mapping Agency)

78. A woman received a statement of her charge account at Old Navy. She spent $93 on purchases last month. She returned an $18 top because she didn't like the color. She also returned a $26 nightshirt because it was damaged. What does she actually owe on her account?

79. Find *x* if the angles below are complementary angles.

80. Find *y* if the angles below are supplementary angles.

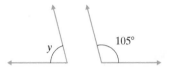

81. A commercial jetliner hits an air pocket and drops 250 feet. After climbing 120 feet, it drops another 178 feet. What is its overall vertical change?

82. In some card games, it is possible to have a negative score. Lavonne Schultz currently has a score of 15 points. She then loses 24 points. What is her new score?

83. The highest point in Africa is Mt. Kilimanjaro, Tanzania, at an elevation of 19,340 feet. The lowest point is Lake Assal, Djibouti, at 512 feet below sea level. How much higher is Mt. Kilimanjaro than Lake Assal? (*Source:* National Geographic Society)

84. The airport in Bishop, California, is at an elevation of 4101 feet above sea level. The nearby Furnace Creek Airport in Death Valley, California, is at an elevation of 226 feet below sea level. How much higher in elevation is the Bishop Airport than the Furnace Creek Airport? (*Source:* National Climatic Data Center)

Find each unknown complementary or supplementary angle.

85.

86.

Mixed Practice–Translating (Sections 5.4, 5.5) *Translate each phrase to an algebraic expression. Use "x" to represent "a number."*

87. The sum of -5 and a number.

88. The difference of -3 and a number.

89. Subtract a number from -20.

90. Add a number and -36.

Review

Multiply or divide as indicated. See Sections 2.4 and 2.5.

91. $\dfrac{5}{8} \cdot 0$

92. $\dfrac{2}{3} \div \dfrac{3}{2}$

93. $1\dfrac{2}{3} \div 2\dfrac{1}{6}$

94. $3\dfrac{1}{2} \cdot \dfrac{11}{14}$

Concept Extensions

Recall the bar graph from Section 5.4. It shows each month's average daily low temperature in degrees Fahrenheit for Barrow, Alaska. Use this graph to answer Exercises 95 through 98.

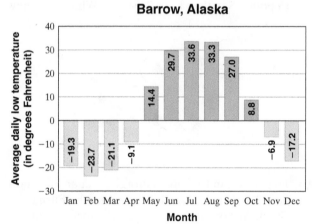

Source: National Climatic Data Center

95. Record the monthly increases and decreases in the low temperature from the previous month.

Month	Monthly Increase or Decrease (from the previous month)
February	
March	
April	
May	
June	

96. Record the monthly increases and decreases in the low temperature from the previous month.

Month	Monthly Increase or Decrease (from the previous month)
July	
August	
September	
October	
November	
December	

97. Which month had the greatest increase in temperature?

98. Which month had the greatest decrease in temperature?

99. Find two numbers whose difference is -5.

100. Find two numbers whose difference is -9.

*Each calculation below is **incorrect.** Find the error and correct it.*

101. $9 - (-7) \overset{?}{=} 2$

102. $-4 - 8 \overset{?}{=} 4$

103. $10 - 30 \overset{?}{=} 20$

104. $-3 - (-10) \overset{?}{=} -13$

If p is a positive number and n is a negative number, determine whether each statement is true or false. Explain your answer.

105. $p - n$ is always a positive number.

106. $n - p$ is always a negative number.

107. $|n| - |p|$ is always a positive number.

108. $|n - p|$ is always a positive number.

Without calculating, determine whether each answer is positive or negative. Then use a calculator to find the exact difference.

109. $56,875 - 87,262$

110. $4.362 - 7.0086$

Objectives

A Multiply Real Numbers.

B Find the Reciprocal of a Real Number.

C Divide Real Numbers.

D Evaluate Expressions Using Real Numbers.

E Determine Whether a Number is a Solution of a Given Equation.

F Solve Applications That Involve Multiplication or Division of Real Numbers.

5.6 MULTIPLYING AND DIVIDING REAL NUMBERS

Objective A Multiplying Real Numbers

Multiplication of real numbers is similar to multiplication of whole numbers. We just need to determine when the answer is positive, when it is negative, and when it is zero. To discover sign patterns for multiplication, recall that multiplication is repeated addition. For example, 3(2) means that 2 is added to itself three times, or

$$3(2) = 2 + 2 + 2 = 6$$

Also,

$$3(-2) = (-2) + (-2) + (-2) = -6$$

Since $3(-2) = -6$, this suggests that the product of a positive number and a negative number is a negative number.

What about the product of two negative numbers? To find out, consider the following pattern.

Factor decreases by 1 each time.

$$-3 \cdot 2 = -6$$
$$-3 \cdot 1 = -3 \quad \text{Product increases by 3 each time.}$$
$$-3 \cdot 0 = 0$$
$$-3 \cdot -1 = 3$$
$$-3 \cdot -2 = 6$$

This suggests that the product of two negative numbers is a positive number. Our results are given below.

Multiplying Real Numbers

1. The product of two numbers with the *same* sign is a positive number.
2. The product of two numbers with *different* signs is a negative number.

Examples Multiply.

1. $-7(6) = -42$ Different signs, so the product is negative.
2. $2(-10) = -20$
3. $-2(-14) = 28$ Same sign, so the product is positive.
4. $-\dfrac{2}{3} \cdot \dfrac{4}{7} = -\dfrac{2 \cdot 4}{3 \cdot 7} = -\dfrac{8}{21}$
5. $5(-1.7) = -8.5$
6. $-18(-3) = 54$

● Work Practice 1–6

We already know that the product of 0 and any whole number is 0. This is true of all real numbers.

Products Involving Zero

If b is a real number, then $b \cdot 0 = 0$. Also $0 \cdot b = 0$.

PRACTICE 1–6

Multiply.

1. $-8(3)$ **2.** $5(-30)$

3. $-4(-12)$ **4.** $-\dfrac{5}{6} \cdot \dfrac{1}{4}$

5. $6(-2.3)$ **6.** $-15(-2)$

Answers

1. -24 **2.** -150 **3.** 48 **4.** $-\dfrac{5}{24}$

5. -13.8 **6.** 30

460

Example 7 Multiply.

a. $7(0)(-6)$ **b.** $(-2)(-3)(-4)$ **c.** $(-1)(-5)(-9)(-2)$

Solution:

a. By the order of operations, we multiply from left to right. Notice that because one of the factors is 0, the product is 0.

$$7(0)\,(-6) = 0(-6) = 0$$

b. Multiply two factors at a time, from left to right.

$$(-2)(-3)(-4) = (6)(-4) \quad \text{Multiply } (-2)(-3).$$
$$= -24$$

c. Multiply from left to right.

$$(-1)(-5)(-9)(-2) = (5)(-9)(-2) \quad \text{Multiply } (-1)(-5).$$
$$= -45(-2) \quad \text{Multiply } 5(-9).$$
$$= 90$$

● **Work Practice 7**

✓**Concept Check** What is the sign of the product of five negative numbers? Explain.

Helpful Hint

Have you noticed a pattern when multiplying signed numbers?

If we let $(-)$ represent a negative number and $(+)$ represent a positive number, then

The product of an even number of negative numbers is a positive result.

$$(-)(-) = (+)$$
$$(-)(-)(-) = (-) \longleftarrow$$
$$(-)(-)(-)(-) = (+)$$
$$(-)(-)(-)(-)(-) = (-)$$

The product of an odd number of negative numbers is a negative result.

Now that we know how to multiply positive and negative numbers, let's see how we find the values of $(-5)^2$ and -5^2, for example. Although these two expressions look similar, the difference between the two is the parentheses. In $(-5)^2$, the parentheses tell us that the base, or repeated factor, is -5. In -5^2, only 5 is the base. Thus,

$$(-5)^2 = (-5)(-5) = 25 \quad \text{The base is } -5.$$
$$-5^2 = -(5 \cdot 5) = -25 \quad \text{The base is } 5.$$

Example 8 Evaluate.

a. $(-2)^3$ **b.** -2^3 **c.** $(-3)^2$ **d.** -3^2 **e.** $\left(-\dfrac{2}{3}\right)^2$

Solution:

a. $(-2)^3 = (-2)(-2)(-2) = -8$ The base is -2.
b. $-2^3 = -(2 \cdot 2 \cdot 2) = -8$ The base is 2.
c. $(-3)^2 = (-3)(-3) = 9$ The base is -3.
d. $-3^2 = -(3 \cdot 3) = -9$ The base is 3.
e. $\left(-\dfrac{2}{3}\right)^2 = \left(-\dfrac{2}{3}\right)\left(-\dfrac{2}{3}\right) = \dfrac{4}{9}$ The base is $-\dfrac{2}{3}$.

● **Work Practice 8**

PRACTICE 7

Multiply.
a. $5(0)(-3)$
b. $(-1)(-6)(-7)$
c. $(-2)(4)(-8)(-1)$

PRACTICE 8

Evaluate.
a. $(-2)^4$ **b.** -2^4
c. $(-1)^5$ **d.** -1^5
e. $\left(-\dfrac{7}{9}\right)^2$

Answers

7. a. 0 **b.** -42 **c.** -64 **8. a.** 16
b. -16 **c.** -1 **d.** -1 **e.** $\dfrac{49}{81}$

✓**Concept Check Answer**
negative

Helpful Hint

Be careful when identifying the base of an exponential expression.

$$(-3)^2 \qquad\qquad -3^2$$
$$\text{Base is } -3 \qquad\qquad \text{Base is } 3$$
$$(-3)^2 = (-3)(-3) = 9 \qquad -3^2 = -(3\cdot 3) = -9$$

Objective B Finding Reciprocals

Addition and subtraction are related. Every difference of two numbers $a - b$ can be written as the sum $a + (-b)$. Multiplication and division are related also. For example, the quotient $6 \div 3$ can be written as the product $6 \cdot \frac{1}{3}$. Recall that the pair of numbers 3 and $\frac{1}{3}$ has a special relationship. Their product is 1 and they are called **reciprocals** or **multiplicative inverses** of each other.

Reciprocal or Multiplicative Inverse

Two numbers whose product is 1 are called **reciprocals** or **multiplicative inverses** of each other.

PRACTICE 9

Find the reciprocal of each number.
a. 13   **b.** $\frac{7}{15}$
c. -5 **d.** $-\frac{8}{11}$
e. 7.9

Example 9 Find the reciprocal of each number.

a. 22   Reciprocal is $\frac{1}{22}$ since $22 \cdot \frac{1}{22} = 1$.

b. $\frac{3}{16}$ Reciprocal is $\frac{16}{3}$ since $\frac{3}{16} \cdot \frac{16}{3} = 1$.

c. -10 Reciprocal is $-\frac{1}{10}$ since $-10 \cdot -\frac{1}{10} = 1$.

d. $-\frac{9}{13}$ Reciprocal is $-\frac{13}{9}$ since $-\frac{9}{13} \cdot -\frac{13}{9} = 1$.

e. 1.7   Reciprocal is $\frac{1}{1.7}$ since $1.7 \cdot \frac{1}{1.7} = 1$.

● Work Practice 9

Helpful Hint

The fraction $\frac{1}{1.7}$ is not simplified since the denominator is a decimal number. For the purpose of finding a reciprocal, we will leave the fraction as is.

Does the number 0 have a reciprocal? If it does, it is a number n such that $0 \cdot n = 1$. Notice that this can never be true since $0 \cdot n = 0$. This means that 0 has no reciprocal.

Answers
9. a. $\frac{1}{13}$ **b.** $\frac{15}{7}$ **c.** $-\frac{1}{5}$
d. $-\frac{11}{8}$ **e.** $\frac{1}{7.9}$

Quotients Involving Zero

The number 0 does not have a reciprocal.

Objective ⓒ Dividing Real Numbers

We may now write a quotient as an equivalent product.

Quotient of Two Real Numbers

If a and b are real numbers and b is not 0, then

$$a \div b = \frac{a}{b} = a \cdot \frac{1}{b}$$

In other words, the quotient of two real numbers is the product of the first number and the multiplicative inverse or reciprocal of the second number.

Example 10 Use the definition of the quotient of two numbers to find each quotient. $\left(a \div b = a \cdot \dfrac{1}{b} \right)$

a. $-18 \div 3$ **b.** $\dfrac{-14}{-2}$ **c.** $\dfrac{20}{-4}$

Solution:

a. $-18 \div 3 = -18 \cdot \dfrac{1}{3} = -6$

b. $\dfrac{-14}{-2} = -14 \cdot -\dfrac{1}{2} = 7$

c. $\dfrac{20}{-4} = 20 \cdot -\dfrac{1}{4} = -5$

● Work Practice 10

Since the quotient $a \div b$ can be written as the product $a \cdot \dfrac{1}{b}$, it follows that sign patterns for dividing two real numbers are the same as sign patterns for multiplying two real numbers.

Dividing Real Numbers

1. The quotient of two numbers with the *same* sign is a positive number.

2. The quotient of two numbers with *different* signs is a negative number.

Example 11 Divide.

a. $\dfrac{-30}{-10} = 3$ Same sign, so the quotient is positive.

b. $\dfrac{-100}{5} = -20$

c. $\dfrac{20}{-2} = -10$ Different signs, so the quotient is negative.

d. $\dfrac{42}{-0.6} = -70$ $0.6\overline{)42.0}$ = 70.

● Work Practice 11

✓**Concept Check** What is wrong with the following calculation?

$\dfrac{-36}{-9} = -4$

PRACTICE 10

Use the definition of the quotient of two numbers to find each quotient.

a. $-12 \div 4$ **b.** $\dfrac{-20}{-10}$

c. $\dfrac{36}{-4}$

PRACTICE 11

Divide.

a. $\dfrac{-25}{5}$ **b.** $\dfrac{-48}{-6}$

c. $\dfrac{50}{-2}$ **d.** $\dfrac{-72}{0.2}$

Answers

10. **a.** −3 **b.** 2 **c.** −9

11. **a.** −5 **b.** 8 **c.** −25 **d.** −360

✓ **Concept Check Answer**

$\dfrac{-36}{-9} = 4$

In the examples on the previous page, we divided mentally or by long division. When we divide by a fraction, it is usually easier to multiply by its reciprocal.

PRACTICE 12–13

Divide.

12. $-\dfrac{5}{9} \div \dfrac{2}{3}$ **13.** $-\dfrac{2}{7} \div \left(-\dfrac{1}{5}\right)$

Examples Divide.

12. $\dfrac{2}{3} \div \left(-\dfrac{5}{4}\right) = \dfrac{2}{3} \cdot \left(-\dfrac{4}{5}\right) = -\dfrac{8}{15}$

13. $-\dfrac{1}{6} \div \left(-\dfrac{2}{3}\right) = -\dfrac{1}{6} \cdot \left(-\dfrac{3}{2}\right) = \dfrac{3}{12} = \dfrac{\overset{1}{\cancel{3}}}{\cancel{3} \cdot 4} = \dfrac{1}{4}$

● **Work Practice 12–13**

Our definition of the quotient of two real numbers does not allow for division by 0 because 0 does not have a reciprocal. How then do we interpret $\dfrac{3}{0}$? We say that an expression such as this one is **undefined.** Can we divide 0 by a number other than 0? Yes; for example,

$$\frac{0}{3} = 0 \cdot \frac{1}{3} = 0$$

Division Involving Zero

If a is a nonzero number, then $\dfrac{0}{a} = 0$ and $\dfrac{a}{0}$ is undefined.

PRACTICE 14

Divide if possible.

a. $\dfrac{-7}{0}$ **b.** $\dfrac{0}{-2}$

Example 14 Divide, if possible.

a. $\dfrac{1}{0}$ is undefined.   **b.** $\dfrac{0}{-3} = 0$

● **Work Practice 14**

Notice that $\dfrac{12}{-2} = -6$, $-\dfrac{12}{2} = -6$, and $\dfrac{-12}{2} = -6$. This means that

$$\frac{12}{-2} = -\frac{12}{2} = \frac{-12}{2}$$

In other words, a single negative sign in a fraction can be written in the denominator, in the numerator, or in front of the fraction without changing the value of the fraction.

If a and b are real numbers, and $b \neq 0$, then $\dfrac{a}{-b} = \dfrac{-a}{b} = -\dfrac{a}{b}$.

PRACTICE 15

Use order of operations to evaluate each expression.

a. $\dfrac{0(-5)}{3}$

b. $-3(-9) - 4(-4)$

c. $(-3)^2 + 2[(5 - 15) - |-4 - 1|]$

d. $\dfrac{-7(-4) + 2}{-10 - (-5)}$

e. $\dfrac{5(-2)^3 + 52}{-4 + 1}$

Objective ⒟ Evaluating Expressions

Examples combining basic arithmetic operations along with the principles of the order of operations help us to review these concepts of multiplying and dividing real numbers.

Example 15 Use order of operations to evaluate each expression.

a. $\dfrac{0(-8)}{2}$ **b.** $-4(-11) - 5(-2)$

c. $(-2)^2 + 3[(-3 - 2) - |4 - 6|]$ **d.** $\dfrac{(-12)(-3) + 4}{-7 - (-2)}$

e. $\dfrac{2(-3)^2 - 20}{|-5| + 4}$

Answers

12. $-\dfrac{5}{6}$ **13.** $\dfrac{10}{7}$ **14. a.** undefined

b. 0 **15. a.** 0 **b.** 43 **c.** −21

d. −6 **e.** −4

Solution:

a. $\dfrac{0(-8)}{2} = \dfrac{0}{2} = 0$

b. $(-4)(-11) - 5(-2) = 44 - (-10)$ Find the products.

$\qquad\qquad\qquad\qquad = 44 + 10$ Add 44 to the opposite of -10.

$\qquad\qquad\qquad\qquad = 54$ Add.

c. $(-2)^2 + 3[(-3 - 2) - |4 - 6|] = (-2)^2 + 3[(-5) - |-2|]$ Simplify within innermost sets of grouping symbols.

$\qquad\qquad\qquad\qquad = (-2)^2 + 3[-5 - 2]$ Write $|-2|$ as 2.

$\qquad\qquad\qquad\qquad = (-2)^2 + 3(-7)$ Combine.

$\qquad\qquad\qquad\qquad = 4 + (-21)$ Evaluate $(-2)^2$ and multiply $3(-7)$.

$\qquad\qquad\qquad\qquad = -17$ Add.

For parts d and e, first simplify the numerator and denominator separately; then divide.

d. $\dfrac{(-12)(-3) + 4}{-7 - (-2)} = \dfrac{36 + 4}{-7 + 2}$

$\qquad\qquad\qquad = \dfrac{40}{-5}$

$\qquad\qquad\qquad = -8$ Divide.

e. $\dfrac{2(-3)^2 - 20}{|-5| + 4} = \dfrac{2 \cdot 9 - 20}{5 + 4} = \dfrac{18 - 20}{9} = \dfrac{-2}{9} = -\dfrac{2}{9}$

● **Work Practice 15**

Using what we have learned about multiplying and dividing real numbers, we continue to practice evaluating algebraic expressions.

Example 16 Evaluate each expression when $x = -2$ and $y = -4$.

a. $\dfrac{3x}{2y}$ **b.** $x^3 - y^2$ **c.** $\dfrac{x - y}{-x}$

Solution: Replace x with -2 and y with -4 and simplify.

a. $\dfrac{3x}{2y} = \dfrac{3(-2)}{2(-4)} = \dfrac{-6}{-8} = \dfrac{6}{8} = \dfrac{\cancel{2} \cdot 3}{\cancel{2} \cdot 4} = \dfrac{3}{4}$

b. $x^3 - y^2 = (-2)^3 - (-4)^2$ Substitute the given values for the variables.

$\qquad\qquad = -8 - (16)$ Evaluate $(-2)^3$ and $(-4)^2$.

$\qquad\qquad = -8 + (-16)$ Write as a sum.

$\qquad\qquad = -24$ Add.

c. $\dfrac{x - y}{-x} = \dfrac{-2 - (-4)}{-(-2)} = \dfrac{-2 + 4}{2} = \dfrac{2}{2} = 1$

● **Work Practice 16**

PRACTICE 16

Evaluate each expression when $x = -1$ and $y = -5$.

a. $\dfrac{3y}{45x}$

b. $x^2 - y^3$

c. $\dfrac{x + y}{3x}$

Answers

16. **a.** $\dfrac{1}{3}$ **b.** 126 **c.** 2

Helpful Hint

Remember: For additional help when replacing variables with replacement values, first place parentheses about any variables.

Evaluate $3x - y^2$ when $x = 5$ and $y = -4$.

$$3x - y^2 = 3(x) - (y)^2 \quad \text{Place parentheses about variables only.}$$
$$= 3(5) - (-4)^2 \quad \text{Replace variables with values.}$$
$$= 15 - 16 \quad \text{Simplify.}$$
$$= -1$$

Objective ⓔ Solutions of Equations

We use our skills in multiplying and dividing real numbers to check possible solutions of an equation.

PRACTICE 17

Determine whether -8 is a solution of $\dfrac{x}{4} - 3 = x + 3$.

Example 17 Determine whether -10 is a solution of $\dfrac{-20}{x} + 15 = 2x$.

Solution:
$$\frac{-20}{x} + 15 = 2x \quad \text{Original equation}$$
$$\frac{-20}{-10} + 15 \stackrel{?}{=} 2(-10) \quad \text{Replace } x \text{ with } -10.$$
$$2 + 15 \stackrel{?}{=} -20 \quad \text{Divide and multiply.}$$
$$17 = -20 \quad \text{False}$$

Since we have a false statement, -10 is *not* a solution of the equation.

● Work Practice 17

Objective ⓕ Solving Applications That Involve Multiplying or Dividing Numbers

Many real-life problems involve multiplication and division of numbers.

PRACTICE 18

A card player had a score of -13 for each of four games. Find the total score.

Example 18 Calculating a Total Golf Score

A professional golfer finished seven strokes under par (-7) for each of three days of a tournament. What was her total score for the tournament?

Solution:

1. **UNDERSTAND.** Read and reread the problem. Although the key word is "total," since this is repeated addition of the same number we multiply.
2. **TRANSLATE.**

In words:	golfer's total score	=	number of days	·	score each day
	↓	↓	↓	↓	↓
Translate:	golfer's total	=	3	·	(-7)

3. **SOLVE** $3 \cdot (-7) = -21$

4. **INTERPRET.** Check and state your conclusion: The golfer's total score was -21, or 21 strokes under par.

● Work Practice 18

Answers

17. -8 is a solution.   18. -52

Calculator Explorations

Entering Negative Numbers on a Scientific Calculator

To enter a negative number on a scientific calculator, find a key marked $\boxed{+/-}$. (On some calculators, this key is marked $\boxed{\text{CHS}}$ for "change sign.") To enter -8, for example, press the keys $\boxed{8}$ $\boxed{+/-}$. The display will read $\boxed{-8}$.

Entering Negative Numbers on a Graphing Calculator

To enter a negative number on a graphing calculator, find a key marked $\boxed{(-)}$. Do not confuse this key with the key $\boxed{-}$, which is used for subtraction. To enter -8, for example, press the keys $\boxed{(-)}$ $\boxed{8}$. The display will read $\boxed{-8}$.

Operations with Real Numbers

To evaluate $-2(7 - 9) - 20$ on a calculator, press the keys

$\boxed{2}$ $\boxed{+/-}$ $\boxed{\times}$ $\boxed{(}$ $\boxed{7}$ $\boxed{-}$ $\boxed{9}$ $\boxed{)}$ $\boxed{-}$ $\boxed{2}$ $\boxed{0}$

$\boxed{=}$, or $\boxed{(-)}$ $\boxed{2}$ $\boxed{(}$ $\boxed{7}$ $\boxed{-}$ $\boxed{9}$ $\boxed{)}$ $\boxed{-}$ $\boxed{2}$ $\boxed{0}$

$\boxed{\text{ENTER}}$.

The display will read $\boxed{-16}$ or $\boxed{\begin{array}{r} -2(7 - 9) - 20 \\ -16 \end{array}}$

Use a calculator to simplify each expression.

1. $-38(26 - 27)$

2. $-59(-8) + 1726$

3. $134 + 25(68 - 91)$

4. $45(32) - 8(218)$

5. $\dfrac{-50(294)}{175 - 205}$

6. $\dfrac{-444 - 444.8}{-181 - (-181)}$

7. $9^5 - 4550$

8. $5^8 - 6259$

9. $(-125)^2$ (Be careful.)

10. -125^2 (Be careful.)

Vocabulary and Readiness Check

Use the choices below to fill in each blank. Each choice may be used more than once.

negative   0

positive   undefined

1. The product of a negative number and a positive number is a(n) _____ number.
2. The product of two negative numbers is a(n) _____ number.
3. The quotient of two negative numbers is a(n) _____ number.
4. The quotient of a negative number and a positive number is a(n) _____ number.
5. The product of a negative number and zero is _____.
6. The reciprocal of a negative number is a _____ number.
7. The quotient of 0 and a negative number is _____.
8. The quotient of a negative number and 0 is _____.

5.6 Exercise Set

Objective A *Multiply. See Examples 1 through 7.*

1. $-6(4)$ **2.** $-8(5)$ **3.** $2(-1)$ **4.** $7(-4)$

5. $-5(-10)$ **6.** $-6(-11)$ **7.** $-3 \cdot 15$ **8.** $-2 \cdot 37$

9. $-\dfrac{1}{2}\left(-\dfrac{3}{5}\right)$ **10.** $-\dfrac{1}{8}\left(-\dfrac{1}{3}\right)$ **11.** $5(-1.4)$ **12.** $6(-2.5)$

13. $(-1)(-3)(-5)$ **14.** $(-2)(-3)(-6)$ **15.** $(2)(-1)(-3)(0)$ **16.** $(3)(-5)(-2)(0)$

Evaluate. See Example 8.

17. $(-4)^2$ **18.** $(-3)^3$ **19.** -4^2 **20.** -6^2

21. $\left(-\dfrac{3}{4}\right)^2$ **22.** $\left(-\dfrac{2}{7}\right)^2$ **23.** -0.7^2 **24.** -0.8^2

Objective B *Find each reciprocal. See Example 9.*

25. $\dfrac{2}{3}$ **26.** $\dfrac{1}{7}$ **27.** -14 **28.** -8

29. $-\dfrac{3}{11}$ **30.** $-\dfrac{6}{13}$ **31.** 0.2 **32.** 1.5

Objective ◯ *Divide. See Examples 10 through 14.*

33. $\dfrac{18}{-2}$ **34.** $\dfrac{36}{-9}$ **35.** $-48 \div 12$ **36.** $-60 \div 5$

37. $\dfrac{0}{-4}$ **38.** $\dfrac{0}{-9}$ **39.** $\dfrac{5}{0}$ **40.** $\dfrac{8}{0}$

41. $\dfrac{6}{7} \div \left(-\dfrac{1}{3}\right)$ **42.** $\dfrac{4}{5} \div \left(-\dfrac{1}{2}\right)$ **43.** $-3.2 \div -0.02$ **44.** $-4.9 \div -0.07$

Objectives ◯ ◯ **Mixed Practice** *Perform the indicated operation. See Examples 1–14.*

45. $(-8)(-8)$ **46.** $(-7)(-7)$ **47.** $\dfrac{2}{3}\left(-\dfrac{4}{9}\right)$ **48.** $\dfrac{2}{7}\left(-\dfrac{2}{11}\right)$ **49.** $\dfrac{-12}{-4}$

50. $\dfrac{-45}{-9}$ **51.** $\dfrac{30}{-2}$ **52.** $\dfrac{14}{-2}$ **53.** $(-5)^3$ **54.** $(-2)^5$

55. $(-0.2)^3$ **56.** $(-0.3)^3$ **57.** $-\dfrac{3}{4}\left(-\dfrac{8}{9}\right)$ **58.** $-\dfrac{5}{6}\left(-\dfrac{3}{10}\right)$ **59.** $-\dfrac{5}{9} \div \left(-\dfrac{3}{4}\right)$

60. $-\dfrac{1}{10} \div \left(-\dfrac{8}{11}\right)$ **61.** $-2.1(-0.4)$ **62.** $-1.3(-0.6)$ **63.** $\dfrac{-48}{1.2}$ **64.** $\dfrac{-86}{2.5}$

65. $(-3)^4$ **66.** -3^4 **67.** -1^7 **68.** $(-1)^7$

69. Multiply -11 by 11.   **70.** Multiply -12 by 12.

71. Find the quotient of $-\dfrac{4}{9}$ and $\dfrac{4}{9}$.   **72.** Find the quotient of $-\dfrac{5}{12}$ and $\dfrac{5}{12}$.

Mixed Practice (Sections 5.4, 5.5, 5.6) *Perform the indicated operation.*

73. $-9 - 10$ **74.** $-8 - 11$ **75.** $-9(-10)$ **76.** $-8(-11)$

77. $7(-12)$ **78.** $6(-15)$ **79.** $7 + (-12)$ **80.** $6 + (-15)$

Objective **D** *Evaluate each expression. See Example 15.*

81. $\dfrac{-9(-3)}{-6}$

82. $\dfrac{-6(-3)}{-4}$

83. $-3(2 - 8)$

84. $-4(3 - 9)$

85. $-7(-2) - 3(-1)$

86. $-8(-3) - 4(-1)$

87. $2^2 - 3[(2 - 8) - (-6 - 8)]$

88. $3^2 - 2[(3 - 5) - (2 - 9)]$

89. $\dfrac{-6^2 + 4}{-2}$

90. $\dfrac{3^2 + 4}{5}$

91. $\dfrac{-3 - 5^2}{2(-7)}$

92. $\dfrac{-2 - 4^2}{3(-6)}$

93. $\dfrac{22 + (3)(-2)^2}{-5 - 2}$

94. $\dfrac{-20 + (-4)^2(3)}{1 - 5}$

95. $\dfrac{(-4)^2 - 16}{4 - 12}$

96. $\dfrac{(-2)^2 - 4}{4 - 9}$

97. $\dfrac{6 - 2(-3)}{4 - 3(-2)}$

98. $\dfrac{8 - 3(-2)}{2 - 5(-4)}$

99. $\dfrac{|5 - 9| + |10 - 15|}{|2(-3)|}$

100. $\dfrac{|-3 + 6| + |-2 + 7|}{|-2 \cdot 2|}$

101. $\dfrac{-7(-1) + (-3)4}{(-2)(5) + (-6)(-8)}$

102. $\dfrac{8(-7) + (-2)(-6)}{(-9)(3) + (-10)(-11)}$

Evaluate each expression when $x = -5$ and $y = -3$. See Example 16.

103. $\dfrac{2x - 5}{y - 2}$

104. $\dfrac{2y - 12}{x - 4}$

105. $\dfrac{6 - y}{x - 4}$

106. $\dfrac{10 - y}{x - 8}$

107. $\dfrac{4 - 2x}{y + 3}$

108. $\dfrac{2y + 3}{-5 - x}$

109. $\dfrac{x^2 + y}{3y}$

110. $\dfrac{y^2 - x}{2x}$

Objective **E** *Decide whether the given number is a solution of the given equation. See Example 17.*

111. $-3x - 5 = -20; \quad 5$

112. $17 - 4x = x + 27; \quad -2$

113. $\dfrac{x}{5} + 2 = -1; \quad 15$

114. $\dfrac{x}{6} - 3 = 5; \quad 48$

115. $\dfrac{x - 3}{7} = -2; \quad -11$

116. $\dfrac{x + 4}{5} = -6; \quad -30$

Objective **F** Translating *Translate each phrase to an expression. Use x to represent "a number." See Example 18.*

117. The product of −71 and a number

118. The quotient of −8 and a number

119. Subtract a number from −16.

120. The sum of a number and −12

121. −29 increased by a number

122. The difference of a number and −10

123. Divide a number by −33.

124. Multiply a number by −17.

Solve. See Example 18.

125. A football team lost four yards on each of three consecutive plays. Represent the total loss as a product of signed numbers and find the total loss.

126. Joe Norstrom lost $400 on each of seven consecutive days in the stock market. Represent his total loss as a product of signed numbers and find his total loss.

127. A deep-sea diver must move up or down in the water in short steps in order to keep from getting a physical condition called the "bends." Suppose a diver moves down from the surface in five steps of 20 feet each. Represent his total movement as a product of signed numbers and find the product.

128. A weather forecaster predicts that the temperature will drop five degrees each hour for the next six hours. Represent this drop as a product of signed numbers and find the total drop in temperature.

Review

Find the perimeter of each figure.

129.

Square
8 in.

130. Parallelogram
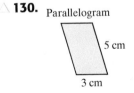
5 cm
3 cm

131. Rectangle
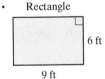
6 ft
9 ft

132. Triangle
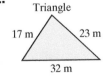
17 m   23 m
32 m

Concept Extensions

State whether each statement is true or false.

133. The product of three negative integers is negative.

134. The product of three positive integers is positive.

135. The product of four negative integers is negative.

136. The product of four positive integers is positive.

Study the bar graph below showing the average surface temperatures of planets. Use Exercises 137 and 138 to complete the planet temperatures on the graph. (Pluto is now classified as a dwarf planet.)

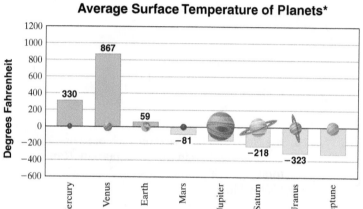

Average Surface Temperature of Planets*

137. The surface temperature of Jupiter is twice the temperature of Mars. Find this temperature.

138. The surface temperature of Neptune is equal to the temperature of Mercury divided by -1. Find this temperature.

*(For some planets, the temperature given is the temperature where the atmosphere pressure equals 1 Earth atmosphere; Source: *The World Almanac*)

139. Explain why the product of an even number of negative numbers is a positive number.

140. If a and b are any real numbers, is the statement $a \cdot b = b \cdot a$ always true? Why or why not?

141. Find two real numbers that are their own reciprocal. Explain why there are only two.

142. Explain why 0 has no reciprocal.

Mixed Practice (5.4, 5.5, 5.6) *Write each as an algebraic expression. Then simplify the expression.*

143. 7 subtracted from the quotient of 0 and 5

144. Twice the sum of -3 and -4

145. -1 added to the product of -8 and -5

146. The difference of -9 and the product of -4 and -6

5.7 PROPERTIES OF REAL NUMBERS

Objective ⒶUsing the Commutative and Associative Properties

In this section we review properties of real numbers with which we are already familiar. Throughout this section, the variables a, b, and c represent real numbers.

We know that order does not matter when adding numbers. For example, we know that $7 + 5$ is the same as $5 + 7$. This property is given a special name—the **commutative property of addition.** We also know that order does not matter when multiplying numbers. For example, we know that $-5(6) = 6(-5)$. This property means that multiplication is commutative also and is called the **commutative property of multiplication.**

Commutative Properties

Addition:	$a + b = b + a$
Multiplication:	$a \cdot b = b \cdot a$

These properties state that the *order* in which any two real numbers are added or multiplied does not change their sum or product. For example, if we let $a = 3$ and $b = 5$, then the commutative properties guarantee that

$$3 + 5 = 5 + 3 \quad \text{and} \quad 3 \cdot 5 = 5 \cdot 3$$

Helpful Hint

Is subtraction also commutative? Try an example. Is $3 - 2 = 2 - 3$? **No!** The left side of this statement equals 1; the right side equals -1. There is no commutative property of subtraction. Similarly, there is no commutative property of division. For example, $10 \div 2$ does not equal $2 \div 10$.

Example 1 Use a commutative property to complete each statement.

a. $x + 5 =$ _____
b. $3 \cdot x =$ _____

Solution:

a. $x + 5 = 5 + x$ By the commutative property of addition
b. $3 \cdot x = x \cdot 3$ By the commutative property of multiplication

● Work Practice 1

✓Concept Check Which of the following pairs of actions are commutative?

a. "raking the leaves" and "bagging the leaves"
b. "putting on your left glove" and "putting on your right glove"
c. "putting on your coat" and "putting on your shirt"
d. "reading a novel" and "reading a newspaper"

Objectives

Ⓐ Use the Commutative and Associative Properties.

Ⓑ Use the Distributive Property.

Ⓒ Use the Identity and Inverse Properties.

PRACTICE 1

Use a commutative property to complete each statement.
a. $7 \cdot y =$ _____
b. $4 + x =$ _____

Answers
1. **a.** $y \cdot 7$ **b.** $x + 4$

✓ **Concept Check Answer**
b, d

473

Let's now discuss grouping numbers. When we add three numbers, the way in which they are grouped or associated does not change their sum. For example, we know that $2 + (3 + 4) = 2 + 7 = 9$. This result is the same if we group the numbers differently. In other words, $(2 + 3) + 4 = 5 + 4 = 9$, also. Thus, $2 + (3 + 4) = (2 + 3) + 4$. This property is called the **associative property of addition.**

In the same way, changing the grouping of numbers when multiplying does not change their product. For example, $2 \cdot (3 \cdot 4) = (2 \cdot 3) \cdot 4$ (check it). This is the **associative property of multiplication.**

Associative Properties

Addition: $(a + b) + c = a + (b + c)$

Multiplication: $(a \cdot b) \cdot c = a \cdot (b \cdot c)$

These properties state that the way in which three numbers are *grouped* does not change their sum or their product.

PRACTICE 2

Use an associative property to complete each statement.

a. $5 \cdot (-3 \cdot 6) = $ _____
b. $(-2 + 7) + 3 = $ _____
c. $(q + r) + 17 = $ _____
d. $(ab) \cdot 21 = $ _____

Example 2 Use an associative property to complete each statement.

a. $5 + (4 + 6) = $ _____   b. $(-1 \cdot 2) \cdot 5 = $ _____
c. $(m + n) + 9 = $ _____   d. $(xy) \cdot 12 = $ _____

Solution:

a. $5 + (4 + 6) = (5 + 4) + 6$ By the associative property of addition
b. $(-1 \cdot 2) \cdot 5 = -1 \cdot (2 \cdot 5)$ By the associative property of multiplication
c. $(m + n) + 9 = m + (n + 9)$ By the associative property of addition
d. $(xy) \cdot 12 = x \cdot (y \cdot 12)$ Recall that xy means $x \cdot y$.

● Work Practice 2

Helpful Hint

Remember the difference between the commutative properties and the associative properties. The commutative properties have to do with the *order* of numbers and the associative properties have to do with the *grouping* of numbers.

PRACTICE 3–4

Determine whether each statement is true by an associative property or a commutative property.

3. $5 \cdot (4 \cdot 7) = 5 \cdot (7 \cdot 4)$
4. $-2 + (4 + 9)$
   $= (-2 + 4) + 9$

Examples Determine whether each statement is true by an associative property or a commutative property.

3. $(7 + 10) + 4 = (10 + 7) + 4$ Since the order of two numbers was changed and their grouping was not, this is true by the commutative property of addition.

4. $2 \cdot (3 \cdot 1) = (2 \cdot 3) \cdot 1$ Since the grouping of the numbers was changed and their order was not, this is true by the associative property of multiplication.

● Work Practice 3–4

Answers
2. a. $(5 \cdot -3) \cdot 6$ b. $-2 + (7 + 3)$
c. $q + (r + 17)$ d. $a \cdot (b \cdot 21)$
3. commutative 4. associative

Let's now illustrate how these properties can help us simplify expressions.

Examples Simplify each expression.

5. $10 + (x + 12) = 10 + (12 + x)$ By the commutative property of addition
$= (10 + 12) + x$ By the associative property of addition
$= 22 + x$ Add.

6. $-3(7x) = (-3 \cdot 7)x$ By the associative property of multiplication
$= -21x$ Multiply.

● Work Practice 5–6

Objective B Using the Distributive Property

The **distributive property of multiplication over addition** is used repeatedly throughout algebra. It is useful because it allows us to write a product as a sum or a sum as a product.

We know that $7(2 + 4) = 7(6) = 42$. Compare that with

$7(2) + 7(4) = 14 + 28 = 42$

Since both original expressions equal 42, they must equal each other, or

$7(2 + 4) = 7(2) + 7(4)$

This is an example of the distributive property. The product on the left side of the equal sign is equal to the sum on the right side. We can think of the 7 as being distributed to each number inside the parentheses.

Distributive Property of Multiplication Over Addition

$$a(b + c) = ab + ac$$

Since multiplication is commutative, this property can also be written as

$$(b + c)a = ba + ca$$

The distributive property can also be extended to more than two numbers inside the parentheses. For example,

$3(x + y + z) = 3(x) + 3(y) + 3(z)$
$= 3x + 3y + 3z$

Since we define subtraction in terms of addition, the distributive property is also true for subtraction. For example,

$2(x - y) = 2(x) - 2(y)$
$= 2x - 2y$

Examples Use the distributive property to write each expression without parentheses. Then simplify the result.

7. $2(x + y) = 2(x) + 2(y)$
$= 2x + 2y$

8. $-5(-3 + 2z) = -5(-3) + (-5)(2z)$
$= 15 - 10z$

9. $5(x + 3y - z) = 5(x) + 5(3y) - 5(z)$
$= 5x + 15y - 5z$

Continued on next page

Continued on next page

10. $-1(2 - y) = (-1)(2) - (-1)(y)$
$$= -2 + y$$

11. $-(3 + x - w) = -1(3 + x - w)$
$$= (-1)(3) + (-1)(x) - (-1)(w)$$
$$= -3 - x + w$$

Helpful Hint
Notice in Example 11 that $-(3 + x - w)$ can be rewritten as $-1(3 + x - w)$.

12. $\dfrac{1}{2}(6x + 14) + 10 = \dfrac{1}{2}(6x) + \dfrac{1}{2}(14) + 10$ Apply the distributive property.
$$= 3x + 7 + 10$$ Multiply.
$$= 3x + 17$$ Add.

● **Work Practice 7–12**

The distributive property can also be used to write a sum as a product.

PRACTICE 13–14

Use the distributive property to write each sum as a product.
13. $9 \cdot 3 + 9 \cdot y$
14. $4x + 4y$

Examples Use the distributive property to write each sum as a product.

13. $8 \cdot 2 + 8 \cdot x = 8(2 + x)$
14. $7s + 7t = 7(s + t)$

● **Work Practice 13–14**

Objective ◉ Using the Identity and Inverse Properties

Next, we look at the **identity properties.**

The number 0 is called the identity for addition because when 0 is added to any real number, the result is the same real number. In other words, the *identity* of the real number is not changed.

The number 1 is called the identity for multiplication because when a real number is multiplied by 1, the result is the same real number. In other words, the *identity* of the real number is not changed.

> ### Identities for Addition and Multiplication
>
> 0 is the identity element for addition.
> $$a + 0 = a \quad \text{and} \quad 0 + a = a$$
> 1 is the identity element for multiplication.
> $$a \cdot 1 = a \quad \text{and} \quad 1 \cdot a = a$$

Notice that 0 is the *only* number that can be added to any real number with the result that the sum is the same real number. Also, 1 is the *only* number that can be multiplied by any real number with the result that the product is the same real number.

Additive inverses or **opposites** were introduced in Section 5.4. Two numbers are called additive inverses or opposites if their sum is 0. The additive inverse or opposite of 6 is -6 because $6 + (-6) = 0$. The additive inverse or opposite of -5 is 5 because $-5 + 5 = 0$.

Reciprocals or **multiplicative inverses** were introduced in Section 5.6. Two nonzero numbers are called reciprocals or multiplicative inverses if their product is 1. The reciprocal or multiplicative inverse of $\dfrac{2}{3}$ is $\dfrac{3}{2}$ because $\dfrac{2}{3} \cdot \dfrac{3}{2} = 1$. Likewise, the reciprocal of -5 is $-\dfrac{1}{5}$ because $-5\left(-\dfrac{1}{5}\right) = 1$.

Answers
13. $9(3 + y)$ **14.** $4(x + y)$

Additive or Multiplicative Inverses

The numbers a and $-a$ are additive inverses or opposites of each other because their sum is 0; that is,

$$a + (-a) = 0$$

The numbers b and $\dfrac{1}{b}$ (for $b \neq 0$) are reciprocals or multiplicative inverses of each other because their product is 1; that is,

$$b \cdot \dfrac{1}{b} = 1$$

✓ **Concept Check** Which of the following is

a. the opposite of $-\dfrac{3}{10}$, and

b. the reciprocal of $-\dfrac{3}{10}$?

$$1, \ -\dfrac{10}{3}, \ \dfrac{3}{10}, \ 0, \ \dfrac{10}{3}, \ -\dfrac{3}{10}$$

Examples Name the property illustrated by each true statement.

15. $3(x + y) = 3 \cdot x + 3 \cdot y$ Distributive property

16. $(x + 7) + 9 = x + (7 + 9)$ Associative property of addition (grouping changed)

17. $(b + 0) + 3 = b + 3$ Identity element for addition

18. $2 \cdot (z \cdot 5) = 2 \cdot (5 \cdot z)$ Commutative property of multiplication (order changed)

19. $-2 \cdot \left(-\dfrac{1}{2}\right) = 1$ Multiplicative inverse property

20. $-2 + 2 = 0$ Additive inverse property

21. $-6 \cdot (y \cdot 2) = (-6 \cdot 2) \cdot y$ Commutative and associative properties of multiplication (order and grouping changed)

● **Work Practice 15–21**

PRACTICE 15–21

Name the property illustrated by each true statement.

15. $7(a + b) = 7 \cdot a + 7 \cdot b$

16. $12 + y = y + 12$

17. $-4 \cdot (6 \cdot x) = (-4 \cdot 6) \cdot x$

18. $6 + (z + 2) = 6 + (2 + z)$

19. $3\left(\dfrac{1}{3}\right) = 1$

20. $(x + 0) + 23 = x + 23$

21. $(7 \cdot y) \cdot 10 = y \cdot (7 \cdot 10)$

Answers

15. distributive property
16. commutative property of addition
17. associative property of multiplication   **18.** commutative property of addition
19. multiplicative inverse property
20. identity element for addition
21. commutative and associative properties of multiplication

✓ **Concept Check Answers**

a. $\dfrac{3}{10}$ **b.** $-\dfrac{10}{3}$

Vocabulary and Readiness Check

Use the choices below to fill in each blank.

distributive property   associative property of multiplication   commutative property of addition

opposites or additive inverses   associative property of addition

reciprocals or multiplicative inverses   commutative property of multiplication

1. $x + 5 = 5 + x$ is a true statement by the _____.

2. $x \cdot 5 = 5 \cdot x$ is a true statement by the _____.

3. $3(y + 6) = 3 \cdot y + 3 \cdot 6$ is true by the _____.

4. $2 \cdot (x \cdot y) = (2 \cdot x) \cdot y$ is a true statement by the _____.

5. $x + (7 + y) = (x + 7) + y$ is a true statement by the _____.

6. The numbers $-\dfrac{2}{3}$ and $-\dfrac{3}{2}$ are called _____.

7. The numbers $-\dfrac{2}{3}$ and $\dfrac{2}{3}$ are called _____.

5.7 Exercise Set

FOR EXTRA HELP
MyMathLab   Powered by CourseCompass™ and MathXL™
Math XL   PRACTICE   WATCH   DOWNLOAD   READ   REVIEW

Objective A *Use a commutative property to complete each statement. See Examples 1 and 3.*

1. $x + 16 =$ **2.** $8 + y =$ **3.** $-4 \cdot y =$ **4.** $-2 \cdot x =$

5. $xy =$ **6.** $ab =$ **7.** $2x + 13 =$ **8.** $19 + 3y =$

Use an associative property to complete each statement. See Examples 2 and 4.

9. $(xy) \cdot z =$ _____   **10.** $3 \cdot (x \cdot y) =$ _____   **11.** $2 + (a + b) =$ _____

12. $(y + 4) + z =$ _____   **13.** $4 \cdot (ab) =$ _____   **14.** $(-3y) \cdot z =$ _____

15. $(a + b) + c =$ _____   **16.** $6 + (r + s) =$ _____

Use the commutative and associative properties to simplify each expression. See Examples 5 and 6.

17. $8 + (9 + b)$ **18.** $(r + 3) + 11$ **19.** $4(6y)$ **20.** $2(42x)$ **21.** $\dfrac{1}{5}(5y)$

22. $\dfrac{1}{8}(8z)$ **23.** $(13 + a) + 13$ **24.** $7 + (x + 4)$ **25.** $-9(8x)$ **26.** $-3(12y)$

27. $\dfrac{3}{4}\left(\dfrac{4}{3}s\right)$ **28.** $\dfrac{2}{7}\left(\dfrac{7}{2}r\right)$ **29.** $-\dfrac{1}{2}(5x)$ **30.** $-\dfrac{1}{3}(7x)$

Objective Ⓑ *Use the distributive property to write each expression without parentheses. Then simplify the result, if possible. See Examples 7 through 12.*

31. $4(x + y)$ **32.** $7(a + b)$ **33.** $9(x - 6)$ **34.** $11(y - 4)$

35. $2(3x + 5)$ **36.** $5(7 + 8y)$ **37.** $7(4x - 3)$ **38.** $3(8x - 1)$

39. $3(6 + x)$ **40.** $2(x + 5)$ **41.** $-2(y - z)$ **42.** $-3(z - y)$

43. $-\dfrac{1}{3}(3y + 5)$ **44.** $-\dfrac{1}{2}(2r + 11)$ **45.** $5(x + 4m + 2)$ **46.** $8(3y + z - 6)$

47. $-4(1 - 2m + n) + 4$ **48.** $-4(4 + 2p + 5) + 16$ **49.** $-(5x + 2)$ **50.** $-(9r + 5)$

51. $-(r - 3 - 7p)$ **52.** $-(q - 2 + 6r)$ **53.** $\dfrac{1}{2}(6x + 7) + \dfrac{1}{2}$ **54.** $\dfrac{1}{4}(4x - 2) - \dfrac{7}{2}$

55. $-\dfrac{1}{3}(3x - 9y)$ **56.** $-\dfrac{1}{5}(10a - 25b)$ **57.** $3(2r + 5) - 7$ **58.** $10(4s + 6) - 40$

59. $-9(4x + 8) + 2$ **60.** $-11(5x + 3) + 10$ **61.** $-0.4(4x + 5) - 0.5$ **62.** $-0.6(2x + 1) - 0.1$

Use the distributive property to write each sum as a product. See Examples 13 and 14.

63. $4 \cdot 1 + 4 \cdot y$ **64.** $14 \cdot z + 14 \cdot 5$ **65.** $11x + 11y$ **66.** $9a + 9b$

67. $(-1) \cdot 5 + (-1) \cdot x$ **68.** $(-3)a + (-3)y$ **69.** $30a + 30b$ **70.** $25x + 25y$

Objectives Ⓐ Ⓒ **Mixed Practice** *Name the property illustrated by each true statement. See Examples 15 through 21.*

71. $3 \cdot 5 = 5 \cdot 3$ **72.** $4(3 + 8) = 4 \cdot 3 + 4 \cdot 8$

73. $2 + (x + 5) = (2 + x) + 5$ **74.** $9 \cdot (x \cdot 7) = (9 \cdot x) \cdot 7$

75. $(x + 9) + 3 = (9 + x) + 3$ **76.** $1 \cdot 9 = 9$

77. $(4 \cdot y) \cdot 9 = 4 \cdot (y \cdot 9)$ **78.** $-4 \cdot (8 \cdot 3) = (8 \cdot 3) \cdot (-4)$

79. $0 + 6 = 6$

80. $(a + 9) + 6 = a + (9 + 6)$

81. $-4(y + 7) = -4 \cdot y + (-4) \cdot 7$

82. $(11 + r) + 8 = (r + 11) + 8$

83. $6 \cdot \dfrac{1}{6} = 1$

84. $r + 0 = r$

85. $-6 \cdot 1 = -6$

86. $-\dfrac{3}{4}\left(-\dfrac{4}{3}\right) = 1$

Review

Perform each indicated operation. See Sections 1.3, 1.4, 1.6, and 1.7.

87. $45 \cdot 90$ **88.** $90 \div 45$ **89.** $90 - 45$ **90.** $45 + 90$

Concept Extensions

Fill in the table with the opposite (additive inverse), the reciprocal (multiplicative inverse), or the expression. Assume that the value of each expression is not 0.

	91.	92.	93.	94.	95.	96.
Expression	8	$-\dfrac{2}{3}$	x	$4y$		
Opposite						$7x$
Reciprocal					$\dfrac{1}{2x}$	

Decide whether each statement is true or false. See the second Concept Check in this section.

97. The opposite of $-\dfrac{a}{2}$ is $-\dfrac{2}{a}$.

98. The reciprocal of $-\dfrac{a}{2}$ is $\dfrac{a}{2}$.

Determine which pairs of actions are commutative. See the first Concept Check in this section.

99. "taking a test" and "studying for the test"

100. "putting on your shoes" and "putting on your socks"

101. "putting on your left shoe" and "putting on your right shoe"

102. "reading the sports section" and "reading the comics section"

103. "mowing the lawn" and "trimming the hedges"

104. "baking a cake" and "eating the cake"

105. "feeding the dog" and "feeding the cat"

106. "dialing a number" and "turning on the cell phone"

Name the property illustrated by each step.

107. a. $\triangle + (\square + \bigcirc) = (\square + \bigcirc) + \triangle$

b. $\qquad\qquad = (\bigcirc + \square) + \triangle$

c. $\qquad\qquad = \bigcirc + (\square + \triangle)$

108. a. $(x + y) + z = x + (y + z)$

b. $\qquad\qquad = (y + z) + x$

c. $\qquad\qquad = (z + y) + x$

109. Explain why 0 is called the identity element for addition.

110. Explain why 1 is called the identity element for multiplication.

111. Write an example that shows that division is not commutative.

112. Write an example that shows that subtraction is not commutative.

5.8 SIMPLIFYING EXPRESSIONS

As we explore in this section, we will see that an expression such as $3x + 2x$ is not written as simply as possible. This is because—even without replacing x by a value—we can perform the indicated addition.

Objective **A** Identifying Terms, Like Terms, and Unlike Terms

Before we practice simplifying expressions, we must learn some new language. A **term** is a number or the product of a number and variables raised to powers.

Terms

$$-y, \quad 2x^3, \quad -5, \quad 3xz^2, \quad \frac{2}{y}, \quad 0.8z$$

The **numerical coefficient** of a term is the numerical factor. The numerical coefficient of $3x$ is 3. Recall that $3x$ means $3 \cdot x$.

Term	Numerical Coefficient
$3x$	3
$\dfrac{y^3}{5}$	$\dfrac{1}{5}$ since $\dfrac{y^3}{5}$ means $\dfrac{1}{5} \cdot y^3$
$-0.7ab^3c^5$	-0.7
z	1
$-y$	-1
-5	-5

Helpful Hint

The term z means $1z$ and thus has a numerical coefficient of 1.
The term $-y$ means $-1y$ and thus has a numerical coefficient of -1.

PRACTICE 1

Identify the numerical coefficient of each term.
a. $-4x$ **b.** $15y^3$ **c.** x
d. $-y$ **e.** $\dfrac{z}{4}$

Example 1 Identify the numerical coefficient of each term.

a. $-3y$ **b.** $22z^4$ **c.** y **d.** $-x$ **e.** $\dfrac{x}{7}$

Solution:

a. The numerical coefficient of $-3y$ is -3.
b. The numerical coefficient of $22z^4$ is 22.
c. The numerical coefficient of y is 1, since y is $1y$.
d. The numerical coefficient of $-x$ is -1, since $-x$ is $-1x$.
e. The numerical coefficient of $\dfrac{x}{7}$ is $\dfrac{1}{7}$, since $\dfrac{x}{7}$ is $\dfrac{1}{7} \cdot x$.

● **Work Practice 1**

Answers
1. **a.** -4 **b.** 15   **c.** 1
d. -1 **e.** $\dfrac{1}{4}$

Terms with the same variables raised to exactly the same powers are called **like terms.** Terms that aren't like terms are called **unlike terms.**

Like Terms	Unlike Terms	Reason Why
$3x, 2x$	$5x, 5x^2$	Why? Same variable x, but different powers of x and x^2
$-6x^2y, 2x^2y, 4x^2y$	$7y, 3z, 8x^2$	Why? Different variables
$2ab^2c^3, ac^3b^2$	$6abc^3, 6ab^2$	Why? Different variables and different powers

Helpful Hint

In like terms, each variable and its exponent must match exactly, but these factors don't need to be in the same order.

$2x^2y$ and $3yx^2$ are like terms.

Example 2 Determine whether the terms are like or unlike.

a. $2x, 3x^2$ **b.** $4x^2y, x^2y, -2x^2y$ **c.** $-2yz, -3zy$
d. $-x^4, x^4$ **e.** $-8a^5, 8a^5$

Solution:

a. Unlike terms, since the exponents on x are not the same.
b. Like terms, since each variable and its exponent match.
c. Like terms, since $zy = yz$ by the commutative property.
d. Like terms. The variable and its exponent match.
e. Like terms. The variable and its exponent match.

● Work Practice 2

Objective ⓑ Combining Like Terms

An algebraic expression containing the sum or difference of like terms can be simplified by applying the distributive property. For example, by the distributive property, we rewrite the sum of the like terms $6x + 2x$ as

$$6x + 2x = (6 + 2)x = 8x$$

Also,

$$-y^2 + 5y^2 = (-1 + 5)y^2 = 4y^2$$

Simplifying the sum or difference of like terms is called **combining like terms.**

Example 3 Simplify each expression by combining like terms.

a. $7x - 3x$ **b.** $10y^2 + y^2$
c. $8x^2 + 2x - 3x$ **d.** $9n^2 - 5n^2 + n^2$

Solution:

a. $7x - 3x = (7 - 3)x = 4x$
b. $10y^2 + y^2 = (10 + 1)y^2 = 11y^2$
c. $8x^2 + 2x - 3x = 8x^2 + (2 - 3)x = 8x^2 - 1x$ or $8x^2 - x$
d. $9n^2 - 5n^2 + n^2 = (9 - 5 + 1)n^2 = 5n^2$

● Work Practice 3

PRACTICE 2

Determine whether the terms are like or unlike.
a. $7x^2, -6x^3$
b. $3x^2y^2, -x^2y^2, 4x^2y^2$
c. $-5ab, 3ba$
d. $2x^3, 4y^3$
e. $-7m^4, 7m^4$

PRACTICE 3

Simplify each expression by combining like terms.
a. $9y - 4y$
b. $11x^2 + x^2$
c. $5y - 3x + 4x$
d. $14m^2 - m^2 + 3m^2$

Answers
2. a. unlike   **b.** like   **c.** like
d. unlike   **e.** like   **3. a.** $5y$ **b.** $12x^2$
c. $5y + x$ **d.** $16m^2$

The preceding examples suggest the following.

> ### Combining Like Terms
>
> To **combine like terms,** combine the numerical coefficients and multiply the result by the common variable factors.

PRACTICE 4–7

Simplify each expression by combining like terms.
4. $7y + 2y + 6 + 10$
5. $-2x + 4 + x - 11$
6. $3z - 3z^2$
7. $8.9y + 4.2y - 3$

Examples   Simplify each expression by combining like terms.

4. $2x + 3x + 5 + 2 = (2 + 3)x + (5 + 2)$
   $$= 5x + 7$$

5. $-5a - 3 + a + 2 = -5a + 1a + (-3 + 2)$
   $$= (-5 + 1)a + (-3 + 2)$$
   $$= -4a - 1$$

6. $4y - 3y^2$ These two terms cannot be combined because they are unlike terms.

7. $2.3x + 5x - 6 = (2.3 + 5)x - 6$
   $$= 7.3x - 6$$

● **Work Practice 4–7**

Objective ⒸSimplifyingExpressions Containing Parentheses

In simplifying expressions we make frequent use of the distributive property to remove parentheses.

It may be helpful to study the examples below.

$$+(3a + 2) = +1(3a + 2) = +1(3a) + (+1)(2) = 3a + 2$$
→ means →

$$-(3a + 2) = -1(3a + 2) = -1(3a) + (-1)(2) = -3a - 2$$
→ means →

PRACTICE 8–10

Find each product by using the distributive property to remove parentheses.
8. $3(11y + 6)$
9. $-4(x + 0.2y - 3)$
10. $-(3x + 2y + z - 1)$

Examples   Find each product by using the distributive property to remove parentheses.

8. $5(3x + 2) = 5(3x) + 5(2)$ Apply the distributive property.
   $$= 15x + 10$$ Multiply.

9. $-2(y + 0.3z - 1) = -2(y) + (-2)(0.3z) - (-2)(1)$ Apply the distributive property.
   $$= -2y - 0.6z + 2$$ Multiply.

10. $-(9x + y - 2z + 6) = -1(9x + y - 2z + 6)$ Distribute -1 over each term.
    $$= -1(9x) + (-1)(y) - (-1)(2z) + (-1)(6)$$
    $$= -9x - y + 2z - 6$$

● **Work Practice 8–10**

Answers
4. $9y + 16$ 5. $-x - 7$
6. $3z - 3z^2$ 7. $13.1y - 3$
8. $33y + 18$ 9. $-4x - 0.8y + 12$
10. $-3x - 2y - z + 1$

Helpful Hint

If a "−" sign precedes parentheses, the sign of each term inside the parentheses is changed when the distributive property is applied to remove the parentheses.

Examples:

$$-(2x + 1) = -2x - 1$$
$$-(x - 2y) = -x + 2y$$
$$-(-5x + y - z) = 5x - y + z$$
$$-(-3x - 4y - 1) = 3x + 4y + 1$$

When simplifying an expression containing parentheses, we often use the distributive property first to remove parentheses and then again to combine any like terms.

Examples   Simplify each expression.

11. $3(2x - 5) + 1 = 6x - 15 + 1$ Apply the distributive property.
$$= 6x - 14 \qquad \text{Combine like terms.}$$

12. $8 - (7x + 2) + 3x = 8 - 7x - 2 + 3x$ Apply the distributive property.
$$= -7x + 3x + 8 - 2$$
$$= -4x + 6 \qquad \text{Combine like terms.}$$

13. $-2(4x + 7) - (3x - 1) = -8x - 14 - 3x + 1$ Apply the distributive property.
$$= -11x - 13 \qquad \text{Combine like terms.}$$

14. $9 + 3(4x - 10) = 9 + 12x - 30$ Apply the distributive property.
$$= -21 + 12x \qquad \text{Combine like terms.}$$
$$\text{or } 12x - 21$$

● **Work Practice 11–14**

PRACTICE 11–14

Simplify each expression.
11. $4(4x - 6) + 20$
12. $5 - (3x + 9) + 6x$
13. $-3(7x + 1) - (4x - 2)$
14. $8 + 11(2y - 9)$

Helpful Hint   Don't forget to use the distributive property and multiply before adding or subtracting like terms.

Example 15   Subtract $4x - 2$ from $2x - 3$.

Solution: We first note that "subtract $4x - 2$ from $2x - 3$" translates to $(2x - 3) - (4x - 2)$. Notice that parentheses were placed around each given expression. This is to ensure that the entire expression after the subtraction sign is subtracted. Next, we simplify the algebraic expression.

$$(2x - 3) - (4x - 2) = 2x - 3 - 4x + 2 \qquad \text{Apply the distributive property.}$$
$$= -2x - 1 \qquad \text{Combine like terms.}$$

● **Work Practice 15**

PRACTICE 15

Subtract $9x - 10$ from $4x - 3$.

Objective ⓓ Writing Algebraic Expressions

To prepare for problem solving, we next practice writing word phrases as algebraic expressions.

Answers
11. $16x - 4$ **12.** $3x - 4$
13. $-25x - 1$ **14.** $-91 + 22y$
15. $-5x + 7$

PRACTICE 16–19

Write each phrase as an algebraic expression and simplify if possible. Let *x* represent the unknown number.

16. Three times a number, subtracted from 10

17. The sum of a number and 2, divided by 5

18. Three times a number, added to the sum of a number and 6

19. Seven times the difference of a number and 4.

 Write each phrase as an algebraic expression and simplify if possible. Let *x* represent the unknown number.

16. 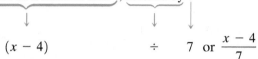 Twice a number, plus 6

$$2x \qquad + \ 6$$

This expression cannot be simplified.

17. 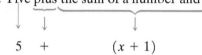 The difference of a number and 4, divided by 7

$$(x - 4) \qquad \div \quad 7 \ \text{or} \ \frac{x - 4}{7}$$

This expression cannot be simplified.

18. Five plus the sum of a number and 1

$$5 \quad + \qquad (x + 1)$$

We can simplify this expression.

$$5 + (x + 1) = 5 + x + 1$$
$$= 6 + x$$

19. Four times the sum of a number and 3

$$4 \quad \cdot \qquad (x + 3)$$

Use the distributive property to simplify the expression.

$$4 \cdot (x + 3) = 4(x + 3)$$
$$= 4 \cdot x + 4 \cdot 3$$
$$= 4x + 12$$

● **Work Practice 16–19**

Answers

16. $10 - 3x$ **17.** $(x + 2) \div 5$ or $\dfrac{x + 2}{5}$
18. $4x + 6$ **19.** $7x - 28$

Vocabulary and Readiness Check

Use the choices below to fill in each blank. Some choices may be used more than once.

numerical coefficient   expression   unlike   distributive

combine like terms   like   term

1. $14y^2 + 2x - 23$ is called a(n) _____ while $14y^2, 2x,$ and -23 are each called a(n) _____.

2. To multiply $3(-7x + 1)$, we use the _____ property.

3. To simplify an expression like $y + 7y$, we _____.

4. The term z has an understood _____ of 1.

5. The terms $-x$ and $5x$ are _____ terms and the terms $5x$ and $5y$ are _____ terms.

6. For the term $-3x^2y$, -3 is called the _____.

Objective Ⓐ *Identify the numerical coefficient of each term. See Example 1.*

7. $-7y$ **8.** $3x$ **9.** x **10.** $-y$ **11.** $17x^2y$ **12.** $1.2xyz$

Indicate whether the terms in each list are like or unlike. See Example 2.

13. $5y, -y$ **14.** $-2x^2y, 6xy$ **15.** $2z, 3z^2$

16. $ab^2, -7ab^2$ **17.** $8wz, \frac{1}{7}zw$ **18.** $7.4p^3q^2, 6.2p^3q^2r$

5.8 Exercise Set

Objective Ⓑ *Simplify each expression by combining any like terms. See Examples 3 through 7.*

1. $7y + 8y$ **2.** $3x + 2x$ **3.** $8w - w + 6w$

4. $c - 7c + 2c$ **5.** $3b - 5 - 10b - 4$ **6.** $6g + 5 - 3g - 7$

7. $m - 4m + 2m - 6$ **8.** $a + 3a - 2 - 7a$ **9.** $5g - 3 - 5 - 5g$

10. $8p + 4 - 8p - 15$ **11.** $6.2x - 4 + x - 1.2$ **12.** $7.9y - 0.7 - y + 0.2$

13. $2k - k - 6$ **14.** $7c - 8 - c$ **15.** $-9x + 4x + 18 - 10x$

16. $5y - 14 + 7y - 20y$ **17.** $6x - 5x + x - 3 + 2x$ **18.** $8h + 13h - 6 + 7h - h$

19. $7x^2 + 8x^2 - 10x^2$ **20.** $8x^3 + x^3 - 11x^3$ **21.** $3.4m - 4 - 3.4m - 7$

22. $2.8w - 0.9 - 0.5 - 2.8w$ **23.** $6x + 0.5 - 4.3x - 0.4x + 3$ **24.** $0.4y - 6.7 + y - 0.3 - 2.6y$

Objective **C** *Simplify each expression. Use the distributive property to remove any parentheses. See Examples 8 through 10.*

25. $5(y + 4)$ **26.** $7(r + 3)$ **27.** $-2(x + 2)$ **28.** $-4(y + 6)$

29. $-5(2x - 3y + 6)$ **30.** $-2(4x - 3z - 1)$ **31.** $-(3x - 2y + 1)$ **32.** $-(y + 5z - 7)$

Objectives **B** **C** Mixed Practice   *Remove parentheses and simplify each expression. See Examples 8 through 14.*

33. $7(d - 3) + 10$ **34.** $9(z + 7) - 15$ **35.** $-4(3y - 4) + 12y$

36. $-3(2x + 5) - 6x$ **37.** $3(2x - 5) - 5(x - 4)$ **38.** $2(6x - 1) - (x - 7)$

39. $-2(3x - 4) + 7x - 6$ **40.** $8y - 2 - 3(y + 4)$ **41.** $5k - (3k - 10)$

42. $-11c - (4 - 2c)$ **43.** $(3x + 4) - (6x - 1)$ **44.** $(8 - 5y) - (4 + 3y)$

45. $5(x + 2) - (3x - 4)$ **46.** $4(2x - 3) - (x + 1)$ **47.** $\frac{1}{3}(7y - 1) + \frac{1}{6}(4y + 7)$

48. $\frac{1}{5}(9y + 2) + \frac{1}{10}(2y - 1)$ **49.** $2 + 4(6x - 6)$ **50.** $8 + 4(3x - 4)$

51. $0.5(m + 2) + 0.4m$ **52.** $0.2(k + 8) - 0.1k$ **53.** $10 - 3(2x + 3y)$

54. $14 - 11(5m + 3n)$ **55.** $6(3x - 6) - 2(x + 1) - 17x$ **56.** $7(2x + 5) - 4(x + 2) - 20x$

57. $\frac{1}{2}(12x - 4) - (x + 5)$ **58.** $\frac{1}{3}(9x - 6) - (x - 2)$

Perform each indicated operation. Don't forget to simplify if possible. See Example 15.

59. Add $6x + 7$ to $4x - 10$.   **60.** Add $3y - 5$ to $y + 16$.   **61.** Subtract $7x + 1$ from $3x - 8$.

62. Subtract $4x - 7$ from $12 + x$.   **63.** Subtract $5m - 6$ from $m - 9$.   **64.** Subtract $m - 3$ from $2m - 6$.

Objective **D** *Write each phrase as an algebraic expression and simplify if possible. Let x represent the unknown number. See Examples 16 through 19.*

65. Twice a number, decreased by four

66. The difference of a number and two, divided by five

67. Three-fourths of a number, increased by twelve

68. Eight more than triple a number

69. The sum of 5 times a number and −2, added to 7 times the number

70. The sum of 3 times a number and 10, **subtracted from** 9 times the number

71. Eight times the sum of a number and six

72. Six times the difference of a number and five

73. Double a number minus the sum of the number and ten

74. Half a number minus the product of the number and eight

Review

Evaluate each expression for the given values. See Section 5.3 and 5.6.

75. If $x = -1$ and $y = 3$, find $y - x^2$

76. If $g = 0$ and $h = -4$, find $gh - h^2$

77. If $a = 2$ and $b = -5$, find $a - b^2$

78. If $x = -3$, find $x^3 - x^2 + 4$

79. If $y = -5$ and $z = 0$, find $yz - y^2$

80. If $x = -2$, find $x^3 - x^2 - x$

Concept Extensions

Given the following information, determine whether each scale on the next page is balanced or not.

1 cone balances 1 cube

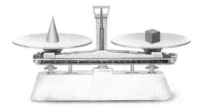

1 cylinder balances 2 cubes

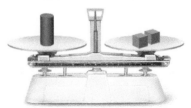

81.

82.

83.

84.

Write each algebraic expression described.

85. Write an expression with 4 terms that simplifies to $3x - 4$.

86. Write an expression of the form ____ (____ + ____) whose product is $6x + 24$.

△ **87.** Given the following rectangle, express the perimeter as an algebraic expression containing the variable x.

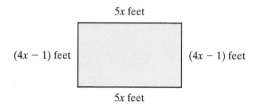

5x feet

$(4x - 1)$ feet $(4x - 1)$ feet

5x feet

△ **88.** Given the following triangle, express its perimeter as an algebraic expression containing the variable x.

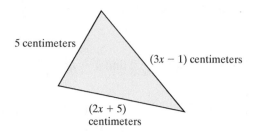

5 centimeters

$(3x - 1)$ centimeters

$(2x + 5)$ centimeters

△ **89.** To convert from feet to inches, we multiply by 12. For example, the number of inches in 2 feet is $12 \cdot 2$ inches. If one board has a length of $(x + 2)$ *feet* and a second board has a length of $(3x - 1)$ *inches*, express their total length in inches as an algebraic expression.

90. The value of 7 nickels is $5 \cdot 7$ cents. Likewise, the value of x nickels is $5x$ cents. If the money box in a drink machine contains x *nickels*, $3x$ *dimes*, and $(30x - 1)$ *quarters*, express their total value in cents as an algebraic expression.

✐ **91.** In your own words, explain how to combine like terms.

✐ **92.** Do like terms always contain the same numerical coefficients? Explain your answer.

5 Chapter Highlights

Definitions and Concepts	Examples
Section 5.1 Square Roots and the Pythagorean Theorem	

SQUARE ROOT OF A NUMBER

A **square root** of a number a is a number b whose square is a. We use the radical sign $\sqrt{}$ to name square roots.

$$\sqrt{9} = 3, \sqrt{100} = 10, \sqrt{1} = 1$$

PYTHAGOREAN THEOREM

$$(\text{leg})^2 + (\text{other leg})^2 = (\text{hypotenuse})^2$$

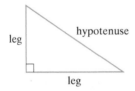

To Find an Unknown Length of a Right Triangle

$$\text{hypotenuse} = \sqrt{(\text{leg})^2 + (\text{other leg})^2}$$
$$\text{leg} = \sqrt{(\text{hypotenuse})^2 - (\text{other leg})^2}$$

Find the hypotenuse of the given triangle.

3 in.   hypotenuse   8 in.

$$\text{hypotenuse} = \sqrt{(\text{leg})^2 + (\text{other leg})^2}$$
$$= \sqrt{(3)^2 + (8)^2} \quad \text{The legs are 3 and 8 inches.}$$
$$= \sqrt{9 + 64}$$
$$= \sqrt{73} \text{ inches}$$
$$\approx 8.5 \text{ inches}$$

| **Section 5.2   Symbols and Sets of Numbers** | |

A **set** is a collection of objects, called **elements,** enclosed in braces.

$\{a, c, e\}$

Given the set $\left\{ -3.4, \sqrt{3}, 0, \dfrac{2}{3}, 5, -4 \right\}$ list the numbers that belong to the set of

Natural numbers: $\{1, 2, 3, 4, \dots\}$

Natural numbers: 5

Whole numbers: $\{0, 1, 2, 3, 4, \dots\}$

Whole numbers: 0, 5

Integers: $\{\dots, -3, -2, -1, 0, 1, 2, 3, \dots\}$

Integers: $-4, 0, 5$

Rational numbers: { real numbers that can be expressed as a quotient of integers }

Rational numbers: $-3.4, 0, \dfrac{2}{3}, 5, -4$

Irrational numbers: { real numbers that cannot be expressed as a quotient of integers }

Irrational numbers: $\sqrt{3}$

A line used to picture numbers is called a **number line.**

Real numbers: { all numbers that correspond to points on the number line }

Real numbers: $-3.4, \sqrt{3}, 0, \dfrac{2}{3}, 5, -4$

(continued)

Definitions and Concepts	**Examples**

Section 5.2   Symbols and Sets of Numbers (*continued*)

The **absolute value** of a real number a denoted by $\lvert a \rvert$ is the distance between a and 0 on a number line.	$\lvert 5 \rvert = 5 \quad \lvert 0 \rvert = 0 \quad \lvert -2 \rvert = 2$
Symbols: $=$ is equal to $\neq$ is not equal to $>$ is greater than $<$ is less than $\leq$ is less than or equal to $\geq$ is greater than or equal to **Order Property for Real Numbers** For any two real numbers a and b, a is less than b if a is to the left of b on the number line.	$-7 = -7$ $3 \neq -3$ $4 > 1$ $1 < 4$ $6 \leq 6$ $18 \geq -\dfrac{1}{3}$ $0 > -3$ $-3 < 0 \quad\quad 0 < 2.5 \quad 2.5 > 0$ $\xleftarrow{\hspace{1cm}} \begin{array}{ccccccccccc} -5 & -4 & -3 & -2 & -1 & 0 & 1 & 2 & 3 & 4 & 5 \end{array} \xrightarrow{\hspace{1cm}}$

Section 5.3   Exponents, Order of Operations, and Variable Expressions

The expression a^n is an **exponential expression.** The number a is called the **base;** it is the repeated factor. The number n is called the **exponent;** it is the number of times that the base is a factor.	$4^3 = 4 \cdot 4 \cdot 4 = 64$ $7^2 = 7 \cdot 7 = 49$
Order of Operations 1. Perform all operations within grouping symbols first, starting with the innermost set. 2. Evaluate exponential expressions. 3. Multiply or divide in order from left to right. 4. Add or subtract in order from left to right.	$\dfrac{8^2 + 5(7 - 3)}{3 \cdot 7} = \dfrac{8^2 + 5(4)}{21}$ $= \dfrac{64 + 5(4)}{21}$ $= \dfrac{64 + 20}{21}$ $= \dfrac{84}{21}$ $= 4$
A symbol used to represent a number is called a **variable.**	Examples of variables are q, x, z
An **algebraic expression** is a collection of numbers, variables, operation symbols, and grouping symbols.	Examples of algebraic expressions are $5x, \quad 2(y - 6), \quad \dfrac{q^2 - 3q + 1}{6}$
To **evaluate an algebraic expression** containing a variable, substitute a given number for the variable and simplify.	Evaluate $x^2 - y^2$ when $x = 5$ and $y = 3$. $\begin{aligned} x^2 - y^2 &= (5)^2 - 3^2 \\ &= 25 - 9 \\ &= 16 \end{aligned}$
A mathematical statement that two expressions are equal is called an **equation.**	Equations: $3x - 9 = 20$ $A = \pi r^2$
A **solution** of an equation is a value for the variable that makes the equation a true statement.	Determine whether 4 is a solution of $5x + 7 = 27$. $\begin{aligned} 5x + 7 &= 27 \\ 5(4) + 7 &\overset{?}{=} 27 \\ 20 + 7 &\overset{?}{=} 27 \\ 27 &= 27 \quad \text{True} \end{aligned}$ 4 is a solution.

Definitions and Concepts	**Examples**

Section 5.4   Adding Real Numbers

To ADD Two NUMBERS WITH THE SAME SIGN	Add.
1. Add their absolute values.	$10 + 7 = 17$
2. Use their common sign as the sign of the sum.	$-3 + (-8) = -11$
To ADD Two NUMBERS WITH DIFFERENT SIGNS	
1. Subtract their absolute values.	$-25 + 5 = -20$
2. Use the sign of the number whose absolute value is larger as the sign of the sum.	$14 + (-9) = 5$
Two numbers that are the same distance from 0 but lie on opposite sides of 0 are called **opposites** or **additive inverses**. The opposite of a number a is denoted by $-a$.	The opposite of -7 is 7. The opposite of 123 is -123.

Section 5.5   Subtracting Real Numbers

To subtract two numbers a and b, add the first number a to the opposite of the second number, b. $$a - b = a + (-b)$$	Subtract. $$3 - (-44) = 3 + 44 = 47$$ $$-5 - 22 = -5 + (-22) = -27$$ $$-30 - (-30) = -30 + 30 = 0$$

Section 5.6   Multiplying and Dividing Real Numbers

MULTIPLYING REAL NUMBERS	Multiply.
The product of two numbers with the same sign is a positive number. The product of two numbers with different signs is a negative number.	$$7 \cdot 8 = 56 \qquad -7 \cdot (-8) = 56$$ $$-2 \cdot 4 = -8 \qquad 2 \cdot (-4) = -8$$
PRODUCTS INVOLVING ZERO	
The product of 0 and any number is 0. $$b \cdot 0 = 0 \quad \text{and} \quad 0 \cdot b = 0$$	$$-4 \cdot 0 = 0 \qquad 0 \cdot \left(-\frac{3}{4}\right) = 0$$
QUOTIENT OF TWO REAL NUMBERS	Divide.
$$\frac{a}{b} = a \cdot \frac{1}{b}$$	$$\frac{42}{2} = 42 \cdot \frac{1}{2} = 21$$
DIVIDING REAL NUMBERS	
The quotient of two numbers with the same sign is a positive number. The quotient of two numbers with different signs is a negative number.	$$\frac{90}{10} = 9 \qquad \frac{-90}{-10} = 9$$ $$\frac{42}{-6} = -7 \qquad \frac{-42}{6} = -7$$
QUOTIENTS INVOLVING ZERO	
Let a be a nonzero number. $\dfrac{0}{a} = 0$ and $\dfrac{a}{0}$ is undefined.	$$\frac{0}{18} = 0 \qquad \frac{0}{-47} = 0 \qquad \frac{-85}{0} \text{ is undefined.}$$

Definitions and Concepts	**Examples**

Section 5.7   Properties of Real Numbers

COMMUTATIVE PROPERTIES

Addition: $a + b = b + a$

Multiplication: $a \cdot b = b \cdot a$

$3 + (-7) = -7 + 3$

$-8 \cdot 5 = 5 \cdot (-8)$

ASSOCIATIVE PROPERTIES

Addition: $(a + b) + c = a + (b + c)$

Multiplication: $(a \cdot b) \cdot c = a \cdot (b \cdot c)$

$(5 + 10) + 20 = 5 + (10 + 20)$

$(-3 \cdot 2) \cdot 11 = -3 \cdot (2 \cdot 11)$

Two numbers whose product is 1 are called **multiplicative inverses** or **reciprocals.** The reciprocal of a nonzero number a is $\dfrac{1}{a}$ because $a \cdot \dfrac{1}{a} = 1$.

The reciprocal of 3 is $\dfrac{1}{3}$.

The reciprocal of $-\dfrac{2}{5}$ is $-\dfrac{5}{2}$.

DISTRIBUTIVE PROPERTY

$$a(b + c) = a \cdot b + a \cdot c$$

$5(6 + 10) = 5 \cdot 6 + 5 \cdot 10$

$-2(3 + x) = -2 \cdot 3 + (-2)(x)$

IDENTITIES

$a + 0 = a \qquad 0 + a = a$

$a \cdot 1 = a \qquad 1 \cdot a = a$

$5 + 0 = 5 \qquad 0 + (-2) = -2$

$-14 \cdot 1 = -14 \qquad 1 \cdot 27 = 27$

INVERSES

Additive or opposite: $a + (-a) = 0$

Multiplicative or reciprocal: $b \cdot \dfrac{1}{b} = 1, \qquad b \neq 0$

$7 + (-7) = 0$

$3 \cdot \dfrac{1}{3} = 1$

Section 5.8   Simplifying Expressions

The **numerical coefficient** of a **term** is its numerical factor.

Term	**Numerical Coefficient**
$-7y$	-7
x	1
$\dfrac{1}{5}a^2 b$	$\dfrac{1}{5}$

Terms with the same variables raised to exactly the same powers are **like terms.**

Like Terms	**Unlike Terms**
$12x, -x$	$3y, 3y^2$
$-2xy, 5yx$	$7a^2 b, -2ab^2$

To combine like terms, add the numerical coefficients and multiply the result by the common variable factor.

$9y + 3y = 12y$

$-4z^2 + 5z^2 - 6z^2 = -5z^2$

To remove parentheses, apply the distributive property.

$-4(x + 7) + 10(3x - 1)$

$= -4x - 28 + 30x - 10$

$= 26x - 38$

Chapter 5 Review

(5.1) *Simplify.*

1. $\sqrt{64}$

2. $\sqrt{144}$

3. $\sqrt{\dfrac{4}{25}}$

4. $\sqrt{\dfrac{1}{100}}$

Find the unknown length of each given right triangle. If necessary, round to the nearest tenth.

5. leg = 12, leg = 5

6. leg = 20, leg = 21

7. leg = 9, hypotenuse = 14

8. leg = 124, hypotenuse = 155

9. A baseball diamond is in the shape of a square and has sides of length 90 feet. Find the distance across the diamond from third base to first base, to the nearest tenth of a foot.

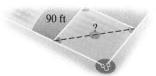

10. Find the height of the building rounded to the nearest tenth.

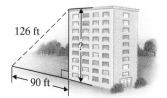

(5.2) *Insert* $<$, $>$, *or* $=$ *in the appropriate space to make each statement true.*

11. 8   10

12. 7   2

13. -4 -5

14. $\dfrac{12}{2}$ -8

15. $|-7|$ $|-8|$

16. $|-9|$ -9

17. $-|-1|$ -1

18. $|-14|$ $-(-14)$

19. 1.2   1.02

20. $-\dfrac{3}{2}$ $-\dfrac{3}{4}$

Translate each statement into symbols.

21. Four is greater than or equal to negative three.

22. Six is not equal to five.

23. 0.03 is less than 0.3.

24. New York City has 155 museums and 400 art galleries. Write an inequality comparing the numbers 155 and 400. (*Source:* Absolute Trivia.com)

Given the sets of numbers below, list the numbers in each set that also belong to the set of:

a. Natural numbers   **b.** Whole numbers
c. Integers   **d.** Rational numbers
e. Irrational numbers   **f.** Real numbers

25. $\left\{ -6, 0, 1, 1\frac{1}{2}, 3, \pi, 9.62 \right\}$

26. $\left\{ -3, -1.6, 2, 5, \frac{11}{2}, 15.1, \sqrt{5}, 2\pi \right\}$

The following chart shows the gains and losses in dollars of Density Oil and Gas stock for a particular week. Use this chart to answer Exercises 33 and 34.

Day	Gain or Loss (in dollars)
Monday	+1
Tuesday	−2
Wednesday	+5
Thursday	+1
Friday	−4

27. Which day showed the greatest loss?

28. Which day showed the greatest gain?

(5.3) *Choose the correct answer for each statement.*

29. The expression $6 \cdot 3^2 + 2 \cdot 8$ simplifies to
   a. −52   **b.** 448   **c.** 70   **d.** 64

30. The expression $68 - 5 \cdot 2^3$ simplifies to
   a. −232   **b.** 28   **c.** 38   **d.** 504

Simplify each expression.

31. $3(1 + 2 \cdot 5) + 4$

32. $8 + 3(2 \cdot 6 - 1)$

33. $\dfrac{4 + |6 - 2| + 8^2}{4 + 6 \cdot 4}$

34. $5[3(2 + 5) - 5]$

Translate each word statement to symbols.

35. The difference of twenty and twelve is equal to the product of two and four.

36. The quotient of nine and two is greater than negative five.

Evaluate each expression when $x = 6$, $y = 2$, and $z = 8$.

37. $2x + 3y$

38. $x(y + 2z)$

39. $\dfrac{x}{y} + \dfrac{z}{2y}$

40. $x^2 - 3y^2$

41. The expression $180 - a - b$ represents the measure of the unknown angle of the given triangle. Replace a with 37 and b with 80 to find the measure of the unknown angle.

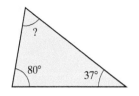

42. The expression $360 - a - b - c$ represents the measure of the unknown angle of the given quadrilateral. Replace a with 93, b with 80, and c with 82 to find the measure of the unknown angle.

Decide whether the given number is a solution to the given equation.

43. $7x - 3 = 18$;   3

44. $3x^2 + 4 = x - 1$;   1

(5.4) *Find the additive inverse or opposite of each number.*

45. -9

46. $\dfrac{2}{3}$

47. $|-2|$

48. $-|-7|$

Add.

49. $-15 + 4$

50. $-6 + (-11)$

51. $\dfrac{1}{16} + \left(-\dfrac{1}{4}\right)$

52. $-8 + |-3|$

53. $-4.6 + (-9.3)$

54. $-2.8 + 6.7$

(5.5) *Perform each indicated operation.*

55. $6 - 20$

56. $-3.1 - 8.4$

57. $-6 - (-11)$

58. $4 - 15$

59. $-21 - 16 + 3(8 - 2)$

60. $\dfrac{11 - (-9) + 6(8 - 2)}{2 + 3 \cdot 4}$

Evaluate each expression for $x = 3$, $y = -6$, and $z = -9$. Then choose the correct evaluation.

61. $2x^2 - y + z$

    a. 15   **b.** 3   **c.** 27   **d.** -3

62. $\dfrac{|y - 4x|}{2x}$

    a. 3   **b.** 1   **c.** -1 **d.** -3

63. At the beginning of the week the price of Density Oil and Gas stock from Exercises 17 and 18 is $50 per share. Find the price of a share of stock at the end of the week.

64. Find the price of a share of stock by the end of the day on Wednesday.

Find each multiplicative inverse or reciprocal.

65. -6

66. $\dfrac{3}{5}$

(5.6) *Simplify each expression.*

67. $6(-8)$

68. $(-2)(-14)$

69. $\dfrac{-18}{-6}$

70. $\dfrac{42}{-3}$

71. $-3(-6)(-2)$

72. $(-4)(-3)(0)(-6)$

73. $\dfrac{4(-3) + (-8)}{2 + (-2)}$

74. $\dfrac{3(-2)^2 - 5}{-14}$

(5.7) *Name the property illustrated in each equation.*

75. $-6 + 5 = 5 + (-6)$

76. $6 \cdot 1 = 6$

77. $3(8 - 5) = 3 \cdot 8 + 3 \cdot (-5)$

78. $4 + (-4) = 0$

79. $2 + (3 + 9) = (2 + 3) + 9$

80. $2 \cdot 8 = 8 \cdot 2$

81. $6(8 + 5) = 6 \cdot 8 + 6 \cdot 5$

82. $(3 \cdot 8) \cdot 4 = 3 \cdot (8 \cdot 4)$

83. $4 \cdot \dfrac{1}{4} = 1$

84. $8 + 0 = 8$

85. $4(8 + 3) = 4(3 + 8)$

86. $5(2 + 1) = 5 \cdot 2 + 5 \cdot 1$

(5.8) *Simplify each expression.*

87. $5x - x + 2x$

88. $0.2z - 4.6z - 7.4z$

89. $\dfrac{1}{2}x + 3 + \dfrac{7}{2}x - 5$

90. $\dfrac{4}{5}y + 1 + \dfrac{6}{5}y + 2$

91. $2(n - 4) + n - 10$

92. $3(w + 2) - (12 - w)$

93. Subtract $7x - 2$ from $x + 5$.

94. Subtract $1.4y - 3$ from $y - 0.7$.

Write each phrase as an algebraic expression. Simplify if possible.

95. Three times a number decreased by 7

96. Twice the sum of a number and 2.8, added to 3 times the number

Answers to Selected Exercises

Chapter 5 Real Numbers and Introduction to Algebra

Section 5.1

Calculator Explorations **1.** 32 **3.** 5.568 **5.** 9.849

Vocabulary and Readiness Check **1.** 10 **3.** squaring **5.**

Exercise Set 5.1 **1.** 2 **3.** 11 **5.** $\frac{1}{9}$ **7.** $\frac{4}{8} = \frac{1}{2}$ **9.** 1.732 **11.** 3.873 **13.** 6.856 **15.** 5.099 **17.** 6,7 **19.** 10,11 **21.** 16 **23.** 9.592 **25.** $\frac{7}{12}$ **27.** 8.426
29. 13 in. **31.** 6.633 cm **33.** 52.802 m **35.** 117 mm **37.** 5 **39.** 12 **41.** 17.205 **43.** 44.822 **45.** 42.426 **47.** 1.732 **49.** 8.5 **51.** 141.42 yd **53.** 25.0 ft
55. 340 ft **57.** $n = 4$ **59.** $n = 45$ **61.** $n = 6$ **63.** 6 **65.** 10 **67.** answers may vary **69.** yes **71.** $\sqrt{80} - 6 \approx 2.94$ in.

Section 5.2

Vocabulary and Readiness Check **1.** whole **3.** inequality **5.** real **7.** 0 **9.** absolute value

Exercise Set 5.2 **1.** < **3.** > **5.** = **7.** < **9.** $32 < 212$ **11.** $30 \le 45$ **13.** true **15.** false **17.** true **19.** false **21.** $20 \le 25$
23. $6 > 0$ **25.** $-12 < -10$ **27.** $7 < 11$ **29.** $5 \ge 4$ **31.** $15 \ne -2$ **33.** 14,494; -282 **35.** $-28,000$ **37.** 475; -195
39. **41.** **43.** **45.** whole, integers,

rational, real **47.** integers, rational, real **49.** natural, whole, integers, rational, real **51.** rational, real **53.** false **55.** true **57.** false **59.** false
61. 8.9 **63.** 20 **65.** $\frac{9}{2}$ **67.** $\frac{12}{13}$ **69.** > **71.** = **73.** < **75.** < **77.** 109 **79.** 8 **81.** 905 thousand > 823 thousand, or 905,000 > 823,000
83. decreased by 24 or -24 thousand bushels **85.** 49 million > 16 million, or 49,000,000 > 16,000,000 **87.** 38 million pounds less, or -38 million
89. $-0.04 > -26.7$ **91.** sun **93.** sun **95.** answers may vary

Section 5.3

Calculator Explorations **1.** 125 **3.** 59,049 **5.** 30 **7.** 9857 **9.** 2376

Vocabulary and Readiness Check **1.** base; exponent **3.** multiplication **5.** subtraction **7.** expression **9.** expression; variables **11.** equation

Exercise Set 5.3 **1.** 243 **3.** 27 **5.** 1 **7.** 5 **9.** 49 **11.** $\frac{16}{81}$ **13.** $\frac{1}{125}$ **15.** 1.44 **17.** 0.343 **19.** 5^2 sq m **21.** 17 **23.** 20 **25.** 12 **27.** 21
29. 45 **31.** 0 **33.** $\frac{2}{7}$ **35.** 30 **37.** 2 **39.** $\frac{7}{18}$ **41.** $\frac{27}{10}$ **43.** $\frac{7}{5}$ **45.** 32 **47.** $\frac{23}{27}$ **49.** 9 **51.** 1 **53.** 1 **55.** 11 **57.** 8 **59.** 45 **61.** 27 **63.** 132
65. $\frac{37}{18}$ **67.** solution **69.** not a solution **71.** not a solution **73.** solution **75.** not a solution **77.** solution **79.** $x + 15$ **81.** $x - 5$ **83.** $\frac{x}{4}$
85. $3x + 22$ **87.** $1 + 2 = 9 \div 3$ **89.** $3 \ne 4 \div 2$ **91.** $5 + x = 20$ **93.** $7.6x = 17$ **95.** $13 - 3x = 13$ **97.** 35 **99.** 360 **101.** no; answers may vary
103. a. 64 **b.** 43 **c.** 19 **d.** 22 **105.** 14 in., 12 sq in. **107.** 14 in., 9.01 sq in. **109.** Rectangles with the same perimeter can have different areas.
111. $(20 - 4) \cdot 4 \div 2$ **113. a.** expression **b.** equation **c.** equation **d.** expression **e.** expression **115.** answers may vary **117.** answers may
vary, for example, $2(6) - 1$.

Section 5.4

Vocabulary and Readiness Check **1.** 0 **3.** a

Exercise Set 5.4 **1.** 3 **3.** -14 **5.** 1 **7.** -12 **9.** -5 **11.** -12 **13.** -4 **15.** 7 **17.** -2 **19.** 0 **21.** -19 **23.** 31 **25.** -47 **27.** -2.1
29. 38 **31.** -13.1 **33.** $\frac{1}{4}$ **35.** $-\frac{3}{16}$ **37.** $-\frac{13}{10}$ **39.** -8 **41.** -8 **43.** -59 **45.** -9 **47.** 5 **49.** 11 **51.** -18 **53.** 19 **55.** -7 **57.** -26
59. -6 **61.** 2 **63.** 0 **65.** -6 **67.** -2 **69.** 7 **71.** 7.9 **73.** $5z$ **75.** $\frac{2}{3}$ **77.** -70 **79.** 3 **81.** 19 **83.** -10 **85.** $0 + (-215) + (-16) = -231$;
231 ft below the surface **87.** 107°F **89.** -95 m **91.** -21 **93.** $-\$6.9$ million **95.** 72.01 **97.** 141 **99.** July **101.** October **103.** 4.7°F
105. answers may vary **107.** -3 **109.** -22 **111.** true **113.** false **115.** answers may vary

Section 5.5

Vocabulary and Readiness Check **1.** $a + (-b)$; b **3.** $-10 - (-14)$; d

Exercise Set 5.5 **1.** -10 **3.** -5 **5.** 19 **7.** 11 **9.** -8 **11.** -11 **13.** 37 **15.** 5 **17.** -71 **19.** 0 **21.** $\frac{2}{11}$ **23.** -6.4 **25.** 4.1 **27.** $-\frac{1}{6}$ **29.** $-\frac{11}{12}$
31. 8.92 **33.** -8.92 **35.** 13 **37.** -5 **39.** -1 **41.** -23 **43.** -26 **45.** -24 **47.** 3 **49.** -45 **51.** -4 **53.** 13 **55.** 6 **57.** 9 **59.** -9 **61.** $\frac{7}{5}$
63. -7 **65.** 21 **67.** $\frac{1}{4}$ **69.** not a solution **71.** not a solution **73.** solution **75.** 265°F **77.** 35,653 ft **79.** 30° **81.** -308 ft **83.** 19,852 ft
85. 130° **87.** $-5 + x$ **89.** $-20 - x$ **91.** 0 **93.** $\frac{10}{13}$ **95.** $-4.4°, 2.6°, 12°, 23.5°, 15.3°$ **97.** May **99.** answers may vary **101.** 16 **103.** -20
105. true; answers may vary **107.** false; answers may vary **109.** negative, $-30,387$

Section 5.6

Calculator Explorations   **1.** 38   **3.** -441 **5.** 490   **7.** 54,499   **9.** 15,625

Vocabulary and Readiness Check   **1.** negative   **3.** positive   **5.** 0   **7.** 0

Exercise Set 5.6   **1.** -24 **3.** -2 **5.** 50   **7.** -45 **9.** $\frac{3}{10}$ **11.** -7 **13.** -15 **15.** 0   **17.** 16   **19.** -16 **21.** $\frac{9}{16}$ **23.** -0.49 **25.** $\frac{3}{2}$ **27.** $-\frac{1}{14}$
29. $-\frac{11}{3}$ **31.** $\frac{1}{0.2}$ **33.** -9 **35.** -4 **37.** 0   **39.** undefined   **41.** $-\frac{18}{7}$ **43.** 160   **45.** 64   **47.** $-\frac{8}{27}$ **49.** 3   **51.** -15 **53.** -125 **55.** -0.008
57. $\frac{2}{3}$ **59.** $\frac{20}{27}$ **61.** 0.84   **63.** -40 **65.** 81   **67.** -1 **69.** -121 **71.** -1 **73.** -19 **75.** 90   **77.** -84 **79.** -5 **81.** $-\frac{9}{2}$ **83.** 18   **85.** 17   **87.** -20
89. 16   **91.** 2   **93.** $-\frac{34}{7}$ **95.** 0   **97.** $\frac{6}{5}$ **99.** $\frac{3}{2}$ **101.** $-\frac{5}{38}$ **103.** 3   **105.** -1 **107.** undefined   **109.** $-\frac{22}{9}$ **111.** solution   **113.** not a solution
115. solution   **117.** $-71 \cdot x$ or $-71x$ **119.** $-16 - x$ **121.** $-29 + x$ **123.** $\frac{x}{-33}$ or $x \div (-33)$ **125.** $3 \cdot (-4) = -12$; a loss of 12 yd
127. $5(-20) = -100$; a depth of 100 ft   **129.** 32 in.   **131.** 30 ft   **133.** true   **135.** false   **137.** $-162°F$ **139.** answers may vary
141. 1, -1; answers may vary   **143.** $\frac{0}{5} - 7 = -7$ **145.** $-8(-5) + (-1) = 39$

Section 5.7

Vocabulary and Readiness Check   **1.** commutative property of addition   **3.** distributive property   **5.** associative property of addition
7. opposites or additive inverses

Exercise Set 5.7   **1.** $16 + x$ **3.** $y \cdot (-4)$ **5.** yx **7.** $13 + 2x$ **9.** $x \cdot (yz)$ **11.** $(2 + a) + b$ **13.** $(4a) \cdot b$ **15.** $a + (b + c)$ **17.** $17 + b$ **19.** $24y$
21. y **23.** $26 + a$ **25.** $-72x$ **27.** s **29.** $-\frac{5}{2}x$ **31.** $4x + 4y$ **33.** $9x - 54$ **35.** $6x + 10$ **37.** $28x - 21$ **39.** $18 + 3x$ **41.** $-2y + 2z$ **43.** $-y - \frac{5}{3}$
45. $5x + 20m + 10$ **47.** $8m - 4n$ **49.** $-5x - 2$ **51.** $-r + 3 + 7p$ **53.** $3x + 4$ **55.** $-x + 3y$ **57.** $6r + 8$ **59.** $-36x - 70$ **61.** $-1.6x - 2.5$
63. $4(1 + y)$ **65.** $11(x + y)$ **67.** $-1(5 + x)$ **69.** $30(a + b)$ **71.** commutative property of multiplication   **73.** associative property of addition
75. commutative property of addition   **77.** associative property of multiplication   **79.** identity element for addition   **81.** distributive property
83. multiplicative inverse property   **85.** identity element for multiplication   **87.** 4050   **89.** 45   **91.** $-8; \frac{1}{8}$ **93.** $-x; \frac{1}{x}$ **95.** $2x; -2x$ **97.** false
99. no   **101.** yes   **103.** yes   **105.** yes   **107. a.** commutative property of addition   **b.** commutative property of addition   **c.** associative property of
addition   **109.** answers may vary   **111.** answers may vary

Section 5.8

Vocabulary and Readiness Check   **1.** expression   **3.** combine like terms   **5.** like; unlike   **7.** -7 **9.** 1   **11.** 17   **13.** like   **15.** unlike   **17.** like

Exercise Set 5.8   **1.** $15y$ **3.** $13w$ **5.** $-7b - 9$ **7.** $-m - 6$ **9.** -8 **11.** $7.2x - 5.2$ **13.** $k - 6$ **15.** $-15x + 18$ **17.** $4x - 3$ **19.** $5x^2$ **21.** -11
23. $1.3x + 3.5$ **25.** $5y + 20$ **27.** $-2x - 4$ **29.** $-10x + 15y - 30$ **31.** $-3x + 2y - 1$ **33.** $7d - 11$ **35.** 16   **37.** $x + 5$ **39.** $x + 2$
41. $2k + 10$ **43.** $-3x + 5$ **45.** $2x + 14$ **47.** $3y + \frac{5}{6}$ **49.** $-22 + 24x$ **51.** $0.9m + 1$ **53.** $10 - 6x - 9y$ **55.** $-x - 38$ **57.** $5x - 7$
59. $10x - 3$ **61.** $-4x - 9$ **63.** $-4m - 3$ **65.** $2x - 4$ **67.** $\frac{3}{4}x + 12$ **69.** $12x - 2$ **71.** $8x + 48$ **73.** $x - 10$ **75.** 2   **77.** -23 **79.** -25
81. balanced   **83.** balanced   **85.** answers may vary   **87.** $(18x - 2)$ ft   **89.** $(15x + 23)$ in.   **91.** answers may vary

Chapter 5 Review   **1.** 8   **2.** 12   **3.** $\frac{2}{5}$ **4.** $\frac{1}{10}$ **5.** 13   **6.** 29   **7.** 10.7   **8.** 93   **9.** 127.3 ft   **10.** 88.2 ft   **11.** $<$ **12.** $>$ **13.** $>$ **14.** $>$ **15.** $<$ **16.** $>$
17. $=$ **18.** $=$ **19.** $>$ **20.** $<$ **21.** $4 \geq -3$ **22.** $6 \neq 5$ **23.** $0.03 < 0.3$ **24.** $155 < 400$ **25. a.** 1,3   **b.** 0,1,3   **c.** $-6,0,1,3$
d. $-6, 0, 1, 1\frac{1}{2}, 3, 9.62$ **e.** π **f.** all numbers in set   **26. a.** 2,5   **b.** 2,5   **c.** $-3, 2, 5$ **d.** $-3, -1.6, 2, 5, \frac{11}{2}, 15.1$ **e.** $\sqrt{5}, 2\pi$
f. all numbers in set   **27.** Friday   **28.** Wednesday   **29.** c   **30.** b   **31.** 37   **32.** 41   **33.** $\frac{18}{7}$ **34.** 80   **35.** $20 - 12 = 2 \cdot 4$ **36.** $\frac{9}{2} > -5$
37. 18   **38.** 108   **39.** 5   **40.** 24   **41.** $63°$ **42.** $105°$ **43.** solution   **44.** not a solution   **45.** 9   **46.** $-\frac{2}{3}$ **47.** -2 **48.** 7   **49.** -11 **50.** -17 **51.** $-\frac{3}{16}$
52. -5 **53.** -13.9 **54.** 3.9   **55.** -14 **56.** -11.5 **57.** 5   **58.** -11 **59.** -19 **60.** 4   **61.** a   **62.** a   **63.** \$51   **64.** \$54   **65.** $-\frac{1}{6}$ **66.** $\frac{5}{3}$ **67.** -48
68. 28   **69.** 3   **70.** -14 **71.** -36 **72.** 0   **73.** undefined   **74.** $-\frac{1}{2}$ **75.** commutative property of addition   **76.** identity element for multiplication
77. distributive property   **78.** additive inverse property   **79.** associative property of addition   **80.** commutative property of multiplication
81. distributive property   **82.** associative property of multiplication   **83.** multiplicative inverse property   **84.** identity element for addition
85. commutative property of addition   **86.** distributive property   **87.** $6x$ **88.** $-11.8z$ **89.** $4x - 2$ **90.** $2y + 3$ **91.** $3n - 18$ **92.** $4w - 6$
93. $-6x + 7$ **94.** $-0.4y + 2.3$ **95.** $3x - 7$ **96.** $5x + 5.6$

Equations, Inequalities and Problem Solving

6

A Use the Addition Property of Equality to Solve Linear Equations.

B Simplify an Equation and Then Use the Addition Property of Equality.

C Write Word Phrases as Algebraic Expressions.

Helpful Hint

Simply stated, an equation contains "=" while an expression does not. Also, we *simplify* expressions and *solve* equations.

6.1 THE ADDITION PROPERTY OF EQUALITY

Let's recall from Section 5.3 the difference between an equation and an expression. A combination of operations on variables and numbers is an expression, and an equation is of the form "expression = expression."

Equations	Expressions
$3x - 1 = -17$	$3x - 1$
area = length · width	$5(20 - 3) + 10$
$8 + 16 = 16 + 8$	y^3
$-9a + 11b = 14b + 3$	$-x^2 + y - 2$

Now, let's concentrate on equations.

Objective **A** Using the Addition Property

A value of the variable that makes an equation a true statement is called a solution or root of the equation. The process of finding the solution of an equation is called **solving** the equation for the variable. In this section, we concentrate on solving *linear equations* in one variable.

Linear Equation in One Variable

A **linear equation in one variable** can be written in the form

$$Ax + B = C$$

where A, B, and C are real numbers and $A \neq 0$.

Evaluating each side of a linear equation for a given value of the variable, as we did in Section 5.3, can tell us whether that value is a solution. But we can't rely on this as our method of solving it—with what value would we start?

Instead, to solve a linear equation in x, we write a series of simpler equations, all *equivalent* to the original equation, so that the final equation has the form

$$x = \text{number} \qquad \text{or} \qquad \text{number} = x$$

Equivalent equations are equations that have the same solution. This means that the "number" above is the solution to the original equation.

The first property of equality that helps us write simpler equivalent equations is the **addition property of equality.**

Addition Property of Equality

Let a, b, and c represent numbers. Then

$$a = b$$
and $a + c = b + c$
are equivalent equations.

Also, $a = b$
and $a - c = b - c$
are equivalent equations.

In other words, **the same number may be added to or subtracted from both sides** of an equation without changing the solution of the equation. (We may subtract the same number from both sides since subtraction is defined in terms of addition.)

Let's visualize how we use the addition property of equality to solve an equation. Picture the equation $x - 2 = 1$ as a balanced scale. The left side of the equation has the same value (weight) as the right side.

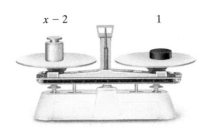

If the same weight is added to each side of a scale, the scale remains balanced. Likewise, if the same number is added to each side of an equation, the left side continues to have the same value as the right side.

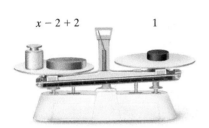 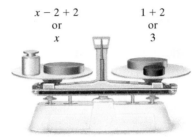

We use the addition property of equality to write equivalent equations until the variable is alone (by itself on one side of the equation) and the equation looks like "$x = $ number" or "number $= x$."

✓**Concept Check** Use the addition property to fill in the blanks so that the middle equation simplifies to the last equation.

$$x - 5 = 3$$
$$x - 5 + \underline{} = 3 + \underline{}$$
$$x = 8$$

Example 1 Solve $x - 7 = 10$ for x.

Solution: To solve for x, we first get x alone on one side of the equation. To do this, we add 7 to both sides of the equation.

$$x - 7 = 10$$
$$x - 7 + 7 = 10 + 7 \quad \text{Add 7 to both sides.}$$
$$x = 17 \qquad \text{Simplify.}$$

The solution of the equation $x = 17$ is obviously 17.
Since we are writing equivalent equations, the solution of the equation $x - 7 = 10$ is also 17.

Check: To check, replace x with 17 in the original equation.

$$x - 7 = 10 \quad \text{Original equation.}$$
$$17 - 7 \stackrel{?}{=} 10 \quad \text{Replace } x \text{ with 17.}$$
$$10 = 10 \quad \text{True}$$

Since the statement is true, 17 is the solution.

● **Work Practice 1**

Example 2 Solve: $y + 0.6 = -1.0$

Solution: To solve for y (get y alone on one side of the equation), we subtract 0.6 from both sides of the equation.

Continued on next page

PRACTICE 1

Solve: $x - 5 = 8$ for x.

PRACTICE 2

Solve: $y + 1.7 = 0.3$

Answers
1. $x = 13$ **2.** $y = -1.4$

✓ **Concept Check Answer**
5

$$y + 0.6 = -1.0$$
$$y + 0.6 - 0.6 = -1.0 - 0.6 \quad \text{Subtract 0.6 from both sides.}$$
$$y = -1.6 \quad \text{Combine like terms.}$$

Check:
$$y + 0.6 = -1.0 \quad \text{Original equation.}$$
$$-1.6 + 0.6 \overset{?}{=} -1.0 \quad \text{Replace } y \text{ with } -1.6.$$
$$-1.0 = -1.0 \quad \text{True}$$

The solution is -1.6.

● **Work Practice 2**

PRACTICE 3

Solve: $\dfrac{7}{8} = y - \dfrac{1}{3}$

Example 3 Solve: $\dfrac{1}{2} = x - \dfrac{3}{4}$

Solution: To get x alone, we add $\dfrac{3}{4}$ to both sides.

$$\frac{1}{2} = x - \frac{3}{4}$$
$$\frac{1}{2} + \frac{3}{4} = x - \frac{3}{4} + \frac{3}{4} \quad \text{Add } \frac{3}{4} \text{ to both sides.}$$
$$\frac{1}{2} \cdot \frac{2}{2} + \frac{3}{4} = x \quad \text{The LCD is 4.}$$
$$\frac{2}{4} + \frac{3}{4} = x \quad \text{Add the fractions.}$$
$$\frac{5}{4} = x$$

Helpful Hint We may solve an equation so that the variable is alone on *either* side of the equation. For example, $\dfrac{5}{4} = x$ is equivalent to $x = \dfrac{5}{4}$.

Check:
$$\frac{1}{2} = x - \frac{3}{4} \quad \text{Original equation.}$$
$$\frac{1}{2} \overset{?}{=} \frac{5}{4} - \frac{3}{4} \quad \text{Replace } x \text{ with } \frac{5}{4}.$$
$$\frac{1}{2} \overset{?}{=} \frac{2}{4} \quad \text{Subtract.}$$
$$\frac{1}{2} = \frac{1}{2} \quad \text{True}$$

The solution is $\dfrac{5}{4}$.

● **Work Practice 3**

PRACTICE 4

Solve: $3x + 10 = 4x$

Example 4 Solve: $5t - 5 = 6t$

Solution: To solve for t, we first want all terms containing t on one side of the equation and numbers on the other side. Notice that if we subtract $5t$ from both sides of the equation, then variable terms will be on one side of the equation and the number -5 will be alone on the other side.

$$5t - 5 = 6t$$
$$5t - 5 - 5t = 6t - 5t \quad \text{Subtract } 5t \text{ from both sides.}$$
$$-5 = t \quad \text{Combine like terms.}$$

Helpful Hint For Example 4, why not subtract $6t$ from both sides? The addition property allows us to do this, and we would have $-t - 5 = 0$. We are just no closer to our goal of having variable terms on one side of the equation and numbers on the other.

Check:
$$5t - 5 = 6t \quad \text{Original equation.}$$
$$5(-5) - 5 \overset{?}{=} 6(-5) \quad \text{Replace } t \text{ with } -5.$$
$$-25 - 5 \overset{?}{=} -30$$
$$-30 = -30 \quad \text{True}$$

The solution is -5.

● **Work Practice 4**

Answers

3. $y = \dfrac{29}{24}$ **4.** $x = 10$

Objective ⓑ Simplifying Equations

Many times, it is best to simplify one or both sides of an equation before applying the addition property of equality.

Example 5 Solve: $2x + 3x - 5 + 7 = 10x + 3 - 6x - 4$

Solution: First we simplify both sides of the equation.

$$2x + 3x - 5 + 7 = 10x + 3 - 6x - 4$$
$$5x + 2 = 4x - 1 \qquad \text{Combine like terms on each}$$
$$\text{side of the equation.}$$

Next, we want all terms with a variable on one side of the equation and all numbers on the other side.

$$5x + 2 - 4x = 4x - 1 - 4x \qquad \text{Subtract } 4x \text{ from both sides.}$$
$$x + 2 = -1 \qquad \text{Combine like terms.}$$
$$x + 2 - 2 = -1 - 2 \qquad \text{Subtract 2 from both sides to get } x \text{ alone.}$$
$$x = -3 \qquad \text{Combine like terms.}$$

Check:
$$2x + 3x - 5 + 7 = 10x + 3 - 6x - 4 \qquad \text{Original equation.}$$
$$2(-3) + 3(-3) - 5 + 7 \stackrel{?}{=} 10(-3) + 3 - 6(-3) - 4 \qquad \text{Replace } x \text{ with } -3.$$
$$-6 - 9 - 5 + 7 \stackrel{?}{=} -30 + 3 + 18 - 4 \qquad \text{Multiply.}$$
$$-13 = -13 \qquad \text{True}$$

The solution is -3.

● **Work Practice 5**

PRACTICE 5
Solve:
$$10w + 3 - 4w + 4$$
$$= -2w + 3 + 7w$$

If an equation contains parentheses, we use the distributive property to remove them, as before. Then we combine any like terms.

Example 6 Solve: $6(2a - 1) - (11a + 6) = 7$

Solution: $6(2a - 1) - 1(11a + 6) = 7$

$$6(2a) + 6(-1) - 1(11a) - 1(6) = 7 \qquad \text{Apply the distributive property.}$$
$$12a - 6 - 11a - 6 = 7 \qquad \text{Multiply.}$$
$$a - 12 = 7 \qquad \text{Combine like terms.}$$
$$a - 12 + 12 = 7 + 12 \qquad \text{Add 12 to both sides.}$$
$$a = 19 \qquad \text{Simplify.}$$

Check: Check by replacing a with 19 in the original equation.

● **Work Practice 6**

PRACTICE 6
Solve:
$$3(2w - 5) - (5w + 1) = -3$$

Example 7 Solve: $3 - x = 7$

Solution: First we subtract 3 from both sides.

$$3 - x = 7$$
$$3 - x - 3 = 7 - 3 \qquad \text{Subtract 3 from both sides.}$$
$$-x = 4 \qquad \text{Simplify.}$$

We have not yet solved for x since x is not alone. However, this equation does say that the opposite of x is 4. If the opposite of x is 4, then x is the opposite of 4, or $x = -4$.

If $\quad -x = 4,$
then $\quad x = -4.$

PRACTICE 7
Solve: $12 - y = 9$

Answers
5. $w = -4$ **6.** $w = 13$ **7.** $y = 3$

Check: $3 - x = 7$ Original equation.

$3 - (-4) \overset{?}{=} 7$ Replace x with -4.

$3 + 4 \overset{?}{=} 7$ Add.

$7 = 7$ True

The solution is -4.

● Work Practice 7

Objective ⓒ Writing Algebraic Expressions

In this section, we continue to practice writing algebraic expressions.

Example 8

a. The sum of two numbers is 8. If one number is 3, find the other number.
b. The sum of two numbers is 8. If one number is x, write an expression representing the other number.

Solution:

a. If the sum of two numbers is 8 and one number is 3, we find the other number by subtracting 3 from 8. The other number is $8 - 3$, or 5.

c. If the sum of two numbers is 8 and one number is x, we find the other number by subtracting x from 8. The other number is represented by $8 - x$.

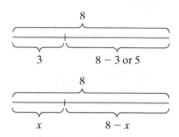

● Work Practice 8

Example 9

The Verrazano-Narrows Bridge in New York City is the longest suspension bridge in North America. The Golden Gate Bridge in San Francisco is 60 feet shorter than the Verrazano-Narrows Bridge. If the length of the Verrazano-Narrows Bridge is m feet, express the length of the Golden Gate Bridge as an algebraic expression in m. (*Source:* Survey of State Highway Engineers)

Solution: Since the Golden Gate Bridge is 60 feet shorter than the Verrazano-Narrows Bridge, we have that its length is

In words:	Length of Verrazano-Narrows Bridge	minus	60
Translate:	m	$-$	60

The Golden Gate Bridge is $(m - 60)$ feet long.

● Work Practice 9

PRACTICE 8

a. The sum of two numbers is 11. If one number is 4, find the other number.
b. The sum of two numbers is 11. If one number is x, write an expression representing the other number.
c. The sum of two numbers is 56. If one number is a, write an expression representing the other number.

PRACTICE 9

In a recent House of Representatives race in California, Mike Thompson received 100,445 more votes than Zane Starkewolf. If Zane received n votes, how many did Mike receive? (*Source:* Voter News Service)

Answers

8. a. $11 - 4$ or 7   **b.** $11 - x$
c. $56 - a$ **9.** $(n + 100,445)$ votes

Vocabulary and Readiness Check

Use the choices below to fill in each blank. Some choices may be used more than once or not at all.

equation	multiplication	addition
expression	solution	equivalent

1. A combination of operations on variables and numbers is called a(n) _____.
2. A statement of the form "expression = expression" is called a(n) _____.
3. A(n) _____ contains an equal sign (=).
4. A(n) _____ does not contain an equal sign (=).
5. A(n) _____ may be simplified and evaluated while a(n) _____ may be solved.
6. A(n) _____ of an equation is a number that when substituted for a variable makes the equation a true statement.
7. _____ equations have the same solution.
8. By the _____ property of equality, the same number may be added to or subtracted from both sides of an equation without changing the solution of the equation.

Solve each equation mentally. See Examples 1 and 2.

9. $x + 4 = 6$

10. $x + 7 = 17$

11. $n + 18 = 30$

12. $z + 22 = 40$

13. $b - 11 = 6$

14. $d - 16 = 5$

6.1 Exercise Set

FOR EXTRA HELP

MyMathLab   Math XP   PRACTICE   WATCH   DOWNLOAD   READ   REVIEW

Objective Ⓐ *Solve each equation. Check each solution. See Examples 1 through 4.*

1. $x + 7 = 10$

2. $x + 14 = 25$

3. $x - 2 = -4$

4. $y - 9 = 1$

5. $-11 = 3 + x$

6. $-8 = 8 + z$

7. $r - 8.6 = -8.1$

8. $t - 9.2 = -6.8$

9. $x - \dfrac{2}{5} = -\dfrac{3}{20}$

10. $y - \dfrac{4}{7} = -\dfrac{3}{14}$

11. $\dfrac{1}{3} + f = \dfrac{3}{4}$

12. $c + \dfrac{1}{6} = \dfrac{3}{8}$

Objective Ⓑ *Solve each equation. Don't forget to first simplify each side of the equation, if possible. Check each solution. See Examples 5 through 7.*

13. $7x + 2x = 8x - 3$

14. $3n + 2n = 7 + 4n$

15. $\dfrac{5}{6}x + \dfrac{1}{6}x = -9$

16. $\dfrac{13}{11}y - \dfrac{2}{11}y = -3$

17. $2y + 10 = 5y - 4y$

18. $4x - 4 = 10x - 7x$

19. $-5(n - 2) = 8 - 4n$

20. $-4(z - 3) = 2 - 3z$

21. $\dfrac{3}{7}x + 2 = -\dfrac{4}{7}x - 5$

22. $\dfrac{1}{5}x - 1 = -\dfrac{4}{5}x - 13$

23. $5x - 6 = 6x - 5$

24. $2x + 7 = x - 10$

25. $8y + 2 - 6y = 3 + y - 10$

26. $4p - 11 - p = 2 + 2p - 20$

27. $-3(x - 4) = -4x$

28. $-2(x - 1) = -3x$

29. $\dfrac{3}{8}x - \dfrac{1}{6} = -\dfrac{5}{8}x - \dfrac{2}{3}$

30. $\dfrac{2}{5}x - \dfrac{1}{12} = -\dfrac{3}{5}x - \dfrac{3}{4}$

31. $2(x - 4) = x + 3$

32. $3(y + 7) = 2y - 5$

33. $3(n - 5) - (6 - 2n) = 4n$

34. $5(3 + z) - (8z + 9) = -4z$

35. $-2(x + 6) + 3(2x - 5) = 3(x - 4) + 10$

36. $-5(x + 1) + 4(2x - 3) = 2(x + 2) - 8$

Objectives Ⓐ Ⓑ Mixed Practice *Solve. See Examples 1 through 7.*

37. $13x - 3 = 14x$

38. $18x - 9 = 19x$

39. $5b - 0.7 = 6b$

40. $9x + 5.5 = 10x$

41. $3x - 6 = 2x + 5$

42. $7y + 2 = 6y + 2$

43. $13x - 9 + 2x - 5 = 12x - 1 + 2x$

44. $15x + 20 - 10x - 9 = 25x + 8 - 21x - 7$

45. $7(6 + w) = 6(2 + w)$

46. $6(5 + c) = 5(c - 4)$

47. $n + 4 = 3.6$

48. $m + 2 = 7.1$

49. $10 - (2x - 4) = 7 - 3x$

50. $15 - (6 - 7k) = 2 + 6k$

51. $\frac{1}{3} = x + \frac{2}{3}$

52. $\frac{1}{11} = y + \frac{10}{11}$

53. $-6.5 - 4x - 1.6 - 3x = -6x + 9.8$

54. $-1.4 - 7x - 3.6 - 2x = -8x + 4.4$

Objective Ⓒ *Write each algebraic expression described. See Examples 8 and 9.*

55. A 10-foot board is cut into two pieces. If one piece is x feet long, express the other length in terms of x.

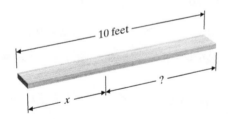

56. A 5-foot piece of string is cut into two pieces. If one piece is x feet long, express the other length in terms of x.

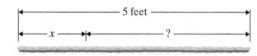

△ 57. Recall that two angles are *supplementary* if their sum is 180°. If one angle measures $x°$, express the measure of its supplement in terms of x.

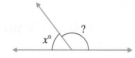

△ 58. Recall that two angles are *complementary* if their sum is 90°. If one angle measures $x°$, express the measure of its complement in terms of x.

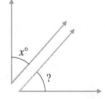

59. In 2009, the number of graduate students at the University of Texas at Austin was approximately 28,000 fewer than the number of undergraduate students. If the number of undergraduate students was n, how many graduate students attend UT Austin? (*Source:* University of Texas at Austin)

60. The longest interstate highway in the U.S. is I-90, which connects Seattle, Washington, and Boston, Massachusetts. The second longest interstate highway, I-80 (connecting San Francisco, California, and Teaneck, New Jersey), is 178.5 miles shorter than I-90. If the length of I-80 is m miles, express the length of I-90 as an algebraic expression in m. (*Source:* U.S. Department of Transportation— Federal Highway Administration)

61. The area of the Sahara Desert in Africa is 7 times the area of the Gobi Desert in Asia. If the area of the Gobi Desert is x square miles, express the area of the Sahara Desert as an algebraic expression in x.

62. The largest meteorite in the world is the Hoba West located in Namibia. Its weight is 3 times the weight of the Armanty meteorite located in Outer Mongolia. If the weight of the Armanty meteorite is y kilograms, express the weight of the Hoba West meteorite as an algebraic expression in y.

Review

Find each multiplicative inverse or reciprocal. See Section 5.7.

63. $\dfrac{5}{8}$ **64.** $\dfrac{7}{6}$ **65.** 2   **66.** 5   **67.** $-\dfrac{1}{9}$ **68.** $-\dfrac{3}{5}$

Perform each indicated operation and simplify. See Sections 5.6 and 5.7.

69. $\dfrac{3x}{3}$ **70.** $\dfrac{-2y}{-2}$ **71.** $-5\left(-\dfrac{1}{5}y\right)$ **72.** $7\left(\dfrac{1}{7}r\right)$ **73.** $\dfrac{3}{5}\left(\dfrac{5}{3}x\right)$ **74.** $\dfrac{9}{2}\left(\dfrac{2}{9}x\right)$

Concept Extensions

75. Write two terms whose sum is $-3x$.

76. Write four terms whose sum is $2y - 6$.

Use the addition property to fill in the blank so that the middle equation simplifies to the last equation. See the Concept Check in this section.

77.
$$x - 4 = -9$$
$$x - 4 + (\ \ ) = -9 + (\ \ )$$
$$x = -5$$

78.
$$a + 9 = 15$$
$$a + 9 + (\ \ ) = 15 + (\ \ )$$
$$a = 6$$

Fill in the blanks with numbers of your choice so that each equation has the given solution. Note: Each blank will be replaced with a different number.

79. ____ $+ x =$ ____ ; Solution: -3

80. $x -$ ____ $=$ ____ ; Solution: -10

Solve.

△ **81.** The sum of the angles of a triangle is 180°. If one angle of a triangle measures $x°$ and a second angle measures $(2x + 7)°$, express the measure of the third angle in terms of x. Simplify the expression.

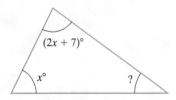

△ **82.** A quadrilateral is a four-sided figure (like the one shown in the figure) whose angle sum is 360°. If one angle measures $x°$, a second angle measures $3x°$, and a third angle measures $5x°$, express the measure of the fourth angle in terms of x. Simplify the expression.

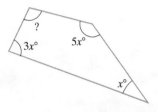

✎ **83.** In your own words, explain what is meant by the solution of an equation.

✎ **84.** In your own words, explain how to check a solution of an equation.

Use a calculator to determine the solution of each equation.

▦ **85.** $36.766 + x = -108.712$

▦ **86.** $-85.325 = x - 97.985$

6.2 THE MULTIPLICATION PROPERTY OF EQUALITY

Objectives

(A) **Use the Multiplication Property of Equality to Solve Linear Equations.**

(B) **Use Both the Addition and Multiplication Properties of Equality to Solve Linear Equations.**

(C) **Write Word Phrases as Algebraic Expressions.**

Objective (A) Using the Multiplication Property

As useful as the addition property of equality is, it cannot help us solve every type of linear equation in one variable. For example, adding or subtracting a value on both sides of the equation does not help solve

$$\frac{5}{2}x = 15$$

because the variable x is being multiplied by a number (other than 1). Instead, we apply another important property of equality, the **multiplication property of equality.**

> ### Multiplication Property of Equality
>
> Let $a, b,$ and c represent numbers and let $c \neq 0$. Then
>
> | $a = b$ | Also, $a = b$ |
> |---|---|
> | and $a \cdot c = b \cdot c$ | and $\dfrac{a}{c} = \dfrac{b}{c}$ |
> | are equivalent equations. | are equivalent equations. |

In other words, **both sides** of an equation **may be multiplied or divided by the same nonzero number** without changing the solution of the equation. (We may divide both sides by the same nonzero number since division is defined in terms of multiplication.)

| $2x$ | 6 | $\frac{2x}{2}$ or x | $\frac{6}{2}$ or 3 |

Example 1 Solve: $\dfrac{5}{2}x = 15$

Solution: To get x alone, we multiply both sides of the equation by the reciprocal (or multiplicative inverse) of $\dfrac{5}{2}$, which is $\dfrac{2}{5}$.

$$\frac{5}{2}x = 15$$

$$\frac{2}{5} \cdot \left(\frac{5}{2}x\right) = \frac{2}{5} \cdot 15 \qquad \text{Multiply both sides by } \frac{2}{5}.$$

$$\left(\frac{2}{5} \cdot \frac{5}{2}\right)x = \frac{2}{5} \cdot 15 \qquad \text{Apply the associative property.}$$

$$1x = 6 \qquad \text{Simplify.}$$

or

$$x = 6$$

PRACTICE 1

Solve: $\dfrac{3}{7}x = 9$

Answer
1. $x = 21$

Continued on next page

Check: Replace x with 6 in the original equation.

$$\frac{5}{2}x = 15 \quad \text{Original equation.}$$

$$\frac{5}{2}(6) \stackrel{?}{=} 15 \quad \text{Replace } x \text{ with 6.}$$

$$15 = 15 \quad \text{True}$$

The solution is 6.

● **Work Practice 1**

In the equation $\frac{5}{2}x = 15$, $\frac{5}{2}$ is the coefficient of x. When the coefficient of x is a *fraction*, we will get x alone by multiplying by the reciprocal. When the coefficient of x is an integer or a decimal, it is usually more convenient to divide both sides by the coefficient. (Dividing by a number is, of course, the same as multiplying by the reciprocal of the number.)

PRACTICE 2

Solve: $7x = 42$

Example 2 Solve: $5x = 30$

Solution: To get x alone, we divide both sides of the equation by 5, the coefficient of x.

$$5x = 30$$

$$\frac{5x}{5} = \frac{30}{5} \quad \text{Divide both sides by 5.}$$

$$1 \cdot x = 6 \quad \text{Simplify.}$$

$$x = 6$$

Check: $5x = 30$ Original equation.

$$5 \cdot 6 \stackrel{?}{=} 30 \quad \text{Replace } x \text{ with 6.}$$

$$30 = 30 \quad \text{True}$$

The solution is 6.

● **Work Practice 2**

PRACTICE 3

Solve: $-4x = 52$

Example 3 Solve: $-3x = 33$

Solution: Recall that $-3x$ means $-3 \cdot x$. To get x alone, we divide both sides by the coefficient of x, that is, -3.

$$-3x = 33$$

$$\frac{-3x}{-3} = \frac{33}{-3} \quad \text{Divide both sides by } -3.$$

$$1x = -11 \quad \text{Simplify.}$$

$$x = -11$$

Check: $-3x = 33$ Original equation.

$$-3(-11) \stackrel{?}{=} 33 \quad \text{Replace } x \text{ with } -11.$$

$$33 = 33 \quad \text{True}$$

The solution is -11.

● **Work Practice 3**

Answers

2. $x = 6$ **3.** $x = -13$

Example 4 Solve: $\frac{y}{7} = 20$

Solution: Recall that $\frac{y}{7} = \frac{1}{7}y$. To get y alone, we multiply both sides of the equation by 7, the reciprocal of $\frac{1}{7}$.

$$\frac{y}{7} = 20$$

$$\frac{1}{7}y = 20$$

$$7 \cdot \frac{1}{7}y = 7 \cdot 20 \quad \text{Multiply both sides by 7.}$$

$$1y = 140 \quad \text{Simplify.}$$

$$y = 140$$

Check: $\quad \frac{y}{7} = 20 \quad \text{Original equation.}$

$$\frac{140}{7} \stackrel{?}{=} 20 \quad \text{Replace } y \text{ with 140.}$$

$$20 = 20 \quad \text{True}$$

The solution is 140.

● **Work Practice 4**

PRACTICE 4

Solve: $\frac{y}{5} = 13$

Example 5 Solve: $3.1x = 4.96$

Solution: $\quad 3.1x = 4.96$

$$\frac{3.1x}{3.1} = \frac{4.96}{3.1} \quad \text{Divide both sides by 3.1.}$$

$$1x = 1.6 \quad \text{Simplify.}$$

$$x = 1.6$$

Check: Check by replacing x with 1.6 in the original equation. The solution is 1.6.

● **Work Practice 5**

PRACTICE 5

Solve: $2.6x = 13.52$

Example 6 Solve: $-\frac{2}{3}x = -\frac{5}{2}$

Solution: To get x alone, we multiply both sides of the equation by $-\frac{3}{2}$, the reciprocal of the coefficient of x.

$$-\frac{2}{3}x = -\frac{5}{2}$$

$$-\frac{3}{2} \cdot -\frac{2}{3}x = -\frac{3}{2} \cdot -\frac{5}{2} \quad \text{Multiply both sides by } -\frac{3}{2}, \text{ the reciprocal of } -\frac{2}{3}.$$

$$x = \frac{15}{4} \quad \text{Simplify.}$$

Check: Check by replacing x with $\frac{15}{4}$ in the original equation. The solution is $\frac{15}{4}$.

● **Work Practice 6**

PRACTICE 6

Solve: $-\frac{5}{6}y = -\frac{3}{5}$

Answers

4. $y = 65$ **5.** $x = 5.2$ **6.** $y = \frac{18}{25}$

Objective B Using Both the Addition and Multiplication Properties

We are now ready to combine the skills learned in the last section with the skills learned in this section to solve equations by applying more than one property.

PRACTICE 7

Solve: $-x + 7 = -12$

Example 7 Solve: $-z - 4 = 6$

Solution: First, let's get $-z$, the term containing the variable, alone. To do so, we add 4 to both sides of the equation.

$$-z - 4 + 4 = 6 + 4 \quad \text{Add 4 to both sides.}$$
$$-z = 10 \quad \text{Simplify.}$$

Next, recall that $-z$ means $-1 \cdot z$. Thus to get z alone, we either multiply or divide both sides of the equation by -1. In this example, we divide.

$$-z = 10$$
$$\frac{-z}{-1} = \frac{10}{-1} \quad \text{Divide both sides by the coefficient } -1.$$
$$1z = -10 \quad \text{Simplify.}$$
$$z = -10$$

Check: $\quad -z - 4 = 6 \quad$ Original equation.
$$-(-10) - 4 \overset{?}{=} 6 \quad \text{Replace } z \text{ with } -10.$$
$$10 - 4 \overset{?}{=} 6$$
$$6 = 6 \quad \text{True}$$

The solution is -10.

● **Work Practice 7**

Don't forget to first simplify one or both sides of an equation, if possible.

PRACTICE 8

Solve:
$-7x + 2x + 3 - 20 = -2$

Example 8 Solve: $a + a - 10 + 7 = -13$

Solution: First, we simplify the left side of the equation by combining like terms.

$$a + a - 10 + 7 = -13$$
$$2a - 3 = -13 \quad \text{Combine like terms.}$$
$$2a - 3 + 3 = -13 + 3 \quad \text{Add 3 to both sides.}$$
$$2a = -10 \quad \text{Simplify.}$$
$$\frac{2a}{2} = \frac{-10}{2} \quad \text{Divide both sides by 2.}$$
$$a = -5 \quad \text{Simplify.}$$

Check: To check, replace a with -5 in the original equation. The solution is -5.

● **Work Practice 8**

PRACTICE 9

Solve: $10x - 4 = 7x + 14$

Example 9 Solve: $7x - 3 = 5x + 9$

Solution: To get x alone, let's first use the addition property to get variable terms on one side of the equation and numbers on the other side. One way to get variable terms on one side is to subtract $5x$ from both sides.

$$7x - 3 = 5x + 9$$
$$7x - 3 - 5x = 5x + 9 - 5x \quad \text{Subtract } 5x \text{ from both sides.}$$
$$2x - 3 = 9 \quad \text{Simplify.}$$

Answers
7. $x = 19$ **8.** $x = -3$ **9.** $x = 6$

Now, to get numbers on the other side, let's add 3 to both sides.

$$2x - 3 + 3 = 9 + 3 \quad \text{Add 3 to both sides.}$$

$$2x = 12 \qquad \text{Simplify.}$$

Use the multiplication property to get x alone.

$$\frac{2x}{2} = \frac{12}{2} \qquad \text{Divide both sides by 2.}$$

$$x = 6 \qquad \text{Simplify.}$$

Check: To check, replace x with 6 in the original equation to see that a true statement results. The solution is 6.

Work Practice 9

If an equation has parentheses, don't forget to use the distributive property to remove them. Then combine any like terms.

Example 10   Solve: $5(2x + 3) = -1 + 7$

Solution:

$$5(2x + 3) = -1 + 7$$
$$5(2x) + 5(3) = -1 + 7 \qquad \text{Apply the distributive property.}$$
$$10x + 15 = 6 \qquad \text{Multiply and write } -1 + 7 \text{ as 6.}$$
$$10x + 15 - 15 = 6 - 15 \qquad \text{Subtract 15 from both sides.}$$
$$10x = -9 \qquad \text{Simplify.}$$
$$\frac{10x}{10} = -\frac{9}{10} \qquad \text{Divide both sides by 10.}$$
$$x = -\frac{9}{10} \qquad \text{Simplify.}$$

Check: To check, replace x with $-\dfrac{9}{10}$ in the original equation to see that a true statement results. The solution is $-\dfrac{9}{10}$.

Work Practice 10

Objective ⓒ Writing Algebraic Expressions

We continue to sharpen our problem-solving skills by writing algebraic expressions.

Example 11   Writing an Expression for Consecutive Integers

If x is the first of three consecutive integers, express the sum of the three integers in terms of x. Simplify if possible.

Solution: An example of three consecutive integers is 7, 8, and 9.

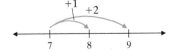

Continued on next page

PRACTICE 10

Solve: $4(3x - 2) = -1 + 4$

PRACTICE 11

a. If x is the first of two consecutive integers, express the sum of the two integers in terms of x. Simplify if possible.

b. If x is the first of two consecutive odd integers (see next page), express the sum of the two integers in terms of x. Simplify if possible.

Answers

10. $x = \dfrac{11}{12}$ **11. a.** $2x + 1$ **b.** $2x + 2$

The second consecutive integer is always 1 more than the first, and the third consecutive integer is 2 more than the first. If x is the first of three consecutive integers, the three consecutive integers are $x, x + 1$, and $x + 2$.

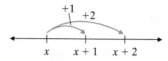

Their sum is shown below.

In words:	first integer	$+$	second integer	$+$	third integer
Translate:	x	$+$	$(x + 1)$	$+$	$(x + 2)$

This simplifies to $3x + 3$.

● **Work Practice 11**

Study these examples of consecutive even and consecutive odd integers.

Consecutive even integers:

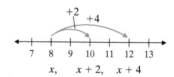

Consecutive odd integers:

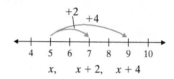

Helpful Hint

If x is an odd integer, then $x + 2$ is the next odd integer. This 2 simply means that odd integers are always 2 units from each other.

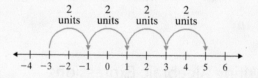

Vocabulary and Readiness Check

Use the choices below to fill in each blank. Some choices may be used more than once. Many of these questions are an important review of Section 6.1 also.

equation	multiplication	addition
expression	solution	equivalent

1. By the _____ property of equality, both sides of an equation may be multiplied or divided by the same nonzero number without changing the solution of the equation.
2. By the _____ property of equality, the same number may be added to or subtracted from both sides of an equation without changing the solution of the equation.
3. A(n) _____ may be solved while a(n) _____ may be simplified and evaluated.
4. A(n) _____ contains an equal sign (=) while a(n) _____ does not.
5. _____ equations have the same solution.
6. A(n) _____ of an equation is a number that when substituted for a variable makes the equation a true statement.

Solve each equation mentally. See Examples 2 and 3.

7. $3a = 27$　　　**8.** $9c = 54$　　　**9.** $5b = 10$　　　**10.** $7t = 14$　　　**11.** $6x = -30$　　　**12.** $8r = -64$

6.2 Exercise Set

FOR EXTRA HELP

MyMathLab

 PRACTICE　 WATCH　 DOWNLOAD　 READ　 REVIEW

Objective A *Solve each equation. Check each solution. See Examples 1 through 6.*

1. $-5x = -20$　　　**2.** $-7x = -49$　　　**3.** $3x = 0$　　　**4.** $2x = 0$

5. $-x = -12$　　　**6.** $-y = 8$　　　**7.** $\dfrac{2}{3}x = -8$　　　**8.** $\dfrac{3}{4}n = -15$

9. $\dfrac{1}{6}d = \dfrac{1}{2}$　　　**10.** $\dfrac{1}{8}v = \dfrac{1}{4}$　　　**11.** $\dfrac{a}{2} = 1$　　　**12.** $\dfrac{d}{15} = 2$

13. $\dfrac{k}{-7} = 0$　　　**14.** $\dfrac{f}{-5} = 0$　　　**15.** $1.7x = 10.71$　　　**16.** $8.5y = 19.55$

Objective B *Solve each equation. Check each solution. See Examples 7 and 8.*

17. $2x - 4 = 16$　　　**18.** $3x - 1 = 26$　　　**19.** $-x + 2 = 22$　　　**20.** $-x + 4 = -24$

21. $6a + 3 = 3$　　　**22.** $8t + 5 = 5$　　　**23.** $\dfrac{x}{3} - 2 = -5$　　　**24.** $\dfrac{b}{4} - 1 = -7$

25. $6z - 8 - z + 3 = 0$　　　**26.** $4a + 1 + a - 11 = 0$　　　**27.** $1 = 0.4x - 0.6x - 5$　　　**28.** $19 = 0.4x - 0.9x - 6$

29. $\dfrac{2}{3}y - 11 = -9$　　　**30.** $\dfrac{3}{5}x - 14 = -8$　　　**31.** $\dfrac{3}{4}t - \dfrac{1}{2} = \dfrac{1}{3}$　　　**32.** $\dfrac{2}{7}z - \dfrac{1}{5} = \dfrac{1}{2}$

Solve each equation. See Examples 9 and 10.

33. $8x + 20 = 6x + 18$ **34.** $11x + 13 = 9x + 9$ **35.** $3(2x + 5) = -18 + 9$ **36.** $2(4x + 1) = -12 + 6$

37. $2x - 5 = 20x + 4$ **38.** $6x - 4 = -2x - 10$ **39.** $2 + 14 = -4(3x - 4)$ **40.** $8 + 4 = -6(5x - 2)$

41. $-6y - 3 = -5y - 7$ **42.** $-17z - 4 = -16z - 20$ **43.** $\frac{1}{2}(2x - 1) = -\frac{1}{7} - \frac{3}{7}$

44. $\frac{1}{3}(3x - 1) = -\frac{1}{10} - \frac{2}{10}$ **45.** $-10z - 0.5 = -20z + 1.6$ **46.** $-14y - 1.8 = -24y + 3.9$

47. $-4x + 20 = 4x - 20$ **48.** $-3x + 15 = 3x - 15$

Objectives Ⓐ Ⓑ **Mixed Practice** *See Examples 1 through 10.*

49. $42 = 7x$ **50.** $81 = 3x$ **51.** $4.4 = -0.8x$

52. $6.3 = -0.6x$ **53.** $6x + 10 = -20$ **54.** $10y + 15 = -5$

55. $5 - 0.3k = 5$ **56.** $2 - 0.4p = 2$ **57.** $13x - 5 = 11x - 11$

58. $20x - 20 = 16x - 40$ **59.** $9(3x + 1) = 4x - 5x$ **60.** $7(2x + 1) = 18x - 19x$

61. $-\frac{3}{7}p = -2$ **62.** $-\frac{4}{5}r = -5$ **63.** $-\frac{4}{3}x = 12$

64. $-\frac{10}{3}x = 30$ **65.** $-2x - \frac{1}{2} = \frac{7}{2}$ **66.** $-3n - \frac{1}{3} = \frac{8}{3}$

67. $10 = 2x - 1$ **68.** $12 = 3j - 4$ **69.** $10 - 3x - 6 - 9x = 7$

70. $12x + 30 + 8x - 6 = 10$ **71.** $z - 5z = 7z - 9 - z$ **72.** $t - 6t = -13 + t - 3t$

73. $-x - \frac{4}{5} = x + \frac{1}{2} + \frac{2}{5}$ **74.** $x + \frac{3}{7} = -x + \frac{1}{3} + \frac{4}{7}$

75. $-15 + 37 = -2(x + 5)$ **76.** $-19 + 74 = -5(x + 3)$

Objective ⓒ *Write each algebraic expression described. Simplify if possible. See Example 11.*

77. If x represents the first of two consecutive odd integers, express the sum of the two integers in terms of x.

78. If x is the first of three consecutive even integers, write their sum as an algebraic expression in x.

79. If x is the first of four consecutive integers, express the sum of the first integer and the third integer as an algebraic expression containing the variable x.

80. If x is the first of two consecutive integers, express the sum of 20 and the second consecutive integer as an algebraic expression containing the variable x.

81. Classrooms on one side of the science building are all numbered with consecutive even integers. If the first room on this side of the building is numbered x, write an expression in x for the sum of five classroom numbers in a row. Then simplify this expression.

82. Two sides of a quadrilateral have the same length, x, while the other two sides have the same length, both being the next consecutive odd integer. Write the sum of these lengths. Then simplify this expression.

Review

Simplify each expression. See Section 5.8.

83. $5x + 2(x - 6)$

84. $-7y + 2y - 3(y + 1)$

85. $6(2z + 4) + 20$

86. $-(3a - 3) + 2a - 6$

87. $-(x - 1) + x$

88. $8(z - 6) + 7z - 1$

Concept Extensions

Fill in the blank with a number of your choice so that each equation has the given solution.

89. $6x = $ _____ ; solution: -8

90. _____ $x = 10$; solution: $\dfrac{1}{2}$

91. The equation $3x + 6 = 2x + 10 + x - 4$ is true for all real numbers. Substitute a few real numbers for x to see that this is so and then try solving the equation. Describe what happens.

92. The equation $6x + 2 - 2x = 4x + 1$ has no solution. Try solving this equation for x and describe what happens.

93. From the results of Exercises 91 and 92, when do you think an equation has all real numbers as its solutions?

94. From the results of Exercises 91 and 92, when do you think an equation has no solution?

Solve.

95. $0.07x - 5.06 = -4.92$

96. $0.06y + 2.63 = 2.5562$

Objectives

A Apply the General Strategy for Solving a Linear Equation.

B Solve Equations Containing Fractions or Decimals.

C Recognize Identities and Equations with No Solution.

6.3 FURTHER SOLVING LINEAR EQUATIONS

Objective **A** Solving Linear Equations

Let's begin by restating the formal definition of a linear equation in one variable.

A **linear equation in one variable** can be written in the form

$$Ax + B = C$$

where $A, B,$ and C are real numbers and $A \neq 0$.

We now combine our knowledge from the previous sections into a general strategy for solving linear equations.

To Solve Linear Equations in One Variable

Step 1: If an equation contains fractions, multiply both sides by the LCD to clear the equation of fractions.

Step 2: Use the distributive property to remove parentheses if they are present.

Step 3: Simplify each side of the equation by combining like terms.

Step 4: Get all variable terms on one side and all numbers on the other side by using the addition property of equality.

Step 5: Get the variable alone by using the multiplication property of equality.

Step 6: Check the solution by substituting it into the original equation.

We will use these steps to solve the equations in Examples 1–5.

Example 1 Solve: $4(2x - 3) + 7 = 3x + 5$

Solution: There are no fractions, so we begin with Step 2.

$$4(2x - 3) + 7 = 3x + 5$$

Step 2: $8x - 12 + 7 = 3x + 5$ Use the distributive property.

Step 3: $8x - 5 = 3x + 5$ Combine like terms.

Step 4: Get all variable terms on one side of the equation and all numbers on the other side. One way to do this is by subtracting $3x$ from both sides and then adding 5 to both sides.

$$8x - 5 - 3x = 3x + 5 - 3x$$ Subtract $3x$ from both sides.
$$5x - 5 = 5$$ Simplify.
$$5x - 5 + 5 = 5 + 5$$ Add 5 to both sides.
$$5x = 10$$ Simplify.

Step 5: Use the multiplication property of equality to get x alone.

$$\frac{5x}{5} = \frac{10}{5}$$ Divide both sides by 5.
$$x = 2$$ Simplify.

Step 6: Check.

$$4(2x - 3) + 7 = 3x + 5$$ Original equation
$$4[2(2) - 3] + 7 \stackrel{?}{=} 3(2) + 5$$ Replace x with 2.
$$4(4 - 3) + 7 \stackrel{?}{=} 6 + 5$$
$$4(1) + 7 \stackrel{?}{=} 11$$
$$4 + 7 \stackrel{?}{=} 11$$
$$11 = 11$$ True

The solution is 2.

PRACTICE 1

Solve:

$$5(3x - 1) + 2 = 12x + 6$$

Answer

1. $x = 3$

518

Work Practice 1

Copyright 2011 Pearson Education, Inc.

Example 2 Solve: $8(2 - t) = -5t$

Solution: First, we apply the distributive property.

$$8(\overset{\frown}{2 - t}) = -5t$$

Step 2: $16 - 8t = -5t$ Use the distributive property.

Step 4: $16 - 8t + 8t = -5t + 8t$ Add $8t$ to both sides.

$16 = 3t$ Combine like terms.

Step 5: $\dfrac{16}{3} = \dfrac{3t}{3}$ Divide both sides by 3.

$\dfrac{16}{3} = t$ Simplify.

Step 6: Check.

$$8(2 - t) = -5t \quad \text{Original equation}$$
$$8\left(2 - \frac{16}{3}\right) \overset{?}{=} -5\left(\frac{16}{3}\right) \quad \text{Replace } t \text{ with } \frac{16}{3}.$$
$$8\left(\frac{6}{3} - \frac{16}{3}\right) \overset{?}{=} -\frac{80}{3} \quad \text{The LCD is 3.}$$
$$8\left(-\frac{10}{3}\right) \overset{?}{=} -\frac{80}{3} \quad \text{Subtract fractions.}$$
$$-\frac{80}{3} = -\frac{80}{3} \quad \text{True}$$

The solution is $\dfrac{16}{3}$.

● **Work Practice 2**

Objective Ⓑ Solving Equations Containing Fractions or Decimals

If an equation contains fractions, we can clear the equation of fractions by multiplying both sides by the LCD of all denominators. By doing this, we avoid working with time-consuming fractions.

Example 3 Solve: $\dfrac{x}{2} - 1 = \dfrac{2}{3}x - 3$

Solution: We begin by clearing fractions. To do this, we multiply both sides of the equation by the LCD, which is 6.

$$\frac{x}{2} - 1 = \frac{2}{3}x - 3$$

Step 1: $6\left(\dfrac{x}{2} - 1\right) = 6\left(\dfrac{2}{3}x - 3\right)$ Multiply both sides by the LCD, 6.

Step 2: $6\left(\dfrac{x}{2}\right) - 6(1) = 6\left(\dfrac{2}{3}x\right) - 6(3)$ Use the distributive property.

$3x - 6 = 4x - 18$ Simplify.

There are no longer grouping symbols and no like terms on either side of the equation, so we continue with Step 4.

Continued on next page

Solve: $9(5 - x) = -3x$

Helpful Hint When checking solutions, use the original equation.

PRACTICE 3

Solve: $\dfrac{5}{2}x - 1 = \dfrac{3}{2}x - 4$

Helpful Hint Don't forget to multiply *each* term by the LCD.

Answers

2. $x = \dfrac{15}{2}$ **3.** $x = -3$

$$3x - 6 = 4x - 18$$

Step 4: $3x - 6 - 3x = 4x - 18 - 3x$ Subtract $3x$ from both sides.

$$-6 = x - 18$$ Simplify.

$$-6 + 18 = x - 18 + 18$$ Add 18 to both sides.

$$12 = x$$ Simplify.

Step 5: The variable is now alone, so there is no need to apply the multiplication property of equality.

Step 6: Check.

$$\frac{x}{2} - 1 = \frac{2}{3}x - 3$$ Original equation

$$\frac{12}{2} - 1 \overset{?}{=} \frac{2}{3} \cdot 12 - 3$$ Replace x with 12.

$$6 - 1 \overset{?}{=} 8 - 3$$ Simplify.

$$5 = 5$$ True

The solution is 12.

● Work Practice 3

PRACTICE 4

Solve: $\dfrac{3(x - 2)}{5} = 3x + 6$

Example 4 Solve: $\dfrac{2(a + 3)}{3} = 6a + 2$

Solution: We clear the equation of fractions first.

$$\frac{2(a + 3)}{3} = 6a + 2$$

Step 1: $3 \cdot \dfrac{2(a + 3)}{3} = 3(6a + 2)$ Clear the fraction by multiplying both sides by the LCD, 3.

$$2(a + 3) = 3(6a + 2)$$ Simplify.

Step 2: Next, we use the distributive property to remove parentheses.

$$2a + 6 = 18a + 6$$ Use the distributive property.

Step 4: $2a + 6 - 18a = 18a + 6 - 18a$ Subtract $18a$ from both sides.

$$-16a + 6 = 6$$ Simplify.

$$-16a + 6 - 6 = 6 - 6$$ Subtract 6 from both sides.

$$-16a = 0$$

Step 5: $\dfrac{-16a}{-16} = \dfrac{0}{-16}$ Divide both sides by -16.

$$a = 0$$ Simplify.

Step 6: To check, replace a with 0 in the original equation. The solution is 0.

● Work Practice 4

Helpful Hint

Remember: When solving an equation, it makes no difference on which side of the equation variable terms lie. Just make sure that constant terms lie on the other side.

When solving a problem about money, you may need to solve an equation containing decimals. If you choose, you may multiply to clear the equation of decimals.

Answer

4. $x = -3$

Example 5 Solve: $0.25x + 0.10(x - 3) = 1.1$

Solution: First we clear this equation of decimals by multiplying both sides of the equation by 100. Recall that multiplying a decimal number by 100 has the effect of moving the decimal point 2 places to the right.

$$0.25x + 0.10(x - 3) = 1.1$$

Step 1: $0.25x + 0.10(x - 3) = 1.10$ Multiply both sides by 100.

$$25x + 10(x - 3) = 110$$

Step 2: $25x + 10x - 30 = 110$ Apply the distributive property.

Step 3: $35x - 30 = 110$ Combine like terms.

Step 4: $35x - 30 + 30 = 110 + 30$ Add 30 to both sides.

$$35x = 140$$ Combine like terms.

Step 5: $\dfrac{35x}{35} = \dfrac{140}{35}$ Divide both sides by 35.

$$x = 4$$

Step 6: To check, replace x with 4 in the original equation. The solution is 4.

● **Work Practice 5**

Objective ⓒ Recognizing Identities and Equations with No Solution

So far, each equation that we have solved has had a single solution. However, not every equation in one variable has a single solution. Some equations have no solution, while others have an infinite number of solutions. For example,

$$x + 5 = x + 7$$

has **no solution** since no matter which real number we replace x with, the equation is false.

    real number + 5 = same real number + 7   FALSE

On the other hand,

$$x + 6 = x + 6$$

has infinitely many solutions since x can be replaced by any real number and the equation will always be true.

    real number + 6 = same real number + 6   TRUE

The equation $x + 6 = x + 6$ is called an **identity.** The next two examples illustrate special equations like these.

Example 6 Solve: $-2(x - 5) + 10 = -3(x + 2) + x$

Solution:

$$-2(x - 5) + 10 = -3(x + 2) + x$$
$$-2x + 10 + 10 = -3x - 6 + x$$ Apply the distributive property on both sides.
$$-2x + 20 = -2x - 6$$ Combine like terms.
$$-2x + 20 + 2x = -2x - 6 + 2x$$ Add 2x to both sides.
$$20 = -6$$ Combine like terms.

The final equation contains no variable terms, and the result is the false statement $20 = -6$. This means that there is no value for x that makes $20 = -6$ a true equation. Thus, we conclude that there is **no solution** to this equation.

● **Work Practice 6**

PRACTICE 5

Solve:
$0.06x - 0.10(x - 2) = -0.16$

Helpful Hint
If you have trouble with this step, try removing parentheses first.

$0.25x + 0.10(x - 3) = 1.1$
$0.25x + 0.10x - 0.3 = 1.1$
$0.25x + 0.10x - 0.30 = 1.10$
$25x + 10x - 30 = 110$

PRACTICE 6

Solve:
$5(2 - x) + 8x = 3(x - 6)$

Answers
5. $x = 9$ **6.** no solution

PRACTICE 7

Solve:

$-6(2x + 1) - 14$
$= -10(x + 2) - 2x$

Example 7 Solve: $3(x - 4) = 3x - 12$

Solution: $3(x - 4) = 3x - 12$

   $3x - 12 = 3x - 12$ Apply the distributive property.

The left side of the equation is now identical to the right side. Every real number may be substituted for x and a true statement will result. We arrive at the same conclusion if we continue.

$$3x - 12 = 3x - 12$$
$$3x - 12 - 3x = 3x - 12 - 3x \quad \text{Subtract } 3x \text{ from both sides.}$$
$$-12 = -12 \quad\quad \text{Combine like terms.}$$

Again, the final equation contains no variables, but this time the result is the true statement $-12 = -12$. This means that one side of the equation is identical to the other side. Thus, $3(x - 4) = 3x - 12$ is an **identity** and **every real number** is a solution.

● **Work Practice 7**

Answer

7. Every real number is a solution.

✓ **Concept Check Answer**

a. Every real number is a solution.
b. The solution is 0.
c. There is no solution.

✓ **Concept Check** Suppose you have simplified several equations and obtained the following results. What can you conclude about the solutions to the original equation?

a. $7 = 7$ **b.** $x = 0$ **c.** $7 = -4$

Calculator Explorations   **Checking Equations**

We can use a calculator to check possible solutions of equations. To do this, replace the variable by the possible solution and evaluate each side of the equation separately.

Equation: $3x - 4 = 2(x + 6)$ Solution: $x = 16$
   $3x - 4 = 2(x + 6)$ Original equation
   $3(16) - 4 \stackrel{?}{=} 2(16 + 6)$ Replace x with 16.

Now evaluate each side with your calculator.

Evaluate left side: | 3 | × | 16 | − | 4 | = |

or

Display: | 44 | | ENTER |

Evaluate right side: | 2 | (| 16 | + | 6 |) | = |

or

Display: | 44 | | ENTER |

Since the left side equals the right side, the equation checks.

Use a calculator to check the possible solutions to each equation.

1. $2x = 48 + 6x; \quad x = -12$

2. $-3x - 7 = 3x - 1; \quad x = -1$

3. $5x - 2.6 = 2(x + 0.8); \quad x = 4.4$

4. $-1.6x - 3.9 = -6.9x - 25.6; \quad x = 5$

5. $\dfrac{564x}{4} = 200x - 11(649); \quad x = 121$

6. $20(x - 39) = 5x - 432; \quad x = 23.2$

Vocabulary and Readiness Check

Throughout algebra, it is important to be able to identify equations and expressions.

Remember,
- an equation contains an equal sign and
- an expression does not.

Among other things,
- we solve equations and
- we simplify or perform operations on expressions.

Identify each as an equation or an expression.

1. $x = -7$ _____

2. $x - 7$ _____

3. $4y - 6 + 9y + 1$ _____

4. $4y - 6 = 9y + 1$ _____

5. $\dfrac{1}{x} - \dfrac{x-1}{8}$ _____

6. $\dfrac{1}{x} - \dfrac{x-1}{8} = 6$ _____

7. $0.1x + 9 = 0.2x$ _____

8. $0.1x^2 + 9y - 0.2x^2$ _____

6.3 Exercise Set

Objective A *Solve each equation. See Examples 1 and 2.*

1. $-4y + 10 = -2(3y + 1)$

2. $-3x + 1 = -2(4x + 2)$

3. $15x - 8 = 10 + 9x$

4. $15x - 5 = 7 + 12x$

5. $-2(3x - 4) = 2x$

6. $-(5x - 10) = 5x$

7. $5(2x - 1) - 2(3x) = 1$

8. $3(2 - 5x) + 4(6x) = 12$

9. $-6(x - 3) - 26 = -8$

10. $-4(n - 4) - 23 = -7$

11. $8 - 2(a + 1) = 9 + a$

12. $5 - 6(2 + b) = b - 14$

13. $4x + 3 = -3 + 2x + 14$

14. $6y - 8 = -6 + 3y + 13$

15. $-2y - 10 = 5y + 18$

16. $-7n + 5 = 8n - 10$

Objective B *Solve each equation. See Examples 3 through 5.*

17. $\dfrac{2}{3}x + \dfrac{4}{3} = -\dfrac{2}{3}$

18. $\dfrac{4}{5}x - \dfrac{8}{5} = -\dfrac{16}{5}$

19. $\dfrac{3}{4}x - \dfrac{1}{2} = 1$

20. $\dfrac{2}{9}x - \dfrac{1}{3} = 1$

21. $0.50x + 0.15(70) = 35.5$

22. $0.40x + 0.06(30) = 9.8$

23. $\dfrac{2(x + 1)}{4} = 3x - 2$

24. $\dfrac{3(y + 3)}{5} = 2y + 6$

25. $x + \dfrac{7}{6} = 2x - \dfrac{7}{6}$

26. $\dfrac{5}{2}x - 1 = x + \dfrac{1}{4}$

27. $0.12(y - 6) + 0.06y = 0.08y - 0.7$

28. $0.60(z - 300) + 0.05z = 0.70z - 205$

Objective Ⓒ *Solve each equation. See Examples 6 and 7.*

29. $4(3x + 2) = 12x + 8$

30. $14x + 7 = 7(2x + 1)$

31. $\dfrac{x}{4} + 1 = \dfrac{x}{4}$

32. $\dfrac{x}{3} - 2 = \dfrac{x}{3}$

33. $3x - 7 = 3(x + 1)$

34. $2(x - 5) = 2x + 10$

35. $-2(6x - 5) + 4 = -12x + 14$

36. $-5(4y - 3) + 2 = -20y + 17$

Objectives Ⓐ Ⓑ Ⓒ **Mixed Practice** *Solve. See Examples 1 through 7.*

37. $\dfrac{6(3 - z)}{5} = -z$

38. $\dfrac{4(5 - w)}{3} = -w$

39. $-3(2t - 5) + 2t = 5t - 4$

40. $-(4a - 7) - 5a = 10 + a$

41. $5y + 2(y - 6) = 4(y + 1) - 2$

42. $9x + 3(x - 4) = 10(x - 5) + 7$

43. $\dfrac{3(x - 5)}{2} = \dfrac{2(x + 5)}{3}$

44. $\dfrac{5(x - 1)}{4} = \dfrac{3(x + 1)}{2}$

45. $0.7x - 2.3 = 0.5$

46. $0.9x - 4.1 = 0.4$

47. $5x - 5 = 2(x + 1) + 3x - 7$

48. $3(2x - 1) + 5 = 6x + 2$

49. $4(2n + 1) = 3(6n + 3) + 1$

50. $4(4y + 2) = 2(1 + 6y) + 8$

51. $x + \dfrac{5}{4} = \dfrac{3}{4}x$

52. $\dfrac{7}{8}x + \dfrac{1}{4} = \dfrac{3}{4}x$

53. $\dfrac{x}{2} - 1 = \dfrac{x}{5} + 2$

54. $\dfrac{x}{5} - 7 = \dfrac{x}{3} - 5$

55. $2(x + 3) - 5 = 5x - 3(1 + x)$

56. $4(2 + x) + 1 = 7x - 3(x - 2)$

57. $0.06 - 0.01(x + 1) = -0.02(2 - x)$

58. $-0.01(5x + 4) = 0.04 - 0.01(x + 4)$

59. $\dfrac{9}{2} + \dfrac{5}{2}y = 2y - 4$

60. $3 - \dfrac{1}{2}x = 5x - 8$

61. $\dfrac{3}{4}x - 1 + \dfrac{1}{2}x = \dfrac{5}{12}x + \dfrac{1}{6}$

62. $\dfrac{5}{9}x + 2 - \dfrac{1}{6}x = \dfrac{11}{18}x + \dfrac{1}{3}$

63. $3x + \dfrac{5}{16} = \dfrac{3}{4} - \dfrac{1}{8}x - \dfrac{1}{2}$

64. $2x - \dfrac{1}{10} = \dfrac{2}{5} - \dfrac{1}{4}x - \dfrac{17}{20}$

Review

Translating   *Write each algebraic expression described. See Section 5.8. (Recall that the perimeter of a figure is the total distance around the figure.)*

65. A plot of land is in the shape of a triangle. If one side is x meters, a second side is $(2x - 3)$ meters, and a third side is $(3x - 5)$ meters, express the perimeter of the lot as a simplified expression in x.

66. A portion of a board has length x feet. The other part has length $(7x - 9)$ feet. Express the total length of the board as a simplified expression in x.

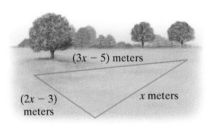

(3x − 5) meters

(2x − 3) meters

x meters

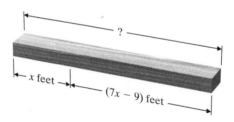

?

x feet

(7x − 9) feet

Translating *Write each phrase as an algebraic expression. Use x for the unknown number. See Section 5.8.*

67. A number subtracted from -8

68. Three times a number

69. The sum of -3 and twice a number

70. The difference of 8 and twice a number

71. The product of 9 and the sum of a number and 20

72. The quotient of -12 and the difference of a number and 3

Concept Extensions

See the Concept Check in this section.

73. a. Solve: $x + 3 = x + 3$

   b. If you simplify an equation (such as the one in part a) and get a true statement such as $3 = 3$ or $0 = 0$, what can you conclude about the solution(s) of the original equation?

   c. On your own, construct an equation for which every real number is a solution.

74. a. Solve: $x + 3 = x + 5$

   b. If you simplify an equation (such as the one in part a) and get a false statement such as $3 = 5$ or $10 = 17$, what can you conclude about the solution(s) of the original equation?

   c. On your own, construct an equation that has no solution.

Match each equation in the first column with its solution in the second column. Items in the second column may be used more than once.

75. $5x + 1 = 5x + 1$

76. $3x + 1 = 3x + 2$

77. $2x - 6x - 10 = -4x + 3 - 10$

78. $x - 11x - 3 = -10x - 1 - 2$

79. $9x - 20 = 8x - 20$

80. $-x + 15 = x + 15$

a. all real numbers

b. no solution

c. 0

81. Explain the difference between simplifying an expression and solving an equation.

82. On your own, write an expression and then an equation. Label each.

For Exercises 83 and 84, **a.** *Write an equation for perimeter.* **b.** *Solve the equation in part (a).* **c.** *Find the length of each side.*

△ **83.** The perimeter of the following pentagon (five-sided figure) is 28 centimeters.

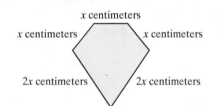

△ **84.** The perimeter of the following triangle is 35 meters.

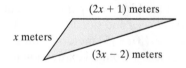

Fill in the blanks with numbers of your choice so that each equation has the given solution. Note: Each blank may be replaced by a different number.

85. $x +$ ____ $= 2x -$ ____; solution: 9

86. $-5x -$ ____ $=$ ____; solution: 2

Solve.

▦ **87.** $1000(7x - 10) = 50(412 + 100x)$

▦ **88.** $1000(x + 40) = 100(16 + 7x)$

▦ **89.** $0.035x + 5.112 = 0.010x + 5.107$

▦ **90.** $0.127x - 2.685 = 0.027x - 2.38$

6.4 A FURTHER INTRODUCTION TO PROBLEM SOLVING

Objectives

A Solve Problems Involving Direct Translations.

B Solve Problems Involving Relationships Among Unknown Quantities.

C Solve Problems Involving Consecutive Integers.

First, let's review a list of key words and phrases from Section 5.3 to help us translate.

Helpful Hint

Order matters when subtracting and also dividing, so be especially careful with these translations.

Addition (+)	Subtraction (−)	Multiplication (·)	Division (÷)	Equality (=)
Sum	Difference of	Product	Quotient	Equals
Plus	Minus	Times	Divide	Gives
Added to	Subtracted from	Multiply	Into	Is/was/ should be
More than	Less than	Twice	Ratio	Yields
Increased by	Decreased by	Of	Divided by	Amounts to
Total	Less			Represents
				Is the same as

Now, we review our general strategy for problem-solving, first introduced in Section 1.8. Notice that Step 1 now includes choosing a variable.

General Strategy for Problem Solving

1. UNDERSTAND the problem. During this step, become comfortable with the problem. Some ways of doing this are:

   Read and reread the problem.

   Choose a variable to represent the unknown.

   Construct a drawing.

   Propose a solution and check. Pay careful attention to how you check your proposed solution. This will help when writing an equation to model the problem.

2. TRANSLATE the problem into an equation.

3. SOLVE the equation.

4. INTERPRET the results: *Check* the proposed solution in the stated problem and *state* your conclusion.

Objective A Solving Direct Translation Problems

Much of problem solving involves a direct translation from a sentence to an equation.

Example 1 Finding an Unknown Number

Twice a number, added to seven, is the same as three subtracted from the number. Find the number.

Solution: Translate the sentence into an equation and solve.

In words:	twice a number	added to	seven	is the same as	three subtracted from the number
	↓	↓	↓	↓	↓
Translate:	$2x$	$+$	7	$=$	$x - 3$

Continued on next page

PRACTICE 1

Three times a number, minus 6, is the same as two times the number, plus 3. Find the number.

Answer
1. The number is 9.

To solve, begin by subtracting x from both sides to isolate the variable term.

$$2x + 7 = x - 3$$
$$2x + 7 - x = x - 3 - x \qquad \text{Subtract } x \text{ from both sides.}$$
$$x + 7 = -3 \qquad \text{Combine like terms.}$$
$$x + 7 - 7 = -3 - 7 \qquad \text{Subtract 7 from both sides.}$$
$$x = -10 \qquad \text{Combine like terms.}$$

Check the solution in the problem as it was originally stated. To do so, replace "number" in the sentence with -10. Twice "-10" added to 7 is the same as 3 subtracted from "-10."

$$2(-10) + 7 = -10 - 3$$
$$-13 = -13$$

The unknown number is -10.

⬤ **Work Practice 1**

> **Helpful Hint**
>
> When checking solutions, go back to the original stated problem rather than to your equation in case errors have been made in translating to an equation.

PRACTICE 2

Three times the difference of a number and 5 is the same as twice the number decreased by 3. Find the number.

Example 2 Finding an Unknown Number

Twice the sum of a number and 4 is the same as four times the number decreased by 12. Find the number.

Solution:

1. **UNDERSTAND.** Read and reread the problem. If we let $x =$ the unknown number, then
   "the sum of a number and 4" translates to "$x + 4$" and
   "four times the number" translates to "$4x$"

2. **TRANSLATE.**

twice	sum of a number and 4	is the same as	four times the number	decreased by	12
↓	↓	↓	↓	↓	↓
2	$(x + 4)$	$=$	$4x$	$-$	12

3. **SOLVE**

$$2(x + 4) = 4x - 12$$
$$2x + 8 = 4x - 12 \qquad \text{Apply the distributive property.}$$
$$2x + 8 - 4x = 4x - 12 - 4x \qquad \text{Subtract } 4x \text{ from both sides.}$$
$$-2x + 8 = -12$$
$$-2x + 8 - 8 = -12 - 8 \qquad \text{Subtract 8 from both sides.}$$
$$-2x = -20$$
$$\frac{-2x}{-2} = \frac{-20}{-2} \qquad \text{Divide both sides by } -2.$$
$$x = 10$$

4. **INTERPRET.**

Check: Check this solution in the problem as it was originally stated. To do so, replace "number" with 10. Twice the sum of "10" and 4 is 28, which is the same as 4 times "10" decreased by 12.

State: The number is 10.

⬤ **Work Practice 2**

Answer

2. The number is 12.

Objective Ⓑ Solving Problems Involving Relationships Among Unknown Quantities

Example 3 Finding the Length of a Board

A 10-foot board is to be cut into two pieces so that the length of the longer piece is 4 times the length of the shorter. Find the length of each piece.

Solution:

1. UNDERSTAND the problem. To do so, read and reread the problem. You may also want to propose a solution. For example, if 3 feet represents the length of the shorter piece, then $4(3) = 12$ feet is the length of the longer piece, since it is 4 times the length of the shorter piece. This guess gives a total board length of 3 feet + 12 feet = 15 feet, which is too long. However, the purpose of proposing a solution is not to guess correctly, but to help better understand the problem and how to model it.

   In general, if we let

   x = length of shorter piece, then

   $4x$ = length of longer piece

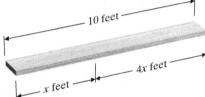

2. TRANSLATE the problem. First, we write the equation in words.

length of shorter piece	added to	length of longer piece	equals	total length of board
↓	↓	↓	↓	↓
x	$+$	$4x$	$=$	10

3. SOLVE.

$$x + 4x = 10$$
$$5x = 10 \quad \text{Combine like terms.}$$
$$\frac{5x}{5} = \frac{10}{5} \quad \text{Divide both sides by 5.}$$
$$x = 2$$

4. INTERPRET.

Check: Check the solution in the stated problem. If the length of the shorter piece of board is 2 feet, the length of the longer piece is $4 \cdot (2 \text{ feet}) = 8$ feet and the sum of the lengths of the two pieces is 2 feet + 8 feet = 10 feet.

State: The shorter piece of board is 2 feet and the longer piece of board is 8 feet.

● Work Practice 3

Helpful Hint

Make sure that units are included in your answer, if appropriate.

Example 4 Finding the Number of Republican and Democratic Senators

The 111th Congress, which began at noon on January 3, 2009, had a total of 434 Democrats and Republicans. There were 78 more Democratic representatives than Republican. Find the number of representatives from each party. (*Source: New York Times*)

Continued on next page

Solution:

1. UNDERSTAND the problem. Read and re-read the problem. Let's suppose that there are 200 Republican representatives. Since there are 78 more Democrats than Republicans, there must be $200 + 78 = 278$ Democrats. The total number of Republicans and Democrats is then $200 + 278 = 478$. This is incorrect since the total should be 434, but we now have a better understanding of the problem.

In general, if we let

x = number of Republicans, then

$x + 78$ = number of Democrats

2. TRANSLATE the problem. First, we write the equation in words.

number of Republicans	added to	number of Democrats	equals	434
↓	↓	↓	↓	↓
x	$+$	$(x + 78)$	$=$	434

3. SOLVE.

$$x + (x + 78) = 434$$
$$2x + 78 = 434 \quad \text{Combine like terms.}$$
$$2x + 78 - 78 = 434 - 78 \quad \text{Subtract 78 from both sides.}$$
$$2x = 356$$
$$\frac{2x}{2} = \frac{356}{2} \quad \text{Divide both sides by 2.}$$
$$x = 178$$

4. INTERPRET.

Check: If there were 178 Republican representatives, then there were $178 + 78 = 256$ Democratic representatives. The total number of representatives is then $178 + 256 = 434$. The results check.

State: There were 178 Republican and 256 Democratic representatives at the beginning of the 111th Congress.

● **Work Practice 4**

Example 5 Calculating Hours on the Job

A computer science major at a local university has a part-time job working on computers for his clients. He charges $20 to come to your home or office and then $25 per hour. During one month he visited 10 homes or offices and his total income was $575. How many hours did he spend working on computers?

Solution:

1. UNDERSTAND. Read and reread the problem. Let's propose that the student spent 20 hours working on computers. Pay careful attention as to how his income is calculated. For 20 hours and 10 visits, his income is $20(\$25) + 10(\$20) = \$700$, which is more than $575. We now have a better understanding of the problem and know that the time working on computers is less than 20 hours.

Let's let

x = hours working on computers. Then

$25x$ = amount of money made while working on computers

PRACTICE 5

A car rental agency charges $28 a day and $0.15 a mile. If you rent a car for a day and your bill (before taxes) is $52, how many miles did you drive?

Answer

5. 160 miles

2. TRANSLATE.

money made while working on computers	plus	money made for visits	is equal to	575
↓	↓	↓	↓	↓
$25x$	$+$	$10(20)$	$=$	575

3. SOLVE.

$$25x + 200 = 575$$
$$25x + 200 - 200 = 575 - 200 \qquad \text{Subtract 200 from both sides.}$$
$$25x = 375 \qquad \text{Simplify.}$$
$$\frac{25x}{25} = \frac{375}{25} \qquad \text{Divide both sides by 25.}$$
$$x = 15 \qquad \text{Simplify.}$$

4. INTERPRET.

Check: If the student works 15 hours and makes 10 visits, his income is $15(\$25) + 10(\$20) = \$575$.

State: The student spent 15 hours working on computers.

● **Work Practice 5**

△ **Example 6** Finding Angle Measures

If the two walls of the Vietnam Veterans Memorial in Washington, D.C., were connected, an isosceles triangle would be formed. The measure of the third angle is 97.5° more than the measure of either of the two equal angles. Find the measure of the third angle. (*Source:* National Park Service)

Solution:

1. **UNDERSTAND.** Read and reread the problem. We then draw a diagram (recall that an isosceles triangle has two angles with the same measure) and let

$$x = \text{degree measure of one angle}$$
$$x = \text{degree measure of the second equal angle}$$
$$x + 97.5 = \text{degree measure of the third angle}$$

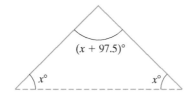

PRACTICE 6

The measure of the second angle of a triangle is twice the measure of the smallest angle. The measure of the third angle of the triangle is three times the measure of the smallest angle. Find the measures of the angles.

Continued on next page

Answer
6. smallest: 30°; second: 60°; third: 90°

2. TRANSLATE. Recall that the sum of the measures of the angles of a triangle equals 180.

measure of first angle	+	measure of second angle	+	measure of third angle	equal	180
↓		↓		↓	↓	↓
x	+	x	+ $(x + 97.5)$		=	180

3. SOLVE.

$$x + x + (x + 97.5) = 180$$
$$3x + 97.5 = 180 \quad\quad \text{Combine like terms.}$$
$$3x + 97.5 - 97.5 = 180 - 97.5 \quad \text{Subtract 97.5 from both sides.}$$
$$3x = 82.5$$
$$\frac{3x}{3} = \frac{82.5}{3} \quad\quad \text{Divide both sides by 3.}$$
$$x = 27.5$$

4. INTERPRET.

Check: If $x = 27.5$, then the measure of the third angle is $x + 97.5 = 125$. The sum of the angles is then $27.5 + 27.5 + 125 = 180$, the correct sum.

State: The third angle measures 125°.*

🔵 **Work Practice 6**

Objective ⓒ Solving Consecutive Integer Problems

The next example has to do with consecutive integers. Recall what we have learned thus far about these integers.

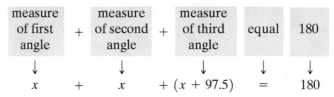

	Example	General Representation
Consecutive Integers	11, 12, 13	Let x be an integer. $x,$ $x + 1,$ $x + 2$
Consecutive Even Integers	38, 40, 42	Let x be an even integer. $x,$ $x + 2,$ $x + 4$
Consecutive Odd Integers	57, 59, 61	Let x be an odd integer. $x,$ $x + 2,$ $x + 4$

The next example has to do with consecutive integers.

---

*The two walls actually meet at an angle of 125 degrees 12 minutes. The measurement of 97.5° given in the problem is an approximation.

Example 7 Some states have a single area code for the entire state. Two such states have area codes that are consecutive odd integers. If the sum of these integers is 1208, find the two area codes. (*Source: World Almanac*)

Solution:

1. UNDERSTAND. Read and reread the problem. If we let

   x = the first odd integer, then
   $x + 2$ = the next odd integer

2. TRANSLATE.

first odd integer	added to	next odd integer	is	1208
↓	↓	↓		
x	$+$	$(x + 2)$	$=$	1208

3. SOLVE.

$$x + x + 2 = 1208$$
$$2x + 2 = 1208$$
$$2x + 2 - 2 = 1208 - 2$$
$$2x = 1206$$
$$\frac{2x}{2} = \frac{1206}{2}$$
$$x = 603$$

4. INTERPRET.

Check: If $x = 603$, then the next odd integer $x + 2 = 603 + 2 = 605$. Notice their sum, $603 + 605 = 1208$, as needed.

State: The area codes are 603 and 605.

Note: New Hampshire's area code is 603 and South Dakota's area code is 605.

● **Work Practice 7**

PRACTICE 7

The sum of three consecutive even integers is 144. Find the integers.

Helpful Hint
Remember, the 2 here means that odd integers are 2 units apart, for example, the odd integers 13 and $13 + 2 = 15$.

Answer
7. 46, 48, 50

Vocabulary and Readiness Check

Fill in the table.

1.	A number: x	→	Double the number:	→	Double the number, decreased by 31:
2.	A number: x	→	Three times the number:	→	Three times the number, increased by 17:
3.	A number: x	→	The sum of the number and 5:	→	Twice the sum of the number and 5:
4.	A number: x	→	The difference of the number and 11:	→	Seven times the difference of the number and 11:
5.	A number: y	→	The difference of 20 and the number:	→	The difference of 20 and the number, divided by 3:
6.	A number: y	→	The sum of -10 and the number:	→	The sum of -10 and the number, divided by 9:

6.4 Exercise Set

FOR EXTRA HELP

MyMathLab   MathXL   PRACTICE   WATCH   DOWNLOAD   READ   REVIEW

Objective A *Solve. For Exercises 1 through 4, write each of the following as equations. Then solve. See Examples 1 and 2.*

1. The sum of twice a number and 7 is equal to the sum of the number and 6. Find the number.

2. The difference of three times a number and 1 is the same as twice the number. Find the number.

3. Three times a number, minus 6, is equal to two times the number, plus 8. Find the number.

4. The sum of 4 times a number and -2 is equal to the sum of 5 times the number and -2. Find the number.

5. Twice the difference of a number and 8 is equal to three times the sum of the number and 3. Find the number.

6. Five times the sum of a number and -1 is the same as 6 times the number. Find the number.

7. The product of twice a number and three is the same as the difference of five times the number and $\frac{3}{4}$. Find the number.

8. If the difference of a number and four is doubled, the result is $\frac{1}{4}$ less than the number. Find the number.

Objective **B** *Solve. For Exercises 9 and 10, the solutions have been started for you. See Examples 3 and 4.*

9. A 25-inch piece of steel is cut into three pieces so that the second piece is twice as long as the first piece, and the third piece is one inch more than five times the length of the first piece. Find the lengths of the pieces.

Start the solution:

1. UNDERSTAND the problem. Reread it as many times as needed.

2. TRANSLATE into an equation. (Fill in the blanks below.)

total length of steel	equals	length of first piece	plus	length of second piece	plus	length of third piece
↓	↓	↓	↓	↓	↓	↓
25	=	——	+	——	+	——

Finish with:

3. SOLVE and 4. INTERPRET

10. A 46-foot piece of rope is cut into three pieces so that the second piece is three times as long as the first piece, and the third piece is two feet more than seven times the length of the first piece. Find the lengths of the pieces.

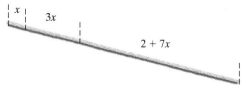

Start the solution:

1. UNDERSTAND the problem. Reread it as many times as needed.

2. TRANSLATE into an equation. (Fill in the blanks below.)

total length of rope	equals	length of first piece	plus	length of second piece	plus	length of third piece
↓	↓	↓	↓	↓	↓	↓
46	=	——	+	——	+	——

Finish with:

3. SOLVE and 4. INTERPRET

11. A 40-inch board is to be cut into three pieces so that the second piece is twice as long as the first piece and the third piece is 5 times as long as the first piece. If x represents the length of the first piece, find the lengths of all three pieces.

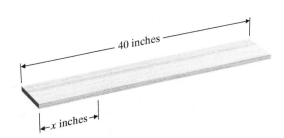

12. A 21-foot beam is to be divided so that the longer piece is 1 foot more than 3 times the length of the shorter piece. If x represents the length of the shorter piece, find the lengths of both pieces.

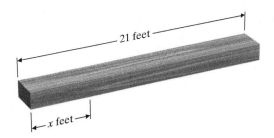

13. In 2008, New Mexico produced 15 million pounds more pecans than Texas. Together, the two states produced 75 million pounds of pecans. Find the amount of pecans grown in New Mexico and Texas in 2008. (*Source:* National Agriculture Statistics Service)

14. In the 2008 Summer Olympics, the U.S. team won 13 more gold medals than the Russian team. If the total number of gold medals won by both teams was 59, find the number of gold medals won by each team. (*Source:* Beijing 2008 Olympic Games)

Solve. See Example 5.

15. A car rental agency advertised renting a Buick Century for $24.95 per day and $0.29 per mile. If you rent this car for 2 days, how many whole miles can you drive on a $100 budget?

16. A plumber gave an estimate for the renovation of a kitchen. Her hourly pay is $27 per hour and the plumbing parts will cost $80. If her total estimate is $404, how many hours does she expect this job to take?

17. In one U.S. city, the taxi cost is $3 plus $0.80 per mile. If you are traveling from the airport, there is an additional charge of $4.50 for tolls. How far can you travel from the airport by taxi for $27.50?

18. A professional carpet cleaning service charges $30 plus $25.50 per hour to come to your home. If your total bill from this company is $119.25 before taxes, for how many hours were you charged?

Solve. See Example 6.

19. The flag of Equatorial Guinea contains an isosceles triangle. (Recall that an isosceles triangle contains two angles with the same measure.) If the measure of the third angle of the triangle is 30° more than twice the measure of either of the other two angles, find the measure of each angle of the triangle. (*Hint:* Recall that the sum of the measures of the angles of a triangle is 180°.)

△ **20.** The flag of Brazil contains a parallelogram. One angle of the parallelogram is 15° less than twice the measure of the angle next to it. Find the measure of each angle of the parallelogram. (*Hint:* Recall that opposite angles of a parallelogram have the same measure and that the sum of the measures of the angles is 360°.)

21. The sum of the measures of the angles of a parallelogram is 360°. In the parallelogram below, angles A and D have the same measure as well as angles C and B. If the measure of angle C is twice the measure of angle A, find the measure of each angle.

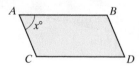

22. Recall that the sum of the measures of the angles of a triangle is 180°. In the triangle below, angle C has the same measure as angle B, and angle A measures 42° less than angle B. Find the measure of each angle.

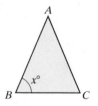

Objective **C** *Solve. See Example 7. Fill in the table. Most of the first row has been completed for you.*

First Integer →	Next Integers	→	Indicated Sum
Integer: x	$x + 1$	$x + 2$	Sum of the three consecutive integers, simplified:
Integer: x			Sum of the second and third consecutive integers, simplified:
Even integer: x			Sum of the first and third even consecutive integers, simplified:
Odd integer: x			Sum of the three consecutive odd integers, simplified:
Integer: x			Sum of the four consecutive integers, simplified:
Integer: x			Sum of the first and fourth consecutive integers, simplified:
Odd integer: x			Sum of the second and third consecutive odd integers, simplified:
Even integer: x			Sum of the three consecutive even integers, simplified:

23. Three consecutive integers:

24. Three consecutive integers:

25. Three consecutive even integers:

26. Three consecutive odd integers:

27. Four consecutive integers:

28. Four consecutive integers:

29. Three consecutive odd integers:

30. Three consecutive even integers:

Solve. See Example 7

31. The left and right page numbers of an open book are two consecutive integers whose sum is 469. Find these page numbers.

32. The room numbers of two adjacent classrooms are two consecutive even numbers. If their sum is 654, find the classroom numbers.

33. To make an international telephone call, you need the code for the country you are calling. The codes for Belgium, France, and Spain are three consecutive integers whose sum is 99. Find the code for each country. (*Source: The World Almanac and Book of Facts*)

34. The code to unlock a student's combination lock happens to be three consecutive odd integers whose sum is 51. Find the integers.

Objectives **A** **B** **C** Mixed Practice *Solve. See Examples 1 through 7.*

35. A 17-foot piece of string is cut into two pieces so that the longer piece is 2 feet longer than twice the length of the shorter piece. Find the lengths of both pieces.

36. A 25-foot wire is to be cut so that the longer piece is one foot longer than 5 times the length of the shorter piece. Find the length of each piece.

37. Currently, the two fastest trains are the Japanese Maglev and the French TGV. The sum of their fastest speeds is 718.2 miles per hour. If the speed of the Maglev is 3.8 mph faster than the speed of the TGV, find the speeds of each.

38. The Pentagon is the world's largest office building in terms of floor space. It has three times the amount of floor space as the Empire State Building. If the total floor space for these two buildings is approximately 8700 thousand square feet, find the floor space of each building.

39. Two angles are supplementary if their sum is 180°. The larger angle below measures eight degrees more than three times the measure of the smaller angle. If x represents the measure of the smaller angle and these two angles are supplementary, find the measure of each angle.

40. Two angles are complementary if their sum is 90°. Given the measures of the complementary angles shown, find the measure of each angle.

41. The measures of the angles of a triangle are 3 consecutive even integers. Find the measure of each angle.

42. A quadrilateral is a polygon with 4 sides. The sum of the measures of the 4 angles in a quadrilateral is 360°. If the measures of the angles of a quadrilateral are consecutive odd integers, find the measures.

43. The sum of $\frac{1}{5}$ and twice a number is equal to $\frac{4}{5}$ subtracted from three times the number. Find the number.

44. The sum of $\frac{2}{3}$ and four times a number is equal to $\frac{5}{6}$ subtracted from five times the number. Find the number.

45. Hertz Car Rental charges a daily rate of $39 plus $0.20 per mile for a certain car. Suppose that you rent that car for a day and your bill (before taxes) is $95. How many miles did you drive?

46. A woman's $15,000 estate is to be divided so that her husband receives twice as much as her son. Find the amount of money that her husband receives and the amount of money that her son receives.

47. During the 2009 Rose Bowl, University of Southern California beat Pennsylvania State University by 14 points. If their combined scores totaled 62, find the individual team scores.

48. After a recent election, there were 8 more Democratic governors than Republican governors in the United States. How many Democrats and how many Republicans held governors' offices after this election? (*Source:* National Governors Association)

49. The number of counties in California and the number of counties in Montana are consecutive even integers whose sum is 114. If California has more counties than Montana, how many counties does each state have? (*Source: The World Almanac and Book of Facts*)

50. A student is building a bookcase with stepped shelves for her dorm room. She buys a 48-inch board and wants to cut the board into three pieces with lengths equal to three consecutive even integers. Find the three board lengths.

51. Over the past few years the satellite Voyager II has passed by the planets Saturn, Uranus, and Neptune, continually updating information about these planets, including the number of moons for each. Uranus is now believed to have 13 more moons than Neptune. Also, Saturn is now believed to have 2 more than twice the number of moons of Neptune. If the total number of moons for these planets is 47, find the number of moons for each planet. (*Source: National Space Science Data Center*)

52. The Mars Odyssey spacecraft was launched in 2001, beginning a multiyear mission to observe and map the planet Mars. Mars Odyssey was launched on Boeing's Delta II 7925 launch vehicle using nine strap-on solid rocket motors. Each solid rocket motor has a height that is 8 meters more than 5 times its diameter. If the sum of the height and the diameter for a single solid rocket motor is 14 meters, find each dimension. (Recently, NASA approved a continuation of the Odyssey mission through September 2010.) (*Source: NASA*)

53. If the sum of a number and five is tripled, the result is one less than twice the number. Find the number.

54. Twice the sum of a number and six equals three times the sum of the number and four. Find the number.

55. The area of the Sahara Desert is 7 times the area of the Gobi Desert. If the sum of their areas is 4,000,000 square miles, find the area of each desert.

56. The largest meteorite in the world is the Hoba West, located in Namibia. Its weight is 3 times the weight of the Armanty meteorite, located in Outer Mongolia. If the sum of their weights is 88 tons, find the weight of each.

57. In the 2008 Summer Olympics, Korea won more gold medals than Germany, which won more gold medals than Australia. If the numbers of gold medals won by these three countries are three consecutive integers whose sum is 21, find the number of gold medals won by each. (*Source:* Beijing 2008 Olympics)

58. To make an international telephone call, you need the code for the country you are calling. The codes for Mali Republic, Côte d'Ivoire, and Niger are three consecutive odd integers whose sum is 675. Find the code for each country.

59. In a runoff election in Georgia for a seat in the U.S. Senate, incumbent Senator Saxby Chambliss received 315,217 more votes than challenger Jim Martin. If the total number of votes cast was 2,126,491, find the number of votes for each candidate. (*Source: New York Times*)

60. In Season 7 of *American Idol*, David Cook received 11.7 million more votes than runner-up David Archuleta. If 97.5 million votes were cast in the season finale, find the number of votes for each contestant. (*Source: Los Angeles Times*)

61. A geodesic dome, based on the design by Buckminster Fuller, is composed of two different types of triangular panels. One of these is an isosceles triangle. In one geodesic dome, the measure of the third angle is 76.5° more than the measure of either of the two equal angles. Find the measure of the three angles. (*Source:* Buckminster Fuller Institute)

62. The measures of the angles of a particular triangle are such that the second and third angles are each four times the measure of the smallest angle. Find the measures of the angles of this triangle.

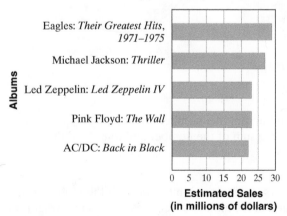

The graph below shows the best-selling albums of all time. Use this graph for Exercises 63 through 66.

Best-Selling Albums of All Time
(U.S. sales)

Albums

Eagles: *Their Greatest Hits, 1971–1975*

Michael Jackson: *Thriller*

Led Zeppelin: *Led Zeppelin IV*

Pink Floyd: *The Wall*

AC/DC: *Back in Black*

0 5 10 15 20 25 30

Estimated Sales
(in millions of dollars)

Source: Recording Industry Association of America

63. Which album is the best-selling album of all time?

64. Which albums sold between $20 million and $25 million?

65. *Thriller* and *The Wall* had sales worth a total of $50 million. *Thriller* brought in $4 million more than *The Wall*. Find the amount of sales that each album brought in.

66. Eagles: *Their Greatest Hits, 1971–1975*, and AC/DC: *Back in Black* had sales worth $51 million. Eagles: *Their Greatest Hits, 1971–1975*, sold $7 million more than AC/DC: *Back in Black*. Find the amount of sales for each album.

Compare the lengths of the bars in the graph with your results for the exercises below. Are your answers reasonable?

67. Exercise 65

68. Exercise 66

Review

Evaluate each expression for the given values. See Section 5.8.

69. $2W + 2L$; $W = 7$ and $L = 10$

70. $\frac{1}{2}Bh$; $B = 14$ and $h = 22$

71. πr^2; $r = 15$

72. $r \cdot t$; $r = 15$ and $t = 2$

Concept Extensions

73. A golden rectangle is a rectangle whose length is approximately 1.6 times its width. The early Greeks thought that a rectangle with these dimensions was the most pleasing to the eye and examples of the golden rectangle are found in many early works of art. For example, the Parthenon in Athens contains many examples of golden rectangles.

Mike Hallahan would like to plant a rectangular garden in the shape of a golden rectangle. If he has 78 feet of fencing available, find the dimensions of the garden.

74. Dr. Dorothy Smith gave the students in her geometry class at the University of New Orleans the following question. Is it possible to construct a triangle such that the second angle of the triangle has a measure that is twice the measure of the first angle and the measure of the third angle is 5 times the measure of the first? If so, find the measure of each angle. (*Hint:* Recall that the sum of the measures of the angles of a triangle is 180°.)

75. Only male crickets chirp. They chirp at different rates depending on their species and the temperature of their environment. Suppose a certain species is currently chirping at a rate of 90 chirps per minute. At this rate, how many chirps occur in one hour? In one 24-hour day? In one year?

76. The human eye blinks once every 5 seconds on average. How many times does the average eye blink in one hour? In one 16-hour day while awake? In one year while awake?

77. In your own words, explain why a solution of a word problem should be checked using the original wording of the problem and not the equation written from the wording.

78. Give an example of how you recently solved a problem using mathematics.

Recall from Exercise 73 that a golden rectangle is a rectangle whose length is approximately 1.6 times its width.

△ **79.** It is thought that for about 75% of adults, a rectangle in the shape of the golden rectangle is the most pleasing to the eye. Draw three rectangles, one in the shape of the golden rectangle, and poll your class. Do the results agree with the percentage given above?

△ **80.** Examples of golden rectangles can be found today in architecture and manufacturing packaging. Find an example of a golden rectangle in your home. A few suggestions: the front face of a book, the floor of a room, the front of a box of food.

For Exercises 81 and 82, measure the dimensions of each rectangle and decide which one best approximates the shape of a golden rectangle.

△ **81.**

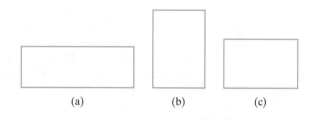

(a)   (b)   (c)

△ **82.**

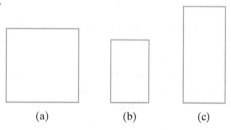

(a)   (b)   (c)

6.5 FORMULAS AND PROBLEM SOLVING

Objectives

A Use Formulas to Solve Problems.

B Solve a Formula or Equation for One of Its Variables.

Objective **A** Using Formulas to Solve Problems

A **formula** describes a known relationship among quantities. Many formulas are given as equations. For example, the formula

$$d = r \cdot t$$

stands for the relationship

$$\text{distance} = \text{rate} \cdot \text{time}$$

Let's look at one way that we can use this formula.

If we know we traveled a distance of 100 miles at a rate of 40 miles per hour, we can replace the variables d and r in the formula $d = rt$ and find our travel time, t.

$d = rt$ Formula

$100 = 40t$ Replace d with 100 and r with 40.

To solve for t, we divide both sides of the equation by 40.

$$\frac{100}{40} = \frac{40t}{40} \quad \text{Divide both sides by 40.}$$

$$\frac{5}{2} = t \quad \text{Simplify.}$$

The travel times was $\frac{5}{2}$ hours, or $2\frac{1}{2}$ hours, or 2.5 hours.

In this section, we solve problems that can be modeled by known formulas. We use the same problem-solving strategy that was used in the previous section.

Example 1 Finding Time Given Rate and Distance

A glacier is a giant mass of rocks and ice that flows downhill like a river. Portage Glacier in Alaska is about 6 miles, or 31,680 *feet,* long and moves 400 *feet* per year. Icebergs are created when the front end of the glacier flows into Portage Lake. How long does it take for ice at the head (beginning) of the glacier to reach the lake?

Solution:

1. UNDERSTAND. Read and reread the problem. The appropriate formula needed to solve this problem is the distance formula, $d = rt$. To become familiar with this formula, let's find the distance that ice traveling at a rate of 400 feet per year travels in 100 years. To do so, we let time t be 100 years and rate r be the given 400 feet per year, and substitute these values into the formula $d = rt$. We then have that distance $d = 400(100) = 40{,}000$ feet. Since we are interested in finding how long it takes ice to travel 31,680 feet, we now know that it is less than 100 years.

Continued on next page

PRACTICE 1

A family is planning their vacation to visit relatives. They will drive from Cincinnati, Ohio, to Rapid City, South Dakota, a distance of 1180 miles. They plan to average a rate of 50 miles per hour. How much time will they spend driving?

Answer
1. 23.6 hours

543

Since we are using the formula $d = rt$, we let

t = the time in years for ice to reach the lake

r = rate or speed of ice

d = distance from beginning of glacier to lake

2. **TRANSLATE.** To translate to an equation, we use the formula $d = rt$ and let distance $d = 31{,}680$ feet and rate $r = 400$ feet per year.

$$d = r \cdot t$$
$$31{,}680 = 400 \cdot t \quad \text{Let } d = 31{,}680 \text{ and } r = 400.$$

3. **SOLVE.** Solve the equation for t. To solve for t, we divide both sides by 400.

$$\frac{31{,}680}{400} = \frac{400 \cdot t}{400} \quad \text{Divide both sides by 400.}$$
$$79.2 = t \quad \text{Simplify.}$$

4. **INTERPRET.**

Check: To check, substitute 79.2 for t and 400 for r in the distance formula and check to see that the distance is 31,680 feet.

State: It takes 79.2 years for the ice at the head of Portage Glacier to reach the lake.

● Work Practice 1

Helpful Hint
Don't forget to include units, if appropriate.

△ **PRACTICE 2**

A wood deck is being built behind a house. The width of the deck must be 18 feet because of the shape of the house. If there is 450 square feet of decking material, find the length of the deck.

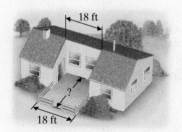

△ **Example 2**   Calculating the Length of a Garden

Charles Pecot can afford enough fencing to enclose a rectangular garden with a perimeter of 140 feet. If the width of his garden is to be 30 feet, find the length.

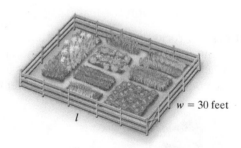

$w = 30$ feet

l

Solution:

1. **UNDERSTAND.** Read and reread the problem. The formula needed to solve this problem is the formula for the perimeter of a rectangle, $P = 2l + 2w$. Before continuing, let's become familar with this formula.

   l = the length of the rectangular garden

   w = the width of the rectangular garden

   P = perimeter of the garden

2. **TRANSLATE.** To translate to an equation, we use the formula $P = 2l + 2w$ and let perimeter $P = 140$ feet and width $w = 30$ feet.

$$P = 2l + 2w \quad \text{Let } P = 140 \text{ and } w = 30.$$
$$140 = 2l + 2(30)$$

Answer

2. 25 feet

3. SOLVE.

$$140 = 2l + 2(30)$$
$$140 = 2l + 60 \qquad \text{Multiply } 2(30).$$
$$140 - 60 = 2l + 60 - 60 \qquad \text{Subtract 60 from both sides.}$$
$$80 = 2l \qquad \text{Combine like terms.}$$
$$40 = l \qquad \text{Divide both sides by 2.}$$

4. INTERPRET.

Check: Substitute 40 for l and 30 for w in the perimeter formula and check to see that the perimeter is 140 feet.

State: The length of the rectangular garden is 40 feet.

● Work Practice 2

Example 3 Finding an Equivalent Temperature

The average maximum temperature for January in Algiers, Algeria, is 59° Fahrenheit. Find the equivalent temperature in degrees Celsius.

Solution:

1. UNDERSTAND. Read and reread the problem. A formula that can be used to solve this problem is the formula for converting degrees Celsius to degrees Fahrenheit, $F = \frac{9}{5}C + 32$. Before continuing, become familiar with this formula. Using this formula, we let

   C = temperature in degrees Celsius, and
   F = temperature in degrees Fahrenheit.

2. TRANSLATE. To translate to an equation, we use the formula $F = \frac{9}{5}C + 32$ and let degrees Fahrenheit $F = 59$.

   Formula: $F = \frac{9}{5}C + 32$

   Substitute: $59 = \frac{9}{5}C + 32$ Let $F = 59$.

3. SOLVE.

$$59 = \frac{9}{5}C + 32$$
$$59 - 32 = \frac{9}{5}C + 32 - 32 \qquad \text{Subtract 32 from both sides}$$
$$27 = \frac{9}{5}C \qquad \text{Combine like terms.}$$
$$\frac{5}{9} \cdot 27 = \frac{5}{9} \cdot \frac{9}{5}C \qquad \text{Multiply both sides by } \frac{5}{9}.$$
$$15 = C \qquad \text{Simplify.}$$

4. INTERPRET.

Check: To check, replace C with 15 and F with 59 in the formula and see that a true statement results.

State: Thus, 59° Fahrenheit is equivalent to 15° Celsius.

● Work Practice 3

PRACTICE 3

Convert the temperature 5°C to Fahrenheit.

Answer
3. 41°F

In the next example, we again use the formula for perimeter of a rectangle as in Example 2. In Example 2, we knew the width of the rectangle. In this example, both the length and width are unknown.

PRACTICE 4

The length of a rectangle is one meter more than 4 times its width. Find the dimensions if the perimeter is 52 meters.

Example 4 Finding Road Sign Dimensions

The length of a rectangular road sign is 2 feet less than three times its width. Find the dimensions if the perimeter is 28 feet.

Solution:

1. UNDERSTAND. Read and reread the problem. Recall that the formula for the perimeter of a rectangle is $P = 2l + 2w$. Draw a rectangle and guess the solution. If the width of the rectangular sign is 5 feet, its length is 2 feet less than 3 times the width, or $3(5 \text{ feet}) - 2 \text{ feet} = 13 \text{ feet}$. The perimeter P of the rectangle is then $2(13 \text{ feet}) + 2(5 \text{ feet}) = 36 \text{ feet}$, too much. We now know that the width is less than 5 feet.

Proposed rectangle:

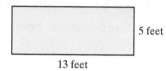

5 feet

13 feet

Let

w = the width of the rectangular sign; then
$3w - 2$ = the length of the sign.

w

$3w - 2$

Draw a rectangle and label it with the assigned variables.

2. TRANSLATE.

Formula: $P = 2l + 2w$
Substitute: $28 = 2(3w - 2) + 2w$

3. SOLVE.

$$28 = 2(3w - 2) + 2w$$
$$28 = 6w - 4 + 2w \qquad \text{Apply the distributive property.}$$
$$28 = 8w - 4$$
$$28 + 4 = 8w - 4 + 4 \qquad \text{Add 4 to both sides.}$$
$$32 = 8w$$
$$\frac{32}{8} = \frac{8w}{8} \qquad \text{Divide both sides by 8.}$$
$$4 = w$$

4. INTERPRET.

Check: If the width of the sign is 4 feet, the length of the sign is $3(4 \text{ feet}) - 2 \text{ feet} = 10 \text{ feet}$. This gives the rectangular sign a perimeter of $P = 2(4 \text{ feet}) + 2(10 \text{ feet}) = 28 \text{ feet}$, the correct perimeter.

State: The width of the sign is 4 feet and the length of the sign is 10 feet.

Answer

4. length: 21 m; width: 5 m

● **Work Practice 4**

Objective ⓑ Solving a Formula for a Variable

We say that the formula

$$d = rt$$

is solved for d because d is alone on one side of the equation and the other side contains no d's. Suppose that we have a large number of problems to solve where we are given distance d and rate r and asked to find time t. In this case, it may be easier to first solve the formula $d = rt$ for t. To solve for t, we divide both sides of the equation by r.

$$d = rt$$

$$\frac{d}{r} = \frac{rt}{r} \quad \text{Divide both sides by } r.$$

$$\frac{d}{r} = t \quad \text{Simplify.}$$

To solve a formula or an equation for a specified variable, we use the same steps as for solving a linear equation except that we treat the specified variable as the only variable in the equation. These steps are listed next.

Solving Equations for a Specified Variable

Step 1: Multiply on both sides to clear the equation of fractions if they appear.

Step 2: Use the distributive property to remove parentheses if they appear.

Step 3: Simplify each side of the equation by combining like terms.

Step 4: Get all terms containing the specified variable on one side and all other terms on the other side by using the addition property of equality.

Step 5: Get the specified variable alone by using the multiplication property of equality.

△ **Example 5** Solve $V = lwh$ for l.

Solution: This formula is used to find the volume of a box. To solve for l, we divide both sides by wh.

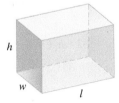

$$V = lwh$$

$$\frac{V}{wh} = \frac{lwh}{wh} \quad \text{Divide both sides by } wh.$$

$$\frac{V}{wh} = l \quad \text{Simplify.}$$

Since we have l alone on one side of the equation, we have solved for l in terms of V, w, and h. Remember that it does not matter on which side of the equation we get the variable alone.

● Work Practice 5

PRACTICE 5

Solve $C = 2\pi r$ for r. (This formula is used to find the circumference, C, of a circle given its radius, r.)

Answer

5. $r = \dfrac{C}{2\pi}$

PRACTICE 6

Solve $P = 2l + 2w$ for l.

Example 6 Solve $y = mx + b$ for x.

Solution: First we get mx alone by subtracting b from both sides.

$$y = mx + b$$
$$y - b = mx + b - b \quad \text{Subtract } b \text{ from both sides.}$$
$$y - b = mx \quad\quad\quad\quad \text{Combine like terms.}$$

Next we solve for x by dividing both sides by m.

$$\frac{y - b}{m} = \frac{mx}{m}$$
$$\frac{y - b}{m} = x \quad \text{Simplify.}$$

● **Work Practice 6**

✓**Concept Check** Solve:

a. ⬤ = ⬛ − ⬛ for ⬛

b. ⬤ = ⬛ · ▲ − ⬛ for ⬛

PRACTICE 7

Solve $P = 2a + b - c$ for a.

Example 7 Solve $P = 2l + 2w$ for w.

Solution: This formula relates the perimeter of a rectangle to its length and width. Find the term containing the variable w. To get this term, $2w$, alone, subtract $2l$ from both sides.

$$P = 2l + 2w$$
$$P - 2l = 2l + 2w - 2l \quad \text{Subtract } 2l \text{ from both sides.}$$
$$P - 2l = 2w \quad\quad\quad\quad \text{Combine like terms.}$$
$$\frac{P - 2l}{2} = \frac{2w}{2} \quad\quad\quad \text{Divide both sides by 2.}$$
$$\frac{P - 2l}{2} = w \quad\quad\quad\quad \text{Simplify.}$$

Helpful Hint

The 2s may *not* be divided out here. Although 2 is a factor of the denominator, 2 is *not* a factor of the numerator since it is not a factor of both terms in the numerator.

● **Work Practice 7**

The next example has an equation containing a fraction. We will first clear the equation of fractions and then solve for the specified variable.

PRACTICE 8

Solve $A = \dfrac{a + b}{2}$ for b.

Example 8 Solve $F = \dfrac{9}{5}C + 32$ for C.

Solution:
$$F = \frac{9}{5}C + 32$$
$$5(F) = 5\left(\frac{9}{5}C + 32\right) \quad \text{Clear the fraction by multiplying both sides by the LCD.}$$
$$5F = 9C + 160 \quad \text{Distribute the 5.}$$
$$5F - 160 = 9C + 160 - 160 \quad \text{To get the term containing the variable } C \text{ alone, subtract 160 from both sides.}$$
$$5F - 160 = 9C \quad \text{Combine like terms.}$$
$$\frac{5F - 160}{9} = \frac{9C}{9} \quad \text{Divide both sides by 9.}$$
$$\frac{5F - 160}{9} = C \quad \text{Simplify.}$$

● **Work Practice 8**

Answers

6. $l = \dfrac{P - 2w}{2}$ **7.** $a = \dfrac{P - b + c}{2}$

8. $b = 2A - a$

✓**Concept Check Answer**

a. ⬤ + ⬛   b. ⬤ + ⬛
⠀⠀⠀⠀⠀⠀⠀⠀⠀▲

Objective A *Substitute the given values into each given formula and solve for the unknown variable. See Examples 1 through 4.*

△ **1.** $A = bh$; $A = 45, b = 15$ (Area of a parallelogram)

2. $d = rt$; $d = 195, t = 3$ (Distance formula)

△ **3.** $S = 4lw + 2wh$; $S = 102, l = 7, w = 3$ (Surface area of a special rectangular box)

△ **4.** $V = lwh$; $l = 14, w = 8, h = 3$ (Volume of a rectangular box)

△ **5.** $A = \frac{1}{2}h(B + b)$; $A = 180, B = 11, b = 7$ (Area of a trapezoid)

△ **6.** $A = \frac{1}{2}h(B + b)$; $A = 60, B = 7, b = 3$ (Area of a trapezoid)

△ **7.** $P = a + b + c$; $P = 30, a = 8, b = 10$ (Perimeter of a triangle)

△ **8.** $V = \frac{1}{3}Ah$; $V = 45, h = 5$ (Volume of a pyramid)

△ **9.** $C = 2\pi r$; $C = 15.7$ (Circumference of a circle) (Use the approximation 3.14 for π.)

△ **10.** $A = \pi r^2$; $r = 4$ (Area of a circle) (Use the approximation 3.14 for π.)

Objective B *Solve each formula for the specified variable. See Examples 5 through 8.*

11. $f = 5gh$ for h

△ **12.** $x = 4\pi y$ for y

13. $V = lwh$ for w

14. $T = mnr$ for n

15. $3x + y = 7$ for y

16. $-x + y = 13$ for y

17. $A = P + PRT$ for R

18. $A = P + PRT$ for T

△ **19.** $V = \frac{1}{3}Ah$ for A

20. $D = \frac{1}{4}fk$ for k

△ **21.** $P = a + b + c$ for a

22. $PR = x + y + z + w$ for z

23. $S = 2\pi rh + 2\pi r^2$ for h

△ **24.** $S = 4lw + 2wh$ for h

549

Objective Ⓐ *Solve. For Exercises 25 and 26, the solutions have been started for you. See Examples 1 through 4.*

△ **25.** The iconic NASDAQ sign in New York's Times Square has a width of 84 feet and an area of 10,080 square feet. Find the height of the sign. (*Source:* livedesignonline.com)

Start the solution:

1. UNDERSTAND the problem. Reread it as many times as needed.

2. TRANSLATE into an equation. (Fill in the blanks below.)

Area	=	length	times	width
↓	↓	↓	↓	↓
____	=	x	·	____

Finish with:

3. SOLVE and 4. INTERPRET

△ **26.** The world's largest sign for Coca-Cola is located in Arica, Chile. The rectangular sign has a length of 400 feet and an area of 52,400 square feet. Find the width of the sign. (*Source:* Fabulous Facts about Coca-Cola, Atlanta, GA)

Start the solution:

1. UNDERSTAND the problem. Reread it as many times as needed.

2. TRANSLATE into an equation. (Fill in the blanks below.)

Area	=	length	times	width
↓	↓	↓	↓	↓
____	=	____	·	x

Finish with:

3. SOLVE and 4. INTERPRET

△ **27.** A frame shop charges according to both the amount of framing needed to surround the picture and the amount of glass needed to cover the picture.

a. Find the area and perimeter of the picture below.

b. Identify whether the frame has to do with perimeter or area and the same with the glass.

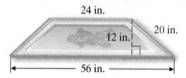

24 in.
12 in.   20 in.
56 in.

△ **28.** A decorator is painting and placing a border completely around the parallelogram-shaped wall.

a. Find the area and perimeter of the wall below.

b. Identify whether the border has to do with perimeter or area and the same with paint.

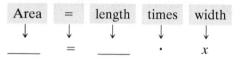

11.7 ft
7 ft
9.3 ft

△ **29.** For the purpose of purchasing new baseboard and carpet,

a. Find the area and perimeter of the room below (neglecting doors).

b. Identify whether baseboard has to do with area or perimeter and the same with carpet.

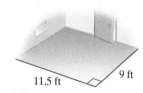

11.5 ft   9 ft

△ **30.** For the purpose of purchasing lumber for a new fence and seed to plant grass,

a. Find the area and perimeter of the yard below.

b. Identify whether a fence has to do with area or perimeter and the same with grass seed.

$$\left(A = \frac{1}{2}bh \right)$$

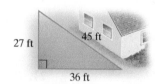

27 ft   45 ft
36 ft

🔌 **31.** Convert Nome, Alaska's 14°F high temperature to Celsius.

32. Convert Paris, France's low temperature of −5°C to Fahrenheit.

33. The X-30 is a "space plane" that skims the edge of space at 4000 miles per hour. Neglecting altitude, if the circumference of Earth is approximately 25,000 miles, how long will it take for the X-30 to travel around Earth?

34. In the United States, a notable hang glider flight was a 303-mile, $8\frac{1}{2}$-hour flight from New Mexico to Kansas. What was the average rate during this flight?

35. An architect designs a rectangular flower garden such that the width is exactly two-thirds of the length. If 260 feet of antique picket fencing are to be used to enclose the garden, find the dimensions of the garden.

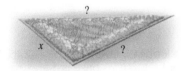

36. If the length of a rectangular parking lot is 10 meters less than twice its width, and the perimeter is 400 meters, find the length of the parking lot.

x meters

37. A flower bed is in the shape of a triangle with one side twice the length of the shortest side, and the third side is 30 feet more than the length of the shortest side. Find the dimensions if the perimeter is 102 feet.

x

38. The perimeter of a yield sign in the shape of an isosceles triangle is 22 feet. If the shortest side is 2 feet less than the other two sides, find the length of the shortest side. (*Hint:* An isosceles triangle has two sides the same length.)

x feet   *x* feet

39. The Cat is a high-speed catamaran auto ferry that operates between Bar Harbor, Maine, and Yarmouth, Nova Scotia. The Cat can make the trip in about $2\frac{1}{2}$ hours at a speed of 55 mph. About how far apart are Bar Harbor and Yarmouth? (*Source:* Bay Ferries)

40. A family is planning their vacation to Disney World. They will drive from a small town outside New Orleans, Louisiana, to Orlando, Florida, a distance of 700 miles. They plan to average a rate of 55 mph. How long will this trip take?

Dolbear's Law states the relationship between the rate at which Snowy Tree Crickets chirp and the air temperature of their environment. The formula is

$$T = 50 + \frac{N - 40}{4}, where \quad \begin{array}{l} T = \text{temperature in degrees Fahrenheit and} \\ N = \text{number of chirps per minute} \end{array}$$

41. If $N = 86$, find the temperature in degrees Fahrenheit, T.

42. If $N = 94$, find the temperature in degrees Fahrenheit, T.

43. If $T = 55°F$, find the number of chirps per minute.

44. If $T = 65°F$, find the number of chirps per minute.

Use the results of Exercises 41–44 to complete each sentence with "increases" or "decreases."

45. As the number of cricket chirps per minute increases, the air temperature of their environment

_____.

46. As the air temperature of their environment decreases, the number of cricket chirps per minute

_____.

Solve. See Examples 1 through 4.

△ **47.** Piranha fish require 1.5 cubic feet of water per fish to maintain a healthy environment. Find the maximum number of piranhas you could put in a tank measuring 8 feet by 3 feet by 6 feet.

6 feet

3 feet   8 feet

△ **48.** Find the maximum number of goldfish you can put in a cylindrical tank whose diameter is 8 meters and whose height is 3 meters, if each goldfish needs 2 cubic meters of water. ($V = \pi r^2 h$)

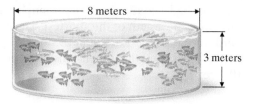

8 meters

3 meters

△ **49.** A lawn is in the shape of a trapezoid with a height of 60 feet and bases of 70 feet and 130 feet. How many bags of fertilizer must be purchased to cover the lawn if each bag covers 4000 square feet?

$$\left(A = \frac{1}{2}h(B + b) \right)$$

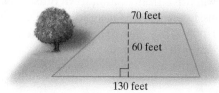

70 feet

60 feet

130 feet

△ **50.** If the area of a right-triangularly shaped sail is 20 square feet and its base is 5 feet, find the height of the sail. $\left(A = \frac{1}{2}bh \right)$

?

5 feet

△ **51.** Maria's Pizza sells one 16-inch cheese pizza or two 10-inch cheese pizzas for $9.99. Determine which size gives more pizza. ($A = \pi r^2$)

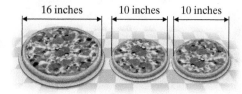

16 inches   10 inches   10 inches

△ **52.** Find how much rope is needed to wrap around Earth at the equator, if the radius of Earth is 4000 miles. (*Hint:* Use 3.14 for π and the formula for circumference.)

53. A Japanese "bullet" train set a new world record for train speed at 552 kilometers per hour during a manned test run on the Yamanashi Maglev Test Line in April 1999. The Yamanashi Maglev Test Line is 42.8 kilometers long. How many *minutes* would a test run on the Yamanashi Line last at this record-setting speed? Round to the nearest hundredth of a minute. (*Source:* Japan Railways Central Co.)

54. In 1983, the Hawaiian volcano Kilauea began erupting in a series of episodes still occurring at the time of this writing. At times, the lava flows advanced at speeds of up to 0.5 kilometer per hour. In 1983 and 1984 lava flows destroyed 16 homes in the Royal Gardens subdivision, about 6 km away from the eruption site. Roughly how long did it take the lava to reach Royal Gardens? (*Source:* U.S. Geological Survey Hawaiian Volcano Observatory)

55. The perimeter of an equilateral triangle is 7 inches more than the perimeter of a square, and the side of the triangle is 5 inches longer than the side of the square. Find the side of the triangle. (*Hint:* An equilateral triangle has three sides the same length.)

56. A square animal pen and a pen shaped like an equilateral triangle have equal perimeters. Find the length of the sides of each pen if the sides of the triangular pen are fifteen less than twice a side of the square pen. (*Hint:* An equilateral triangle has three sides the same length.)

57. Find how long it takes Tran Nguyen to drive 135 miles on I-10 if he merges onto I-10 at 10 a.m. and drives nonstop with his cruise control set on 60 mph.

58. Beaumont, Texas, is about 150 miles from Toledo Bend. If Leo Miller leaves Beaumont at 4 a.m. and averages 45 mph, when should he arrive at Toledo Bend?

59. The longest runway at Los Angeles International Airport has the shape of a rectangle and an area of 1,813,500 square feet. This runway is 150 feet wide. How long is the runway? (*Source:* Los Angeles World Airports)

60. The return stroke of a bolt of lightning can travel at a speed of 87,000 miles per second (almost half the speed of light). At this speed, how many times can an object travel around the world in one second? (See Exercise 52.) Round to the nearest tenth. (*Source: The Handy Science Answer Book*)

61. The highest temperature ever recorded in Europe was 122°F in Seville, Spain, in August of 1881. Convert this record high temperature to Celsius. (*Source:* National Climatic Data Center)

62. The lowest temperature ever recorded in Oceania was −10°C at the Haleakala Summit in Maui, Hawaii, in January 1961. Convert this record low temperature to Fahrenheit. (*Source:* National Climatic Data Center)

△ **63.** The CART FedEx Championship Series is an open-wheeled race car competition based in the United States. A CART car has a maximum length of 199 inches, a maximum width of 78.5 inches, and a maximum height of 33 inches. When the CART series travels to another country for a grand prix, teams must ship their cars. Find the volume of the smallest shipping crate needed to ship a CART car of maximum dimensions. (*Source:* Championship Auto Racing Teams, Inc.)

CART Racing Car

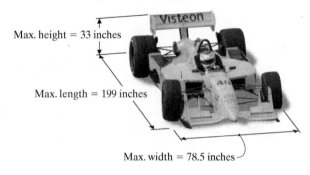

Max. height = 33 inches

Max. length = 199 inches

Max. width = 78.5 inches

64. On a road course, a CART car's speed can average up to around 105 mph. Based on this speed, how long would it take a CART driver to travel from Los Angeles to New York City, a distance of about 2810 miles by road, without stopping? Round to the nearest tenth of an hour.

△ **65.** The Hoberman Sphere is a toy ball that expands and contracts. When it is completely closed, it has a diameter of 9.5 inches. Find the volume of the Hoberman Sphere when it is completely closed. Use 3.14 for π. Round to the nearest whole cubic inch. (*Hint:* volume of a sphere $= \dfrac{4}{3}\pi r^3$. *Source:* Hoberman Designs, Inc.)

△ **66.** When the Hoberman Sphere (see Exercise 65) is completely expanded, its diameter is 30 inches. Find the volume of the Hoberman Sphere when it is completely expanded. Use 3.14 for π. (*Source:* Hoberman Designs, Inc.)

67. The average temperature on the planet Mercury is 167°C. Convert this temperature to degrees Fahrenheit. Round to the nearest degree. (*Source:* National Space Science Data Center)

68. The average temperature on the planet Jupiter is −227°F. Convert this temperature to degrees Celsius. Round to the nearest degree. (*Source:* National Space Science Data Center)

Review

Write each percent as a decimal. See Section 4.3.

69. 32%   **70.** 8%   **71.** 200%   **72.** 0.5%

Write each decimal as a percent. See Section 4.3.

73. 0.17   **74.** 0.03   **75.** 7.2   **76.** 5

Concept Extensions

Solve.

77. $N = R + \dfrac{V}{G}$ for V (Urban forestry: tree plantings per year)

78. $B = \dfrac{F}{P - V}$ for V (Business: break-even point)

79. The formula $V = lwh$ is used to find the volume of a box. If the length of a box is doubled, the width is doubled, and the height is doubled, how does this affect the volume? Explain your answer.

80. The formula $A = bh$ is used to find the area of a parallelogram. If the base of a parallelogram is doubled and its height is doubled, how does this affect the area? Explain your answer.

81. Use the Dolbear's Law formula for Exercises 41–46 and calculate when the number of cricket chirps per minute is the same as the temperature in degrees Fahrenheit. (*Hint:* Replace T with N and solve for N or replace N with T and solve for T.)

82. Find the temperature at which the Celsius measurement and the Fahrenheit measurement are the same number.

Solve. See the Concept Check in this section.

83. ▲ − ● · ▮ = ▮   for ●

84. ⬠ · ▮ + ▲ = ●   for ▮

85. Flying fish do not *actually* fly, but glide. They have been known to travel a distance of 1300 feet at a rate of 20 miles per hour. How many seconds would it take to travel this distance? (*Hint:* First convert miles per hour to feet per second. Recall that 1 mile = 5280 feet.) Round to the nearest tenth of a second.

86. A glacier is a giant mass of rocks and ice that flows downhill like a river. Exit Glacier, near Seward, Alaska, moves at a rate of 20 inches a day. Find the distance in feet the glacier moves in a year. (Assume 365 days a year.) Round to two decimal places.

Substitute the given values into each given formula and solve for the unknown variable. If necessary, round to one decimal place.

87. $I = PRT$; $I = 1{,}056{,}000, R = 0.055, T = 6$
(Simple interest formula)

88. $I = PRT$; $I = 3750, P = 25{,}000, R = 0.05$
(Simple interest formula)

89. $V = \dfrac{4}{3}\pi r^3$; $r = 3$ (Volume of a sphere) (Use a calculator approximation for π.)

90. $V = \dfrac{1}{3}\pi r^2 h$; $V = 565.2, r = 6$ (Volume of a cone) (Use a calculator approximation for π.)

6.6 LINEAR INEQUALITIES AND PROBLEM SOLVING

In Chapters 1 and 5, we reviewed these inequality symbols and their meanings:

$<$ means "is less than" $\leq$ means "is less than or equal to"
$>$ means "is greater than" $\geq$ means "is greater than or equal to"

An **inequality** is a statement that contains one of the symbols above.

Equations	Inequalities
$x = 3$	$x \leq 3$
$5n - 6 = 14$	$5n - 6 > 14$
$12 = 7 - 3y$	$12 \leq 7 - 3y$
$\frac{x}{4} - 6 = 1$	$\frac{x}{4} - 6 > 1$

Objective **A** Graphing Inequalities on a Number Line

Recall that the single solution to the equation $x = 3$ is 3. The solutions of the inequality $x \leq 3$ include 3 and *all real numbers less than 3* (for example, $-10, \frac{1}{2}, 2$, and 2.9). Because we can't list all numbers less than 3, we show instead a picture of the solutions by graphing them on a number line.

To graph the solutions of $x \leq 3$, we shade the numbers to the left of 3 since they are less than 3. Then we place a closed circle on the point representing 3. The closed circle indicates that 3 *is* a solution: 3 *is* less than or equal to 3.

To graph the solutions of $x < 3$, we shade the numbers to the left of 3. Then we place an open circle on the point representing 3. The open circle indicates that 3 *is not* a solution: 3 *is not* less than 3.

Example 1 Graph: $x \geq -1$

Solution: To graph the solutions of $x \geq -1$, we place a closed circle at -1 since the inequality symbol is $\geq$ and -1 is greater than or equal to -1. Then we shade to the right of -1.

● Work Practice 1

Example 2 Graph: $-1 > x$

Solution: Recall from Section 5.2 that $-1 > x$ means the same as $x < -1$. The graph of the solutions of $x < -1$ is shown below.

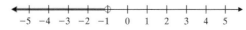

● Work Practice 2

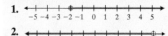 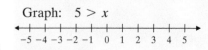
557

PRACTICE 3

Graph: $-3 \leq x < 1$

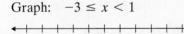

Example 3 Graph: $-4 < x \leq 2$

Solution: We read $-4 < x \leq 2$ as " -4 is less than x and x is less than or equal to 2," or as "x is greater than -4 and x is less than or equal to 2." To graph the solutions of this inequality, we place an open circle at -4 (-4 is not part of the graph), a closed circle at 2 (2 is part of the graph), and we shade all numbers between -4 and 2. Why? All numbers between -4 and 2 are greater than -4 *and* less than 2.

● Work Practice 3

Objective Ⓑ Using the Addition Property

When solutions of a linear inequality are not immediately obvious, they are found through a process similar to the one used to solve a linear equation. Our goal is to get the variable alone on one side of the inequality. We use properties of inequality similar to properties of equality.

Addition Property of Inequality

If a, b, and c are real numbers, then

$$a < b \quad \text{and} \quad a + c < b + c$$

are equivalent inequalities.

This property also holds true for subtracting values, since subtraction is defined in terms of addition. In other words, adding or subtracting the same quantity from both sides of an inequality does not change the solutions of the inequality.

PRACTICE 4

Solve $x - 6 \geq -11$. Graph the solutions.

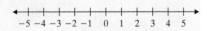

Example 4 Solve $x + 4 \leq -6$. Graph the solutions.

Solution: To solve for x, subtract 4 from both sides of the inequality.

$$x + 4 \leq -6 \qquad \text{Original inequality}$$
$$x + 4 - 4 \leq -6 - 4 \qquad \text{Subtract 4 from both sides.}$$
$$x \leq -10 \qquad \text{Simplify.}$$

The graph of the solutions is shown below.

● Work Practice 4

Helpful Hint

Notice that any number less than or equal to -10 is a solution to $x \leq -10$. For example, solutions include

$$-10, \quad -200, \quad -11\frac{1}{2}, \quad -\sqrt{130}, \quad \text{and} \quad -50.3$$

Objective Ⓒ Using the Multiplication Property

An important difference between solving linear equations and solving linear inequalities is shown when we multiply or divide both sides of an inequality by a nonzero real number. For example, start with the true statement $6 < 8$ and multiply both sides by 2. As we see below, the resulting inequality is also true.

$$6 < 8 \qquad \text{True}$$
$$2(6) < 2(8) \qquad \text{Multiply both sides by 2.}$$
$$12 < 16 \qquad \text{True}$$

Answers

3.

4. $x \geq -5$

But if we start with the same true statement $6 < 8$ and multiply both sides by -2, the resulting inequality is not a true statement.

$6 < 8$ True

$-2(6) < -2(8)$ Multiply both sides by -2.

$-12 < -16$ False

Notice, however, that if we reverse the direction of the inequality symbol, the resulting inequality is true.

$-12 < -16$ False

$-12 > -16$ True

This demonstrates the multiplication property of inequality.

Multiplication Property of Inequality

1. If a, b, and c are real numbers, and c is **positive,** then

$a < b$ and $ac < bc$

are equivalent inequalities.

2. If a, b, and c are real numbers, and c is **negative,** then

$a < b$ and $ac > bc$

are equivalent inequalities.

Because division is defined in terms of multiplication, this property also holds true when dividing both sides of an inequality by a nonzero number: If we multiply or divide both sides of an inequality by a negative number, **the direction of the inequality sign must be reversed for the inequalities to remain equivalent.**

✔**Concept Check** Fill in the box with $<$, $>$, $\leq$, or $\geq$.

a. Since $-8 < -4$, then $3(-8) \,\square\, 3(-4)$.

b. Since $5 \geq -2$, then $\dfrac{5}{-7} \,\square\, \dfrac{-2}{-7}$.

c. If $a < b$, then $2a \,\square\, 2b$.

d. If $a \geq b$, then $\dfrac{a}{-3} \,\square\, \dfrac{b}{-3}$.

Example 5 Solve $-2x \leq -4$. Graph the solutions.

Solution: Remember to reverse the direction of the inequality symbol when dividing by a negative number.

$-2x \leq -4$

$\dfrac{-2x}{-2} \geq \dfrac{-4}{-2}$ Divide both sides by -2 and reverse the inequality sign.

$x \geq 2$ Simplify.

The graph of the solutions is shown.

● **Work Practice 5**

PRACTICE 5

Solve $-3x \leq 12$. Graph the solutions.

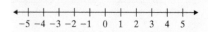

Answer

5. $x \geq -4$

✔ **Concept Check Answer**

a. $<$ **b.** $\leq$ **c.** $<$ **d.** $\leq$

PRACTICE 6

Solve $5x > -20$. Graph the solutions.

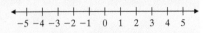

Example 6 Solve $2x < -4$. Graph the solutions.

Solution: $2x < -4$

$$\frac{2x}{2} < \frac{-4}{2}$$ Divide both sides by 2.   Do not reverse the inequality sign.

$$x < -2$$ Simplify.

The graph of the solutions is shown.

● Work Practice 6

Since we cannot list all solutions to an inequality such as $x < -2$, we will use the set notation $\{x \mid x < -2\}$. Recall from Section 5.2 that this is read "the set of all x such that x is less than -2." We will use this notation when solving inequalities.

Objective ⒟ Using Both Properties of Inequality

The following steps may be helpful when solving inequalities in one variable. Notice that these steps are similar to the ones given in Section 6.3 for solving equations.

> ### To Solve Linear Inequalities in One Variable
>
> **Step 1:** If an inequality contains fractions, multiply both sides by the LCD to clear the inequality of fractions.
>
> **Step 2:** Use the distributive property to remove parentheses if they appear.
>
> **Step 3:** Simplify each side of the inequality by combining like terms.
>
> **Step 4:** Get all variable terms on one side and all numbers on the other side by using the addition property of inequality.
>
> **Step 5:** Get the variable alone by using the multiplication property of inequality.

Helpful Hint

Don't forget that if both sides of an inequality are multiplied or divided by a negative number, the direction of the inequality sign must be reversed.

PRACTICE 7

Solve $-3x + 11 \leq -13$. Graph the solution set.

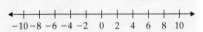

Example 7 Solve $-4x + 7 \geq -9$. Graph the solution set.

Solution: $-4x + 7 \geq -9$

$$-4x + 7 - 7 \geq -9 - 7$$ Subtract 7 from both sides.

$$-4x \geq -16$$ Simplify.

$$\frac{-4x}{-4} \leq \frac{-16}{-4}$$ Divide both sides by -4 and reverse the direction of the inequality sign.

$$x \leq 4$$ Simplify.

The graph of the solution set $\{x \mid x \leq 4\}$ is shown.

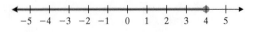

● Work Practice 7

Answers

6. $x > -4$

7. $\{x \mid x \geq 8\}$

Example 8 Solve $-5x + 7 < 2(x - 3)$. Graph the solution set.

Solution:  $-5x + 7 < 2(x - 3)$

$-5x + 7 < 2x - 6$	Apply the distributive property.
$-5x + 7 - 2x < 2x - 6 - 2x$	Subtract $2x$ from both sides.
$-7x + 7 < -6$	Combine like terms.
$-7x + 7 - 7 < -6 - 7$	Subtract 7 from both sides.
$-7x < -13$	Combine like terms.
$\dfrac{-7x}{-7} > \dfrac{-13}{-7}$	Divide both sides by -7 and reverse the direction of the inequality sign.
$x > \dfrac{13}{7}$	Simplify.

The graph of the solution set $\left\{ x \mid x > \dfrac{13}{7} \right\}$ is shown.

$$\underleftarrow{}\overset{\frac{13}{7}}{\underset{-5 \quad -4 \quad -3 \quad -2 \quad -1 \quad 0 \quad 1 \quad 2 \quad 3 \quad 4 \quad 5}{+\!+\!+\!+\!+\!+\!+\!\circ\!+\!+\!+\!+}}\overrightarrow{}$$

● **Work Practice 8**

Example 9 Solve: $2(x - 3) - 5 \le 3(x + 2) - 18$

Solution: $2(x - 3) - 5 \le 3(x + 2) - 18$

$2x - 6 - 5 \le 3x + 6 - 18$	Apply the distributive property.
$2x - 11 \le 3x - 12$	Combine like terms.
$-x - 11 \le -12$	Subtract $3x$ from both sides.
$-x \le -1$	Add 11 to both sides.
$\dfrac{-x}{-1} \ge \dfrac{-1}{-1}$	Divide both sides by -1 and reverse the direction of the inequality sign.
$x \ge 1$	Simplify.

The solution set is $\{ x \mid x \ge 1 \}$.

● **Work Practice 9**

Objective ⒠ Solving Problems Modeled by Inequalities

Problems containing words such as "at least," "at most," "between," "no more than," and "no less than" usually indicate that an inequality should be solved instead of an equation. In solving applications involving linear inequalities, we use the same procedure we used to solve applications involving linear equations.

Some Inequality Translations			
$\ge$	$\le$	$<$	$>$
at least	at most	is less than	is greater than
no less than	no more than		

Example 10 12 subtracted from 3 times a number is less than 21. Find all numbers that make this statement true.

Solution:

1. **UNDERSTAND.** Read and reread the problem. This is a direct translation problem, and let's let

    x = the unknown number

PRACTICE 8

Solve $2x - 3 > 4(x - 1)$. Graph the solution set.

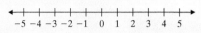

PRACTICE 9

Solve:
$3(x + 5) - 1 \ge 5(x - 1) + 7$

PRACTICE 10

Twice a number, subtracted from 35, is greater than 15. Find all numbers that make this true.

Answers

8. $\left\{ x \mid x < \dfrac{1}{2} \right\}$

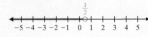

9. $\{ x \mid x \le 6 \}$

10. all numbers less than 10

2. TRANSLATE.

12	subtracted from	three times a number	is less than	21

$$3x \quad - \quad 12 \qquad < \qquad 21$$

3. SOLVE. $3x - 12 < 21$

$$3x < 33 \qquad \text{Add 12 to both sides.}$$

$$\frac{3x}{3} < \frac{33}{3} \qquad \text{Divide both sides by 3 and do not reverse the direction of the inequality sign.}$$

$$x < 11 \qquad \text{Simplify.}$$

4. INTERPRET.

Check: Check the translation; then let's choose a number less than 11 to see if it checks. For example, let's check 10. 12 subtracted from 3 times 10 is 12 subtracted from 30, or 18. Since 18 is less than 21, the number 10 checks.

State: All numbers less than 11 make the original statement true.

● **Work Practice 10**

PRACTICE 11

Alex earns $600 per month plus 4% of all his sales. Find the minimum sales that will allow Alex to earn at least $3000 per month.

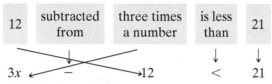 **Example 11** Budgeting for a Wedding

Marie Chase and Jonathan Edwards are having their wedding reception at the Gallery reception hall. They may spend at most $1000 for the reception. If the reception hall charges a $100 cleanup fee plus $14 per person, find the greatest number of people that they can invite and still stay within their budget.

Solution:

1. UNDERSTAND. Read and reread the problem. Suppose that 50 people attend the reception. The cost is then $100 + $14(50) = $100 + $700 = $800.
Let x = the number of people who attend the reception.

2. TRANSLATE.

cleanup fee	+	cost per person	times	number of people	must be less than or equal to	$1000
100	+	14	·	x	≤	1000

3. SOLVE.

$$100 + 14x \leq 1000$$

$$14x \leq 900 \qquad \text{Subtract 100 from both sides.}$$

$$x \leq 64\frac{2}{7} \qquad \text{Divide both sides by 14.}$$

4. INTERPRET.

Check: Since x represents the number of people, we round down to the nearest whole, or 64. Notice that if 64 people attend, the cost is $100 + $14(64) = $996. If 65 people attend, the cost is $100 + $14(65) = $1010, which is more than the given $1000.

State: Marie Chase and Jonathan Edwards can invite at most 64 people to the reception.

● **Work Practice 11**

Answer

11. $60,000

Vocabulary and Readiness Check

Identify each as an equation, expression, or inequality.

1. $6x - 7(x + 9)$ _____

2. $6x = 7(x + 9)$ _____

3. $6x < 7(x + 9)$ _____

4. $5y - 2 \geq -38$ _____

5. $\dfrac{9}{7} = \dfrac{x + 2}{14}$ _____

6. $\dfrac{9}{7} - \dfrac{x + 2}{14}$ _____

Decide which number listed is not a solution to each given inequality.

7. $x \geq -3$; $-3, 0, -5, \pi$ _____

8. $x < 6$; $-6, |-6|, 0, -3.2$ _____

9. $x < 4.01$; $4, -4.01, 4.1, -4.1$ _____

10. $x \geq -3$; $-4, -3, -2, -(-2)$ _____

6.6 Exercise Set

FOR EXTRA HELP

MyMathLab   PRACTICE   WATCH   DOWNLOAD   READ   REVIEW

Objective Ⓐ *Graph each inequality on the number line. See Examples 1 and 2.*

1. $x \leq -1$
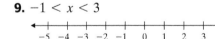
$$-5 \ -4 \ -3 \ -2 \ -1 \ 0 \ 1 \ 2 \ 3 \ 4 \ 5$$

2. $y < 0$
$$-5 \ -4 \ -3 \ -2 \ -1 \ 0 \ 1 \ 2 \ 3 \ 4 \ 5$$

3. $x > \dfrac{1}{2}$
$$-5 \ -4 \ -3 \ -2 \ -1 \ 0 \ 1 \ 2 \ 3 \ 4 \ 5$$

4. $z \geq -\dfrac{2}{3}$
$$-5 \ -4 \ -3 \ -2 \ -1 \ 0 \ 1 \ 2 \ 3 \ 4 \ 5$$

5. $y < 4$
$$-5 \ -4 \ -3 \ -2 \ -1 \ 0 \ 1 \ 2 \ 3 \ 4 \ 5$$

6. $x > 3$
$$-5 \ -4 \ -3 \ -2 \ -1 \ 0 \ 1 \ 2 \ 3 \ 4 \ 5$$

7. $-2 \leq m$
$$-5 \ -4 \ -3 \ -2 \ -1 \ 0 \ 1 \ 2 \ 3 \ 4 \ 5$$

8. $-5 \geq x$
$$-5 \ -4 \ -3 \ -2 \ -1 \ 0 \ 1 \ 2 \ 3 \ 4 \ 5$$

Graph each inequality on the number line. See Example 3.

9. $-1 < x < 3$
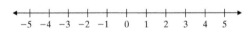
$$-5 \ -4 \ -3 \ -2 \ -1 \ 0 \ 1 \ 2 \ 3 \ 4 \ 5$$

10. $-2 \leq x \leq 3$

$$-5 \ -4 \ -3 \ -2 \ -1 \ 0 \ 1 \ 2 \ 3 \ 4 \ 5$$

11. $0 \leq y < 2$
$$-5 \ -4 \ -3 \ -2 \ -1 \ 0 \ 1 \ 2 \ 3 \ 4 \ 5$$

12. $-4 < x \leq 0$
$$-5 \ -4 \ -3 \ -2 \ -1 \ 0 \ 1 \ 2 \ 3 \ 4 \ 5$$

Objective Ⓑ *Solve each inequality. Graph the solution set. Write each answer using solution set notation. See Example 4.*

13. $x - 2 \geq -7$

$$-5 \ -4 \ -3 \ -2 \ -1 \ 0 \ 1 \ 2 \ 3 \ 4 \ 5$$

14. $x + 4 \leq 1$
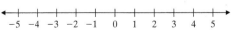
$$-5 \ -4 \ -3 \ -2 \ -1 \ 0 \ 1 \ 2 \ 3 \ 4 \ 5$$

15. $-9 + y < 0$

16. $-3 + m > 5$

17. $3x - 5 > 2x - 8$

18. $3 - 7x \geq 10 - 8x$

19. $4x - 1 \leq 5x - 2x$

20. $7x + 3 < 9x - 3x$

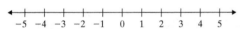

Objective **C** *Solve each inequality. Graph the solution set. See Examples 5 and 6.*

21. $2x < -6$

22. $3x > -9$

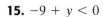 **23.** $-8x \leq 16$

24. $-5x < 20$

25. $-x > 0$

26. $-y \geq 0$

27. $\dfrac{3}{4}y \geq -2$

28. $\dfrac{5}{6}x \leq -8$

29. $-0.6y < -1.8$

30. $-0.3x > -2.4$

Objectives **B** **C** **D** Mixed Practice *Solve each inequality. Write each answer using solution set notation. See Examples 4 through 9.*

31. $-8 < x + 7$

32. $-11 > x + 4$

33. $7(x + 1) - 6x \geq -4$

34. $10(x + 2) - 9x \leq -1$

35. $4x > 1$

36. $6x < 5$

37. $-\dfrac{2}{3}y \leq 8$

38. $-\dfrac{3}{4}y \geq 9$

39. $4(2z + 1) < 4$

40. $6(2 - z) \geq 12$

41. $3x - 7 < 6x + 2$

42. $2x - 1 \geq 4x - 5$

43. $5x - 7x \leq x + 2$

44. $4 - x < 8x + 2x$

45. $-6x + 2 \geq 2(5 - x)$

46. $-7x + 4 > 3(4 - x)$

47. $3(x - 5) < 2(2x - 1)$

48. $5(x - 2) \le 3(2x - 1)$

49. $4(3x - 1) \le 5(2x - 4)$

50. $3(5x - 4) \le 4(3x - 2)$

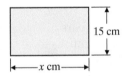 **51.** $3(x + 2) - 6 > -2(x - 3) + 14$

52. $7(x - 2) + x \le -4(5 - x) - 12$

53. $-5(1 - x) + x \le -(6 - 2x) + 6$

54. $-2(x - 4) - 3x < -(4x + 1) + 2x$

55. $\dfrac{1}{4}(x + 4) < \dfrac{1}{5}(2x + 3)$

56. $\dfrac{1}{2}(x - 5) < \dfrac{1}{3}(2x - 1)$

57. $-5x + 4 \le -4(x - 1)$

58. $-6x + 2 < -3(x + 4)$

Objective Ⓔ *Solve the following. For Exercises 61 and 62, the solutions have been started for you. See Examples 10 and 11.*

59. Six more than twice a number is greater than negative fourteen. Find all numbers that make this statement true.

60. One more than five times a number is less than or equal to ten. Find all such numbers.

△ **61.** The perimeter of a rectangle is to be no greater than 100 centimeters and the width must be 15 centimeters. Find the maximum length of the rectangle.

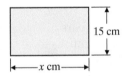

△ **62.** One side of a triangle is three times as long as another side, and the third side is 12 inches long. If the perimeter can be no longer than 32 inches, find the maximum lengths of the other two sides.

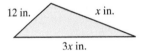

Start the solution:

1. UNDERSTAND the problem. Reread it as many times as needed.

2. TRANSLATE into an equation. (Fill in the blanks below.)

the perimeter of the rectangle	is less than or equal to	100
↓	↓	↓
$\overbrace{x + 15 + x + 15}$	_____	100

Finish with:

3. SOLVE and **4.** INTERPRET

Start the solution:

1. UNDERSTAND the problem. Reread it as many times as needed.

2. TRANSLATE into an equation. (Fill in the blanks below.)

the perimeter of the triangle	is less than or equal to	87
↓	↓	↓
$\overbrace{12 + 4x + x}$	_____	87

Finish with:

3. SOLVE and **4.** INTERPRET

63. Ben Holladay bowled 146 and 201 in his first two games. What must he bowl in his third game to have an average of at least 180? (*Hint:* The average of a list of numbers is their sum divided by the number of numbers in the list.)

64. On an NBA team the two forwards measure 6′8″ and 6′6″ tall and the two guards measure 6′0″ and 5′9″ tall. How tall should the center be if they wish to have a starting team average height of at least 6′5″?

65. Dennis and Nancy Wood are celebrating their 30th wedding anniversary by having a reception at Tiffany Oaks reception hall. They have budgeted $3000 for their reception. If the reception hall charges a $50.00 cleanup fee plus $34 per person, find the greatest number of people that they may invite and still stay within their budget.

66. A surprise retirement party is being planned for Pratap Puri. A total of $860 has been collected for the event, which is to be held at a local reception hall. This reception hall charges a cleanup fee of $40 and $15 per person for drinks and light snacks. Find the greatest number of people that may be invited and still stay within the $860 budget.

67. A 150-pound person uses 5.8 calories per minute when walking at a speed of 4 mph. How long must a person walk at this speed to use at least 200 calories? Round up to the nearest minute. (*Source:* Home & Garden Bulletin No. 72)

68. A 170-pound person uses 5.3 calories per minute when bicycling at a speed of 5.5 mph. How long must a person ride a bike at this speed in order to use at least 200 calories? Round up to the nearest minute. (*Source:* Same as Exercise 67)

Review

Evaluate each expression. See Section 5.3.

69. 3^4 **70.** 4^3 **71.** 1^8 **72.** 0^7 **73.** $\left(\dfrac{7}{8}\right)^2$ **74.** $\left(\dfrac{2}{3}\right)^3$

The graph shows the number of U.S. Starbucks locations from 2002 to 2008. The height of the graph for each year shown corresponds to the number of Starbucks locations in the United States. Use this graph to answer Exercises 75 through 80. See Appendix B.1.)

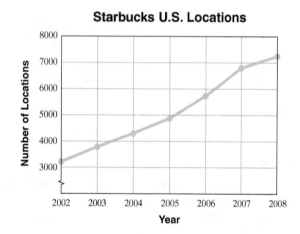

Starbucks U.S. Locations

75. How many Starbucks locations were there in 2002?

76. How many Starbucks locations were there in 2007?

77. Between which two years did the greatest increase in the number of Starbucks locations occur?

78. In what year were there approximately 4900 Starbucks locations?

79. During which year did the number of Starbucks locations rise above 5000?

80. During which year did the number of Starbucks locations rise above 6000?

Concept Extensions

Fill in the box with $<, >, \le, or \ge$. See the Concept Check in this section.

81. Since $3 < 5$, then $3(-4) \,\square\, 5(-4)$.

82. If $m \le n$, then $2m \,\square\, 2n$.

83. If $m \le n$, then $-2m \,\square\, -2n$.

84. If $-x < y$, then $x \,\square\, -y$.

85. When solving an inequality, when must you reverse the direction of the inequality symbol?

86. If both sides of the inequality $-3x < -30$ are divided by 3, do you reverse the direction of the inequality symbol? Why or why not?

Solve.

87. Eric Daly has scores of 75, 83, and 85 on his history tests. Use an inequality to find the scores he can make on his final exam to receive a B in the class. The final exam counts as **two** tests, and a B is received if the final course average is greater than or equal to 80.

88. Maria Lipco has scores of 85, 95, and 92 on her algebra tests. Use an inequality to find the scores she can make on her final exam to receive an A in the course. The final exam counts as **three** tests, and an A is received if the final course average is greater than or equal to 90. Round to one decimal place.

Helpful Hint 📱 Are you preparing for your test? Use the Chapter Test Prep Videos to see the fully worked-out solutions to any of the exercises you want to review.

6 Chapter Highlights

Definitions and Concepts	Examples
Section 6.1 The Addition Property of Equality	

A **linear equation in one variable** can be written in the form $Ax + B = C$ where A, B, and C are real numbers and $A \neq 0$.

$$-3x + 7 = 2$$
$$3(x - 1) = -8(x + 5) + 4$$

Equivalent equations are equations that have the same solution.

$x - 7 = 10$ and $x = 17$ are equivalent equations.

ADDITION PROPERTY OF EQUALITY

Adding the same number to or subtracting the same number from both sides of an equation does not change its solution.

$$y + 9 = 3$$
$$y + 9 - 9 = 3 - 9$$
$$y = -6$$

| **Section 6.2   The Multiplication Property of Equality** | |

MULTIPLICATION PROPERTY OF EQUALITY

Multiplying both sides or dividing both sides of an equation by the same nonzero number does not change its solution.

$$\frac{2}{3}a = 18$$
$$\frac{3}{2}\left(\frac{2}{3}a\right) = \frac{3}{2}(18)$$
$$a = 27$$

| **Section 6.3   Further Solving Linear Equations** | |

TO SOLVE LINEAR EQUATIONS

Solve: $\dfrac{5(-2x + 9)}{6} + 3 = \dfrac{1}{2}$

1. Clear the equation of fractions.

1. $6 \cdot \dfrac{5(-2x + 9)}{6} + 6 \cdot 3 = 6 \cdot \dfrac{1}{2}$

2. Remove any grouping symbols such as parentheses.

2. $5(-2x + 9) + 18 = 3$

$-10x + 45 + 18 = 3$ Apply the distributive property.

3. Simplify each side by combining like terms.

3. $\qquad\qquad -10x + 63 = 3$ Combine like terms.

4. Get all variable terms on one side and all numbers on the other side by using the addition property of equality.

4. $\qquad -10x + 63 - 63 = 3 - 63$ Subtract 63.

$\qquad\qquad\qquad -10x = -60$

5. Get the variable alone by using the multiplication property of equality.

5. $\qquad\qquad \dfrac{-10x}{-10} = \dfrac{-60}{-10}$ Divide by -10.

$\qquad\qquad\qquad x = 6$

6. Check the solution by substituting it into the original equation.

Definitions and Concepts	**Examples**

Section 6.4   A Further Introduction to Problem Solving

PROBLEM-SOLVING STEPS

1. UNDERSTAND the problem.

The height of the Hudson volcano in Chile is twice the height of the Kiska volcano in the Aleutian Islands. If the sum of their heights is 12,870 feet, find the height of each.

1. Read and reread the problem. Guess a solution and check your guess.
Let x be the height of the Kiska volcano. Then $2x$ is the height of the Hudson volcano.

2. TRANSLATE the problem.

2.

height of Kiska	added to	height of Hudson	is	12,870
↓	↓	↓	↓	↓
x	$+$	$2x$	$=$	$12{,}870$

3. SOLVE the equation.

3. $x + 2x = 12{,}870$
$3x = 12{,}870$
$x = 4290$

4. INTERPRET the results.

4. *Check:* If x is 4290, then $2x$ is $2(4290)$ or 8580. Their sum is $4290 + 8580$ or 12,870, the required amount.

State: The Kiska volcano is 4290 feet tall, and the Hudson volcano is 8580 feet tall.

Section 6.5   Formulas and Problem Solving

An equation that describes a known relationship among quantities is called a **formula.**

To solve a formula for a specified variable, use the same steps as for solving a linear equation. Treat the specified variable as the only variable of the equation.

$A = lw$ (area of a rectangle)
$I = PRT$ (simple interest)

Solve: $P = 2l + 2w$ for l.
$P = 2l + 2w$
$P - 2w = 2l + 2w - 2w$ Subtract 2w.
$P - 2w = 2l$
$\dfrac{P - 2w}{2} = \dfrac{2l}{2}$ Divide by 2.
$\dfrac{P - 2w}{2} = l$

Definitions and Concepts	**Examples**
Section 6.6 Linear Inequalities and Problem Solving	

Properties of inequalities are similar to properties of equations. However, if you multiply or divide both sides of an inequality by the same *negative* number, you must reverse the direction of the inequality symbol.	$-2x \leq 4$ $\dfrac{-2x}{-2} \geq \dfrac{4}{-2}$ Divide by -2; reverse the inequality symbol. $x \geq -2$ 
TO SOLVE LINEAR INEQUALITIES	*Solve:* $3(x + 2) \leq -2 + 8$
1. Clear the inequality of fractions.	**1.** $3(x + 2) \leq -2 + 8$ No fractions to clear.
2. Remove grouping symbols.	**2.** $3x + 6 \leq -2 + 8$ Apply the distributive property.
3. Simplify each side by combining like terms.	**3.** $3x + 6 \leq 6$ Combine like terms.
4. Write all variable terms on one side and all numbers on the other side using the addition property of inequality.	**4.** $3x + 6 - 6 \leq 6 - 6$ Subtract 6. $3x \leq 0$
5. Get the variable alone by using the multiplication property of inequality.	**5.** $\dfrac{3x}{3} \leq \dfrac{0}{3}$ Divide by 3. $x \leq 0$
	The solution set is $\{x \mid x \leq 0\}$.

Chapter 6 Review

(6.1) *Solve each equation.*

1. $8x + 4 = 9x$

2. $5y - 3 = 6y$

3. $\dfrac{2}{7}x + \dfrac{5}{7}x = 6$

4. $3x - 5 = 4x + 1$

5. $2x - 6 = x - 6$

6. $4(x + 3) = 3(1 + x)$

7. $6(3 + n) = 5(n - 1)$

8. $5(2 + x) - 3(3x + 2) = -5(x - 6) + 2$

Choose the correct algebraic expression.

9. The sum of two numbers is 10. If one number is x, express the other number in terms of x.

 a. $x - 10$
 b. $10 - x$
 c. $10 + x$
 d. $10x$

10. Mandy is 5 inches taller than Melissa. If x inches represents the height of Mandy, express Melissa's height in terms of x.

 a. $x - 5$
 b. $5 - x$
 c. $5 + x$
 d. $5x$

△ **11.** If one angle measures $x°$, express the measure of its complement in terms of x.

 a. $(180 - x)°$
 b. $(90 - x)°$
 c. $(x - 180)°$
 d. $(x - 90)°$

△ **12.** If one angle measures $(x + 5)°$, express the measure of its supplement in terms of x.

 a. $(185 + x)°$
 b. $(95 + x)°$
 c. $(175 - x)°$
 d. $(x - 170)°$

(6.2) *Solve each equation.*

13. $\dfrac{3}{4}x = -9$

14. $\dfrac{x}{6} = \dfrac{2}{3}$

15. $-5x = 0$

16. $-y = 7$

17. $0.2x = 0.15$

18. $\dfrac{-x}{3} = 1$

19. $-3x + 1 = 19$

20. $5x + 25 = 20$

21. $7(x - 1) + 9 = 5x$

22. $7x - 6 = 5x - 3$

23. $-5x + \dfrac{3}{7} = \dfrac{10}{7}$

24. $5x + x = 9 + 4x - 1 + 6$

25. Write the sum of three consecutive integers as an expression in x. Let x be the first integer.

26. Write the sum of the first and fourth of four consecutive even integers. Let x be the first even integer.

(6.3) *Solve each equation.*

27. $\dfrac{5}{3}x + 4 = \dfrac{2}{3}x$

28. $\dfrac{7}{8}x + 1 = \dfrac{5}{8}x$

29. $-(5x + 1) = -7x + 3$

30. $-4(2x + 1) = -5x + 5$

31. $-6(2x - 5) = -3(9 + 4x)$

32. $3(8y - 1) = 6(5 + 4y)$

33. $\dfrac{3(2 - z)}{5} = z$

34. $\dfrac{4(n + 2)}{5} = -n$

35. $0.5(2n - 3) - 0.1 = 0.4(6 + 2n)$

36. $-9 - 5a = 3(6a - 1)$

37. $\dfrac{5(c + 1)}{6} = 2c - 3$

38. $\dfrac{2(8 - a)}{3} = 4 - 4a$

▦ **39.** $200(70x - 3560) = -179(150x - 19{,}300)$

40. $1.72y - 0.04y = 0.42$

(6.4) *Solve each of the following.*

41. The height of the Washington Monument is 50.5 inches more than 10 times the length of a side of its square base. If the sum of these two dimensions is 7327 inches, find the height of the Washington Monument. (*Source:* National Park Service)

42. A 12-foot board is to be divided into two pieces so that one piece is twice as long as the other. If *x* represents the length of the shorter piece, find the length of each piece.

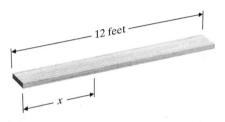

43. The Harvard University library system and the Cornell University library system consist of a total of 119 different library sites. The number of Harvard libraries is two more than twice the number of Cornell libraries. How many libraries does each university support? (*Source*: Harvard University, Cornell University)

44. Find three consecutive integers whose sum is −114.

45. The quotient of a number and 3 is the same as the difference of the number and two. Find the number.

46. Double the sum of a number and 6 is the opposite of the number. Find the number.

(6.5) *Substitute the given values into the given formulas and solve for the unknown variable.*

47. $P = 2l + 2w$; $P = 46, l = 14$

48. $V = lwh$; $V = 192, l = 8, w = 6$

Solve each equation for the indicated variable or constant.

49. $y = mx + b$ for m

50. $r = vst - 5$ for s

51. $2y - 5x = 7$ for x

52. $3x - 6y = -2$ for y

△ **53.** $C = \pi D$ for π

△ **54.** $C = 2\pi r$ for π

△ **55.** A swimming pool holds 900 cubic meters of water. If its length is 20 meters and its height is 3 meters, find its width.

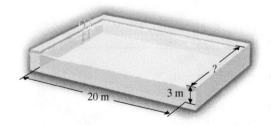

56. The perimeter of a rectangular billboard is 60 feet and the billboard has a length 6 feet longer than its width. Find the dimensions of the billboard.

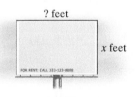

57. A charity 10K race is given annually to benefit a local hospice organization. How long will it take to run/walk a 10K race (10 kilometers or 10,000 meters) if your average pace is 125 **meters** per minute? Give your time in hours and minutes.

58. On April 28, 2001, the highest temperature recorded in the United States was 104°F, which occurred in Death Valley, California. Convert this temperature to degrees Celsius. (*Source:* National Weather Service)

(6.6) *Graph on a number line.*

71. $x \leq -2$

72. $0 < x \leq 5$

Solve each inequality.

73. $x - 5 \leq -4$ **74.** $x + 7 > 2$ **75.** $-2x \geq -20$ **76.** $-3x > 12$

77. $5x - 7 > 8x + 5$ **78.** $x + 4 \geq 6x - 16$ **79.** $\dfrac{2}{3}y > 6$

80. $-0.5y \leq 7.5$ **81.** $-2(x - 5) > 2(3x - 2)$ **82.** $4(2x - 5) \leq 5x - 1$

83. Carol Abolafia earns $175 per week plus a 5% commission on all her sales. Find the minimum amount of sales she must make to ensure that she earns at least $300 per week.

84. Joseph Barrow shot rounds of 76, 82, and 79 golfing. What must he shoot on his next round so that his average will be below 80?

Answers to Selected Exercises

Chapter 6 Equations, Inequalities, and Problem Solving

Section 6.1

Vocabulary and Readiness Check **1.** expression **3.** equation **5.** expression; equation **7.** Equivalent **9.** 2 **11.** 12 **13.** 17

Exercise Set 6.1 **1.** 3 **3.** -2 **5.** -14 **7.** 0.5 **9.** $\frac{1}{4}$ **11.** $\frac{5}{12}$ **13.** -3 **15.** -9 **17.** -10 **19.** 2 **21.** -7 **23.** -1 **25.** -9 **27.** -12 **29.** $-\frac{1}{2}$

31. 11 **33.** 21 **35.** 25 **37.** -3 **39.** -0.7 **41.** 11 **43.** 13 **45.** -30 **47.** -0.4 **49.** -7 **51.** $-\frac{1}{3}$ **53.** -17.9 **55.** $(10 - x)$ ft **57.** $(180 - x)°$

59. $n - 28{,}000$ **61.** $7x$ sq mi **63.** $\frac{8}{5}$ **65.** $\frac{1}{2}$ **67.** -9 **69.** x **71.** y **73.** x **75.** answers may vary **77.** 4 **79.** answers may vary **81.** $(173 - 3x)°$
83. answers may vary **85.** -145.478

Section 6.2

Vocabulary and Readiness Check **1.** multiplication **3.** equation; expression **5.** Equivalent **7.** 9 **9.** 2 **11.** -5

Exercise Set 6.2 **1.** 4 **3.** 0 **5.** 12 **7.** -12 **9.** 3 **11.** 2 **13.** 0 **15.** 6.3 **17.** 10 **19.** -20 **21.** 0 **23.** -9 **25.** 1 **27.** -30 **29.** 3 **31.** $\frac{10}{9}$

33. -1 **35.** -4 **37.** $-\frac{1}{2}$ **39.** 0 **41.** 4 **43.** $-\frac{1}{14}$ **45.** 0.21 **47.** 5 **49.** 6 **51.** -5.5 **53.** -5 **55.** 0 **57.** -3 **59.** $-\frac{9}{28}$ **61.** $\frac{14}{3}$ **63.** -9

65. -2 **67.** $\frac{11}{2}$ **69.** $-\frac{1}{4}$ **71.** $\frac{9}{10}$ **73.** $-\frac{17}{20}$ **75.** -16 **77.** $2x + 2$ **79.** $2x + 2$ **81.** $5x + 20$ **83.** $7x - 12$ **85.** $12z + 44$ **87.** 1 **89.** -48
91. answers may vary **93.** answers may vary **95.** 2

Section 6.3

Calculator Explorations **1.** solution **3.** not a solution **5.** solution

Vocabulary and Readiness Check **1.** equation **3.** expression **5.** expression **7.** equation

Exercise Set 6.3 **1.** -6 **3.** 3 **5.** 1 **7.** $\frac{3}{2}$ **9.** 0 **11.** -1 **13.** 4 **15.** -4 **17.** -3 **19.** 2 **21.** 50 **23.** 1 **25.** $\frac{7}{3}$ **27.** 0.2 **29.** all real numbers

31. no solution **33.** no solution **35.** all real numbers **37.** 18 **39.** $\frac{19}{9}$ **41.** $\frac{14}{3}$ **43.** 13 **45.** 4 **47.** all real numbers **49.** $-\frac{3}{5}$ **51.** -5 **53.** 10

55. no solution **57.** 3 **59.** -17 **61.** $\frac{7}{5}$ **63.** $-\frac{1}{50}$ **65.** $(6x - 8)$ m **67.** $-8 - x$ **69.** $-3 + 2x$ **71.** $9(x + 20)$ **73. a.** all real numbers
b. answers may vary **c.** answers may vary **75.** a **77.** b **79.** c **81.** answers may vary **83. a.** $x + x + x + 2x + 2x = 28$ **b.** $x = 4$
c. $x = 4$ cm; $2x = 8$ cm **85.** answers may vary **87.** 15.3 **89.** -0.2

Section 6.4

Vocabulary and Readiness Check **1.** $2x; 2x - 31$ **3.** $x + 5; 2(x + 5)$ **5.** $20 - y; \dfrac{20 - y}{3}$ or $(20 - y) \div 3$

Exercise Set 6.4 **1.** $2x + 7 = x + 6; -1$ **3.** $3x - 6 = 2x + 8; 14$ **5.** -25 **7.** $-\frac{3}{4}$ **9.** 3 in.; 6 in.; 16 in. **11.** 1st piece: 5 in.; 2nd piece: 10 in.;
3rd piece: 25 in. **13.** Texas: 30 million pounds; New Mexico: 45 million pounds **15.** 172 mi **17.** 25 mi **19.** 1st angle: 37.5°; 2nd angle: 37.5°;
3rd angle: 105° **21.** A: 60°; B: 120°; C: 120°; D: 60° **23.** $3x + 3$ **25.** $x + 2; x + 4; 2x + 4$ **27.** $x + 1; x + 2; x + 3; 4x + 6$
29. $x + 2; x + 4; 2x + 6$ **31.** 234, 235 **33.** Belgium: 32; France: 33; Spain: 34 **35.** 5 ft, 12 ft **37.** Maglev: 361 mph; TGV: 357.2 mph **39.** 43°, 137°
41. 58°, 60°, 62° **43.** 1 **45.** 280 mi **47.** USC: 38; Penn State: 24 **49.** Montana: 56 counties; California: 58 counties **51.** Neptune: 8 moons;
Uranus: 21 moons; Saturn: 18 moons **53.** -16 **55.** Sahara: 3,500,000 sq mi; Gobi: 500,000 sq mi **57.** Australia: 6; Germany: 7; Korea: 8
59. Chambliss: 1,220,854; Martin: 905,637 **61.** 34.5°; 34.5°; 111° **63.** Eagles: *Their Greatest Hits, 1971–1975* **65.** *Thriller*: $27 million; *The Wall*: $23 million
67. answers may vary **69.** 34 **71.** 225π **73.** 15 ft by 24 ft **75.** 5400 chirps per hour; 129,600 chirps per day; 47,304,000 chirps per year
77. answers may vary **79.** answers may vary **81.** c

Section 6.5

Exercise Set 6.5 **1.** $h = 3$ **3.** $h = 3$ **5.** $h = 20$ **7.** $c = 12$ **9.** $r = 2.5$ **11.** $h = \dfrac{f}{5g}$ **13.** $w = \dfrac{V}{lh}$ **15.** $y = 7 - 3x$ **17.** $R = \dfrac{A - P}{PT}$

19. $A = \dfrac{3V}{h}$ **21.** $a = P - b - c$ **23.** $h = \dfrac{S - 2\pi r^2}{2\pi r}$ **25.** 120 ft **27. a.** area: 480 sq in.; perimeter: 120 in. **b.** frame: perimeter; glass: area
29. a. area: 103.5 sq ft; perimeter: 41 ft **b.** baseboard: perimeter; carpet: area **31.** $-10°$C **33.** 6.25 hr **35.** length: 78 ft; width: 52 ft
37. 18 ft, 36 ft, 48 ft **39.** 137.5 mi **41.** 61.5°F **43.** 60 chirps per minute **45.** increases **47.** 96 piranhas **49.** 2 bags **51.** one 16-in. pizza
53. 4.65 min **55.** 13 in. **57.** 2.25 hr **59.** 12,090 ft **61.** 50°C **63.** at least 515,509.5 cu in. **65.** 449 cu in. **67.** 333°F **69.** 0.32 **71.** 2.00 or 2

73. 17% **75.** 720% **77.** $V = G(N - R)$ **79.** multiplies the volume by 8; answers may vary **81.** $53\frac{1}{3}$ **83.** $\bigcirc = \dfrac{\triangle - \square}{\blacksquare}$ **85.** 44.3 sec
87. $P = 3{,}200{,}000$ **89.** $V = 113.1$

Section 6.6

Vocabulary and Readiness Check   **1.** expression   **3.** inequality   **5.** equation   **7.** -5 **9.** 4.1

Exercise Set 6.6   **1.** (number line, closed circle at -1)   **3.** (number line, open circle at $\frac{1}{2}$)   **5.** (number line, open circle at 4)   **7.** (number line, closed circle at -2)

9. (number line, open circles at -1 and 3)   **11.** (number line, closed circle at 0, open circle at 2)   **13.** $\{x \mid x \geq -5\}$ (number line, closed circle at -5)

15. $\{y \mid y < 9\}$ (number line, open circle at 9)   **17.** $\{x \mid x > -3\}$ (number line, open circle at -3)   **19.** $\{x \mid x \leq 1\}$ (number line, closed circle at 1)

21. $\{x \mid x < -3\}$ (number line, open circle at -3)   **23.** $\{x \mid x \geq -2\}$ (number line, closed circle at -2)   **25.** $\{x \mid x < 0\}$ (number line, open circle at 0)

27. $\left\{y \mid y \geq -\frac{8}{3}\right\}$ (number line, closed circle at $-\frac{8}{3}$)   **29.** $\{y \mid y > 3\}$ (number line, open circle at 3)   **31.** $\{x \mid x > -15\}$ **33.** $\{x \mid x \geq -11\}$

35. $\left\{x \mid x > \frac{1}{4}\right\}$ **37.** $\{y \mid y \geq -12\}$ **39.** $\{z \mid z < 0\}$ **41.** $\{x \mid x > -3\}$ **43.** $\left\{x \mid x \geq -\frac{2}{3}\right\}$ **45.** $\{x \mid x \leq -2\}$ **47.** $\{x \mid x > -13\}$

49. $\{x \mid x \leq -8\}$ **51.** $\{x \mid x > 4\}$ **53.** $\left\{x \mid x \leq \frac{5}{4}\right\}$ **55.** $\left\{x \mid x > \frac{8}{3}\right\}$ **57.** $\{x \mid x \geq 0\}$ **59.** all numbers greater than -10

61. 35 cm   **63.** at least 193   **65.** 86 people   **67.** at least 35 min   **69.** 81   **71.** 1   **73.** $\frac{49}{64}$ **75.** about 3200   **77.** 2006 and 2007   **79.** 2005   **81.** $>$

83. $\geq$ **85.** when multiplying or dividing by a negative number   **87.** final exam score ≥ 78.5

Chapter 6 Review   **1.** 4   **2.** -3 **3.** 6   **4.** -6 **5.** 0   **6.** -9 **7.** -23 **8.** 28   **9.** b   **10.** a   **11.** b   **12.** c   **13.** -12 **14.** 4   **15.** 0   **16.** -7

17. 0.75   **18.** -3 **19.** -6 **20.** -1 **21.** -1 **22.** $\frac{3}{2}$ **23.** $-\frac{1}{5}$ **24.** 7   **25.** $3x + 3$ **26.** $2x + 6$ **27.** -4 **28.** -4 **29.** 2   **30.** -3 **31.** no solution

32. no solution   **33.** $\frac{3}{4}$ **34.** $-\frac{8}{9}$ **35.** 20   **36.** $-\frac{6}{23}$ **37.** $\frac{23}{7}$ **38.** $-\frac{2}{5}$ **39.** 102   **40.** 0.25   **41.** 6665.5 in.   **42.** short piece: 4 ft; long piece: 8 ft

43. Harvard: 80; Cornell: 39   **44.** $-39, -38, -37$ **45.** 3   **46.** -4 **47.** $w = 9$ **48.** $h = 4$ **49.** $m = \dfrac{y - b}{x}$ **50.** $s = \dfrac{r + 5}{vt}$ **51.** $x = \dfrac{2y - 7}{5}$

52. $y = \dfrac{2 + 3x}{6}$ **53.** $\pi = \dfrac{C}{D}$ **54.** $\pi = \dfrac{C}{2r}$ **55.** 15 m   **56.** 18 ft by 12 ft   **57.** 1 hr and 20 min   **58.** 40°C   **59.** 20%   **60.** 70%   **61.** 110   **62.** 1280

63. mark-up: $209; new price: $2109   **64.** 50,844 people   **65.** 40% solution: 10 gal; 10% solution: 20 gal   **66.** 1.9% increase   **67.** 18%

68. swerving into another lane   **69.** 966 customers   **70.** no; answers may vary   **71.** (number line, closed circle at -2)   **72.** (number line, open circle at 0, closed circle at 5)

73. $\{x \mid x \leq 1\}$ **74.** $\{x \mid x > -5\}$ **75.** $\{x \mid x \leq 10\}$ **76.** $\{x \mid x < -4\}$ **77.** $\{x \mid x < -4\}$ **78.** $\{x \mid x \leq 4\}$ **79.** $\{y \mid y > 9\}$

80. $\{y \mid y \geq -15\}$ **81.** $\left\{x \mid x < \frac{7}{4}\right\}$ **82.** $\left\{x \mid x \leq \frac{19}{3}\right\}$ **83.** $2500   **84.** score must be less than 83

7

Graphing Equations and Inequalities

574

7.1 THE RECTANGULAR COORDINATE SYSTEM

Objectives

A Plot Ordered Pairs of Numbers on the Rectangular Coordinate System.

B Graph Paired Data to Create a Scatter Diagram.

C Find the Missing Coordinate of an Ordered Pair Solution, Given One Coordinate of the Pair.

The broken line graph below shows the relationship between the time before and after smoking a cigarette and pulse rate. The horizontal line or axis shows time in minutes and the vertical line or axis shows the pulse rate in heartbeats per minute. Notice that there are two numbers associated with each point of the graph. For example, the graph shows that 15 minutes after "lighting up," the pulse rate is 80 beats per minute. If we agree to write the time first and the pulse rate second, we can say there is a point on the graph corresponding to the **ordered pair** of numbers (15, 80). A few more ordered pairs are shown alongside their corresponding points.

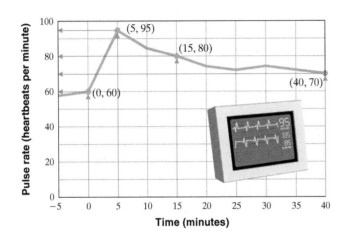

Objective **A** Plotting Ordered Pairs of Numbers

In general, we use the idea of ordered pairs to describe the location of a point in a plane (such as a piece of paper). We start with a horizontal and a vertical axis. Each axis is a number line, and for the sake of consistency we construct our axes to intersect at the 0 coordinate of both. This point of intersection is called the **origin.** Notice that these two number lines or axes divide the plane into four regions called **quadrants.** The quadrants are usually numbered with Roman numerals as shown. The axes are not considered to be in any quadrant.

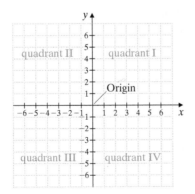

    It is helpful to label axes, so we label the horizontal axis the ***x*-axis** and the vertical axis the ***y*-axis.** We call the system described above the **rectangular coordinate system,** or the **coordinate plane.** Just as with other graphs shown, we can then describe the locations of points by ordered pairs of numbers. We list the horizontal ***x*-axis** measurement first and the vertical ***y*-axis** measurement second.

To plot or graph the point corresponding to the ordered pair (a, b) we start at the origin. We then move a units left or right (right if a is positive, left if a is negative). From there, we move b units up or down (up if b is positive, down if b is negative). For example, to plot the point corresponding to the ordered pair $(3, 2)$, we start at the origin, move 3 units right, and from there move 2 units up. (See the figure below.) The x-value, 3, is also called the **x-coordinate** and the y-value, 2, is also called the **y-coordinate**. From now on, we will call the point with coordinates $(3, 2)$ simply the point $(3, 2)$. The point $(-2, 5)$ is also graphed below.

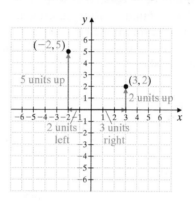

PRACTICE 1

On a single coordinate system, plot each ordered pair. State in which quadrant, or on which axis, each point lies.

a. $(4, 2)$ **b.** $(-1, -3)$

c. $(2, -2)$ **d.** $(-5, 1)$

e. $(0, 3)$ **f.** $(3, 0)$

g. $(0, -4)$ **h.** $\left(-2\frac{1}{2}, 0\right)$

i. $\left(1, -3\frac{3}{4}\right)$

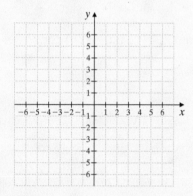

Answers

1.

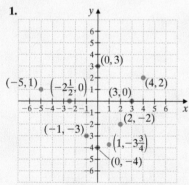

a. Point $(4, 2)$ lies in quadrant I.

b. Point $(-1, -3)$ lies in quadrant III.

c. Point $(2, -2)$ lies in quadrant IV.

d. Point $(-5, 1)$ lies in quadrant II.

e.–h. Points $(3, 0)$ and $\left(-2\frac{1}{2}, 0\right)$ lie on the x-axis. Points $(0, 3)$ and $(0, -4)$ lie on the y-axis.

i. Point $\left(1, -3\frac{3}{4}\right)$ lies in quadrant IV.

✓ Concept Check Answer

The graph of point $(-5, 1)$ lies in quadrant II and the graph of point $(1, -5)$ lies in quadrant IV. They are *not* in the same location.

Helpful Hint

Don't forget that **each ordered pair corresponds to exactly one point in the plane and that each point in the plane corresponds to exactly one ordered pair.**

✓ Concept Check Is the graph of the point $(-5, 1)$ in the same location as the graph of the point $(1, -5)$? Explain.

Example 1 On a single coordinate system, plot each ordered pair. State in which quadrant, or on which axis, each point lies.

a. $(5, 3)$ **b.** $(-2, -4)$ **c.** $(1, -2)$ **d.** $(-5, 3)$ **e.** $(0, 0)$

f. $(0, 2)$ **g.** $(-5, 0)$ **h.** $\left(0, -5\frac{1}{2}\right)$ **i.** $\left(4\frac{2}{3}, -3\right)$

Solution:

a. Point $(5, 3)$ lies in quadrant I.

b. Point $(-2, -4)$ lies in quadrant III.

c. Point $(1, -2)$ lies in quadrant IV.

d. Point $(-5, 3)$ lies in quadrant II.

e.–h. Points $(0, 0)$, $(0, 2)$, and $\left(0, -5\frac{1}{2}\right)$ lie on the y-axis. Points $(0, 0)$ and $(-5, 0)$ lie on the x-axis.

i. Point $\left(4\frac{2}{3}, -3\right)$ lies in quadrant IV.

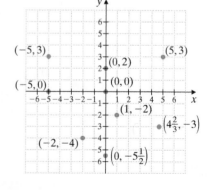

Work Practice 1

Helpful Hint

In Example 1, notice that the point $(0, 0)$ lies on both the x-axis and the y-axis. It is the only point in the entire rectangular coordinate system that has this feature. Why? It is the only point of intersection of the x-axis and the y-axis.

✓**Concept Check** For each description of a point in the rectangular coordinate system, write an ordered pair that represents it.

a. Point A is located three units to the left of the y-axis and five units above the x-axis.

b. Point B is located six units below the origin.

From Example 1, notice that the y-coordinate of any point on the x-axis is 0. For example, the point $(-5, 0)$ lies on the x-axis. Also, the x-coordinate of any point on the y-axis is 0. For example, the point $(0, 2)$ lies on the y-axis.

Objective B Creating Scatter Diagrams

Data that can be represented as ordered pairs are called **paired data**. Many types of data collected from the real world are paired data. For instance, the annual measurements of a child's height can be written as ordered pairs of the form (year, height in inches) and are paired data. The graph of paired data as points in a rectangular coordinate system is called a **scatter diagram**. Scatter diagrams can be used to look for patterns and trends in paired data.

Example 2 The table gives the annual net sales for PetSmart for the years shown. (*Source:* PetSmart)

Year	PetSmart Net Sales (in billions of dollars)
2003	3.0
2004	3.4
2005	3.8
2006	4.2
2007	4.7
2008	5.1
2009	5.3

a. Write this paired data as a set of ordered pairs of the form (year, net sales in billions of dollars).

b. Create a scatter diagram of the paired data.

c. What trend in the paired data does the scatter diagram show?

Solution:

a. The ordered pairs are (2003, 3.0), (2004, 3.4), (2005, 3.8), (2006, 4.2), (2007, 4.7), (2008, 5.1), and (2009, 5.3).

b. We begin by plotting the ordered pairs. Because the x-coordinate in each ordered pair is a year, we label the x-axis "Year" and mark the horizontal axis with the years given. Then we label the y-axis or vertical axis "Net Sales (in billions of dollars)." In this case, it is convenient to mark the vertical axis in multiples of 0.5, starting with 0. In Practice 2, since there are no years when the number of tornadoes is less than 1000, we use the notation ⚡ to skip to 1000, and then proceed by multiples of 100.

PetSmart Net Sales

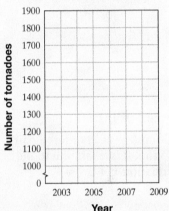

c. The scatter diagram shows that PetSmart net sales steadily increased over the years 2003–2009.

● **Work Practice 2**

PRACTICE 2

The table gives the number of tornadoes that have occurred in the United States for the years shown. (*Source:* Storm Prediction Center, National Weather Service)

Year	Tornadoes
2003	1376
2004	1817
2005	1264
2006	1106
2007	1098
2008	1691
2009	1156

a. Write this paired data as a set of ordered pairs of the form (year, number of tornadoes).

b. Create a scatter diagram of the paired data.

U.S. Tornadoes

c. What trend in the paired data, if any, does the scatter diagram show?

Answers

2. a. (2003, 1376), (2004, 1817), (2005, 1264), (2006, 1106), (2007, 1098), (2008, 1691), (2009, 1156)

b. **U.S. Tornadoes**

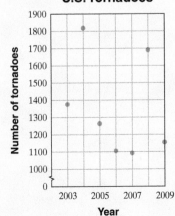

c. The number of tornadoes varies greatly from year to year.

✓ **Concept Check Answers**

a. $(-3, 5)$ **b.** $(0, -6)$

Objective ⓒ Completing Ordered Pair Solutions

Let's see how we can use ordered pairs to record solutions of equations containing two variables. An equation in one variable such as $x + 1 = 5$ has one solution, 4: the number 4 is the value of the variable x that makes the equation true.

An equation in two variables, such as $2x + y = 8$, has solutions consisting of two values, one for x and one for y. For example, $x = 3$ and $y = 2$ is a solution of $2x + y = 8$ because, if x is replaced with 3 and y with 2, we get a true statement.

$$2x + y = 8$$
$$2(3) + 2 \overset{?}{=} 8 \quad \text{Replace } x \text{ with 3 and } y \text{ with 2.}$$
$$8 = 8 \quad \text{True}$$

The solution $x = 3$ and $y = 2$ can be written as $(3, 2)$, an ordered pair of numbers.

> In general, an ordered pair is a **solution** of an equation in two variables if replacing the variables by the values of the ordered pair results in a *true statement*.

For example, another ordered pair solution of $2x + y = 8$ is $(5, -2)$. Replacing x with 5 and y with -2 results in a true statement.

$$2x + y = 8$$
$$2(5) + (-2) \overset{?}{=} 8 \quad \text{Replace } x \text{ with 5 and } y \text{ with } -2.$$
$$10 - 2 \overset{?}{=} 8$$
$$8 = 8 \quad \text{True}$$

PRACTICE 3

Complete each ordered pair so that it is a solution to the equation $x + 2y = 8$.

a. $(0, \ )$
b. $(\ , 3)$
c. $(-4, \ )$

Example 3 Complete each ordered pair so that it is a solution to the equation $3x + y = 12$.

a. $(0, \ )$ **b.** $(\ , 6)$ **c.** $(-1, \ )$

Solution:

a. In the ordered pair $(0, \ )$, the x-value is 0. We let $x = 0$ in the equation and solve for y.

$$3x + y = 12$$
$$3(0) + y = 12 \quad \text{Replace } x \text{ with 0.}$$
$$0 + y = 12$$
$$y = 12$$

The completed ordered pair is $(0, 12)$.

b. In the ordered pair $(\ , 6)$, the y-value is 6. We let $y = 6$ in the equation and solve for x.

$$3x + y = 12$$
$$3x + 6 = 12 \quad \text{Replace } y \text{ with 6.}$$
$$3x = 6 \quad \text{Subtract 6 from both sides.}$$
$$x = 2 \quad \text{Divide both sides by 3.}$$

The ordered pair is $(2, 6)$.

c. In the ordered pair $(-1, \ )$, the x-value is -1. We let $x = -1$ in the equation and solve for y.

$$3x + y = 12$$
$$3(-1) + y = 12 \quad \text{Replace } x \text{ with } -1.$$
$$-3 + y = 12$$
$$y = 15 \quad \text{Add 3 to both sides.}$$

The ordered pair is $(-1, 15)$.

● **Work Practice 3**

Solutions of equations in two variables can also be recorded in a **table of paired values,** as shown in the next example.

Example 4 Complete the table for the equation $y = 3x$.

	x	y
a.	−1	
b.		0
c.		−9

PRACTICE 4

Complete the table for the equation $y = -2x$.

	x	y
a.	−3	
b.		0
c.		10

Solution:

a. We replace x with -1 in the equation and solve for y.

$$y = 3x$$
$$y = 3(-1) \quad \text{Let } x = -1.$$
$$y = -3$$

The ordered pair is $(-1, -3)$.

b. We replace y with 0 in the equation and solve for x.

$$y = 3x$$
$$0 = 3x \quad \text{Let } y = 0.$$
$$0 = x \quad \text{Divide both sides by 3.}$$

The ordered pair is $(0, 0)$.

c. We replace y with -9 in the equation and solve for x.

$$y = 3x$$
$$-9 = 3x \quad \text{Let } y = -9.$$
$$-3 = x \quad \text{Divide both sides by 3.}$$

The ordered pair is $(-3, -9)$.
The completed table is shown to the right.

x	y
−1	−3
0	0
−3	−9

● **Work Practice 4**

Example 5 Complete the table for the equation
$$y = \frac{1}{2}x - 5.$$

	x	y
a.	−2	
b.	0	
c.		0

PRACTICE 5

Complete the table for the equation $y = \frac{1}{3}x - 1$.

	x	y
a.	−3	
b.	0	
c.		0

Solution:

a. Let $x = -2$.

$$y = \frac{1}{2}x - 5$$
$$y = \frac{1}{2}(-2) - 5$$
$$y = -1 - 5$$
$$y = -6$$

b. Let $x = 0$.

$$y = \frac{1}{2}x - 5$$
$$y = \frac{1}{2}(0) - 5$$
$$y = 0 - 5$$
$$y = -5$$

c. Let $y = 0$.

$$y = \frac{1}{2}x - 5$$
$$0 = \frac{1}{2}x - 5 \quad \text{Now, solve for } x.$$
$$5 = \frac{1}{2}x \quad \text{Add 5.}$$
$$10 = x \quad \text{Multiply by 2.}$$

Ordered Pairs: $(-2, -6)$ $(0, -5)$ $(10, 0)$

The completed table is

x	−2	0	10
y	−6	−5	0

Answers

4.

	x	y
a.	−3	6
b.	0	0
c.	−5	10

5.

	x	y
a.	−3	−2
b.	0	−1
c.	3	0

● **Work Practice 5**

By now, you have noticed that equations in two variables often have more than one solution. We discuss this more in the next section.

A table showing ordered pair solutions may be written vertically or horizontally, as shown in the previous example.

PRACTICE 6

A company purchased a fax machine for $400. The business manager of the company predicts that the fax machine will be used for 7 years and the value in dollars y of the machine in x years is $y = -50x + 400$. Complete the table.

x	1	2	3	4	5	6	7
y							

Example 6 A small business purchased a computer for $2000. The business predicts that the computer will be used for 5 years and the value in dollars y of the computer in x years is $y = -300x + 2000$. Complete the table.

x	0	1	2	3	4	5
y						

Solution:

To find the value of y when x is 0, we replace x with 0 in the equation. We use this same procedure to find y when x is 1 and when x is 2.

When x = 0,

$y = -300x + 2000$
$y = -300 \cdot 0 + 2000$
$y = 0 + 2000$
$y = 2000$

When x = 1,

$y = -300x + 2000$
$y = -300 \cdot 1 + 2000$
$y = -300 + 2000$
$y = 1700$

When x = 2,

$y = -300x + 2000$
$y = -300 \cdot 2 + 2000$
$y = -600 + 2000$
$y = 1400$

We have the ordered pairs (0, 2000), (1, 1700), and (2, 1400). This means that in 0 years the value of the computer is $2000, in 1 year the value of the computer is $1700, and in 2 years the value is $1400. To complete the table of values, we continue the procedure for $x = 3$, $x = 4$, and $x = 5$.

When x = 3,

$y = -300x + 2000$
$y = -300 \cdot 3 + 2000$
$y = -900 + 2000$
$y = 1100$

When x = 4,

$y = -300x + 2000$
$y = -300 \cdot 4 + 2000$
$y = -1200 + 2000$
$y = 800$

When x = 5,

$y = -300x + 2000$
$y = -300 \cdot 5 + 2000$
$y = -1500 + 2000$
$y = 500$

The completed table is shown below.

x	0	1	2	3	4	5
y	2000	1700	1400	1100	800	500

● **Work Practice 6**

The ordered pair solutions recorded in the completed table for Example 6 are another set of paired data. They are graphed next. Notice that this scatter diagram gives a visual picture of the decrease in value of the computer.

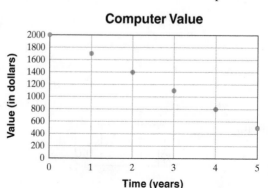

Computer Value

Answer

6.

x	1	2	3	4	5	6	7
y	350	300	250	200	150	100	50

Vocabulary and Readiness Check

Use the choices below to fill in each blank. The exercises below all have to do with the rectangular coordinate system.

origin   *x*-coordinate   *x*-axis   scatter diagram   four

quadrants   *y*-coordinate   *y*-axis   solution   one

1. The horizontal axis is called the _____ .

2. The vertical axis is called the _____ .

3. The intersection of the horizontal axis and the vertical axis is a point called the _____ .

4. The axes divide the plane into regions, called _____ . There are _____ of these regions.

5. In the ordered pair of numbers $(-2, 5)$, the number -2 is called the _____ and the number 5 is called the _____ .

6. Each ordered pair of numbers corresponds to _____ point in the plane.

7. An ordered pair is a(n) _____ of an equation in two variables if replacing the variables by the coordinates of the ordered pair results in a true statement.

8. The graph of paired data as points in a rectangular coordinate system is called a(n) _____ .

7.1 Exercise Set

FOR EXTRA HELP

MyMathLab   MathXP PRACTICE   WATCH   DOWNLOAD   READ   REVIEW

Objective A *Plot each ordered pair. State in which quadrant or on which axis each point lies. See Example 1.*

1. a. $(1, 5)$ **b.** $(-5, -2)$ **c.** $(-3, 0)$ **d.** $(0, -1)$
   e. $(2, -4)$ **f.** $\left(-1, 4\frac{1}{2}\right)$ **g.** $(3.7, 2.2)$ **h.** $\left(\frac{1}{2}, -3\right)$

2. a. $(2, 4)$ **b.** $(0, 2)$ **c.** $(-2, 1)$ **d.** $(-3, -3)$
   e. $\left(3\frac{3}{4}, 0\right)$ **f.** $(5, -4)$ **g.** $(-3.4, 4.8)$ **h.** $\left(\frac{1}{3}, -5\right)$

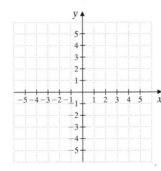
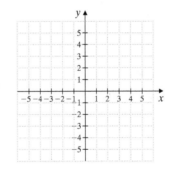

Find the x- and y-coordinates of each labeled point. See Example 1.

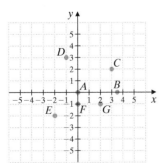

3. *A*

4. *B*

5. *C*

6. *D*

7. *E*

8. *F*

9. *G*

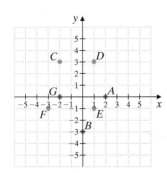

10. *A*

11. *B*

12. *C*

13. *D*

14. *E*

15. *F*

16. *G*

Objective **B** *Solve. See Example 2.*

17. The table shows the domestic box office (in billions of dollars) for the U.S. movie industry during the years shown. (*Source:* Motion Picture Association of America)

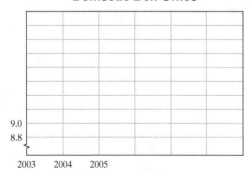

Year	Box Office (in billions of dollars)
2003	9.2
2004	9.2
2005	8.8
2006	9.1
2007	9.6
2008	9.8
2009	10.6

a. Write this paired data as a set of ordered pairs of the form (year, box office).

b. In your own words, write the meaning of the ordered pair (2006, 9.1).

c. Create a scatter diagram of the paired data. Be sure to label the axes appropriately.

Domestic Box Office

9.0

8.8

2003   2004   2005

d. What trend in the paired data does the scatter diagram show?

18. The table shows the amount of money (in billions of dollars) that Americans spent on their pets for the years shown. (*Source:* American Pet Products Manufacturers Association)

Year	Pet-Related Expenditures (in billions of dollars)
2005	36.3
2006	38.5
2007	41.2
2008	43.4

a. Write this paired data as a set of ordered pairs of the form (year, pet-related expenditures).

b. In your own words, write the meaning of the ordered pair (2007, 41.2).

c. Create a scatter diagram of the paired data. Be sure to label the axes appropriately.

Pet-Related Expenditures

35

30

2005   2006

d. What trend in the paired data does the scatter diagram show?

19. Minh, a psychology student, kept a record of how much time she spent studying for each of her 20-point psychology quizzes and her score on each quiz.

Hours Spent Studying	0.50	0.75	1.00	1.25	1.50	1.50	1.75	2.00
Quiz Score	10	12	15	16	18	19	19	20

a. Write the data as ordered pairs of the form (hours spent studying, quiz score).

Minh's Chart for Psychology

b. In your own words, write the meaning of the ordered pair (1.25, 16).

c. Create a scatter diagram of the paired data. Be sure to label the axes appropriately.

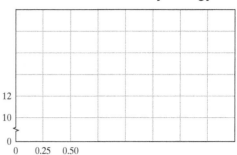

d. What might Minh conclude from the scatter diagram?

20. A local lumberyard uses quantity pricing. The table shows the price per board for different amounts of lumber purchased.

Price per Board (in dollars)	Number of Boards Purchased
8.00	1
7.50	10
6.50	25
5.00	50
2.00	100

c. Create a scatter diagram of the paired data. Be sure to label the axes appropriately.

Lumberyard Board Pricing

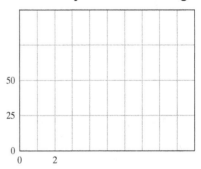

a. Write the data as ordered pairs of the form (price per board, number of boards purchased).

b. In your own words, write the meaning of the ordered pair (2.00, 100).

d. What trend in the paired data does the scatter diagram show?

Objective Ⓒ *Complete each ordered pair so that it is a solution of the given linear equation. See Example 3.*

21. $x - 4y = 4$; (, −2), (4,)

22. $x - 5y = -1$; (, −2), (4,)

23. $y = \frac{1}{4}x - 3$; (−8,), (, 1)

24. $y = \frac{1}{5}x - 2$; (−10,), (, 1)

Complete the table of ordered pairs for each linear equation. See Examples 4 and 5.

25. $y = -7x$

x	y
0	
−1	
	2

26. $y = -9x$

x	y
	0
−3	
	2

27. $x = -y + 2$

x	y
0	
	0
−3	

28. $x = -y + 4$

x	y
	0
0	
	-3

29. $y = \dfrac{1}{2}x$

x	y
0	
-6	
	1

30. $y = \dfrac{1}{3}x$

x	y
0	
-6	
	1

31. $x + 3y = 6$

x	y
0	
	0
	1

32. $2x + y = 4$

x	y
0	
	0
	2

33. $y = 2x - 12$

x	y
0	
	-2
3	

34. $y = 5x + 10$

x	y
	0
	5
0	

35. $2x + 7y = 5$

x	y
0	
	0
	1

36. $x - 6y = 3$

x	y
0	
1	
	-1

Objectives Ⓐ Ⓑ Ⓒ **Mixed Practice** *Complete the table of ordered pairs for each equation. Then plot the ordered pair solutions. See Examples 1 through 5.*

37. $x = -5y$

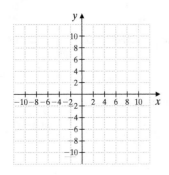

x	y
	0
	1
10	

38. $y = -3x$

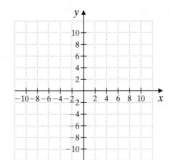

x	y
0	
-2	
	9

39. $y = \dfrac{1}{3}x + 2$

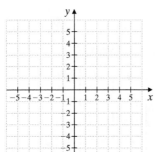

x	y
0	
-3	
	0

40. $y = \dfrac{1}{2}x + 3$

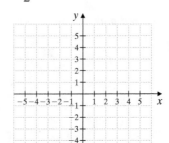

x	y
0	
-4	
	0

Solve. See Example 6.

41. The cost in dollars y of producing x computer desks is given by $y = 80x + 5000$.

  a. Complete the table.

x	100	200	300
y			

  b. Find the number of computer desks that can be produced for $8600. (*Hint:* Find x when $y = 8600$.)

42. The hourly wage y of an employee at a certain production company is given by $y = 0.25x + 9$ where x is the number of units produced by the employee in an hour.

  a. Complete the table.

x	0	1	5	10
y				

  b. Find the number of units that an employee must produce each hour to earn an hourly wage of $12.25. (*Hint:* Find x when $y = 12.25$.)

43. The average annual cinema admission price y (in dollars) from 2000 through 2008 is given by $y = 0.2x + 5.39$. In this equation, x represents the number of years after 2000. (*Source:* Motion Picture Association of America)

  a. Complete the table.

x	1	3	5
y			

  b. Find the year in which the average cinema admission price was approximately $6.40. (*Hint:* Find x when $y = 6.40$ and round to the nearest whole number.)

  c. Use the given equation to predict when the cinema admission price might be $8.00. (Use the hint for part b.)

44. The amount y of land occupied by farms in the United States (in millions of acres) from 1997 through 2007 is given by $y = -4x + 967$. In the equation, x represents the number of years after 1997. (*Source:* National Agricultural Statistics Service)

  a. Complete the table.

x	4	7	10
y			

  b. Find the year in which there were approximately 930 million acres of land occupied by farms. (*Hint:* Find x when $y = 930$ and round to the nearest whole number.)

  c. Use the given equation to predict when the land occupied by farms might be 900 million acres. (Use the hint for part b.)

Review

Solve each equation for y. See Section 6.5.

45. $x + y = 5$

46. $x - y = 3$

47. $2x + 4y = 5$

48. $5x + 2y = 7$

49. $10x = -5y$

50. $4y = -8x$

Concept Extensions

Answer each exercise with true or false.

51. Point $(-1, 5)$ lies in quadrant IV.

52. Point $(3, 0)$ lies on the y-axis.

53. For the point $\left(-\dfrac{1}{2}, 1.5\right)$, the first value, $-\dfrac{1}{2}$, is the x-coordinate and the second value, 1.5, is the y-coordinate.

54. The ordered pair $\left(2, \dfrac{2}{3}\right)$ is a solution of $2x - 3y = 6$.

For Exercises 55 through 59, fill in each blank with "0," "positive," or "negative." For Exercises 60 and 61, fill in each blank with "x" or "y."

	Point	Location
55.	(_____, _____)	quadrant III
56.	(_____, _____)	quadrant I
57.	(_____, _____)	quadrant IV
58.	(_____, _____)	quadrant II
59.	(_____, _____)	origin
60.	(number, 0)	__-axis
61.	(0, number)	__-axis

62. Give an example of an ordered pair whose location is in (or on)

    a. quadrant I   **b.** quadrant II   **c.** quadrant III   **d.** quadrant IV   **e.** *x*-axis   **f.** *y*-axis

Solve. See the Concept Checks in this section.

63. Is the graph of $(3, 0)$ in the same location as the graph of $(0, 3)$? Explain why or why not.

64. Give the coordinates of a point such that if the coordinates are reversed, the location is the same.

65. In general, what points can have coordinates reversed and still have the same location?

66. In your own words, describe how to plot or graph an ordered pair of numbers.

67. Discuss any similarities in the graphs of the ordered pair solutions for Exercises 37–40.

68. Discuss any differences in the graphs of the ordered pair solutions for Exercises 37–40.

Write an ordered pair for each point described.

69. Point *C* is four units to the right of the *y*-axis and seven units below the *x*-axis.

70. Point *D* is three units to the left of the origin.

71. Find the perimeter of the rectangle whose vertices are the points with coordinates $(-1, 5), (3, 5), (3, -4)$, and $(-1, -4)$.

72. Find the area of the rectangle whose vertices are the points with coordinates $(5, 2), (5, -6), (0, -6)$, and $(0, 2)$.

The scatter diagram below shows Target's annual revenues. The horizontal axis represents the number of years after 2003.

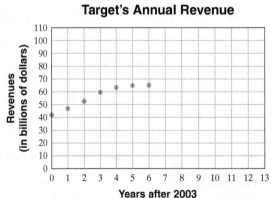

Target's Annual Revenue

73. Estimate the annual revenues for years 1, 2, 3, and 4.

74. Use a straightedge or ruler and this scatter diagram to predict Target's revenue in the year 2015.

7.2 GRAPHING LINEAR EQUATIONS

Objective

Ⓐ Graph a Linear Equation by Finding and Plotting Ordered Pair Solutions.

In the previous section, we found that equations in two variables may have more than one solution. For example, both $(2, 2)$ and $(0, 4)$ are solutions of the equation $x + y = 4$. In fact, this equation has an infinite number of solutions. Other solutions include $(-2, 6)$, $(4, 0)$, and $(6, -2)$. Notice the pattern that appears in the graph of these solutions.

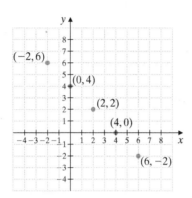

These solutions all appear to lie on the same line, as seen in the second graph. It can be shown that every ordered pair solution of the equation corresponds to a point on this line, and every point on this line corresponds to an ordered pair solution. Thus, we say that this line is the **graph of the equation** $x + y = 4$. Notice that we can show only a part of a line on a graph. The arrowheads on each end of the line below remind us that the line actually extends indefinitely in both directions.

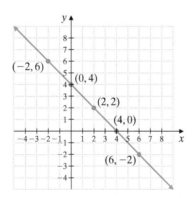

The equation $x + y = 4$ is called a *linear equation in two variables* and *the graph of every linear equation in two variables is a straight line.*

Linear Equation in Two Variables

A **linear equation in two variables** is an equation that can be written in the form

$$Ax + By = C$$

where A, B, and C are real numbers and A and B are not both 0. This form is called **standard form. The graph of a linear equation in two variables is a straight line.**

A linear equation in two variables may be written in many forms. Standard form, $Ax + By = C$, is just one of many of these forms.

Following are examples of linear equations in two variables.

$$2x + y = 8 \qquad -2x = 7y \qquad y = \frac{1}{3}x + 2 \qquad y = 7$$

(Standard Form)

Objective Ⓐ Graphing Linear Equations

From geometry, we know that a straight line is determined by just two points. Thus, to graph a linear equation in two variables, we need to find just two of its infinitely many solutions. Once we do so, we plot the solution points and draw the line connecting the points. Usually, we find a third solution as well, as a check.

PRACTICE 1

Graph the linear equation $x + 3y = 6$.

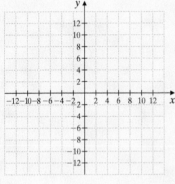

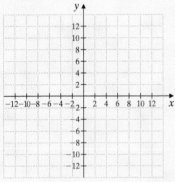

> **Helpful Hint**
>
> All three points should fall on the same straight line. If not, check your ordered pair solutions for a mistake.

Answer

1.

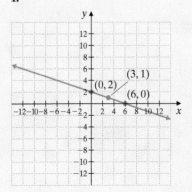

Example 1 Graph the linear equation $2x + y = 5$.

Solution: To graph this equation, we find three ordered pair solutions of $2x + y = 5$. To do this, we choose a value for one variable, x or y, and solve for the other variable. For example, if we let $x = 1$, then $2x + y = 5$ becomes

$$2x + y = 5$$
$$2(1) + y = 5 \quad \text{Replace } x \text{ with 1.}$$
$$2 + y = 5 \quad \text{Multiply.}$$
$$y = 3 \quad \text{Subtract 2 from both sides.}$$

Since $y = 3$ when $x = 1$, the ordered pair $(1, 3)$ is a solution of $2x + y = 5$. Next, we let $x = 0$.

$$2x + y = 5$$
$$2(0) + y = 5 \quad \text{Replace } x \text{ with 0.}$$
$$0 + y = 5$$
$$y = 5$$

The ordered pair $(0, 5)$ is a second solution.

The two solutions found so far allow us to draw the straight line that is the graph of all solutions of $2x + y = 5$. However, we will find a third ordered pair as a check. Let $y = -1$.

$$2x + y = 5$$
$$2x + (-1) = 5 \quad \text{Replace } y \text{ with } -1.$$
$$2x - 1 = 5$$
$$2x = 6 \quad \text{Add 1 to both sides.}$$
$$x = 3 \quad \text{Divide both sides by 2.}$$

The third solution is $(3, -1)$. These three ordered pair solutions are listed in the table and plotted on the coordinate plane. The graph of $2x + y = 5$ is the line through the three points.

x	y
1	3
0	5
3	−1

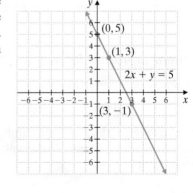

● **Work Practice 1**

Example 2 Graph the linear equation $-5x + 3y = 15$.

Solution: We find three ordered pair solutions of $-5x + 3y = 15$.

Let $x = 0$.	**Let $y = 0$.**	**Let $x = -2$.**
$-5x + 3y = 15$	$-5x + 3y = 15$	$-5x + 3y = 15$
$-5 \cdot 0 + 3y = 15$	$-5x + 3 \cdot 0 = 15$	$-5 \cdot -2 + 3y = 15$
$0 + 3y = 15$	$-5x + 0 = 15$	$10 + 3y = 15$
$3y = 15$	$-5x = 15$	$3y = 5$
$y = 5$	$x = -3$	$y = \dfrac{5}{3}$ or $1\dfrac{2}{3}$

The ordered pairs are $(0, 5)$, $(-3, 0)$, and $\left(-2, 1\dfrac{2}{3}\right)$. The graph of $-5x + 3y = 15$ is the line through the three points.

x	y
0	5
−3	0
−2	$1\dfrac{2}{3}$

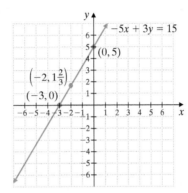

● **Work Practice 2**

Example 3 Graph the linear equation $y = 3x$.

Solution: We find three ordered pair solutions. Since this equation is solved for y, we'll choose three x-values.

If $x = 2$, $y = 3 \cdot 2 = 6$.
If $x = 0$, $y = 3 \cdot 0 = 0$.
If $x = -1$, $y = 3 \cdot -1 = -3$.

Next, we plot the ordered pair solutions and draw a line through the plotted points. The line is the graph of $y = 3x$.

Think about the following for a moment: A line is made up of an infinite number of points. Every point on the line defined by $y = 3x$ represents an ordered pair solution of the equation and every ordered pair solution is a point on this line.

x	y
2	6
0	0
−1	−3

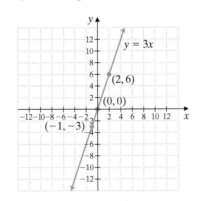

● **Work Practice 3**

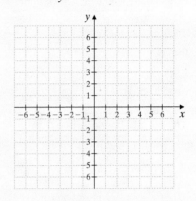
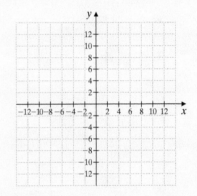
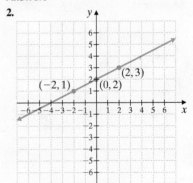
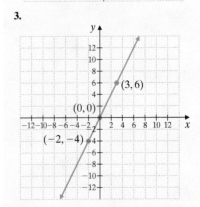

PRACTICE 4

Graph the linear equation
$y = -\frac{1}{2}x + 4$.

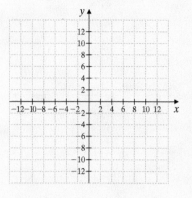

PRACTICE 5

Graph the linear equation
$x = 3$.

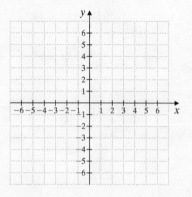

Answers

4.

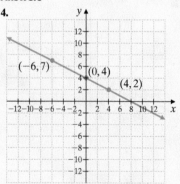

5.

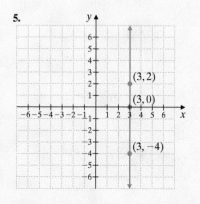

Helpful Hint

When graphing a linear equation in two variables, if it is

- solved for y, it may be easier to find ordered pair solutions by choosing x-values. If it is
- solved for x, it may be easier to find ordered pair solutions by choosing y-values.

Example 4 Graph the linear equation $y = -\frac{1}{3}x + 2$.

Solution: We find three ordered pair solutions, plot the solutions, and draw a line through the plotted solutions. To avoid fractions, we'll choose x-values that are multiples of 3 to substitute into the equation.

If $x = 6$, then $y = -\frac{1}{3} \cdot 6 + 2 = -2 + 2 = 0$

If $x = 0$, then $y = -\frac{1}{3} \cdot 0 + 2 = 0 + 2 = 2$

If $x = -3$, then $y = -\frac{1}{3} \cdot -3 + 2 = 1 + 2 = 3$

x	y
6	0
0	2
−3	3

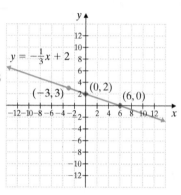

● **Work Practice 4**

Let's take a moment and compare the graphs in Examples 3 and 4. The graph of $y = 3x$ tilts upward (as we follow the line from left to right) and the graph of $y = -\frac{1}{3}x + 2$ tilts downward (as we follow the line from left to right). We will learn more about the tilt, or slope, of a line in Section 7.4.

Example 5 Graph the linear equation $y = -2$.

Solution: The equation $y = -2$ can be written in standard form as $0x + y = -2$. No matter what value we replace x with, y is always -2.

x	y
0	−2
3	−2
−2	−2

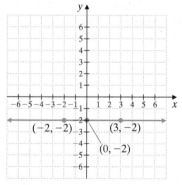

Notice that the graph of $y = -2$ is a horizontal line.

● **Work Practice 5**

Linear equations are often used to model real data, as seen in the next example.

Example 6 Estimating the Number of Registered Nurses

One of the occupations expected to have the most growth in the next few years is registered nurse. The number of people y (in thousands) employed as registered nurses in the United States can be estimated by the linear equation $y = 46.7x + 2279$, where x is the number of years after the year 2003. (*Source:* Based on data from the Bureau of Labor Statistics)

a. Graph the equation.

b. Use the graph to predict the number of registered nurses in the year 2014.

Solution:

a. To graph $y = 46.7x + 2279$, choose x-values and substitute in the equation.

If $x = 0$, then $y = 46.7(0) + 2279 = 2279$.

If $x = 2$, then $y = 46.7(2) + 2279 = 2372.4$.

If $x = 5$, then $y = 46.7(5) + 2279 = 2512.5$.

x	y
0	2279
2	2372.4
5	2512.5

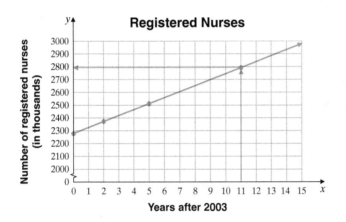

b. To use the graph to *predict* the number of registered nurses in the year 2014, we need to find the y-coordinate that corresponds to $x = 11$. (11 years after 2003 is the year 2014.) To do so, find 11 on the x-axis. Move vertically upward to the graphed line and then horizontally to the left. We approximate the number on the y-axis to be 2800. Thus, in the year 2014, we predict that there will be 2800 thousand registered nurses. (The actual value, using 11 for x, is 2792.7.)

⬤ **Work Practice 6**

Helpful Hint   From Example 5, we learned that equations such as $y = -2$ are linear equations since $y = -2$ can be written as $0x + y = -2$.

Helpful Hint

Make sure you understand that models are mathematical approximations of the data for the known years. (For example, see the model in Example 6.) Any number of unknown factors can affect future years, so be cautious when using models to make predictions.

Answer
6. 2840 thousand

Calculator Explorations   Graphing

In this section, we begin an optional study of graphing calculators and graphing software packages for computers. These graphers use the same point plotting technique that was introduced in this section. The advantage of this graphing technology is, of course, that graphing calculators and computers can find and plot ordered pair solutions much faster than we can. Note, however, that the features described in these boxes may not be available on all graphing calculators.

The rectangular screen where a portion of the rectangular coordinate system is displayed is called a **window.** We call it a **standard window** for graphing when both the x- and y-axes show coordinates between -10 and 10. This information is often displayed in the window menu on a graphing calculator as follows.

Xmin = -10

Xmax = 10

Xscl = 1 The scale on the x-axis is one unit per tick mark.

Ymin = -10

Ymax = 10

Yscl = 1 The scale on the y-axis is one unit per tick mark.

To use a graphing calculator to graph the equation $y = 2x + 3$, press the $\boxed{Y=}$ key and enter the keystrokes $\boxed{2}$ $\boxed{x}$ $\boxed{+}$ $\boxed{3}$. The top row should now read $Y_1 = 2x + 3$. Next press the $\boxed{\text{GRAPH}}$ key, and the display should look like this:

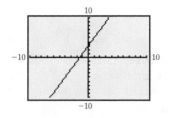

Graph the following linear equations. (Unless otherwise stated, use a standard window when graphing.)

1. $y = -3x + 7$

2. $y = -x + 5$

3. $y = 2.5x - 7.9$

4. $y = -1.3x + 5.2$

5. $y = -\dfrac{3}{10}x + \dfrac{32}{5}$

6. $y = \dfrac{2}{9}x - \dfrac{22}{3}$

Objective Ⓐ *For each equation, find three ordered pair solutions by completing the table. Then use the ordered pairs to graph the equation. See Examples 1 through 5.*

1. $x - y = 6$

x	y
	0
4	
	-1

2. $x - y = 4$

x	y
0	
	2
-1	

3. $y = -4x$

x	y
1	
0	
-1	

4. $y = -5x$

x	y
1	
0	
-1	

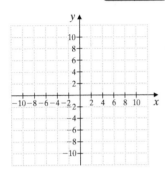 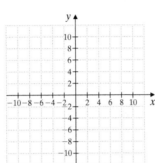 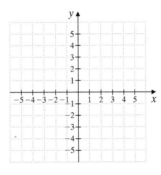 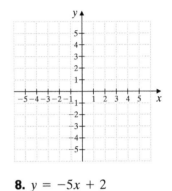

5. $y = \frac{1}{3}x$

x	y
0	
6	
-3	

6. $y = \frac{1}{2}x$

x	y
0	
-4	
2	

7. $y = -4x + 3$

x	y
0	
1	
2	

8. $y = -5x + 2$

x	y
0	
1	
2	

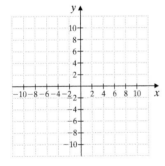 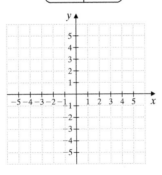 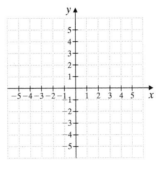 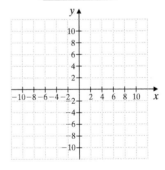

Graph each linear equation. See Examples 1 through 5.

9. $x + y = 1$

10. $x + y = 7$

11. $x - y = -2$

12. $-x + y = 6$

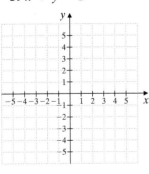 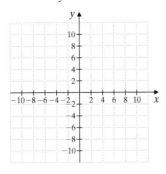 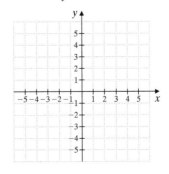 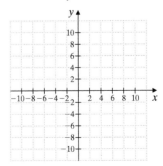

13. $x - 2y = 6$

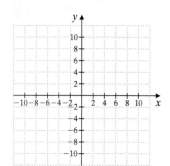

14. $-x + 5y = 5$

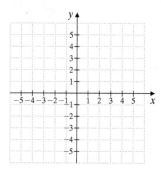

15. $y = 6x + 3$

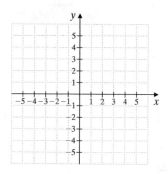

16. $y = -2x + 7$

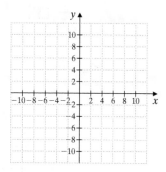

17. $x = -4$

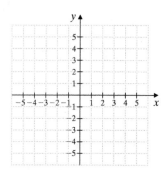

18. $y = 5$

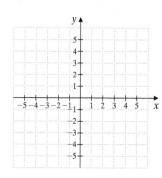

19. $y = 3$

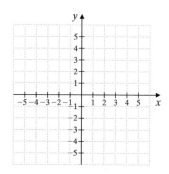

20. $x = -1$

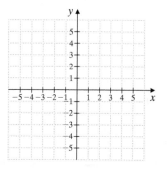

21. $y = x$

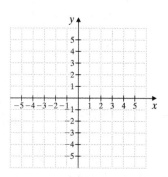

22. $y = -x$

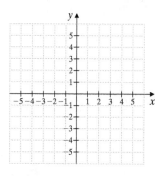

23. $x = -3y$

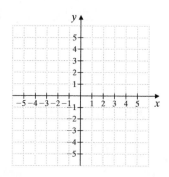

24. $x = 4y$

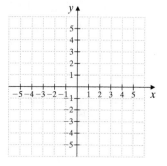

25. $x + 3y = 9$

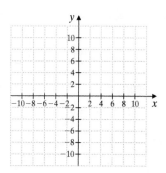

26. $2x + y = 2$

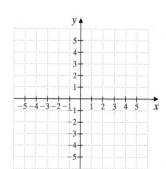

27. $y = \dfrac{1}{2}x + 2$

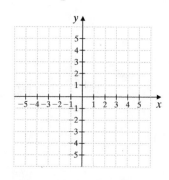

28. $y = \dfrac{1}{4}x + 3$

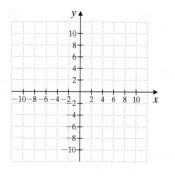

29. $3x - 2y = 12$

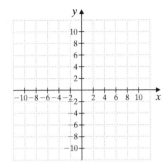

30. $2x - 7y = 14$

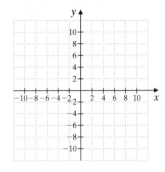

31. $y = -3.5x + 4$

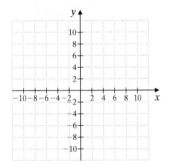

32. $y = -1.5x - 3$

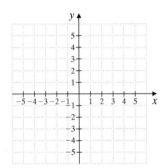

Solve. See Example 6.

33. One American rite of passage is a driver's license. The number of people y (in millions) who have a driver's license can be estimated by the linear equation $y = 2.2x + 145$, where x is the number of years after 1990. (*Source:* Based on data from the Federal Highway Administration)

   a. Graph the linear equation. The break in the vertical axis means that the numbers between 0 and 100 have been skipped.

   b. Does the point (20, 189) lie on the line? If so, what does this ordered pair mean?

34. College is getting more expensive every year. The average cost for tuition and fees at a public two-year college y from 1978 through 2009 can be approximated by the linear equation $y = 45x + 1089$, where x is the number of years after 1978. (*Source:* The College Board: Trends in College Pricing 2008)

   a. Graph the linear equation. The break in the vertical axis means that the numbers between 0 and 1000 have been skipped.

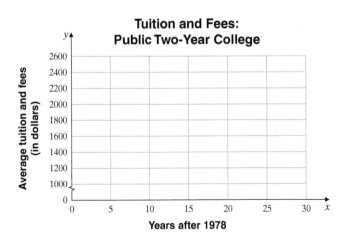

   b. Does the point (15, 1764) lie on the line? If so, what does this ordered pair mean?

35. The percent of U.S. households y that have at least one computer can be approximated by the linear equation $y = 5.6x + 38.5$, where x is the number of years since 1998. (*Source: Statistical Abstract of the United States*)

a. Graph the linear equation.

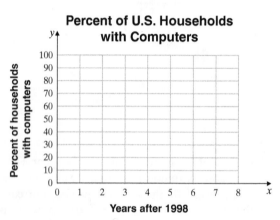

b. Complete the ordered pair (5,).
c. Write a sentence explaining the meaning of the ordered pair found in part b.

36. The restaurant industry is still busier than ever. The yearly revenue for restaurants in the United States can be estimated by $y = 13.4x + 6.2$, where x is the number of years after 1970 and y is the revenue in billions of dollars. (*Source:* National Restaurant Association)

a. Graph the linear equation.

b. Complete the ordered pair (25,).
c. Write a sentence explaining the meaning of the ordered pair found in part b.

Review

37. The coordinates of three vertices of a rectangle are $(-2, 5)$, $(4, 5)$, and $(-2, -1)$. Find the coordinates of the fourth vertex. See Section 7.1.

38. The coordinates of two vertices of a square are $(-3, -1)$ and $(2, -1)$. Find the coordinates of two pairs of points possible for the third and fourth vertices. See Section 7.1.

Complete each table. See Section 7.1.

39. $x - y = -3$

x	y
0	
	0

40. $y - x = 5$

x	y
0	
	0

41. $y = 2x$

x	y
0	
	0

42. $x = -3y$

x	y
0	
	0

Concept Extensions

Graph each pair of linear equations on the same set of axes. Discuss how the graphs are similar and how they are different.

43. $y = 5x$

$y = 5x + 4$

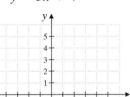

44. $y = 2x$

$y = 2x + 5$

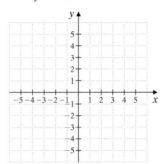

45. $y = -2x$

$y = -2x - 3$

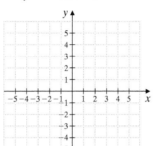

46. $y = x$

$y = x - 7$

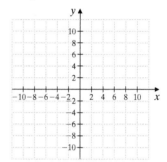

47. Graph the nonlinear equation $y = x^2$ by completing the table shown. Plot the ordered pairs and connect them with a smooth curve. This curve is "U" shaped.

x	y
0	
1	
−1	
2	
−2	

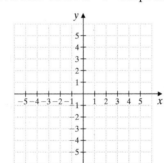

48. Graph the nonlinear equation $y = |x|$ by completing the table shown. Plot the ordered pairs and connect them. This curve is "V" shaped.

x	y
0	
1	
−1	
2	
−2	

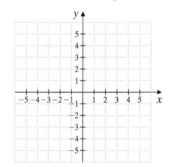

49. The perimeter of the trapezoid below is 22 centimeters. Write a linear equation in two variables for the perimeter. Find y if x is 3 centimeters.

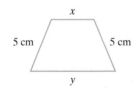

50. The perimeter of the rectangle below is 50 miles. Write a linear equation in two variables for the perimeter. Use this equation to find x when y is 20 miles.

51. If (a, b) is an ordered pair solution of $x + y = 5$, is (b, a) also a solution? Explain why or why not.

52. If (a, b) is an ordered pair solution of $x - y = 5$, is (b, a) also a solution? Explain why or why not.

Objectives

Ⓐ Identify Intercepts of a Graph.

Ⓑ Graph a Linear Equation by Finding and Plotting Intercept Points.

Ⓒ Identify and Graph Vertical and Horizontal Lines.

7.3 INTERCEPTS

Objective Ⓐ Identifying Intercepts

The graph of $y = 4x - 8$ is shown below. Notice that this graph crosses the y-axis at the point $(0, -8)$. This point is called the **y-intercept.** Likewise the graph crosses the x-axis at $(2, 0)$. This point is called the **x-intercept.**

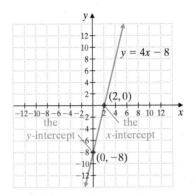

The intercepts are $(2, 0)$ and $(0, -8)$.

Helpful Hint

If a graph crosses the x-axis at $(2, 0)$ and the y-axis at $(0, -8)$, then

$$\underbrace{(2, 0)}_{\uparrow} \qquad \underbrace{(0, -8)}_{\uparrow}$$
$$x\text{-intercept} \qquad y\text{-intercept}$$

Notice that for the x-intercept, the y-value is 0 and for the y-intercept, the x-value is 0.

Note: Sometimes in mathematics, you may see just the number -8 stated as the y-intercept, and 2 stated as the x-intercept.

PRACTICE 1

Identify the x- and y-intercepts.

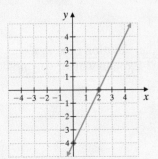

Answer
1. x-intercept: $(2, 0)$; y-intercept: $(0, -4)$

598

Examples Identify the x- and y-intercepts.

1.

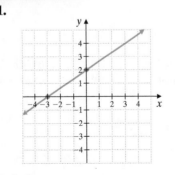

Solution:

x-intercept: $(-3, 0)$

y-intercept: $(0, 2)$

2.

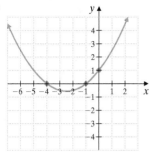

Solution:

 x-intercepts: $(-4, 0)$, $(-1, 0)$

 y-intercept: $(0, 1)$

3.

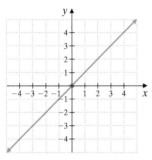

Solution:

 x-intercept: $(0, 0)$

 y-intercept: $(0, 0)$

Here, the *x*- and *y*-intercepts happen to be the same point.

● **Work Practice 1–3**

Objective Ⓑ Finding and Plotting Intercepts

Given an equation of a line, we can usually find intercepts easily since one coordinate is 0.

　To find the *x*-intercept of a line from its equation, let $y = 0$, since a point on the *x*-axis has a *y*-coordinate of 0. To find the *y*-intercept of a line from its equation, let $x = 0$, since a point on the *y*-axis has an *x*-coordinate of 0.

> ### Finding x- and y-Intercepts
>
> To find the *x*-intercept, let $y = 0$ and solve for *x*.
> To find the *y*-intercept, let $x = 0$ and solve for *y*.

Example 4 Graph $x - 3y = 6$ by finding and plotting its intercepts.

Solution: We let $y = 0$ to find the *x*-intercept and $x = 0$ to find the *y*-intercept.

Let $y = 0$.	Let $x = 0$.
$x - 3y = 6$	$x - 3y = 6$
$x - 3(0) = 6$	$0 - 3y = 6$
$x - 0 = 6$	$-3y = 6$
$x = 6$	$y = -2$

The *x*-intercept is $(6, 0)$ and the *y*-intercept is $(0, -2)$. We find a third ordered pair solution to check our work. If we let $y = -1$, then $x = 3$. We plot the points $(6, 0)$,

Continued on next page

Identify the *x*- and *y*-intercepts.

2.

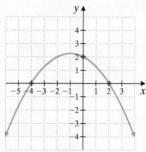

3.

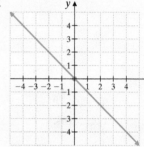

> ### Helpful Hint
> Notice that any time $(0, 0)$ is a point of a graph, then it is an *x*-intercept and a *y*-intercept. Why? It is the *only* point that lies on both axes.

PRACTICE 4

Graph $2x - y = 4$ by finding and plotting its intercepts.

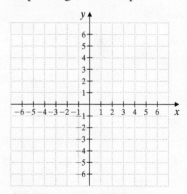

Answers

2. *x*-intercepts: $(-4, 0)$ $(2, 0)$; *y*-intercept: $(0, 2)$

3. *x*-intercept and *y*-intercept: $(0, 0)$

4. See page 610.

$(0, -2)$, and $(3, -1)$. The graph of $x - 3y = 6$ is the line drawn through these points as shown.

x	y
6	0
0	−2
3	−1

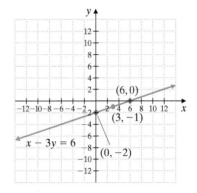

● **Work Practice 4**

PRACTICE 5

Graph $y = 3x$ by finding and plotting its intercepts.

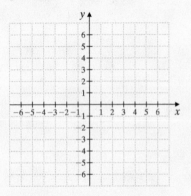

Example 5 Graph $x = -2y$ by finding and plotting its intercepts.

Solution: We let $y = 0$ to find the x-intercept and $x = 0$ to find the y-intercept.

Let $y = 0$.   Let $x = 0$.
$$x = -2y \qquad x = -2y$$
$$x = -2(0) \qquad 0 = -2y$$
$$x = 0 \qquad 0 = y$$

Both the x-intercept and y-intercept are $(0, 0)$. In other words, when $x = 0$, then $y = 0$, which gives the ordered pair $(0, 0)$. Also, when $y = 0$, then $x = 0$, which gives the same ordered pair, $(0, 0)$. This happens when the graph passes through the origin. Since two points are needed to determine a line, we must find at least one more ordered pair that satisfies $x = -2y$. Since the equation is solved for x, we choose y-values so that there is no need to solve to find the corresponding x-value. We let $y = -1$ to find a second ordered pair solution and let $y = 1$ as a check point.

Let $y = -1$.
$$x = -2(-1)$$
$$x = 2 \qquad \text{Multiply.}$$
Let $y = 1$.
$$x = -2(1)$$
$$x = -2 \qquad \text{Multiply.}$$

The ordered pairs are $(0, 0)$, $(2, -1)$, and $(-2, 1)$. We plot these points to graph $x = -2y$.

Answers

4.

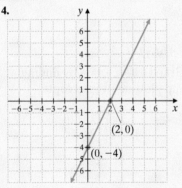

5.

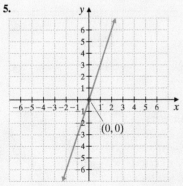

x	y
0	0
2	−1
−2	1

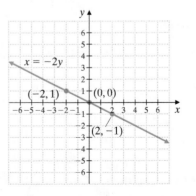

● **Work Practice 5**

Objective ⓒ Graphing Vertical and Horizontal Lines

The equation $x = 2$ is a linear equation in two variables because it can be written in the form $x + 0y = 2$. The graph of this equation is a vertical line, as shown in the next example.

Example 6 Graph: $x = 2$

Solution: The equation $x = 2$ can be written as $x + 0y = 2$. For any y-value chosen, notice that x is 2. No other value for x satisfies $x + 0y = 2$. Any ordered pair whose x-coordinate is 2 is a solution of $x + 0y = 2$. We will use the ordered pair solutions $(2, 3)$, $(2, 0)$, and $(2, -3)$ to graph $x = 2$.

x	y
2	3
2	0
2	-3

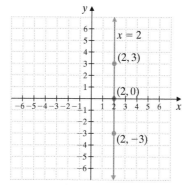

The graph is a vertical line with x-intercept 2. Note that this graph has no y-intercept because x is never 0.

● Work Practice 6

In general, we have the following.

Vertical Lines

The graph of $x = c$, where c is a real number, is a **vertical line** with x-intercept $(c, 0)$.

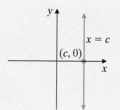

Example 7 Graph: $y = -3$

Solution: The equation $y = -3$ can be written as $0x + y = -3$. For any x-value chosen, y is -3. If we choose 4, 1, and -2 as x-values, the ordered pair solutions are $(4, -3)$, $(1, -3)$, and $(-2, -3)$. We use these ordered pairs to graph $y = -3$. The graph is a horizontal line with y-intercept -3 and no x-intercept.

x	y
4	-3
1	-3
-2	-3

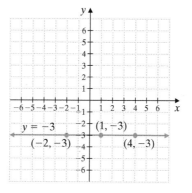

● Work Practice 7

PRACTICE 6

Graph: $x = -3$

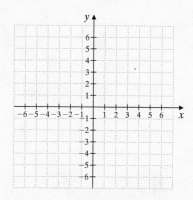

PRACTICE 7

Graph: $y = 4$

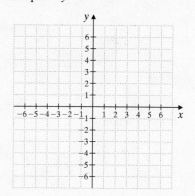

Answers

6.

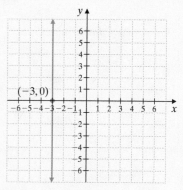

7. See page 612.

In general, we have the following.

Answer

7.

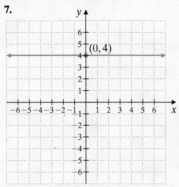

Horizontal Lines

The graph of $y = c$, where c is a real number, is a **horizontal line** with y-intercept $(0, c)$.

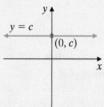

Calculator Explorations   Graphing

You may have noticed that to use the $\boxed{Y=}$ key on a graphing calculator to graph an equation, the equation must be solved for y. For example, to graph $2x + 3y = 7$, we solve this equation for y.

$$2x + 3y = 7$$

$$3y = -2x + 7 \qquad \text{Subtract } 2x \text{ from both sides.}$$

$$\frac{3y}{3} = -\frac{2x}{3} + \frac{7}{3} \qquad \text{Divide both sides by 3.}$$

$$y = -\frac{2}{3}x + \frac{7}{3} \qquad \text{Simplify.}$$

To graph $2x + 3y = 7$ or $y = -\frac{2}{3}x + \frac{7}{3}$, press the $\boxed{Y=}$ key and enter

$$Y_1 = -\frac{2}{3}x + \frac{7}{3}$$

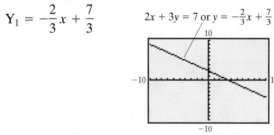

Graph each linear equation.

1. $x = 3.78y$

2. $-2.61y = x$

3. $3x + 7y = 21$

4. $-4x + 6y = 12$

5. $-2.2x + 6.8y = 15.5$

6. $5.9x - 0.8y = -10.4$

Vocabulary and Readiness Check

Use the choices below to fill in each blank. Some choices may be used more than once. Exercises 1 and 2 come from Section 7.2.

x	vertical	x-intercept	linear
y	horizontal	y-intercept	standard

1. An equation that can be written in the form $Ax + By = C$ is called a(n) _____ equation in two variables.
2. The form $Ax + By = C$ is called _____ form.
3. The graph of the equation $y = -1$ is a(n) _____ line.
4. The graph of the equation $x = 5$ is a(n) _____ line.
5. A point where a graph crosses the y-axis is called a(n) _____.
6. A point where a graph crosses the x-axis is called a(n) _____.
7. Given an equation of a line, to find the x-intercept (if there is one), let _____ = 0 and solve for _____.
8. Given an equation of a line, to find the y-intercept (if there is one), let _____ = 0 and solve for _____.

Answer the following true or false.

9. All lines have an x-intercept *and* a y-intercept.
10. The graph of $y = 4x$ contains the point $(0, 0)$.
11. The graph of $x + y = 5$ has an x-intercept of $(5, 0)$ and a y-intercept of $(0, 5)$.
12. The graph of $y = 5x$ contains the point $(5, 1)$.

7.3 Exercise Set

Objective Ⓐ *Identify the intercepts. See Examples 1 through 3.*

1.
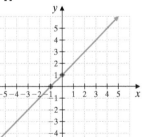

2.
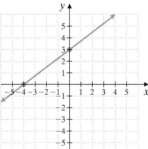

3.
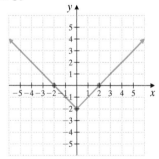

4.
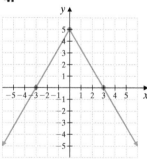

5.
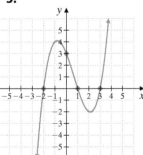

6.
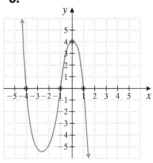

7.
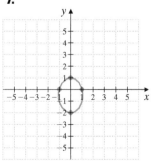

8.
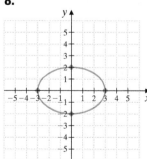

Objective Ⓑ *Graph each linear equation by finding and plotting its intercepts. See Examples 4 and 5.*

9. $x - y = 3$

10. $x - y = -4$

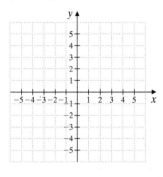

11. $x = 5y$

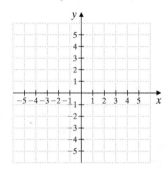

12. $x = 2y$

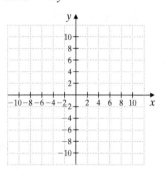

13. $-x + 2y = 6$

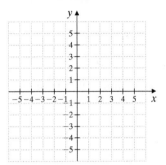

14. $x - 2y = -8$

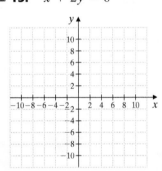

15. $2x - 4y = 8$

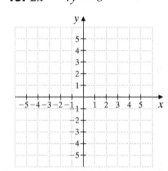

16. $2x + 3y = 6$

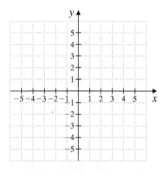

17. $y = 2x$

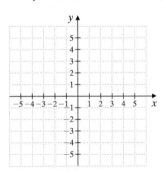

18. $y = -2x$

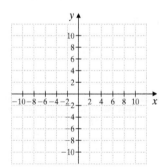

19. $y = 3x + 6$

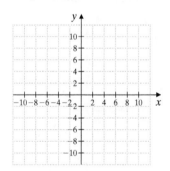

20. $y = 2x + 10$

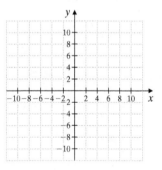

Objective Ⓒ *Graph each linear equation. See Examples 6 and 7.*

21. $x = -1$

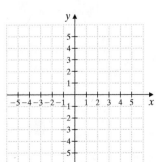

22. $y = 5$

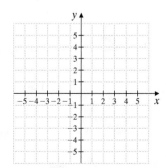

23. $y = 0$

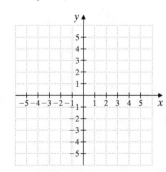

24. $x = 0$

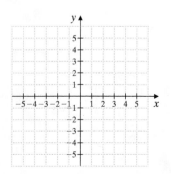

25. $y + 7 = 0$

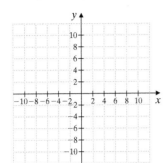

26. $x - 2 = 0$

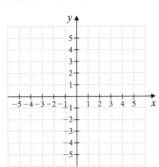

27. $x + 3 = 0$

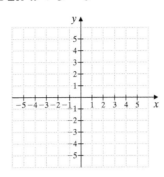

28. $y - 6 = 0$

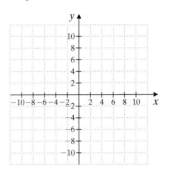

Objectives **B** **C** **Mixed Practice** *Graph each linear equation. See Examples 4 through 7.*

29. $x = y$

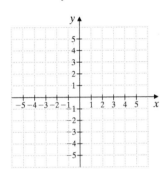

30. $x = -y$

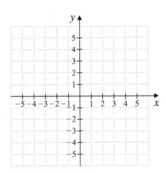

31. $x + 8y = 8$

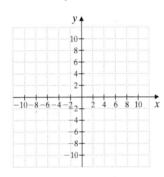

32. $x + 3y = 9$

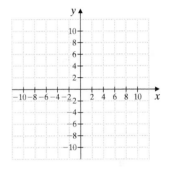

33. $5 = 6x - y$

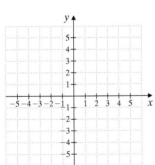

34. $4 = x - 3y$

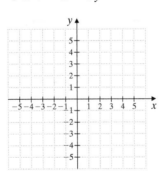

35. $-x + 10y = 11$

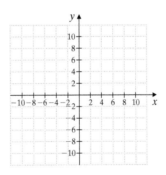

36. $-x + 9y = 10$

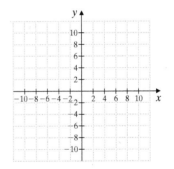

37. $x = -4\dfrac{1}{2}$

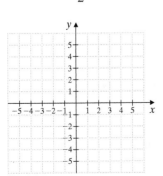

38. $x = -1\dfrac{3}{4}$

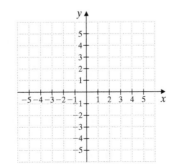

39. $y = 3\dfrac{1}{4}$

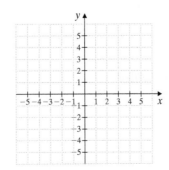

40. $y = 2\dfrac{1}{2}$

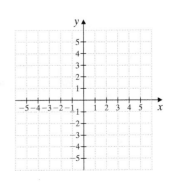

41. $y = -\dfrac{2}{3}x + 1$

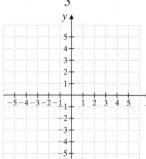

42. $y = -\dfrac{3}{5}x + 3$

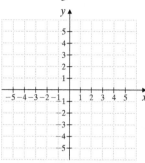

43. $4x - 6y + 2 = 0$

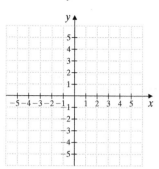

44. $9x - 6y + 3 = 0$

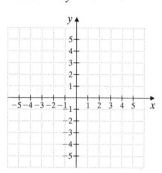

Review

Simplify. See Sections 5.3, 5.5, and 5.6.

45. $\dfrac{-6 - 3}{2 - 8}$

46. $\dfrac{4 - 5}{-1 - 0}$

47. $\dfrac{-8 - (-2)}{-3 - (-2)}$

48. $\dfrac{12 - 3}{10 - 9}$

49. $\dfrac{0 - 6}{5 - 0}$

50. $\dfrac{2 - 2}{3 - 5}$

Concept Extensions

Match each equation with its graph.

51. $y = 3$

a.

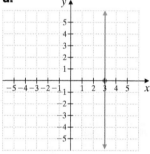

52. $y = 2x + 2$

b.

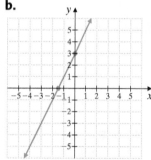

53. $x = 3$

c.

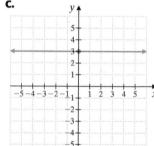

54. $y = 2x + 3$

d.

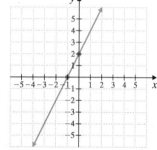

55. What is the greatest number of x- and y-intercepts that a line can have?

56. What is the smallest number of x- and y-intercepts that a line can have?

57. What is the smallest number of x- and y-intercepts that a circle can have?

58. What is the greatest number of x- and y-intercepts that a circle can have?

59. Discuss whether a vertical line ever has a y-intercept.

60. Discuss whether a horizontal line ever has an x-intercept.

The production supervisor at Alexandra's Office Products finds that it takes 3 hours to manufacture a particular office chair and 6 hours to manufacture an office desk. A total of 1200 hours is available to produce office chairs and desks of this style. The linear equation that models this situation is $3x + 6y = 1200$, where x represents the number of chairs produced and y the number of desks manufactured.

61. Complete the ordered pair solution $(0, \quad)$ of this equation. Describe the manufacturing situation that corresponds to this solution.

62. Complete the ordered pair solution $(\quad, 0)$ of this equation. Describe the manufacturing situation that corresponds to this solution.

63. If 50 desks are manufactured, find the greatest number of chairs that can be made.

64. If 50 chairs are manufactured, find the greatest number of desks that can be made.

*Two lines in the same plane that do not intersect are called **parallel lines.***

65. Use your own graph paper to draw a line parallel to the line $y = -1$ that intersects the y-axis at -4. What is the equation of this line?

66. Use your own graph paper to draw a line parallel to the line $x = 5$ that intersects the x-axis at 1. What is the equation of this line?

Solve.

67. It has been said that newspapers are disappearing, replaced by various electronic media. The average circulation of newspapers in the United States y, in millions, from 2003 to 2007 can be modeled by the equation $y = -1.9x + 59$, where x represents the number of years after 2003. (*Source:* Newspaper Association of America)

    a. Find the x-intercept of this equation (round to the nearest tenth).

    b. What does this x-intercept mean?

68. The number of a certain chain of stores y for the years 2003–2007 can be modeled by the equation $y = -198x + 3991$, where x represents the number of years after 2003. (*Source:* Limited Brands)

    a. Find the y-intercept of this equation.

    b. What does this y-intercept mean?

7.4 SLOPE AND RATE OF CHANGE

Objective **A** Finding the Slope of a Line Given Two Points

Thus far, much of this chapter has been devoted to graphing lines. You have probably noticed by now that a key feature of a line is its slant or steepness. In mathematics, the slant or steepness of a line is formally known as its **slope.** We measure the slope of a line by the ratio of vertical change (rise) to the corresponding horizontal change (run) as we move along the line.

On the line below, for example, suppose that we begin at the point $(1, 2)$ and move to the point $(4, 6)$. The vertical change is the change in y-coordinates: $6 - 2$ or 4 units. The corresponding horizontal change is the change in x-coordinates: $4 - 1 = 3$ units. The ratio of these changes is

$$\text{slope} = \frac{\text{change in } y \text{ (vertical change or rise)}}{\text{change in } x \text{ (horizontal change or run)}} = \frac{4}{3}$$

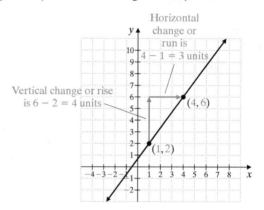

The slope of this line, then, is $\frac{4}{3}$. This means that for every 4 units of change in y-coordinates, there is a corresponding change of 3 units in x-coordinates.

Helpful Hint

It makes no difference what two points of a line are chosen to find its slope. The slope of a line is the same everywhere on the line.

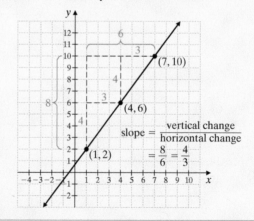

To find the slope of a line, then, choose two points of the line. Label the two x-coordinates of the two points x_1 and x_2 (read "x sub one" and "x sub two"), and label the corresponding y-coordinates y_1 and y_2.

The vertical change or **rise** between these points is the difference in the y-coordinates: $y_2 - y_1$. The horizontal change or **run** between the points is the difference of the x-coordinates: $x_2 - x_1$. The slope of the line is the ratio of $y_2 - y_1$ to $x_2 - x_1$, and we traditionally use the letter m to denote slope $m = \dfrac{y_2 - y_1}{x_2 - x_1}$.

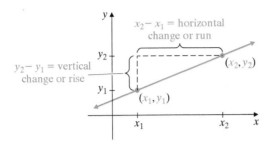

Slope of a Line

The slope m of the line containing the points (x_1, y_1) and (x_2, y_2) is given by

$$m = \frac{\text{rise}}{\text{run}} = \frac{\text{change in } y}{\text{change in } x} = \frac{y_2 - y_1}{x_2 - x_1}, \qquad \text{as long as } x_2 \ne x_1$$

Example 1 Find the slope of the line through $(-1, 5)$ and $(2, -3)$. Graph the line.

Solution: Let (x_1, y_1) be $(-1, 5)$ and (x_2, y_2) be $(2, -3)$. Then, by the definition of slope, we have the following.

$$m = \frac{y_2 - y_1}{x_2 - x_1}$$

$$= \frac{-3 - 5}{2 - (-1)}$$

$$= \frac{-8}{3} = -\frac{8}{3}$$

The slope of the line is $-\dfrac{8}{3}$.

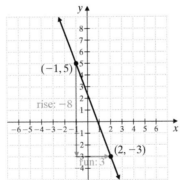

● **Work Practice 1**

PRACTICE 1

Find the slope of the line through $(-2, 3)$ and $(4, -1)$. Graph the line.

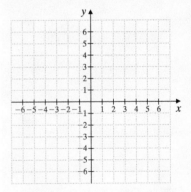

Answer

1. $-\dfrac{2}{3}$

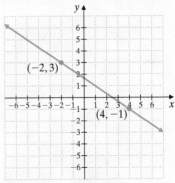

Helpful Hint

When finding slope, it makes no difference which point is identified as (x_1, y_1) and which is identified as (x_2, y_2). Just remember that whatever y-value is first in the numerator, its corresponding x-value is first in the denominator. Another way to calculate the slope in Example 1 is

$$m = \frac{y_2 - y_1}{x_2 - x_1} = \frac{5 - (-3)}{-1 - 2} = \frac{8}{-3} \text{ or } -\frac{8}{3} \quad \leftarrow \text{Same slope as found in Example 1}$$

✓**Concept Check** The points $(-2, -5)$, $(0, -2)$, $(4, 4)$, and $(10, 13)$ all lie on the same line. Work with a partner and verify that the slope is the same no matter which points are used to find slope.

✓ **Concept Check Answer**

$m = \dfrac{3}{2}$

PRACTICE 2

Find the slope of the line through $(-2, 1)$ and $(3, 5)$. Graph the line.

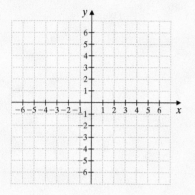

Example 2 Find the slope of the line through $(-1, -2)$ and $(2, 4)$. Graph the line.

Solution: Let (x_1, y_1) be $(2, 4)$ and (x_2, y_2) be $(-1, -2)$.

$$m = \frac{y_2 - y_1}{x_2 - x_1}$$

$$= \frac{-2 - 4}{-1 - 2} \quad \begin{array}{l} y\text{-value} \\ \text{corresponding } x\text{-value} \end{array}$$

$$= \frac{-6}{-3} = 2$$

The slope is 2.

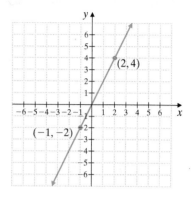

⬤ **Work Practice 2**

✓**Concept Check** What is wrong with the following slope calculation for the points $(3, 5)$ and $(-2, 6)$?

$$m = \frac{5 - 6}{-2 - 3} = \frac{-1}{-5} = \frac{1}{5}$$

Notice that the slope of the line in Example 1 is negative and that the slope of the line in Example 2 is positive. Let your eye follow the line with negative slope from left to right and notice that the line "goes down." If you follow the line with positive slope from left to right, you will notice that the line "goes up." This is true in general.

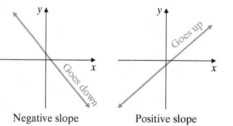

Negative slope   Positive slope

Helpful Hint To decide whether a line "goes up" or "goes down," always follow the line from left to right.

Answer

2. $\dfrac{4}{5}$

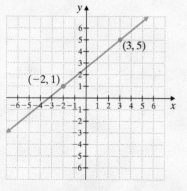

✓ **Concept Check Answer**

$m = \dfrac{5 - 6}{3 - (-2)} = \dfrac{-1}{5} = -\dfrac{1}{5}$

Objective ⓑ Finding the Slope of a Line Given Its Equation

As we have seen, the slope of a line is defined by two points on the line. Thus, if we know the equation of a line, we can find its slope by finding two of its points. For example, let's find the slope of the line

$$y = 3x - 2$$

To find two points, we can choose two values for x and substitute to find corresponding y-values. If $x = 0$, for example, $y = 3 \cdot 0 - 2$ or $y = -2$. If $x = 1$, $y = 3 \cdot 1 - 2$ or $y = 1$. This gives the ordered pairs $(0, -2)$ and $(1, 1)$. Using the definition for slope, we have

$$m = \frac{1 - (-2)}{1 - 0} = \frac{3}{1} = 3 \qquad \text{The slope is 3.}$$

Notice that the slope, 3, is the same as the coefficient of x in the equation $y = 3x - 2$. This is true in general.

If a linear equation is solved for y, the coefficient of x is the line's slope. In other words, the slope of the line given by $y = mx + b$ is m, the coefficient of x.

$$y = \underset{\text{slope}}{m}x + b$$

Example 3 Find the slope of the line $-2x + 3y = 11$.

Solution: When we solve for y, the coefficient of x is the slope.

$$-2x + 3y = 11$$
$$3y = 2x + 11 \qquad \text{Add } 2x \text{ to both sides.}$$
$$y = \frac{2}{3}x + \frac{11}{3} \qquad \text{Divide both sides by 3.}$$

The slope is $\frac{2}{3}$.

● **Work Practice 3**

PRACTICE 3

Find the slope of the line $5x + 4y = 10$.

Example 4 Find the slope of the line $-y = 5x - 2$.

Solution: Remember, the equation must be solved for y (not $-y$) in order for the coefficient of x to be the slope.
To solve for y, let's divide both sides of the equation by -1.

$$-y = 5x - 2$$
$$\frac{-y}{-1} = \frac{5x}{-1} - \frac{2}{-1} \qquad \text{Divide both sides by } -1.$$
$$y = -5x + 2 \qquad \text{Simplify.}$$

The slope is -5.

● **Work Practice 4**

PRACTICE 4

Find the slope of the line $-y = -2x + 7$.

Objective ○ Finding Slopes of Horizontal and Vertical Lines

Example 5 Find the slope of the line $y = -1$.

Solution: Recall that $y = -1$ is a horizontal line with y-intercept -1. To find the slope, we find two ordered pair solutions of $y = -1$, knowing that solutions of $y = -1$ must have a y-value of -1. We will use $(2, -1)$ and $(-3, -1)$. We let (x_1, y_1) be $(2, -1)$ and (x_2, y_2) be $(-3, -1)$.

$$m = \frac{y_2 - y_1}{x_2 - x_1} = \frac{-1 - (-1)}{-3 - 2} = \frac{0}{-5} = 0$$

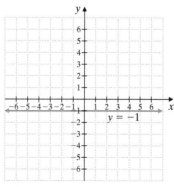

PRACTICE 5

Find the slope of $y = 3$.

The slope of the line $y = -1$ is 0. Since the y-values will have a difference of 0 for every horizontal line, we can say that all **horizontal lines have a slope of 0.**

● **Work Practice 5**

Answers

3. $-\dfrac{5}{4}$ **4.** 2 **5.** 0

PRACTICE 6

Find the slope of the line $x = -2$.

Slope of 0 and undefined slope are not the same. Vertical lines have undefined slope, while horizontal lines have a slope of 0.

Example 6 Find the slope of the line $x = 5$.

Solution: Recall that the graph of $x = 5$ is a vertical line with x-intercept 5. To find the slope, we find two ordered pair solutions of $x = 5$. Ordered pair solutions of $x = 5$ must have an x-value of 5. We will use $(5, 0)$ and $(5, 4)$. We let $(x_1, y_1) = (5, 0)$ and $(x_2, y_2) = (5, 4)$.

$$m = \frac{y_2 - y_1}{x_2 - x_1} = \frac{4 - 0}{5 - 5} = \frac{4}{0}$$

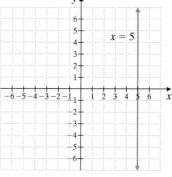

Since $\frac{4}{0}$ is undefined, we say that the slope of the vertical line $x = 5$ is undefined.

Since the x-values will have a difference of 0 for every vertical line, we can say that all **vertical lines have undefined slope.**

● **Work Practice 6**

Here is a general review of slope.

Summary of Slope

Slope m of the line through (x_1, y_1) and (x_2, y_2) is given by the equation

$$m = \frac{y_2 - y_1}{x_2 - x_1}.$$

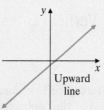

Upward line

Positive slope: $m > 0$

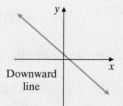

Downward line

Negative slope: $m < 0$

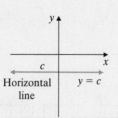

Horizontal line $y = c$

Zero slope: $m = 0$

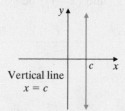

Vertical line $x = c$

No slope or undefined slope

Objective ⒟ Slopes of Parallel and Perpendicular Lines

Two lines in the same plane are **parallel** if they do not intersect. Slopes of lines can help us determine whether lines are parallel. Since parallel lines have the same steepness, it follows that they have the same slope.

Answer
6. undefined slope

For example, the graphs of

$$y = -2x + 4$$

and

$$y = -2x - 3$$

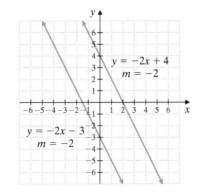

are shown. These lines have the same slope, -2. They also have different y-intercepts, so the lines are parallel. (If the y-intercepts were the same also, the lines would be the same.)

Parallel Lines

Nonvertical parallel lines have the same slope and different y-intercepts.

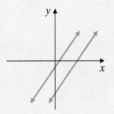

Two lines are **perpendicular** if they lie in the same plane and meet at a 90° (right) angle. How do the slopes of perpendicular lines compare? The product of the slopes of two perpendicular lines is -1.

For example, the graphs of

$$y = 4x + 1$$

and

$$y = -\frac{1}{4}x - 3$$

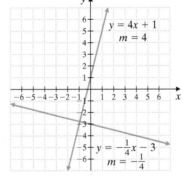

are shown. The slopes of the lines are 4 and $-\dfrac{1}{4}$. Their product is $4\left(-\dfrac{1}{4}\right) = -1$, so the lines are perpendicular.

Perpendicular Lines

If the product of the slopes of two lines is -1, then the lines are perpendicular.

(Two nonvertical lines are perpendicular if the slope of one is the negative reciprocal of the slope of the other.)

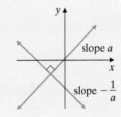

Helpful Hint

Here are examples of numbers that are negative (opposite) reciprocals.

Number	Negative Reciprocal	Their product is −1.
$\frac{2}{3}$	$-\frac{3}{2}$	$\frac{2}{3} \cdot -\frac{3}{2} = -\frac{6}{6} = -1$
-5 or $-\frac{5}{1}$	$\frac{1}{5}$	$-5 \cdot \frac{1}{5} = -\frac{5}{5} = -1$

Here are a few important points about vertical and horizontal lines.
- Two distinct vertical lines are parallel.
- Two distinct horizontal lines are parallel.
- A horizontal line and a vertical line are always perpendicular.

PRACTICE 7

Determine whether each pair of lines is parallel, perpendicular, or neither.

a. $x + y = 5$
$2x + y = 5$

b. $5y = 2x - 3$
$5x + 2y = 1$

c. $y = 2x + 1$
$4x - 2y = 8$

Example 7 Determine whether each pair of lines is parallel, perpendicular, or neither.

a. $y = -\frac{1}{5}x + 1$

$2x + 10y = 3$

b. $x + y = 3$
$-x + y = 4$

c. $3x + y = 5$
$2x + 3y = 6$

Solution:

a. The slope of the line $y = -\frac{1}{5}x + 1$ is $-\frac{1}{5}$. We find the slope of the second line by solving its equation for y.

$2x + 10y = 3$

$10y = -2x + 3$ Subtract $2x$ from both sides.

$y = \frac{-2}{10}x + \frac{3}{10}$ Divide both sides by 10.

$y = -\frac{1}{5}x + \frac{3}{10}$ Simplify.

The slope of this line is $-\frac{1}{5}$ also. Since the lines have the same slope and different y-intercepts, they are parallel, as shown in the figure on the left below.

b. To find each slope, we solve each equation for y.

$x + y = 3$ $-x + y = 4$

$y = -x + 3$ $y = x + 4$

The slope is -1.   The slope is 1.

The slopes are not the same, so the lines are not parallel. Next we check the product of the slopes: $(-1)(1) = -1$. Since the product is -1, the lines are perpendicular, as shown in the figure on the right.

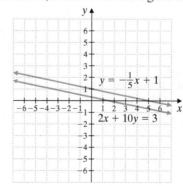

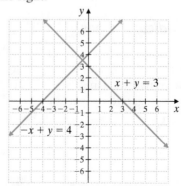

Answers

7. **a.** neither   **b.** perpendicular
c. parallel

c. We solve each equation for y to find each slope. The slopes are -3 and $-\frac{2}{3}$. The slopes are not the same and their product is not -1. Thus, the lines are neither parallel nor perpendicular.

⬤ Work Practice 7

✓ Concept Check Consider the line $-6x + 2y = 1$.

a. Write the equations of two lines parallel to this line.
b. Write the equations of two lines perpendicular to this line.

Objective Ⓔ Slope as a Rate of Change

Slope can also be interpreted as a rate of change. In other words, slope tells us how fast y is changing with respect to x. To see this, let's look at a few of the many real-world applications of slope. For example, the pitch of a roof, used by builders and architects, is its slope. The pitch of the roof on the right is $\frac{7}{10}\left(\frac{\text{rise}}{\text{run}}\right)$. This means that the roof rises vertically 7 feet for every horizontal 10 feet. The rate of change for the roof is 7 vertical feet (y) per 10 horizontal feet (x).

The grade of a road is its slope written as a percent. A 7% grade, as shown below, means that the road rises (or falls) 7 feet for every horizontal 100 feet. $\Big($ Recall that $7\% = \frac{7}{100}.\Big)$ Here, the slope of $\frac{7}{100}$ gives us the rate of change. The road rises (in our diagram) 7 vertical feet (y) for every 100 horizontal feet (x).

$\frac{7}{100} = 7\%\ \text{grade}$ 7 feet

100 feet

▬▬ **Example 8** Finding the Grade of a Road

At one part of the road to the summit of Pike's Peak, the road rises 15 feet for a horizontal distance of 250 feet. Find the grade of the road.

Solution: Recall that the grade of a road is its slope written as a percent.

$$\text{grade} = \frac{\text{rise}}{\text{run}} = \frac{15}{250} = 0.06 = 6\%$$

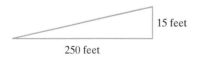

15 feet

250 feet

The grade is 6%.

⬤ Work Practice 8

PRACTICE 8

Find the grade of the road shown.

3 feet

20 feet

Answer
8. 15%

✓ **Concept Check Answers**
Answers may vary; for example,
a. $y = 3x - 3, y = 3x - 1$
b. $y = -\frac{1}{3}x, y = -\frac{1}{3}x + 1$

Slope can also be interpreted as a rate of change. In other words, slope tells us how fast y is changing with respect to x.

PRACTICE 9

The following graph shows the cost y (in cents) of a nationwide long-distance telephone call from Texas with a certain telephone-calling plan, where x is the length of the call in minutes. Find the slope of the line and attach the proper units for the rate of change. Then write a sentence explaining the meaning of slope in this application.

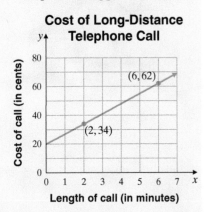

Example 9 Finding the Slope of a Line

This graph represents annual food and drink sales y (in billions of dollars) for year x. Find the slope of the line and write the slope as a rate of change. Write a sentence explaining the meaning of slope in this application.

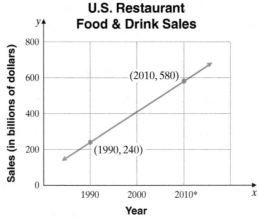

Source: National Restaurant Assn.
* projected

Solution: Use $(1990, 240)$ and $(2010, 580)$ to calculate slope.

$$m = \frac{580 - 240}{2010 - 1990} = \frac{340}{20} = \frac{17 \text{ billion dollars}}{1 \text{ year}}$$

The U.S. Restaurant food and drink sales is increasing at a rate of \$17 billion dollars per year.

● **Work Practice 9**

Answer

9. $m = \dfrac{7 \text{ cents}}{1 \text{ minute}}$; This means that the rate of change of a phone call is 7 cents per 1 minute, or the cost of the phone call is 7 cents per minute.

Calculator Explorations   Graphing

It is possible to use a graphing calculator and sketch the graph of more than one equation on the same set of axes. This feature can be used to see that parallel lines have the same slope. For example, graph the equations $y = \frac{2}{5}x$, $y = \frac{2}{5}x + 7$, and $y = \frac{2}{5}x - 4$ on the same set of axes. To do so, press the $\boxed{\text{Y=}}$ key and enter the equations on the first three lines.

$$Y_1 = \left(\frac{2}{5}\right)x$$

$$Y_2 = \left(\frac{2}{5}\right)x + 7$$

$$Y_3 = \left(\frac{2}{5}\right)x - 4$$

The displayed equations should look like this:

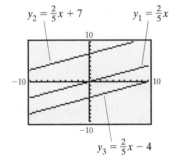

These lines are parallel as expected since they all have a slope of $\frac{2}{5}$. The graph of $y = \frac{2}{5}x + 7$ is the graph of $y = \frac{2}{5}x$ moved 7 units upward with a y-intercept of 7. Also, the graph of $y = \frac{2}{5}x - 4$ is the graph of $y = \frac{2}{5}x$ moved 4 units downward with a y-intercept of -4.

Graph the parallel lines on the same set of axes. Describe the similarities and differences in their graphs.

1. $y = 3.8x$, $y = 3.8x - 3$, $y = 3.8x + 9$

2. $y = -4.9x$, $y = -4.9x + 1$, $y = -4.9x + 8$

3. $y = \frac{1}{4}x$, $y = \frac{1}{4}x + 5$, $y = \frac{1}{4}x - 8$

4. $y = -\frac{3}{4}x$, $y = -\frac{3}{4}x - 5$, $y = -\frac{3}{4}x + 6$

Vocabulary and Readiness Check

Use the choices below to fill in each blank. Not all choices will be used.

m	x	0	positive	undefined
b	y	slope	negative	

1. The measure of the steepness or tilt of a line is called _____ .
2. If an equation is written in the form $y = mx + b$, the value of the letter _____ is the value of the slope of the graph.
3. The slope of a horizontal line is _____ .
4. The slope of a vertical line is _____ .
5. If the graph of a line moves upward from left to right, the line has _____ slope.
6. If the graph of a line moves downward from left to right, the line has _____ slope.
7. Given two points of a line, slope $= \dfrac{\text{change in} \underline{\hspace{1.5cm}}}{\text{change in} \underline{\hspace{1.5cm}}}$.

State whether the slope of the line is positive, negative, 0, or undefined.

8. 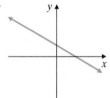   9. 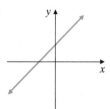   10. 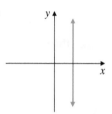   11.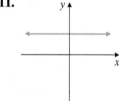

Decide whether a line with the given slope slants upward or downward or is horizontal or vertical.

12. $m = \dfrac{7}{6}$ _____   13. $m = -3$ _____   14. $m = 0$ _____   15. m is undefined. _____

7.4 Exercise Set

Objective Ⓐ Find the slope of the line that passes through the given points. See Examples 1 and 2.

1. $(-1, 5)$ and $(6, -2)$ 2. $(-1, 16)$ and $(3, 4)$ 3. $(1, 4)$ and $(5, 3)$ 4. $(3, 1)$ and $(2, 6)$

5. $(5, 1)$ and $(-2, 1)$ 6. $(-8, 3)$ and $(-2, 3)$ 7. $(-4, 3)$ and $(-4, 5)$ 8. $(-2, -3)$ and $(-2, 5)$

Use the points shown on each graph to find the slope of each line. See Examples 1 and 2.

9. 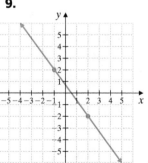   10. 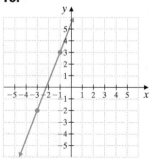   11. 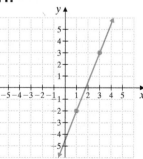   12.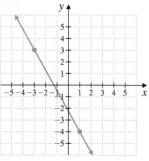

For each graph, determine which line has the greater slope.

13.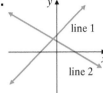

14.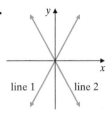

15.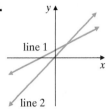

16.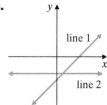

Objectives **B** **C** Mixed Practice *Find the slope of each line. See Examples 3 through 6.*

17. $y = 5x - 2$

18. $y = -2x + 6$

19. $y = -0.3x + 2.5$

20. $y = -7.6x - 0.1$

21. $2x + y = 7$

22. $-5x + y = 10$

23.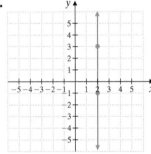

24.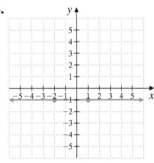

25. $2x - 3y = 10$

26. $3x - 5y = 1$

27. $x = 1$

28. $y = -2$

29. $x = 2y$

30. $x = -4y$

31. $y = -3$

32. $x = 5$

33. $-3x - 4y = 6$

34. $-4x - 7y = 9$

35. $20x - 5y = 1.2$

36. $24x - 3y = 5.7$

△ Objective **D** *Determine whether each pair of lines is parallel, perpendicular, or neither. See Example 7.*

37. $y = \dfrac{2}{9}x + 3$
$y = -\dfrac{2}{9}x$

38. $y = \dfrac{1}{5}x + 20$
$y = -\dfrac{1}{5}x$

39. $x - 3y = -6$
$y = 3x - 9$

40. $y = 4x - 2$
$4x + y = 5$

41. $6x = 5y + 1$
$-12x + 10y = 1$

42. $-x + 2y = -2$
$2x = 4y + 3$

43. $6 + 4x = 3y$
$3x + 4y = 8$

44. $10 + 3x = 5y$
$5x + 3y = 1$

△ *Find the slope of the line that is (a) parallel and (b) perpendicular to the line through each pair of points. See Example 7.*

45. $(-3, -3)$ and $(0, 0)$ **46.** $(6, -2)$ and $(1, 4)$ **47.** $(-8, -4)$ and $(3, 5)$ **48.** $(6, -1)$ and $(-4, -10)$

Objective Ⓔ *The pitch of a roof is its slope. Find the pitch of each roof shown. See Example 8.*

49.

50.

The grade of a road is its slope written as a percent. Find the grade of each road shown. See Example 8.

51.

52.

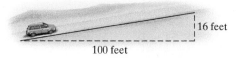

53. One of Japan's superconducting "bullet" trains is researched and tested at the Yamanashi Maglev Test Line near Otsuki City. The steepest section of the track has a rise of 2580 meters for a horizontal distance of 6450 meters. What is the grade (slope written as a percent) of this section of track? (*Source:* Japan Railways Central Co.)

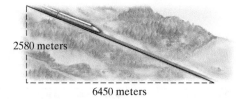

54. Professional plumbers suggest that a sewer pipe should rise 0.25 inch for every horizontal foot. Find the recommended slope for a sewer pipe and write the slope as a grade, or percent. Round to the nearest percent.

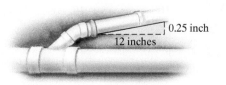

55. There has been controversy over the past few years about the world's steepest street. The *Guinness Book of Records* actually listed Baldwin Street, in Dunedin, New Zealand, as the world's steepest street, but Canton Avenue in the Pittsburgh neighborhood of Beechview may be steeper. Calculate each grade to the nearest percent.

		Grade (%)
Canton Avenue	for every 30 meters of horizontal distance, the vertical change is 11 meters	
Baldwin Street	for every 2.86 meters of horizontal distance, the vertical change is 1 meter	

56. According to federal regulations, a wheelchair ramp should rise no more than 1 foot for a horizontal distance of 12 feet. Write the slope as a grade. Round to the nearest tenth of a percent.

Find the slope of each line and write a sentence using the slope as a rate of change. Don't forget to attach the proper units. See Example 9.

57. This graph approximates the number of U.S. households that have televisions y (in millions) for year x.

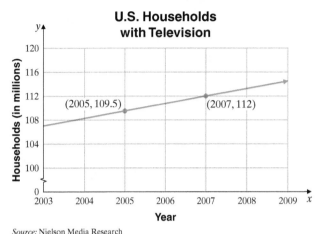

Source: Nielson Media Research

58. The graph approximates the amount of money y (in billions of dollars) spent worldwide on tourism for year x. (*Source:* World Tourism Organization)

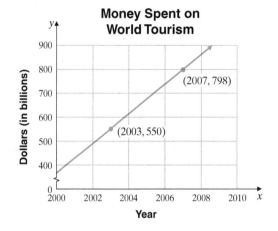

59. Americans are keeping their cars longer. The graph below shows the median age y (in years) of automobiles in the United States for the years shown. (*Source:* Bureau of Transportation Statistics)

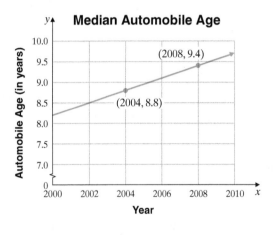

60. The graph below shows the total cost y (in dollars) of owning and operating a compact car (excluding the cost of the car), where x is the number of miles driven.

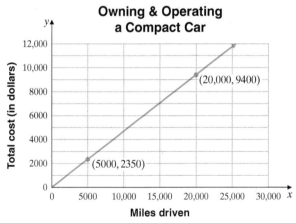

Source: AAA

Review

Solve each equation for y. See Section 6.5.

61. $y - (-6) = 2(x - 4)$

62. $y - 7 = -9(x - 6)$

63. $y - 1 = -6(x - (-2))$

64. $y - (-3) = 4(x - (-5))$

Concept Extensions

Match each line with its slope.

a. $m = 0$

b. undefined slope

c. $m = 3$

d. $m = 1$

e. $m = -\dfrac{1}{2}$

f. $m = -\dfrac{3}{4}$

65.

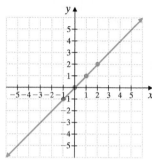

66.

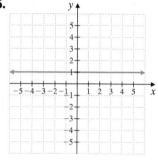

67.

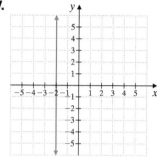

68.

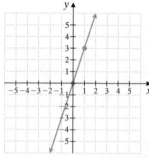

69.

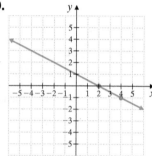

70.

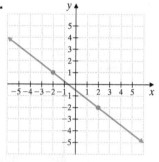

Solve. See a Concept Check in this section.

71. Verify that the points $(2, 1), (0, 0), (-2, -1)$, and $(-4, -2)$ are all on the same line by computing the slope between each pair of points. (See the first Concept Check.)

72. Given the points $(2, 3)$ and $(-5, 1)$, can the slope of the line through these points be calculated by $\dfrac{1 - 3}{2 - (-5)}$? Why or why not? (See the second Concept Check.)

73. Write the equations of three lines parallel to $10x - 5y = -7$. (See the third Concept Check.)

74. Write the equations of two lines perpendicular to $10x - 5y = -7$. (See the third Concept Check.)

The following line graph shows the average fuel economy (in miles per gallon) of passenger automobiles produced during each of the model years shown. Use this graph to answer Exercises 75 through 80.

75. What was the average fuel economy (in miles per gallon) for automobiles produced during 2004?

76. Find the decrease in average fuel economy for automobiles between the years 1998 and 1999.

77. During which of the model years shown was average fuel economy the lowest?
What was the average fuel economy for that year?

78. During which of the model years shown was average fuel economy the highest?
What was the average fuel economy for that year?

Average Fuel Economy for Autos

Source: Bureau of Transportation Statistics

79. Of the following line segments, which has the greatest slope: from 2002 to 2003, from 2006 to 2007, or from 2007 to 2008?

80. What line segment has a slope of 0?

81. Find x so that the pitch of the roof is $\frac{2}{5}$.

4 feet

x

82. Find x so that the pitch of the roof is $\frac{1}{3}$.

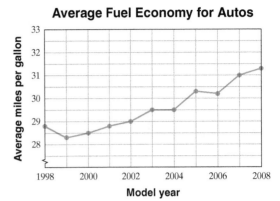

x

18 feet

83. There were approximately 2025 heart transplants performed in the United States in 2004. In 2007, the number of heart transplants in the United States rose to 2208. (*Source:* Organ Procurement and Transplantation Network)

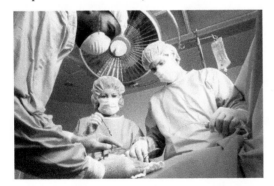

a. Write two ordered pairs of the form (year, number of heart transplants).

b. Find the slope of the line between the two points.

c. Write a sentence explaining the meaning of the slope as a rate of change.

84. The average price of an acre of U.S. farmland was $1210 in 2002. In 2008, the price of an acre rose to $2350. (*Source:* National Agricultural Statistics Services)

a. Write two ordered pairs of the form (year, price of an acre).

b. Find the slope of the line through the two points.

c. Write a sentence explaining the meaning of the slope as a rate of change.

85. Show that the quadrilateral with vertices $(1, 3)$, $(2, 1)$, $(-4, 0)$, and $(-3, -2)$ is a parallelogram.

86. Show that a triangle with vertices at the points $(1, 1)$, $(-4, 4)$, and $(-3, 0)$ is a right triangle.

Find the slope of the line through the given points.

87. $(-3.8, 1.2)$ and $(-2.2, 4.5)$

88. $(2.1, 6.7)$ and $(-8.3, 9.3)$

89. $(14.3, -10.1)$ and $(9.8, -2.9)$

90. $(2.3, 0.2)$ and $(7.9, 5.1)$

91. The graph of $y = \dfrac{1}{2}x$ has a slope of $\dfrac{1}{2}$. The graph of $y = 3x$ has a slope of 3. The graph of $y = 5x$ has a slope of 5. Graph all three equations on a single coordinate system. As the slope becomes larger, how does the steepness of the line change?

92. The graph of $y = -\dfrac{1}{3}x + 2$ has a slope of $-\dfrac{1}{3}$. The graph of $y = -2x + 2$ has a slope of -2. The graph of $y = -4x + 2$ has a slope of -4. Graph all three equations on a single coordinate system. As the absolute value of the slope becomes larger, how does the steepness of the line change?

7.5 EQUATIONS OF LINES

Objectives

A Use the Slope-Intercept Form to Graph a Linear Equation.

B Use the Slope-Intercept Form to Write an Equation of a Line.

C Use the Point-Slope Form to Find an Equation of a Line Given Its Slope and a Point of the Line.

D Use the Point-Slope Form to Find an Equation of a Line Given Two Points of the Line.

E Use the Point-Slope Form to Solve Problems.

We know that when a linear equation is solved for y, the coefficient of x is the slope of the line. For example, the slope of the line whose equation is $y = 3x + 1$ is 3. In this equation, $y = 3x + 1$, what does 1 represent? To find out, let $x = 0$ and watch what happens.

$$y = 3x + 1$$
$$y = 3 \cdot 0 + 1 \quad \text{Let } x = 0.$$
$$y = 1$$

We now have the ordered pair $(0, 1)$, which means that 1 is the y-intercept.
 This is true in general. To see this, let $x = 0$ and solve for y in $y = mx + b$.

$$y = m \cdot 0 + b \quad \text{Let } x = 0.$$
$$y = b$$

We obtain the ordered pair $(0, b)$, which means that point is the y-intercept.
 The form $y = mx + b$ is appropriately called the *slope-intercept form* of a linear equation.

y-intercept is $(0, b)$

slope

Slope-Intercept Form

When a linear equation in two variables is written in **slope-intercept form**,

$$y = mx + b$$

slope $(0, b)$, y-intercept

then m is the slope of the line and $(0, b)$ is the y-intercept of the line.

Objective **A** Using the Slope-Intercept Form to Graph an Equation

We can use the slope-intercept form of the equation of a line to graph a linear equation.

Example 1 Use the slope-intercept form to graph the equation

$$y = \frac{3}{5}x - 2.$$

Solution: Since the equation $y = \frac{3}{5}x - 2$ is written in slope-intercept form $y = mx + b$, the slope of its graph is $\frac{3}{5}$ and the y-intercept is $(0, -2)$. To graph this equation, we begin by plotting the point $(0, -2)$. From this point, we can find another point of the graph by using the slope $\frac{3}{5}$ and recalling that slope is $\frac{\text{rise}}{\text{run}}$. We start at the y-intercept and move 3 units up since the

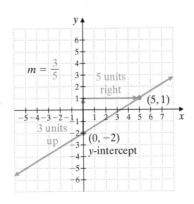

Continued on next page

PRACTICE 1

Use the slope-intercept form to graph the equation $y = \frac{2}{3}x - 4$.

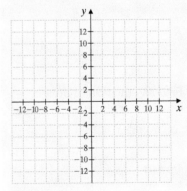

Answer

1.

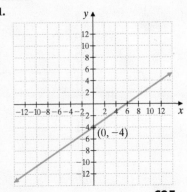

numerator of the slope is 3; then we move 5 units to the right since the denominator of the slope is 5. We stop at the point $(5, 1)$. The line through $(0, -2)$ and $(5, 1)$ is the graph of $y = \dfrac{3}{5}x - 2$.

● **Work Practice 1**

PRACTICE 2

Use the slope-intercept form to graph $3x + y = 2$.

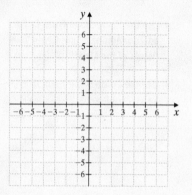

Example 2 Use the slope-intercept form to graph the equation $4x + y = 1$.

Solution: First we write the given equation in slope-intercept form.

$$4x + y = 1$$
$$y = -4x + 1$$

The graph of this equation will have slope -4 and y-intercept $(0, 1)$. To graph this line, we first plot the point $(0, 1)$. To find another point of the graph, we use the slope -4, which can be written as $\dfrac{-4}{1}$ $\left(\dfrac{4}{-1} \text{ could also be used} \right)$. We start at the point $(0, 1)$ and move 4 units down (since the numerator of the slope is -4), and then 1 unit to the right (since the denominator of the slope is 1).

    We arrive at the point $(1, -3)$. The line through $(0, 1)$ and $(1, -3)$ is the graph of $4x + y = 1$.

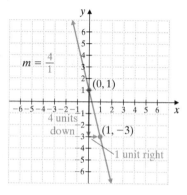

● **Work Practice 2**

Helpful Hint

In Example 2, if we interpret the slope of -4 as $\dfrac{4}{-1}$, we arrive at $(-1, 5)$ for a second point. Notice that this point is also on the line.

Objective Ⓑ Using the Slope-Intercept Form to Write an Equation

The slope-intercept form can also be used to write the equation of a line when we know its slope and y-intercept.

PRACTICE 3

Find an equation of the line with y-intercept $(0, -4)$ and slope of $\dfrac{1}{5}$.

Example 3 Find an equation of the line with y-intercept $(0, -3)$ and slope of $\dfrac{1}{4}$.

Solution: We are given the slope and the y-intercept. We let $m = \dfrac{1}{4}$ and $b = -3$ and write the equation in slope-intercept form, $y = mx + b$.

$$y = mx + b$$
$$y = \dfrac{1}{4}x + (-3) \quad \text{Let } m = \dfrac{1}{4} \text{ and } b = -3.$$
$$y = \dfrac{1}{4}x - 3 \quad \text{Simplify.}$$

● **Work Practice 3**

Answers

2.

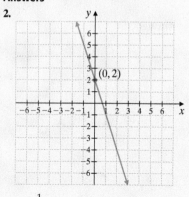

3. $y = \dfrac{1}{5}x - 4$

Objective ⓒ Writing an Equation Given Its Slope and a Point

Thus far, we have written an equation of a line by knowing its slope and y-intercept. We can also write an equation of a line if we know its slope and any point on the line. To see how we do this, let m represent slope and (x_1, y_1) represent the point on the line. Then if (x, y) is any other point of the line, we have that

$$\frac{y - y_1}{x - x_1} = m$$

$$y - y_1 = m(x - x_1) \quad \text{Multiply both sides by } (x - x_1).$$

$$\uparrow$$

slope

This is the *point-slope form* of the equation of a line.

Point-Slope Form of the Equation of a Line

The **point-slope form** of the equation of a line is $y - y_1 = m(x - x_1)$, where m is the slope of the line and (x_1, y_1) is a point on the line.

Example 4 Find an equation of the line with slope -2 that passes through $(-1, 5)$. Write the equation in slope-intercept form, $y = mx + b$, and in standard form, $Ax + By = C$.

Solution: Since the slope and a point on the line are given, we use point-slope form $y - y_1 = m(x - x_1)$ to write the equation. Let $m = -2$ and $(-1, 5) = (x_1, y_1)$.

$$y - y_1 = m(x - x_1)$$

$$y - 5 = -2[x - (-1)] \quad \text{Let } m = -2 \text{ and } (x_1, y_1) = (-1, 5).$$

$$y - 5 = -2(x + 1) \quad \text{Simplify.}$$

$$y - 5 = -2x - 2 \quad \text{Use the distributive property.}$$

To write the equation in slope-intercept form, $y = mx + b$, we simply solve the equation for y. To do this, we add 5 to both sides.

$$y - 5 = -2x - 2$$

$$y = -2x + 3 \quad \text{Slope-intercept form}$$

$$2x + y = 3 \quad \text{Add } 2x \text{ to both sides and we have standard form.}$$

● **Work Practice 4**

PRACTICE 4

Find an equation of the line with slope -3 that passes through $(2, -4)$. Write the equation in slope-intercept form, $y = mx + b$, and in standard form, $Ax + By = C$.

Objective ⓓ Writing an Equation Given Two Points

We can also find the equation of a line when we are given any two points of the line.

Example 5 Find an equation of the line through $(2, 5)$ and $(-3, 4)$. Write the equation in the form $Ax + By = C$.

Solution: First, use the two given points to find the slope of the line.

$$m = \frac{4 - 5}{-3 - 2} = \frac{-1}{-5} = \frac{1}{5}$$

Next we use the slope $\frac{1}{5}$ and either one of the given points to write the equation in point-slope form. We use $(2, 5)$. Let $x_1 = 2$, $y_1 = 5$, and $m = \frac{1}{5}$.

PRACTICE 5

Find an equation of the line through $(1, 3)$ and $(5, -2)$. Write the equation in the form $Ax + By = C$.

Answers

4. $y = -3x + 2$; $3x + y = 2$

5. $5x + 4y = 17$

Continued on next page

$$y - y_1 = m(x - x_1) \qquad \text{Use point-slope form.}$$

$$y - 5 = \frac{1}{5}(x - 2) \qquad \text{Let } x_1 = 2, y_1 = 5, \text{ and } m = \frac{1}{5}.$$

$$5(y - 5) = 5 \cdot \frac{1}{5}(x - 2) \qquad \text{Multiply both sides by 5 to clear fractions.}$$

$$5y - 25 = x - 2 \qquad \text{Use the distributive property and simplify.}$$

$$-x + 5y - 25 = -2 \qquad \text{Subtract } x \text{ from both sides.}$$

$$-x + 5y = 23 \qquad \text{Add 25 to both sides.}$$

● **Work Practice 5**

Helpful Hint

When you multiply both sides of the equation from Example 5, $-x + 5y = 23$, by -1, it becomes $x - 5y = -23$.

Both $-x + 5y = 23$ and $x - 5y = -23$ are in the form $Ax + By = C$ and both are equations of the same line.

Objective ⓔ Using the Point-Slope Form to Solve Problems

Problems occurring in many fields can be modeled by linear equations in two variables. The next example is from the field of marketing and shows how consumer demand for a product depends on the price of the product.

PRACTICE 6

The Pool Entertainment Company learned that by pricing a new pool toy at $10, local sales will reach 200 a week. Lowering the price to $9 will cause sales to rise to 250 a week.

a. Assume that the relationship between sales price and number of toys sold is linear, and write an equation describing this relationship. Write the equation in slope-intercept form. Use ordered pairs of the form (sales price, number sold).

b. Predict the weekly sales of the toy if the price is $7.50.

Example 6 The Whammo Company has learned that by pricing a newly released Frisbee at $6, sales will reach 2000 Frisbees per day. Raising the price to $8 will cause the sales to fall to 1500 Frisbees per day.

a. Assume that the relationship between sales price and number of Frisbees sold is linear and write an equation describing this relationship. Write the equation in slope-intercept form. Use ordered pairs of the form (sales price, number sold).

b. Predict the daily sales of Frisbees if the sales price is $7.50.

Solution:

a. We use the given information and write two ordered pairs. Our ordered pairs are $(6, 2000)$ and $(8, 1500)$. To use the point-slope form to write an equation, we find the slope of the line that contains these points.

$$m = \frac{2000 - 1500}{6 - 8} = \frac{500}{-2} = -250$$

Next we use the slope and either one of the points to write the equation in point-slope form. We use $(6, 2000)$.

$$y - y_1 = m(x - x_1) \qquad \text{Use point-slope form.}$$

$$y - 2000 = -250(x - 6) \qquad \text{Let } x_1 = 6, y_1 = 2000, \text{ and } m = -250.$$

$$y - 2000 = -250x + 1500 \qquad \text{Use the distributive property.}$$

$$y = -250x + 3500 \qquad \text{Write in slope-intercept form.}$$

Answers

6. a. $y = -50x + 700$ **b.** 325

b. To predict the sales if the price is $7.50, we find y when $x = 7.50$.

$y = -250x + 3500$

$y = -250(7.50) + 3500$ Let $x = 7.50$.

$y = -1875 + 3500$

$y = 1625$

If the sales price is $7.50, sales will reach 1625 Frisbees per day.

● Work Practice 6

We could have solved Example 6 by using ordered pairs of the form (number sold, sales price).

Here is a summary of our discussion on linear equations thus far.

Forms of Linear Equations

$Ax + By = C$	**Standard form** of a linear equation.
	A and B are not both 0.
$y = mx + b$	**Slope-intercept form** of a linear equation.
	The slope is m and the y-intercept is $(0, b)$.
$y - y_1 = m(x - x_1)$	**Point-slope form** of a linear equation.
	The slope is m and (x_1, y_1) is a point on the line.
$y = c$	**Horizontal line**
	The slope is 0 and the y-intercept is $(0, c)$.
$x = c$	**Vertical line**
	The slope is undefined and the x-intercept is $(c, 0)$.

Parallel and Perpendicular Lines

Nonvertical parallel lines have the same slope.

The product of the slopes of two nonvertical perpendicular lines is -1.

Calculator Explorations   Graphing

A graphing calculator is a very useful tool for discovering patterns. To discover the change in the graph of a linear equation caused by a change in slope, try the following. Use a standard window and graph a linear equation in the form $y = mx + b$. Recall that the graph of such an equation will have slope m and y-intercept $(0, b)$.

First graph $y = x + 3$. To do so, press the ⬚ Y= ⬚ key and enter $Y_1 = x + 3$. Notice that this graph has slope 1 and that the y-intercept is 3. Next, on the same set of axes, graph $y = 2x + 3$ and $y = 3x + 3$ by pressing ⬚ Y= ⬚ and entering $Y_2 = 2x + 3$ and $Y_3 = 3x + 3$.

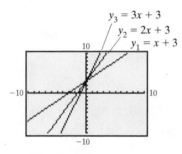

Notice the difference in the graph of each equation as the slope changes from 1 to 2 to 3. How would the graph of $y = 5x + 3$ appear? To see the change in the graph caused by a change in negative slope, try graphing $y = -x + 3$, $y = -2x + 3$, and $y = -3x + 3$ on the same set of axes.

Use a graphing calculator to graph the following equations. For each exercise, graph the first equation and use its graph to predict the appearance of the other equations. Then graph the other equations on the same set of axes and check your prediction.

1. $y = x; y = 6x, y = -6x$

2. $y = -x; y = -5x, y = -10x$

3. $y = \dfrac{1}{2}x + 2; y = \dfrac{3}{4}x + 2, y = x + 2$

4. $y = x + 1; y = \dfrac{5}{4}x + 1, y = \dfrac{5}{2}x + 1$

Vocabulary and Readiness Check

Use the choices below to fill in each blank. Some choices may be used more than once and some not at all.

b	(y_1, x_1)	point-slope	vertical	standard
m	(x_1, y_1)	slope-intercept	horizontal	

1. The form $y = mx + b$ is called _____ form. When a linear equation in two variables is written in this form, _____ is the slope of its graph and (0, _____) is its y-intercept.

2. The form $y - y_1 = m(x - x_1)$ is called _____ form. When a linear equation in two variables is written in this form, _____ is the slope of its graph and _____ is a point on the graph.

For Exercises 3 through 6 identify the form that the linear equation in two variables is written in. For Exercises 7 and 8, identify the appearance of the graph of the equation.

3. $y - 7 = 4(x + 3)$; _____ form

4. $5x - 9y = 11$; _____ form

5. $y = \dfrac{3}{4}x - \dfrac{1}{3}$; _____ form

6. $y + 2 = \dfrac{-1}{3}(x - 2)$; _____ form

7. $y = \dfrac{1}{2}$; _____ line

8. $x = -17$; _____ line

7.5 Exercise Set

FOR EXTRA HELP

 PRACTICE   WATCH   DOWNLOAD   READ   REVIEW

Objective A *Use the slope-intercept form to graph each equation. See Examples 1 and 2.*

1. $y = 2x + 1$

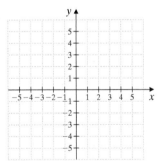

2. $y = -4x - 1$

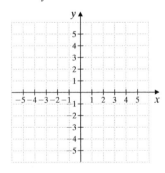

3. $y = \dfrac{2}{3}x + 5$

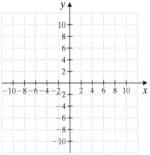

4. $y = \dfrac{1}{4}x - 3$

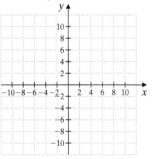

5. $y = -5x$

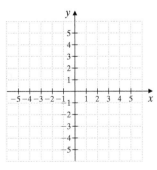

6. $y = -6x$

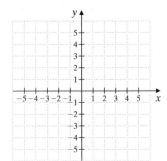

7. $4x + y = 6$

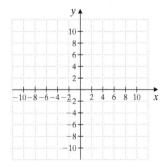

8. $-3x + y = 2$

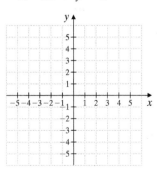

631

9. $4x - 7y = -14$

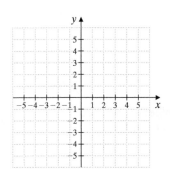

10. $3x - 4y = 4$

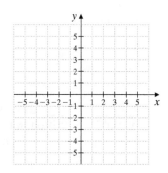

11. $x = \frac{5}{4}y$

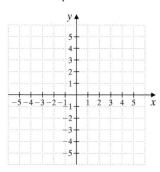

12. $x = \frac{3}{2}y$

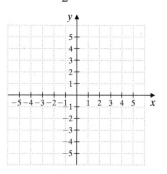

Objective Ⓑ *Write an equation of the line with each given slope, m, and y-intercept, (0, b). See Example 3.*

13. $m = 5, b = 3$

14. $m = -3, b = -3$

15. $m = -4, b = -\frac{1}{6}$

16. $m = 2, b = \frac{3}{4}$

17. $m = \frac{2}{3}, b = 0$

18. $m = -\frac{4}{5}, b = 0$

19. $m = 0, b = -8$

20. $m = 0, b = -2$

21. $m = -\frac{1}{5}, b = \frac{1}{9}$

22. $m = \frac{1}{2}, b = -\frac{1}{3}$

Objective Ⓒ *Find an equation of each line with the given slope that passes through the given point. Write the equation in the form $Ax + By = C$. See Example 4.*

23. $m = 6;$ $(2, 2)$

24. $m = 4;$ $(1, 3)$

25. $m = -8;$ $(-1, -5)$

26. $m = -2;$ $(-11, -12)$

27. $m = \frac{3}{2};$ $(5, -6)$

28. $m = \frac{2}{3};$ $(-8, 9)$

29. $m = -\frac{1}{2};$ $(-3, 0)$

30. $m = -\frac{1}{5};$ $(4, 0)$

Objective Ⓓ *Find an equation of the line passing through each pair of points. Write the equation in the form $Ax + By = C$. See Example 5.*

31. $(3, 2)$ and $(5, 6)$

32. $(6, 2)$ and $(8, 8)$

33. $(-1, 3)$ and $(-2, -5)$

34. $(-4, 0)$ and $(6, -1)$

35. $(2, 3)$ and $(-1, -1)$

36. $(7, 10)$ and $(-1, -1)$

37. $(0, 0)$ and $\left(-\frac{1}{8}, \frac{1}{13}\right)$

38. $(0, 0)$ and $\left(-\frac{1}{2}, \frac{1}{3}\right)$

Objectives Ⓐ Ⓒ Ⓓ **Mixed Practice** *See Examples 3 through 5. Find an equation of each line described. Write each equation in slope-intercept form when possible.*

39. With slope $-\frac{1}{2}$, through $\left(0, \frac{5}{3}\right)$

40. With slope $\frac{5}{7}$, through $(0, -3)$

41. Through $(10, 7)$ and $(7, 10)$

42. Through $(5, -6)$ and $(-6, 5)$

43. With undefined slope, through $\left(-\frac{3}{4}, 1\right)$

44. With slope 0, through $(6.7, 12.1)$

45. Slope 1, through $(-7, 9)$

46. Slope 5, through $(6, -8)$

47. Slope -5, y-intercept $(0, 7)$

48. Slope -2, y-intercept $(0, -4)$

49. Through $(1, 2)$, parallel to $y = 5$

50. Through $(1, -5)$, parallel to the y-axis

51. Through $(2, 3)$ and $(0, 0)$

52. Through $(4, 7)$ and $(0, 0)$

53. Through $(-2, -3)$, perpendicular to the y-axis

54. Through $(0, 12)$, perpendicular to the x-axis

55. Slope $-\frac{4}{7}$, through $(-1, -2)$

56. Slope $-\frac{3}{5}$, through $(4, 4)$

Objective Ⓔ *Solve. Assume each exercise describes a linear relationship. Write the equations in slope-intercept form. See Example 6.*

57. In 2003, there were 302 million magazine subscriptions in the United States. By 2007, this number was 322 million. (*Source:* Audit Bureau of Circulation, Magazine Publishers Association)

   a. Write two ordered pairs of the form (years after 2003, millions of magazine subscriptions) for this situation.

   b. Assume the relationship between years after 2003 and millions of magazine subscriptions is linear over this period. Use the ordered pairs from part (a) to write an equation for the line relating year after 2003 to millions of magazine subscriptions.

   c. Use this linear equation in part (b) to estimate the millions of magazine subscriptions in 2005.

58. In 2000, crude oil field production in the United States was 2130 thousand barrels. In 2007, U.S. crude oil field production dropped to 1850 thousand barrels. (*Source:* Energy Information Administration)

   a. Write two ordered pairs of the form (years after 2000, crude oil production).

   b. Assume the relationship between years after 2000 and crude oil production is linear over this period. Use the ordered pairs from part (a) to write an equation of the line relating years after 2000 to crude oil production.

   c. Use the linear equation from part (b) to estimate crude oil production in the United States in 2010, if this trend were to continue.

59. A rock is dropped from the top of a 400-foot cliff. After 1 second, the rock is traveling 32 feet per second. After 3 seconds, the rock is traveling 96 feet per second.

400 feet

a. Assume that the relationship between time and speed is linear and write an equation describing this relationship. Use ordered pairs of the form (time, speed).

b. Use this equation to determine the speed of the rock 4 seconds after it is dropped.

61. In 2004 there were approximately 83,000 gas-electric hybrid vehicles sold in the United States. In 2007, there were approximately 353,000 such vehicles sold. (*Source:* Energy Information Administration, Department of Energy)

a. Assume the relationship between years past 2004 and the number of vehicles sold is linear over this period. Write an equation describing the relationship between time and the number of vehicles sold. Use ordered pairs of the form (years past 2004, number of vehicles sold).

b. Use this equation to estimate the number of gas-electric hybrid sales in 2009.

63. In 2007 there were approximately 5540 cinema sites in the United States. In 2003 there were 5700 cinema sites. (*Source:* National Association of Theater Owners)

a. Assume the relationship between years past 2003 and the number of cinema sites is linear over this period. Write an equation describing this relationship. Use ordered pairs of the form (years past 2003, number of cinema sites).

b. Use this equation to predict the number of cinema sites in 2010.

60. A Hawaiian fruit company is studying the sales of a pineapple sauce to see if this product is to be continued. At the end of its first year, profits on this product amounted to $30,000. At the end of the fourth year, profits were $66,000.

a. Assume that the relationship between years on the market and profit is linear and write an equation describing this relationship. Use ordered pairs of the form (years on the market, profit).

b. Use this equation to predict the profit at the end of 7 years.

62. In 2008, there were approximately 945 thousand restaurants in the United States. In 2004, there were 875 thousand restaurants. (*Source:* National Restaurant Association)

a. Assume the relationship between years past 2004 and the number of restaurants is linear over this period. Write an equation describing the relationship between time and the number of restaurants. Use ordered pairs of the form (years past 2004, numbers of restaurants in thousands).

b. Use this equation to predict the number of eating establishments in 2012.

64. In 2006, the U.S. population per square mile of land area was approximately 83.6. In 2000, the population per square mile was 79.6.

a. Assume the relationship between years past 2000 and population per square mile is linear over this period. Write an equation describing the relationship between year and population per square mile. Use ordered pairs of the form (years past 2000, population per square mile).

b. Use this equation to predict the population per square mile in 2010.

65. The Pool Fun Company has learned that, by pricing a newly released Fun Noodle at $3, sales will reach 10,000 Fun Noodles per day during the summer. Raising the price to $5 will cause sales to fall to 8000 Fun Noodles per day.

    a. Assume that the relationship between price and number of Fun Noodles sold is linear and write an equation describing this relationship. Use ordered pairs of the form (price, number sold).

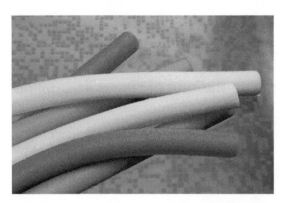

    b. Predict the daily sales of Fun Noodles if the price is $3.50.

66. The value of a building bought in 1995 may be depreciated (or decreased) as time passes for income tax purposes. Seven years after the building was bought, this value was $225,000 and 12 years after it was bought, this value was $195,000.

    a. If the relationship between number of years past 1995 and the depreciated value of the building is linear, write an equation describing this relationship. Use ordered pairs of the form (years past 1995, value of building).

    b. Use this equation to estimate the depreciated value of the building in 2013.

Review

Find the value of $x^2 - 3x + 1$ for each given value of x. See Section 5.3.

67. 2   **68.** 5   **69.** -1 **70.** -3

Concept Extensions

Match each linear equation with its graph.

71. $y = 2x + 1$ **72.** $y = -x + 1$ **73.** $y = -3x - 2$ **74.** $y = \dfrac{5}{3}x - 2$

a. 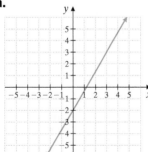   **b.** 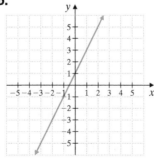   **c.** 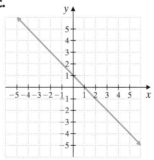   **d.**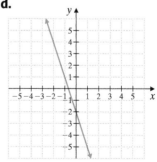

75. Write an equation in standard form of the line that contains the point $(-1, 2)$ and is parallel to (has the same slope as) the line $y = 3x - 1$.

76. Write an equation in standard form of the line that contains the point $(4, 0)$ and is parallel to (has the same slope as) the line $y = -2x + 3$.

77. Write an equation in standard form of the line that contains the point $(-1, 2)$ and is perpendicular to the line $y = 3x - 1$.

78. Write an equation in standard form of the line that contains the point $(4, 0)$ and is perpendicular to the line $y = -2x + 3$.

A Determine Whether an Ordered Pair Is a Solution of a Linear Inequality in Two Variables.

B Graph a Linear Inequality in Two Variables

7.6 GRAPHING LINEAR INEQUALITIES IN TWO VARIABLES

Recall that a linear equation in two variables is an equation that can be written in the form $Ax + By = C$, where A, B, and C are real numbers and A and B are not both 0. A **linear inequality in two variables** is an inequality that can be written in one of the forms

$$Ax + By < C \qquad Ax + By \leq C$$
$$Ax + By > C \qquad Ax + By \geq C$$

where A, B, and C are real numbers and A and B are not both 0.

Objective **A** Determining Solutions of Linear Inequalities in Two Variables

Just as for linear equations in x and y, an ordered pair is a **solution** of an inequality in x and y if replacing the variables with the coordinates of the ordered pair results in a true statement.

PRACTICE 1

Determine whether each ordered pair is a solution of $x - 4y > 8$.
a. $(-3, 2)$
b. $(9, 0)$

Example 1 Determine whether each ordered pair is a solution of the inequality $2x - y < 6$.

a. $(5, -1)$ **b.** $(2, 7)$

Solution:

a. We replace x with 5 and y with -1 and see if a true statement results.

$$2x - y < 6$$
$$2(5) - (-1) < 6 \quad \text{Replace } x \text{ with 5 and } y \text{ with } -1.$$
$$10 + 1 < 6$$
$$11 < 6 \quad \text{False}$$

The ordered pair $(5, -1)$ is not a solution since $11 < 6$ is a false statement.

b. We replace x with 2 and y with 7 and see if a true statement results.

$$2x - y < 6$$
$$2(2) - (7) < 6 \quad \text{Replace } x \text{ with 2 and } y \text{ with 7.}$$
$$4 - 7 < 6$$
$$-3 < 6 \quad \text{True}$$

The ordered pair $(2, 7)$ is a solution since $-3 < 6$ is a true statement.

Work Practice 1

Objective **B** Graphing Linear Inequalities in Two Variables

The linear equation $x - y = 1$ is graphed next. Recall that all points on the line correspond to ordered pairs that satisfy the equation $x - y = 1$.

Notice that the line defined by $x - y = 1$ divides the rectangular coordinate system plane into 2 sides. All points on one side of the line satisfy the inequality $x - y < 1$ and all points on the other side satisfy the inequality $x - y > 1$. The graph on the next page shows a few examples of this.

Answers
1. a. no   **b.** yes

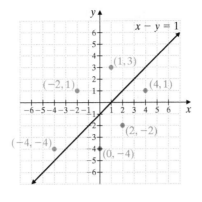

$x - y < 1$
$1 - 3 < 1$ True
$-2 - 1 < 1$ True
$-4 - (-4) < 1$ True

$x - y > 1$
$4 - 1 > 1$ True
$2 - (-2) > 1$ True
$0 - (-4) > 1$ True

The graph of $x - y < 1$ is the region shaded blue and the graph of $x - y > 1$ is the region shaded red below.

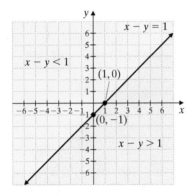

   The region to the left of the line and the region to the right of the line are called **half-planes.** Every line divides the plane (similar to a sheet of paper extending indefinitely in all directions) into two half-planes; the line is called the **boundary.**
   Recall that the inequality $x - y \leq 1$ means

$$x - y = 1 \quad \text{or} \quad x - y < 1$$

Thus, the graph of $x - y \leq 1$ is the half-plane $x - y < 1$ along with the boundary line $x - y = 1$.

To Graph a Linear Inequality in Two Variables

Step 1: Graph the boundary line found by replacing the inequality sign with an equal sign. If the inequality sign is $>$ or $<$, graph a dashed boundary line (indicating that the points on the line are not solutions of the inequality). If the inequality sign is $\geq$ or $\leq$, graph a solid boundary line (indicating that the points on the line are solutions of the inequality).

Step 2: Choose a point *not* on the boundary line as a test point. Substitute the coordinates of this test point into the *original* inequality.

Step 3: If a true statement is obtained in Step 2, shade the half-plane that contains the test point. If a false statement is obtained, shade the half-plane that does not contain the test point.

PRACTICE 2

Graph: $x - y > 3$

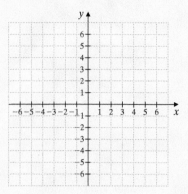

Example 2 Graph: $x + y < 7$

Solution:

Step 1: First we graph the boundary line by graphing the equation $x + y = 7$. We graph this boundary as a *dashed line* because the inequality sign is $<$, and thus the points on the line are not solutions of the inequality $x + y < 7$.

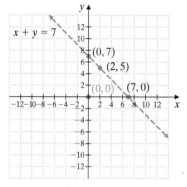

Step 2: Next we choose a test point, being careful *not* to choose a point on the boundary line. We choose $(0, 0)$ and substitute the coordinates of $(0, 0)$ into $x + y < 7$.

$x + y < 7$ Original inequality

$0 + 0 < 7$ Replace x with 0 and y with 0.

$\quad 0 < 7$ True

Step 3: Since the result is a true statement, $(0, 0)$ is a solution of $x + y < 7$, and every point in the same half-plane as $(0, 0)$ is also a solution. To indicate this, we shade the entire half-plane containing $(0, 0)$, as shown.

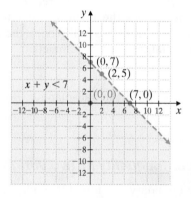

● **Work Practice 2**

Answer

2.

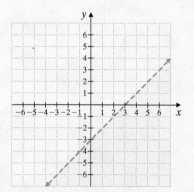

✓**Concept Check** Determine whether $(0, 0)$ is included in the graph of

a. $y \geq 2x + 3$

b. $x < 7$

c. $2x - 3y < 6$

✓ **Concept Check Answers**

a. no   **b.** yes   **c.** yes

Example 3 Graph: $2x - y \geq 3$

Solution:

Step 1: We graph the boundary line by graphing $2x - y = 3$. We draw this line as a solid line because the inequality sign is $\geq$, and thus the points on the line are solutions of $2x - y \geq 3$.

Step 2: Once again, $(0, 0)$ is a convenient test point since it is not on the boundary line.
We substitute 0 for x and 0 for y into the original inequality.

$$2x - y \geq 3$$

$$2(0) - 0 \geq 3 \quad \text{Let } x = 0 \text{ and } y = 0.$$

$$0 \geq 3 \quad \text{False}$$

Step 3: Since the statement is false, no point in the half-plane containing $(0, 0)$ is a solution. Therefore, we shade the half-plane that does not contain $(0, 0)$. Every point in the shaded half-plane and every point on the boundary line is a solution of $2x - y \geq 3$.

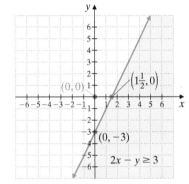

● **Work Practice 3**

Helpful Hint

When graphing an inequality, make sure the test point is substituted into the **original inequality.** For Example 3, we substituted the test point $(0, 0)$ into the **original inequality** $2x - y \geq 3$, *not* $2x - y = 3$.

Example 4 Graph: $x > 2y$

Solution:

Step 1: We find the boundary line by graphing $x = 2y$. The boundary line is a dashed line since the inequality symbol is $>$.

Step 2: We cannot use $(0, 0)$ as a test point because it is a point on the boundary line. We choose instead $(0, 2)$.

$$x > 2y$$

$$0 > 2(2) \quad \text{Let } x = 0 \text{ and } y = 2.$$

$$0 > 4 \quad \text{False}$$

Step 3: Since the statement is false, we shade the half-plane that does not contain the test point $(0, 2)$, as shown.

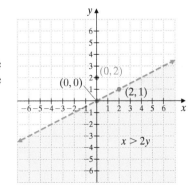

● **Work Practice 4**

PRACTICE 3
Graph: $x - 4y \leq 4$

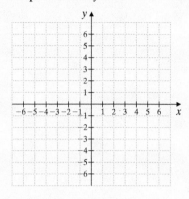

PRACTICE 4
Graph: $y < 3x$

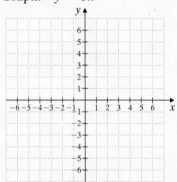

Answers
3.

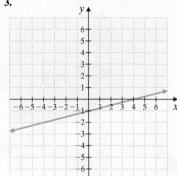

4.

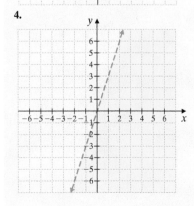

PRACTICE 5

Graph: $3x + 2y \geq 12$

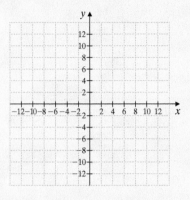

PRACTICE 6

Graph: $x < 2$

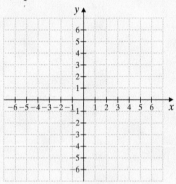

Answers

5.

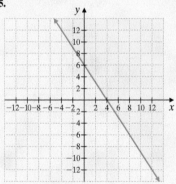

6.

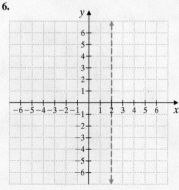

Example 5 Graph: $5x + 4y \leq 20$

Solution: We graph the solid boundary line $5x + 4y = 20$ and choose $(0, 0)$ as the test point.

$$5x + 4y \leq 20$$
$$5(0) + 4(0) \leq 20 \quad \text{Let } x = 0 \text{ and } y = 0.$$
$$0 \leq 20 \quad \text{True}$$

We shade the half-plane that contains $(0, 0)$, as shown.

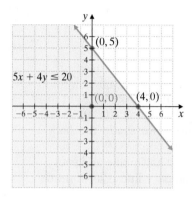

● **Work Practice 5**

Example 6 Graph: $y > 3$

Solution: We graph the dashed boundary line $y = 3$ and choose $(0, 0)$ as the test point. (Recall that the graph of $y = 3$ is a horizontal line with y-intercept 3.)

$$y > 3$$
$$0 > 3 \quad \text{Let } y = 0.$$
$$0 > 3 \quad \text{False}$$

We shade the half-plane that does not contain $(0, 0)$, as shown.

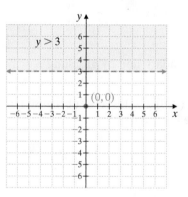

● **Work Practice 6**

Example 7 Graph: $y \le \frac{2}{3}x - 4$

Solution: Graph the solid boundary line $y = \frac{2}{3}x - 4$. This equation is in slope-intercept form with slope $\frac{2}{3}$ and y-intercept -4.

We use this information to graph the line. Then we choose $(0, 0)$ as our test point.

$$y \le \frac{2}{3}x - 4$$

$$0 \le \frac{2}{3} \cdot 0 - 4$$

$$0 \le -4 \quad \text{False}$$

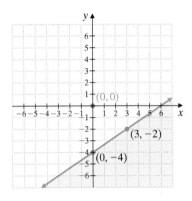

We shade the half-plane that does not contain $(0, 0)$, as shown.

🔵 **Work Practice 7**

PRACTICE 7

Graph: $y \ge \frac{1}{4}x + 3$

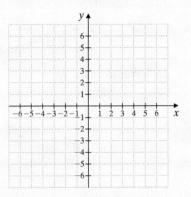

Answer

7.

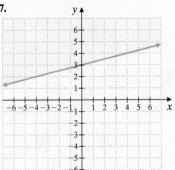

Vocabulary and Readiness Check

Use the choices below to fill in each blank. Some choices may be used more than once, and some not at all.

true	$x > 2$	$y > 2$	half-planes
false	$x \geq 2$	$y \geq 2$	linear inequality in two variables

1. The statement $5x - 6y < 7$ is an example of a _____.
2. A boundary line divides a plane into two regions called _____.
3. True or false: The graph of $5x - 6y < 7$ includes its corresponding boundary line. _____
4. True or false: When graphing a linear inequality, to determine which side of the boundary line to shade, choose a point *not* on the boundary line. _____
5. True or false: The boundary line for the inequality $5x - 6y < 7$ is the graph of $5x - 6y = 7$. _____

6. The graph of _____ is

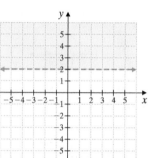

7.6 Exercise Set

FOR EXTRA HELP

MyMathLab®   Math XL   PRACTICE   WATCH   DOWNLOAD   READ   REVIEW

Objective Ⓐ *Determine whether the ordered pairs given are solutions of the linear inequality in two variables. See Example 1.*

1. $x - y > 3$; $(0, 3)$, $(2, -1)$

2. $y - x < -2$; $(2, 1)$, $(5, -1)$

3. $3x - 5y \leq -4$; $(2, 3)$, $(-1, -1)$

4. $2x + y \geq 10$; $(0, 11)$, $(5, 0)$

5. $x < -y$; $(0, 2)$, $(-5, 1)$

6. $y > 3x$; $(0, 0)$, $(1, 4)$

Objective Ⓑ *Graph each inequality. See Examples 2 through 7.*

7. $x + y \leq 1$

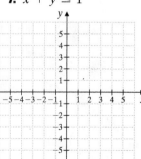

8. $x + y \geq -2$

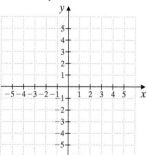

9. $2x - y > -4$

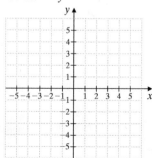

10. $x - 3y < 3$

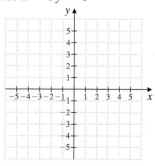

11. $y \geq 2x$

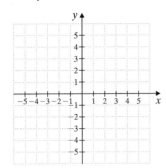

12. $y \leq 3x$

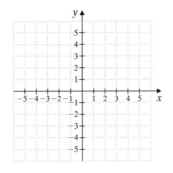

13. $x < -3y$

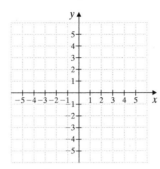

14. $x > -2y$

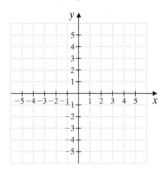

15. $y \geq x + 5$

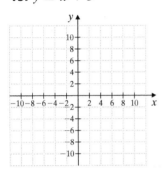

16. $y \leq x + 1$

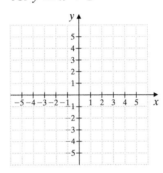

17. $y < 4$

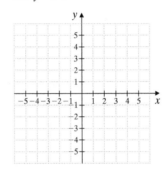

18. $y > 2$

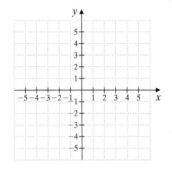

19. $x \geq -3$

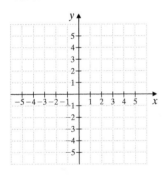

20. $x \leq -1$

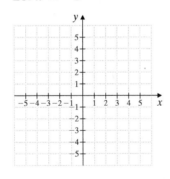

21. $5x + 2y \leq 10$

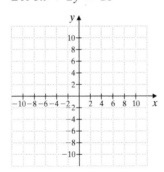

22. $4x + 3y \geq 12$

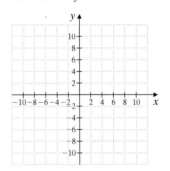

23. $x > y$

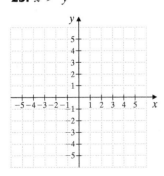

24. $x \leq -y$

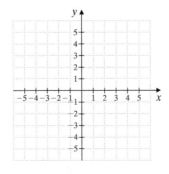

25. $x - y \leq 6$

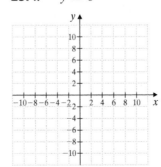

26. $x - y > 10$

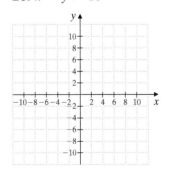

27. $x \geq 0$

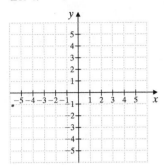

28. $y \leq 0$

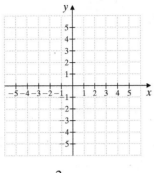

29. $2x + 7y > 5$

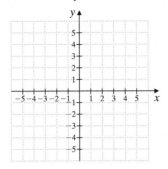

30. $3x + 5y \leq -2$

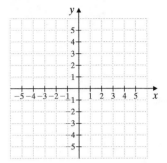

31. $y \geq \dfrac{1}{2}x - 4$

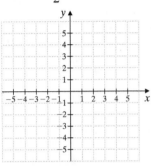

32. $y < \dfrac{2}{5}x - 3$

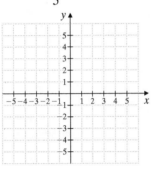

Review

Approximate the coordinates of each point of intersection. See Section 7.1.

33.

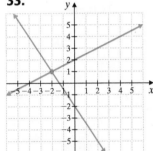

34.

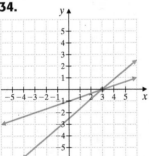

35.

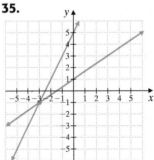

36.

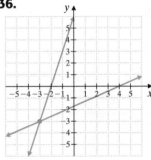

Concept Extensions

Match each inequality with its graph.

a. $x > 2$

b. $y < 2$

c. $y \leq 2x$

d. $y \leq -3x$

37.

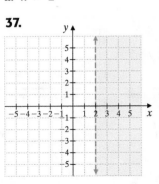

38.

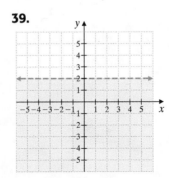

39.

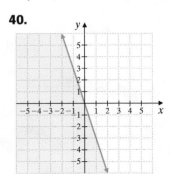

40.

41. Explain why a point on the boundary line should not be chosen as the test point.

42. Write an inequality whose solutions are all points with coordinates whose sum is at least 13.

Determine whether $(1, 1)$ *is included in each graph. See the Concept Check in this section.*

43. $3x + 4y < 8$

44. $y > 5x$

45. $y \geq -\dfrac{1}{2}x$

46. $x > 3$

47. It's the end of the budgeting period for Dennis Fernandes and he has $500 left in his budget for car rental expenses. He plans to spend this budget on a sales trip throughout southern Texas. He will rent a car that costs $30 per day and $0.15 per mile and he can spend no more than $500.

   a. Write an inequality describing this situation. Let x = number of days and let y = number of miles.

   b. Graph this inequality below.

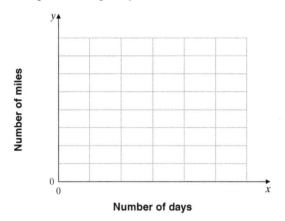

Number of days

   c. Why is the grid showing quadrant I only?

48. Scott Sambracci and Sara Thygeson are planning their wedding. They have calculated that they want the cost of their wedding ceremony x plus the cost of their reception y to be no more than $5000.

   a. Write an inequality describing this relationship.

   b. Graph this inequality below.

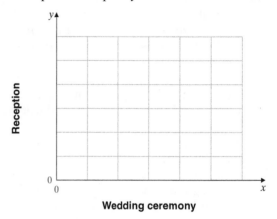

Wedding ceremony

   c. Why is the grid showing quadrant I only?

7 Chapter Highlights

Helpful Hint 📱 Are you preparing for your test? Use the Chapter Test Prep Videos to see the fully worked-out solutions to any of the exercises you want to review.

Definitions and Concepts	**Examples**

Section 7.1   The Rectangular Coordinate System

The **rectangular coordinate system** consists of a plane and a vertical and a horizontal number line intersecting at their 0 coordinates. The vertical number line is called the **y-axis** and the horizontal number line is called the **x-axis.** The point of intersection of the axes is called the **origin.**

To **plot** or **graph** an ordered pair means to find its corresponding point on a rectangular coordinate system.

To plot or graph an ordered pair such as $(3, -2)$, start at the origin. Move 3 units to the right and from there, 2 units down.

To plot or graph $(-3, 4)$, start at the origin. Move 3 units to the left and from there, 4 units up.

An ordered pair is a **solution** of an equation in two variables if replacing the variables with the coordinates of the ordered pair results in a true statement.

If one coordinate of an ordered pair solution of an equation is known, the other value can be determined by substitution.

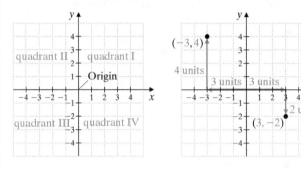

Complete the ordered pair $(0, \quad)$ for the equation $x - 6y = 12$.

$$x - 6y = 12$$
$$0 - 6y = 12 \quad \text{Let } x = 0.$$
$$\frac{-6y}{-6} = \frac{12}{-6} \quad \text{Divide by } -6.$$
$$y = -2$$

The ordered pair solution is $(0, -2)$.

Section 7.2   Graphing Linear Equations

A **linear equation in two variables** is an equation that can be written in the form $Ax + By = C$, where A and B are not both 0. The form $Ax + By = C$ is called **standard form.**

To graph a linear equation in two variables, find three ordered pair solutions. Plot the solution points and draw the line connecting the points.

$$3x + 2y = -6 \qquad x = -5$$
$$y = 3 \qquad y = -x + 10$$

$x + y = 10$ is in standard form.

Graph: $x - 2y = 5$

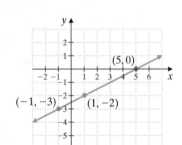

x	y
5	0
1	-2
-1	-3

Definitions and Concepts	**Examples**

Section 7.3   Intercepts

An **intercept** of a graph is a point where the graph intersects an axis. If a graph intersects the x-axis at a, then $(a, 0)$ is an **x-intercept.** If a graph intersects the y-axis at b, then $(0, b)$ is a **y-intercept.**

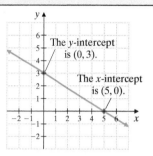

To find the x-intercept(s), let $y = 0$ and solve for x.
To find the y-intercept(s), let $x = 0$ and solve for y.

Find the intercepts for $2x - 5y = -10$ and graph the line.

If $y = 0$, then
$$2x - 5 \cdot 0 = -10$$
$$2x = -10$$
$$\frac{2x}{2} = \frac{-10}{2}$$
$$x = -5$$

If $x = 0$, then
$$2 \cdot 0 - 5y = -10$$
$$-5y = -10$$
$$\frac{-5y}{-5} = \frac{-10}{-5}$$
$$y = 2$$

The x-intercept is $(-5, 0)$. The y-intercept is $(0, 2)$.

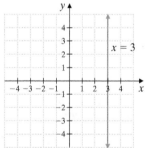

The graph of $x = c$ is a vertical line with x-intercept $(c, 0)$.

The graph of $y = c$ is a horizontal line with y-intercept $(0, c)$.

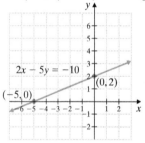

Section 7.4   Slope and Rate of Change

The **slope m** of the line through points (x_1, y_1) and (x_2, y_2) is given by

$$m = \frac{y_2 - y_1}{x_2 - x_1} \qquad \text{as long as } x_2 \neq x_1$$

A horizontal line has slope 0.
The slope of a vertical line is undefined.
Nonvertical parallel lines have the same slope.
Two nonvertical lines are perpendicular if the slope of one is the negative reciprocal of the slope of the other.

The slope of the line through points $(-1, 6)$ and $(-5, 8)$ is

$$m = \frac{y_2 - y_1}{x_2 - x_1} = \frac{8 - 6}{-5 - (-1)} = \frac{2}{-4} = -\frac{1}{2}$$

The slope of the line $y = -5$ is 0.
The line $x = 3$ has undefined slope.

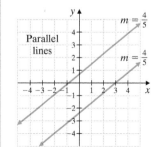

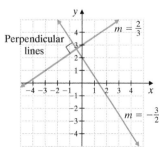

Definitions and Concepts	**Examples**

Section 7.5   Equations of Lines

SLOPE-INTERCEPT FORM

$$y = mx + b$$

m is the slope of the line.
$(0, b)$ is the y-intercept.

POINT-SLOPE FORM

$$y - y_1 = m(x - x_1)$$

m is the slope.
(x_1, y_1) is a point of the line.

Find the slope and the y-intercept of the line $2x + 3y = 6$.
Solve for y:

$$2x + 3y = 6$$
$$3y = -2x + 6 \quad \text{Subtract } 2x.$$
$$y = -\frac{2}{3}x + 2 \quad \text{Divide by 3.}$$

The slope of the line is $-\dfrac{2}{3}$ and the y-intercept is $(0, 2)$.

Find an equation of the line with slope $\dfrac{3}{4}$ that contains the point $(-1, 5)$.

$$y - 5 = \frac{3}{4}[x - (-1)]$$
$$4(y - 5) = 3(x + 1) \quad \text{Multiply by 4.}$$
$$4y - 20 = 3x + 3 \quad \text{Distribute.}$$
$$-3x + 4y = 23 \quad \text{Subtract } 3x \text{ and add 20.}$$

Section 7.6   Graphing Linear Inequalities in Two Variables

A **linear inequality in two variables** is an inequality that can be written in one of these forms:

$$Ax + By < C \qquad Ax + By \le C$$
$$Ax + By > C \qquad Ax + By \ge C$$

where A and B are not both 0.

$$2x - 5y < 6 \qquad x \ge -5$$
$$y > -8x \qquad y \le 2$$

TO GRAPH A LINEAR INEQUALITY

1. Graph the boundary line by graphing the related equation. Draw the line solid if the inequality symbol is $\le$ or $\ge$. Draw the line dashed if the inequality symbol is $<$ or $>$.

2. Choose a test point not on the line. Substitute its coordinates into the original inequality.

3. If the resulting inequality is true, shade the half-plane that contains the test point. If the inequality is not true, shade the half-plane that does not contain the test point.

Graph: $2x - y \le 4$

1. Graph $2x - y = 4$. Draw a solid line because the inequality symbol is $\le$.

2. Check the test point $(0, 0)$ in the original inequality, $2x - y \le 4$.

$$2 \cdot 0 - 0 \le 4 \quad \text{Let } x = 0 \text{ and } y = 0.$$
$$0 \le 4 \quad \text{True}$$

3. The inequality is true, so shade the half-plane containing $(0, 0)$ as shown.

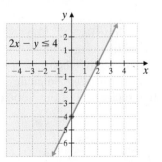

Chapter 7 Review

Plot each ordered pair on the same rectangular coordinate system.

1. $(-7, 0)$

2. $\left(0, 4\dfrac{4}{5}\right)$

3. $(-2, -5)$

4. $(1, -3)$

5. $(0.7, 0.7)$

6. $(-6, 4)$

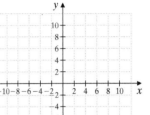

Complete each ordered pair so that it is a solution of the given equation.

7. $-2 + y = 6x; (7, \ )$

8. $y = 3x + 5; (\ , -8)$

Complete the table of values for each given equation.

9. $9 = -3x + 4y$

x	y
	0
	3
9	

10. $y = 5$

x	y
7	
-7	
0	

11. $x = 2y$

x	y
	0
	5
	-5

12. The cost in dollars of producing x compact disc holders is given by $y = 5x + 2000$.

    a. Complete the table.

x	1	100	1000
y			

    b. Find the number of compact disc holders that can be produced for $6430.

Graph each linear equation.

13. $x - y = 1$

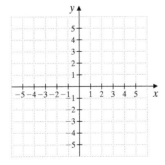

14. $x + y = 6$

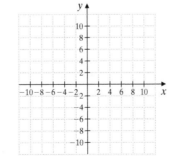

15. $x - 3y = 12$

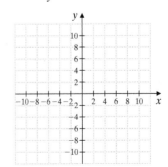

16. $5x - y = -8$

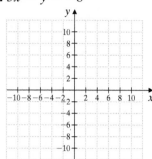

17. $x = 3y$

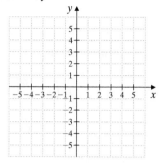

18. $y = -2x$

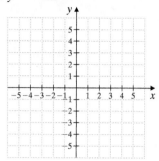

(7.3) *Identify the intercepts in each graph.*

19.

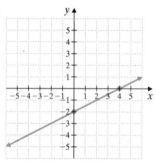

20.

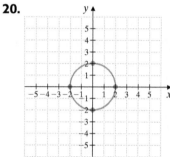

Graph each linear equation.

21. $y = -3$

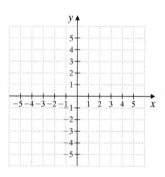

22. $x = 5$

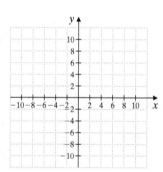

Find the intercepts of each equation.

23. $x - 3y = 12$

24. $-4x + y = 8$

(7.4) *Find the slope of each line.*

25.

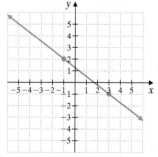

26.

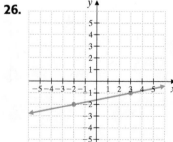

Match each line with its slope.

a.

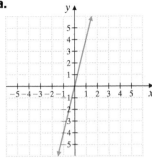

b.

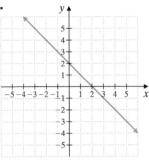

c.

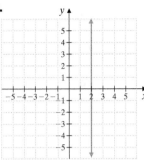

d.

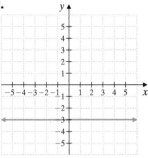

27. $m = 0$

28. $m = -1$

29. undefined slope

30. $m = 4$

Find the slope of the line that passes through each pair of points.

31. $(2, 5)$ and $(6, 8)$

32. $(4, 7)$ and $(1, 2)$

33. $(1, 3)$ and $(-2, -9)$

34. $(-4, 1)$ and $(3, -6)$

Find the slope of each line.

35. $y = 3x + 7$

36. $x - 2y = 4$

37. $y = -2$

38. $x = 0$

△ *Determine whether each pair of lines is parallel, perpendicular, or neither.*

39. $x - y = -6$
  $x + y = 3$

40. $3x + y = 7$
  $-3x - y = 10$

41. $y = 4x + \dfrac{1}{2}$
  $4x + 2y = 1$

42. $y = 6x - \dfrac{1}{3}$
  $x + 6y = 6$

Find the slope of each line and write the slope as a rate of change. Don't forget to attach the proper units.

43. The graph below approximates the number of U.S. college students (in millions) earning a bachelor's degree for each year x.

44. The graph below approximates the number of kidney transplants y in the United States for year x.

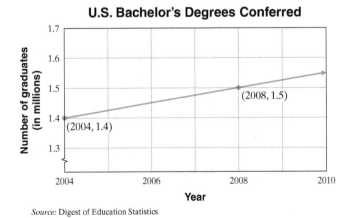

Source: Digest of Education Statistics

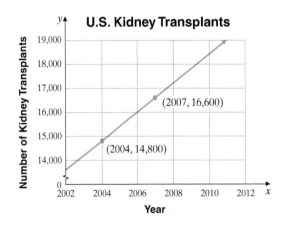

(7.5) *Determine the slope and the y-intercept of the graph of each equation.*

45. $x - 6y = -1$

46. $3x + y = 7$

Write an equation of each line.

47. slope -5; y-intercept $\left(0, \dfrac{1}{2}\right)$

48. slope $\dfrac{2}{3}$; y-intercept $(0, 6)$

Match each equation with its graph.

49. $y = 2x + 1$ **50.** $y = -4x$ **51.** $y = 2x$ **52.** $y = 2x - 1$

a.
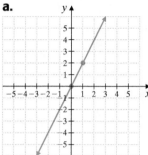

b.
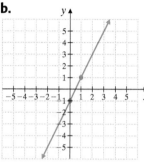

c.
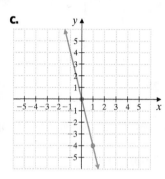

d.
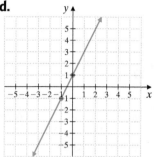

Write an equation of the line with the given slope that passes through the given point. Write the equation in the form $Ax + By = C$.

53. $m = 4$; $(2, 0)$ **54.** $m = -3$; $(0, -5)$ **55.** $m = \dfrac{3}{5}$; $(1, 4)$ **56.** $m = -\dfrac{1}{3}$; $(-3, 3)$

Write an equation of the line passing through each pair of points. Write the equation in the form $y = mx + b$.

57. $(1, 7)$ and $(2, -7)$

58. $(-2, 5)$ and $(-4, 6)$

(7.6) *Graph each inequality.*

59. $x + 6y < 6$

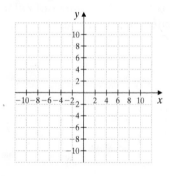

60. $x + y > -2$

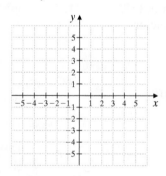

61. $y \geq -7$

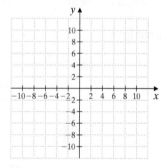

62. $y \leq -4$

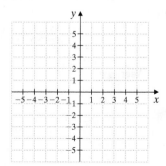

63. $-x \leq y$

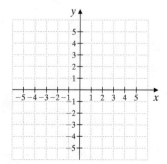

64. $x \geq -y$

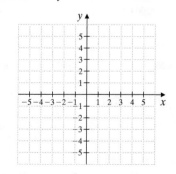

Answers to Selected Exercises

Chapter 7 Graphing Equations and Inequalities

Section 7.1

Vocabulary and Readiness Check **1.** x-axis **3.** origin **5.** x-coordinate; y-coordinate **7.** solution

Exercise Set 7.1 **1.** 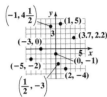 $(1,5)$ and $(3.7, 2.2)$ are in quadrant I, $\left(-1, 4\frac{1}{2}\right)$ is in quadrant II, $(-5, -2)$ is in quadrant III, $(2, -4)$ and $\left(\frac{1}{2}, -3\right)$ are in quadrant IV, $(-3, 0)$ lies on the x-axis, $(0, -1)$ lies on the y-axis **3.** $(0,0)$ **5.** $(3,2)$ **7.** $(-2, -2)$ **9.** $(2, -1)$ **11.** $(0, -3)$ **13.** $(1, 3)$ **15.** $(-3, -1)$ **17. a.** $(2003, 9.2), (2004, 9.2), (2005, 8.8), (2006, 9.1), (2007, 9.6), (2008, 9.8); (2009, 10.6)$ **b.** In the year 2006, the domestic box office was $9.1 billion. **c.**

d. answers may vary **19. a.** $(0.50, 10), (0.75, 12), (1.00, 15), (1.25, 16), (1.50, 18), (1.50, 19), (1.75, 19), (2.00, 20)$ **b.** When Minh studied 1.25 hours, her quiz score was 16. **c.**

d. answers may vary **21.** $(-4, -2), (4, 0)$ **23.** $(-8, -5), (16, 1)$ **25.** $0; 7; -\frac{2}{7}$ **27.** $2; 2; 5$ **29.** $0; -3; 2$ **31.** $2; 6; 3$ **33.** $-12; 5; -6$ **35.** $\frac{5}{7}; \frac{5}{2}; -1$ **37.** $0; -5; -2$ **39.** $2; 1; -6$

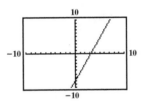
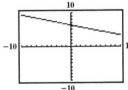

41. a. $13{,}000; 21{,}000; 29{,}000$ **b.** 45 desks **43. a.** $5.59; 5.99; 6.39$ **b.** 2005 **c.** 2013 **45.** $y = 5 - x$ **47.** $y = \dfrac{5 - 2x}{4}$ **49.** $y = -2x$ **51.** false
53. true **55.** negative; negative **57.** positive; negative **59.** $0; 0$ **61.** y **63.** no; answers may vary **65.** answers may vary **67.** answers may vary
69. $(4, -7)$ **71.** 26 units **73.** $47 billion; $53 billion; $59 billion; $63 billion

Section 7.2

Calculator Explorations 1.

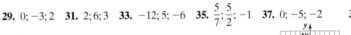

3. **5.**

Exercise Set 7.2 **1.** $6; -2; 5$ **3.** $-4; 0; 4$ **5.** $0; 2; -1$ **7.** $3; -1; -5$

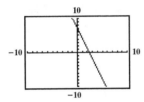 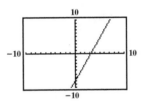 

9. **11.** **13.** **15.** **17.** **19.**

21. **23.** **25.** **27.** **29.** **31.**

A15

33. a.

b. yes; answers may vary **35. a.** 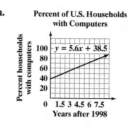 **b.** $(5, 66.5)$

c. In 2003, 66.5% of American households had at least one computer.

37. $(4, -1)$ **39.** $3; -3$ **41.** $0; 0$ **43.** **45.** 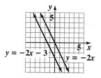 **47.** $0; 1; 1; 4; 4$ **49.** $x + y = 12; 9$ cm

51. yes; answers may vary

Section 7.3

Calculator Explorations **1.**  **3.** 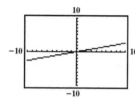 **5.**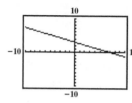

Vocabulary and Readiness Check **1.** linear **3.** horizontal **5.** y-intercept **7.** $y; x$ **9.** false **11.** true

Exercise Set 7.3 **1.** $(-1, 0); (0, 1)$ **3.** $(-2, 0); (2, 0); (0, -2)$ **5.** $(-2, 0); (1, 0); (3, 0); (0, 3)$ **7.** $(-1, 0); (1, 0); (0, 1); (0, -2)$

9. **11.** **13.** **15.** **17.** **19.**

21. **23.** **25.** **27.** **29.** **31.**

33. **35.** **37.** **39.** **41.** **43.**

45. $\dfrac{3}{2}$ **47.** 6 **49.** $-\dfrac{6}{5}$ **51.** c **53.** a **55.** infinite **57.** 0 **59.** answers may vary **61.** $(0, 200)$; no chairs and 200 desks are manufactured.

63. 300 chairs **65.** $y = -4$ **67. a.** $(31.1, 0)$ **b.** 31.1 years after 2003, there may be no newspaper circulation.

Section 7.4

Calculator Explorations **1.** 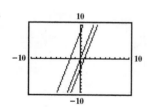 **3.**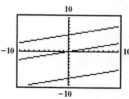

Vocabulary and Readiness Check **1.** slope **3.** 0 **5.** positive **7.** $y; x$ **9.** positive **11.** 0 **13.** downward **15.** vertical

Exercise Set 7.4 **1.** $m = -1$ **3.** $m = -\dfrac{1}{4}$ **5.** $m = 0$ **7.** undefined slope **9.** $m = -\dfrac{4}{3}$ **11.** $m = \dfrac{5}{2}$ **13.** line 1 **15.** line 2 **17.** $m = 5$

19. $m = -0.3$ **21.** $m = -2$ **23.** undefined slope **25.** $m = \dfrac{2}{3}$ **27.** undefined slope **29.** $m = \dfrac{1}{2}$ **31.** $m = 0$ **33.** $m = -\dfrac{3}{4}$ **35.** $m = 4$

37. neither **39.** neither **41.** parallel **43.** perpendicular **45. a.** 1 **b.** -1 **47. a.** $\dfrac{9}{11}$ **b.** $-\dfrac{11}{9}$ **49.** $\dfrac{3}{5}$ **51.** 12.5% **53.** 40% **55.** 37%; 35%

57. $m = \dfrac{5}{4}$; Every 4 years, there are/should be 5 million more U.S. households with televisions. **59.** $m = 0.15$; Every year, the median age of U.S.

automobiles increases by 0.15 year. **61.** $y = 2x - 14$ **63.** $y = -6x - 11$ **65.** d **67.** b **69.** e **71.** $m = \dfrac{1}{2}$ **73.** answers may vary **75.** 29.5

77. 1999; 28.3 mi per gal **79.** from 2006 to 2007 **81.** $x = 20$ **83. a.** (2004, 2025), (2007, 2208) **b.** 61 **c.** For the years 2004 through 2007, the number of heart transplants increased at a rate of 61 per year. **85.** Opposite sides are parallel since their slopes are equal, so the figure is a parallelogram. **87.** 2.0625 **89.** -1.6 **91.** The line becomes steeper.

Section 7.5

Calculator Explorations 1.

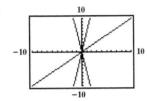

3.

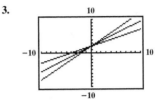

Vocabulary and Readiness Check 1. slope-intercept; m; b **3.** point-slope **5.** slope-intercept **7.** horizontal

Exercise Set 7.5 1.

3.

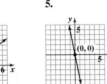

5.

7.

9.

11.

13. $y = 5x + 3$ **15.** $y = -4x - \dfrac{1}{6}$ **17.** $y = \dfrac{2}{3}x$ **19.** $y = -8$ **21.** $y = -\dfrac{1}{5}x + \dfrac{1}{9}$ **23.** $-6x + y = -10$ **25.** $8x + y = -13$ **27.** $3x - 2y = 27$

29. $x + 2y = -3$ **31.** $2x - y = 4$ **33.** $8x - y = -11$ **35.** $4x - 3y = -1$ **37.** $8x + 13y = 0$ **39.** $y = -\dfrac{1}{2}x + \dfrac{5}{3}$ **41.** $y = -x + 17$ **43.** $x = -\dfrac{3}{4}$

45. $y = x + 16$ **47.** $y = -5x + 7$ **49.** $y = 2$ **51.** $y = \dfrac{3}{2}x$ **53.** $y = -3$ **55.** $y = -\dfrac{4}{7}x - \dfrac{18}{7}$ **57. a.** (0, 302), (4, 322) **b.** $y = 5x + 302$

c. 312 million **59. a.** $s = 32t$ **b.** 128 ft/sec **61. a.** $y = 90{,}000x + 83{,}000$ **b.** 533,000 vehicles **63. a.** $y = -40x + 5700$ **b.** 5420 cinema sites **65. a.** $S = -1000p + 13{,}000$ **b.** 9500 Fun Noodles **67.** -1 **69.** 5 **71.** b **73.** d **75.** $3x - y = -5$ **77.** $x + 3y = 5$

Section 7.6

Vocabulary and Readiness Check 1. linear inequality in two variables **3.** false **5.** true

Exercise Set 7.6 1. no; no **3.** yes; no **5.** no; yes **7.**

9.

11.

13.

15.

17.

19.

21.

23.

25.

27.

29.

31.

33. $(-2, 1)$ **35.** $(-3, -1)$ **37.** a **39.** b **41.** answers may vary **43.** yes **45.** yes

47. a. $30x + 0.15y \le 500$ **b.**

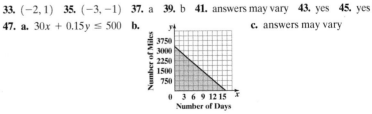

c. answers may vary

Chapter 7 Review **1–6.**

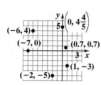

7. $(7, 44)$ **8.** $\left(-\dfrac{13}{3}, -8\right)$ **9.** $-3; 1; 9$ **10.** $5; 5; 5$ **11.** $0; 10; -10$ **12. a.** $2005; 2500; 7000$

b. 886 compact disc holders

13.   **14.**   **15.**   **16.**   **17.**   **18.**

19. $(4, 0); (0, -2)$ **20.** $(-2, 0); (2, 0); (0, 2); (0, -2)$ **21.**   **22.**

23. $(12, 0), (0, -4)$ **24.** $(-2, 0), (0, 8)$

25. $m = -\dfrac{3}{4}$ **26.** $m = \dfrac{1}{5}$ **27.** d **28.** b

29. c **30.** a **31.** $m = \dfrac{3}{4}$ **32.** $m = \dfrac{5}{3}$

33. $m = 4$ **34.** $m = -1$

35. $m = 3$ **36.** $m = \dfrac{1}{2}$ **37.** $m = 0$ **38.** undefined slope **39.** perpendicular **40.** parallel **41.** neither **42.** perpendicular

43. $m = 0.025$; Every 1 year, 0.025 million (25,000) more students graduate with a bachelor's degree. **44.** $m = 600$; Every 1 year, 600 more people get a kidney transplant. **45.** $m = \dfrac{1}{6}; \left(0, \dfrac{1}{6}\right)$ **46.** $m = -3; (0, 7)$ **47.** $y = -5x + \dfrac{1}{2}$ **48.** $y = \dfrac{2}{3}x + 6$ **49.** d **50.** c **51.** a **52.** b

53. $-4x + y = -8$ **54.** $3x + y = -5$ **55.** $-3x + 5y = 17$ **56.** $x + 3y = 6$ **57.** $y = -14x + 21$ **58.** $y = -\dfrac{1}{2}x + 4$

59.   **60.**   **61.**   **62.**   **63.**   **64.**

Exponents and Polynomials

8

Objectives

A Evaluate Exponential Expressions.

B Use the Product Rule for Exponents.

C Use the Power Rule for Exponents.

D Use the Power Rules for Products and Quotients.

E Use the Quotient Rule for Exponents, and Define a Number Raised to the 0 Power.

F Decide Which Rule(s) to Use to Simplify an Expression.

PRACTICE 1–6

Evaluate each expression.

1. 3^4 **2.** 7^1

3. $(-2)^3$ **4.** -2^3

5. $\left(\dfrac{2}{3}\right)^2$ **6.** $5 \cdot 6^2$

Answers

1. 81   **2.** 7   **3.** -8 **4.** -8

5. $\dfrac{4}{9}$ **6.** 180

654

8.1 EXPONENTS

Objective **A** Evaluating Exponential Expressions

In this section, we continue our work with integer exponents. Recall from Section 1.9 that repeated multiplication of the same factor can be written using exponents. For example,

$$2 \cdot 2 \cdot 2 \cdot 2 \cdot 2 = 2^5$$

The exponent 5 tells us how many times 2 is a factor. The expression 2^5 is called an **exponential expression**. It is also called the fifth **power** of 2, or we can say that 2 is **raised** to the fifth power.

$$5^6 = \underbrace{5 \cdot 5 \cdot 5 \cdot 5 \cdot 5 \cdot 5}_{\text{6 factors; each factor is } 5} \quad \text{and} \quad (-3)^4 = \underbrace{(-3) \cdot (-3) \cdot (-3) \cdot (-3)}_{\text{4 factors; each factor is } -3}$$

The **base** of an exponential expression is the repeated factor. The **exponent** is the number of times that the base is used as a factor.

$$a^{\overset{\text{exponent or power}}{n}} = \underbrace{a \cdot a \cdot a \cdots a}_{\substack{\uparrow \\ \text{base} \quad n \text{ factors; each factor is } a}}$$

Examples Evaluate each expression.

1. $2^3 = 2 \cdot 2 \cdot 2 = 8$

2. $3^1 = 3$. To raise 3 to the first power means to use 3 as a factor only once. When no exponent is shown, the exponent is assumed to be 1.

3. $(-4)^2 = (-4)(-4) = 16$

4. $-4^2 = -(4 \cdot 4) = -16$

5. $\left(\dfrac{1}{2}\right)^4 = \dfrac{1}{2} \cdot \dfrac{1}{2} \cdot \dfrac{1}{2} \cdot \dfrac{1}{2} = \dfrac{1}{16}$

6. $4 \cdot 3^2 = 4 \cdot 9 = 36$

● **Work Practice 1–6**

Notice how similar -4^2 is to $(-4)^2$ in the examples above. The difference between the two is the parentheses. In $(-4)^2$, the parentheses tell us that the base, or the repeated factor, is -4. In -4^2, only 4 is the base.

Helpful Hint

Be careful when identifying the base of an exponential expression. Pay close attention to the use of parentheses.

$(-3)^2$	-3^2	$2 \cdot 3^2$
The base is -3.	The base is 3.	The base is 3.
$(-3)^2 = (-3)(-3) = 9$	$-3^2 = -(3 \cdot 3) = -9$	$2 \cdot 3^2 = 2 \cdot 3 \cdot 3 = 18$

An exponent has the same meaning whether the base is a number or a variable. If x is a real number and n is a positive integer, then x^n is the product of n factors, each of which is x.

$$x^n = \underbrace{x \cdot x \cdot x \cdot x \cdot x \cdots x}_{n \text{ factors; each factor is } x}$$

Example 7 Evaluate each expression for the given value of x.

a. $2x^3$ when x is 5 **b.** $\dfrac{9}{x^2}$ when x is -3

Solution:

a. When x is 5, $2x^3 = 2 \cdot 5^3$

$$= 2 \cdot (5 \cdot 5 \cdot 5)$$

$$= 2 \cdot 125$$

$$= 250$$

b. When x is -3, $\dfrac{9}{x^2} = \dfrac{9}{(-3)^2}$

$$= \dfrac{9}{(-3)(-3)}$$

$$= \dfrac{9}{9} = 1$$

● **Work Practice 7**

PRACTICE 7

Evaluate each expression for the given value of x.

a. $3x^2$ when x is 4

b. $\dfrac{x^4}{-8}$ when x is -2

Objective Ⓑ Using the Product Rule

Exponential expressions can be multiplied, divided, added, subtracted, and themselves raised to powers. Let's see if we can discover a shortcut method for multiplying exponential expressions with the same base. By our definition of an exponent,

$$5^4 \cdot 5^3 = \underbrace{(5 \cdot 5 \cdot 5 \cdot 5)}_{4 \text{ factors of } 5} \cdot \underbrace{(5 \cdot 5 \cdot 5)}_{3 \text{ factors of } 5}$$

$$= \underbrace{5 \cdot 5 \cdot 5 \cdot 5 \cdot 5 \cdot 5 \cdot 5}_{7 \text{ factors of } 5}$$

$$= 5^7$$

Also,

$$x^2 \cdot x^3 = \underbrace{(x \cdot x)}_{2 \text{ factors of } x} \cdot \underbrace{(x \cdot x \cdot x)}_{3 \text{ factors of } x}$$

$$= x \cdot x \cdot x \cdot x \cdot x$$

$$= x^5$$

In both cases, notice that the result is exactly the same if the exponents are added.

$$5^4 \cdot 5^3 = 5^{4+3} = 5^7 \quad \text{and} \quad x^2 \cdot x^3 = x^{2+3} = x^5$$

This suggests the following rule.

Product Rule for Exponents

If m and n are positive integers and a is a real number, then

$$a^m \cdot a^n = a^{m+n} \quad \leftarrow \text{Add exponents.}$$

$\qquad \uparrow$ —— Keep common base.

For example,

$$3^5 \cdot 3^7 = 3^{5+7} = 3^{12} \quad \leftarrow \text{Add exponents.}$$

$\qquad \uparrow$ —— Keep common base.

Answers

7. a. 48 **b.** -2

Helpful Hint

Don't forget that

$$3^5 \cdot 3^7 \neq 9^{12} \quad \leftarrow \text{Add exponents.}$$

$\uparrow$ _____ Common base *not* kept.

$$3^5 \cdot 3^7 = \underbrace{3 \cdot 3 \cdot 3 \cdot 3 \cdot 3}_{5 \text{ factors of } 3} \cdot \underbrace{3 \cdot 3 \cdot 3 \cdot 3 \cdot 3 \cdot 3 \cdot 3}_{7 \text{ factors of } 3}$$

$$= 3^{12} \quad 12 \text{ factors of } 3, not \ 9$$

In other words, to multiply two exponential expressions with the **same base**, we keep the base and add the exponents. We call this **simplifying** the exponential expression.

PRACTICE 8–12

Use the product rule to simplify each expression.

8. $7^3 \cdot 7^2$ **9.** $x^4 \cdot x^9$

10. $r^5 \cdot r$ **11.** $s^6 \cdot s^2 \cdot s^3$

12. $(-3)^9 \cdot (-3)$

Examples Use the product rule to simplify each expression.

8. $4^2 \cdot 4^5 = 4^{2+5} = 4^7 \quad \leftarrow \text{Add exponents.}$

$\uparrow$ _____ Keep common base.

9. $x^2 \cdot x^5 = x^{2+5} = x^7$

10. $y^3 \cdot y = y^3 \cdot y^1$

$\qquad = y^{3+1}$

$\qquad = y^4$

Helpful Hint Don't forget that if no exponent is written, it is assumed to be 1.

 11. $y^3 \cdot y^2 \cdot y^7 = y^{3+2+7} = y^{12}$

 12. $(-5)^7 \cdot (-5)^8 = (-5)^{7+8} = (-5)^{15}$

● **Work Practice 8–12**

✓**Concept Check**   Where possible, use the product rule to simplify the expression.

a. $z^2 \cdot z^{14}$ **b.** $x^2 \cdot z^{14}$ **c.** $9^8 \cdot 9^3$ **d.** $9^8 \cdot 2^7$

PRACTICE 13

Use the product rule to simplify $(6x^3)(-2x^9)$.

Example 13 Use the product rule to simplify $(2x^2)(-3x^5)$.

Solution: Recall that $2x^2$ means $2 \cdot x^2$ and $-3x^5$ means $-3 \cdot x^5$.

$$(2x^2)(-3x^5) = (2 \cdot x^2) \cdot (-3 \cdot x^5)$$

$$= (2 \cdot -3) \cdot (x^2 \cdot x^5) \quad \text{Group factors with common bases (using commutative and associative properties).}$$

$$= -6x^7 \quad \text{Simplify.}$$

● **Work Practice 13**

PRACTICE 14–15

Simplify.

14. $(m^5n^{10})(mn^8)$

15. $(-x^9y)(4x^2y^{11})$

Examples Simplify.

14. $(x^2y)(x^3y^2) = (x^2 \cdot x^3) \cdot (y^1 \cdot y^2) \quad \text{Group like bases and write } y \text{ as } y^1.$

$$= x^5 \cdot y^3 \quad \text{or} \quad x^5y^3 \quad \text{Multiply.}$$

15 $(-a^7b^4)(3ab^9) = (-1 \cdot 3) \cdot (a^7 \cdot a^1) \cdot (b^4 \cdot b^9)$

$$= -3a^8b^{13}$$

● **Work Practice 14–15**

Answers

8. 7^5 **9.** x^{13} **10.** r^6 **11.** s^{11}

12. $(-3)^{10}$ **13.** $-12x^{12}$

14. m^6n^{18} **15.** $-4x^{11}y^{12}$

✓**Concept Check Answers**

a. z^{16} **b.** cannot be simplified

c. 9^{11} **d.** cannot be simplified

Helpful Hint

These examples will remind you of the difference between adding and multiplying terms.

Addition

$$5x^3 + 3x^3 = (5 + 3)x^3 = 8x^3 \qquad \text{By the distributive property}$$
$$7x + 4x^2 = 7x + 4x^2 \qquad \text{Cannot be combined}$$

Multiplication

$$(5x^3)(3x^3) = 5 \cdot 3 \cdot x^3 \cdot x^3 = 15x^{3+3} = 15x^6 \quad \text{By the product rule}$$
$$(7x)(4x^2) = 7 \cdot 4 \cdot x \cdot x^2 = 28x^{1+2} = 28x^3 \quad \text{By the product rule}$$

Objective C Using the Power Rule

Exponential expressions can themselves be raised to powers. Let's try to discover a rule that simplifies an expression like $(x^2)^3$. By the definition of a^n,

$$(x^2)^3 = (x^2)(x^2)(x^2) \quad (x^2)^3 \text{ means 3 factors of } (x^2).$$

which can be simplified by the product rule for exponents.

$$(x^2)^3 = (x^2)(x^2)(x^2) = x^{2+2+2} = x^6$$

Notice that the result is exactly the same if we multiply the exponents.

$$(x^2)^3 = x^{2\cdot3} = x^6$$

The following rule states this result.

Power Rule for Exponents

If m and n are positive integers and a is a real number, then

$$(a^m)^n = a^{mn} \quad \leftarrow \text{ Multiply exponents.}$$
$$\qquad\qquad \uparrow\text{_____ Keep the base.}$$

For example,

$$(7^2)^5 = 7^{2\cdot5} = 7^{10} \quad \leftarrow \text{ Multiply exponents.}$$
$$\qquad\qquad \uparrow\text{_____ Keep the base.}$$

$$[(-5)^3]^7 = (-5)^{3\cdot7} = (-5)^{21} \quad \leftarrow \text{Multiply exponents.}$$
$$\qquad\qquad\qquad \uparrow\text{_____ Keep the base.}$$

In other words, to raise an exponential expression to a power, we keep the base and multiply the exponents.

Examples Use the power rule to simplify each expression.

16. $(5^3)^6 = 5^{3\cdot6} = 5^{18}$
17. $(y^8)^2 = y^{8\cdot2} = y^{16}$

● Work Practice 16–17

PRACTICE 16–17

Use the power rule to simplify each expression.
16. $(9^4)^{10}$ **17.** $(z^6)^3$

Helpful Hint

Take a moment to make sure that you understand when to apply the product rule and when to apply the power rule.

Product Rule → Add Exponents	Power Rule → Multiply Exponents
$x^5 \cdot x^7 = x^{5+7} = x^{12}$	$(x^5)^7 = x^{5\cdot7} = x^{35}$
$y^6 \cdot y^2 = y^{6+2} = y^8$	$(y^6)^2 = y^{6\cdot2} = y^{12}$

Answers
16. 9^{40} **17.** z^{18}

Objective ⓓ Using the Power Rules for Products and Quotients

When the base of an exponential expression is a product, the definition of a^n still applies. For example, simplify $(xy)^3$ as follows.

$$(xy)^3 = (xy)(xy)(xy) \quad \text{\small $(xy)^3$ means 3 factors of (xy).}$$
$$= x \cdot x \cdot x \cdot y \cdot y \cdot y \quad \text{\small Group factors with common bases.}$$
$$= x^3 y^3 \quad \text{\small Simplify.}$$

Notice that to simplify the expression $(xy)^3$, we raise each factor within the parentheses to a power of 3.

$$(xy)^3 = x^3 y^3$$

In general, we have the following rule.

> **Power of a Product Rule**
>
> If n is a positive integer and a and b are real numbers, then
> $$(ab)^n = a^n b^n$$
> For example,
> $$(3x)^5 = 3^5 x^5$$

In other words, to raise a product to a power, we raise each factor to the power.

PRACTICE 18–21

Simplify each expression.
18. $(xy)^7$ 19. $(3y)^4$
20. $(-2p^4q^2r)^3$ 21. $(-a^4b)^7$

Examples Simplify each expression.

18. $(st)^4 = s^4 \cdot t^4 = s^4 t^4$ Use the power of a product rule.
19. $(2a)^3 = 2^3 \cdot a^3 = 8a^3$ Use the power of a product rule.
20. $(-5x^2y^3z)^2 = (-5)^2 \cdot (x^2)^2 \cdot (y^3)^2 \cdot (z^1)^2$ Use the power of a product rule.
$$= 25x^4y^6z^2$$
21. $(-xy^3)^5 = (-1xy^3)^5 = (-1)^5 \cdot x^5 \cdot (y^3)^5$ Use the power of a product rule.
$$= -1x^5y^{15} \quad \text{or} \quad -x^5y^{15}$$

● Work Practice 18–21

Let's see what happens when we raise a quotient to a power. For example, we simplify $\left(\dfrac{x}{y}\right)^3$ as follows.

$$\left(\frac{x}{y}\right)^3 = \left(\frac{x}{y}\right)\left(\frac{x}{y}\right)\left(\frac{x}{y}\right) \quad \text{\small $\left(\frac{x}{y}\right)^3$ means 3 factors of $\left(\frac{x}{y}\right)$.}$$
$$= \frac{x \cdot x \cdot x}{y \cdot y \cdot y} \quad \text{\small Multiply fractions.}$$
$$= \frac{x^3}{y^3} \quad \text{\small Simplify.}$$

Notice that to simplify the expression $\left(\dfrac{x}{y}\right)^3$, we raise both the numerator and the denominator to a power of 3.

$$\left(\frac{x}{y}\right)^3 = \frac{x^3}{y^3}$$

In general, we have the following rule.

Answers
18. x^7y^7 19. $81y^4$ 20. $-8p^{12}q^6r^3$
21. $-a^{28}b^7$

Power of a Quotient Rule

If n is a positive integer and a and c are real numbers, then

$$\left(\frac{a}{c}\right)^n = \frac{a^n}{c^n}, \quad c \neq 0$$

For example,

$$\left(\frac{y}{7}\right)^3 = \frac{y^3}{7^3}$$

In other words, to raise a quotient to a power, we raise both the numerator and the denominator to the power.

Examples Simplify each expression.

22. $\left(\dfrac{m}{n}\right)^7 = \dfrac{m^7}{n^7}, \quad n \neq 0$ Use the power of a quotient rule.

23. $\left(\dfrac{2x^4}{3y^5}\right)^4 = \dfrac{2^4 \cdot (x^4)^4}{3^4 \cdot (y^5)^4}$ Use the power of a quotient rule and the power of a product rule.

$$= \dfrac{16x^{16}}{81y^{20}}, \quad y \neq 0 \quad \text{Use the power rule for exponents.}$$

● **Work Practice 22–23**

PRACTICE 22–23
Simplify each expression.
22. $\left(\dfrac{r}{s}\right)^6$ **23.** $\left(\dfrac{5x^6}{9y^3}\right)^2$

Objective ⓔ Using the Quotient Rule and Defining the Zero Exponent

Another pattern for simplifying exponential expressions involves quotients.

$$\frac{x^5}{x^3} = \frac{x \cdot x \cdot x \cdot x \cdot x}{x \cdot x \cdot x}$$

$$= \frac{x \cdot x \cdot x \cdot x \cdot x}{x \cdot x \cdot x}$$

$$= 1 \cdot 1 \cdot 1 \cdot x \cdot x$$

$$= x \cdot x$$

$$= x^2$$

Notice that the result is exactly the same if we subtract exponents of the common bases.

$$\frac{x^5}{x^3} = x^{5-3} = x^2$$

The following rule states this result in a general way.

Quotient Rule for Exponents

If m and n are positive integers and a is a real number, then

$$\frac{a^m}{a^n} = a^{m-n}, \quad a \neq 0$$

For example,

$$\frac{x^6}{x^2} = x^{6-2} = x^4, \quad x \neq 0$$

Answers

22. $\dfrac{r^6}{s^6}, \quad s \neq 0$ **23.** $\dfrac{25x^{12}}{81y^6}, \quad y \neq 0$

In other words, to divide one exponential expression by another with a common base, we keep the base and subtract the exponents.

PRACTICE 24–27

Simplify each quotient.

24. $\dfrac{y^7}{y^3}$ **25.** $\dfrac{5^9}{5^6}$

26. $\dfrac{(-2)^{14}}{(-2)^{10}}$ **27.** $\dfrac{7a^4b^{11}}{ab}$

Examples Simplify each quotient.

24. $\dfrac{x^5}{x^2} = x^{5-2} = x^3$ Use the quotient rule.

25. $\dfrac{4^7}{4^3} = 4^{7-3} = 4^4 = 256$ Use the quotient rule.

26. $\dfrac{(-3)^5}{(-3)^2} = (-3)^3 = -27$ Use the quotient rule.

27. $\dfrac{2x^5y^2}{xy} = 2 \cdot \dfrac{x^5}{x^1} \cdot \dfrac{y^2}{y^1}$

$\qquad = 2 \cdot (x^{5-1}) \cdot (y^{2-1})$ Use the quotient rule.

$\qquad = 2x^4y^1$ or $2x^4y$

● **Work Practice 24–27**

$\dfrac{x^3}{x^3}$ Let's now give meaning to an expression such as x^0. To do so, we will simplify $\dfrac{x^3}{x^3}$ in two ways and compare the results.

$$\dfrac{x^3}{x^3} = x^{3-3} = x^0 \qquad \text{Apply the quotient rule.}$$

$$\dfrac{x^3}{x^3} = \dfrac{x \cdot x \cdot x}{x \cdot x \cdot x} = 1 \qquad \text{Divide the numerator and denominator by all common factors.}$$

Since $\dfrac{x^3}{x^3} = x^0$ and $\dfrac{x^3}{x^3} = 1$, we define that $x^0 = 1$ as long as x is not 0.

> ### Zero Exponent
>
> $a^0 = 1$, as long as a is not 0.
>
> For example, $5^0 = 1$.

In other words, a base raised to the 0 power is 1, as long as the base is not 0.

PRACTICE 28–32

Simplify each expression.
28. 8^0 **29.** $(2r^2s)^0$
30. $(-7)^0$ **31.** -7^0
32. $7y^0$

Examples Simplify each expression.

28. $3^0 = 1$
29. $(5x^3y^2)^0 = 1$
30. $(-4)^0 = 1$
31. $-4^0 = -1 \cdot 4^0 = -1 \cdot 1 = -1$
32. $5x^0 = 5 \cdot x^0 = 5 \cdot 1 = 5$

● **Work Practice 28–32**

Answers
24. y^4 **25.** 125 **26.** 16 **27.** $7a^3b^{10}$
28. 1 **29.** 1 **30.** 1 **31.** -1
32. 7

✓Concept Check Suppose you are simplifying each expression. Tell whether you would *add* the exponents, *subtract* the exponents, *multiply* the exponents, *divide* the exponents, or *none of these.*

a. $(x^{63})^{21}$ **b.** $\dfrac{y^{15}}{y^3}$ **c.** $z^{16} + z^8$ **d.** $w^{45} \cdot w^9$

Objective ⓕ Deciding Which Rule to Use

Let's practice deciding which rule to use to simplify an expression. We will continue this discussion with more examples in the next section.

Example 33 Simplify each expression.

a. $x^7 \cdot x^4$ **b.** $\left(\dfrac{t}{2}\right)^4$ **c.** $(9y^5)^2$

Solution:

a. Here, we have a product, so we use the product rule to simplify.

$x^7 \cdot x^4 = x^{7+4} = x^{11}$

b. This is a quotient raised to a power, so we use the power of a quotient rule.

$\left(\dfrac{t}{2}\right)^4 = \dfrac{t^4}{2^4} = \dfrac{t^4}{16}$

c. This is a product raised to a power, so we use the power of a product rule.

$(9y^5)^2 = 9^2(y^5)^2 = 81y^{10}$

⬤ **Work Practice 33**

Example 34 Simplify each expression.

a. $4^2 - 4^0$ **b.** $(x^0)^3 + (2^0)^5$ **c.** $\left(\dfrac{3y^7}{6x^5}\right)^2$ **d.** $\dfrac{(2a^3b^4)^3}{-8a^9b^2}$

Solution:

a. $4^2 - 4^0 = 16 - 1 = 15$ Remember that $4^0 = 1$.

b. $(x^0)^3 + (2^0)^5 = 1^3 + 1^5 = 1 + 1 = 2$

c. $\left(\dfrac{3y^7}{6x^5}\right)^2 = \dfrac{3^2(y^7)^2}{6^2(x^5)^2} = \dfrac{9 \cdot y^{14}}{36 \cdot x^{10}} = \dfrac{y^{14}}{4x^{10}}$

d. $\dfrac{(2a^3b^4)^3}{-8a^9b^2} = \dfrac{2^3(a^3)^3(b^4)^3}{-8a^9b^2} = \dfrac{8a^9b^{12}}{-8a^9b^2} = -1 \cdot (a^{9-9}) \cdot (b^{12-2})$

$= -1 \cdot a^0 \cdot b^{10} = -1 \cdot 1 \cdot b^{10} = -b^{10}$

⬤ **Work Practice 34**

PRACTICE 33

Simplify each expression.

a. $\dfrac{x^7}{x^4}$ **b.** $(3y^4)^4$ **c.** $\left(\dfrac{x}{4}\right)^3$

PRACTICE 34

Simplify each expression.

a. $2^3 - 2^0$ **b.** $(y^0)^7 + (5^0)^3$

c. $\left(\dfrac{7x^9}{14y^6}\right)^2$ **d.** $\dfrac{(3a^2b^5)^3}{-27a^6b^4}$

Answers

33. a. x^3 **b.** $81y^{16}$ **c.** $\dfrac{x^3}{64}$

34. a. 7 **b.** 2 **c.** $\dfrac{x^{18}}{4y^{12}}$ **d.** $-b^{11}$

✓ **Concept Check Answers**

a. multiply **b.** subtract

c. none of these **d.** add

Vocabulary and Readiness Check

Use the choices below to fill in each blank. Some choices may be used more than once.

0	base	add
1	exponent	multiply

1. Repeated multiplication of the same factor can be written using a(n) _____.
2. In 5^2, the 2 is called the _____ and the 5 is called the _____.
3. To simplify $x^2 \cdot x^7$, keep the base and _____ the exponents.
4. To simplify $(x^3)^6$, keep the base and _____ the exponents.
5. The understood exponent on the term y is _____.
6. If $x^\square = 1$, the exponent is _____.

For each of the following expressions, state the exponent shown and its corresponding base.

7. 3^2

8. $(-3)^6$

9. -4^2

10. $5 \cdot 3^4$

11. $5x^2$

12. $(5x)^2$

8.1 Exercise Set

FOR EXTRA HELP

PRACTICE   WATCH   DOWNLOAD   READ   REVIEW

Objective A *Evaluate each expression. See Examples 1 through 6.*

1. 7^2

2. -3^2

3. $(-5)^1$

4. $(-3)^2$

5. -2^4

6. -4^3

7. $(-2)^4$

8. $(-4)^3$

9. $\left(\dfrac{1}{3}\right)^3$

10. $\left(-\dfrac{1}{9}\right)^2$

11. $7 \cdot 2^4$

12. $9 \cdot 2^2$

Evaluate each expression with the given replacement values. See Example 7.

13. x^2 when $x = -2$

14. x^3 when $x = -2$

15. $5x^3$ when $x = 3$

16. $4x^2$ when $x = 5$

17. $2xy^2$ when $x = 3$ and $y = -5$

18. $-4x^2y^3$ when $x = 2$ and $y = -1$

19. $\dfrac{2z^4}{5}$ when $z = -2$

20. $\dfrac{10}{3y^3}$ when $y = -3$

Objective B *Use the product rule to simplify each expression. See Examples 8 through 15.*

21. $x^2 \cdot x^5$

22. $y^2 \cdot y$

23. $(-3)^3 \cdot (-3)^9$

24. $(-5)^7 \cdot (-5)^6$

25. $(5y^4)(3y)$

26. $(-2z^3)(-2z^2)$

27. $(x^9y)(x^{10}y^5)$

28. $(a^2b)(a^{13}b^{17})$

29. $(-8mn^6)(9m^2n^2)$

30. $(-7a^3b^3)(7a^{19}b)$

31. $(4z^{10})(-6z^7)(z^3)$

32. $(12x^5)(-x^6)(x^4)$

△ **33.** The rectangle below has width $4x^2$ feet and length $5x^3$ feet. Find its area as an expression in x.

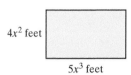

$4x^2$ feet

$5x^3$ feet

△ **34.** The parallelogram below has base length $9y^7$ meters and height $2y^{10}$ meters. Find its area as an expression in y.

$2y^{10}$ meters

$9y^7$ meters

Objectives 🅒 🅓 Mixed Practice *Use the power rule and the power of a product or quotient rule to simplify each expression. See Examples 16 through 23.*

35. $(x^9)^4$

36. $(y^7)^5$

37. $(pq)^8$

38. $(ab)^6$

39. $(2a^5)^3$

40. $(4x^6)^2$

41. $(x^2y^3)^5$

42. $(a^4b)^7$

43. $(-7a^2b^5c)^2$

44. $(-3x^7yz^2)^3$

45. $\left(\dfrac{r}{s}\right)^9$

46. $\left(\dfrac{q}{t}\right)^{11}$

47. $\left(\dfrac{mp}{n}\right)^9$

48. $\left(\dfrac{xy}{7}\right)^2$

49. $\left(\dfrac{-2xz}{y^5}\right)^2$

50. $\left(\dfrac{xy^4}{-3z^3}\right)^3$

△ **51.** The square shown has sides of length $8z^5$ decimeters. Find its area.

$8z^5$
decimeters

△ **52.** Given the circle below with radius $5y$ centimeters, find its area. Do not approximate π.

$5y$ cm

△ **53.** The vault below is in the shape of a cube. If each side is $3y^4$ feet, find its volume.

$3y^4$ feet $3y^4$ feet

$3y^4$ feet

△ **54.** The silo shown is in the shape of a cylinder. If its radius is $4x$ meters and its height is $5x^3$ meters, find its volume. Do not approximate π.

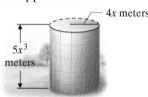

$4x$ meters

$5x^3$ meters

Objective 🅔 *Use the quotient rule and simplify each expression. See Examples 24 through 27.*

55. $\dfrac{x^3}{x}$

56. $\dfrac{y^{10}}{y^9}$

57. $\dfrac{(-4)^6}{(-4)^3}$

58. $\dfrac{(-6)^{13}}{(-6)^{11}}$

59. $\dfrac{p^7q^{20}}{pq^{15}}$

60. $\dfrac{x^8y^6}{xy^5}$

61. $\dfrac{7x^2y^6}{14x^2y^3}$

62. $\dfrac{9a^4b^7}{27ab^2}$

Simplify each expression. See Examples 28 through 32.

63. 7^0

64. 23^0

65. $(2x)^0$

66. $(4y)^0$

67. $-7x^0$

68. $-2x^0$

69. $5^0 + y^0$

70. $-3^0 + 4^0$

Objectives Ⓐ Ⓑ Ⓒ Ⓓ Ⓔ Ⓕ **Mixed Practice** *Simplify each expression. See Examples 1 through 6, and 8 through 34.*

71. -9^2

72. $(-9)^2$

73. $\left(\dfrac{1}{4}\right)^3$

74. $\left(\dfrac{2}{3}\right)^3$

75. $b^4 b^2$

76. $y^4 y$

77. $a^2 a^3 a^4$

78. $x^2 x^{15} x^9$

79. $(2x^3)(-8x^4)$

80. $(3y^4)(-5y)$

81. $(a^7 b^{12})(a^4 b^8)$

82. $(y^2 z^2)(y^{15} z^{13})$

83. $(-2mn^6)(-13m^8 n)$

84. $(-3s^5 t)(-7st^{10})$

85. $(z^4)^{10}$

86. $(t^5)^{11}$

87. $(4ab)^3$

88. $(2ab)^4$

89. $(-6xyz^3)^2$

90. $(-3xy^2 a^3)^3$

91. $\dfrac{3x^5}{x^4}$

92. $\dfrac{5x^9}{x^3}$

93. $(9xy)^2$

94. $(2ab)^5$

95. $2^3 + 2^0$

96. $7^2 - 7^0$

97. $\left(\dfrac{3y^5}{6x^4}\right)^3$

98. $\left(\dfrac{2ab}{6yz}\right)^4$

99. $\dfrac{2x^3 y^2 z}{xyz}$

100. $\dfrac{x^{12} y^{13}}{x^5 y^7}$

101. $(5^0)^3 + (y^0)^7$

102. $(9^0)^4 + (z^0)^5$

103. $\left(\dfrac{5x^9}{10y^{11}}\right)^2$

104. $\left(\dfrac{3a^4}{9b^5}\right)^2$

105. $\dfrac{(2a^5 b^3)^4}{-16a^{20} b^7}$

106. $\dfrac{(2x^6 y^2)^5}{-32x^{20} y^{10}}$

Review

Subtract. See Section 5.5.

107. $5 - 7$

108. $9 - 12$

109. $3 - (-2)$

110. $5 - (-10)$

111. $-11 - (-4)$

112. $-15 - (-21)$

Concept Extensions

Solve. See the Concept Checks in this section. For Exercises 113 through 116, match the expression with the operation needed to simplify each. A letter may be used more than once and a letter may not be used at all.

113. $(x^{14})^{23}$

114. $x^{14} \cdot x^{23}$

115. $x^{14} + x^{23}$

116. $\dfrac{x^{35}}{x^{17}}$

a. Add the exponents.

b. Subtract the exponents.

c. Multiply the exponents.

d. Divide the exponents.

e. None of these

Fill in the boxes so that each statement is true. (More than one answer is possible for each exercise.)

117. $x^\square \cdot x^\square = x^{12}$

118. $(x^\square)^\square = x^{20}$

119. $\dfrac{y^\square}{y^\square} = y^7$

120. $(y^\square)^\square \cdot (y^\square)^\square = y^{30}$

△ **121.** The formula $V = x^3$ can be used to find the volume V of a cube with side length x. Find the volume of a cube with side length 7 meters. (Volume is measured in cubic units.)

△ **122.** The formula $S = 6x^2$ can be used to find the surface area S of a cube with side length x. Find the surface area of a cube with side length 5 meters. (Surface area is measured in square units.)

△ **123.** To find the amount of water that a swimming pool in the shape of a cube can hold, do we use the formula for volume of the cube or surface area of the cube? (See Exercises 121 and 122.)

△ **124.** To find the amount of material needed to cover an ottoman in the shape of a cube, do we use the formula for volume of the cube or surface area of the cube? (See Exercises 121 and 122.)

✎ **125.** Explain why $(-5)^4 = 625$, while $-5^4 = -625$.

✎ **126.** Explain why $5 \cdot 4^2 = 80$, while $(5 \cdot 4)^2 = 400$.

✎ **127.** In your own words, explain why $5^0 = 1$.

✎ **128.** In your own words, explain when $(-3)^n$ is positive and when it is negative.

Simplify each expression. Assume that variables represent positive integers.

129. $x^{5a} x^{4a}$

130. $b^{9a} b^{4a}$

131. $(a^b)^5$

132. $(2a^{4b})^4$

133. $\dfrac{x^{9a}}{x^{4a}}$

134. $\dfrac{y^{15b}}{y^{6b}}$

Objectives

A Simplify Expressions Containing Negative Exponents.

B Use the Rules and Definitions for Exponents to Simplify Exponential Expressions.

C Write Numbers in Scientific Notation.

D Convert Numbers in Scientific Notation to Standard Form.

8.2 NEGATIVE EXPONENTS AND SCIENTIFIC NOTATION

Objective **A** Simplifying Expressions Containing Negative Exponents

Our work with exponential expressions so far has been limited to exponents that are positive integers or 0. Here we will also give meaning to an expression like x^{-3}.

Suppose that we wish to simplify the expression $\dfrac{x^2}{x^5}$. If we use the quotient rule for exponents, we subtract exponents:

$$\frac{x^2}{x^5} = x^{2-5} = x^{-3}, \quad x \neq 0$$

But what does x^{-3} mean? Let's simplify $\dfrac{x^2}{x^5}$ using the definition of a^n.

$$\frac{x^2}{x^5} = \frac{x \cdot x}{x \cdot x \cdot x \cdot x \cdot x}$$

$$= \frac{x \cdot x}{x \cdot x \cdot x \cdot x \cdot x} \qquad \text{\small Divide numerator and denominator by common factors.}$$

$$= \frac{1}{x^3}$$

If the quotient rule is to hold true for negative exponents, then x^{-3} must equal $\dfrac{1}{x^3}$. From this example, we state the definition for negative exponents.

Negative Exponents

If a is a real number other than 0 and n is an integer, then

$$a^{-n} = \frac{1}{a^n}$$

For example,

$$x^{-3} = \frac{1}{x^3}$$

In other words, another way to write a^{-n} is to take its reciprocal and change the sign of its exponent.

PRACTICE 1–4

Simplify by writing each expression with positive exponents only.

1. 5^{-3} **2.** $7x^{-4}$

3. $5^{-1} + 3^{-1}$ **4.** $(-3)^{-4}$

Examples Simplify by writing each expression with positive exponents only.

1. $3^{-2} = \dfrac{1}{3^2} = \dfrac{1}{9}$ *Use the definition of negative exponents.*

2. $2x^{-3} = 2^1 \cdot \dfrac{1}{x^3} = \dfrac{2^1}{x^3}$ or $\dfrac{2}{x^3}$ *Use the definition of negative exponents.*

3. $2^{-1} + 4^{-1} = \dfrac{1}{2} + \dfrac{1}{4} = \dfrac{2}{4} + \dfrac{1}{4} = \dfrac{3}{4}$

4. $(-2)^{-4} = \dfrac{1}{(-2)^4} = \dfrac{1}{(-2)(-2)(-2)(-2)} = \dfrac{1}{16}$

Helpful Hint Don't forget that since there are no parentheses, only x is the base for the exponent -3.

● **Work Practice 1–4**

Answers

1. $\dfrac{1}{125}$ **2.** $\dfrac{7}{x^4}$ **3.** $\dfrac{8}{15}$ **4.** $\dfrac{1}{81}$

🗨 **Helpful Hint**

A negative exponent *does not affect* the sign of its base.
Remember: Another way to write a^{-n} is to take its reciprocal and change the sign of its exponent: $a^{-n} = \dfrac{1}{a^n}$. For example,

$$x^{-2} = \frac{1}{x^2}, \qquad\qquad 2^{-3} = \frac{1}{2^3} \quad \text{or} \quad \frac{1}{8}$$

$$\frac{1}{y^{-4}} = \frac{1}{\frac{1}{y^4}} = y^4, \qquad \frac{1}{5^{-2}} = 5^2 \quad \text{or} \quad 25$$

From the preceding Helpful Hint, we know that $x^{-2} = \dfrac{1}{x^2}$ and $\dfrac{1}{y^{-4}} = y^4$. We can use this to include another statement in our definition of negative exponents.

Negative Exponents

If a is a real number other than 0 and n is an integer, then

$$a^{-n} = \frac{1}{a^n} \quad \text{and} \quad \frac{1}{a^{-n}} = a^n$$

Examples Simplify each expression. Write each result using positive exponents only.

5. $\left(\dfrac{2}{x}\right)^{-3} = \dfrac{2^{-3}}{x^{-3}} = \dfrac{2^{-3}}{1} \cdot \dfrac{1}{x^{-3}} = \dfrac{1}{2^3} \cdot \dfrac{x^3}{1} = \dfrac{x^3}{2^3} = \dfrac{x^3}{8}$ Use the negative exponents rule.

6. $\dfrac{y}{y^{-2}} = \dfrac{y^1}{y^{-2}} = y^{1-(-2)} = y^3$ Use the quotient rule.

7. $\dfrac{p^{-4}}{q^{-9}} = p^{-4} \cdot \dfrac{1}{q^{-9}} = \dfrac{1}{p^4} \cdot q^9 = \dfrac{q^9}{p^4}$ Use the negative exponents rule.

8. $\dfrac{x^{-5}}{x^7} = x^{-5-7} = x^{-12} = \dfrac{1}{x^{12}}$

⬤ **Work Practice 5–8**

Objective Ⓑ Simplifying Exponential Expressions

All the previously stated rules for exponents apply for negative exponents also. Here is a summary of the rules and definitions for exponents.

Summary of Exponent Rules

If m and n are integers and a, b, and c are real numbers, then

Product rule for exponents: $a^m \cdot a^n = a^{m+n}$
Power rule for exponents: $(a^m)^n = a^{m \cdot n}$
Power of a product: $(ab)^n = a^n b^n$
Power of a quotient: $\left(\dfrac{a}{c}\right)^n = \dfrac{a^n}{c^n}, \quad c \neq 0$
Quotient rule for exponents: $\dfrac{a^m}{a^n} = a^{m-n}, \quad a \neq 0$
Zero exponent: $a^0 = 1, \quad a \neq 0$
Negative exponent: $a^{-n} = \dfrac{1}{a^n}, \quad a \neq 0$

PRACTICE 5–8

Simplify each expression. Write each result using positive exponents only.

5. $\left(\dfrac{6}{7}\right)^{-2}$ **6.** $\dfrac{x}{x^{-4}}$

7. $\dfrac{y^{-9}}{z^{-5}}$ **8.** $\dfrac{y^{-4}}{y^6}$

Answers

5. $\dfrac{49}{36}$ **6.** x^5 **7.** $\dfrac{z^5}{y^9}$ **8.** $\dfrac{1}{y^{10}}$

PRACTICE 9-16

Simplify each expression. Write each result using positive exponents only.

9. $\dfrac{(3x^5)^3 x}{x^4}$ 　　**10.** $\left(\dfrac{9x^3}{y}\right)^{-2}$

11. $(a^{-4}b^7)^{-5}$ 　　**12.** $\dfrac{y^{-10}}{(y^5)^4}$

13. $(4a^2)^{-3}$ 　　**14.** $\dfrac{5x^7 y^3 z^0}{15x y^8 z^3}$

15. $-\dfrac{32x^{-3}y^{-6}}{8x^{-5}y^{-2}}$ 　　**16.** $\dfrac{(3x^{-2}y)^{-2}}{(2x^7 y)^3}$

Examples Simplify each expression. Write each result using positive exponents only.

9. $\dfrac{(2x^3)^4 x}{x^7} = \dfrac{2^4 \cdot x^{12} \cdot x}{x^7} = \dfrac{16 \cdot x^{12+1}}{x^7} = \dfrac{16 \cdot x^{13}}{x^7} = 16 \cdot x^{13-7} = 16x^6$　Use the power rule.

10. $\left(\dfrac{3a^2}{b}\right)^{-3} = \dfrac{3^{-3}(a^2)^{-3}}{b^{-3}}$　Raise each factor in the numerator and the denominator to the -3 power.

　　　　$= \dfrac{3^{-3}a^{-6}}{b^{-3}}$　Use the power rule.

　　　　$= \dfrac{b^3}{3^3 a^6}$　Use the negative exponent rule.

　　　　$= \dfrac{b^3}{27a^6}$　Write 3^3 as 27.

11. $(y^{-3}z^6)^{-6} = (y^{-3})^{-6}(z^6)^{-6}$　Raise each factor to the -6 power.

　　　　$= y^{18}z^{-36} = \dfrac{y^{18}}{z^{36}}$

12. $\dfrac{x^{-7}}{(x^4)^3} = \dfrac{x^{-7}}{x^{12}} = x^{-7-12} = x^{-19} = \dfrac{1}{x^{19}}$

13. $(5y^3)^{-2} = 5^{-2}(y^3)^{-2} = 5^{-2}y^{-6} = \dfrac{1}{5^2 y^6} = \dfrac{1}{25y^6}$

14. $\dfrac{3a^4 b^0 c^6}{6ab^2 c^8} = \dfrac{3}{6} \cdot a^{4-1} \cdot b^{0-2} \cdot c^{6-8} = \dfrac{1}{2} \cdot a^3 b^{-2} c^{-2} = \dfrac{a^3}{2b^2 c^2}$

Note: Since $b^0 = 1$, another way to proceed above is to first replace b^0 with 1, then continue.

15. $-\dfrac{22a^7 b^{-5}}{11a^{-2}b^3} = -\dfrac{22}{11} \cdot a^{7-(-2)}b^{-5-3} = -2a^9 b^{-8} = -\dfrac{2a^9}{b^8}$

16. $\dfrac{(2xy)^{-3}}{(x^2 y^3)^2} = \dfrac{2^{-3}x^{-3}y^{-3}}{(x^2)^2(y^3)^2} = \dfrac{2^{-3}x^{-3}y^{-3}}{x^4 y^6} = 2^{-3}x^{-3-4}y^{-3-6}$

　　　　$= 2^{-3}x^{-7}y^{-9} = \dfrac{1}{2^3 x^7 y^9}$　or　$\dfrac{1}{8x^7 y^9}$

● **Work Practice 9-16**

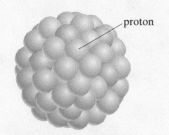

proton

Mass of proton is approximately
$0.000\,000\,000\,000\,000\,000\,000\,000\,00165$ gram

Objective ⒞ Writing Numbers in Scientific Notation

Both very large and very small numbers frequently occur in many fields of science. For example, the distance between the sun and the dwarf planet Pluto is approximately 5,906,000,000 kilometers, and the mass of a proton is approximately 0.00000000000000000000000165 gram. It can be tedious to write these numbers in this standard decimal notation, so **scientific notation** is used as a convenient shorthand for expressing very large and very small numbers.

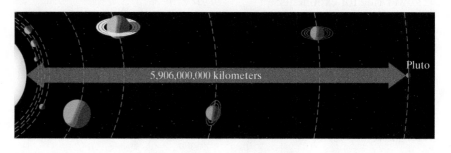

5,906,000,000 kilometers　Pluto

Answers

9. $27x^{12}$ 　**10.** $\dfrac{y^2}{81x^6}$ 　**11.** $\dfrac{a^{20}}{b^{35}}$ 　**12.** $\dfrac{1}{y^{30}}$

13. $\dfrac{1}{64a^6}$ 　**14.** $\dfrac{x^6}{3y^5 z^3}$ 　**15.** $-\dfrac{4x^2}{y^4}$

16. $\dfrac{1}{72x^{17}y^5}$

Scientific Notation

A positive number is written in scientific notation if it is written as the product of a number a, where $1 \le a < 10$, and an integer power r of 10: $a \times 10^r$.

The following numbers are written in scientific notation. The $\times$ sign for multiplication is used as part of the notation.

2.03×10^2 7.362×10^7 5.906×10^9 (Distance between the sun and Pluto)

1×10^{-3} 8.1×10^{-5} 1.65×10^{-24} (Mass of a proton)

The following steps are useful when writing numbers in scientific notation.

To Write a Number in Scientific Notation

Step 1: Move the decimal point in the original number so that the new number has a value between 1 and 10.

Step 2: Count the number of decimal places the decimal point is moved in Step 1. If the original number is 10 or greater, the count is positive. If the original number is less than 1, the count is negative.

Step 3: Multiply the new number in Step 1 by 10 raised to an exponent equal to the count found in Step 2.

Example 17 Write each number in scientific notation.

a. 367,000,000
b. 0.000003
c. 20,520,000,000
d. 0.00085

Solution:

a. Step 1: Move the decimal point until the number is between 1 and 10.
367,000,000.
8 places
Step 2: The decimal point is moved 8 places and the original number is 10 or greater, so the count is positive 8.
Step 3: $367,000,000 = 3.67 \times 10^8$
b. Step 1: Move the decimal point until the number is between 1 and 10.
0.000003
6 places
Step 2: The decimal point is moved 6 places and the original number is less than 1, so the count is -6.
Step 3: $0.000003 = 3.0 \times 10^{-6}$
c. $20,520,000,000 = 2.052 \times 10^{10}$
d. $0.00085 = 8.5 \times 10^{-4}$

● **Work Practice 17**

Objective D Converting Numbers to Standard Form

A number written in scientific notation can be rewritten in standard form. For example, to write 8.63×10^3 in standard form, recall that $10^3 = 1000$.

$8.63 \times 10^3 = 8.63(1000) = 8630$

Notice that the exponent on the 10 is positive 3, and we moved the decimal point 3 places to the right.

Write each number in scientific notation.
a. 420,000   **b.** 0.00017
c. 9,060,000,000   **d.** 0.000007

Answers
17. a. 4.2×10^5 **b.** 1.7×10^{-4}
c. 9.06×10^9 **d.** 7×10^{-6}

To write 7.29×10^{-3} in standard form, recall that $10^{-3} = \dfrac{1}{10^3} = \dfrac{1}{1000}$.

$$7.29 \times 10^{-3} = 7.29\left(\frac{1}{1000}\right) = \frac{7.29}{1000} = 0.00729$$

The exponent on the 10 is negative 3, and we moved the decimal to the left 3 places.

In general, **to write a scientific notation number in standard form**, move the decimal point the same number of places as the exponent on 10. If the exponent is positive, move the decimal point to the right; if the exponent is negative, move the decimal point to the left.

✔**Concept Check** Which number in each pair is larger?

a. 7.8×10^3 or 2.1×10^5

b. 9.2×10^{-2} or 2.7×10^4

c. 5.6×10^{-4} or 6.3×10^{-5}

PRACTICE 18

Write the numbers in standard form, without exponents.

a. 3.062×10^{-4}

b. 5.21×10^4

c. 9.6×10^{-5}

d. 6.002×10^6

Example 18 Write each number in standard form, without exponents.

a. 1.02×10^5 **b.** 7.358×10^{-3}
c. 8.4×10^7 **d.** 3.007×10^{-5}

Solution:

a. Move the decimal point 5 places to the right.

$1.02 \times 10^5 = 102,000.$

b. Move the decimal point 3 places to the left.

$7.358 \times 10^{-3} = 0.007358$

c. $8.4 \times 10^7 = 84,000,000.$ 7 places to the right

d. $3.007 \times 10^{-5} = 0.00003007$ 5 places to the left

● **Work Practice 18**

Performing operations on numbers written in scientific notation makes use of the rules and definitions for exponents.

PRACTICE 19

Perform each indicated operation. Write each result in standard decimal notation.

a. $(9 \times 10^7)(4 \times 10^{-9})$

b. $\dfrac{8 \times 10^4}{2 \times 10^{-3}}$

Example 19 Perform each indicated operation. Write each result in standard decimal notation.

a. $(8 \times 10^{-6})(7 \times 10^3)$

b. $\dfrac{12 \times 10^2}{6 \times 10^{-3}}$

Solution:

a. $(8 \times 10^{-6})(7 \times 10^3) = 8 \cdot 7 \cdot 10^{-6} \cdot 10^3$
$= 56 \times 10^{-3}$
$= 0.056$

b. $\dfrac{12 \times 10^2}{6 \times 10^{-3}} = \dfrac{12}{6} \times 10^{2-(-3)} = 2 \times 10^5 = 200,000$

● **Work Practice 19**

Answers
18. a. 0.0003062 **b.** 52,100
c. 0.000096 **d.** 6,002,000
19. a. 0.36 **b.** 40,000,000

✔**Concept Check Answers**
a. 2.1×10^5 **b.** 2.7×10^4
c. 5.6×10^{-4}

Calculator Explorations   Scientific Notation

To enter a number written in scientific notation on a scientific calculator, locate the scientific notation key, which may be marked $\boxed{\text{EE}}$ or $\boxed{\text{EXP}}$. To enter 3.1×10^7, press $\boxed{3.1}$ $\boxed{\text{EE}}$ $\boxed{7}$. The display should read $\boxed{3.1 \quad 07}$.

Enter each number written in scientific notation on your calculator.

1. 5.31×10^3
2. -4.8×10^{14}
3. 6.6×10^{-9}

4. -9.9811×10^{-2}

Multiply each of the following on your calculator. Notice the form of the result.

5. $3{,}000{,}000 \times 5{,}000{,}000$
6. $230{,}000 \times 1000$

Multiply each of the following on your calculator. Write the product in scientific notation.

7. $(3.26 \times 10^6)(2.5 \times 10^{13})$

Vocabulary and Readiness Check

Fill in each blank with the correct choice.

1. The expression x^{-3} equals _____.

    a. $-x^3$ **b.** $\dfrac{1}{x^3}$ **c.** $\dfrac{-1}{x^3}$ **d.** $\dfrac{1}{x^{-3}}$

2. The expression 5^{-4} equals _____.

    a. -20 **b.** -625 **c.** $\dfrac{1}{20}$ **d.** $\dfrac{1}{625}$

3. The number 3.021×10^{-3} is written in _____.

    a. standard form **b.** expanded form
    c. scientific notation

4. The number 0.0261 is written in _____.

    a. standard form **b.** expanded form
    c. scientific notation

Write each expression using positive exponents only.

5. $5x^{-2}$ **6.** $3x^{-3}$ **7.** $\dfrac{1}{y^{-6}}$ **8.** $\dfrac{1}{x^{-3}}$ **9.** $\dfrac{4}{y^{-3}}$ **10.** $\dfrac{16}{y^{-7}}$

8.2 Exercise Set

FOR EXTRA HELP

MyMathLab   *Powered by CourseCompass™ and MathXL®*

 Math XL PRACTICE   WATCH   DOWNLOAD   READ   REVIEW

Objective A *Simplify each expression. Write each result using positive exponents only. See Examples 1 through 8.*

1. 4^{-3} **2.** 6^{-2} **3.** $7x^{-3}$ **4.** $(7x)^{-3}$ **5.** $\left(-\dfrac{1}{4}\right)^{-3}$ **6.** $\left(-\dfrac{1}{8}\right)^{-2}$

7. $3^{-1} + 2^{-1}$ **8.** $4^{-1} + 4^{-2}$ **9.** $\dfrac{1}{p^{-3}}$ **10.** $\dfrac{1}{q^{-5}}$ **11.** $\dfrac{p^{-5}}{q^{-4}}$ **12.** $\dfrac{r^{-5}}{s^{-2}}$

13. $\dfrac{x^{-2}}{x}$ **14.** $\dfrac{y}{y^{-3}}$ **15.** $\dfrac{z^{-4}}{z^{-7}}$ **16.** $\dfrac{x^{-4}}{x^{-1}}$ **17.** $3^{-2} + 3^{-1}$ **18.** $4^{-2} - 4^{-3}$

19. $(-3)^{-2}$ **20.** $(-2)^{-6}$ **21.** $\dfrac{-1}{p^{-4}}$ **22.** $\dfrac{-1}{y^{-6}}$ **23.** $-2^0 - 3^0$ **24.** $5^0 + (-5)^0$

Objective B *Simplify each expression. Write each result using positive exponents only. See Examples 9 through 16.*

25. $\dfrac{x^2 x^5}{x^3}$ **26.** $\dfrac{y^4 y^5}{y^6}$ **27.** $\dfrac{p^2 p}{p^{-1}}$ **28.** $\dfrac{y^3 y}{y^{-2}}$ **29.** $\dfrac{(m^5)^4 m}{m^{10}}$ **30.** $\dfrac{(x^2)^8 x}{x^9}$

31. $\dfrac{r}{r^{-3} r^{-2}}$ **32.** $\dfrac{p}{p^{-3} p^{-5}}$ **33.** $(x^5 y^3)^{-3}$ **34.** $(z^5 x^5)^{-3}$ **35.** $\dfrac{(x^2)^3}{x^{10}}$ **36.** $\dfrac{(y^4)^2}{y^{12}}$

37. $\dfrac{(a^5)^2}{(a^3)^4}$ **38.** $\dfrac{(x^2)^5}{(x^4)^3}$ **39.** $\dfrac{8k^4}{2k}$ **40.** $\dfrac{27r^6}{3r^4}$ **41.** $\dfrac{-6m^4}{-2m^3}$ **42.** $\dfrac{15a^4}{-15a^5}$

43. $\dfrac{-24a^6 b}{6ab^2}$ **44.** $\dfrac{-5x^4 y^5}{15x^4 y^2}$ **45.** $\dfrac{6x^2 y^3 z^0}{-7x^2 y^5 z^5}$ **46.** $\dfrac{-8xa^2 b^0}{-5xa^5 b}$ **47.** $(3a^2 b^{-4})^3$ **48.** $(5x^3 y^{-2})^2$

49. $(a^{-5}b^2)^{-6}$

50. $(4^{-1}x^5)^{-2}$

51. $\left(\dfrac{x^{-2}y^4z^0}{x^3y^7}\right)^2$

52. $\left(\dfrac{a^5bc^0}{a^7b^{-2}}\right)^{-3}$

53. $\dfrac{4^2z^{-3}}{4^3z^{-5}}$

54. $\dfrac{5^{-1}z^7}{5^{-2}z^9}$

55. $\dfrac{3^{-1}x^4}{3^3x^{-7}}$

56. $\dfrac{2^{-3}x^{-4}}{2^2x}$

57. $\dfrac{7ab^{-4}}{7^{-1}a^{-3}b^2}$

58. $\dfrac{6^{-5}x^{-1}y^2}{6^{-2}x^{-4}y^4}$

59. $\dfrac{-12m^5n^{-7}}{4m^{-2}n^{-3}}$

60. $\dfrac{-15r^{-6}s}{5r^{-4}s^{-3}}$

61. $\left(\dfrac{a^{-5}b}{ab^3}\right)^{-4}$

62. $\left(\dfrac{r^{-2}s^{-3}}{r^{-4}s^{-3}}\right)^{-3}$

63. $(5^2)(8)(2^0)$

64. $(3^4)(7^0)(2)$

65. $\dfrac{(xy^3)^5}{(xy)^{-4}}$

66. $\dfrac{(rs)^{-3}}{(r^2s^3)^2}$

67. $\dfrac{(-2xy^{-3})^{-3}}{(xy^{-1})^{-1}}$

68. $\dfrac{(-3x^2y^2)^{-2}}{(xyz)^{-2}}$

69. $\dfrac{(a^4b^{-7})^{-5}}{(5a^2b^{-1})^{-2}}$

70. $\dfrac{(a^6b^{-2})^4}{(4a^{-3}b^{-3})^3}$

△ **71.** Find the volume of the cube.

$\dfrac{3x^{-2}}{z}$ inches

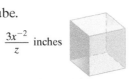

△ **72.** Find the area of the triangle.

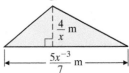

$\dfrac{4}{x}$ m

$\dfrac{5x^{-3}}{7}$ m

Objective ◯ *Write each number in scientific notation. See Example 17.*

73. 78,000

74. 9,300,000,000

75. 0.00000167

76. 0.00000017

77. 0.00635

78. 0.00194

79. 1,160,000

80. 700,000

81. As of this writing, the world's largest optical telescope is the Gran Telescopio Canaris, located in La Palma, Canary Islands, Spain. The elevation of this telescope is 2400 meters above sea level. Write 2400 in scientific notation.

82. In January 2009, the twin Mars rovers, Spirit and Opportunity, celebrated their fifth anniversary of landing on Mars. These rovers, which were expected to last about 90 days, have defied all expectations, and have been transmitting signals back to Earth from as far away as 250,000,000 miles. Write 250,000,000 in scientific notation. (*Source:* NASA)

Objective Ⓓ *Write each number in standard form. See Example 18.*

83. 8.673×10^{-10}

84. 9.056×10^{-4}

85. 3.3×10^{-2}

86. 4.8×10^{-6}

87. 2.032×10^{4}

88. 9.07×10^{10}

89. Each second, the sun converts 7.0×10^{8} tons of hydrogen into helium and energy in the form of gamma rays. Write this number in standard form. (*Source:* Students for the Exploration and Development of Space)

90. In chemistry, Avogadro's number is the number of atoms in one mole of an element. Avogadro's number is $6.02214199 \times 10^{23}$. Write this number in standard form. (*Source:* National Institute of Standards and Technology)

Objectives Ⓒ Ⓓ **Mixed Practice** *See Examples 17 and 18. Below are some interesting facts about selected countries' national debts during a certain time period. If a number is written in standard form, write it in scientific notation. If a number is written in scientific notation, write it in standard form. (Source: CIA World Factbook)*

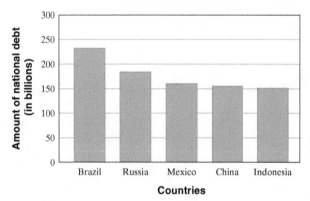

Selected Countries and Their National Debt

91. The national debt of Russia during a certain time period was $184,000,000,000.

92. The amount by which Russia's debt is greater than Mexico's debt is $24,000,000,000.

93. At a certain time period, China's national debt was 1.55×10^{11}.

94. At a certain time period, the national debt of the United States was 1.1×10^{13}.

95. At a certain time period, the estimated per person share of the United States' national debt was 3.5×10^{4}.

96. The bar graph shows the national debt of five different countries. Estimate the height of the tallest bar and the shortest bar in standard form. Then write each number in scientific notation.

Objective Ⓓ *Evaluate each expression using exponential rules. Write each result in standard form. See Example 19.*

97. $(1.2 \times 10^{-3})(3 \times 10^{-2})$

98. $(2.5 \times 10^{6})(2 \times 10^{-6})$

99. $(4 \times 10^{-10})(7 \times 10^{-9})$

100. $(5 \times 10^{6})(4 \times 10^{-8})$

101. $\dfrac{8 \times 10^{-1}}{16 \times 10^{5}}$

102. $\dfrac{25 \times 10^{-4}}{5 \times 10^{-9}}$

103. $\dfrac{1.4 \times 10^{-2}}{7 \times 10^{-8}}$

104. $\dfrac{0.4 \times 10^{5}}{0.2 \times 10^{11}}$

105. Although the actual amount varies by season and time of day, the average volume of water that flows over Niagara Falls (the American and Canadian falls combined) each second is 7.5×10^{5} gallons. How much water flows over Niagara Falls in an hour? Write the result in scientific notation. (*Hint:* 1 hour equals 3600 seconds.) (*Source:* niagarafallslive.com)

106. A beam of light travels 9.460×10^{12} kilometers per year. How far does light travel in 10,000 years? Write the result in scientific notation.

Review

Simplify each expression by combining any like terms. See Section 5.8.

107. $3x - 5x + 7$

108. $7w + w - 2w$

109. $y - 10 + y$

110. $-6z + 20 - 3z$

111. $7x + 2 - 8x - 6$

112. $10y - 14 - y - 14$

Concept Extensions

For Exercises 113–118, write each number in standard form. Then write the number in scientific notation.

113. The Facebook Web site has more than 90 million active users.

114. Facebook has more than 24 million photos uploaded daily.

115. There are over 1 billion Internet users worldwide.

116. The English version of Wikipedia has more than 2.3 million articles.

117. The estimated number of Google users in a day is 0.44 billion.

118. The estimated number of Wikipedia users in a day is 0.13 billion.

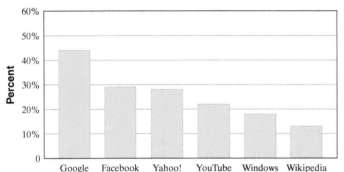

Most Visited Websites
(Global Internet Users in a Day)

119. Do the percents in the bar graph have a sum of 100%? Why or why not?

120. Give a value for x so that x^{-1} is a positive number, and then a value for x so that x^{-1} is a negative number. In general, what does this mean?

Simplify.

121. $(2a^3)^3 a^4 + a^5 a^8$

122. $(2a^3)^3 a^{-3} + a^{11} a^{-5}$

Fill in the boxes so that each statement is true. (More than one answer may be possible for these exercises.)

123. $x^{\square} = \dfrac{1}{x^5}$

124. $7^{\square} = \dfrac{1}{49}$

125. $z^{\square} \cdot z^{\square} = z^{-10}$

126. $(x^{\square})^{\square} = x^{-15}$

127. Which is larger? See the Concept Check in this section.

    a. 9.7×10^{-2} or 1.3×10^1

    b. 8.6×10^5 or 4.4×10^7

    c. 6.1×10^{-2} or 5.6×10^{-4}

128. Determine whether each statement is true or false.

    a. $5^{-1} < 5^{-2}$

    b. $\left(\dfrac{1}{5}\right)^{-1} < \left(\dfrac{1}{5}\right)^{-2}$

    c. $a^{-1} < a^{-2}$ for all nonzero numbers.

129. It was stated earlier that for an integer n,

$$x^{-n} = \frac{1}{x^n}, \quad x \neq 0$$

Explain why x may not equal 0.

130. The quotient rule states that

$$\frac{a^m}{a^n} = a^{m-n}, a \neq 0.$$

Explain why a may not equal 0.

Simplify each expression. Assume that variables represent positive integers.

131. $(x^{-3s})^3$

132. $a^{-4m} \cdot a^{5m}$

133. $a^{4m+1} \cdot a^4$

134. $(3y^{2z})^3$

A Define Term and Coefficient of a Term.

B Define Polynomial, Monomial, Binomial, Trinomial, and Degree.

C Evaluate Polynomials for Given Replacement Values.

D Simplify a Polynomial by Combining Like Terms.

E Simplify a Polynomial in Several Variables.

F Write a Polynomial in Descending Powers of the Variable and with No Missing Powers of the Variable.

8.3 INTRODUCTION TO POLYNOMIALS

Objective A Defining Term and Coefficient

In this section, we introduce a special algebraic expression called a polynomial. Let's first review some definitions presented in Section 5.8.

Recall that a term is a number or the product of a number and variables raised to powers. The terms of an expression are separated by plus signs. The terms of the expression $4x^2 + 3x$ are $4x^2$ and $3x$. The terms of the expression $9x^4 - 7x - 1$, or $9x^4 + (-7x) + (-1)$, are $9x^4, -7x$, and -1.

Expression	Terms
$4x^2 + 3x$	$4x^2, 3x$
$9x^4 - 7x - 1$	$9x^4, -7x, -1$
$7y^3$	$7y^3$

The **numerical coefficient** of a term, or simply the **coefficient,** is the numerical factor of each term. If no numerical factor appears in the term, then the coefficient is understood to be 1. If the term is a number only, it is called a **constant term** or simply a **constant.**

Term	Coefficient
x^5	1
$3x^2$	3
$-4x$	-4
$-x^2y$	-1
3 (constant)	3

PRACTICE 1

Complete the table for the expression
$-6x^6 + 4x^5 + 7x^3 - 9x^2 - 1$.

Term	Coefficient
$7x^3$	
	-9
$-6x^6$	
	4
-1	

Example 1 Complete the table for the expression $7x^5 - 8x^4 + x^2 - 3x + 5$.

Term	Coefficient
x^2	
	-8
$-3x$	
	7
5	

Solution: The completed table is shown below.

Term	Coefficient
x^2	1
$-8x^4$	-8
$-3x$	-3
$7x^5$	7
5	5

● Work Practice 1

Answer
1. term: $-9x^2, 4x^5$; coefficient: $7, -6, -1$

Objective B Defining Polynomial, Monomial, Binomial, Trinomial, and Degree

Now we are ready to define what we mean by a polynomial.

Polynomial

A **polynomial in x** is a finite sum of terms of the form ax^n, where a is a real number and n is a whole number.

For example,

$$x^5 - 3x^3 + 2x^2 - 5x + 1$$

is a polynomial in x. Notice that this polynomial is written in **descending powers** of x, because the powers of x decrease from left to right. (Recall that the term 1 can be thought of as $1x^0$.)

On the other hand,

$$x^{-5} + 2x - 3$$

is **not** a polynomial because one of its terms contains a variable with an exponent, -5, that is not a whole number.

Types of Polynomials

A **monomial** is a polynomial with exactly one term.
A **binomial** is a polynomial with exactly two terms.
A **trinomial** is a polynomial with exactly three terms.

The following are examples of monomials, binomials, and trinomials. Each of these examples is also a polynomial.

Polynomials			
Monomials	**Binomials**	**Trinomials**	**More than Three Terms**
ax^2	$x + y$	$x^2 + 4xy + y^2$	$5x^3 - 6x^2 + 3x - 6$
$-3z$	$3p + 2$	$x^5 + 7x^2 - x$	$-y^5 + y^4 - 3y^3 - y^2 + y$
4	$4x^2 - 7$	$-q^4 + q^3 - 2q$	$x^6 + x^4 - x^3 + 1$

Each term of a polynomial has a degree. The **degree of a term in one variable** is the exponent on the variable.

Example 2 Identify the degree of each term of the trinomial $12x^4 - 7x + 3$.

Solution: The term $12x^4$ has degree 4.
The term $-7x$ has degree 1 since $-7x$ is $-7x^1$.
The term 3 has degree 0 since 3 is $3x^0$.

● Work Practice 2

Each polynomial also has a degree.

Degree of a Polynomial

The **degree of a polynomial** is the greatest degree of any term of the polynomial.

PRACTICE 2

Identify the degree of each term of the trinomial $-15x^3 + 2x^2 - 5$.

Answer
2. 3; 2; 0

PRACTICE 3

Find the degree of each polynomial and tell whether the polynomial is a monomial, binomial, trinomial, or none of these.
a. $-6x + 14$
b. $9x - 3x^6 + 5x^4 + 2$
c. $10x^2 - 6x - 6$

Example 3 Find the degree of each polynomial and tell whether the polynomial is a monomial, binomial, trinomial, or none of these.

a. $-2t^2 + 3t + 6$ **b.** $15x - 10$ **c.** $7x + 3x^3 + 2x^2 - 1$

Solution:

a. The degree of the trinomial $-2t^2 + 3t + 6$ is 2, the greatest degree of any of its terms.

b. The degree of the binomial $15x - 10$ or $15x^1 - 10$ is 1.

c. The degree of the polynomial $7x + 3x^3 + 2x^2 - 1$ is 3. The polynomial is neither a monomial, binomial, nor trinomial.

● **Work Practice 3**

Objective ⓒ Evaluating Polynomials

Polynomials have different values depending on the replacement values for the variables. When we find the value of a polynomial for a given replacement value, we are evaluating the polynomial for that value.

PRACTICE 4

Evaluate each polynomial when $x = -1$.
a. $-2x + 10$
b. $6x^2 + 11x - 20$

Example 4 Evaluate each polynomial when $x = -2$.

a. $-5x + 6$ **b.** $3x^2 - 2x + 1$

Solution:

a. $-5x + 6 = -5(-2) + 6$　Replace x with -2.
$\qquad\qquad = 10 + 6$
$\qquad\qquad = 16$

b. $3x^2 - 2x + 1 = 3(-2)^2 - 2(-2) + 1$　Replace x with -2.
$\qquad\qquad\qquad = 3(4) + 4 + 1$
$\qquad\qquad\qquad = 12 + 4 + 1$
$\qquad\qquad\qquad = 17$

● **Work Practice 4**

Many physical phenomena can be modeled by polynomials.

PRACTICE 5

Find the height of the object in Example 5 when $t = 2$ seconds and $t = 4$ seconds.

Example 5 Finding Free-Fall Time

The Swiss Re Building, completed in London in 2003, is a unique building. Londoners often refer to it as the "pickle building." The building is 592.1 feet tall. An object is dropped from the highest point of this building. Neglecting air resistance, the height in feet of the object above ground at time t seconds is given by the polynomial $-16t^2 + 592.1$. Find the height of the object when $t = 1$ second and when $t = 6$ seconds.

Solution: To find each height, we evaluate the polynomial when $t = 1$ and when $t = 6$.

$-16t^2 + 592.1 = -16(1)^2 + 592.1$　Replace t with 1.
$\qquad\qquad\qquad = -16(1) + 592.1$
$\qquad\qquad\qquad = -16 + 592.1$
$\qquad\qquad\qquad = 576.1$

The height of the object at 1 second is 576.1 feet.

$-16t^2 + 592.1 = -16(6)^2 + 592.1$　Replace t with 6.
$\qquad\qquad\qquad = -16(36) + 592.1$
$\qquad\qquad\qquad = -576 + 592.1 = 16.1$

Answers
3. a. binomial, 1 **b.** none of these, 6
c. trinomial, 2 **4. a.** 12 **b.** -25
5. 528.1 feet, 336.1 feet

The height of the object at 6 seconds is 16.1 feet.

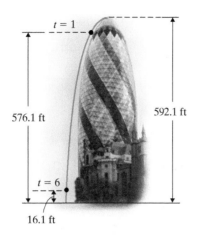

● Work Practice 5

Objective ⓓ Simplifying Polynomials by Combining Like Terms

We can simplify polynomials with like terms by combining the like terms. Recall from Section 5.8 that like terms are terms that contain exactly the same variables raised to exactly the same powers.

Like Terms	Unlike Terms
$5x^2, -7x^2$	$3x, 3y$
$y, 2y$	$-2x^2, -5x$
$\frac{1}{2}a^2b, -a^2b$	$6st^2, 4s^2t$

Only like terms can be combined. We combine like terms by applying the distributive property.

Examples Simplify each polynomial by combining any like terms.

6. $-3x + 7x = (-3 + 7)x = 4x$

7. $11x^2 + 5 + 2x^2 - 7 = 11x^2 + 2x^2 + 5 - 7$
$$= 13x^2 - 2$$

8. $9x^3 + x^3 = 9x^3 + 1x^3$ Write x^3 as $1x^3$.
$$= 10x^3$$

9. $5x^2 + 6x - 9x - 3 = 5x^2 - 3x - 3$ Combine like terms $6x$ and $-9x$.

10. $\frac{2}{5}x^4 + \frac{2}{3}x^3 - x^2 + \frac{1}{10}x^4 - \frac{1}{6}x^3$

$$= \left(\frac{2}{5} + \frac{1}{10}\right)x^4 + \left(\frac{2}{3} - \frac{1}{6}\right)x^3 - x^2$$

$$= \left(\frac{4}{10} + \frac{1}{10}\right)x^4 + \left(\frac{4}{6} - \frac{1}{6}\right)x^3 - x^2$$

$$= \frac{5}{10}x^4 + \frac{3}{6}x^3 - x^2$$

$$= \frac{1}{2}x^4 + \frac{1}{2}x^3 - x^2$$

● Work Practice 6–10

PRACTICE 6–10

Simplify each polynomial by combining any like terms.

6. $-6y + 8y$

7. $14y^2 + 3 - 10y^2 - 9$

8. $7x^3 + x^3$

9. $23x^2 - 6x - x - 15$

10. $\frac{2}{7}x^3 - \frac{1}{4}x + 2 - \frac{1}{2}x^3 + \frac{3}{8}x$

Answers

6. $2y$ **7.** $4y^2 - 6$ **8.** $8x^3$

9. $23x^2 - 7x - 15$

10. $-\frac{3}{14}x^3 + \frac{1}{8}x + 2$

PRACTICE 11

Write a polynomial that describes the total area of the squares and rectangles shown below. Then simplify the polynomial.

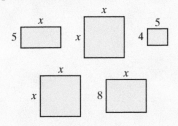

Example 11 Write a polynomial that describes the total area of the squares and rectangles shown below. Then simplify the polynomial.

Solution: Recall that the area of a rectangle is length times width.

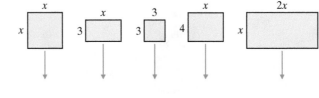

Area: $x \cdot x \ + \ 3 \cdot x \ + \ 3 \cdot 3 \ + \ 4 \cdot x \ + \ x \cdot 2x$

$$= x^2 + 3x + 9 + 4x + 2x^2$$
$$= 3x^2 + 7x + 9 \qquad \text{Combine like terms.}$$

● Work Practice 11

Objective Ⓔ Simplifying Polynomials Containing Several Variables

A polynomial may contain more than one variable. One example is

$$5x + 3xy^2 - 6x^2y^2 + x^2y - 2y + 1$$

We call this expression a polynomial in several variables.

The **degree of a term** with more than one variable is the sum of the exponents on the variables. The **degree of a polynomial** in several variables is still the greatest degree of the terms of the polynomial.

PRACTICE 12

Identify the degrees of the terms and the degree of the polynomial $-2x^3y^2 + 4 - 8xy + 3x^3y + 5xy^2$.

Example 12 Identify the degrees of the terms and the degree of the polynomial $5x + 3xy^2 - 6x^2y^2 + x^2y - 2y + 1$.

Solution: To organize our work, we use a table.

Terms of Polynomial	Degree of Term	Degree of Polynomial
$5x$	1	
$3xy^2$	1 + 2, or 3	
$-6x^2y^2$	2 + 2, or 4	4 (greatest degree)
x^2y	2 + 1, or 3	
$-2y$	1	
1	0	

● Work Practice 12

To simplify a polynomial containing several variables, we combine any like terms.

PRACTICE 13–14

Simplify each polynomial by combining any like terms.

13. $11ab - 6a^2 - ba + 8b^2$

14. $7x^2y^2 + 2y^2 - 4y^2x^2 + x^2 - y^2 + 5x^2$

Examples Simplify each polynomial by combining any like terms.

13. $3xy - 5y^2 + 7yx - 9x^2 = (3 + 7)xy - 5y^2 - 9x^2$
$$= 10xy - 5y^2 - 9x^2$$

14. $9a^2b - 6a^2 + 5b^2 + a^2b - 11a^2 + 2b^2$
$$= 10a^2b - 17a^2 + 7b^2$$

Helpful Hint
This term can be written as $7yx$ or $7xy$.

Answers

11. $5x + x^2 + 20 + x^2 + 8x$;
$\quad 2x^2 + 13x + 20$
12. $5, 0, 2, 4, 3; 5$
13. $10ab - 6a^2 + 8b^2$
14. $3x^2y^2 + y^2 + 6x^2$

● Work Practice 13–14

Objective ⑤ Inserting "Missing" Terms

To prepare for dividing polynomials in Section 8.7, let's practice writing a polynomial in descending powers of the variable and with no "missing" powers.

Recall from Objective ⑧ that a polynomial such as

$$x^5 - 3x^3 + 2x^2 - 5x + 1$$

is written in descending powers of x because the powers of x decrease from left to right. Study the decreasing powers of x and notice that there is a "missing" power of x. This missing power is x^4. Writing a polynomial in decreasing powers of the variable helps you immediately determine important features of the polynomial, such as its degree. It is also sometimes helpful to write a polynomial so that there are no "missing" powers of x. For our polynomial above, if we simply insert a term of $0x^4$, which equals 0, we have an equivalent polynomial with no missing powers of x.

$$x^5 - 3x^3 + 2x^2 - 5x + 1 = x^5 + 0x^4 - 3x^3 + 2x^2 - 5x + 1$$

Example 15 Write each polynomial in descending powers of the variable with no missing powers.

a. $x^2 - 4$
b. $3m^3 - m + 1$
c. $2x + x^4$

Solution:

a. $x^2 - 4 = x^2 + 0x^1 - 4$ or $x^2 + 0x - 4$ Insert a missing term of $0x^1$ or $0x$.
b. $3m^3 - m + 1 = 3m^3 + 0m^2 - m + 1$ Insert a missing term of $0m^2$.
c. $2x + x^4 = x^4 + 2x$ Write in descending powers of variable.
      $= x^4 + 0x^3 + 0x^2 + 2x + 0x^0$ Insert missing terms of $0x^3$, $0x^2$, and $0x^0$ (or 0).

● Work Practice 15

Helpful Hint

Since there is no constant as a last term, we insert a $0x^0$. This $0x^0$ (or 0) is the final power of x in our polynomial.

PRACTICE 15

Write each polynomial in descending powers of the variable with no missing powers.
a. $x^2 + 9$
b. $9m^3 + m^2 - 5$
c. $-3a^3 + a^4$

Answers
15. a. $x^2 + 0x + 9$
b. $9m^3 + m^2 + 0m - 5$
c. $a^4 - 3a^3 + 0a^2 + 0a + 0a^0$

Vocabulary and Readiness Check

Use the choices below to fill in each blank. Not all choices will be used.

least	monomial	trinomial	coefficient
greatest	binomial	constant	

1. A _____ is a polynomial with exactly two terms.
2. A _____ is a polynomial with exactly one term.
3. A _____ is a polynomial with exactly three terms.
4. The numerical factor of a term is called the _____.
5. A number term is also called a _____.
6. The degree of a polynomial is the _____ degree of any term of the polynomial.

8.3 Exercise Set

FOR EXTRA HELP

MyMathLab   MathXL   PRACTICE   WATCH   DOWNLOAD   READ   REVIEW

Objective Ⓐ *Complete each table for each polynomial. See Example 1.*

1. $x^2 - 3x + 5$

Term	Coefficient
x^2	
	-3
5	

2. $2x^3 - x + 4$

Term	Coefficient
	2
$-x$	
4	

3. $-5x^4 + 3.2x^2 + x - 5$

Term	Coefficient
$-5x^4$	
$3.2x^2$	
x	
-5	

4. $9.7x^7 - 3x^5 + x^3 - \dfrac{1}{4}x^2$

Term	Coefficient
$9.7x^7$	
$-3x^5$	
x^3	
$-\dfrac{1}{4}x^2$	

Objective Ⓑ *Find the degree of each polynomial and determine whether it is a monomial, binomial, trinomial, or none of these. See Examples 2 and 3.*

5. $x + 2$

6. $-6y + 4$

7. $9m^3 - 5m^2 + 4m - 8$

8. $a + 5a^2 + 3a^3 - 4a^4$

9. $12x^4 - x^6 - 12x^2$

10. $7r^2 + 2r - 3r^5$

11. $3z - 5z^4$

12. $5y^6 + 2$

Objective Ⓒ *Evaluate each polynomial when* (a) $x = 0$ *and* (b) $x = -1$. *See Examples 4 and 5.*

13. $5x - 6$

14. $2x - 10$

15. $x^2 - 5x - 2$

16. $x^2 + 3x - 4$

17. $-x^3 + 4x^2 - 15$

18. $-2x^3 + 3x^2 - 6$

A rocket is fired upward from the ground with an initial velocity of 200 feet per second. Neglecting air resistance, the height of the rocket at any time t can be described in feet by the polynomial $-16t^2 + 200t$. Find the height of the rocket at the time given in Exercises 19 through 22. See Example 5.

	Time, t (in seconds)	Height $-16t^2 + 200t$
19.	1	
20.	5	
21.	7.6	
22.	10.3	

Apostle Islands
National Shoreline

Cedar Breaks
National Monument

23. The polynomial $-7.5x^2 + 93x - 100$ models the yearly number of visitors (in thousands) x years after 2000 at Apostle Islands National Park. Use this polynomial to estimate the number of visitors to the park in 2008 ($x = 8$).

24. The polynomial $8x^2 - 90.6x + 752$ models the yearly number of visitors (in thousands) x years after 2000 at Cedar Breaks National Park. Use this polynomial to estimate the number of visitors to the park in 2007 ($x = 7$).

25. The number of wireless telephone subscribers (in millions) x years after 1995 is given by the polynomial $0.52x^2 + 11.4x + 27.87$ for 1995 through 2008. Use this model to predict the number of wireless telephone subscribers in 2012 ($x = 17$). (*Source:* Based on data from Cellular Telecommunications & Internet Association)

26. The penetration rate of American wireless telephone subscribers—that is, the percent of the population who have cell phones—x years after 1995 is given by $0.1x^2 + 4.4x + 10.7$ for 1995 through 2008. Assuming the same rate of growth, use this model to predict the penetration rate of wireless subscribers in the United States in 2010 ($x = 15$). (*Source:* Based on data from Cellular Telecommunications & Internet Association)

Objective D *Simplify each expression by combining like terms. See Examples 6 through 10.*

27. $9x - 20x$

28. $14y - 30y$

29. $14x^3 + 9x^3$

30. $18x^3 + 4x^3$

31. $7x^2 + 3 + 9x^2 - 10$

32. $8x^2 + 4 + 11x^2 - 20$

33. $15x^2 - 3x^2 - 13$

34. $12k^3 - 9k^3 + 11$

35. $8s - 5s + 4s$

36. $5y + 7y - 6y$

37. $0.1y^2 - 1.2y^2 + 6.7 - 1.9$

38. $7.6y + 3.2y^2 - 8y - 2.5y^2$

39. $\frac{2}{3}x^4 + 12x^3 + \frac{1}{6}x^4 - 19x^3 - 19$

40. $\frac{2}{5}x^4 - 23x^2 + \frac{1}{15}x^4 + 5x^2 - 5$

41. $\frac{3}{20}x^3 + \frac{1}{10} - \frac{3}{10}x - \frac{1}{5} - \frac{7}{20}x + 6x^2$

42. $\frac{5}{16}x^3 - \frac{1}{8} + \frac{3}{8}x + \frac{1}{4} - \frac{9}{16}x - 14x^2$

Write a polynomial that describes the total area of each set of rectangles and squares shown in Exercises 43 and 44. Then simplify the polynomial. See Example 11.

△ **43.**

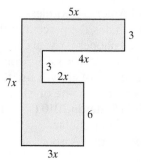

△ **44.**

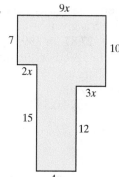

Recall that the perimeter of a figure such as the ones shown in Exercises 45 and 46 is the sum of the lengths of its sides. Write each perimeter as a polynomial. Then simplify the polynomial.

△ **45.**

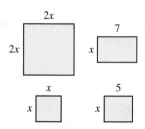

△ **46.**

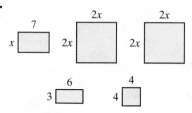

Objective Ⓔ *Identify the degrees of the terms and the degree of the polynomial. See Example 12.*

47. $9ab - 6a + 5b - 3$

48. $y^4 - 6y^3x + 2x^2y^2 - 5y^2 + 3$

49. $x^3y - 6 + 2x^2y^2 + 5y^3$

50. $2a^2b + 10a^4b - 9ab + 6$

Simplify each polynomial by combining any like terms. See Examples 13 and 14.

51. $3ab - 4a + 6ab - 7a$

52. $-9xy + 7y - xy - 6y$

53. $4x^2 - 6xy + 3y^2 - xy$

54. $3a^2 - 9ab + 4b^2 - 7ab$

55. $5x^2y + 6xy^2 - 5yx^2 + 4 - 9y^2x$

56. $17a^2b - 16ab^2 + 3a^3 + 4ba^3 - b^2a$

57. $14y^3 - 9 + 3a^2b^2 - 10 - 19b^2a^2$

58. $18x^4 + 2x^3y^3 - 1 - 2y^3x^3 - 17x^4$

Objective **F** *Write each polynomial in descending powers of the variable and with no missing powers. See Example 15.*

59. $7x^2 + 3$

60. $5x^2 - 2$

61. $x^3 - 64$

62. $x^3 - 8$

63. $5y^3 + 2y - 10$

64. $6m^3 - 3m + 4$

65. $8y + 2y^4$

66. $11z + 4z^4$

67. $6x^5 + x^3 - 3x + 15$

68. $9y^5 - y^2 + 2y - 11$

Review

Simplify each expression. See Section 5.8.

69. $4 + 5(2x + 3)$　　　**70.** $9 - 6(5x + 1)$　　　**71.** $2(x - 5) + 3(5 - x)$　　　**72.** $-3(w + 7) + 5(w + 1)$

Concept Extensions

73. Describe how to find the degree of a term.

74. Describe how to find the degree of a polynomial.

75. Explain why xyz is a monomial while $x + y + z$ is a trinomial.

76. Explain why the degree of the term $5y^3$ is 3 and the degree of the polynomial $2y + y + 2y$ is 1.

Simplify, if possible.

77. $x^4 \cdot x^9$

78. $x^4 + x^9$

79. $a \cdot b^3 \cdot a^2 \cdot b^7$

80. $a + b^3 + a^2 + b^7$

81. $(y^5)^4 + (y^2)^{10}$

82. $x^5 y^2 + y^2 x^5$

Fill in the boxes so that the terms in each expression can be combined. Then simplify. Each exercise has more than one solution.

83. $7x^{\square} + 2x^{\square}$

84. $(3y^2)^{\square} + (4y^3)^{\square}$

85. Explain why the height of the rocket in Exercises 19 through 22 increases and then decreases as time passes.

86. Approximate (to the nearest tenth of a second) how long before the rocket in Exercises 19 through 22 hits the ground.

Simplify each polynomial by combining like terms.

87. $1.85x^2 - 3.76x + 9.25x^2 + 10.76 - 4.21x$

88. $7.75x + 9.16x^2 - 1.27 - 14.58x^2 - 18.34$

8.4 ADDING AND SUBTRACTING POLYNOMIALS

Objective Ⓐ Adding Polynomials

To add polynomials, we use commutative and associative properties and then combine like terms. To see if you are ready to add polynomials, try the Concept Check.

✓Concept Check When combining like terms in the expression $5x - 8x^2 - 8x$, which of the following is the proper result?

a. $-11x^2$ **b.** $-3x - 8x^2$ **c.** $-11x$ **d.** $-11x^4$

To Add Polynomials

To add polynomials, combine all like terms.

Examples Add.

PRACTICE 1–2
Add.
1. $(3x^5 - 7x^3 + 2x - 1)$
   $+ (3x^3 - 2x)$
2. $(5x^2 - 2x + 1)$
   $+ (-6x^2 + x - 1)$

1. $(4x^3 - 6x^2 + 2x + 7) + (5x^2 - 2x)$

   $= 4x^3 - 6x^2 + 2x + 7 + 5x^2 - 2x$ Remove parentheses.

   $= 4x^3 + (-6x^2 + 5x^2) + (2x - 2x) + 7$ Combine like terms.

   $= 4x^3 - x^2 + 7$ Simplify.

2. $(-2x^2 + 5x - 1) + (-2x^2 + x + 3)$

   $= -2x^2 + 5x - 1 - 2x^2 + x + 3$ Remove parentheses.

   $= (-2x^2 - 2x^2) + (5x + 1x) + (-1 + 3)$ Combine like terms.

   $= -4x^2 + 6x + 2$ Simplify.

● Work Practice 1–2

Just as we can add numbers vertically, polynomials can be added vertically if we line up like terms underneath one another.

Example 3 Add $(7y^3 - 2y^2 + 7)$ and $(6y^2 + 1)$ using a vertical format.

Solution: Vertically line up like terms and add.

$$\begin{array}{r} 7y^3 - 2y^2 + 7 \\ 6y^2 + 1 \\ \hline 7y^3 + 4y^2 + 8 \end{array}$$

● Work Practice 3

Objective Ⓑ Subtracting Polynomials

To subtract one polynomial from another, recall the definition of subtraction. To subtract a number, we add its opposite: $a - b = a + (-b)$. To subtract a polynomial, we also add its opposite. Just as $-b$ is the opposite of b, $-(x^2 + 5)$ is the opposite of $(x^2 + 5)$.

To Subtract Polynomials

To subtract two polynomials, change the signs of the terms of the polynomial being subtracted and then add.

PRACTICE 4

Subtract:

$(9x + 5) - (4x - 3)$

Example 4 Subtract: $(5x - 3) - (2x - 11)$

Solution: From the definition of subtraction, we have

$$(5x - 3) - (2x - 11) = (5x - 3) + [-(2x - 11)] \quad \text{Add the opposite.}$$
$$= (5x - 3) + (-2x + 11) \quad \text{Apply the distributive property.}$$
$$= 5x - 3 - 2x + 11 \quad \text{Remove parentheses.}$$
$$= 3x + 8 \quad \text{Combine like terms.}$$

● Work Practice 4

PRACTICE 5

Subtract:

$(4x^3 - 10x^2 + 1)$
$-(-4x^3 + x^2 - 11)$

Example 5 Subtract: $(2x^3 + 8x^2 - 6x) - (2x^3 - x^2 + 1)$

Solution: First, we change the sign of each term of the second polynomial; then we add.

$$(2x^3 + 8x^2 - 6x) - (2x^3 - x^2 + 1)$$
$$= (2x^3 + 8x^2 - 6x) + (-2x^3 + x^2 - 1)$$
$$= 2x^3 + 8x^2 - 6x - 2x^3 + x^2 - 1$$
$$= 2x^3 - 2x^3 + 8x^2 + x^2 - 6x - 1$$
$$= 9x^2 - 6x - 1 \quad \text{Combine like terms.}$$

● Work Practice 5

Just as polynomials can be added vertically, so can they be subtracted vertically.

PRACTICE 6

Subtract $(6y^2 - 3y + 2)$ from $(2y^2 - 2y + 7)$ using a vertical format.

Example 6 Subtract $(5y^2 + 2y - 6)$ from $(-3y^2 - 2y + 11)$ using a vertical format.

Solution: Arrange the polynomials in a vertical format, lining up like terms.

$$\begin{array}{r} -3y^2 - 2y + 11 \\ -(5y^2 + 2y - 6) \\ \hline \end{array} \qquad \begin{array}{r} -3y^2 - 2y + 11 \\ -5y^2 - 2y + 6 \\ \hline -8y^2 - 4y + 17 \end{array}$$

● Work Practice 6

Helpful Hint

Don't forget to change the sign of each term in the polynomial being subtracted.

Objective ○ Adding and Subtracting Polynomials in One Variable

Let's practice adding and subtracting polynomials in one variable.

PRACTICE 7

Subtract $(3x + 1)$ from the sum of $(4x - 3)$ and $(12x - 5)$.

Example 7 Subtract $(5z - 7)$ from the sum of $(8z + 11)$ and $(9z - 2)$.

Solution: Notice that $(5z - 7)$ is to be subtracted **from** a sum. The translation is

$$[(8z + 11) + (9z - 2)] - (5z - 7)$$
$$= 8z + 11 + 9z - 2 - 5z + 7 \quad \text{Remove grouping symbols.}$$
$$= 8z + 9z - 5z + 11 - 2 + 7 \quad \text{Group like terms.}$$
$$= 12z + 16 \quad \text{Combine like terms.}$$

● Work Practice 7

Answers

4. $5x + 8$ **5.** $8x^3 - 11x^2 + 12$
6. $-4y^2 + y + 5$ **7.** $13x - 9$

Objective ⓓ Adding and Subtracting Polynomials in Several Variables

Now that we know how to add or subtract polynomials in one variable, we can also add and subtract polynomials in several variables.

Examples Add or subtract as indicated.

8. $(3x^2 - 6xy + 5y^2) + (-2x^2 + 8xy - y^2)$
$= 3x^2 - 6xy + 5y^2 - 2x^2 + 8xy - y^2$
$= x^2 + 2xy + 4y^2$ 　　　　　　Combine like terms.

9. $(9a^2b^2 + 6ab - 3ab^2) - (5b^2a + 2ab - 3 - 9b^2)$
$= 9a^2b^2 + 6ab - 3ab^2 - 5b^2a - 2ab + 3 + 9b^2$
$= 9a^2b^2 + 4ab - 8ab^2 + 9b^2 + 3$ 　　Combine like terms.

● **Work Practice 8–9**

PRACTICE 8–9

Add or subtract as indicated.
8. $(2a^2 - ab + 6b^2)$
$+ (-3a^2 + ab - 7b^2)$
9. $(5x^2y^2 + 3 - 9x^2y + y^2)$
$- (-x^2y^2 + 7 - 8xy^2 + 2y^2)$

✓**Concept Check** If possible, simplify each expression by performing the indicated operation.

a. $2y + y$
b. $2y \cdot y$
c. $-2y - y$
d. $(-2y)(-y)$
e. $2x + y$

Answers
8. $-a^2 - b^2$
9. $6x^2y^2 - 4 - 9x^2y + 8xy^2 - y^2$

✓**Concept Check Answers**
a. $3y$ 　**b.** $2y^2$ 　**c.** $-3y$ 　**d.** $2y^2$
e. cannot be simplified

Vocabulary and Readiness Check

Simplify by combining like terms if possible.

1. $-9y - 5y$

2. $6m^5 + 7m^5$

3. $x + 6x$

4. $7z - z$

5. $5m^2 + 2m$

6. $8p^3 + 3p^2$

8.4 Exercise Set

FOR EXTRA HELP
MyMathLab
Powered by CourseCompass™ and MathXL®

 PRACTICE   WATCH   DOWNLOAD   READ   REVIEW

Objective Ⓐ *Add. See Examples 1 and 2.*

1. $(3x + 7) + (9x + 5)$

2. $(-y - 2) + (3y + 5)$

3. $(-7x + 5) + (-3x^2 + 7x + 5)$

4. $(3x - 8) + (4x^2 - 3x + 3)$

5. $(-5x^2 + 3) + (2x^2 + 1)$

6. $(3x^2 + 7) + (3x^2 + 9)$

7. $(-3y^2 - 4y) + (2y^2 + y - 1)$

8. $(7x^2 + 2x - 9) + (-3x^2 + 5)$

9. $(1.2x^3 - 3.4x + 7.9) + (6.7x^3 + 4.4x^2 - 10.9)$

10. $(9.6y^3 + 2.7y^2 - 8.6) + (1.1y^3 - 8.8y + 11.6)$

11. $\left(\dfrac{3}{4}m^2 - \dfrac{2}{5}m + \dfrac{1}{8}\right) + \left(-\dfrac{1}{4}m^2 - \dfrac{3}{10}m + \dfrac{11}{16}\right)$

12. $\left(-\dfrac{4}{7}n^2 + \dfrac{5}{6}m - \dfrac{1}{20}\right) + \left(\dfrac{3}{7}n^2 - \dfrac{5}{12}m - \dfrac{3}{10}\right)$

Add using a vertical format. See Example 3.

13. $\begin{aligned} 3t^2 + 4 \\ \underline{5t^2 - 8} \end{aligned}$

14. $\begin{aligned} 7x^3 + 3 \\ \underline{2x^3 - 7} \end{aligned}$

15. $\begin{aligned} 10a^3 - 8a^2 + 4a + 9 \\ \underline{5a^3 + 9a^2 - 7a + 7} \end{aligned}$

16. $\begin{aligned} 2x^3 - 3x^2 + \ x - 4 \\ \underline{5x^3 + 2x^2 - 3x + 2} \end{aligned}$

Objective Ⓑ *Subtract. See Examples 4 and 5.*

17. $(2x + 5) - (3x - 9)$

18. $(4 + 5a) - (-a - 5)$

19. $(5x^2 + 4) - (-2y^2 + 4)$

20. $(-7y^2 + 5) - (-8y^2 + 12)$

21. $3x - (5x - 9)$

22. $4 - (-y - 4)$

23. $(2x^2 + 3x - 9) - (-4x + 7)$

24. $(-7x^2 + 4x + 7) - (-8x + 2)$

25. $(5x + 8) - (-2x^2 - 6x + 8)$

26. $(-6y^2 + 3y - 4) - (9y^2 - 3y)$

27. $(0.7x^2 + 0.2x - 0.8) - (0.9x^2 + 1.4)$

28. $(-0.3y^2 + 0.6y - 0.3) - (0.5y^2 + 0.3)$

29. $\left(\dfrac{1}{4}z^2 - \dfrac{1}{5}z\right) - \left(-\dfrac{3}{20}z^2 + \dfrac{1}{10}z - \dfrac{7}{20}\right)$

30. $\left(\dfrac{1}{3}x^2 - \dfrac{2}{7}x\right) - \left(\dfrac{4}{21}x^2 + \dfrac{1}{21}x - \dfrac{2}{3}\right)$

Subtract using a vertical format. See Example 6.

31. $\quad 4z^2 - 8z + 3$
$\quad \underline{-(6z^2 + 8z - 3)}$

32. $\quad 7a^2 - 9a + 6$
$\quad \underline{-(11a^2 - 4a + 2)}$

33. $\quad 5u^5 - 4u^2 + 3u - 7$
$\quad \underline{-(3u^5 + 6u^2 - 8u + 2)}$

34. $\quad 5x^3 - 4x^2 + 6x - 2$
$\quad \underline{-(3x^3 - 2x^2 - \ x - 4)}$

Objectives Ⓐ Ⓑ Ⓒ **Mixed Practice** *Add or subtract as indicated. See Examples 1 through 7.*

35. $(3x + 5) + (2x - 14)$

36. $(2y + 20) + (5y - 30)$

37. $(9x - 1) - (5x + 2)$

38. $(7y + 7) - (y - 6)$

39. $(14y + 12) + (-3y - 5)$

40. $(26y + 17) + (-20y - 10)$

41. $(x^2 + 2x + 1) - (3x^2 - 6x + 2)$

42. $(5y^2 - 3y - 1) - (2y^2 + y + 1)$

43. $(3x^2 + 5x - 8) + (5x^2 + 9x + 12) - (8x^2 - 14)$

44. $(2x^2 + 7x - 9) + (x^2 - x + 10) - (3x^2 - 30)$

45. $(-a^2 + 1) - (a^2 - 3) + (5a^2 - 6a + 7)$

46. $(-m^2 + 3) - (m^2 - 13) + (6m^2 - m + 1)$

Translating *Perform each indicated operation. See Examples 3, 6, and 7.*

47. Subtract $4x$ from $(7x - 3)$.

48. Subtract y from $(y^2 - 4y + 1)$.

49. Add $(4x^2 - 6x + 1)$ and $(3x^2 + 2x + 1)$.

50. Add $(-3x^2 - 5x + 2)$ and $(x^2 - 6x + 9)$.

51. Subtract $(5x + 7)$ from $(7x^2 + 3x + 9)$.

52. Subtract $(5y^2 + 8y + 2)$ from $(7y^2 + 9y - 8)$.

53. Subtract $(4y^2 - 6y - 3)$ from the sum of $(8y^2 + 7)$ and $(6y + 9)$.

54. Subtract $(4x^2 - 2x + 2)$ from the sum of $(x^2 + 7x + 1)$ and $(7x + 5)$.

55. Subtract $(3x^2 - 4)$ from the sum of $(x^2 - 9x + 2)$ and $(2x^2 - 6x + 1)$.

56. Subtract $(y^2 - 9)$ from the sum of $(3y^2 + y + 4)$ and $(2y^2 - 6y - 10)$.

Objective D *Add or subtract as indicated. See Examples 8 and 9.*

57. $(9a + 6b - 5) + (-11a - 7b + 6)$

58. $(3x - 2 + 6y) + (7x - 2 - y)$

59. $(4x^2 + y^2 + 3) - (x^2 + y^2 - 2)$

60. $(7a^2 - 3b^2 + 10) - (-2a^2 + b^2 - 12)$

61. $(x^2 + 2xy - y^2) + (5x^2 - 4xy + 20y^2)$

62. $(a^2 - ab + 4b^2) + (6a^2 + 8ab - b^2)$

63. $(11r^2s + 16rs - 3 - 2r^2s^2) - (3sr^2 + 5 - 9r^2s^2)$

64. $(3x^2y - 6xy + x^2y^2 - 5) - (11x^2y^2 - 1 + 5yx^2)$

For Exercises 65 through 68, find the perimeter of each figure.

65.

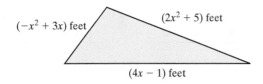

(−x² + 3x) feet   (2x² + 5) feet

(4x − 1) feet

66.

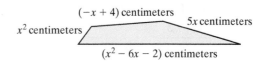

(−x + 4) centimeters   5x centimeters

x² centimeters

(x² − 6x − 2) centimeters

67.

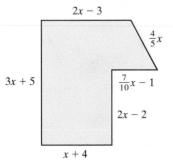

2x − 3

$\frac{4}{5}x$

3x + 5

$\frac{7}{10}x - 1$

2x − 2

x + 4

68.

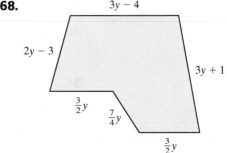

3y − 4

2y − 3

3y + 1

$\frac{3}{2}y$

$\frac{7}{4}y$

$\frac{3}{2}y$

69. A wooden beam is $(4y^2 + 4y + 1)$ meters long. If a piece $(y^2 - 10)$ meters is cut off, express the length of the remaining piece of beam as a polynomial in *y*.

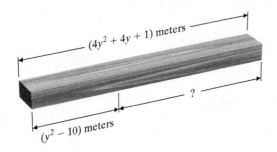

(4y² + 4y + 1) meters

?

(y² − 10) meters

70. A piece of quarter-round molding is $(13x - 7)$ inches long. If a piece $(2x + 2)$ inches long is removed, express the length of the remaining piece of molding as a polynomial in *x*.

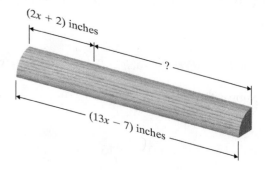

(2x + 2) inches

?

(13x − 7) inches

Perform each indicated operation.

71. $[(1.2x^2 - 3x + 9.1) - (7.8x^2 - 3.1 + 8)] + (1.2x - 6)$

72. $[(7.9y^4 - 6.8y^3 + 3.3y) + (6.1y^3 - 5)] - (4.2y^4 + 1.1y - 1)$

Review

Multiply. See Section 8.1.

73. $3x(2x)$ **74.** $-7x(x)$ **75.** $(12x^3)(-x^5)$ **76.** $6r^3(7r^{10})$ **77.** $10x^2(20xy^2)$ **78.** $-z^2y(11zy)$

Concept Extensions

Fill in the squares so that each is a true statement.

79. $3x^{\square} + 4x^2 = 7x^{\square}$

80. $9y^7 + 3y^{\square} = 12y^7$

81. $2x^{\square} + 3x^{\square} - 5x^{\square} + 4x^{\square} = 6x^4 - 2x^3$

82. $3y^{\square} + 7y^{\square} - 2y^{\square} - y^{\square} = 10y^5 - 3y^2$

Match each expression on the left with its simplification on the right. Not all letters on the right must be used and a letter may be used more than once.

83. $10y - 6y^2 - y$

84. $5x + 5x$

85. $(5x - 3) + (5x - 3)$

86. $(15x - 3) - (5x - 3)$

a. $3y$

b. $9y - 6y^2$

c. $10x$

d. $25x^2$

e. $10x - 6$

f. none of these

Simplify each expression by performing the indicated operation. Explain how you arrived at each answer. See the last Concept Check in this section.

87. a. $z + 3z$
  b. $z \cdot 3z$
  c. $-z - 3z$
  d. $(-z)(-3z)$

88. a. $2y + y$
  b. $2y \cdot y$
  c. $-2y - y$
  d. $(-2y)(-y)$

89. a. $m \cdot m \cdot m$
  b. $m + m + m$
  c. $(-m)(-m)(-m)$
  d. $-m - m - m$

90. a. $x + x$
  b. $x \cdot x$
  c. $-x - x$
  d. $(-x)(-x)$

91. The polynomial $-20x^2 + 156x + 14{,}437$ represents the electricity generated (in gigawatts) by geothermal sources in the United States during 2002–2007. The polynomial $894x^2 - 90x + 10{,}939$ represents the electricity generated (in gigawatts) by wind power in the United States during 2002–2007. In both polynomials, x represents the number of years after 2002. Find a polynomial for the total electricity generated by both geothermal and wind power during 2002–2007. (*Source:* Based on information from the Energy Information Administration)

92. The polynomial $-0.92x^2 + 2.43x + 34.85$ represents the number of Americans (in millions) under age 65 covered by public health programs during 1999–2007. The polynomial $0.07x^2 - 0.64x + 180.96$ represents the number of Americans (in millions) under age 65 covered by private health insurance during 1999–2007. In both polynomials, x represents the number of years since 1999. Find a polynomial for the total number of Americans (in millions) under age 65 with some form of health coverage during this period. (*Source:* Based on data from U.S. Census Bureau)

8.5 MULTIPLYING POLYNOMIALS

Objective A Multiplying Monomials

Recall from Section 8.1 that to multiply two monomials such as $(-5x^3)$ and $(-2x^4)$, we use the associative and commutative properties and regroup. Remember also that to multiply exponential expressions with a common base, we use the product rule for exponents and add exponents.

$$(-5x^3)(-2x^4) = (-5)(-2)(x^3 \cdot x^4) \qquad \text{Use the commutative and associative properties.}$$
$$= 10x^7 \qquad \text{Multiply.}$$

Examples Multiply.

1. $6x \cdot 4x = (6 \cdot 4)(x \cdot x)$ Use the commutative and associative properties.
   $\qquad = 24x^2$ Multiply.
2. $-7x^2 \cdot 2x^5 = (-7 \cdot 2)(x^2 \cdot x^5)$
   $\qquad = -14x^7$
3. $(-12x^5)(-x) = (-12x^5)(-1x)$
   $\qquad = (-12)(-1)(x^5 \cdot x)$
   $\qquad = 12x^6$

● **Work Practice 1–3**

✓ **Concept Check** Simplify.

a. $3x \cdot 2x$ **b.** $3x + 2x$

Objective B Multiplying Monomials by Polynomials

To multiply a monomial such as $7x$ by a trinomial such as $x^2 + 2x + 5$, we use the distributive property.

Examples Multiply.

4. $7x(x^2 + 2x + 5) = 7x(x^2) + 7x(2x) + 7x(5)$ Apply the distributive property.
   $\qquad\qquad = 7x^3 + 14x^2 + 35x$ Multiply.

5. $5x(2x^3 + 6) = 5x(2x^3) + 5x(6)$ Apply the distributive property.
   $\qquad\qquad = 10x^4 + 30x$ Multiply.

6. $-3x^2(5x^2 + 6x - 1)$ Apply the distributive property.
   $\qquad = (-3x^2)(5x^2) + (-3x^2)(6x) + (-3x^2)(-1)$ Multiply.
   $\qquad = -15x^4 - 18x^3 + 3x^2$

● **Work Practice 4–6**

Answers
1. $90x^2$ 2. $-88x^{10}$ 3. $5x^5$
4. $4x^3 + 16x^2 + 12x$ 5. $56x^5 + 8x$
6. $-6x^5 + 2x^4 - 4x^3$

✓ **Concept Check Answers**
a. $6x^2$ **b.** $5x$

Objective ⓒ Multiplying Two Polynomials

We also use the distributive property to multiply two binomials.

Example 7 Multiply.

a. $(m + 4)(m + 6)$ 　　　　**b.** $(3x + 2)(2x - 5)$

Solution:

a. $(m + 4)(m + 6) = m(m + 6) + 4(m + 6)$ 　Use the distributive property.

$= m \cdot m + m \cdot 6 + 4 \cdot m + 4 \cdot 6$ 　Use the distributive property.

$= m^2 + 6m + 4m + 24$ 　Multiply.

$= m^2 + 10m + 24$ 　Combine like terms.

b. $(3x + 2)(2x - 5) = 3x(2x - 5) + 2(2x - 5)$ 　Use the distributive property.

$= 3x(2x) + 3x(-5) + 2(2x) + 2(-5)$

$= 6x^2 - 15x + 4x - 10$ 　Multiply.

$= 6x^2 - 11x - 10$ 　Combine like terms.

● **Work Practice 7**

This idea can be expanded so that we can multiply any two polynomials.

> **To Multiply Two Polynomials**
>
> Multiply each term of the first polynomial by each term of the second polynomial, and then combine like terms.

Examples Multiply.

8. $(2x - y)^2$

$= (2x - y)(2x - y)$ 　Using the meaning of an exponent, we have 2 factors of $(2x - y)$.

$= 2x(2x) + 2x(-y) + (-y)(2x) + (-y)(-y)$

$= 4x^2 - 2xy - 2xy + y^2$ 　Multiply.

$= 4x^2 - 4xy + y^2$ 　Combine like terms.

9. $(t + 2)(3t^2 - 4t + 2)$

$= t(3t^2) + t(-4t) + t(2) + 2(3t^2) + 2(-4t) + 2(2)$

$= 3t^3 - 4t^2 + 2t + 6t^2 - 8t + 4$

$= 3t^3 + 2t^2 - 6t + 4$ 　Combine like terms.

● **Work Practice 8–9**

✓**Concept Check** Square where indicated. Simplify if possible.

a. $(4a)^2 + (3b)^2$ 　　**b.** $(4a + 3b)^2$

Objective ⓓ Multiplying Polynomials Vertically

Another convenient method for multiplying polynomials is to multiply vertically, similar to the way we multiply real numbers. This method is shown in the next examples.

PRACTICE 7

Multiply:

a. $(x + 5)(x + 10)$

b. $(4x + 5)(3x - 4)$

PRACTICE 8–9

Multiply.

8. $(3x - 2y)^2$

9. $(x + 3)(2x^2 - 5x + 4)$

Answers

7. a. $x^2 + 15x + 50$

b. $12x^2 - x - 20$

8. $9x^2 - 12xy + 4y^2$

9. $2x^3 + x^2 - 11x + 12$

✓ **Concept Check Answers**

a. $16a^2 + 9b^2$ 　**b.** $16a^2 + 24ab + 9b^2$

PRACTICE 10

Multiply vertically:
$(3y^2 + 1)(y^2 - 4y + 5)$

Example 10 Multiply vertically: $(2y^2 + 5)(y^2 - 3y + 4)$

Solution:

$$
\begin{array}{r}
y^2 - 3y + 4 \\
2y^2 + 5 \\
\hline
5y^2 - 15y + 20 \\
2y^4 - 6y^3 + 8y^2 \\
\hline
2y^4 - 6y^3 + 13y^2 - 15y + 20
\end{array}
$$

Multiply $y^2 - 3y + 4$ by 5.

Multiply $y^2 - 3y + 4$ by $2y^2$.

Combine like terms.

● **Work Practice 10**

PRACTICE 11

Find the product of
$(4x^2 - x - 1)$ and
$(3x^2 + 6x - 2)$ using a vertical
format.

Example 11 Find the product of $(2x^2 - 3x + 4)$ and $(x^2 + 5x - 2)$ using a vertical format.

Solution: First, we arrange the polynomials in a vertical format. Then we multiply each term of the second polynomial by each term of the first polynomial.

$$
\begin{array}{r}
2x^2 - 3x + 4 \\
x^2 + 5x - 2 \\
\hline
-4x^2 + 6x - 8 \\
10x^3 - 15x^2 + 20x \\
2x^4 - 3x^3 + 4x^2 \\
\hline
2x^4 + 7x^3 - 15x^2 + 26x - 8
\end{array}
$$

Multiply $2x^2 - 3x + 4$ by -2.

Multiply $2x^2 - 3x + 4$ by $5x$.

Multiply $2x^2 - 3x + 4$ by x^2.

Combine like terms.

● **Work Practice 11**

Answers

10. $3y^4 - 12y^3 + 16y^2 - 4y + 5$

11. $12x^4 + 21x^3 - 17x^2 - 4x + 2$

Vocabulary and Readiness Check

Fill in each blank with the correct choice.

1. The expression $5x(3x + 2)$ equals $5x \cdot 3x + 5x \cdot 2$ by the _____ property.
   a. commutative   **b.** associative   **c.** distributive

2. The expression $(x + 4)(7x - 1)$ equals $x(7x - 1) + 4(7x - 1)$ by the _____ property.
   a. commutative   **b.** associative   **c.** distributive

3. The expression $(5y - 1)^2$ equals _____.
   a. $2(5y - 1)$ **b.** $(5y - 1)(5y + 1)$ **c.** $(5y - 1)(5y - 1)$

4. The expression $9x \cdot 3x$ equals _____.
   a. $27x$ **b.** $27x^2$ **c.** $12x$ **d.** $12x^2$

Perform the indicated operation, if possible.

5. $x^3 \cdot x^5$

6. $x^2 \cdot x^6$

7. $x^3 + x^5$

8. $x^2 + x^6$

9. $x^7 \cdot x^7$

10. $x^{11} \cdot x^{11}$

11. $x^7 + x^7$

12. $x^{11} + x^{11}$

13. $9y^2 \cdot 11y^2$

14. $6z^3 \cdot 7z^3$

15. $9y^2 + 11y^2$

16. $6z^3 + 7z^3$

8.5 Exercise Set

Objective Ⓐ *Multiply. See Examples 1 through 3.*

1. $8x^2 \cdot 3x$

2. $6x \cdot 3x^2$

3. $(-x^3)(-x)$

4. $(-x^6)(-x)$

5. $-4n^3 \cdot 7n^7$

6. $9t^6(-3t^5)$

7. $(-3.1x^3)(4x^9)$

8. $(-5.2x^4)(3x^4)$

9. $\left(-\dfrac{1}{3}y^2\right)\left(\dfrac{2}{5}y\right)$

10. $\left(-\dfrac{3}{4}y^7\right)\left(\dfrac{1}{7}y^4\right)$

11. $(2x)(-3x^2)(4x^5)$

12. $(x)(5x^4)(-6x^7)$

Objective Ⓑ *Multiply. See Examples 4 through 6.*

13. $3x(2x + 5)$

14. $2x(6x + 3)$

15. $7x(x^2 + 2x - 1)$

16. $5y(y^2 + y - 10)$

17. $-2a(a + 4)$

18. $-3a(2a + 7)$

19. $3x(2x^2 - 3x + 4)$

20. $4x(5x^2 - 6x - 10)$

21. $3a^2(4a^3 + 15)$

22. $9x^3(5x^2 + 12)$

23. $-2a^2(3a^2 - 2a + 3)$

24. $-4b^2(3b^3 - 12b^2 - 6)$

25. $3x^2y(2x^3 - x^2y^2 + 8y^3)$

26. $4xy^2(7x^3 + 3x^2y^2 - 9y^3)$

27. $-y(4x^3 - 7x^2y + xy^2 + 3y^3)$

28. $-x(6y^3 - 5xy^2 + x^2y - 5x^3)$

29. $\dfrac{1}{2}x^2(8x^2 - 6x + 1)$

30. $\dfrac{1}{3}y^2(9y^2 - 6y + 1)$

Objective C *Multiply. See Examples 7 through 9.*

31. $(x + 4)(x + 3)$

32. $(x + 2)(x + 9)$

33. $(a + 7)(a - 2)$

34. $(y - 10)(y + 11)$

35. $\left(x + \dfrac{2}{3}\right)\left(x - \dfrac{1}{3}\right)$

36. $\left(x + \dfrac{3}{5}\right)\left(x - \dfrac{2}{5}\right)$

37. $(3x^2 + 1)(4x^2 + 7)$

38. $(5x^2 + 2)(6x^2 + 2)$

39. $(4x - 3)(3x - 5)$

40. $(8x - 3)(2x - 4)$

41. $(1 - 3a)(1 - 4a)$

42. $(3 - 2a)(2 - a)$

43. $(2y - 4)^2$

44. $(6x - 7)^2$

45. $(x - 2)(x^2 - 3x + 7)$

46. $(x + 3)(x^2 + 5x - 8)$

47. $(x + 5)(x^3 - 3x + 4)$

48. $(a + 2)(a^3 - 3a^2 + 7)$

49. $(2a - 3)(5a^2 - 6a + 4)$

50. $(3 + b)(2 - 5b - 3b^2)$

51. $(7xy - y)^2$

52. $(x^2 - 4)^2$

Objective D *Multiply vertically. See Examples 10 and 11.*

53. $(2x - 11)(6x + 1)$

54. $(4x - 7)(5x + 1)$

55. $(x + 3)(2x^2 + 4x - 1)$

56. $(4x - 5)(8x^2 + 2x - 4)$

57. $(x^2 + 5x - 7)(2x^2 - 7x - 9)$

58. $(3x^2 - x + 2)(x^2 + 2x + 1)$

Objectives A B C D Mixed Practice *Multiply. See Examples 1 through 11.*

59. $-1.2y(-7y^6)$

60. $-4.2x(-2x^5)$

61. $-3x(x^2 + 2x - 8)$

62. $-5x(x^2 - 3x + 10)$

63. $(x + 19)(2x + 1)$

64. $(3y + 4)(y + 11)$

65. $\left(x + \dfrac{1}{7}\right)\left(x - \dfrac{3}{7}\right)$

66. $\left(m + \dfrac{2}{9}\right)\left(m - \dfrac{1}{9}\right)$

67. $(3y + 5)^2$

68. $(7y + 2)^2$

69. $(a + 4)(a^2 - 6a + 6)$

70. $(t + 3)(t^2 - 5t + 5)$

Express as the product of polynomials. Then multiply.

71. Find the area of the rectangle.

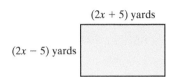

(2x + 5) yards

(2x − 5) yards

72. Find the area of the square field.

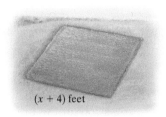

(x + 4) feet

73. Find the area of the triangle.

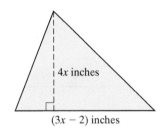

4x inches

(3x − 2) inches

74. Find the volume of the cube-shaped glass block.

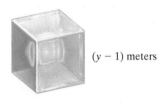

(y − 1) meters

Review

In this section, we review operations on monomials. Study the box below, then proceed. See Sections 5.8, 8.1, and 8.2.

Operations on Monomials	
Multiply	Review the product rule for exponents.
Divide	Review the quotient rule for exponents.
Add or Subtract	Remember, we may only combine like terms.

Perform the operations on the monomials, if possible. The first two rows have been completed for you.

	Monomials	Add	Subtract	Multiply	Divide
	$6x, 3x$	$6x + 3x = 9x$	$6x - 3x = 3x$	$6x \cdot 3x = 18x^2$	$\dfrac{6x}{3x} = 2$
	$-12x^2, 2x$	$-12x^2 + 2x$; can't be simplified	$-12x^2 - 2x$; can't be simplified	$-12x^2 \cdot 2x = -24x^3$	$\dfrac{-12x^2}{2x} = -6x$
75.	$5a, 15a$				
76.	$4y^3, 4y^7$				
77.	$-3y^5, 9y^4$				
78.	$-14x^2, 2x^2$				

Concept Extensions

79. Perform each indicated operation. Explain the difference between the two expressions.

   a. $(3x + 5) + (3x + 7)$
   b. $(3x + 5)(3x + 7)$

80. Perform each indicated operation. Explain the difference between the two expressions.

   a. $(8x - 3) - (5x - 2)$
   b. $(8x - 3)(5x - 2)$

Mixed Practice *Perform the indicated operations. See Sections 8.4 and 8.5.*

81. $(3x - 1) + (10x - 6)$ **82.** $(2x - 1) + (10x - 7)$ **83.** $(3x - 1)(10x - 6)$

84. $(2x - 1)(10x - 7)$ **85.** $(3x - 1) - (10x - 6)$ **86.** $(2x - 1) - (10x - 7)$

87. The area of the largest rectangle below is $x(x + 3)$. Find another expression for this area by finding the sum of the areas of the smaller rectangles.

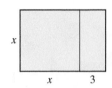

88. The area of the figure below is $(x + 2)(x + 3)$. Find another expression for this area by finding the sum of the areas of the smaller rectangles.

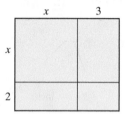

89. Write an expression for the area of the largest rectangle below in two different ways.

90. Write an expression for the area of the figure below in two different ways.

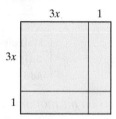

Simplify. See the Concept Checks in this section.

91. $5a + 6a$ **92.** $5a \cdot 6a$

Square where indicated. Simplify if possible.

93. $(5x)^2 + (2y)^2$ **94.** $(5x + 2y)^2$

95. Multiply each of the following polynomials.
   a. $(a + b)(a - b)$
   b. $(2x + 3y)(2x - 3y)$
   c. $(4x + 7)(4x - 7)$
   d. Can you make a general statement about all products of the form $(x + y)(x - y)$?

96. Evaluate each of the following.
   a. $(2 + 3)^2; 2^2 + 3^2$
   b. $(8 + 10)^2; 8^2 + 10^2$
   c. Does $(a + b)^2 = a^2 + b^2$ no matter what the values of a and b are? Why or why not?

8.6 SPECIAL PRODUCTS

Objectives

A Multiply Two Binomials Using the FOIL Method.

B Square a Binomial.

C Multiply the Sum and Difference of Two Terms.

D Use Special Products to Multiply Binomials.

Objective A Using the FOIL Method

In this section, we multiply binomials using special products. First, we introduce a special order for multiplying binomials called the FOIL order or method. This order, or pattern, is a result of the distributive property. We demonstrate by multiplying $(3x + 1)$ by $(2x + 5)$.

The FOIL Method

F stands for the product of the **First** terms.

$(3x + 1)(2x + 5)$

$(3x)(2x) = 6x^2$ F

O stands for the product of the **Outer** terms.

$(3x + 1)(2x + 5)$

$(3x)(5) = 15x$ O

I stands for the product of the **Inner** terms.

$(3x + 1)(2x + 5)$

$(1)(2x) = 2x$ I

L stands for the product of the **Last** terms.

$(3x + 1)(2x + 5)$

$(1)(5) = 5$ L

$$\overset{\text{F}}{} \quad \overset{\text{O}}{} \quad \overset{\text{I}}{} \quad \overset{\text{L}}{}$$
$$(3x + 1)(2x + 5) = 6x^2 + 15x + 2x + 5$$
$$= 6x^2 + 17x + 5 \qquad \text{Combine like terms.}$$

Let's practice multiplying binomials using the FOIL method.

Example 1   Multiply: $(x - 3)(x + 4)$

Solution:

$$(x - 3)(x + 4) = \overset{\text{F}}{(x)(x)} + \overset{\text{O}}{(x)(4)} + \overset{\text{I}}{(-3)(x)} + \overset{\text{L}}{(-3)(4)}$$
$$= x^2 + 4x - 3x - 12$$
$$= x^2 + x - 12 \qquad \text{Combine like terms.}$$

● Work Practice 1

Example 2   Multiply: $(5x - 7)(x - 2)$

Solution:

$$(5x - 7)(x - 2) = \overset{\text{F}}{5x(x)} + \overset{\text{O}}{5x(-2)} + \overset{\text{I}}{(-7)(x)} + \overset{\text{L}}{(-7)(-2)}$$
$$= 5x^2 - 10x - 7x + 14$$
$$= 5x^2 - 17x + 14 \qquad \text{Combine like terms.}$$

● Work Practice 2

PRACTICE 1

Multiply: $(x + 7)(x - 5)$

Helpful Hint   Remember that the FOIL order for multiplying can be used only for the product of 2 binomials.

PRACTICE 2

Multiply: $(6x - 1)(x - 4)$

Answers
1. $x^2 + 2x - 35$ 2. $6x^2 - 25x + 4$

Multiply: $(2y^2 + 3)(y - 4)$

Example 3 Multiply: $(y^2 + 6)(2y - 1)$

Solution: F   O   I   L

$(y^2 + 6)(2y - 1) = 2y^3 - 1y^2 + 12y - 6$

Notice in this example that there are no like terms that can be combined, so the product is $2y^3 - y^2 + 12y - 6$.

● Work Practice 3

Objective B Squaring Binomials

An expression such as $(3y + 1)^2$ is called the square of a binomial. Since $(3y + 1)^2 = (3y + 1)(3y + 1)$, we can use the FOIL method to find this product.

PRACTICE 4

Multiply: $(2x + 9)^2$

Example 4 Multiply: $(3y + 1)^2$

Solution: $(3y + 1)^2 = (3y + 1)(3y + 1)$

                 F   O   I   L

$= (3y)(3y) + (3y)(1) + 1(3y) + 1(1)$

$= 9y^2 + 3y + 3y + 1$

$= 9y^2 + 6y + 1$

● Work Practice 4

Notice the pattern that appears in Example 4.

$(3y + 1)^2 = 9y^2 + 6y + 1$

→ $9y^2$ is the first term of the binomial squared: $(3y)^2 = 9y^2$.

→ $6y$ is 2 times the product of both terms of the binomial: $(2)(3y)(1) = 6y$.

→ 1 is the second term of the binomial squared: $(1)^2 = 1$.

This pattern leads to the formulas below, which can be used when squaring a binomial. We call these **special products.**

Squaring a Binomial

A binomial squared is equal to the square of the first term plus or minus twice the product of both terms plus the square of the second term.

$$(a + b)^2 = a^2 + 2ab + b^2$$
$$(a - b)^2 = a^2 - 2ab + b^2$$

The first product can be visualized geometrically.

The area of the large square is side · side.
Area $= (a + b)(a + b) = (a + b)^2$
The area of the large square is also the sum of the areas of the smaller rectangles.
Area $= a^2 + ab + ab + b^2 = a^2 + 2ab + b^2$
Thus, $(a + b)^2 = a^2 + 2ab + b^2$.

Answers
3. $2y^3 - 8y^2 + 3y - 12$
4. $4x^2 + 36x + 81$

Examples Use a special product to square each binomial.

first term squared	plus or minus	twice the product of the terms	plus	second term squared

5. $(t + 2)^2 = \quad t^2 + \quad 2(t)(2) + \quad 2^2 = t^2 + 4t + 4$
6. $(p - q)^2 = \quad p^2 - \quad 2(p)(q) + \quad q^2 = p^2 - 2pq + q^2$
7. $(2x + 5)^2 = (2x)^2 + \quad 2(2x)(5) + \quad 5^2 = 4x^2 + 20x + 25$
8. $(x^2 - 7y)^2 = (x^2)^2 - \quad 2(x^2)(7y) + \quad (7y)^2 = x^4 - 14x^2y + 49y^2$

● Work Practice 5–8

PRACTICE 5–8

Use a special product to square each binomial.
5. $(y + 3)^2$
6. $(r - s)^2$
7. $(6x + 5)^2$
8. $(x^2 - 3y)^2$

Helpful Hint

Notice that

$(a + b)^2 \neq a^2 + b^2$ The middle term, $2ab$, is missing.

$(a + b)^2 = (a + b)(a + b) = a^2 + 2ab + b^2$

Likewise,

$(a - b)^2 \neq a^2 - b^2$

$(a - b)^2 = (a - b)(a - b) = a^2 - 2ab + b^2$

Objective ◉ Multiplying the Sum and Difference of Two Terms

Another special product is the product of the sum and difference of the same two terms, such as $(x + y)(x - y)$. Finding this product by the FOIL method, we see a pattern emerge.

$$(x + y)(x - y) = \overset{F}{x^2} - \overset{O}{xy} + \overset{I}{xy} - \overset{L}{y^2}$$
$$= x^2 - y^2$$

Notice that the two middle terms subtract out. This is because the **O**uter product is the opposite of the **I**nner product. Only the **difference of squares** remains.

Multiplying the Sum and Difference of Two Terms

The product of the sum and difference of two terms is the square of the first term minus the square of the second term.

$$(a + b)(a - b) = a^2 - b^2$$

Answers
5. $y^2 + 6y + 9$ 6. $r^2 - 2rs + s^2$
7. $36x^2 + 60x + 25$
8. $x^4 - 6x^2y + 9y^2$

Use a special product to multiply.

9. $(x + 9)(x - 9)$

10. $(5 + 4y)(5 - 4y)$

11. $\left(x - \dfrac{1}{3}\right)\left(x + \dfrac{1}{3}\right)$

12. $(3a - b)(3a + b)$

13. $(2x^2 - 6y)(2x^2 + 6y)$

Examples Use a special product to multiply.

first term squared	minus	second term squared
↓	↓	↓

9. $(x + 4)(x - 4) = x^2 \quad - \quad 4^2 = x^2 - 16$

10. $(6t + 7)(6t - 7) = (6t)^2 \quad - \quad 7^2 = 36t^2 - 49$

11. $\left(x - \dfrac{1}{4}\right)\left(x + \dfrac{1}{4}\right) = x^2 \quad - \quad \left(\dfrac{1}{4}\right)^2 = x^2 - \dfrac{1}{16}$

12. $(2p - q)(2p + q) = (2p)^2 - q^2 = 4p^2 - q^2$

13. $(3x^2 - 5y)(3x^2 + 5y) = (3x^2)^2 - (5y)^2 = 9x^4 - 25y^2$

● **Work Practice 9–13**

✔**Concept Check** Match each expression on the left to the equivalent expression or expressions in the list on the right.

$(a + b)^2$

$(a + b)(a - b)$

a. $(a + b)(a + b)$

b. $a^2 - b^2$

c. $a^2 + b^2$

d. $a^2 - 2ab + b^2$

e. $a^2 + 2ab + b^2$

Objective ⓓ Using Special Products

Let's now practice using our special products on a variety of multiplication problems. This practice will help us recognize when to apply what special product formula.

Use a special product to multiply, if possible.

14. $(7x - 1)^2$

15. $(5y + 3)(2y - 5)$

16. $(2a - 1)(2a + 1)$

17. $\left(5y - \dfrac{1}{9}\right)^2$

Examples Use a special product to multiply, if possible.

14. $(4x - 9)(4x + 9)$ This is the sum and difference of the same two terms.

$= (4x)^2 - 9^2 = 16x^2 - 81$

15. $(3y + 2)^2$ This is a binomial squared.

$= (3y)^2 + 2(3y)(2) + 2^2$

$= 9y^2 + 12y + 4$

16. $(6a + 1)(a - 7)$ No special product applies. Use the FOIL method.

$\quad\text{F}\qquad\text{O}\qquad\text{I}\qquad\text{L}$

$= 6a \cdot a + 6a(-7) + 1 \cdot a + 1(-7)$

$= 6a^2 - 42a + a - 7$

$= 6a^2 - 41a - 7$

17. $\left(4x - \dfrac{1}{11}\right)^2$ This is a binomial squared.

$= (4x)^2 - 2(4x)\left(\dfrac{1}{11}\right) + \left(\dfrac{1}{11}\right)^2$

$= 16x^2 - \dfrac{8}{11}x + \dfrac{1}{121}$

● **Work Practice 14–17**

Answers

9. $x^2 - 81$ **10.** $25 - 16y^2$

11. $x^2 - \dfrac{1}{9}$ **12.** $9a^2 - b^2$

13. $4x^4 - 36y^2$ **14.** $49x^2 - 14x + 1$

15. $10y^2 - 19y - 15$ **16.** $4a^2 - 1$

17. $25y^2 - \dfrac{10}{9}y + \dfrac{1}{81}$

✔ **Concept Check Answer**

a and e, b

Helpful Hint

- When multiplying two binomials, you may always use the FOIL order or method.
- When multiplying any two polynomials, you may always use the distributive property to find the product.

Vocabulary and Readiness Check

Answer each exercise true or false.

1. $(x + 4)^2 = x^2 + 16$

3. $(x + 4)(x - 4) = x^2 + 16$

2. For $(x + 6)(2x - 1)$, the product of the first terms is $2x^2$.

4. The product $(x - 1)(x^3 + 3x - 1)$ is a polynomial of degree 5.

8.6 Exercise Set

FOR EXTRA HELP  PRACTICE WATCH DOWNLOAD READ REVIEW

Objective **A** *Multiply using the FOIL method. See Examples 1 through 3.*

1. $(x + 3)(x + 4)$

2. $(x + 5)(x + 1)$

3. $(x - 5)(x + 10)$

4. $(y - 12)(y + 4)$

5. $(5x - 6)(x + 2)$

6. $(3y - 5)(2y + 7)$

7. $(y - 6)(4y - 1)$

8. $(2x - 9)(x - 11)$

9. $(2x + 5)(3x - 1)$

10. $(6x + 2)(x - 2)$

11. $(y^2 + 7)(6y + 4)$

12. $(y^2 + 3)(5y + 6)$

13. $\left(x - \dfrac{1}{3}\right)\left(x + \dfrac{2}{3}\right)$

14. $\left(x - \dfrac{2}{5}\right)\left(x + \dfrac{1}{5}\right)$

15. $(0.4 - 3a)(0.2 - 5a)$

16. $(0.3 - 2a)(0.6 - 5a)$

17. $(x + 5y)(2x - y)$

18. $(x + 4y)(3x - y)$

Objective **B** *Multiply. See Examples 4 through 8.*

19. $(x + 2)^2$

20. $(x + 7)^2$

21. $(2a - 3)^2$

22. $(7x - 3)^2$

23. $(3a - 5)^2$

24. $(5a - 2)^2$

25. $(x^2 + 0.5)^2$

26. $(x^2 + 0.3)^2$

27. $\left(y - \dfrac{2}{7}\right)^2$

28. $\left(y - \dfrac{3}{4}\right)^2$

29. $(2x - 1)^2$

30. $(5b - 4)^2$

31. $(5x + 9)^2$

32. $(6s + 2)^2$

33. $(3x - 7y)^2$

34. $(4s - 2y)^2$

35. $(4m + 5n)^2$

36. $(3n + 5m)^2$

37. $(5x^4 - 3)^2$

38. $(7x^3 - 6)^2$

Objective **C** *Multiply. See Examples 9 through 13.*

39. $(a - 7)(a + 7)$ | **40.** $(b + 3)(b - 3)$ | **41.** $(x + 6)(x - 6)$ | **42.** $(x - 8)(x + 8)$

43. $(3x - 1)(3x + 1)$ | **44.** $(7x - 5)(7x + 5)$ | **45.** $(x^2 + 5)(x^2 - 5)$ | **46.** $(a^2 + 6)(a^2 - 6)$

47. $(2y^2 - 1)(2y^2 + 1)$ | **48.** $(3x^2 + 1)(3x^2 - 1)$ | **49.** $(4 - 7x)(4 + 7x)$ | **50.** $(8 - 7x)(8 + 7x)$

51. $\left(3x - \dfrac{1}{2}\right)\left(3x + \dfrac{1}{2}\right)$ | **52.** $\left(10x + \dfrac{2}{7}\right)\left(10x - \dfrac{2}{7}\right)$ | **53.** $(9x + y)(9x - y)$ | **54.** $(2x - y)(2x + y)$

55. $(2m + 5n)(2m - 5n)$ | **56.** $(5m + 4n)(5m - 4n)$

Objective **D** **Mixed Practice** *Multiply. See Examples 14 through 17.*

57. $(a + 5)(a + 4)$ | **58.** $(a + 5)(a + 7)$ | **59.** $(a - 7)^2$ | **60.** $(b - 2)^2$

61. $(4a + 1)(3a - 1)$ | **62.** $(6a + 7)(6a + 5)$ | **63.** $(x + 2)(x - 2)$ | **64.** $(x - 10)(x + 10)$

65. $(3a + 1)^2$ | **66.** $(4a + 2)^2$ | **67.** $(x + y)(4x - y)$ | **68.** $(3x + 2)(4x - 2)$

69. $\left(\dfrac{1}{3}a^2 - 7\right)\left(\dfrac{1}{3}a^2 + 7\right)$ | **70.** $\left(\dfrac{a}{2} + 4y\right)\left(\dfrac{a}{2} - 4y\right)$ | **71.** $(3b + 7)(2b - 5)$ | **72.** $(3y - 13)(y - 3)$

73. $(x^2 + 10)(x^2 - 10)$ | **74.** $(x^2 + 8)(x^2 - 8)$ | **75.** $(4x + 5)(4x - 5)$ | **76.** $(3x + 5)(3x - 5)$

77. $(5x - 6y)^2$ | **78.** $(4x - 9y)^2$ | **79.** $(2r - 3s)(2r + 3s)$ | **80.** $(6r - 2x)(6r + 2x)$

Express each as a product of polynomials in x. Then multiply and simplify.

△ **81.** Find the area of the square rug if its side is $(2x + 1)$ feet.

$(2x + 1)$ feet

$(2x + 1)$ feet

△ **82.** Find the area of the rectangular canvas if its length is $(3x - 2)$ inches and its width is $(x - 4)$ inches.

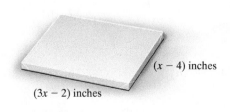

$(x - 4)$ inches

$(3x - 2)$ inches

Review

Simplify each expression. See Sections 8.1 and 8.2.

83. $\dfrac{50b^{10}}{70b^5}$

84. $\dfrac{60y^6}{80y^2}$

85. $\dfrac{8a^{17}b^5}{-4a^7b^{10}}$

86. $\dfrac{-6a^8y}{3a^4y}$

87. $\dfrac{2x^4y^{12}}{3x^4y^4}$

88. $\dfrac{-48ab^6}{32ab^3}$

Concept Extensions

Match each expression on the left to the equivalent expression on the right. See the Concept Check in this section. (Not all choices will be used.)

89. $(a - b)^2$

90. $(a - b)(a + b)$

91. $(a + b)^2$

92. $(a + b)^2(a - b)^2$

a. $a^2 - b^2$

b. $a^2 + b^2$

c. $a^2 - 2ab + b^2$

d. $a^2 + 2ab + b^2$

e. none of these

Fill in the squares so that a true statement forms.

93. $(x^{\square} + 7)(x^{\square} + 3) = x^4 + 10x^2 + 21$

94. $(5x^{\square} - 2)^2 = 25x^6 - 20x^3 + 4$

Find the area of the shaded figure. To do so, subtract the area of the smaller square(s) from the area of the larger geometric figure.

△ **95.**

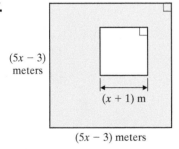

△ **96.**

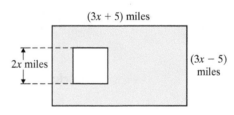

△ **97.**

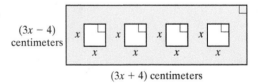

△ **98.**

99. In your own words, describe the different methods that can be used to find the product: $(2x - 5)(3x + 1)$.

100. In your own words, describe the different methods that can be used to find the product: $(5x + 1)^2$.

101. Suppose that a classmate asked you why $(2x + 1)^2$ is **not** $(4x^2 + 1)$. Write down your response to this classmate.

102. Suppose that a classmate asked you why $(2x + 1)^2$ **is** $(4x^2 + 4x + 1)$. Write down your response to this classmate.

8.7 DIVIDING POLYNOMIALS

Objective **A** Dividing by a Monomial

To divide a polynomial by a monomial, recall addition of fractions. Fractions that have a common denominator are added by adding the numerators:

$$\frac{a}{c} + \frac{b}{c} = \frac{a + b}{c}$$

If we read this equation from right to left and let a, b, and c be monomials, $c \neq 0$, we have the following.

> ### To Divide a Polynomial by a Monomial
>
> Divide each term of the polynomial by the monomial.
>
> $$\frac{a + b}{c} = \frac{a}{c} + \frac{b}{c}, \quad c \neq 0$$

Throughout this section, we assume that denominators are not 0.

PRACTICE 1

Divide: $(25x^3 + 5x^2) \div 5x^2$

Example 1 Divide: $(6m^2 + 2m) \div 2m$

Solution: We begin by writing the quotient in fraction form. Then we divide each term of the polynomial $6m^2 + 2m$ by the monomial $2m$ and use the quotient rule for exponents to simplify.

$$\frac{6m^2 + 2m}{2m} = \frac{6m^2}{2m} + \frac{2m}{2m}$$
$$= 3m + 1 \quad \text{Simplify.}$$

Check: To check, we multiply.

$$2m(3m + 1) = 2m(3m) + 2m(1) = 6m^2 + 2m$$

The quotient $3m + 1$ checks.

● Work Practice 1

✔**Concept Check** In which of the following is $\dfrac{x + 5}{5}$ simplified correctly?

a. $\dfrac{x}{5} + 1$ **b.** x **c.** $x + 1$

PRACTICE 2

Divide: $\dfrac{24x^7 + 12x^2 - 4x}{4x^2}$

Example 2 Divide: $\dfrac{9x^5 - 12x^2 + 3x}{3x^2}$

Solution: $\dfrac{9x^5 - 12x^2 + 3x}{3x^2} = \dfrac{9x^5}{3x^2} - \dfrac{12x^2}{3x^2} + \dfrac{3x}{3x^2}$ Divide each term by $3x^2$.

$$= 3x^3 - 4 + \frac{1}{x} \quad \text{Simplify.}$$

Notice that the quotient is not a polynomial because of the term $\dfrac{1}{x}$. This expression is called a rational expression. Although the quotient of two polynomials is not always a polynomial, we may still check by multiplying.

Answers
1. $5x + 1$ **2.** $6x^5 + 3 - \dfrac{1}{x}$

✔**Concept Check Answer**

a

Check: $3x^2\left(3x^3 - 4 + \dfrac{1}{x}\right) = 3x^2(3x^3) - 3x^2(4) + 3x^2\left(\dfrac{1}{x}\right)$

$$= 9x^5 - 12x^2 + 3x$$

● Work Practice 2

Example 3   Divide: $\dfrac{8x^2y^2 - 16xy + 2x}{4xy}$

Solution: $\dfrac{8x^2y^2 - 16xy + 2x}{4xy} = \dfrac{8x^2y^2}{4xy} - \dfrac{16xy}{4xy} + \dfrac{2x}{4xy}$ · Divide each term by $4xy$.

$$= 2xy - 4 + \dfrac{1}{2y} \qquad \text{Simplify.}$$

Check: $4xy\left(2xy - 4 + \dfrac{1}{2y}\right) = 4xy(2xy) - 4xy(4) + 4xy\left(\dfrac{1}{2y}\right)$

$$= 8x^2y^2 - 16xy + 2x$$

● Work Practice 3

PRACTICE 3

Divide: $\dfrac{12x^3y^3 - 18xy + 6y}{3xy}$

Vocabulary and Readiness Check

Use the choices below to fill in each blank. Choices may be used more than once

    dividend   divisor   quotient

1. In $6\overline{)18}^{\,3}$, the 18 is the _____, the 3 is the _____ and the 6 is the _____.

2. In $x + 1\overline{)x^2 + 3x + 2}^{\,x + 2}$, the $x + 1$ is the _____, the $x^2 + 3x + 2$ is the _____, and the $x + 2$ is the _____.

Simplify each expression mentally.

3. $\dfrac{a^6}{a^4}$ **4.** $\dfrac{p^8}{p^3}$ **5.** $\dfrac{y^2}{y}$ **6.** $\dfrac{a^3}{a}$

8.7 Exercise Set

FOR EXTRA HELP

MyMathLab *Powered by CourseCompass™ and MathXL®*

 Math**XP**

 PRACTICE   WATCH   DOWNLOAD   READ   REVIEW

Objective Ⓐ *Perform each division. See Examples 1 through 3.*

1. $\dfrac{12x^4 + 3x^2}{x}$

2. $\dfrac{15x^2 - 9x^5}{x}$

3. $\dfrac{20x^3 - 30x^2 + 5x + 5}{5}$

4. $\dfrac{8x^3 - 4x^2 + 6x + 2}{2}$

5. $\dfrac{15p^3 + 18p^2}{3p}$

6. $\dfrac{6x^5 + 3x^4}{3x^4}$

7. $\dfrac{-9x^4 + 18x^5}{6x^5}$

8. $\dfrac{14m^2 - 27m^3}{7m}$

9. $\dfrac{-9x^5 + 3x^4 - 12}{3x^3}$

10. $\dfrac{6a^2 - 4a + 12}{-2a^2}$

11. $\dfrac{4x^4 - 6x^3 + 7}{-4x^4}$

12. $\dfrac{-12a^3 + 36a - 15}{3a}$

Objectives Ⓐ Ⓑ **Mixed Practice** *Divide. If the divisor contains 2 or more terms, use long division. See Examples 1 through 3.*

13. $\dfrac{a^2b^2 - ab^3}{ab}$

14. $\dfrac{m^3n^2 - mn^4}{mn}$

15. $\dfrac{8x^2 + 6x - 27}{2x - 3}$

16. $\dfrac{18w^2 + 18w - 8}{3w + 4}$

17. $\dfrac{2x^2y + 8x^2y^2 - xy^2}{2xy}$

18. $\dfrac{11x^3y^3 - 33xy + x^2y^2}{11xy}$

19. $\dfrac{2b^3 + 9b^2 + 6b - 4}{b + 4}$

20. $\dfrac{2x^3 + 3x^2 - 3x + 4}{x + 2}$

21. $\dfrac{y^3 + 3y^2 + 4}{y - 2}$

22. $\dfrac{3x^3 + 11x + 12}{x + 4}$

23. $\dfrac{5 - 6x^2}{x - 2}$

24. $\dfrac{3 - 7x^2}{x - 3}$

25. $\dfrac{x^5 + x^2}{x^2 + x}$

26. $\dfrac{x^6 - x^3}{x^3 - x^2}$

710

8 Chapter Highlights

Definitions and Concepts	Examples

Section 8.1 Exponents

a^n means the product of n factors, each of which is a.

$$3^2 = 3 \cdot 3 = 9$$
$$(-5)^3 = (-5)(-5)(-5) = -125$$
$$\left(\frac{1}{2}\right)^4 = \frac{1}{2} \cdot \frac{1}{2} \cdot \frac{1}{2} \cdot \frac{1}{2} = \frac{1}{16}$$

Let m and n be integers and no denominators be 0.

Product Rule: $a^m \cdot a^n = a^{m+n}$

Power Rule: $(a^m)^n = a^{mn}$

Power of a Product Rule: $(ab)^n = a^n b^n$

Power of a Quotient Rule: $\left(\dfrac{a}{b}\right)^n = \dfrac{a^n}{b^n}$

Quotient Rule: $\dfrac{a^m}{a^n} = a^{m-n}$

Zero Exponent: $a^0 = 1, a \neq 0$

$$x^2 \cdot x^7 = x^{2+7} = x^9$$
$$(5^3)^8 = 5^{3 \cdot 8} = 5^{24}$$
$$(7y)^4 = 7^4 y^4$$
$$\left(\frac{x}{8}\right)^3 = \frac{x^3}{8^3}$$
$$\frac{x^9}{x^4} = x^{9-4} = x^5$$
$$5^0 = 1; x^0 = 1, x \neq 0$$

Section 8.2 Negative Exponents and Scientific Notation

If $a \neq 0$ and n is an integer,

$$a^{-n} = \frac{1}{a^n}$$

$$3^{-2} = \frac{1}{3^2} = \frac{1}{9}; 5x^{-2} = \frac{5}{x^2}$$

Simplify: $\left(\dfrac{x^{-2}y}{x^5}\right)^{-2} = \dfrac{x^4 y^{-2}}{x^{-10}}$

$$= x^{4-(-10)} y^{-2}$$
$$= \frac{x^{14}}{y^2}$$

A positive number is written in scientific notation if it is written as the product of a number a, where $1 \leq a < 10$, and an integer power r of 10.

$$a \times 10^r$$

$$1200 = 1.2 \times 10^3$$

$$0.000000568 = 5.68 \times 10^{-7}$$

Definitions and Concepts	**Examples**
Section 8.3 Introduction to Polynomials	

A **term** is a number or the product of a number and variables raised to powers.	$-5x, 7a^2b, \dfrac{1}{4}y^4, 0.2$
The **numerical coefficient,** or **coefficient,** of a term is its numerical factor.	**Term** **Coefficient** $7x^2$ 7 y 1 $-a^2b$ -1
A **polynomial** is a finite sum of terms of the form ax^n where a is a real number and n is a whole number.	$5x^3 - 6x^2 + 3x - 6$ (Polynomial)
A **monomial** is a polynomial with exactly 1 term.	$\dfrac{5}{6}y^3$ (Monomial)
A **binomial** is a polynomial with exactly 2 terms.	$-0.2a^2b - 5b^2$ (Binomial)
A **trinomial** is a polynomial with exactly 3 terms.	$3x^2 - 2x + 1$ (Trinomial)
The **degree of a polynomial** is the greatest degree of any term of the polynomial.	**Polynomial** **Degree** $5x^2 - 3x + 2$ 2 $7y + 8y^2z^3 - 12$ $2 + 3 = 5$

Section 8.4 Adding and Subtracting Polynomials	

To add polynomials, combine like terms.	Add. $(7x^2 - 3x + 2) + (-5x - 6)$ $= 7x^2 - 3x + 2 - 5x - 6$ $= 7x^2 - 8x - 4$
To subtract two polynomials, change the signs of the terms of the second polynomial, and then add.	Subtract. $(17y^2 - 2y + 1) - (-3y^3 + 5y - 6)$ $= (17y^2 - 2y + 1) + (3y^3 - 5y + 6)$ $= 17y^2 - 2y + 1 + 3y^3 - 5y + 6$ $= 3y^3 + 17y^2 - 7y + 7$

Section 8.5 Multiplying Polynomials	

To multiply two polynomials, multiply each term of one polynomial by each term of the other polynomial, and then combine like terms.	Multiply. $(2x + 1)(5x^2 - 6x + 2)$ $= 2x(5x^2 - 6x + 2) + 1(5x^2 - 6x + 2)$ $= 10x^3 - 12x^2 + 4x + 5x^2 - 6x + 2$ $= 10x^3 - 7x^2 - 2x + 2$

Definitions and Concepts	**Examples**

Section 8.6   Special Products

The **FOIL method** may be used when multiplying two binomials.

Multiply: $(5x - 3)(2x + 3)$

First ⎯⎯ Last ⎯
$(5x - 3)(2x + 3)$
↑ Inner ↑
⎯ Outer ⎯

$$\quad\quad\text{F}\quad\quad\quad\text{O}\quad\quad\quad\text{I}\quad\quad\quad\text{L}$$
$$= (5x)(2x) + (5x)(3) + (-3)(2x) + (-3)(3)$$
$$= 10x^2 + 15x - 6x - 9$$
$$= 10x^2 + 9x - 9$$

Squaring a Binomial

$$(a + b)^2 = a^2 + 2ab + b^2$$

$$(a - b)^2 = a^2 - 2ab + b^2$$

Square each binomial.

$$(x + 5)^2 = x^2 + 2(x)(5) + 5^2$$
$$= x^2 + 10x + 25$$
$$(3x - 2y)^2 = (3x)^2 - 2(3x)(2y) + (2y)^2$$
$$= 9x^2 - 12xy + 4y^2$$

Multiplying the Sum and Difference of Two Terms

$$(a + b)(a - b) = a^2 - b^2$$

Multiply.

$$(6y + 5)(6y - 5) = (6y)^2 - 5^2$$
$$= 36y^2 - 25$$

Section 8.7   Dividing Polynomials

To divide a polynomial by a monomial,

$$\frac{a + b}{c} = \frac{a}{c} + \frac{b}{c}, c \neq 0$$

Divide.

$$\frac{15x^5 - 10x^3 + 5x^2 - 2x}{5x^2}$$
$$= \frac{15x^5}{5x^2} - \frac{10x^3}{5x^2} + \frac{5x^2}{5x^2} - \frac{2x}{5x^2}$$
$$= 3x^3 - 2x + 1 - \frac{2}{5x}$$

To divide a polynomial by a polynomial other than a monomial, use long division.

$$5x - 1 + \frac{-4}{2x + 3}$$
$$2x + 3\overline{)10x^2 + 13x - 7}\quad\quad \text{or } 5x - 1 - \frac{4}{2x + 3}$$
$$\underline{10x^2 + 15x}$$
$$-2x - 7$$
$$\underline{-2x - 3}$$
$$-4$$

Chapter 8 Review

(8.1) *State the base and the exponent for each expression.*

1. 3^2 **2.** $(-5)^4$ **3.** -5^4 **4.** x^6

Evaluate each expression.

5. 8^3 **6.** $(-6)^2$ **7.** -6^2 **8.** $-4^3 - 4^0$ **9.** $(3b)^0$ **10.** $\dfrac{8b}{8b}$

Simplify each expression.

11. $y^2 \cdot y^7$ **12.** $x^9 \cdot x^5$ **13.** $(2x^5)(-3x^6)$ **14.** $(-5y^3)(4y^4)$ **15.** $(x^4)^2$

16. $(y^3)^5$ **17.** $(3y^6)^4$ **18.** $(2x^3)^3$ **19.** $\dfrac{x^9}{x^4}$ **20.** $\dfrac{z^{12}}{z^5}$

21. $\dfrac{3x^4 y^{10}}{12xy^6}$ **22.** $\dfrac{2x^7 y^8}{8xy^2}$ **23.** $5a^7(2a^4)^3$ **24.** $(2x)^2(9x)$ **25.** $\dfrac{(4a^5 b)^2}{-16ab^2}$

26. $\dfrac{(2x^3 y)^4}{-16x^5 y^4}$ **27.** $(-5a)^0 + 7^0 + 8^0$ **28.** $8x^0 + 9^0$

Simplify the given expression and choose the correct result.

29. $\left(\dfrac{3x^4}{4y}\right)^3$

     a. $\dfrac{27x^{64}}{64y^3}$ **b.** $\dfrac{27x^{12}}{64y^3}$

     c. $\dfrac{9x^{12}}{12y^3}$ **d.** $\dfrac{3x^{12}}{4y^3}$

30. $\left(\dfrac{5a^6}{b^3}\right)^2$

     a. $\dfrac{10a^{12}}{b^6}$ **b.** $\dfrac{25a^{36}}{b^9}$

     c. $\dfrac{25a^{12}}{b^6}$ **d.** $25a^{12}b^6$

(8.2) *Simplify each expression.*

31. 7^{-2} **32.** -7^{-2} **33.** $2x^{-4}$ **34.** $(2x)^{-4}$

35. $\left(\dfrac{1}{5}\right)^{-3}$ **36.** $\left(\dfrac{-2}{3}\right)^{-2}$ **37.** $2^0 + 2^{-4}$ **38.** $6^{-1} - 7^{-1}$

Simplify each expression. Write each answer using positive exponents only.

39. $\dfrac{r^{-3}}{r^{-4}}$ **40.** $\dfrac{y^{-2}}{y^{-5}}$ **41.** $\left(\dfrac{bc^{-2}}{bc^{-3}}\right)^4$ **42.** $\left(\dfrac{x^{-3}y^{-4}}{x^{-2}y^{-5}}\right)^{-3}$

43. $\dfrac{10a^3b^4c^0}{50ab^{11}c^3}$ **44.** $\dfrac{8a^0b^4c^5}{40a^6bc^{12}}$ **45.** $\dfrac{9x^{-4}y^{-6}}{x^2y^7}$ **46.** $\dfrac{3a^5b^{-5}}{a^{-5}b^5}$

Write each number in scientific notation.

47. 0.00027 **48.** 0.8868 **49.** 80,800,000 **50.** 868,000

51. In November 2008, approximately 127,000,000 Americans voted in the U.S. presidential election. Write this number in scientific notation. (*Source:* CNN)

52. The approximate diameter of the Milky Way galaxy is 150,000 light years. Write this number in scientific notation. (*Source:* NASA IMAGE/POETRY Education and Public Outreach Program)

150,000 light years

Write each number in standard form.

53. 8.67×10^5 **54.** 3.86×10^{-3} **55.** 8.6×10^{-4} **56.** 8.936×10^5

57. The volume of the planet Jupiter is 1.43128×10^{15} cubic kilometers. Write this number in standard form. (*Source:* National Space Science Data Center)

58. An angstrom is a unit of measure, equal to 1×10^{-10} meter, used for measuring wavelengths or the diameters of atoms. Write this number in standard form. (*Source:* National Institute of Standards and Technology)

Simplify. Express each result in standard form.

59. $(8 \times 10^4)(2 \times 10^{-7})$

60. $\dfrac{8 \times 10^4}{2 \times 10^{-7}}$

(8.3) *Find the degree of each polynomial.*

61. $y^5 + 7x - 8x^4$

62. $9y^2 + 30y + 25$

63. $-14x^2y - 28x^2y^3 - 42x^2y^2$

64. $6x^2y^2z^2 + 5x^2y^3 - 12xyz$

65. The Glass Bridge Skywalk is suspended 4000 feet over the Colorado River at the very edge of the Grand Canyon. Neglecting air resistance, the height of an object dropped from the Skywalk at time t seconds is given by the polynomial $-16t^2 + 4000$. Find the height of the object at the given times below.

t	0 seconds	1 second	3 seconds	5 seconds
$-16t^2 + 4000$				

△ **66.** The surface area of a box with a square base and a height of 5 units is given by the polynomial $2x^2 + 20x$. Fill in the table below by evaluating $2x^2 + 20x$ for the given values of x.

x	1	3	5.1	10
$2x^2 + 20x$				

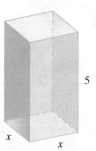

Combine like terms in each expression.

67. $7a^2 - 4a^2 - a^2$

68. $9y + y - 14y$

69. $6a^2 + 4a + 9a^2$

70. $21x^2 + 3x + x^2 + 6$

71. $4a^2b - 3b^2 - 8q^2 - 10a^2b + 7q^2$

72. $2s^{14} + 3s^{13} + 12s^{12} - s^{10}$

(8.4) *Add or subtract as indicated.*

73. $(3x^2 + 2x + 6) + (5x^2 + x)$

74. $(2x^5 + 3x^4 + 4x^3 + 5x^2) + (4x^2 + 7x + 6)$

75. $(-5y^2 + 3) - (2y^2 + 4)$

76. $(2m^7 + 3x^4 + 7m^6) - (8m^7 + 4m^2 + 6x^4)$

77. $(3x^2 - 7xy + 7y^2) - (4x^2 - xy + 9y^2)$

78. $(8x^6 - 5xy - 10y^2) - (7x^6 - 9xy - 12y^2)$

Translating *Perform the indicated operations.*

79. Add $(-9x^2 + 6x + 2)$ and $(4x^2 - x - 1)$.

80. Subtract $(4x^2 + 8x - 7)$ from the sum of $(x^2 + 7x + 9)$ and $(x^2 + 4)$.

(8.5) *Multiply each expression.*

81. $6(x + 5)$

82. $9(x - 7)$

83. $4(2a + 7)$

84. $9(6a - 3)$

85. $-7x(x^2 + 5)$

86. $-8y(4y^2 - 6)$

87. $-2(x^3 - 9x^2 + x)$

88. $-3a(a^2b + ab + b^2)$

89. $(-2a)(3a^3 - 4a + 1)$

90. $(7b)(6b^3 - 4b + 2)$

91. $(2x + 2)(x - 7)$

92. $(2x - 5)(3x + 2)$

93. $(4a - 1)(a + 7)$

94. $(6a - 1)(7a + 3)$

95. $(x + 7)(x^3 + 4x - 5)$

96. $(x + 2)(x^5 + x + 1)$

97. $(x^2 + 2x + 4)(x^2 + 2x - 4)$

98. $(x^3 + 4x + 4)(x^3 + 4x - 4)$

99. $(x + 7)^3$

100. $(2x - 5)^3$

(8.6) *Use special products to multiply each of the following.*

101. $(x + 7)^2$

102. $(x - 5)^2$

103. $(3x - 7)^2$

104. $(4x + 2)^2$

105. $(5x - 9)^2$

106. $(5x + 1)(5x - 1)$

107. $(7x + 4)(7x - 4)$

108. $(a + 2b)(a - 2b)$

109. $(2x - 6)(2x + 6)$

110. $(4a^2 - 2b)(4a^2 + 2b)$

Express each as a product of polynomials in x. Then multiply and simplify.

111. Find the area of the square if its side is $(3x - 1)$ meters.

(3x − 1) meters

112. Find the area of the rectangle.

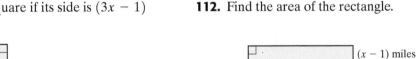

$(x - 1)$ miles

(5x + 2) miles

(8.7) *Divide.*

113. $\dfrac{x^2 + 21x + 49}{7x^2}$

114. $\dfrac{5a^3b - 15ab^2 + 20ab}{-5ab}$

115. $(a^2 - a + 4) \div (a - 2)$

116. $(4x^2 + 20x + 7) \div (x + 5)$

117. $\dfrac{a^3 + a^2 + 2a + 6}{a - 2}$

118. $\dfrac{9b^3 - 18b^2 + 8b - 1}{3b - 2}$

119. $\dfrac{4x^4 - 4x^3 + x^2 + 4x - 3}{2x - 1}$

120. $\dfrac{-10x^2 - x^3 - 21x + 18}{x - 6}$

△ **121.** The area of the rectangle below is $(15x^3 - 3x^2 + 60)$ square feet. If its length is $3x^2$ feet, find its width.

Area is $(15x^3 - 3x^2 + 60)$ sq feet

122. The perimeter of the equilateral triangle below is $(21a^3b^6 + 3a - 3)$ units. Find the length of a side.

Perimeter is
$(21a^3b^6 + 3a - 3)$ units

Answers to Selected Exercises

Chapter 8 Exponents and Polynomials

Section 8.1

Vocabulary and Readiness Check **1.** exponent **3.** add **5.** 1 **7.** exponent: 2; base: 3 **9.** exponent: 2; base 4 **11.** exponent: 2; base x

Exercise Set 8.1 **1.** 49 **3.** -5 **5.** -16 **7.** 16 **9.** $\dfrac{1}{27}$ **11.** 112 **13.** 4 **15.** 135 **17.** 150 **19.** $\dfrac{32}{5}$ **21.** x^7 **23.** $(-3)^{12}$ **25.** $15y^5$ **27.** $x^{19}y^6$
29. $-72m^3n^8$ **31.** $-24z^{20}$ **33.** $20x^5$ sq ft **35.** x^{36} **37.** p^8q^8 **39.** $8a^{15}$ **41.** $x^{10}y^{15}$ **43.** $49a^4b^{10}c^2$ **45.** $\dfrac{r^9}{s^9}$ **47.** $\dfrac{m^9p^9}{n^9}$ **49.** $\dfrac{4x^2z^2}{y^{10}}$ **51.** $64z^{10}$ sq dm
53. $27y^{12}$ cu ft **55.** x^2 **57.** -64 **59.** p^6q^5 **61.** $\dfrac{y^3}{2}$ **63.** 1 **65.** 1 **67.** -7 **69.** 2 **71.** -81 **73.** $\dfrac{1}{64}$ **75.** b^6 **77.** a^9 **79.** $-16x^7$ **81.** $a^{11}b^{20}$
83. $26m^9n^7$ **85.** z^{40} **87.** $64a^3b^3$ **89.** $36x^2y^2z^6$ **91.** $3x$ **93.** $81x^2y^2$ **95.** 9 **97.** $\dfrac{y^{15}}{8x^{12}}$ **99.** $2x^2y$ **101.** 2 **103.** $\dfrac{x^{18}}{4y^{22}}$ **105.** $-b^5$ **107.** -2 **109.** 5
111. -7 **113.** c **115.** e **117.** answers may vary **119.** answers may vary **121.** 343 cu m **123.** volume **125.** answers may vary **127.** answers may vary **129.** x^{9a} **131.** a^{5b} **133.** x^{5a}

Section 8.2

Calculator Explorations **1.** 5.31 EE 3 **3.** 6.6 EE -9 **5.** 1.5×10^{13} **7.** 8.15×10^{19}

Vocabulary and Readiness Check **1.** $\dfrac{1}{x^3}$; b **3.** scientific notation; c **5.** $\dfrac{5}{x^2}$ **7.** y^6 **9.** $4y^3$

Exercise Set 8.2 **1.** $\dfrac{1}{64}$ **3.** $\dfrac{7}{x^3}$ **5.** -64 **7.** $\dfrac{5}{6}$ **9.** p^3 **11.** $\dfrac{q^4}{p^5}$ **13.** $\dfrac{1}{x^3}$ **15.** z^3 **17.** $\dfrac{4}{9}$ **19.** $\dfrac{1}{9}$ **21.** $-p^4$ **23.** -2 **25.** x^4 **27.** p^4 **29.** m^{11}
31. r^6 **33.** $\dfrac{1}{x^{15}y^9}$ **35.** $\dfrac{1}{x^4}$ **37.** $\dfrac{1}{a^2}$ **39.** $4k^3$ **41.** $3m$ **43.** $-\dfrac{4a^5}{b}$ **45.** $-\dfrac{6}{7y^2z^5}$ **47.** $\dfrac{27a^6}{b^{12}}$ **49.** $\dfrac{a^{30}}{b^{12}}$ **51.** $\dfrac{1}{x^{10}y^6}$ **53.** $\dfrac{z^2}{4}$ **55.** $\dfrac{x^{11}}{81}$ **57.** $\dfrac{49a^4}{b^6}$
59. $-\dfrac{3m^7}{n^4}$ **61.** $a^{24}b^8$ **63.** 200 **65.** x^9y^{19} **67.** $-\dfrac{y^8}{8x^2}$ **69.** $\dfrac{25b^{33}}{a^{16}}$ **71.** $\dfrac{27}{z^3x^6}$ cu in. **73.** 7.8×10^4 **75.** 1.67×10^{-6} **77.** 6.35×10^{-3}
79. 1.16×10^6 **81.** 2.4×10^3 **83.** 0.0000000008673 **85.** 0.033 **87.** 20,320 **89.** 700,000,000 **91.** 1.84×10^{11} **93.** 155,000,000,000
95. 35,000 **97.** 0.000036 **99.** 0.0000000000000000028 **101.** 0.0000005 **103.** 200,000 **105.** 2.7×10^9 gal **107.** $-2x + 7$
109. $2y - 10$ **111.** $-x - 4$ **113.** 90,000,000; 9×10^7 **115.** 1,000,000,000; 1×10^9 **117.** 440,000,000; 4.4×10^8
119. no; answers may vary **121.** $9a^{13}$ **123.** -5 **125.** answers may vary **127. a.** 1.3×10^1 **b.** 4.4×10^7 **c.** 6.1×10^{-2}
129. answers may vary **131.** $\dfrac{1}{x^{9s}}$ **133.** a^{4m+5}

Section 8.3

Vocabulary and Readiness Check **1.** binomial **3.** trinomial **5.** constant

Exercise Set 8.3 **1.** 1; $-3x$; 5 **3.** -5; 3.2; 1; -5 **5.** 1; binomial **7.** 3; none of these **9.** 6; trinomial **11.** 4; binomial **13. a.** -6 **b.** -11
15. a. -2 **b.** 4 **17. a.** -15 **b.** -10 **19.** 184 ft **21.** 595.84 ft **23.** 164 thousand **25.** 371.95 million wireless subscribers
27. $-11x$ **29.** $23x^3$ **31.** $16x^2 - 7$ **33.** $12x^2 - 13$ **35.** $7s$ **37.** $-1.1y^2 + 4.8$ **39.** $\dfrac{5}{6}x^4 - 7x^3 - 19$ **41.** $\dfrac{3}{20}x^3 + 6x^2 - \dfrac{13}{20}x - \dfrac{1}{10}$
43. $4x^2 + 7x + x^2 + 5x$; $5x^2 + 12x$ **45.** $5x + 3 + 4x + 3 + 2x + 6 + 3x + 7x$; $21x + 12$ **47.** 2, 1, 1, 0; 2 **49.** 4, 0, 4, 3; 4 **51.** $9ab - 11a$
53. $4x^2 - 7xy + 3y^2$ **55.** $-3xy^2 + 4$ **57.** $14y^3 - 19 - 16a^2b^2$ **59.** $7x^2 + 0x + 3$ **61.** $x^3 + 0x^2 + 0x - 64$ **63.** $5y^3 + 0y^2 + 2y - 10$
65. $2y^4 + 0y^3 + 0y^2 + 8y + 0y^0$ or $2y^4 + 0y^3 + 0y^2 + 8y + 0$ **67.** $6x^5 + 0x^4 + x^3 + 0x^2 - 3x + 15$ **69.** $10x + 19$ **71.** $-x + 5$
73. answers may vary **75.** answers may vary **77.** x^{13} **79.** a^3b^{10} **81.** $2y^{20}$ **83.** answers may vary **85.** answers may vary
87. $11.1x^2 - 7.97x + 10.76$

Section 8.4

Vocabulary and Readiness Check **1.** $-14y$ **3.** $7x$ **5.** $5m^2 + 2m$

Exercise Set 8.4 **1.** $12x + 12$ **3.** $-3x^2 + 10$ **5.** $-3x^2 + 4$ **7.** $-y^2 - 3y - 1$ **9.** $7.9x^3 + 4.4x^2 - 3.4x - 3$ **11.** $\dfrac{1}{2}m^2 - \dfrac{7}{10}m + \dfrac{13}{16}$
13. $8t^2 - 4$ **15.** $15a^3 + a^2 - 3a + 16$ **17.** $-x + 14$ **19.** $5x^2 + 2y^2$ **21.** $-2x + 9$ **23.** $2x^2 + 7x - 16$ **25.** $2x^2 + 11x$
27. $-0.2x^2 + 0.2x - 2.2$ **29.** $\dfrac{2}{5}z^2 - \dfrac{3}{10}z + \dfrac{7}{20}$ **31.** $-2z^2 - 16z + 6$ **33.** $2u^5 - 10u^2 + 11u - 9$ **35.** $5x - 9$ **37.** $4x - 3$ **39.** $11y + 7$
41. $-2x^2 + 8x - 1$ **43.** $14x + 18$ **45.** $3a^2 - 6a + 11$ **47.** $3x - 3$ **49.** $7x^2 - 4x + 2$ **51.** $7x^2 - 2x + 2$ **53.** $4y^2 + 12y + 19$
55. $-15x + 7$ **57.** $-2a - b + 1$ **59.** $3x^2 + 5$ **61.** $6x^2 - 2xy + 19y^2$ **63.** $8r^2s + 16rs - 8 + 7r^2s^2$ **65.** $(x^2 + 7x + 4)$ ft
67. $\left(\dfrac{19}{2}x + 3\right)$ units **69.** $(3y^2 + 4y + 11)$ m **71.** $-6.6x^2 - 1.8x - 1.8$ **73.** $6x^2$ **75.** $-12x^8$ **77.** $200x^3y^2$ **79.** 2; 2
81. 4; 3; 3; 4 **83.** b **85.** e **87. a.** $4z$ **b.** $3z^2$ **c.** $-4z$ **d.** $3z^2$; answers may vary **89. a.** m^3 **b.** $3m$ **c.** $-m^3$ **d.** $-3m$; answers may vary
91. $874x^2 + 66x + 25,376$

Section 8.5

Vocabulary and Readiness Check   **1.** distributive; c   **3.** $(5y-1)(5y-1)$; c   **5.** x^8 **7.** cannot simplify   **9.** x^{14} **11.** $2x^7$ **13.** $99y^4$ **15.** $20y^2$

Exercise Set 8.5   **1.** $24x^3$ **3.** x^4 **5.** $-28n^{10}$ **7.** $-12.4x^{12}$ **9.** $-\dfrac{2}{15}y^3$ **11.** $-24x^8$ **13.** $6x^2+15x$ **15.** $7x^3+14x^2-7x$ **17.** $-2a^2-8a$

19. $6x^3-9x^2+12x$ **21.** $12a^5+45a^2$ **23.** $-6a^4+4a^3-6a^2$ **25.** $6x^5y-3x^4y^3+24x^2y^4$ **27.** $-4x^3y+7x^2y^2-xy^3-3y^4$

29. $4x^4-3x^3+\dfrac{1}{2}x^2$ **31.** $x^2+7x+12$ **33.** $a^2+5a-14$ **35.** $x^2+\dfrac{1}{3}x-\dfrac{2}{9}$ **37.** $12x^4+25x^2+7$ **39.** $12x^2-29x+15$ **41.** $1-7a+12a^2$

43. $4y^2-16y+16$ **45.** $x^3-5x^2+13x-14$ **47.** $x^4+5x^3-3x^2-11x+20$ **49.** $10a^3-27a^2+26a-12$ **51.** $49x^2y^2-14xy^2+y^2$

53. $12x^2-64x-11$ **55.** $2x^3+10x^2+11x-3$ **57.** $2x^4+3x^3-58x^2+4x+63$ **59.** $8.4y^7$ **61.** $-3x^3-6x^2+24x$ **63.** $2x^2+39x+19$

65. $x^2-\dfrac{2}{7}x-\dfrac{3}{49}$ **67.** $9y^2+30y+25$ **69.** $a^3-2a^2-18a+24$ **71.** $(4x^2-25)$ sq yd   **73.** $(6x^2-4x)$ sq in.

75. $5a+15a=20a$; $5a-15a=-10a$; $5a\cdot 15a=75a^2$; $\dfrac{5a}{15a}=\dfrac{1}{3}$ **77.** $-3y^5+9y^4$, can't be simplified; $-3y^5-9y^4$, can't be simplified;

$-3y^5\cdot 9y^4=-27y^9$; $\dfrac{-3y^5}{9y^4}=-\dfrac{y}{3}$ **79. a.** $6x+12$ **b.** $9x^2+36x+35$; answers may vary   **81.** $13x-7$ **83.** $30x^2-28x+6$

85. $-7x+5$ **87.** x^2+3x **89.** $x+2x^2$; $x(1+2x)$ **91.** $11a$ **93.** $25x^2+4y^2$ **95. a.** a^2-b^2 **b.** $4x^2-9y^2$ **c.** $16x^2-49$

d. answers may vary

Section 8.6

Vocabulary and Readiness Check   **1.** false   **3.** false

Exercise Set 8.6   **1.** $x^2+7x+12$ **3.** $x^2+5x-50$ **5.** $5x^2+4x-12$ **7.** $4y^2-25y+6$ **9.** $6x^2+13x-5$ **11.** $6y^3+4y^2+42y+28$

13. $x^2+\dfrac{1}{3}x-\dfrac{2}{9}$ **15.** $0.08-2.6a+15a^2$ **17.** $2x^2+9xy-5y^2$ **19.** x^2+4x+4 **21.** $4a^2-12a+9$ **23.** $9a^2-30a+25$

25. $x^4+x^2+0.25$ **27.** $y^2-\dfrac{4}{7}y+\dfrac{4}{49}$ **29.** $4x^2-4x+1$ **31.** $25x^2+90x+81$ **33.** $9x^2-42xy+49y^2$ **35.** $16m^2+40mn+25n^2$

37. $25x^8-30x^4+9$ **39.** a^2-49 **41.** x^2-36 **43.** $9x^2-1$ **45.** x^4-25 **47.** $4y^4-1$ **49.** $16-49x^2$ **51.** $9x^2-\dfrac{1}{4}$ **53.** $81x^2-y^2$

55. $4m^2-25n^2$ **57.** $a^2+9a+20$ **59.** $a^2-14a+49$ **61.** $12a^2-a-1$ **63.** x^2-4 **65.** $9a^2+6a+1$ **67.** $4x^2+3xy-y^2$

69. $\dfrac{1}{9}a^4-49$ **71.** $6b^2-b-35$ **73.** x^4-100 **75.** $16x^2-25$ **77.** $25x^2-60xy+36y^2$ **79.** $4r^2-9s^2$ **81.** $(4x^2+4x+1)$ sq ft

83. $\dfrac{5b^5}{7}$ **85.** $-\dfrac{2a^{10}}{b^5}$ **87.** $\dfrac{2y^8}{3}$ **89.** c   **91.** d   **93.** 2   **95.** (x^4-3x^2+1) sq m   **97.** $(24x^2-32x+8)$ sq m   **99.** answers may vary

101. answers may vary

Section 8.7

Vocabulary and Readiness Check   **1.** dividend; quotient; divisor   **3.** a^2 **5.** y

Exercise Set 8.7   **1.** $12x^3+3x$ **3.** $4x^3-6x^2+x+1$ **5.** $5p^2+6p$ **7.** $-\dfrac{3}{2x}+3$ **9.** $-3x^2+x-\dfrac{4}{x^3}$ **11.** $-1+\dfrac{3}{2x}-\dfrac{7}{4x^4}$ **13.** $ab-b^2$

15. $4x+9$ **17.** $x+4xy-\dfrac{y}{2}$ **19.** $2b^2+b+2-\dfrac{12}{b+4}$ **21.** $y^2+5y+10+\dfrac{24}{y-2}$ **23.** $-6x-12-\dfrac{19}{x-2}$ **25.** x^3-x^2+x

Chapter 8 Review   **1.** base: 3; exponent: 2   **2.** base: -5; exponent: 4   **3.** base: 5; exponent: 4   **4.** base: x; exponent: 6   **5.** 512   **6.** 36   **7.** -36

8. -65 **9.** 1   **10.** 1   **11.** y^9 **12.** x^{14} **13.** $-6x^{11}$ **14.** $-20y^7$ **15.** x^8 **16.** y^{15} **17.** $81y^{24}$ **18.** $8x^9$ **19.** x^5 **20.** z^7 **21.** $\dfrac{x^3y^4}{4}$ **22.** $\dfrac{x^6y^6}{4}$

23. $40a^{19}$ **24.** $36x^3$ **25.** $-a^9$ **26.** $-x^7$ **27.** 3   **28.** 9   **29.** b   **30.** c   **31.** $\dfrac{1}{49}$ **32.** $-\dfrac{1}{49}$ **33.** $\dfrac{2}{x^4}$ **34.** $\dfrac{1}{16x^4}$ **35.** 125   **36.** $\dfrac{9}{4}$ **37.** $\dfrac{17}{16}$ **38.** $\dfrac{1}{42}$

39. r **40.** y^3 **41.** c^4 **42.** $\dfrac{x^3}{y^3}$ **43.** $\dfrac{a^2}{5b^7c^3}$ **44.** $\dfrac{b^3}{5a^6c^7}$ **45.** $\dfrac{9}{x^6y^{13}}$ **46.** $\dfrac{3a^{10}}{b^{10}}$ **47.** 2.7×10^{-4} **48.** 8.868×10^{-1} **49.** 8.08×10^7 **50.** 8.68×10^5

51. 1.27×10^8 **52.** 1.5×10^5 **53.** $867{,}000$ **54.** 0.00386 **55.** 0.00086 **56.** $893{,}600$ **57.** $1{,}431{,}280{,}000{,}000{,}000$ **58.** 0.0000000001 **59.** 0.016

60. $400{,}000{,}000{,}000$ **61.** 5   **62.** 2   **63.** 5   **64.** 6   **65.** 4000 ft; 3984 ft; 3856 ft; 3600 ft   **66.** 22; 78; 154.02; 400   **67.** $2a^2$ **68.** $-4y$ **69.** $15a^2+4a$

70. $22x^2+3x+6$ **71.** $-6a^2b-3b^2-q^2$ **72.** cannot be combined   **73.** $8x^2+3x+6$ **74.** $2x^5+3x^4+4x^3+9x^2+7x+6$ **75.** $-7y^2-1$

76. $-6m^7-3x^4+7m^6-4m^2$ **77.** $-x^2-6xy-2y^2$ **78.** $x^6+4xy+2y^2$ **79.** $-5x^2+5x+1$ **80.** $-2x^2-x+20$ **81.** $6x+30$

82. $9x-63$ **83.** $8a+28$ **84.** $54a-27$ **85.** $-7x^3-35x$ **86.** $-32y^3+48y$ **87.** $-2x^3+18x^2-2x$ **88.** $-3a^3b-3a^2b-3ab^2$

89. $-6a^4+8a^2-2a$ **90.** $42b^4-28b^2+14b$ **91.** $2x^2-12x-14$ **92.** $6x^2-11x-10$ **93.** $4a^2+27a-7$ **94.** $42a^2+11a-3$

95. $x^4+7x^3+4x^2+23x-35$ **96.** $x^6+2x^5+x^2+3x+2$ **97.** $x^4+4x^3+4x^2-16$ **98.** $x^6+8x^4+16x^2-16$

99. $x^3+21x^2+147x+343$ **100.** $8x^3-60x^2+150x-125$ **101.** $x^2+14x+49$ **102.** $x^2-10x+25$ **103.** $9x^2-42x+49$

104. $16x^2+16x+4$ **105.** $25x^2-90x+81$ **106.** $25x^2-1$ **107.** $49x^2-16$ **108.** a^2-4b^2 **109.** $4x^2-36$ **110.** $16a^4-4b^2$

111. $(9x^2-6x+1)$ sq m   **112.** $(5x^2-3x-2)$ sq mi   **113.** $\dfrac{1}{7}+\dfrac{3}{x}+\dfrac{7}{x^2}$ **114.** $-a^2+3b-4$ **115.** $a+1+\dfrac{6}{a-2}$ **116.** $4x+\dfrac{7}{x+5}$

117. $a^2+3a+8+\dfrac{22}{a-2}$ **118.** $3b^2-4b-\dfrac{1}{3b-2}$ **119.** $2x^3-x^2+2-\dfrac{1}{2x-1}$ **120.** $-x^2-16x-117-\dfrac{684}{x-6}$ **121.** $\left(5x-1+\dfrac{20}{x^2}\right)$ ft

122. $(7a^3b^6+a-1)$ units

Factoring Polynomials

9

A Find the Greatest Common Factor of a List of Numbers.

B Find the Greatest Common Factor of a List of Terms.

C Factor Out the Greatest Common Factor from the Terms of a Polynomial.

D Factor by Grouping.

9.1 THE GREATEST COMMON FACTOR

In the product $2 \cdot 3 = 6$, the numbers 2 and 3 are called **factors** of 6 and $2 \cdot 3$ is a **factored form** of 6. This is true of polynomials also. Since $(x + 2)(x + 3) = x^2 + 5x + 6$, then $(x + 2)$ and $(x + 3)$ are factors of $x^2 + 5x + 6$, and $(x + 2)(x + 3)$ is a factored form of the polynomial.

> The process of writing a polynomial as a product is called **factoring** the polynomial.

Study the examples below and look for a pattern.

Multiplying: $5(x^2 + 3) = 5x^2 + 15$ $2x(x - 7) = 2x^2 - 14x$

Factoring: $5x^2 + 15 = 5(x^2 + 3)$ $2x^2 - 14x = 2x(x - 7)$

Do you see that factoring is the reverse process of multiplying?

$$x^2 + 5x + 6 = (x + 2)(x + 3)$$

✓ **Concept Check** Multiply: $2(x - 4)$
What do you think the result of factoring $2x - 8$ would be? Why?

Objective **A** Finding the Greatest Common Factor of a List of Numbers

The first step in factoring a polynomial is to see whether the terms of the polynomial have a common factor. If there is one, we can write the polynomial as a product by **factoring out** the common factor. We will usually factor out the *greatest* common factor (GCF).

The GCF of a list of integers is the largest integer that is a factor of all the integers in the list. For example, the GCF of 12 and 20 is 4 because 4 is the largest integer that is a factor of both 12 and 20. With large integers, the GCF may not be easily found by inspection. When this happens, we will write each integer as a product of prime numbers. Recall that a prime number is a whole number other than 1, whose only factors are 1 and itself.

Example 1 Find the GCF of each list of numbers.

a. 28 and 40   **b.** 55 and 21   **c.** 15, 18, and 66

Solution:

a. Write each number as a product of primes.

$28 = 2 \cdot 2 \cdot 7 = 2^2 \cdot 7$

$40 = 2 \cdot 2 \cdot 2 \cdot 5 = 2^3 \cdot 5$

There are two common factors, each of which is 2, so the GCF is

$GCF = 2 \cdot 2 = 4$

Find the GCF of each list of numbers.

a. 45 and 75   **b.** 32 and 33
c. 14, 24, and 60

Answers

1. **a.** 15 **b.** 1 **c.** 2

✓ **Concept Check Answer**

$2x - 8$; the result would be $2(x - 4)$ because factoring is the reverse process of multiplying.

720

b. $55 = 5 \cdot 11$
$21 = 3 \cdot 7$
There are no common prime factors; thus, the GCF is 1.

c. $15 = 3 \cdot 5$
$18 = 2 \cdot 3 \cdot 3 = 2 \cdot 3^2$
$66 = 2 \cdot 3 \cdot 11$
The only prime factor common to all three numbers is 3, so the GCF is
$GCF = 3$

◉ Work Practice 1

Objective Ⓑ Finding the Greatest Common Factor of a List of Terms

The greatest common factor of a list of variables raised to powers is found in a similar way. For example, the GCF of x^2, x^3, and x^5 is x^2 because each term contains a factor of x^2 and no higher power of x is a factor of each term.

$$x^2 = x \cdot x$$
$$x^3 = x \cdot x \cdot x$$
$$x^5 = x \cdot x \cdot x \cdot x \cdot x$$

There are two common factors, each of which is x, so the $GCF = x \cdot x$ or x^2. From this example, we see that **the GCF of a list of common variables raised to powers is the variable raised to the smallest exponent in the list.**

Example 2 Find the GCF of each list of terms.

a. x^3, x^7, and x^5
b. y, y^4, and y^7

Solution:

a. The GCF is x^3, since 3 is the smallest exponent to which x is raised.
b. The GCF is y^1 or y, since 1 is the smallest exponent on y.

◉ Work Practice 2

PRACTICE 2

Find the GCF of each list of terms.
a. y^4, y^5, and y^8
b. x and x^{10}

The **greatest common factor (GCF) of a list of terms** is the product of the GCF of the numerical coefficients and the GCF of the variable factors.

$$20x^2y^2 = 2 \cdot 2 \cdot 5 \cdot x \cdot x \cdot y \cdot y$$
$$6xy^3 = 2 \cdot 3 \cdot x \cdot y \cdot y \cdot y$$
$$GCF = 2 \cdot x \cdot y \cdot y = 2xy^2$$

Helpful Hint

Remember that the GCF of a list of terms contains the smallest exponent on each common variable.

Smallest exponent on x
The GCF of x^5y^6, x^2y^7, and x^3y^4 is x^2y^4. Smallest exponent on y

Answers
2. a. y^4 **b.** x

PRACTICE 3

Find the greatest common factor of each list of terms.

a. $6x^2$, $9x^4$, and $-12x^5$

b. $-16y$, $-20y^6$, and $40y^4$

c. a^5b^4, ab^3, and a^3b^2

Example 3 Find the greatest common factor of each list of terms.

a. $6x^2$, $10x^3$, and $-8x$

b. $-18y^2$, $-63y^3$, and $27y^4$

c. a^3b^2, a^5b, and a^6b^2

Solution:

a.
$$6x^2 = 2 \cdot 3 \cdot x^2$$
$$10x^3 = 2 \cdot 5 \cdot x^3$$
$$-8x = -1 \cdot 2 \cdot 2 \cdot 2 \cdot x^1$$

→ The GCF of x^2, x^3, and x^1 is x^1 or x.

$$\text{GCF} = 2 \cdot x^1 \quad \text{or} \quad 2x$$

b.
$$-18y^2 = -1 \cdot 2 \cdot 3 \cdot 3 \cdot y^2$$
$$-63y^3 = -1 \cdot 3 \cdot 3 \cdot 7 \cdot y^3$$
$$27y^4 = 3 \cdot 3 \cdot 3 \cdot y^4$$

→ The GCF of y^2, y^3, and y^4 is y^2.

$$\text{GCF} = 3 \cdot 3 \cdot y^2 \quad \text{or} \quad 9y^2$$

c. The GCF of a^3, a^5, and a^6 is a^3.

The GCF of b^2, b, and b^2 is b.

Thus, the GCF of a^3b^2, a^5b, and a^6b^2 is a^3b.

● **Work Practice 3**

Objective ⓒ Factoring Out the Greatest Common Factor

To factor a polynomial such as $8x + 14$, we first see whether the terms have a greatest common factor other than 1. In this case, they do: The GCF of $8x$ and 14 is 2.

We factor out 2 from each term by writing each term as the product of 2 and the term's remaining factors.

$$8x + 14 = 2 \cdot 4x + 2 \cdot 7$$

Using the distributive property, we can write

$$8x + 14 = 2 \cdot 4x + 2 \cdot 7$$
$$= 2(4x + 7)$$

Thus, a factored form of $8x + 14$ is $2(4x + 7)$. We can check by multiplying:

$$2(4x + 7) = 2 \cdot 4x + 2 \cdot 7 = 8x + 14.$$

Helpful Hint

A factored form of $8x + 14$ is *not*

$$2 \cdot 4x + 2 \cdot 7$$

Although the *terms* have been factored (written as products), the *polynomial* $8x + 14$ has not been factored. A factored form of $8x + 14$ is the *product* $2(4x + 7)$.

✓**Concept Check** Which of the following is/are factored form(s) of $6t + 18$?

a. 6

b. $6 \cdot t + 6 \cdot 3$

c. $6(t + 3)$

d. $3(t + 6)$

Answers

3. **a.** $3x^2$ **b.** $4y$ **c.** ab^2

✓ **Concept Check Answer**

c

Example 4 Factor each polynomial by factoring out the greatest common factor (GCF).

a. $5ab + 10a$ **b.** $y^5 - y^{12}$

Solution:

a. The GCF of terms $5ab$ and $10a$ is $5a$. Thus,

$$5ab + 10a = 5a \cdot b + 5a \cdot 2$$
$$= 5a(b + 2) \quad \text{Apply the distributive property.}$$

We can check our work by multiplying $5a$ and $(b + 2)$.
$5a(b + 2) = 5a \cdot b + 5a \cdot 2 = 5ab + 10a$, the original polynomial.

b. The GCF of y^5 and y^{12} is y^5. Thus,

$$y^5 - y^{12} = y^5(1) - y^5(y^7)$$
$$= y^5(1 - y^7)$$

Helpful Hint Don't forget the 1.

● **Work Practice 4**

Example 5 Factor: $-9a^5 + 18a^2 - 3a$

Solution:

$$-9a^5 + 18a^2 - 3a = 3a(-3a^4) + 3a(6a) + 3a(-1)$$
$$= 3a(-3a^4 + 6a - 1)$$

● **Work Practice 5**

Helpful Hint Don't forget the -1.

In Example 5, we could have chosen to factor out $-3a$ instead of $3a$. If we factor out $-3a$, we have

$$-9a^5 + 18a^2 - 3a = (-3a)(3a^4) + (-3a)(-6a) + (-3a)(1)$$
$$= -3a(3a^4 - 6a + 1)$$

Helpful Hint

Notice the changes in signs when factoring out $-3a$.

Examples Factor.

6. $6a^4 - 12a = 6a(a^3 - 2)$

7. $\frac{3}{7}x^4 + \frac{1}{7}x^3 - \frac{5}{7}x^2 = \frac{1}{7}x^2(3x^2 + x - 5)$

8. $15p^2q^4 + 20p^3q^5 + 5p^3q^3 = 5p^2q^3(3q + 4pq^2 + p)$

● **Work Practice 6–8**

Example 9 Factor: $5(x + 3) + y(x + 3)$

Solution: The binomial $(x + 3)$ is present in both terms and is the greatest common factor. We use the distributive property to factor out $(x + 3)$.

$$5(x + 3) + y(x + 3) = (x + 3)(5 + y)$$

● **Work Practice 9**

Objective Ⓓ Factoring by Grouping

Once the GCF is factored out, we can often continue to factor the polynomial, using a variety of techniques. We discuss here a technique called **factoring by grouping.** This technique can be used to factor some polynomials with four terms.

PRACTICE 10

Factor $ab + 7a + 2b + 14$ by grouping.

Example 10 Factor $xy + 2x + 3y + 6$ by grouping.

Solution: Notice that the first two terms of this polynomial have a common factor of x and the second two terms have a common factor of 3. Because of this, group the first two terms, then the last two terms, and then factor out these common factors.

$xy + 2x + 3y + 6 = (xy + 2x) + (3y + 6)$ Group terms.

$= \underbrace{x(y + 2) + 3(y + 2)}$ Factor out GCF from each grouping.

Helpful Hint Notice that this form, $x(y + 2) + 3(y + 2)$, is *not* a factored form of the original polynomial. It is a sum, not a product.

Next we factor out the common binomial factor, $(y + 2)$.

$x(y + 2) + 3(y + 2) = (y + 2)(x + 3)$

Now the result is a factored form because it is a product. We were able to write the polynomial as a product because of the common binomial factor, $(y + 2)$, that appeared. If this does not happen, try rearranging the terms of the original polynomial.

Check: Multiply $(y + 2)$ by $(x + 3)$.

$(y + 2)(x + 3) = xy + 2x + 3y + 6,$

the original polynomial.
Thus, the factored form of $xy + 2x + 3y + 6$ is the product $(y + 2)(x + 3)$.

● **Work Practice 10**

You may want to try these steps when factoring by grouping.

> ### To Factor by Grouping
>
> **Step 1:** Group the terms in two groups so that each group has a common factor.
>
> **Step 2:** Factor out the GCF from each group.
>
> **Step 3:** If there is a common binomial factor, factor it out.
>
> **Step 4:** If not, rearrange the terms and try these steps again.

PRACTICE 11–13

Factor by grouping.
11. $28x^3 - 7x^2 + 12x - 3$
12. $2xy + 5y^2 - 4x - 10y$
13. $3x^2 + 4xy + 3x + 4y$

Examples Factor by grouping.

11. $15x^3 - 10x^2 + 6x - 4$

$= (15x^3 - 10x^2) + (6x - 4)$ Group the terms.

$= 5x^2(3x - 2) + 2(3x - 2)$ Factor each group.

$= (3x - 2)(5x^2 + 2)$ Factor out the common factor, $(3x - 2)$.

12. $3x^2 + 4xy - 3x - 4y$

$= (3x^2 + 4xy) + (-3x - 4y)$

$= x(3x + 4y) - 1(3x + 4y)$ Factor each group. A -1 is factored from the second pair of terms so that there is a common factor, $(3x + 4y)$.

$= (3x + 4y)(x - 1)$ Factor out the common factor, $(3x + 4y)$.

Answers

10. $(b + 7)(a + 2)$
11. $(4x - 1)(7x^2 + 3)$
12. $(2x + 5y)(y - 2)$
13. $(3x + 4y)(x + 1)$

13. $2a^2 + 5ab + 2a + 5b$

$= (2a^2 + 5ab) + (2a + 5b)$ Factor each group.

$= a(2a + 5b) + 1(2a + 5b)$ An understood 1 is written before $(2a + 5b)$ to help remember that $(2a + 5b)$ is $1(2a + 5b)$.

$= (2a + 5b)(a + 1)$ Factor out the common factor, $(2a + 5b)$.

Work Practice 11–13

Helpful Hint Notice that the factor of 1 is written when $(2a + 5b)$ is factored out.

Examples Factor by grouping.

14. $3x^3 - 2x - 9x^2 + 6$

$= x(3x^2 - 2) - 3(3x^2 - 2)$ Factor each group. A -3 is factored from the second pair of terms so that there is a common factor, $(3x^2 - 2)$.

$= (3x^2 - 2)(x - 3)$ Factor out the common factor, $(3x^2 - 2)$.

15. $3xy + 2 - 3x - 2y$

Notice that the first two terms have no common factor other than 1. However, if we rearrange these terms, a grouping emerges that does lead to a common factor.

$3xy + 2 - 3x - 2y$

$= (3xy - 3x) + (-2y + 2)$

$= 3x(y - 1) - 2(y - 1)$ Factor -2 from the second group.

$= (y - 1)(3x - 2)$ Factor out the common factor, $(y - 1)$.

16. $5x - 10 + x^3 - x^2 = 5(x - 2) + x^2(x - 1)$

There is no common binomial factor that can now be factored out. No matter how we rearrange the terms, no grouping will lead to a common factor. Thus, this polynomial is not factorable by grouping.

Work Practice 14–16

Helpful Hint

Throughout this chapter, we will be factoring polynomials. Even when the instructions do not so state, it is always a good idea to check your answers by multiplying.

PRACTICE 14–16

Factor by grouping.
14. $4x^3 + x - 20x^2 - 5$
15. $3xy - 4 + x - 12y$
16. $2x - 2 + x^3 - 3x^2$

Answers
14. $(4x^2 + 1)(x - 5)$
15. $(3y + 1)(x - 4)$
16. cannot be factored by grouping

Vocabulary and Readiness Check

Use the choices below to fill in each blank. Some choices may be used more than once and some may not be used at all.

greatest common factor   factors   factoring   true   false   least   greatest

1. Since $5 \cdot 4 = 20$, the numbers 5 and 4 are called _____ of 20.
2. The _____ of a list of integers is the largest integer that is a factor of all the integers in the list.
3. The greatest common factor of a list of common variables raised to powers is the variable raised to the _____ exponent in the list.
4. The process of writing a polynomial as a product is called _____ .
5. True or false: A factored form of $7x + 21 + xy + 3y$ is $7(x + 3) + y(x + 3)$. _____
6. True or false: A factored form of $3x^3 + 6x + x^2 + 2$ is $3x(x^2 + 2)$. _____

Write the prime factorization of the following integers.

7. 14   **8.** 15

Write the GCF of the following pairs of integers.

9. 18, 3   **10.** 7, 35   **11.** 20, 15   **12.** 6, 15

9.1 Exercise Set

FOR EXTRA HELP

MyMathLab

MathXP
PRACTICE   WATCH   DOWNLOAD   READ   REVIEW

Objectives A B Mixed Practice Find the GCF for each list. See Examples 1 through 3.

1. 32, 36    **2.** 36, 90   **3.** 18, 42, 84   **4.** 30, 75, 135

5. 24, 14, 21   **6.** 15, 25, 27   **7.** y^2, y^4, y^7 **8.** x^3, x^2, x^5

9. z^7, z^9, z^{11} **10.** y^8, y^{10}, y^{12} **11.** $x^{10}y^2, xy^2, x^3y^3$ **12.** p^7q, p^8q^2, p^9q^3

13. $14x, 21$ **14.** $20y, 15$ **15.** $12y^4, 20y^3$ **16.** $32x^5, 18x^2$

17. $-10x^2, 15x^3$ **18.** $-21x^3, 14x$ **19.** $12x^3, -6x^4, 3x^5$ **20.** $15y^2, 5y^7, -20y^3$

21. $-18x^2y, 9x^3y^3, 36x^3y$ **22.** $7x^3y^3, -21x^2y^2, 14xy^4$ **23.** $20a^6b^2c^8, 50a^7b$ **24.** $40x^7y^2z, 64x^9y$

Objective C Factor out the GCF from each polynomial. See Examples 4 through 9.

25. $3a + 6$ **26.** $18a + 12$ **27.** $30x - 15$ **28.** $42x - 7$ **29.** $x^3 + 5x^2$

30. $y^5 + 6y^4$ **31.** $6y^4 + 2y^3$ **32.** $5x^2 + 10x^6$ **33.** $32xy - 18x^2$ **34.** $10xy - 15x^2$

35. $4x - 8y + 4$ **36.** $7x + 21y - 7$ **37.** $6x^3 - 9x^2 + 12x$ **38.** $12x^3 + 16x^2 - 8x$

39. $a^7b^6 - a^3b^2 + a^2b^5 - a^2b^2$ **40.** $x^9y^6 + x^3y^5 - x^4y^3 + x^3y^3$ **41.** $5x^3y - 15x^2y + 10xy$

42. $14x^3y + 7x^2y - 7xy$ **43.** $8x^5 + 16x^4 - 20x^3 + 12$ **44.** $9y^6 - 27y^4 + 18y^2 + 6$

45. $\dfrac{1}{3}x^4 + \dfrac{2}{3}x^3 - \dfrac{4}{3}x^5 + \dfrac{1}{3}x$ **46.** $\dfrac{2}{5}y^7 - \dfrac{4}{5}y^5 + \dfrac{3}{5}y^2 - \dfrac{2}{5}y$ **47.** $y(x^2 + 2) + 3(x^2 + 2)$

48. $x(y^2 + 1) - 3(y^2 + 1)$ **49.** $z(y + 4) + 3(y + 4)$ **50.** $8(x + 2) - y(x + 2)$

51. $r(z^2 - 6) + (z^2 - 6)$ **52.** $q(b^3 - 5) + (b^3 - 5)$

Factor a " −1" from each polynomial. See Example 5.

53. $-x - 7$ **54.** $-y - 3$ **55.** $-2 + z$

56. $-5 + y$ **57.** $3a - b + 2$ **58.** $2y - z - 11$

Objective **D** *Factor each four-term polynomial by grouping. If this is not possible, write "not factorable by grouping." See Examples 10 through 16.*

59. $x^3 + 2x^2 + 5x + 10$ **60.** $x^3 + 4x^2 + 3x + 12$ **61.** $5x + 15 + xy + 3y$

62. $xy + y + 2x + 2$ **63.** $6x^3 - 4x^2 + 15x - 10$ **64.** $16x^3 - 28x^2 + 12x - 21$

65. $5m^3 + 6mn + 5m^2 + 6n$ **66.** $8w^2 + 7wv + 8w + 7v$ **67.** $2y - 8 + xy - 4x$

68. $6x - 42 + xy - 7y$ **69.** $2x^3 + x^2 + 8x + 4$ **70.** $2x^3 - x^2 - 10x + 5$

71. $3x - 3 + x^3 - 4x^2$ **72.** $7x - 21 + x^3 - 2x^2$ **73.** $4x^2 - 8xy - 3x + 6y$

74. $5xy - 15x - 6y + 18$ **75.** $5q^2 - 4pq - 5q + 4p$ **76.** $6m^2 - 5mn - 6m + 5n$

Objectives C D **Mixed Practice** *Factor out the GCF from each polynomial. Then factor by grouping.*

77. $12x^2y - 42x^2 - 4y + 14$

78. $90 + 15y^2 - 18x - 3xy^2$

79. $6a^2 + 9ab^2 + 6ab + 9b^3$

80. $16x^2 + 4xy^2 + 8xy + 2y^3$

Review

Multiply. See Section 8.5 or 8.6.

81. $(x + 2)(x + 5)$ **82.** $(y + 3)(y + 6)$ **83.** $(b + 1)(b - 4)$ **84.** $(x - 5)(x + 10)$

Fill in the chart by finding two numbers that have the given product and sum. The first column is filled in for you.

		85.	**86.**	**87.**	**88.**	**89.**	**90.**	**91.**	**92.**
Two Numbers	4, 7								
Their Product	28	12	20	8	16	−10	−9	−24	−36
Their Sum	11	8	9	−9	−10	3	0	−5	−5

Concept Extensions

See the Concept Checks in this section.

93. Which of the following is/are factored form(s) of $-2x + 14$?

  a. $-2(x + 7)$ **b.** $-2 \cdot x + 14$

  c. $-2(x - 14)$ **d.** $-2(x - 7)$

94. Which of the following is/are factored form(s) of $8a - 24$?

  a. $8 \cdot a - 24$ **b.** $8(a - 3)$

  c. $4(2a - 12)$ **d.** $8 \cdot a - 2 \cdot 12$

Which of the following expressions are factored?

95. $(a + 6)(a + 2)$

96. $(x + 5)(x + y)$

97. $5(2y + z) - b(2y + z)$

98. $3x(a + 2b) + 2(a + 2b)$

99. The annual cotton crop yield (in 1000 bales) in the United States for the period 2003–2007 can be approximated by the polynomial $-1264x^2 + 5056x + 18,960$, where x is the number of years after 2003. (*Source:* Based on data from the National Agricultural Statistics Service)

  a. Find the approximate amount of the cotton harvest in 2004. To do so, let $x = 1$ and evaluate $-1264x^2 + 5056x + 18,960$.

  b. Find the approximate amount of cotton harvested in 2007.

  c. Factor the polynomial $-1264x^2 + 5056x + 18,960$.

100. The polynomial $-30x^2 + 180x + 210$ represents the approximate number of visitors (in thousands) per year to the White House during 2003–2007. In this polynomial, x represents the years since 2003. (*Source:* Based on data from the National Park Service)

   a. Find the approximate number of visitors to the White House in 2005. To do so, let $x = 2$ and evaluate $-30x^2 + 180x + 210$.

   b. Find the approximate number of visitors to the White House in 2006.

   c. Factor out the GCF from the polynomial $-30x^2 + 180x + 210$.

Write an expression for the area of each shaded region. Then write the expression as a factored polynomial.

△ **101.**

△ **102.**

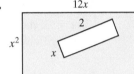

Write an expression for the length of each rectangle. (Hint: Factor the area binomial and recall that Area = width · length.)

△ **103.**

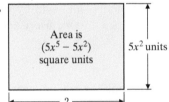

△ **104.**

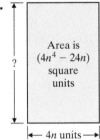

105. Construct a binomial whose greatest common factor is $5a^3$. (*Hint:* Multiply $5a^3$ by a binomial whose terms contain no common factor other than 1: $5a^3(\square + \square)$.)

106. Construct a trinomial whose greatest common factor is $2x^2$. See the hint for Exercise 105.

107. Explain how you can tell whether a polynomial is written in factored form.

108. Construct a four-term polynomial that can be factored by grouping. Explain how you constructed the polynomial.

A Factor Trinomials of the Form
$x^2 + bx + c$.

B Factor Out the Greatest Common
Factor and Then Factor a
Trinomial of the Form
$x^2 + bx + c$.

9.2 FACTORING TRINOMIALS OF THE FORM $x^2 + bx + c$

Objective **A** Factoring Trinomials of the Form $x^2 + bx + c$

In this section, we factor trinomials of the form $x^2 + bx + c$, such as

$$x^2 + 7x + 12, \quad x^2 - 12x + 35, \quad x^2 + 4x - 12, \quad \text{and} \quad r^2 - r - 42$$

Notice that for these trinomials, the coefficient of the squared variable is 1.

Recall that factoring means to write as a product and that factoring and multiplying are reverse processes. Using the FOIL method of multiplying binomials, we have the following.

$$\overset{\text{F} \quad \text{O} \quad \text{I} \quad \text{L}}{(x + 3)(x + 1) = x^2 + 1x + 3x + 3}$$
$$= x^2 + 4x + 3$$

Thus, a factored form of $x^2 + 4x + 3$ is $(x + 3)(x + 1)$.

Notice that the product of the first terms of the binomials is $x \cdot x = x^2$, the first term of the trinomial. Also, the product of the last two terms of the binomials is $3 \cdot 1 = 3$, the third term of the trinomial. The sum of these same terms is $3 + 1 = 4$, the coefficient of the middle, x, term of the trinomial.

The product of these numbers is 3.

$$x^2 + 4x + 3 = (x + 3)(x + 1)$$

The sum of these numbers is 4.

Many trinomials, such as the one above, factor into two binomials. To factor $x^2 + 7x + 10$, let's assume that it factors into two binomials and begin by writing two pairs of parentheses. The first term of the trinomial is x^2, so we use x and x as the first terms of the binomial factors.

$$x^2 + 7x + 10 = (x + \square)(x + \square)$$

To determine the last term of each binomial factor, we look for two integers whose product is 10 and whose sum is 7. The integers are 2 and 5. Thus,

$$x^2 + 7x + 10 = (x + 2)(x + 5)$$

Check: To see if we have factored correctly, we multiply.

$$(x + 2)(x + 5) = x^2 + 5x + 2x + 10$$
$$= x^2 + 7x + 10 \qquad \text{Combine like terms.}$$

Helpful Hint

Since multiplication is commutative, the factored form of $x^2 + 7x + 10$ can be written as either $(x + 2)(x + 5)$ or $(x + 5)(x + 2)$.

To Factor a Trinomial of the Form $x^2 + bx + c$

The product of these numbers is c.

$$x^2 + bx + c = (x + \square)(x + \square)$$

The sum of these numbers is b.

Example 1 Factor: $x^2 + 7x + 12$

Solution: We begin by writing the first terms of the binomial factors.

$$(x + \square)(x + \square)$$

Next we look for two numbers whose product is 12 and whose sum is 7. Since our numbers must have a positive product and a positive sum, we look at pairs of positive factors of 12 only.

Factors of 12	Sum of Factors
1, 12	13
2, 6	8
3, 4	7

Correct sum, so the numbers are 3 and 4.

Thus, $x^2 + 7x + 12 = (x + 3)(x + 4)$

Check: $(x + 3)(x + 4) = x^2 + 4x + 3x + 12 = x^2 + 7x + 12$

● **Work Practice 1**

PRACTICE 1

Factor: $x^2 + 12x + 20$

Example 2 Factor: $x^2 - 12x + 35$

Solution: Again, we begin by writing the first terms of the binomials.

$$(x + \square)(x + \square)$$

Now we look for two numbers whose product is 35 and whose sum is -12. Since our numbers must have a positive product and a negative sum, we look at pairs of negative factors of 35 only.

Factors of 35	Sum of Factors
$-1, -35$	-36
$-5, -7$	-12

Correct sum, so the numbers are -5 and -7.

$x^2 - 12x + 35 = (x - 5)(x - 7)$

Check: To check, multiply $(x - 5)(x - 7)$.

● **Work Practice 2**

PRACTICE 2

Factor each trinomial.
a. $x^2 - 23x + 22$
b. $x^2 - 27x + 50$

Example 3 Factor: $x^2 + 4x - 12$

Solution: $x^2 + 4x - 12 = (x + \square)(x + \square)$

We look for two numbers whose product is -12 and whose sum is 4. Since our numbers must have a negative product, we look at pairs of factors with opposite signs.

Factors of -12	Sum of Factors
$-1, 12$	11
$1, -12$	-11
$-2, 6$	4
$2, -6$	-4
$-3, 4$	1
$3, -4$	-1

Correct sum, so the numbers are -2 and 6.

$x^2 + 4x - 12 = (x - 2)(x + 6)$

● **Work Practice 3**

PRACTICE 3

Factor: $x^2 + 5x - 36$

Answers
1. $(x + 10)(x + 2)$
2. a. $(x - 1)(x - 22)$
   b. $(x - 2)(x - 25)$
3. $(x + 9)(x - 4)$

PRACTICE 4

Factor each trinomial.
a. $q^2 - 3q - 40$
b. $y^2 + 2y - 48$

Example 4 Factor: $r^2 - r - 42$

Solution: Because the variable in this trinomial is r, the first term of each binomial factor is r.

$$r^2 - r - 42 = (r + \square)(r + \square)$$

Now we look for two numbers whose product is -42 and whose sum is -1, the numerical coefficient of r. The numbers are 6 and -7. Therefore,

$$r^2 - r - 42 = (r + 6)(r - 7)$$

● Work Practice 4

PRACTICE 5

Factor: $x^2 + 6x + 15$

Example 5 Factor: $a^2 + 2a + 10$

Solution: Look for two numbers whose product is 10 and whose sum is 2. Neither 1 and 10 nor 2 and 5 give the required sum, 2. We conclude that $a^2 + 2a + 10$ is not factorable with integers. A polynomial such as $a^2 + 2a + 10$ is called a **prime polynomial.**

● Work Practice 5

PRACTICE 6

Factor each trinomial.
a. $x^2 + 9xy + 14y^2$
b. $a^2 - 13ab + 30b^2$

Example 6 Factor: $x^2 + 5xy + 6y^2$

Solution: $x^2 + 5xy + 6y^2 = (x + \square)(x + \square)$

Recall that the middle term, $5xy$, is the same as $5yx$. Thus, we can see that $5y$ is the "coefficient" of x. We then look for two terms whose product is $6y^2$ and whose sum is $5y$. The terms are $2y$ and $3y$ because $2y \cdot 3y = 6y^2$ and $2y + 3y = 5y$. Therefore,

$$x^2 + 5xy + 6y^2 = (x + 2y)(x + 3y)$$

● Work Practice 6

PRACTICE 7

Factor: $x^4 + 8x^2 + 12$

Example 7 Factor: $x^4 + 5x^2 + 6$

Solution: As usual, we begin by writing the first terms of the binomials. Since the greatest power of x in this polynomial is x^4, we write

$$(x^2 + \square)(x^2 + \square) \quad \text{Since } x^2 \cdot x^2 = x^4$$

Now we look for two factors of 6 whose sum is 5. The numbers are 2 and 3. Thus,

$$x^4 + 5x^2 + 6 = (x^2 + 2)(x^2 + 3)$$

● Work Practice 7

If the terms of a polynomial are not written in descending powers of the variable, you may want to rearrange the terms before factoring.

PRACTICE 8

Factor: $48 - 14x + x^2$

Example 8 Factor: $40 - 13t + t^2$

Solution: First, we rearrange terms so that the trinomial is written in descending powers of t.

$$40 - 13t + t^2 = t^2 - 13t + 40$$

Next, try to factor.

$$t^2 - 13t + 40 = (t + \square)(t + \square)$$

Now we look for two factors of 40 whose sum is -13. The numbers are -8 and -5. Thus,

$$t^2 - 13t + 40 = (t - 8)(t - 5)$$

● Work Practice 8

Answers

4. a. $(q - 8)(q + 5)$
   b. $(y + 8)(y - 6)$
5. prime polynomial
6. a. $(x + 2y)(x + 7y)$
   b. $(a - 3b)(a - 10b)$
7. $(x^2 + 6)(x^2 + 2)$
8. $(x - 6)(x - 8)$

The following sign patterns may be useful when factoring trinomials.

Helpful Hint

A positive constant in a trinomial tells us to look for two numbers with the same sign. The sign of the coefficient of the middle term tells us whether the signs are both positive or both negative.

both   same   both   same
positive   sign   negative   sign

$$x^2 + 10x + 16 = (x + 2)(x + 8) \qquad x^2 - 10x + 16 = (x - 2)(x - 8)$$

A negative constant in a trinomial tells us to look for two numbers with opposite signs.

opposite   opposite
signs   signs

$$x^2 + 6x - 16 = (x + 8)(x - 2) \qquad x^2 - 6x - 16 = (x - 8)(x + 2)$$

Objective Ⓑ Factoring Out the Greatest Common Factor

Remember that the first step in factoring any polynomial is to factor out the greatest common factor (if there is one other than 1 or −1).

Example 9 Factor: $3m^2 - 24m - 60$

Solution: First we factor out the greatest common factor, 3, from each term.

$$3m^2 - 24m - 60 = 3(m^2 - 8m - 20)$$

Now we factor $m^2 - 8m - 20$ by looking for two factors of −20 whose sum is −8. The factors are −10 and 2. Therefore, the complete factored form is

$$3m^2 - 24m - 60 = 3(m + 2)(m - 10)$$

● **Work Practice 9**

Helpful Hint

Remember to write the common factor, 3, as part of the factored form.

Example 10 Factor: $2x^4 - 26x^3 + 84x^2$

Solution:

$$2x^4 - 26x^3 + 84x^2 = 2x^2(x^2 - 13x + 42) \quad \text{Factor out common factor, } 2x^2.$$
$$= 2x^2(x - 6)(x - 7) \quad \text{Factor } x^2 - 13x + 42.$$

● **Work Practice 10**

PRACTICE 9

Factor each trinomial.
a. $4x^2 - 24x + 36$
b. $x^3 + 3x^2 - 4x$

PRACTICE 10

Factor: $5x^5 - 25x^4 - 30x^3$

Answers
9. a. $4(x - 3)(x - 3)$
   b. $x(x + 4)(x - 1)$
10. $5x^3(x + 1)(x - 6)$

Vocabulary and Readiness Check

Fill in each blank with "true" or "false."

1. To factor $x^2 + 7x + 6$, we look for two numbers whose product is 6 and whose sum is 7. _____

2. We can write the factorization $(y + 2)(y + 4)$ also as $(y + 4)(y + 2)$. _____

3. The factorization $(4x - 12)(x - 5)$ is completely factored. _____

4. The factorization $(x + 2y)(x + y)$ may also be written as $(x + 2y)^2$. _____

Complete each factored form.

5. $x^2 + 9x + 20 = (x + 4)(x \qquad)$

6. $x^2 + 12x + 35 = (x + 5)(x \qquad)$

7. $x^2 - 7x + 12 = (x - 4)(x \qquad)$

8. $x^2 - 13x + 22 = (x - 2)(x \qquad)$

9. $x^2 + 4x + 4 = (x + 2)(x \qquad)$

10. $x^2 + 10x + 24 = (x + 6)(x \qquad)$

9.2 Exercise Set

FOR EXTRA HELP

MyMathLab   Math XL PRACTICE   WATCH   DOWNLOAD   READ   REVIEW

Objective Ⓐ *Factor each trinomial completely. If a polynomial can't be factored, write "prime." See Examples 1 through 8.*

 1. $x^2 + 7x + 6$

2. $x^2 + 6x + 8$

3. $y^2 - 10y + 9$

4. $y^2 - 12y + 11$

5. $x^2 - 6x + 9$

6. $x^2 - 10x + 25$

 7. $x^2 - 3x - 18$

8. $x^2 - x - 30$

9. $x^2 + 3x - 70$

10. $x^2 + 4x - 32$

11. $x^2 + 5x + 2$

12. $x^2 - 7x + 5$

13. $x^2 + 8xy + 15y^2$

14. $x^2 + 6xy + 8y^2$

15. $a^4 - 2a^2 - 15$

16. $y^4 - 3y^2 - 70$

17. $13 + 14m + m^2$

18. $17 + 18n + n^2$

19. $10t - 24 + t^2$

20. $6q - 27 + q^2$

21. $a^2 - 10ab + 16b^2$

22. $a^2 - 9ab + 18b^2$

Objectives Ⓐ Ⓑ **Mixed Practice** *Factor each trinomial completely. Some of these trinomials contain a greatest common factor (other than 1). Don't forget to factor out the GCF first. See Examples 1 through 10.*

23. $2z^2 + 20z + 32$

24. $3x^2 + 30x + 63$

25. $2x^3 - 18x^2 + 40x$

26. $3x^3 - 12x^2 - 36x$

27. $x^2 - 3xy - 4y^2$

28. $x^2 - 4xy - 77y^2$

29. $x^2 + 15x + 36$

30. $x^2 + 19x + 60$

31. $x^2 - x - 2$

32. $x^2 - 5x - 14$

33. $r^2 - 16r + 48$

34. $r^2 - 10r + 21$

35. $x^2 + xy - 2y^2$

36. $x^2 - xy - 6y^2$

37. $3x^2 + 9x - 30$

38. $4x^2 - 4x - 48$

39. $3x^2 - 60x + 108$

40. $2x^2 - 24x + 70$

41. $x^2 - 18x - 144$

42. $x^2 + x - 42$

43. $r^2 - 3r + 6$

44. $x^2 + 4x - 10$

45. $x^2 - 8x + 15$

46. $x^2 - 9x + 14$

47. $6x^3 + 54x^2 + 120x$

48. $3x^3 + 3x^2 - 126x$

49. $4x^2y + 4xy - 12y$

50. $3x^2y - 9xy + 45y$

51. $x^2 - 4x - 21$

52. $x^2 - 4x - 32$

53. $x^2 + 7xy + 10y^2$

54. $x^2 - 3xy - 4y^2$

55. $64 + 24t + 2t^2$

56. $50 + 20t + 2t^2$

57. $x^3 - 2x^2 - 24x$

58. $x^3 - 3x^2 - 28x$

59. $2t^5 - 14t^4 + 24t^3$

60. $3x^6 + 30x^5 + 72x^4$

61. $5x^3y - 25x^2y^2 - 120xy^3$

62. $7a^3b - 35a^2b^2 + 42ab^3$

63. $162 - 45m + 3m^2$

64. $48 - 20n + 2n^2$

65. $-x^2 + 12x - 11$
(Factor out -1 first.)

66. $-x^2 + 8x - 7$
(Factor out -1 first.)

67. $\dfrac{1}{2}y^2 - \dfrac{9}{2}y - 11$

(Factor out $\dfrac{1}{2}$ first.)

68. $\dfrac{1}{3}y^2 - \dfrac{5}{3}y - 8$

(Factor out $\dfrac{1}{3}$ first.)

69. $x^3y^2 + x^2y - 20x$

70. $a^2b^3 + ab^2 - 30b$

Review

Multiply. See Section 8.5 or 8.6.

71. $(2x + 1)(x + 5)$

72. $(3x + 2)(x + 4)$

73. $(5y - 4)(3y - 1)$

74. $(4z - 7)(7z - 1)$

75. $(a + 3b)(9a - 4b)$

76. $(y - 5x)(6y + 5x)$

Concept Extensions

77. Write a polynomial that factors as $(x - 3)(x + 8)$.

78. To factor $x^2 + 13x + 42$, think of two numbers whose _____ is 42 and whose _____ is 13.

Complete each sentence in your own words.

79. If $x^2 + bx + c$ is factorable and c is negative, then the signs of the last-term factors of the binomials are opposite because . . .

80. If $x^2 + bx + c$ is factorable and c is positive, then the signs of the last-term factors of the binomials are the same because . . .

Remember that perimeter means distance around. Write the perimeter of each rectangle as a simplified polynomial. Then factor the polynomial completely.

△ **81.**

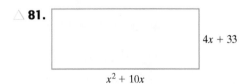

$4x + 33$

$x^2 + 10x$

△ **82.**

$12x^2$

$2x^3 + 16x$

83. An object is thrown upward from the top of an 80-foot building with an initial velocity of 64 feet per second. Neglecting air resistance, the height of the object after t seconds is given by $-16t^2 + 64t + 80$. Factor this polynomial.

84. An object is thrown upward from the top of a 112-foot building with an initial velocity of 96 feet per second. Neglecting air resistance, the height of the object after t seconds is given by $-16t^2 + 96t + 112$. Factor this polynomial.

$-16t^2 + 64t + 80$

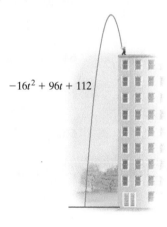

$-16t^2 + 96t + 112$

Factor each trinomial completely.

85. $x^2 + \dfrac{1}{2}x + \dfrac{1}{16}$

86. $x^2 + x + \dfrac{1}{4}$

87. $z^2(x + 1) - 3z(x + 1) - 70(x + 1)$

88. $y^2(x + 1) - 2y(x + 1) - 15(x + 1)$

Find all positive values of c so that each trinomial is factorable.

89. $n^2 - 16n + c$

90. $y^2 - 4y + c$

Find all positive values of b so that each trinomial is factorable.

91. $y^2 + by + 20$

92. $x^2 + bx + 15$

Factor each trinomial. (Hint: Notice that $x^{2n} + 4x^n + 3$ factors as $(x^n + 1)(x^n + 3)$. Remember: $x^n \cdot x^n = x^{n+n}$ or x^{2n}.)

93. $x^{2n} + 8x^n - 20$

94. $x^{2n} + 5x^n + 6$

9.3 FACTORING TRINOMIALS OF THE FORM $ax^2 + bx + c$

Objective Ⓐ Factoring Trinomials of the Form $ax^2 + bx + c$

In this section, we factor trinomials of the form $ax^2 + bx + c$, such as

$$3x^2 + 11x + 6, \quad 8x^2 - 22x + 5, \quad \text{and} \quad 2x^2 + 13x - 7$$

Notice that the coefficient of the squared variable in these trinomials is a number other than 1. We will factor these trinomials using a trial-and-check method based on our work in the last section.

To begin, let's review the relationship between the numerical coefficients of the trinomial and the numerical coefficients of its factored form. For example, since

$$(2x + 1)(x + 6) = 2x^2 + 13x + 6,$$

a factored form of $2x^2 + 13x + 6$ is $(2x + 1)(x + 6)$.

Notice that $2x$ and x are factors of $2x^2$, the first term of the trinomial. Also, 6 and 1 are factors of 6, the last term of the trinomial, as shown:

$$\begin{array}{c} \overbrace{2x \cdot x} \\ 2x^2 + 13x + 6 = (2x + 1)(x + 6) \\ \underbrace{\qquad\qquad}_{1 \cdot 6} \end{array}$$

Also notice that $13x$, the middle term, is the sum of the following products:

$$2x^2 + 13x + 6 = (2x + 1)(x + 6)$$

$$\begin{array}{r} 1x \\ + 12x \\ \hline 13x \end{array} \quad \text{Middle term}$$

Let's use this pattern to factor $5x^2 + 7x + 2$. First, we find factors of $5x^2$. Since all numerical coefficients in this trinomial are positive, we will use factors with positive numerical coefficients only. Thus, the factors of $5x^2$ are $5x$ and x. Let's try these factors as first terms of the binomials. Thus far, we have

$$5x^2 + 7x + 2 = (5x + \square)(x + \square)$$

Next, we need to find positive factors of 2. Positive factors of 2 are 1 and 2. Now we try possible combinations of these factors as second terms of the binomials until we obtain a middle term of $7x$.

$$(5x + 1)(x + 2) = 5x^2 + 11x + 2$$

$$\begin{array}{r} 1x \\ + 10x \\ \hline 11x \end{array} \longrightarrow \text{Incorrect middle term}$$

Let's try switching factors 2 and 1.

$$(5x + 2)(x + 1) = 5x^2 + 7x + 2$$

$$\begin{array}{r} 2x \\ + 5x \\ \hline 7x \end{array} \longrightarrow \text{Correct middle term}$$

Thus a factored form of $5x^2 + 7x + 2$ is $(5x + 2)(x + 1)$. To check, we multiply $(5x + 2)$ and $(x + 1)$. The product is $5x^2 + 7x + 2$.

PRACTICE 1

Factor each trinomial.
a. $5x^2 + 27x + 10$
b. $4x^2 + 12x + 5$

> **Helpful Hint**
> This is true in general: If the terms of a trinomial have no common factor (other than 1), then the terms of each of its binomial factors will contain no common factor (other than 1).

PRACTICE 2

Factor each trinomial.
a. $2x^2 - 11x + 12$
b. $6x^2 - 5x + 1$

Answers
1. a. $(5x + 2)(x + 5)$
  b. $(2x + 5)(2x + 1)$
2. a. $(2x - 3)(x - 4)$
  b. $(3x - 1)(2x - 1)$

✓ **Concept Check Answer**

no; **a, c, d**

Example 1   Factor: $3x^2 + 11x + 6$

Solution: Since all numerical coefficients are positive, we use factors with positive numerical coefficients. We first find factors of $3x^2$.

Factors of $3x^2$: $3x^2 = 3x \cdot x$

If factorable, the trinomial will be of the form

$$3x^2 + 11x + 6 = (3x + \square)(x + \square)$$

Next we factor 6.

Factors of 6: $6 = 1 \cdot 6$, $6 = 2 \cdot 3$

Now we try combinations of factors of 6 until a middle term of $11x$ is obtained. Let's try 1 and 6 first.

$$(3x + 1)(x + 6) = 3x^2 + 19x + 6$$

$1x$
$+18x$
$19x$ $\longrightarrow$ **Incorrect** middle term

Now let's next try 6 and 1.

$$(3x + 6)(x + 1)$$

Before multiplying, notice that the terms of the factor $3x + 6$ have a common factor of 3. The terms of the original trinomial $3x^2 + 11x + 6$ have no common factor other than 1, so the terms of its factors will also contain no common factor other than 1. This means that $(3x + 6)(x + 1)$ is not a factored form.
    Next let's try 2 and 3 as last terms.

$$(3x + 2)(x + 3) = 3x^2 + 11x + 6$$

$2x$
$+9x$
$11x$ $\longrightarrow$ **Correct** middle term

Thus a factored form of $3x^2 + 11x + 6$ is $(3x + 2)(x + 3)$.

● **Work Practice 1**

✓ **Concept Check**   Do the terms of $3x^2 + 29x + 18$ have a common factor? Without multiplying, decide which of the following factored forms could not be a factored form of $3x^2 + 29x + 18$.

a. $(3x + 18)(x + 1)$ **b.** $(3x + 2)(x + 9)$
c. $(3x + 6)(x + 3)$ **d.** $(3x + 9)(x + 2)$

Example 2   Factor: $8x^2 - 22x + 5$

Solution: Factors of $8x^2$: $8x^2 = 8x \cdot x$, $8x^2 = 4x \cdot 2x$

We'll try $8x$ and x.

$$8x^2 - 22x + 5 = (8x + \square)(x + \square)$$

Since the middle term, $-22x$, has a negative numerical coefficient, we factor 5 into negative factors.

Factors of 5: $5 = -1 \cdot -5$

Let's try -1 and -5.

$$(8x - 1)(x - 5) = 8x^2 - 41x + 5$$

$$\begin{aligned} -1x \\ + (-40x) \\ \hline -41x \end{aligned}$$ ⟶ **Incorrect** middle term

Now let's try -5 and -1.

$$(8x - 5)(x - 1) = 8x^2 - 13x + 5$$

$$\begin{aligned} -5x \\ + (-8x) \\ \hline -13x \end{aligned}$$ ⟶ **Incorrect** middle term

Don't give up yet! We can still try other factors of $8x^2$. Let's try $4x$ and $2x$ with -1 and -5.

$$(4x - 1)(2x - 5) = 8x^2 - 22x + 5$$

$$\begin{aligned} -2x \\ + (-20x) \\ \hline -22x \end{aligned}$$ ⟶ **Correct** middle term

A factored form of $8x^2 - 22x + 5$ is $(4x - 1)(2x - 5)$.

● **Work Practice 2**

Example 3 Factor: $2x^2 + 13x - 7$

Solution: Factors of $2x^2$: $2x^2 = 2x \cdot x$

Factors of -7: $-7 = -1 \cdot 7$, $\qquad -7 = 1 \cdot -7$

We try possible combinations of these factors:

$$(2x + 1)(x - 7) = 2x^2 - 13x - 7 \quad \text{Incorrect middle term}$$
$$(2x - 1)(x + 7) = 2x^2 + 13x - 7 \quad \text{Correct middle term}$$

A factored form of $2x^2 + 13x - 7$ is $(2x - 1)(x + 7)$.

● **Work Practice 3**

Example 4 Factor: $10x^2 - 13xy - 3y^2$

Solution: Factors of $10x^2$: $10x^2 = 10x \cdot x$, $\qquad 10x^2 = 2x \cdot 5x$

Factors of $-3y^2$: $-3y^2 = -3y \cdot y$, $\qquad -3y^2 = 3y \cdot -y$

We try some combinations of these factors:

$$\begin{array}{cc} & \text{Correct} \qquad\qquad \text{Correct} \\ & \downarrow \qquad\qquad\quad \downarrow \end{array}$$
$$(10x - 3y)(x + y) = 10x^2 + 7xy - 3y^2$$
$$(x + 3y)(10x - y) = 10x^2 + 29xy - 3y^2$$
$$(5x + 3y)(2x - y) = 10x^2 + xy - 3y^2$$
$$(2x - 3y)(5x + y) = 10x^2 - 13xy - 3y^2 \quad \text{Correct middle term}$$

A factored form of $10x^2 - 13xy - 3y^2$ is $(2x - 3y)(5x + y)$.

● **Work Practice 4**

Example 5 Factor: $3x^4 - 5x^2 - 8$

Solution: Factors of $3x^4$: $3x^4 = 3x^2 \cdot x^2$

Factors of -8: $-8 = -2 \cdot 4, 2 \cdot -4, -1 \cdot 8, 1 \cdot -8$

Continued on next page

PRACTICE 3

Factor each trinomial.
a. $3x^2 + 14x - 5$
b. $35x^2 + 4x - 4$

PRACTICE 4

Factor each trinomial.
a. $14x^2 - 3xy - 2y^2$
b. $12a^2 - 16ab - 3b^2$

PRACTICE 5

Factor: $2x^4 - 5x^2 - 7$

Answers
3. a. $(3x - 1)(x + 5)$
   b. $(5x + 2)(7x - 2)$
4. a. $(7x + 2y)(2x - y)$
   b. $(6a + b)(2a - 3b)$
5. $(2x^2 - 7)(x^2 + 1)$

Try combinations of these factors:

$$Correct \qquad Correct$$
$$\downarrow \qquad\qquad \downarrow$$

$(3x^2 - 2)(x^2 + 4) = 3x^4 + 10x^2 - 8$ **Incorrect** middle term

$(3x^2 + 4)(x^2 - 2) = 3x^4 - 2x^2 - 8$ **Incorrect** middle term

$(3x^2 + 8)(x^2 - 1) = 3x^4 + 5x^2 - 8$ **Incorrect sign** on middle term, so switch signs in binomial factors

$(3x^2 - 8)(x^2 + 1) = 3x^4 - 5x^2 - 8$ **Correct** middle term

⬤ **Work Practice 5**

Helpful Hint

Study the last two lines of Example 5. If a factoring attempt gives you a middle term whose numerical coefficient is the opposite of the desired numerical coefficient, try switching the signs of the last terms in the binomials.

Switched signs
$(3x^2 + 8)(x^2 - 1) = 3x^4 + 5x^4 - 8$ Middle term: $+5x$
$(3x^2 - 8)(x^2 + 1) = 3x^4 - 5x^2 - 8$ Middle term: $-5x$

Objective ⓑ Factoring Out the Greatest Common Factor

Don't forget that the first step in factoring any polynomial is to look for a common factor to factor out.

PRACTICE 6

Factor each trinomial.
a. $3x^3 + 17x^2 + 10x$
b. $6xy^2 + 33xy - 18x$

Example 6 Factor: $24x^4 + 40x^3 + 6x^2$

Solution: Notice that all three terms have a common factor of $2x^2$. Thus we factor out $2x^2$ first.

$$24x^4 + 40x^3 + 6x^2 = 2x^2(12x^2 + 20x + 3)$$

Next we factor $12x^2 + 20x + 3$.

Factors of $12x^2$: $12x^2 = 4x \cdot 3x$, $12x^2 = 12x \cdot x$, $12x^2 = 6x \cdot 2x$

Since all terms in the trinomial have positive numerical coefficients, we factor 3 using positive factors only.

Factors of 3: $3 = 1 \cdot 3$

We try some combinations of the factors.

$$2x^2(4x + 3)(3x + 1) = 2x^2(12x^2 + 13x + 3)$$
$$2x^2(12x + 1)(x + 3) = 2x^2(12x^2 + 37x + 3)$$
$$2x^2(2x + 3)(6x + 1) = 2x^2(12x^2 + 20x + 3)$$ **Correct** middle term

A factored form of $24x^4 + 40x^3 + 6x^2$ is $2x^2(2x + 3)(6x + 1)$.

⬤ **Work Practice 6**

Helpful Hint
Don't forget to include the common factor in the factored form.

When the term containing the squared variable has a negative coefficient, you may want to first factor out a common factor of -1.

PRACTICE 7

Factor: $-5x^2 - 19x + 4$

Example 7 Factor: $-6x^2 - 13x + 5$

Solution: We begin by factoring out a common factor of -1.

$$-6x^2 - 13x + 5 = -1(6x^2 + 13x - 5)$$ Factor out -1.
$$= -1(3x - 1)(2x + 5)$$ Factor $6x^2 + 13x - 5$.

⬤ **Work Practice 7**

Answers
6. a. $x(3x + 2)(x + 5)$
  b. $3x(2y - 1)(y + 6)$
7. $-1(x + 4)(5x - 1)$

Vocabulary and Readiness Check

Complete each factorization.

1. $2x^2 + 5x + 3$ factors as $(2x + 3)($? $)$.
   a. $(x + 3)$ **b.** $(2x + 1)$ **c.** $(3x + 4)$ **d.** $(x + 1)$

2. $7x^2 + 9x + 2$ factors as $(7x + 2)($? $)$.
   a. $(3x + 1)$ **b.** $(x + 1)$ **c.** $(x + 2)$ **d.** $(7x + 1)$

3. $3x^2 + 31x + 10$ factors as _____.
   a. $(3x + 2)(x + 5)$ **b.** $(3x + 5)(x + 2)$ **c.** $(3x + 1)(x + 10)$

4. $5x^2 + 61x + 12$ factors as _____.
   a. $(5x + 1)(x + 12)$ **b.** $(5x + 3)(x + 4)$ **c.** $(5x + 2)(x + 6)$

9.3 Exercise Set

FOR EXTRA HELP

MyMathLab®   Powered by CourseCompass™ and MathXL®

 Math XP

 PRACTICE   WATCH   DOWNLOAD   READ   REVIEW

Objective Ⓐ *Complete each factored form. See Examples 1 through 5.*

1. $5x^2 + 22x + 8 = (5x + 2)($ $)$ **2.** $2y^2 + 15y + 25 = (2y + 5)($ $)$

3. $50x^2 + 15x - 2 = (5x + 2)($ $)$ **4.** $6y^2 + 11y - 10 = (2y + 5)($ $)$

5. $20x^2 - 7x - 6 = (5x + 2)($ $)$ **6.** $8y^2 - 2y - 55 = (2y + 5)($ $)$

Factor each trinomial completely. See Examples 1 through 5.

7. $2x^2 + 13x + 15$ **8.** $3x^2 + 8x + 4$ **9.** $8y^2 - 17y + 9$ **10.** $21x^2 - 41x + 10$

11. $2x^2 - 9x - 5$ **12.** $36r^2 - 5r - 24$ **13.** $20r^2 + 27r - 8$ **14.** $3x^2 + 20x - 63$

15. $10x^2 + 31x + 3$ **16.** $12x^2 + 17x + 5$ **17.** $x + 3x^2 - 2$ **18.** $y + 8y^2 - 9$

19. $6x^2 - 13xy + 5y^2$ **20.** $8x^2 - 14xy + 3y^2$ **21.** $15m^2 - 16m - 15$ **22.** $25n^2 - 5n - 6$

23. $-9x + 20 + x^2$ **24.** $-7x + 12 + x^2$ **25.** $2x^2 - 7x - 99$ **26.** $2x^2 + 7x - 72$

27. $-27t + 7t^2 - 4$ **28.** $-3t + 4t^2 - 7$ **29.** $3a^2 + 10ab + 3b^2$ **30.** $2a^2 + 11ab + 5b^2$

31. $49p^2 - 7p - 2$ **32.** $3r^2 + 10r - 8$ **33.** $18x^2 - 9x - 14$ **34.** $42a^2 - 43a + 6$

35. $2m^2 + 17m + 10$ **36.** $3n^2 + 20n + 5$ **37.** $24x^2 + 41x + 12$ **38.** $24x^2 - 49x + 15$

Objectives Ⓐ Ⓑ **Mixed Practice** *Factor each trinomial completely. See Examples 1 through 7.*

39. $12x^3 + 11x^2 + 2x$ **40.** $8a^3 + 14a^2 + 3a$ **41.** $21b^2 - 48b - 45$ **42.** $12x^2 - 14x - 10$

43. $7z + 12z^2 - 12$ **44.** $16t + 15t^2 - 15$ **45.** $6x^2y^2 - 2xy^2 - 60y^2$ **46.** $8x^2y + 34xy - 84y$

47. $4x^2 - 8x - 21$ **48.** $6x^2 - 11x - 10$ **49.** $3x^2 - 42x + 63$ **50.** $5x^2 - 75x + 60$

51. $8x^2 + 6xy - 27y^2$ **52.** $54a^2 + 39ab - 8b^2$ **53.** $-x^2 + 2x + 24$ **54.** $-x^2 + 4x + 21$

55. $4x^3 - 9x^2 - 9x$ **56.** $6x^3 - 31x^2 + 5x$ **57.** $24x^2 - 58x + 9$ **58.** $36x^2 + 55x - 14$

59. $40a^2b + 9ab - 9b$ **60.** $24y^2x + 7yx - 5x$ **61.** $30x^3 + 38x^2 + 12x$ **62.** $6x^3 - 28x^2 + 16x$

63. $6y^3 - 8y^2 - 30y$ **64.** $12x^3 - 34x^2 + 24x$ **65.** $10x^4 + 25x^3y - 15x^2y^2$ **66.** $42x^4 - 99x^3y - 15x^2y^2$

67. $-14x^2 + 39x - 10$ **68.** $-15x^2 + 26x - 8$ **69.** $16p^4 - 40p^3 + 25p^2$ **70.** $9q^4 - 42q^3 + 49q^2$

71. $-2x^2 + 9x + 5$ **72.** $-3x^2 + 8x + 16$ **73.** $-4 + 52x - 48x^2$ **74.** $-5 + 55x - 50x^2$

75. $2t^4 + 3t^2 - 27$ **76.** $4r^4 - 17r^2 - 15$ **77.** $5x^2y^2 + 20xy + 1$ **78.** $3a^2b^2 + 12ab + 1$

79. $6a^5 + 37a^3b^2 + 6ab^4$ **80.** $5m^5 + 26m^3h^2 + 5mh^4$

Review

Multiply. See Section 8.6.

81. $(x - 4)(x + 4)$ **82.** $(2x - 9)(2x + 9)$ **83.** $(x + 2)^2$

84. $(x + 3)^2$ **85.** $(2x - 1)^2$ **86.** $(3x - 5)^2$

Concept Extensions

See the Concept Check in this section.

87. Do the terms of $4x^2 + 19x + 12$ have a common factor (other than 1)?

88. Without multiplying, decide which of the following factored forms is not a factored form of $4x^2 + 19x + 12$.
  a. $(2x + 4)(2x + 3)$ **b.** $(4x + 4)(x + 3)$
  c. $(4x + 3)(x + 4)$ **d.** $(2x + 2)(2x + 6)$

Write the perimeter of each figure as a simplified polynomial. Then factor the polynomial completely.

89.

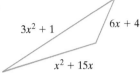

$3x^2 + 1$

$6x + 4$

$x^2 + 15x$

90.

$3y^2$

$-22y + 7$

Factor each trinomial completely.

91. $4x^2 + 2x + \dfrac{1}{4}$

92. $27x^2 + 2x - \dfrac{1}{9}$

93. $4x^2(y - 1)^2 + 25x(y - 1)^2 + 25(y - 1)^2$

94. $3x^2(a + 3)^3 - 28x(a + 3)^3 + 25(a + 3)^3$

Find all positive values of b so that each trinomial is factorable.

95. $3x^2 + bx - 5$

96. $2z^2 + bz - 7$

Find all positive values of c so that each trinomial is factorable.

97. $5x^2 + 7x + c$

98. $3x^2 - 8x + c$

99. In your own words, describe the steps you use to factor a trinomial.

100. A student in your class factored $6x^2 + 7x + 1$ as $(3x + 1)(2x + 1)$. Write down how you would explain the student's error.

9.4 FACTORING TRINOMIALS OF THE FORM $ax^2 + bx + c$ BY GROUPING

Objective ⓐ Using the Grouping Method

There is an alternative method that can be used to factor trinomials of the form $ax^2 + bx + c, a \neq 1$. This method is called the **grouping method** because it uses factoring by grouping as we learned in Section 9.1.

To see how this method works, recall from Section 9.2 that to factor a trinomial such as $x^2 + 11x + 30$, we find two numbers such that

Product is 30.
↓
$$x^2 + 11x + 30$$
↓
Sum is 11.

To factor a trinomial such as $2x^2 + 11x + 12$ by grouping, we use an extension of the method in Section 9.1. Here we look for two numbers such that

Product is $2 \cdot 12 = 24$.
↓
$$2x^2 + 11x + 12$$
↓
Sum is 11.

This time, we use the two numbers to write

$2x^2 + 11x + 12$ as
$= 2x^2 + \square x + \square x + 12$

Then we factor by grouping. Since we want a positive product, 24, and a positive sum, 11, we consider pairs of positive factors of 24 only.

Factors of 24	Sum of Factors
1, 24	25
2, 12	14
3, 8	11

Correct sum

The factors are 3 and 8. Now we use these factors to write the middle term, $11x$, as $3x + 8x$ (or $8x + 3x$). We replace $11x$ with $3x + 8x$ in the original trinomial and then we can factor by grouping.

$$
\begin{aligned}
2x^2 + 11x + 12 &= 2x^2 + 3x + 8x + 12 \\
&= (2x^2 + 3x) + (8x + 12) && \text{Group the terms.} \\
&= x(2x + 3) + 4(2x + 3) && \text{Factor each group.} \\
&= (2x + 3)(x + 4) && \text{Factor out } (2x + 3).
\end{aligned}
$$

In general, we have the following procedure.

To Factor Trinomials by Grouping

Step 1: Factor out a greatest common factor, if there is one other than 1.

Step 2: For the resulting trinomial $ax^2 + bx + c$, find two numbers whose product is $a \cdot c$ and whose sum is b.

Step 3: Write the middle term, bx, using the factors found in Step 2.

Step 4: Factor by grouping.

Example 1 Factor $8x^2 - 14x + 5$ by grouping.

Solution:

Step 1: The terms of this trinomial contain no greatest common factor other than 1.

Step 2: This trinomial is of the form $ax^2 + bx + c$, with $a = 8, b = -14$, and $c = 5$. Find two numbers whose product is $a \cdot c$ or $8 \cdot 5 = 40$, and whose sum is b or -14.

The numbers are -4 and -10.

Factors of 40	Sum of Factors
$-40, -1$	-41
$-20, -2$	-22
$-10, -4$	-14

Correct sum

Step 3: Write $-14x$ as $-4x - 10x$ so that
$$8x^2 - 14x + 5 = 8x^2 - 4x - 10x + 5$$

Step 4: Factor by grouping.
$$8x^2 - 4x - 10x + 5 = 4x(2x - 1) - 5(2x - 1)$$
$$= (2x - 1)(4x - 5)$$

⬤ **Work Practice 1**

Example 2 Factor $6x^2 - 2x - 20$ by grouping.

Solution:

Step 1: First factor out the greatest common factor, 2.
$$6x^2 - 2x - 20 = 2(3x^2 - x - 10)$$

Step 2: Next notice that $a = 3, b = -1$, and $c = -10$ in the resulting trinomial. Find two numbers whose product is $a \cdot c$ or $3(-10) = -30$ and whose sum is $b, -1$. The numbers are -6 and 5.

Step 3: $3x^2 - x - 10 = 3x^2 - 6x + 5x - 10$

Step 4: $3x^2 - 6x + 5x - 10 = 3x(x - 2) + 5(x - 2)$
$$= (x - 2)(3x + 5)$$

The factored form of $6x^2 - 2x - 20 = 2(x - 2)(3x + 5)$.

└─ Don't forget to include the common factor of 2.

⬤ **Work Practice 2**

Example 3 Factor $18y^4 + 21y^3 - 60y^2$ by grouping.

Solution:

Step 1: First factor out the greatest common factor, $3y^2$.
$$18y^4 + 21y^3 - 60y^2 = 3y^2(6y^2 + 7y - 20)$$

Step 2: Notice that $a = 6, b = 7$, and $c = -20$ in the resulting trinomial. Find two numbers whose product is $a \cdot c$ or $6(-20) = -120$ and whose sum is 7. It may help to factor -120 as a product of primes and -1.
$$-120 = 2 \cdot 2 \cdot 2 \cdot 3 \cdot 5 \cdot (-1)$$

Then choose pairings of factors until you have two pairings whose sum is 7.

$$\overset{-8}{\underset{15}{2 \cdot 2 \cdot 2 \cdot 3 \cdot 5 \cdot (-1)}}$$ The numbers are -8 and 15.

Step 3: $6y^2 + 7y - 20 = 6y^2 - 8y + 15y - 20$

Step 4: $6y^2 - 8y + 15y - 20 = 2y(3y - 4) + 5(3y - 4)$
$$= (3y - 4)(2y + 5)$$

The factored form of $18y^4 + 21y^3 - 60y^2$ is $3y^2(3y - 4)(2y + 5)$.

└─Don't forget to include the common factor of $3y^2$.

⬤ **Work Practice 3**

Vocabulary and Readiness Check

For each trinomial $ax^2 + bx + c$, choose two numbers whose product is $a \cdot c$ and whose sum is b.

1. $x^2 + 6x + 8$
   a. 4, 2   b. 7, 1   c. 6, 2   d. 6, 8

2. $x^2 + 11x + 24$
   a. 6, 4   b. 24, 1   c. 8, 3   d. 2, 12

3. $2x^2 + 13x + 6$
   a. 2, 6   b. 12, 1   c. 13, 1   d. 3, 4

4. $4x^2 + 8x + 3$
   a. 4, 3   b. 4, 4   c. 12, 1   d. 2, 6

9.4 Exercise Set

FOR EXTRA HELP

MyMathLab Powered by CourseCompass™ and MathXL™

 Math XL
PRACTICE

 WATCH

 DOWNLOAD

 READ

 REVIEW

Objective Ⓐ *Factor each polynomial by grouping. Notice that Step 3 has already been done in these exercises. See Examples 1 through 3.*

1. $x^2 + 3x + 2x + 6$ 2. $x^2 + 5x + 3x + 15$ 3. $y^2 + 8y - 2y - 16$ 4. $z^2 + 10z - 7z - 70$

5. $8x^2 - 5x - 24x + 15$ 6. $4x^2 - 9x - 32x + 72$ 7. $5x^4 - 3x^2 + 25x^2 - 15$ 8. $2y^4 - 10y^2 + 7y^2 - 35$

Factor each trinomial by grouping. Exercises 9 through 12 are broken into parts to help you get started. See Examples 1 through 3.

9. $6x^2 + 11x + 3$
   a. Find two numbers whose product is $6 \cdot 3 = 18$ and whose sum is 11.
   b. Write $11x$ using the factors from part (a).
   c. Factor by grouping.

10. $8x^2 + 14x + 3$
   a. Find two numbers whose product is $8 \cdot 3 = 24$ and whose sum is 14.
   b. Write $14x$ using the factors from part (a).
   c. Factor by grouping.

11. $15x^2 - 23x + 4$
   a. Find two numbers whose product is $15 \cdot 4 = 60$ and whose sum is -23.
   b. Write $-23x$ using the factors from part (a).
   c. Factor by grouping.

12. $6x^2 - 13x + 5$
   a. Find two numbers whose product is $6 \cdot 5 = 30$ and whose sum is -13.
   b. Write $-13x$ using the factors from part (a).
   c. Factor by grouping.

13. $21y^2 + 17y + 2$ 14. $15x^2 + 11x + 2$ 15. $7x^2 - 4x - 11$ 16. $8x^2 - x - 9$

17. $10x^2 - 9x + 2$ 18. $30x^2 - 23x + 3$ 19. $2x^2 - 7x + 5$ 20. $2x^2 - 7x + 3$

21. $12x + 4x^2 + 9$ 22. $20x + 25x^2 + 4$ 23. $4x^2 - 8x - 21$ 24. $6x^2 - 11x - 10$

25. $10x^2 - 23x + 12$ 26. $21x^2 - 13x + 2$ 27. $2x^3 + 13x^2 + 15x$ 28. $3x^3 + 8x^2 + 4x$

29. $16y^2 - 34y + 18$ 30. $4y^2 - 2y - 12$ 31. $-13x + 6 + 6x^2$ 32. $-25x + 12 + 12x^2$

33. $54a^2 - 9a - 30$ **34.** $30a^2 + 38a - 20$ **35.** $20a^3 + 37a^2 + 8a$ **36.** $10a^3 + 17a^2 + 3a$

37. $12x^3 - 27x^2 - 27x$ **38.** $30x^3 - 155x^2 + 25x$ **39.** $3x^2y + 4xy^2 + y^3$ **40.** $6r^2t + 7rt^2 + t^3$

41. $20z^2 + 7z + 1$ **42.** $36z^2 + 6z + 1$

43. $24a^2 - 6ab - 30b^2$ **44.** $30a^2 + 5ab - 25b^2$

45. $15p^4 + 31p^3q + 2p^2q^2$ **46.** $20s^4 + 61s^3t + 3s^2t^2$

47. $35 + 12x + x^2$ **48.** $33 + 14x + x^2$

49. $6 - 11x + 5x^2$ **50.** $5 - 12x + 7x^2$

Review

Multiply. See Section 8.6.

51. $(x - 2)(x + 2)$ **52.** $(y - 5)(y + 5)$ **53.** $(y + 4)(y + 4)$ **54.** $(x + 7)(x + 7)$

55. $(9z + 5)(9z - 5)$ **56.** $(8y + 9)(8y - 9)$ **57.** $(4x - 3)^2$ **58.** $(2z - 1)^2$

Concept Extensions

Write the perimeter of each figure as a simplified polynomial. Then factor the polynomial.

59.

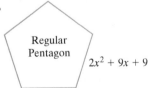

Regular Pentagon $2x^2 + 9x + 9$

60.

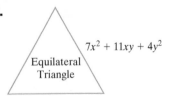

Equilateral Triangle $7x^2 + 11xy + 4y^2$

Factor each polynomial by grouping.

61. $x^{2n} + 2x^n + 3x^n + 6$
(*Hint:* Don't forget that $x^{2n} = x^n \cdot x^n$.)

62. $x^{2n} + 6x^n + 10x^n + 60$

63. $3x^{2n} + 16x^n - 35$ **64.** $12x^{2n} - 40x^n + 25$

65. In your own words, explain how to factor a trinomial by grouping.

66. In your own words, explain how factoring a trinomial by grouping is similar to factoring a four-term polynomial by grouping.

9.5 FACTORING PERFECT SQUARE TRINOMIALS AND THE DIFFERENCE OF TWO SQUARES

Objective Ⓐ Recognizing Perfect Square Trinomials

A trinomial that is the square of a binomial is called a **perfect square trinomial.** For example,

$$(x + 3)^2 = (x + 3)(x + 3)$$
$$= x^2 + 6x + 9$$

Thus $x^2 + 6x + 9$ is a perfect square trinomial.

In Chapter 8, we discovered special product formulas for squaring binomials.

$$(a + b)^2 = a^2 + 2ab + b^2 \quad \text{and} \quad (a - b)^2 = a^2 - 2ab + b^2$$

Because multiplication and factoring are reverse processes, we can now use these special products to help us factor perfect square trinomials. If we reverse these equations, we have the following.

Factoring Perfect Square Trinomials

$$a^2 + 2ab + b^2 = (a + b)^2$$
$$a^2 - 2ab + b^2 = (a - b)^2$$

Helpful Hint

Notice that for both given forms of a perfect square trinomial, the last term is positive. This is because the last term is a square.

To use these equations to help us factor, we must first be able to recognize a perfect square trinomial. A trinomial is a perfect square when

1. two terms, a^2 and b^2, are squares and
2. another term is $2 \cdot a \cdot b$ or $-2 \cdot a \cdot b$. That is, this term is twice the product of a and b, or its opposite.

PRACTICE 1

Decide whether each trinomial is a perfect square trinomial.
a. $x^2 + 12x + 36$
b. $x^2 + 20x + 100$

Example 1 Decide whether $x^2 + 8x + 16$ is a perfect square trinomial.

Solution:

1. Two terms, x^2 and 16, are squares ($16 = 4^2$).
2. Twice the product of x and 4 is the other term of the trinomial.

$$2 \cdot x \cdot 4 = 8x$$

Thus, $x^2 + 8x + 16$ is a perfect square trinomial.

⬤ Work Practice 1

PRACTICE 2

Decide whether each trinomial is a perfect square trinomial.
a. $9x^2 + 20x + 25$
b. $4x^2 + 8x + 11$

Example 2 Decide whether $4x^2 + 10x + 9$ is a perfect square trinomial.

Solution:

1. Two terms, $4x^2$ and 9, are squares.

$$4x^2 = (2x)^2 \quad \text{and} \quad 9 = 3^2$$

2. Twice the product of $2x$ and 3 is *not* the other term of the trinomial.

$$2 \cdot 2x \cdot 3 = 12x, \text{ not } 10x$$

The trinomial is *not* a perfect square trinomial.

⬤ Work Practice 2

Answers
1. a. yes **b.** yes **2. a.** no **b.** no

Example 3 Decide whether $9x^2 - 12xy + 4y^2$ is a perfect square trinomial.

Solution:

1. Two terms, $9x^2$ and $4y^2$, are squares.
   $9x^2 = (3x)^2$ and $4y^2 = (2y)^2$

2. Twice the product of $3x$ and $2y$ is the opposite of the other term of the trinomial.
   $2 \cdot 3x \cdot 2y = 12xy$, the opposite of $-12xy$

Thus, $9x^2 - 12xy + 4y^2$ is a perfect square trinomial.

● **Work Practice 3**

PRACTICE 3

Decide whether each trinomial is a perfect square trinomial.
a. $25x^2 - 10x + 1$
b. $9x^2 - 42x + 49$

Objective ⓑ Factoring Perfect Square Trinomials

Now that we can recognize perfect square trinomials, we are ready to factor them.

Example 4 Factor: $x^2 + 12x + 36$

Solution:

$$x^2 + 12x + 36 = x^2 + 2 \cdot x \cdot 6 + 6^2 \qquad 36 = 6^2 \text{ and } 12x = 2 \cdot x \cdot 6$$
$$a^2 + 2 \cdot a \cdot b + b^2$$
$$= (x + 6)^2$$
$$(a + b)^2$$

● **Work Practice 4**

PRACTICE 4

Factor: $x^2 + 16x + 64$

Example 5 Factor: $25x^2 + 20xy + 4y^2$

Solution:

$$25x^2 + 20xy + 4y^2 = (5x)^2 + 2 \cdot 5x \cdot 2y + (2y)^2$$
$$= (5x + 2y)^2$$

● **Work Practice 5**

PRACTICE 5

Factor: $9r^2 + 24rs + 16s^2$

Example 6 Factor: $4m^4 - 4m^2 + 1$

Solution:

$$4m^4 - 4m^2 + 1 = (2m^2)^2 - 2 \cdot 2m^2 \cdot 1 + 1^2$$
$$a^2 \quad - 2 \cdot a \cdot b + b^2$$
$$= (2m^2 - 1)^2$$
$$(a \quad - b)^2$$

● **Work Practice 6**

PRACTICE 6

Factor: $9n^4 - 6n^2 + 1$

Example 7 Factor: $25x^2 + 50x + 9$

Solution: Notice that this trinomial is not a perfect square trinomial.

$$25x^2 = (5x)^2, 9 = 3^2$$

but

$$2 \cdot 5x \cdot 3 = 30x$$

and $30x$ is not the middle term, $50x$.

Continued on next page

PRACTICE 7

Factor: $9x^2 + 15x + 4$

Answers
3. a. yes **b.** yes **4.** $(x + 8)^2$
5. $(3r + 4s)^2$ **6.** $(3n^2 - 1)^2$
7. $(3x + 1)(3x + 4)$

Copyright 2011 Pearson Education, Inc.

Helpful Hint   A perfect square trinomial can also be factored by the methods found in Sections 9.2 through 9.4.

Although $25x^2 + 50x + 9$ is not a perfect square trinomial, it is factorable. Using techniques we learned in Sections 9.3 or 9.4, we find that

$$25x^2 + 50x + 9 = (5x + 9)(5x + 1)$$

● **Work Practice 7**

PRACTICE 8

Factor:

a. $8n^2 + 40n + 50$

b. $12x^3 - 84x^2 + 147x$

Example 8 Factor: $162x^3 - 144x^2 + 32x$

Solution: Don't forget to first look for a common factor. There is a greatest common factor of $2x$ in this trinomial.

$$162x^3 - 144x^2 + 32x = 2x(81x^2 - 72x + 16)$$
$$= 2x[(9x)^2 - 2 \cdot 9x \cdot 4 + 4^2]$$
$$= 2x(9x - 4)^2$$

● **Work Practice 8**

Objective ○ **Factoring the Difference of Two Squares**

In Chapter 8, we discovered another special product, the product of the sum and difference of two terms a and b:

$$(a + b)(a - b) = a^2 - b^2$$

Reversing this equation gives us another factoring pattern, which we use to factor the difference of two squares.

> **Factoring the Difference of Two Squares**
>
> $$a^2 - b^2 = (a + b)(a - b)$$

To use this equation to help us factor, we must first be able to recognize the difference of two squares. A binomial is a difference of two squares if

1. both terms are squares and
2. the signs of the terms are different.

Let's practice using this pattern.

PRACTICE 9–12

Factor each binomial.

9. $x^2 - 9$ **10.** $a^2 - 16$

11. $c^2 - \dfrac{9}{25}$ **12.** $s^2 + 9$

Examples Factor each binomial.

9. $z^2 - 4 = z^2 - 2^2 = (z + 2)(z - 2)$

$$a^2 - b^2 = (a + b)(a - b)$$

10. $y^2 - 25 = y^2 - 5^2 = (y + 5)(y - 5)$

11. $y^2 - \dfrac{4}{9} = y^2 - \left(\dfrac{2}{3}\right)^2 = \left(y + \dfrac{2}{3}\right)\left(y - \dfrac{2}{3}\right)$

12. $x^2 + 4$

Note that the binomial $x^2 + 4$ is the *sum* of two squares since we can write $x^2 + 4$ as $x^2 + 2^2$. We might try to factor using $(x + 2)(x + 2)$ or $(x - 2)(x - 2)$. But when we multiply to check, we find that neither factoring is correct.

$$(x + 2)(x + 2) = x^2 + 4x + 4$$
$$(x - 2)(x - 2) = x^2 - 4x + 4$$

In both cases, the product is a trinomial, not the required binomial. In fact, $x^2 + 4$ is a prime polynomial.

● **Work Practice 9–12**

Helpful Hint   After the greatest common factor has been removed, the *sum* of two squares cannot be factored further using real numbers.

Answers

8. a. $2(2n + 5)^2$ **b.** $3x(2x - 7)^2$

9. $(x - 3)(x + 3)$

10. $(a - 4)(a + 4)$

11. $\left(c - \dfrac{3}{5}\right)\left(c + \dfrac{3}{5}\right)$

12. prime polynomial

Examples Factor each difference of two squares.

13. $4x^2 - 1 = (2x)^2 - 1^2 = (2x + 1)(2x - 1)$
14. $25a^2 - 9b^2 = (5a)^2 - (3b)^2 = (5a + 3b)(5a - 3b)$
15. $y^4 - 16 = (y^2)^2 - 4^2$

$\qquad = (y^2 + 4)(y^2 - 4)$ Factor the difference of two squares.

$\qquad = (y^2 + 4)(y + 2)(y - 2)$ Factor the difference of two squares.

● **Work Practice 13–15**

PRACTICE 13–15

Factor each difference of two squares.
13. $9s^2 - 1$
14. $16x^2 - 49y^2$
15. $p^4 - 81$

Helpful Hint

1. Don't forget to first see whether there's a greatest common factor (other than 1) that can be factored out.
2. Factor completely. In other words, check to see whether any factors can be factored further (as in Example 15).

Examples Factor each binomial.

16. $4x^3 - 49x = x(4x^2 - 49)$ Factor out the common factor, x.

$\qquad = x[(2x)^2 - 7^2]$

$\qquad = x(2x + 7)(2x - 7)$ Factor the difference of two squares.

17. $162x^4 - 2 = 2(81x^4 - 1)$ Factor out the common factor, 2.

$\qquad = 2(9x^2 + 1)(9x^2 - 1)$ Factor the difference of two squares.

$\qquad = 2(9x^2 + 1)(3x + 1)(3x - 1)$ Factor the difference of two squares.

18. $-49x^2 + 16 = -1(49x^2 - 16)$ Factor out -1.

$\qquad = -1(7x + 4)(7x - 4)$ Factor the difference of two squares.

● **Work Practice 16–18**

PRACTICE 16–18

Factor each binomial.
16. $9x^3 - 25x$
17. $48x^4 - 3$
18. $-9x^2 + 100$

Example 19 Factor: $36 - x^2$

Solution: This is the difference of two squares. Factor as is or if you like, first write the binomial with the variable term first.

Factor as is: $36 - x^2 = 6^2 - x^2 = (6 + x)(6 - x)$

Rewrite binomial: $36 - x^2 = -x^2 + 36 = -1(x^2 - 36)$

$\qquad\qquad\qquad\qquad = -1(x + 6)(x - 6)$

Both factorizations are correct and are equal. To see this, factor -1 from $(6 - x)$ in the first factorization.

● **Work Practice 19**

PRACTICE 19

Factor: $121 - m^2$

Helpful Hint

When rearranging terms, keep in mind that the sign of a term is in front of the term.

Answers
13. $(3s - 1)(3s + 1)$
14. $(4x - 7y)(4x + 7y)$
15. $(p^2 + 9)(p + 3)(p - 3)$
16. $x(3x - 5)(3x + 5)$
17. $3(4x^2 + 1)(2x + 1)(2x - 1)$
18. $-1(3x - 10)(3x + 10)$
19. $(11 + m)(11 - m)$ or
$-1(m + 11)(m - 11)$

Calculator Explorations   Graphing

A graphing calculator is a convenient tool for evaluating an expression at a given replacement value. For example, let's evaluate $x^2 - 6x$ when $x = 2$. To do so, store the value 2 in the variable x and then enter and evaluate the algebraic expression.

```
2→X
              2
X²-6X
             -8
```

The value of $x^2 - 6x$ when $x = 2$ is -8. You may want to use this method for evaluating expressions as you explore the following.

We can use a graphing calculator to explore factoring patterns numerically. Use your calculator to evaluate $x^2 - 2x + 1$, $x^2 - 2x - 1$, and $(x - 1)^2$ for each value of x given in the table. What do you observe?

	$x^2 - 2x + 1$	$x^2 - 2x - 1$	$(x - 1)^2$
$x = 5$			
$x = -3$			
$x = 2.7$			
$x = -12.1$			
$x = 0$			

Notice in each case that $x^2 - 2x - 1 \neq (x - 1)^2$. Because for each x in the table the value of $x^2 - 2x + 1$ and the value of $(x - 1)^2$ are the same, we might guess that $x^2 - 2x + 1 = (x - 1)^2$. We can verify our guess algebraically with multiplication:

$$(x - 1)(x - 1) = x^2 - x - x + 1 = x^2 - 2x + 1$$

Vocabulary and Readiness Check

Use the choices below to fill in each blank. Some choices may be used more than once and some choices may not be used at all.

perfect square trinomial   true $(5y)^2$ $(x + 5y)^2$

difference of two squares   false $(x - 5y)^2$ $5y^2$

1. A _____ is a trinomial that is the square of a binomial.
2. The term $25y^2$ written as a square is _____.
3. The expression $x^2 + 10xy + 25y^2$ is called a _____.
4. The expression $x^2 - 49$ is called a _____.
5. The factorization $(x + 5y)(x + 5y)$ may also be written as _____.
6. True or false: The factorization $(x - 5y)(x + 5y)$ may also be written as $(x - 5y)^2$. _____
7. The trinomial $x^2 - 6x - 9$ is a perfect square trinomial. _____
8. The binomial $y^2 + 9$ factors as $(y + 3)^2$. _____

Write each number or term as a square. For example, 16 written as a square is 4^2.

9. 64

10. 9

11. $121a^2$

12. $81b^2$

13. $36p^4$

14. $4q^4$

9.5 Exercise Set

FOR EXTRA HELP

Objective Ⓐ *Determine whether each trinomial is a perfect square trinomial. See Examples 1 through 3.*

1. $x^2 + 16x + 64$

2. $x^2 + 22x + 121$

3. $y^2 + 5y + 25$

4. $y^2 + 4y + 16$

5. $m^2 - 2m + 1$

6. $p^2 - 4p + 4$

7. $a^2 - 16a + 49$

8. $n^2 - 20n + 144$

9. $4x^2 + 12xy + 8y^2$

10. $25x^2 + 20xy + 2y^2$

11. $25a^2 - 40ab + 16b^2$

12. $36a^2 - 12ab + b^2$

Objective Ⓑ *Factor each trinomial completely. See Examples 4 through 8.*

13. $x^2 + 22x + 121$

14. $x^2 + 18x + 81$

15. $x^2 - 16x + 64$

16. $x^2 - 12x + 36$

17. $16a^2 - 24a + 9$

18. $25x^2 - 20x + 4$

19. $x^4 + 4x^2 + 4$

20. $m^4 + 10m^2 + 25$

21. $2n^2 - 28n + 98$

22. $3y^2 - 6y + 3$

23. $16y^2 + 40y + 25$

24. $9y^2 + 48y + 64$

25. $x^2y^2 - 10xy + 25$ **26.** $4x^2y^2 - 28xy + 49$ **27.** $m^3 + 18m^2 + 81m$ **28.** $y^3 + 12y^2 + 36y$

29. $1 + 6x^2 + x^4$ **30.** $1 + 16x^2 + x^4$ **31.** $9x^2 - 24xy + 16y^2$ **32.** $25x^2 - 60xy + 36y^2$

Objective ⓒ *Factor each binomial completely. See Examples 9 through 19.*

33. $x^2 - 4$ **34.** $x^2 - 36$ **35.** $81 - p^2$ **36.** $100 - t^2$

37. $-4r^2 + 1$ **38.** $-9t^2 + 1$ **39.** $9x^2 - 16$ **40.** $36y^2 - 25$

41. $16r^2 + 1$ **42.** $49y^2 + 1$ **43.** $-36 + x^2$ **44.** $-1 + y^2$

45. $m^4 - 1$ **46.** $n^4 - 16$ **47.** $x^2 - 169y^2$ **48.** $x^2 - 225y^2$

49. $18r^2 - 8$ **50.** $32t^2 - 50$ **51.** $9xy^2 - 4x$ **52.** $36x^2y - 25y$

53. $16x^4 - 64x^2$ **54.** $25y^4 - 100y^2$ **55.** $xy^3 - 9xyz^2$ **56.** $x^3y - 4xy^3$

57. $36x^2 - 64y^2$ **58.** $225a^2 - 81b^2$ **59.** $144 - 81x^2$ **60.** $12x^2 - 27$

61. $25y^2 - 9$ **62.** $49a^2 - 16$ **63.** $121m^2 - 100n^2$ **64.** $169a^2 - 49b^2$

65. $x^2y^2 - 1$ **66.** $a^2b^2 - 16$ **67.** $x^2 - \dfrac{1}{4}$

68. $y^2 - \dfrac{1}{16}$ **69.** $49 - \dfrac{9}{25}m^2$ **70.** $100 - \dfrac{4}{81}n^2$

Objectives Ⓑ Ⓒ **Mixed Practice** *Factor each binomial or trinomial completely. See Examples 4 through 19.*

71. $81a^2 - 25b^2$

72. $49y^2 - 100z^2$

73. $x^2 + 14xy + 49y^2$

74. $x^2 + 10xy + 25y^2$

75. $32n^4 - 112n^2 + 98$

76. $162a^4 - 72a^2 + 8$

77. $x^6 - 81x^2$

78. $n^9 - n^5$

79. $64p^3q - 81pq^3$

80. $100x^3y - 49xy^3$

Review

Solve each equation. See Section 6.3.

81. $x - 6 = 0$

82. $y + 5 = 0$

83. $2m + 4 = 0$

84. $3x - 9 = 0$

85. $5z - 1 = 0$

86. $4a + 2 = 0$

Concept Extensions

Factor each expression completely.

87. $x^2 - \dfrac{2}{3}x + \dfrac{1}{9}$

88. $x^2 - \dfrac{1}{25}$

89. $(x + 2)^2 - y^2$

90. $(y - 6)^2 - z^2$

91. $a^2(b - 4) - 16(b - 4)$

92. $m^2(n + 8) - 9(n + 8)$

93. $(x^2 + 6x + 9) - 4y^2$ (*Hint:* Factor the trinomial in parentheses first.)

94. $(x^2 + 2x + 1) - 36y^2$ (See the hint for Exercise 93.)

95. $x^{2n} - 100$

96. $x^{2n} - 81$

97. Fill in the blank so that $x^2 + \underline{\quad} x + 16$ is a perfect square trinomial.

98. Fill in the blank so that $9x^2 + \underline{\quad} x + 25$ is a perfect square trinomial.

99. Describe a perfect square trinomial.

100. Write a perfect square trinomial that factors as $(x + 3y)^2$.

101. What binomial multiplied by $(x - 6)$ gives the difference of two squares?

102. What binomial multiplied by $(5 + y)$ gives the difference of two squares?

The area of the largest square in the figure is $(a + b)^2$. Use this figure to answer Exercises 103 and 104.

103. Write the area of the largest square as the sum of the areas of the smaller squares and rectangles.

104. What factoring formula from this section is visually represented by this square?

105. The Toroweap Overlook, on the North Rim of the Grand Canyon, lies 3000 vertical feet above the Colorado River. The view is spectacular, and the sheer drop is dramatic. A film crew creating a documentary about the Grand Canyon has suspended a camera platform 296 feet below the Overlook. A camera filter comes loose and falls to the river below. The height of the filter above the river after t seconds is given by the expression $2704 - 16t^2$.

 a. Find the height of the filter above the river after 3 seconds.

 b. Find the height of the filter above the river after 7 seconds.

 c. To the nearest whole second, estimate when the filter lands in the river.

 d. Factor $2704 - 16t^2$.

107. The world's second tallest building is the Taipei 101 in Taipei, Taiwan, at a height of 1671 feet. (*Source:* Council on Tall Buildings and Urban Habitat) Suppose a worker is suspended 71 feet below the top of the pinnacle atop the building, at a height of 1600 feet above the ground. If the worker accidentally drops a bolt, the height of the bolt after t seconds is given by the expression $1600 - 16t^2$. (*Note:* As of January 2010, the Burj Khalifa was officially the tallest building at 2684 feet.)

 a. Find the height of the bolt after 3 seconds.

 b. Find the height of the bolt after 7 seconds.

 c. To the nearest whole second, estimate when the bolt hits the ground.

 d. Factor $1600 - 16t^2$.

106. An object is dropped from the top of Pittsburgh's USX Towers, which is 841 feet tall. (*Source: World Almanac* research) The height of the object after t seconds is given by the expression $841 - 16t^2$.

 a. Find the height of the object after 2 seconds.

 b. Find the height of the object after 5 seconds.

 c. To the nearest whole second, estimate when the object hits the ground.

 d. Factor $841 - 16t^2$.

841 feet

108. A performer with the Moscow Circus is planning a stunt involving a free fall from the top of the Moscow State University building, which is 784 feet tall. (*Source:* Council on Tall Buildings and Urban Habitat) Neglecting air resistance, the performer's height above gigantic cushions positioned at ground level after t seconds is given by the expression $784 - 16t^2$.

 a. Find the performer's height after 2 seconds.

 b. Find the performer's height after 5 seconds.

 c. To the nearest whole second, estimate when the performer reaches the cushions positioned at ground level.

 d. Factor $784 - 16t^2$.

9.6 FACTORING THE SUM AND DIFFERENCES OF TWO CUBES

Objective (A) Factoring the Sum or Difference of Two Cubes

Although the sum of two squares usually cannot be factored, the sum of two cubes, as well as the difference of two cubes, can be factored as follows.

> **Sum and Difference of Two Cubes**
>
> $a^3 + b^3 = (a + b)(a^2 - ab + b^2)$
> $a^3 - b^3 = (a - b)(a^2 + ab + b^2)$

To check the first pattern, let's find the product of $(a + b)$ and $(a^2 - ab + b^2)$.

$$(a + b)(a^2 - ab + b^2) = a(a^2 - ab + b^2) + b(a^2 - ab + b^2)$$
$$= a^3 - a^2b + ab^2 + a^2b - ab^2 + b^3$$
$$= a^3 + b^3$$

Example 1 Factor: $x^3 + 8$

Solution: First we write the binomial in the form $a^3 + b^3$. Then we use the formula

$$a^3 + b^3 = (a + b)(a^2 - a \cdot b + b^2), \text{ where } a \text{ is } x \text{ and } b \text{ is } 2.$$

$$x^3 + 8 = x^3 + 2^3 = (x + 2)(x^2 - x \cdot 2 + 2^2)$$

Thus, $x^3 + 8 = (x + 2)(x^2 - 2x + 4)$

● **Work Practice 1**

PRACTICE 1

Factor: $z^3 + 27$

Example 2 Factor: $p^3 + 27q^3$

Solution:

$$p^3 + 27q^3 = p^3 + (3q)^3$$
$$= (p + 3q)[p^2 - (p)(3q) + (3q)^2]$$
$$= (p + 3q)(p^2 - 3pq + 9q^2)$$

● **Work Practice 2**

PRACTICE 2

Factor: $x^3 + 64y^3$

Example 3 Factor: $y^3 - 64$

Solution: This is a difference of cubes since $y^3 - 64 = y^3 - 4^3$.

From $a^3 - b^3 = (a - b)(a^2 + a \cdot b + b^2)$ we have that

$$y^3 - 4^3 = (y - 4)(y^2 + y \cdot 4 + 4^2)$$
$$= (y - 4)(y^2 + 4y + 16)$$

● **Work Practice 3**

PRACTICE 3

Factor: $y^3 - 8$

Answers
1. $(z + 3)(z^2 - 3z + 9)$
2. $(x + 4y)(x^2 - 4xy + 16y^2)$
3. $(y - 2)(y^2 + 2y + 4)$

Helpful Hint

When factoring sums or differences of cubes, be sure to notice the sign patterns.

Same sign

$$x^3 + y^3 = (x + y)(x^2 - xy + y^2)$$

Opposite sign

Always positive

Same sign

$$x^3 - y^3 = (x - y)(x^2 + xy + y^2)$$

Opposite sign

PRACTICE 4

Factor: $27a^2 - b^3a^2$

Example 4   Factor: $125q^2 - n^3q^2$

Solution: First we factor out a common factor of q^2.

$$125q^2 - n^3q^2 = q^2(125 - n^3)$$
$$= q^2(5^3 - n^3)$$

Opposite sign   Positive

$$= q^2(5 - n)[5^2 + (5)(n) + (n^2)]$$
$$= q^2(5 - n)(25 + 5n + n^2)$$

Thus, $125q^2 - n^3q^2 = q^2(5 - n)(25 + 5n + n^2)$. The trinomial $25 + 5n + n^2$ cannot be factored further.

● **Work Practice 4**

Answers

4. $a^2(3 - b)(9 + 3b + b^2)$

Vocabulary and Readiness Check

Write each term as a square. For example, $25x^2$ as a square is $(5x)^2$.

1. $81y^2$ **2.** $4z^2$ **3.** $64x^6$ **4.** $49y^6$

Write each number or term as a cube.

5. 125 **6.** 216 **7.** $8x^3$ **8.** $27y^3$ **9.** $64x^6$ **10.** x^3y^6

9.6 Exercise Set

Objective A *Factor. See Examples 1 through 4.*

1. $x^3 + 27$ **2.** $y^3 + 1$ **3.** $z^3 - 1$

4. $x^3 - 8$ **5.** $m^3 + n^3$ **6.** $p^3 + 125q^3$

7. $27y^2 - x^3y^2$ **8.** $64q^2 - q^2p^3$ **9.** $8ab^3 + 27a^4$

10. $a^3b + 8b^4$ **11.** $250y^3 - 16x^3$ **12.** $54y^3 - 128$

Objective A Mixed Practice *Factor completely. See Examples 1 through 4.*

13. $x^2 - 12x + 36$ **14.** $x^2 - 18x + 81$ **15.** $18x^2y - 2y$

16. $12xy^2 - 108x$ **17.** $9x^2 - 49$ **18.** $25x^2 - 4$

19. $x^4 - 1$ **20.** $x^4 - 256$

21. $x^6 - y^3$ **22.** $x^3 - y^6$

23. $8x^3 + 27y^3$ **24.** $125x^3 + 8y^3$

25. $4x^2 + 4x + 1 - z^2$ **26.** $9y^2 + 12y + 4 - x^2$

27. $3x^6y^2 + 81y^2$ **28.** $x^2y^9 + x^2y^3$

29. $n^3 - \dfrac{1}{27}$ **30.** $p^3 + \dfrac{1}{125}$

31. $-16y^2 + 64$

32. $-12y^2 + 108$

33. $x^2 - 10x + 25 - y^2$

34. $x^2 - 18x + 81 - y^2$

35. $a^3b^3 + 125$

36. $x^3y^3 + 216$

37. $\dfrac{x^2}{25} - \dfrac{y^2}{9}$

38. $\dfrac{a^2}{4} - \dfrac{b^2}{49}$

39. $(x + y)^3 + 125$

40. $(r + s)^3 + 27$

Review

Solve each equation.

41. $x - 5 = 0$

42. $x + 7 = 0$

43. $3x + 1 = 0$

44. $5x - 15 = 0$

45. $-2x = 0$

46. $3x = 0$

47. $-5x + 25 = 0$

48. $-4x - 16 = 0$

Concept Extensions

Determine whether each polynomial is factored completely or not. See the Concept Check in this section.

49. $5x(x^2 - 4)$

50. $x^2y^2(x^3 - y^3)$

51. $7y(a^2 + a + 1)$

52. $9z(x^2 + 4)$

△ **53.** A manufacturer of metal washers needs to determine the cross-sectional area of each washer. If the outer radius of the washer is R and the radius of the hole is r, express the area of the washer as a polynomial. Factor this polynomial completely.

△ **54.** Express the area of the shaded region as a polynomial. Factor the polynomial completely.

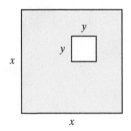

Express the volume of each solid as a polynomial. To do so, subtract the volume of the "hole" from the volume of the larger solid. Then factor the resulting polynomial.

△ **55.**

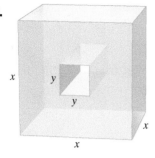

△ **56.**

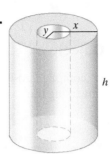

Find the value of c that makes each trinomial a perfect square trinomial.

57. $x^2 + 6x + c$ **58.** $y^2 + 10y + c$ **59.** $m^2 - 14m + c$ **60.** $n^2 - 2n + c$

61. Factor $x^6 - 1$ completely, using the following methods from this chapter.
   a. Factor the expression by treating it as the difference of two squares, $(x^3)^2 - 1^2$.
   b. Factor the expression by treating it as the difference of two cubes, $(x^2)^3 - 1^3$.
   c. Are the answers to parts **(a)** and **(b)** the same? Why or why not?

62. Factor $x^{12} - 1$ completely, using the following methods from this chapter:
   a. Factor the expression by treating it as the difference of two squares, $(x^3)^4 - 1^4$.
   b. Factor the expression by treating it as the difference of two cubes, $(x^4)^3 - 1^3$.
   c. Are the answers to parts (a) and (b) the same? Why or why not?

Factor. Assume that variables used as exponents represent positive integers.

63. $x^{2n} - 25$ **64.** $x^{2n} - 36$ **65.** $36x^{2n} - 49$

66. $25x^{2n} - 81$ **67.** $x^{4n} - 16$ **68.** $x^{4n} - 625$

9.7 FACTORING BY SUBSTITUTION

Objective Ⓐ Factoring by Substitution

A complicated-looking polynomial may be a simpler trinomial "in disguise." Revealing the simpler trinomial is possible by substitution.

PRACTICE 1

Factor: $3(z + 2)^2 - 19(z + 2) + 6$

Example 1 Factor: $2(a + 3)^2 - 5(a + 3) - 7$

Solution: The quantity $(a + 3)$ is in two of the terms of this polynomial. If we *substitute x* for $(a + 3)$, the result is the following simpler trinomial.

$$2(a + 3)^2 - 5(a + 3) - 7 \quad \text{Original trinomial}$$
$$\downarrow \qquad\qquad \downarrow$$
$$= \ 2(x)^2 \ - \ 5(x) \ - 7 \quad \text{Substitute } x \text{ for } (a + 3).$$

Now we can factor $2x^2 - 5x - 7$.

$$2x^2 - 5x - 7 = (2x - 7)(x + 1)$$

But the quantity in the original polynomial was $(a + 3)$, not x. Thus we need to reverse the substitution and replace x with $(a + 3)$.

$$(2x - 7)(x + 1) \qquad\qquad \text{Factored expression}$$
$$\swarrow \qquad\qquad \searrow$$
$$= [2(a + 3) - 7][(a + 3) + 1] \quad \text{Substitute } (a + 3) \text{ for } x.$$
$$= (2a + 6 - 7)(a + 3 + 1) \qquad \text{Remove inside parentheses.}$$
$$= (2a - 1)(a + 4) \qquad\qquad \text{Simplify.}$$

Thus, $2(a + 3)^2 - 5(a + 3) - 7 = (2a - 1)(a + 4)$.

● **Work Practice 1**

PRACTICE 2

Factor: $14x^4 + 23x^2 + 3$

Example 2 Factor: $5x^4 + 29x^2 - 42$

Solution: Again, substitution may help us factor this polynomial more easily. We will let $y = x^2$, so $y^2 = (x^2)^2$, or x^4. Then

$$5x^4 + 29x^2 - 42$$
becomes $\quad \downarrow \qquad \downarrow$
$$5y^2 + 29y - 42$$

which factors as

$$5y^2 + 29y - 42 = (5y - 6)(y + 7)$$

Now we replace y with x^2 to get

$$(5x^2 - 6)(x^2 + 7)$$

● **Work Practice 2**

Solve each exercise by guessing and checking.

1. Find two numbers whose product is 10 and whose sum is 7.

2. Find two numbers whose product is 12 and whose sum is 8.

3. Find two numbers whose product is 24 and whose sum is 11.

4. Find two numbers whose product is 30 and whose sum is 13.

9.7 Exercise Set

Objective A *Use substitution to factor each polynomial completely. See Examples 1 and 2.*

1. $x^4 + x^2 - 6$
2. $x^4 - x^2 - 20$
3. $(5x+1)^2 + 8(5x+1) + 7$

4. $(3x-1)^2 + 5(3x-1) + 6$
5. $x^6 - 7x^3 + 12$
6. $x^6 - 4x^3 - 12$

7. $(a+5)^2 - 5(a+5) - 24$
8. $(3c+6)^2 + 12(3c+6) - 28$

Objective A Mixed Practice *Factor each polynomial completely. See Examples 1 and 2.*

9. $x^2 - 24x - 81$
10. $x^2 - 48x - 100$
11. $x^2 - 15x - 54$
12. $x^2 - 15x + 54$

13. $3x^2 - 6x + 3$
14. $8x^2 - 8x + 2$
15. $3x^2 - 5x - 2$
16. $5x^2 - 14x - 3$

17. $8x^2 - 26x + 15$
18. $12x^2 - 17x + 6$
19. $18x^4 + 21x^3 + 6x^2$
20. $20x^5 + 54x^4 + 10x^3$

21. $x^2 + 8xz + 7z^2$
22. $a^2 - 2ab - 15b^2$
23. $x^2 - x - 12$
24. $x^2 + 4x - 5$

25. $3a^2 + 12ab + 12b^2$
26. $2x^2 + 16xy + 32y^2$
27. $x^2 + 4x + 5$
28. $x^2 + 5x + 8$

29. $2(x+4)^2 + 3(x+4) - 5$
30. $3(x+3)^2 + 2(x+3) - 5$
31. $6x^2 - 49x + 30$

32. $4x^2 - 39x + 27$
33. $x^4 - 5x^2 - 6$
34. $x^4 - 5x^2 + 6$

35. $6x^3 - x^2 - x$
36. $12x^3 + x^2 - x$
37. $12a^2 - 29ab + 15b^2$

38. $16y^2 + 6yx - 27x^2$
39. $9x^2 + 30x + 25$
40. $4x^2 + 12x + 9$

41. $3x^2y - 11xy + 8y$
42. $5xy^2 - 9xy + 4x$
43. $2x^2 + 2x - 12$

44. $3x^2 + 6x - 45$
45. $(x-4)^2 + 3(x-4) - 18$
46. $(x-3)^2 - 2(x-3) - 8$

47. $2x^6 + 3x^3 - 9$
48. $3x^6 - 14x^3 + 8$
49. $72xy^4 - 24xy^2z + 2xz^2$

50. $36xy^2 - 48xyz^2 + 16xz^4$
51. $2x^3y + 2x^2y - 12xy$
52. $3x^2y^3 + 6x^2y^2 - 45x^2y$

53. $x^2 + 6xy + 5y^2$
54. $x^2 + 6xy + 8y^2$

Review

Multiply.

55. $(x - 3)(x + 3)$

56. $(x - 4)(x + 4)$

57. $(2x + 1)^2$

58. $(3x + 5)^2$

59. $(x - 2)(x^2 + 2x + 4)$

60. $(y + 1)(y^2 - y + 1)$

Concept Extensions

61. Find all positive and negative integers b such that $x^2 + bx + 6$ is factorable.

62. Find all positive and negative integers b such that $x^2 + bx - 10$ is factorable.

△ **63.** The volume $V(x)$ of a box in terms of its height x is given by the function $V(x) = x^3 + 2x^2 - 8x$. Factor this expression for $V(x)$.

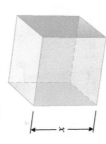

△ **64.** Based on your results from Exercise 63, find the length and width of the box if the height is 5 inches and the dimensions of the box are whole numbers.

65. Suppose that a movie is being filmed in New York City. An action shot requires an object to be thrown upward with an initial velocity of 80 feet per second off the top of 1 Madison Square Plaza, a height of 576 feet. The height $h(t)$ in feet of the object after t seconds is given by the function $h(t) = -16t^2 + 80t + 576$. (*Source: The World Almanac, 2001*)

a. Find the height of the object at $t = 0$ seconds, $t = 2$ seconds, $t = 4$ seconds, and $t = 6$ seconds.

b. Explain why the height of the object increases and then decreases as time passes.

c. Factor the polynomial $-16t^2 + 80t + 576$.

66. Suppose that an object is thrown upward with an initial velocity of 64 feet per second off the edge of a 960-foot-cliff. The height $h(t)$ in feet of the object after t seconds is given by the function

$$h(t) = -16t^2 + 64t + 960$$

a. Find the height of the object at $t = 0$ seconds, $t = 3$ seconds, $t = 6$ seconds, and $t = 9$ seconds.

b. Explain why the height of the object increases and then decreases as time passes.

c. Factor the polynomial $-16t^2 + 64t + 960$.

Factor. Assume that variables used as exponents represent positive integers.

67. $x^{2n} + 10x^n + 16$

68. $x^{2n} - 7x^n + 12$

69. $x^{2n} - 3x^n - 18$

70. $x^{2n} + 7x^n - 18$

71. $2x^{2n} + 11x^n + 5$

72. $3x^{2n} - 8x^n + 4$

73. $4x^{2n} - 12x^n + 9$

74. $9x^{2n} + 24x^n + 16$

Recall that a graphing calculator may be used to check addition, subtraction, and multiplication of polynomials. In the same manner, a graphing calculator may be used to check factoring of polynomials in one variable. For example, to see that

$$2x^3 - 9x^2 - 5x = x(2x + 1)(x - 5)$$

graph $Y_1 = 2x^3 - 9x^2 - 5x$ *and* $Y_2 = x(2x + 1)(x - 5)$. *Then trace along both graphs to see that they coincide. Factor the following and use this method to check your results.*

75. $x^4 + 6x^3 + 5x^2$

76. $x^3 + 6x^2 + 8x$

77. $30x^3 + 9x^2 - 3x$

78. $-6x^4 + 10x^3 - 4x^2$

576 ft

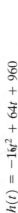

9.8 SOLVING QUADRATIC EQUATIONS BY FACTORING

Objectives

A Solve Quadratic Equations by Factoring.

B Solve Equations with Degree Greater than Two by Factoring.

In this section, we introduce a new type of equation—the **quadratic equation.**

Quadratic Equation

A quadratic equation is one that can be written in the form

$$ax^2 + bx + c = 0$$

where a, b, and c are real numbers and $a \neq 0$.

Some examples of quadratic equations are shown below.

$$x^2 - 9x - 22 = 0 \qquad 4x^2 - 28 = -49 \qquad x(2x - 7) = 4$$

The form $ax^2 + bx + c = 0$ is called the **standard form** of a quadratic equation. The quadratic equation $x^2 - 9x - 22 = 0$ is the only equation above that is in standard form.

Quadratic equations model many real-life situations. For example, let's suppose we want to know how long before a person diving from a 144-foot cliff reaches the ocean. The answer to this question is found by solving the quadratic equation $-16t^2 + 144 = 0$. (See Example 1 in Section 9.9.)

144 feet

Objective **A** Solving Quadratic Equations by Factoring

Some quadratic equations can be solved by making use of factoring and the **zero-factor property.**

Zero-Factor Property

If a and b are real numbers and if $ab = 0$, then $a = 0$ or $b = 0$.

In other words, if the product of two numbers is 0, then at least one of the numbers must be 0.

Example 1 Solve: $(x - 3)(x + 1) = 0$

Solution: If this equation is to be a true statement, then either the factor $x - 3$ must be 0 or the factor $x + 1$ must be 0. In other words, either

$$x - 3 = 0 \qquad \text{or} \qquad x + 1 = 0$$

If we solve these two linear equations, we have

$$x = 3 \qquad \text{or} \qquad x = -1$$

Continued on next page

PRACTICE 1

Solve: $(x - 7)(x + 2) = 0$

Answer
1. 7 and -2

Thus, 3 and -1 are both solutions of the equation $(x - 3)(x + 1) = 0$. To check, we replace x with 3 in the original equation. Then we replace x with -1 in the original equation.

Check:

$$(x - 3)(x + 1) = 0 \qquad\qquad (x - 3)(x + 1) = 0$$

$(3 - 3)(3 + 1) \stackrel{?}{=} 0$ _{Replace x with 3.} $(-1 - 3)(-1 + 1) \stackrel{?}{=} 0$ _{Replace x with -1.}

$0(4) = 0$ _{True} $(-4)(0) = 0$ _{True}

The solutions are 3 and -1.

● **Work Practice 1**

Helpful Hint

The zero-factor property says that *if a product is 0, then a factor is 0.*

If $a \cdot b = 0$, then $a = 0$ or $b = 0$.

If $x(x + 5) = 0$, then $x = 0$ or $x + 5 = 0$.

If $(x + 7)(2x - 3) = 0$, then $x + 7 = 0$ or $2x - 3 = 0$.

Use this property only when the product is 0. For example, if $a \cdot b = 8$, we do not know the value of a or b. The values may be $a = 2$, $b = 4$ or $a = 8$, $b = 1$, or any other two numbers whose product is 8.

PRACTICE 2

Solve: $(x - 10)(3x + 1) = 0$

Example 2   Solve: $(x - 5)(2x + 7) = 0$

Solution: The product is 0. By the zero-factor property, this is true only when a factor is 0. To solve, we set each factor equal to 0 and solve the resulting linear equations.

$$(x - 5)(2x + 7) = 0$$
$$x - 5 = 0 \quad \text{or} \quad 2x + 7 = 0$$
$$x = 5 \qquad\qquad 2x = -7$$
$$x = -\frac{7}{2}$$

Check: Let $x = 5$.

$$(x - 5)(2x + 7) = 0$$
$$(5 - 5)(2 \cdot 5 + 7) \stackrel{?}{=} 0 \quad \text{Replace } x \text{ with 5.}$$
$$0 \cdot 17 \stackrel{?}{=} 0$$
$$0 = 0 \quad \text{True}$$

Let $x = -\dfrac{7}{2}$.

$$(x - 5)(2x + 7) = 0$$
$$\left(-\frac{7}{2} - 5\right)\left(2\left(-\frac{7}{2}\right) + 7\right) \stackrel{?}{=} 0 \quad \text{Replace } x \text{ with } -\frac{7}{2}.$$
$$\left(-\frac{17}{2}\right)(-7 + 7) \stackrel{?}{=} 0$$
$$\left(-\frac{17}{2}\right) \cdot 0 \stackrel{?}{=} 0$$
$$0 = 0 \quad \text{True}$$

The solutions are 5 and $-\dfrac{7}{2}$.

● **Work Practice 2**

Answer

2. 10 and $-\dfrac{1}{3}$

Example 3 Solve: $x(5x - 2) = 0$

Solution: $x(5x - 2) = 0$

$x = 0$ or $5x - 2 = 0$ Use the zero-factor property.

$$5x = 2$$

$$x = \frac{2}{5}$$

Check these solutions in the original equation. The solutions are 0 and $\frac{2}{5}$.

● **Work Practice 3**

PRACTICE 3

Solve each equation.
a. $y(y + 3) = 0$
b. $x(4x - 3) = 0$

Example 4 Solve: $x^2 - 9x - 22 = 0$

Solution: One side of the equation is 0. However, to use the zero-factor property, one side of the equation must be 0 *and* the other side must be written as a product (must be factored). Thus, we must first factor this polynomial.

$$x^2 - 9x - 22 = 0$$
$$(x - 11)(x + 2) = 0$$ Factor.

Now we can apply the zero-factor property.

$x - 11 = 0$ or $x + 2 = 0$
$x = 11$ $x = -2$

Check: Let $x = 11$.   Let $x = -2$.

$x^2 - 9x - 22 = 0$ $x^2 - 9x - 22 = 0$
$11^2 - 9 \cdot 11 - 22 \stackrel{?}{=} 0$ $(-2)^2 - 9(-2) - 22 \stackrel{?}{=} 0$
$121 - 99 - 22 \stackrel{?}{=} 0$ $4 + 18 - 22 \stackrel{?}{=} 0$
$22 - 22 \stackrel{?}{=} 0$ $22 - 22 \stackrel{?}{=} 0$
$0 = 0$ True $0 = 0$ True

The solutions are 11 and -2.

● **Work Practice 4**

PRACTICE 4

Solve: $x^2 - 3x - 18 = 0$

Example 5 Solve: $4x^2 - 28x = -49$

Solution: First we rewrite the equation in standard form so that one side is 0. Then we factor the polynomial.

$$4x^2 - 28x = -49$$
$$4x^2 - 28x + 49 = 0$$ Write in standard form by adding 49 to both sides.
$$(2x - 7)(2x - 7) = 0$$ Factor.

Next we use the zero-factor property and set each factor equal to 0. Since the factors are the same, the related equations will give the same solution.

$2x - 7 = 0$ or $2x - 7 = 0$ Set each factor equal to 0.
$2x = 7$ $2x = 7$ Solve.
$x = \frac{7}{2}$ $x = \frac{7}{2}$

Check this solution in the original equation. The solution is $\frac{7}{2}$.

● **Work Practice 5**

PRACTICE 5

Solve: $9x^2 - 24x = -16$

Answers
3. a. 0 and -3 **b.** 0 and $\frac{3}{4}$
4. 6 and -3 **5.** $\frac{4}{3}$

The following steps may be used to solve a quadratic equation by factoring.

> **To Solve Quadratic Equations by Factoring**
>
> **Step 1:** Write the equation in standard form so that one side of the equation is 0.
>
> **Step 2:** Factor the quadratic equation completely.
>
> **Step 3:** Set each factor containing a variable equal to 0.
>
> **Step 4:** Solve the resulting equations.
>
> **Step 5:** Check each solution in the original equation.

Since it is not always possible to factor a quadratic polynomial, not all quadratic equations can be solved by factoring.

Example 6 Solve: $x(2x - 7) = 4$

Solution: First we write the equation in standard form; then we factor.

$$x(2x - 7) = 4$$
$$2x^2 - 7x = 4 \qquad \text{Multiply.}$$
$$2x^2 - 7x - 4 = 0 \qquad \text{Write in standard form.}$$
$$(2x + 1)(x - 4) = 0 \qquad \text{Factor.}$$
$$2x + 1 = 0 \quad \text{or} \quad x - 4 = 0 \qquad \text{Set each factor equal to zero.}$$
$$2x = -1 \qquad\qquad x = 4 \qquad \text{Solve.}$$
$$x = -\frac{1}{2}$$

Check the solutions in the original equation. The solutions are $-\frac{1}{2}$ and 4.

● **Work Practice 6**

Helpful Hint

To solve the equation $x(2x - 7) = 4$, do **not** set each factor equal to 4. Remember that to apply the zero-factor property, one side of the equation must be 0 and the other side of the equation must be in factored form.

✔ **Concept Check** Explain the error and solve the equation correctly.

$$(x - 3)(x + 1) = 5$$
$$x - 3 = 0 \quad \text{or} \quad x + 1 = 0$$
$$x = 3 \quad \text{or} \qquad x = -1$$

Answers

6. **a.** 5 and −1   **b.** $\frac{2}{3}$ and −3

✔ **Concept Check Answer**
To use the zero-factor property, one side of the equation must be 0, not 5. Correctly, $(x - 3)(x + 1) = 5$, $x^2 - 2x - 3 = 5$, $x^2 - 2x - 8 = 0$, $(x - 4)(x + 2) = 0$, $x - 4 = 0$ or $x + 2 = 0$, $x = 4$ or $x = -2$.

Objective Ⓑ **Solving Equations with Degree Greater than Two by Factoring**

Some equations with degree greater than 2 can be solved by factoring and then using the zero-factor property.

Example 7 Solve: $3x^3 - 12x = 0$

Solution: To factor the left side of the equation, we begin by factoring out the greatest common factor, $3x$.

$$3x^3 - 12x = 0$$
$$3x(x^2 - 4) = 0 \quad \text{Factor out the GCF, } 3x.$$
$$3x(x + 2)(x - 2) = 0 \quad \text{Factor } x^2 - 4, \text{ a difference of two squares.}$$
$$3x = 0 \quad \text{or} \quad x + 2 = 0 \quad \text{or} \quad x - 2 = 0 \quad \text{Set each factor equal to 0.}$$
$$x = 0 \qquad\qquad x = -2 \qquad\qquad x = 2 \quad \text{Solve.}$$

Thus, the equation $3x^3 - 12x = 0$ has three solutions: $0, -2$, and 2.

Check: Replace x with each solution in the original equation.

Let $x = 0$.
$$3(0)^3 - 12(0) \overset{?}{=} 0$$
$$0 = 0 \quad \text{True}$$

Let $x = -2$.
$$3(-2)^3 - 12(-2) \overset{?}{=} 0$$
$$3(-8) + 24 \overset{?}{=} 0$$
$$0 = 0 \quad \text{True}$$

Let $x = 2$.
$$3(2)^3 - 12(2) \overset{?}{=} 0$$
$$3(8) - 24 \overset{?}{=} 0$$
$$0 = 0 \quad \text{True}$$

The solutions are $0, -2$, and 2.

● **Work Practice 7**

PRACTICE 7

Solve: $2x^3 - 18x = 0$

Example 8 Solve: $(5x - 1)(2x^2 + 15x + 18) = 0$

Solution:

$$(5x - 1)(2x^2 + 15x + 18) = 0$$
$$(5x - 1)(2x + 3)(x + 6) = 0 \qquad \text{Factor the trinomial.}$$
$$5x - 1 = 0 \quad \text{or} \quad 2x + 3 = 0 \quad \text{or} \quad x + 6 = 0 \qquad \text{Set each factor equal to 0.}$$
$$5x = 1 \qquad\qquad 2x = -3 \qquad\qquad x = -6 \quad \text{Solve.}$$
$$x = \frac{1}{5} \qquad\qquad x = -\frac{3}{2}$$

Check each solution in the original equation. The solutions are $\frac{1}{5}, -\frac{3}{2}$, and -6.

● **Work Practice 8**

PRACTICE 8

Solve:
$(x + 3)(3x^2 - 20x - 7) = 0$

Answers

7. $0, 3$, and -3 **8.** $-3, -\frac{1}{3}$, and 7

Vocabulary and Readiness Check

Use the choices below to fill in each blank. Not all choices will be used.

$-3, 5$ $a = 0$ or $b = 0$ 0 linear

$3, -5$ quadratic 1

1. An equation that can be written in the form $ax^2 + bx + c = 0$ (with $a \neq 0$) is called a _____ equation.

2. If the product of two numbers is 0, then at least one of the numbers must be _____.

3. The solutions to $(x - 3)(x + 5) = 0$ are _____.

4. If $a \cdot b = 0$, then _____.

9.8 Exercise Set

PRACTICE   WATCH   DOWNLOAD   READ   REVIEW

Objective A *Solve each equation. See Examples 1 through 3.*

1. $(x - 2)(x + 1) = 0$

2. $(x + 3)(x + 2) = 0$

3. $(x - 6)(x - 7) = 0$

4. $(x + 4)(x - 10) = 0$

5. $(x + 9)(x + 17) = 0$

6. $(x - 11)(x - 1) = 0$

7. $x(x + 6) = 0$

8. $x(x - 7) = 0$

9. $3x(x - 8) = 0$

10. $2x(x + 12) = 0$

11. $(2x + 3)(4x - 5) = 0$

12. $(3x - 2)(5x + 1) = 0$

13. $(2x - 7)(7x + 2) = 0$

14. $(9x + 1)(4x - 3) = 0$

15. $\left(x - \dfrac{1}{2}\right)\left(x + \dfrac{1}{3}\right) = 0$

16. $\left(x + \dfrac{2}{9}\right)\left(x - \dfrac{1}{4}\right) = 0$

17. $(x + 0.2)(x + 1.5) = 0$

18. $(x + 1.7)(x + 2.3) = 0$

Solve. See Examples 4 through 6.

19. $x^2 - 13x + 36 = 0$

20. $x^2 + 2x - 63 = 0$

21. $x^2 + 2x - 8 = 0$

22. $x^2 - 5x + 6 = 0$

23. $x^2 - 7x = 0$

24. $x^2 - 3x = 0$

25. $x^2 + 20x = 0$

26. $x^2 + 15x = 0$

27. $x^2 = 16$

28. $x^2 = 9$

29. $x^2 - 4x = 32$

30. $x^2 - 5x = 24$

31. $(x + 4)(x - 9) = 4x$

32. $(x + 3)(x + 8) = x$

33. $x(3x - 1) = 14$

34. $x(4x - 11) = 3$

35. $3x^2 + 19x - 72 = 0$

36. $36x^2 + x - 21 = 0$

Copyright 2011 Pearson Education, Inc.

Objectives Ⓐ Ⓑ and Section 6.3 **Mixed Practice** *Solve each equation. See Examples 1 through 8. (A few exercises are linear equations.)*

37. $4x^3 - x = 0$

38. $4y^3 - 36y = 0$

39. $4(x - 7) = 6$

40. $5(3 - 4x) = 9$

41. $(4x - 3)(16x^2 - 24x + 9) = 0$

42. $(2x + 5)(4x^2 + 20x + 25) = 0$

43. $4y^2 - 1 = 0$

44. $4y^2 - 81 = 0$

45. $(2x + 3)(2x^2 - 5x - 3) = 0$

46. $(2x - 9)(x^2 + 5x - 36) = 0$

47. $x^2 - 15 = -2x$

48. $x^2 - 26 = -11x$

49. $30x^2 - 11x = 30$

50. $9x^2 + 7x = 2$

51. $5x^2 - 6x - 8 = 0$

52. $12x^2 + 7x - 12 = 0$

53. $6y^2 - 22y - 40 = 0$

54. $3x^2 - 6x - 9 = 0$

55. $(y - 2)(y + 3) = 6$

56. $(y - 5)(y - 2) = 28$

57. $x^3 - 12x^2 + 32x = 0$

58. $x^3 - 14x^2 + 49x = 0$

59. $x^2 + 14x + 49 = 0$

60. $x^2 + 22x + 121 = 0$

61. $12y = 8y^2$

62. $9y = 6y^2$

63. $7x^3 - 7x = 0$

64. $3x^3 - 27x = 0$

65. $3x^2 + 8x - 11 = 13 - 6x$

66. $2x^2 + 12x - 1 = 4 + 3x$

67. $3x^2 - 20x = -4x^2 - 7x - 6$

68. $4x^2 - 20x = -5x^2 - 6x - 5$

Review

Perform each indicated operation. Write all results in lowest terms. See Sections 2.4 and 2.8.

69. $\dfrac{3}{5} + \dfrac{4}{9}$

70. $\dfrac{2}{3} + \dfrac{3}{7}$

71. $\dfrac{7}{10} - \dfrac{5}{12}$

72. $\dfrac{5}{9} - \dfrac{5}{12}$

73. $\dfrac{4}{5} \cdot \dfrac{7}{8}$

74. $\dfrac{3}{7} \cdot \dfrac{12}{17}$

Concept Extensions

For Exercises 75 and 76, see the Concept Check in this section.

75. Explain the error and solve correctly:

$$x(x - 2) = 8$$
$$x = 8 \quad \text{or} \quad x - 2 = 8$$
$$x = 10$$

76. Explain the error and solve correctly:

$$(x - 4)(x + 2) = 0$$
$$x = -4 \quad \text{or} \quad x = 2$$

77. Write a quadratic equation that has two solutions, 6 and −1. Leave the polynomial in the equation in factored form.

78. Write a quadratic equation that has two solutions, 0 and −2. Leave the polynomial in the equation in factored form.

79. Write a quadratic equation in standard form that has two solutions, 5 and 7.

80. Write an equation that has three solutions, 0, 1, and 2.

81. A compass is accidentally thrown upward and out of an air balloon at a height of 300 feet. The height, y, of the compass at time x is given by the equation $y = -16x^2 + 20x + 300$.

300 ft

a. Find the height of the compass at the given times by filling in the table below.

Time, x (in seconds)	0	1	2	3	4	5	6
Height, y (in feet)							

b. Use the table to determine when the compass strikes the ground.

c. Use the table to approximate the maximum height of the compass.

82. A rocket is fired upward from the ground with an initial velocity of 100 feet per second. The height, y, of the rocket at any time x is given by the equation $y = -16x^2 + 100x$.

y

a. Find the height of the rocket at the given times by filling in the table below.

Time, x (in seconds)	0	1	2	3	4	5	6	7
Height, y (in feet)								

b. Use the table to determine between what two whole-numbered seconds the rocket strikes the ground.

c. Use the table to approximate the maximum height of the rocket.

Solve each equation.

83. $(x - 3)(3x + 4) = (x + 2)(x - 6)$

84. $(2x - 3)(x + 6) = (x - 9)(x + 2)$

85. $(2x - 3)(x + 8) = (x - 6)(x + 4)$

86. $(x + 6)(x - 6) = (2x - 9)(x + 4)$

9.9 QUADRATIC EQUATIONS AND PROBLEM SOLVING

Objective

A Solve Problems That Can Be Modeled by Quadratic Equations.

Objective **A** Solving Problems Modeled by Quadratic Equations

Some problems may be modeled by quadratic equations. To solve these problems, we use the same problem-solving steps that were introduced in Section 1.8. When solving these problems, keep in mind that a solution of an equation that models a problem may not be a solution to the problem. For example, a person's age or the length of a rectangle is always a positive number. Thus we discard solutions that do not make sense as solutions of the problem.

Example 1 Finding Free-Fall Time

Since the 1940s, one of the top tourist attractions in Acapulco, Mexico, is watching the cliff divers off La Quebrada. The divers' platform is about 144 feet above the sea. These divers must time their descent just right, since they land in the crashing Pacific, in an inlet that is at most $9\frac{1}{2}$ feet deep. Neglecting air resistance, the height h in feet of a cliff diver above the ocean after t seconds is given by the quadratic equation $h = -16t^2 + 144$.

PRACTICE 1

Cliff divers also frequent the falls at Waimea Falls Park in Oahu, Hawaii. Here, a diver can jump from a ledge 64 feet up the waterfall into a rocky pool below. Neglecting air resistance, the height of a diver above the pool after t seconds is $h = -16t^2 + 64$. Find how long it takes the diver to reach the pool.

Find out how long it takes the diver to reach the ocean.

Solution:

1. UNDERSTAND. Read and reread the problem. Then draw a picture of the problem.

    The equation $h = -16t^2 + 144$ models the height of the falling diver at time t. Familiarize yourself with this equation by finding the height of the diver at time $t = 1$ second and $t = 2$ seconds.

    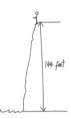

    144 feet

    When $t = 1$ second, the height of the diver is $h = -16(1)^2 + 144 = 128$ feet.
    When $t = 2$ seconds, the height of the diver is $h = -16(2)^2 + 144 = 80$ feet.

2. TRANSLATE. To find out how long it takes the diver to reach the ocean, we want to know the value of t for which $h = 0$.

3. SOLVE. Solve the equation.

    $$0 = -16t^2 + 144$$
    $$0 = -16(t^2 - 9) \qquad \text{Factor out } -16.$$
    $$0 = -16(t - 3)(t + 3) \qquad \text{Factor completely.}$$
    $$t - 3 = 0 \quad \text{or} \quad t + 3 = 0 \qquad \text{Set each factor containing a variable equal to 0.}$$
    $$t = 3 \quad \text{or} \qquad\quad t = -3 \quad \text{Solve.}$$

4. INTERPRET. Since the time t cannot be negative, the proposed solution is 3 seconds.

Check: Verify that the height of the diver when t is 3 seconds is 0.

When $t = 3$ seconds, $h = -16(3)^2 + 144 = -144 + 144 = 0$.

● Work Practice 1

Answer
1. 2 sec

PRACTICE 2

The square of a number minus twice the number is 63. Find the number.

Example 2 Finding a Number

The square of a number plus three times the number is 70. Find the number.

Solution:

1. **UNDERSTAND.** Read and reread the problem. Suppose that the number is 5. The square of 5 is 5^2 or 25. Three times 5 is 15. Then $25 + 15 = 40$, not 70, so the number must be greater than 5. Remember, the purpose of proposing a number, such as 5, is to better understand the problem. Now that we do, we will let x = the number.

2. **TRANSLATE.**

the square of a number	plus	three times the number	is	70
↓	↓	↓	↓	↓
x^2	$+$	$3x$	$=$	70

3. **SOLVE.**

$$x^2 + 3x = 70$$

$$x^2 + 3x - 70 = 0 \qquad \text{Subtract 70 from both sides.}$$

$$(x + 10)(x - 7) = 0 \qquad \text{Factor.}$$

$$x + 10 = 0 \quad \text{or} \quad x - 7 = 0 \quad \text{Set each factor equal to 0.}$$

$$x = -10 \qquad\qquad x = 7 \quad \text{Solve.}$$

4. **INTERPRET.**

Check: The square of -10 is $(-10)^2$, or 100. Three times -10 is $3(-10)$ or -30. Then $100 + (-30) = 70$, the correct sum, so -10 checks.

The square of 7 is 7^2 or 49. Three times 7 is $3(7)$, or 21. Then $49 + 21 = 70$, the correct sum, so 7 checks.

State: There are two numbers. They are -10 and 7.

● **Work Practice 2**

PRACTICE 3

The length of a rectangular garden is 5 feet more than its width. The area of the garden is 176 square feet. Find the length and the width of the garden.

Height = $2x - 2$

Base = x

△ **Example 3** Finding the Dimensions of a Sail

The height of a triangular sail is 2 meters less than twice the length of the base. If the sail has an area of 30 square meters, find the length of its base and the height.

Solution:

1. **UNDERSTAND.** Read and reread the problem. Since we are finding the length of the base and the height, we let

x = the length of the base

Since the height is 2 meters less than twice the length of the base,

$2x - 2$ = the height

An illustration is shown in the margin.

2. **TRANSLATE.** We are given that the area of the triangle is 30 square meters, so we use the formula for area of a triangle.

area of triangle	=	$\frac{1}{2}$	·	base	·	height
↓		↓		↓		↓
30	=	$\frac{1}{2}$	·	x	·	$(2x - 2)$

Answers

2. 9 and -7

3. length: 16 ft; width: 11 ft

3. SOLVE. Now we solve the quadratic equation.

$$30 = \frac{1}{2}x(2x - 2)$$

$30 = x^2 - x$ Multiply.

$0 = x^2 - x - 30$ Write in standard form.

$0 = (x - 6)(x + 5)$ Factor.

$x - 6 = 0$ or $x + 5 = 0$ Set each factor equal to 0.

     $x = 6$ $x = -5$

4. INTERPRET. Since x represents the length of the base, we discard the solution -5. The base of a triangle cannot be negative. The base is then 6 meters and the height is $2(6) - 2 = 10$ meters.

Check: To check this problem, we recall that

$$\text{area} = \frac{1}{2} \cdot \text{base} \cdot \text{height or}$$

$$30 \overset{?}{=} \frac{1}{2}(6)(10)$$

$30 = 30$ True

State: The base of the triangular sail is 6 meters and the height is 10 meters.

 Work Practice 3

The next example has to do with consecutive integers. Study the following diagrams for a review of consecutive integers.

Examples

If x is the first integer, then consecutive integers are

$x, x + 1, x + 2, \ldots$

If x is the first even integer, then consecutive even integers are

$x, x + 2, x + 4, \ldots$

If x is the first odd integer, then consecutive odd integers are

$x, x + 2, x + 4, \ldots$

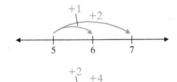

 Example 4 Finding Consecutive Even Integers

Find two consecutive even integers whose product is 34 more than their sum.

Solution:

1. UNDERSTAND. Read and reread the problem. Let's just choose two consecutive even integers to help us better understand the problem. Let's choose 10 and 12. Their product is $10(12) = 120$ and their sum is $10 + 12 = 22$. The product is $120 - 22$, or 98 greater than the sum. Thus our guess is incorrect, but we have a better understanding of this example.

    Let's let x and $x + 2$ be the consecutive even integers.

2. TRANSLATE.

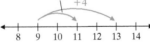

Continued on next page

PRACTICE 4

Find two consecutive odd integers whose product is 23 more than their sum.

Answer
4. 5 and 7 or -5 and -3

3. SOLVE. Now we solve the equation.

$$x(x + 2) = x + (x + 2) + 34$$

$x^2 + 2x = x + x + 2 + 34$	Multiply.
$x^2 + 2x = 2x + 36$	Combine like terms.
$x^2 - 36 = 0$	Write in standard form.
$(x + 6)(x - 6) = 0$	Factor.
$x + 6 = 0$ or $x - 6 = 0$	Set each factor equal to 0.
$x = -6$ $x = 6$	Solve.

4. INTERPRET. If $x = -6$, then $x + 2 = -6 + 2$, or -4.
         If $x = 6$, then $x + 2 = 6 + 2$, or 8.

Check: $-6, -4$

$-6(-4) \overset{?}{=} -6 + (-4) + 34$

$24 \overset{?}{=} -10 + 34$

$24 = 24$ True

$6, 8$

$6(8) \overset{?}{=} 6 + 8 + 34$

$48 \overset{?}{=} 14 + 34$

$48 = 48$ True

State: The two consecutive even integers are -6 and -4 or 6 and 8.

● **Work Practice 4**

The next example makes use of the **Pythagorean theorem**. Before we review this theorem, recall that a **right triangle** is a triangle that contains a 90° or right angle. The **hypotenuse** of a right triangle is the side opposite the right angle and is the longest side of the triangle. The **legs** of a right triangle are the other sides of the triangle.

> **Helpful Hint**
>
> If you use this formula, don't forget that c represents the length of the hypotenuse.

Pythagorean Theorem

In a right triangle, the sum of the squares of the lengths of the two legs is equal to the square of the length of the hypotenuse.

$$(\text{leg})^2 + (\text{leg})^2 = (\text{hypotenuse})^2 \quad \text{or} \quad a^2 + b^2 = c^2$$

Leg b Hypotenuse c

Leg a

PRACTICE 5

The length of one leg of a right triangle is 7 meters less than the length of the other leg. The length of the hypotenuse is 13 meters. Find the lengths of the legs.

Example 5 Finding the Dimensions of a Triangle

Find the lengths of the sides of a right triangle if the lengths can be expressed as three consecutive even integers.

Solution:

1. UNDERSTAND. Read and reread the problem. Let's suppose that the length of one leg of the right triangle is 4 units. Then the other leg is the next even integer, or 6 units, and the hypotenuse of the triangle is the next even integer, or 8 units. Remember that the hypotenuse is the longest side. Let's see if a triangle with sides of these lengths forms a right triangle. To do this, we check to see whether the Pythagorean theorem holds true.

$$4^2 + 6^2 \overset{?}{=} 8^2$$

$$16 + 36 \overset{?}{=} 64$$

$$52 = 64 \quad \text{False}$$

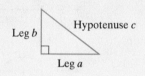

4 units   8 units

6 units

Answer

5. 5 meters, 12 meters

Our proposed numbers do not check, but we now have a better understanding of the problem.

We let x, $x + 2$, and $x + 4$ be three consecutive even integers. Since these integers represent lengths of the sides of a right triangle, we have the following.

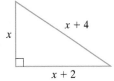

x = one leg

$x + 2$ = other leg

$x + 4$ = hypotenuse (longest side)

2. TRANSLATE. By the Pythagorean theorem, we have that

$$(\text{leg})^2 + (\text{leg})^2 = (\text{hypotenuse})^2$$

$$(x)^2 + (x + 2)^2 = (x + 4)^2$$

3. SOLVE. Now we solve the equation.

$$x^2 + (x + 2)^2 = (x + 4)^2$$

$x^2 + x^2 + 4x + 4 = x^2 + 8x + 16$	Multiply.
$2x^2 + 4x + 4 = x^2 + 8x + 16$	Combine like terms.
$x^2 - 4x - 12 = 0$	Write in standard form.
$(x - 6)(x + 2) = 0$	Factor.
$x - 6 = 0$ or $x + 2 = 0$	Set each factor equal to 0.
$x = 6$ $x = -2$	

5. INTERPRET. We discard $x = -2$ since length cannot be negative. If $x = 6$, then $x + 2 = 8$ and $x + 4 = 10$.

Check: Verify that

$$(\text{leg})^2 + (\text{leg})^2 = (\text{hypotenuse})^2$$

$$6^2 + 8^2 \stackrel{?}{=} 10^2$$

$$36 + 64 \stackrel{?}{=} 100$$

$$100 = 100 \qquad \text{True}$$

State: The sides of the right triangle have lengths 6 units, 8 units, and 10 units.

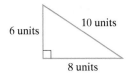

● **Work Practice 5**

Objective Ⓐ *See Examples 1 through 5 for all exercises.*

Translating *For Exercises 1 through 6, represent each given condition using a single variable, x.*

△ **1.** The length and width of a rectangle whose length is 4 centimeters more than its width

△ **2.** The length and width of a rectangle whose length is twice its width

3. Two consecutive odd integers

4. Two consecutive even integers

△ **5.** The base and height of a triangle whose height is one more than four times its base

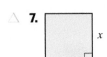

△ **6.** The base and height of a trapezoid whose base is three less than five times its height

base

Use the information given to find the dimensions of each figure.

△ **7.**

x

The *area* of the square is 121 square units. Find the length of its sides.

△ **8.**

$x - 2$

$x + 3$

The *area* of the rectangle is 84 square inches. Find its length and width.

△ **9.**

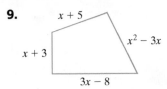

$x + 5$

$x^2 - 3x$

$x + 3$

$3x - 8$

The *perimeter* of the quadrilateral is 120 centimeters. Find the lengths of its sides.

▧ **10.**

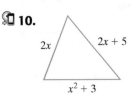

$2x$ $2x + 5$

$x^2 + 3$

The *perimeter* of the triangle is 85 feet. Find the lengths of its sides.

△ **11.**

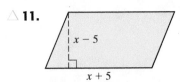

$x - 5$

$x + 5$

The *area* of the parallelogram is 96 square miles. Find its base and height.

△ **12.**

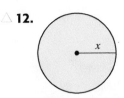

x

The *area* of the circle is 25π square kilometers. Find its radius.

Solve.

13. An object is thrown upward from the top of an 80-foot building with an initial velocity of 64 feet per second. The height h of the object after t seconds is given by the quadratic equation $h = -16t^2 + 64t + 80$. When will the object hit the ground?

14. A hang glider accidentally drops her compass from the top of a 400-foot cliff. The height h of the compass after t seconds is given by the quadratic equation $h = -16t^2 + 400$. When will the compass hit the ground?

15. The width of a rectangle is 7 centimeters less than twice its length. Its area is 30 square centimeters. Find the dimensions of the rectangle.

16. The length of a rectangle is 9 inches more than its width. Its area is 112 square inches. Find the dimensions of the rectangle.

△ *The equation $D = \dfrac{1}{2}n(n - 3)$ gives the number of diagonals D for a polygon with n sides. For example, a polygon with 6 sides has $D = \dfrac{1}{2} \cdot 6(6 - 3)$ or $D = 9$ diagonals. (See if you can count all 9 diagonals. Some are shown in the figure.) Use this equation, $D = \dfrac{1}{2}n(n - 3)$, for Exercises 17 through 20.*

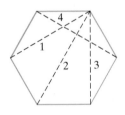

17. Find the number of diagonals for a polygon that has 12 sides.

18. Find the number of diagonals for a polygon that has 15 sides.

19. Find the number of sides n for a polygon that has 35 diagonals.

20. Find the number of sides n for a polygon that has 14 diagonals.

21. The sum of a number and its square is 132. Find the number.

22. The sum of a number and its square is 182. Find the number.

23. The product of two consecutive room numbers is 210. Find the room numbers.

24. The product of two consecutive page numbers is 420. Find the page numbers.

△ **25.** A ladder is leaning against a building so that the distance from the ground to the top of the ladder is one foot less than the length of the ladder. Find the length of the ladder if the distance from the bottom of the ladder to the building is 5 feet.

△ **26.** Use the given figure to find the length of the guy wire.

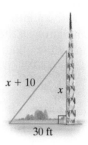

△ **27.** If the sides of a square are increased by 3 inches, the area becomes 64 square inches. Find the length of the sides of the original square.

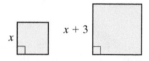

△ **28.** If the sides of a square are increased by 5 meters, the area becomes 100 square meters. Find the length of the sides of the original square.

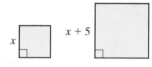

△ **29.** One leg of a right triangle is 4 millimeters longer than the smaller leg and the hypotenuse is 8 millimeters longer than the smaller leg. Find the lengths of the sides of the triangle.

△ **30.** One leg of a right triangle is 9 centimeters longer than the other leg and the hypotenuse is 45 centimeters. Find the lengths of the legs of the triangle.

△ **31.** The length of the base of a triangle is twice its height. If the area of the triangle is 100 square kilometers, find the height.

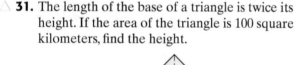

△ **32.** The height of a triangle is 2 millimeters less than the base. If the area is 60 square millimeters, find the base.

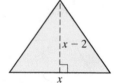

△ **33.** Find the length of the shorter leg of a right triangle if the longer leg is 12 feet more than the shorter leg and the hypotenuse is 12 feet less than twice the shorter leg.

△ **34.** Find the length of the shorter leg of a right triangle if the longer leg is 10 miles more than the shorter leg and the hypotenuse is 10 miles less than twice the shorter leg.

35. An object is dropped from 39 feet below the tip of the pinnacle atop one of the 1483-foot-tall Petronas Twin Towers in Kuala Lumpur, Malaysia. (*Source:* Council on Tall Buildings and Urban Habitat) The height h of the object after t seconds is given by the equation $h = -16t^2 + 1444$. Find how many seconds pass before the object reaches the ground.

36. An object is dropped from the top of 311 South Wacker Drive, a 961-foot-tall office building in Chicago. (*Source:* Council on Tall Buildings and Urban Habitat) The height h of the object after t seconds is given by the equation $h = -16t^2 + 961$. Find how many seconds pass before the object reaches the ground.

37. At the end of 2 years, P dollars invested at an interest rate r compounded annually increases to an amount, A dollars, given by

$$A = P(1 + r)^2$$

Find the interest rate if $100 increased to $144 in 2 years. Write your answer as a percent.

38. At the end of 2 years, P dollars invested at an interest rate r compounded annually increases to an amount, A dollars, given by

$$A = P(1 + r)^2$$

Find the interest rate if $2000 increased to $2420 in 2 years. Write your answer as a percent.

△ **39.** Find the dimensions of a rectangle whose width is 7 miles less than its length and whose area is 120 square miles.

△ **40.** Find the dimensions of a rectangle whose width is 2 inches less than half its length and whose area is 160 square inches.

41. If the cost, C, for manufacturing x units of a certain product is given by $C = x^2 - 15x + 50$, find the number of units manufactured at a cost of $9500.

42. If a switchboard handles n telephones, the number C of telephone connections it can make simultaneously is given by the equation $C = \dfrac{n(n-1)}{2}$. Find how many telephones are handled by a switchboard making 120 telephone connections simultaneously.

Review

The following double line graph shows a comparison of the number of annual visitors (in millions) to Glacier National Park and Gettysburg National Military Park for the years shown. Use this graph to answer Exercises 43 through 49.

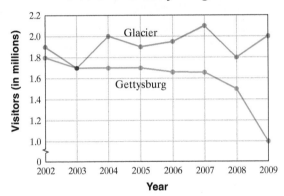

Annual Visitors to Glacier and Gettysburg Parks

43. Approximate the number of visitors to Glacier National Park in 2002.

44. Approximate the number of visitors to Gettysburg National Military Park in 2009.

45. Approximate the number of visitors to Glacier National Park in 2005.

46. Approximate the number of visitors to Gettysburg National Military Park in 2005.

47. Determine the year that the colored lines in this graph intersect.

48. In your own words, explain the meaning of the point of intersection in the graph.

49. Describe the trends shown in this graph and speculate as to why these trends have occurred.

Concept Extensions

△ **50.** Two boats travel at right angles to each other after leaving the same dock at the same time. One hour later the boats are 17 miles apart. If one boat travels 7 miles per hour faster than the other boat, find the rate of each boat.

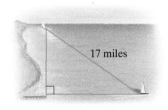

17 miles

△ **51.** The side of a square equals the width of a rectangle. The length of the rectangle is 6 meters longer than its width. The sum of the areas of the square and the rectangle is 176 square meters. Find the side of the square.

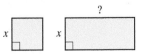

52. The sum of two numbers is 20, and the sum of their squares is 218. Find the numbers.

53. The sum of two numbers is 25, and the sum of their squares is 325. Find the numbers.

△ **54.** A rectangular garden is surrounded by a walk of uniform width. The area of the garden is 180 square yards. If the dimensions of the garden plus the walk are 16 yards by 24 yards, find the width of the walk.

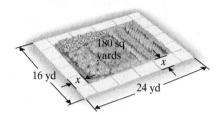

180 sq yards

16 yd   x

24 yd   x

△ **55.** A rectangular pool is surrounded by a walk 4 meters wide. The pool is 6 meters longer than its width. If the total area of the pool and walk is 576 square meters more than the area of the pool, find the dimensions of the pool.

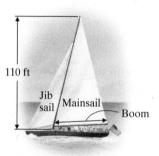

x + 6   x

4   4

△ **56.** According to the International America's Cup Class (IACC) rule, a sailboat competing in the America's Cup match must have a 110-foot-tall mast and a combined mainsail and jib sail area of 3000 square feet. (*Source:* America's Cup Organizing Committee) A design for an IACC-class sailboat calls for the mainsail to be 60% of the combined sail area. If the height of the triangular mainsail is 28 feet more than twice the length of the boom, find the length of the boom and the height of the mainsail.

110 ft

Jib sail   Mainsail   Boom

9 Chapter Highlights

Helpful Hint Are you preparing for your test? Use the Chapter Test Prep Videos to see the fully worked-out solutions to any of the exercises you want to review.

Definitions and Concepts	**Examples**

Section 9.1 The Greatest Common Factor

Factoring is the process of writing an expression as a product.	Factor: $6 = 2 \cdot 3$
	Factor: $x^2 + 5x + 6 = (x + 2)(x + 3)$
The GCF of a list of variable terms contains the smallest exponent on each common variable.	The GCF of z^5, z^3, and z^{10} is z^3.
The GCF of a list of terms is the product of all common factors.	Find the GCF of $8x^2y$, $10x^3y^2$, and $50x^2y^3$.

$$8x^2y = 2 \cdot 2 \cdot 2 \cdot x^2 \cdot y$$
$$10x^3y^2 = 2 \cdot 5 \cdot x^3 \cdot y^2$$
$$50x^2y^3 = 2 \cdot 5 \cdot 5 \cdot x^2 \cdot y^3$$
$$\text{GCF} = 2 \cdot x^2 \cdot y \quad \text{or} \quad 2x^2y$$

To Factor by Grouping

Step 1. Group the terms in two groups so that each group has a common factor.

Step 2. Factor out the GCF from each group.

Step 3. If there is a common binomial factor, factor it out.

Step 4. If not, rearrange the terms and try these steps again.

Factor: $10ax + 15a - 6xy - 9y$

Step 1. $(10ax + 15a) + (-6xy - 9y)$

Step 2. $5a(2x + 3) - 3y(2x + 3)$

Step 3. $(2x + 3)(5a - 3y)$

Section 9.2 Factoring Trinomials of the Form $x^2 + bx + c$

The product of these numbers is c.

$$x^2 + bx + c = (x + \square)(x + \square)$$

The sum of these numbers is b.

Factor: $x^2 + 7x + 12$

$$3 + 4 = 7 \quad 3 \cdot 4 = 12$$
$$x^2 + 7x + 12 = (x + 3)(x + 4)$$

Section 9.3 Factoring Trinomials of the Form $ax^2 + bx + c$

To factor $ax^2 + bx + c$, try various combinations of factors of ax^2 and c until a middle term of bx is obtained when checking.

Factor: $3x^2 + 14x - 5$

Factors of $3x^2$: $3x, x$

Factors of -5: $-1, 5$ and $1, -5$

$$(3x - 1)(x + 5)$$
$$-1x$$
$$+15x$$
$$14x \quad \text{Correct middle term}$$

Definitions and Concepts	**Examples**

Section 9.4   Factoring Trinomials of the Form $ax^2 + bx + c$ by Grouping

TO FACTOR $x^2 + bx + c$ BY GROUPING	Factor: $3x^2 + 14x - 5$
Step 1. Find two numbers whose product is $a \cdot c$ and whose sum is b.	**Step 1.** Find two numbers whose product is $3 \cdot (-5)$ or -15 and whose sum is 14. They are 15 and -1.
Step 2. Rewrite bx using the factors found in Step 1.	**Step 2.** $3x^2 + 14x - 5$ $= 3x^2 + 15x - 1x - 5$
Step 3. Factor by grouping.	**Step 3.** $= 3x(x + 5) - 1(x + 5)$ $= (x + 5)(3x - 1)$

Section 9.5   Factoring Perfect Square Trinomials and the Difference of Two Squares

A **perfect square trinomial** is a trinomial that is the square of some binomial.	**PERFECT SQUARE TRINOMIAL = SQUARE OF BINOMIAL** $x^2 + 4x + 4 = (x + 2)^2$ $25x^2 - 10x + 1 = (5x - 1)^2$
FACTORING PERFECT SQUARE TRINOMIALS $a^2 + 2ab + b^2 = (a + b)^2$ $a^2 - 2ab + b^2 = (a - b)^2$	Factor. $x^2 + 6x + 9 = x^2 + 2 \cdot x \cdot 3 + 3^2 = (x + 3)^2$ $4x^2 - 12x + 9 = (2x)^2 - 2 \cdot 2x \cdot 3 + 3^2$ $= (2x - 3)^2$
DIFFERENCE OF TWO SQUARES $a^2 - b^2 = (a + b)(a - b)$	Factor. $x^2 - 9 = x^2 - 3^2 = (x + 3)(x - 3)$

Section 9.6   Factoring the Sum and Differences of Two Cubes

SUM AND DIFFERENCE OF TWO CUBES $a^3 + b^3 = (a + b)(a^2 - ab + b^2)$ $a^3 - b^3 = (a - b)(a^2 + ab + b^2)$	Factor. $8y^3 + 1 = (2y + 1)(4y^2 - 2y + 1)$ $27p^3 - 64q^3 = (3p - 4q)(9p^2 + 12pq + 16q^2)$

Section 9.7   Factoring by Substitution

FACTORING $ax^2 + bx + c$	Factor: $28x^2 - 27x - 10$
Step 1: Write all pairs of factors of ax^2.	Factors of $28x^2$: $28x$ and x, $2x$ and $14x$, $4x$ and $7x$.
Step 2: Write all pairs of factors of c.	Factors of -10: -2 and 5, 2 and -5, -10 and 1, 10 and -1.
Step 3: Try combinations of these factors until the middle term bx is found.	$28x^2 - 27x - 10 = (7x + 2)(4x - 5)$

Section 9.8   Solving Quadratic Equations by Factoring

A **quadratic equation** is an equation that can be written in the form $ax^2 + bx + c = 0$ with a not 0. The form $ax^2 + bx + c = 0$ is called the **standard form** of a quadratic equation.	**Quadratic Equation** **Standard Form** $x^2 = 16$ $x^2 - 16 = 0$ $y = -2y^2 + 5$ $2y^2 + y - 5 = 0$
ZERO-FACTOR PROPERTY If a and b are real numbers and if $ab = 0$, then $a = 0$ or $b = 0$.	If $(x + 3)(x - 1) = 0$, then $x + 3 = 0$ or $x - 1 = 0$.

Definitions and Concepts	**Examples**

Section 9.8   Solving Quadratic Equations by Factoring (*continued*)

TO SOLVE QUADRATIC EQUATIONS BY FACTORING	Solve: $3x^2 = 13x - 4$
Step 1. Write the equation in standard form so that one side of the equation is 0.	**Step 1.** $3x^2 - 13x + 4 = 0$
Step 2. Factor completely.	**Step 2.** $(3x - 1)(x - 4) = 0$
Step 3. Set each factor containing a variable equal to 0.	**Step 3.** $3x - 1 = 0$ or $x - 4 = 0$
Step 4. Solve the resulting equations.	**Step 4.** $3x = 1$ $x = 4$
Step 5. Check solutions in the original equation.	$x = \dfrac{1}{3}$
	Step 5. Check both $\dfrac{1}{3}$ and 4 in the original equation.

Section 9.9   Quadratic Equations and Problem Solving

PROBLEM-SOLVING STEPS	A garden is in the shape of a rectangle whose length is two feet more than its width. If the area of the garden is 35 square feet, find its dimensions.
1. UNDERSTAND the problem.	**1.** Read and reread the problem. Guess a solution and check your guess. Draw a diagram.
	Let x be the width of the rectangular garden. Then $x + 2$ is the length.
	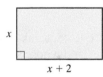
2. TRANSLATE.	**2.** length · width = area
	$(x + 2) \cdot x = 35$
3. SOLVE.	**3.** $(x + 2)x = 35$
	$x^2 + 2x - 35 = 0$
	$(x - 5)(x + 7) = 0$
	$x - 5 = 0$ or $x + 7 = 0$
	$x = 5$ $x = -7$
4. INTERPRET.	**4.** Discard the solution $x = -7$ since x represents width.
	Check: If x is 5 feet, then $x + 2 = 5 + 2 = 7$ feet. The area of a rectangle whose width is 5 feet and whose length is 7 feet is (5 feet)(7 feet) or 35 square feet.
	State: The garden is 5 feet by 7 feet.

Chapter 9 Review

(9.1) *Complete each factoring.*

1. $6x^2 - 15x = 3x($ $)$

2. $4x^5 + 2x - 10x^4 = 2x($ $)$

Factor out the GCF from each polynomial.

3. $5m + 30$

4. $20x^3 + 12x^2 + 24x$

5. $3x(2x + 3) - 5(2x + 3)$

6. $5x(x + 1) - (x + 1)$

Factor each polynomial by grouping.

7. $3x^2 - 3x + 2x - 2$

8. $3a^2 + 9ab + 3b^2 + ab$

9. $10a^2 + 5ab + 7b^2 + 14ab$

10. $6x^2 + 10x - 3x - 5$

(9.2) *Factor each trinomial.*

11. $x^2 + 6x + 8$

12. $x^2 - 11x + 24$

13. $x^2 + x + 2$

14. $x^2 - 5x - 6$

15. $x^2 + 2x - 8$

16. $x^2 + 4xy - 12y^2$

17. $x^2 + 8xy + 15y^2$

18. $72 - 18x - 2x^2$

19. $32 + 12x - 4x^2$

20. $5y^3 - 50y^2 + 120y$

21. To factor $x^2 + 2x - 48$, think of two numbers whose product is _____ and whose sum is _____.

22. What is the first step in factoring $3x^2 + 15x + 30$?

(9.3) or (9.4) *Factor each trinomial.*

23. $2x^2 + 13x + 6$

24. $4x^2 + 4x - 3$

25. $6x^2 + 5xy - 4y^2$

26. $x^2 - x + 2$

27. $2x^2 - 23x - 39$

28. $18x^2 - 9xy - 20y^2$

29. $10y^3 + 25y^2 - 60y$

30. $60y^3 - 39y^2 + 6y$

Write the perimeter of each figure as a simplified polynomial. Then factor each polynomial completely.

△ **31.**

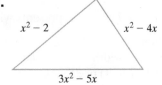

$x^2 - 2$ $x^2 - 4x$

$3x^2 - 5x$

△ **32.**

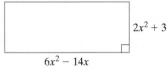

$2x^2 + 3$

$6x^2 - 14x$

(9.5) *Determine whether each polynomial is a perfect square trinomial.*

33. $x^2 + 6x + 9$

34. $x^2 + 8x + 64$

35. $9m^2 - 12m + 16$

36. $4y^2 - 28y + 49$

Determine whether each binomial is a difference of two squares.

37. $x^2 - 9$

38. $x^2 + 16$

39. $4x^2 - 25y^2$

40. $9a^3 - 1$

786

Factor each polynomial completely.

41. $x^2 - 81$

42. $x^2 + 12x + 36$

43. $4x^2 - 9$

44. $9t^2 - 25s^2$

45. $16x^2 + y^2$

46. $n^2 - 18n + 81$

47. $3r^2 + 36r + 108$

48. $9y^2 - 42y + 49$

49. $5m^8 - 5m^6$

50. $4x^2 - 28xy + 49y^2$

51. $3x^2y + 6xy^2 + 3y^3$

52. $16x^4 - 1$

(9.6) *Factor each polynomial completely.*

53. $x^2 - 100$

54. $x^2 - 81$

55. $2x^2 - 32$

56. $6x^2 - 54$

57. $81 - x^4$

58. $16 - y^4$

59. $(y + 2)^2 - 25$

60. $(x - 3)^2 - 16$

61. $x^3 + 216$

62. $y^3 + 512$

63. $8 - 27y^3$

64. $1 - 64y^3$

65. $6x^4y + 48xy$

66. $2x^5 + 16x^2y^3$

67. $x^2 - 2x + 1 - y^2$

68. $x^2 - 6x + 9 - 4y^2$

69. $4x^2 + 12x + 9$

70. $16a^2 - 40ab + 25b^2$

(9.7) *Factor each polynomial completely.*

71. $x^2 - 14x - 72$

72. $x^2 + 16x - 80$

73. $2x^2 - 18x + 28$

74. $3x^2 + 33x + 54$

75. $2x^3 - 7x^2 - 9x$

76. $3x^2 + 2x - 16$

77. $6x^2 + 17x + 10$

78. $15x^2 - 91x + 6$

79. $4x^2 + 2x - 12$

80. $9x^2 - 12x - 12$

81. $y^2(x + 6)^2 - 2y(x + 6)^2 - 3(x + 6)^2$

82. $(x + 5)^2 + 6(x + 5) + 8$

83. $x^4 - 6x^2 - 16$

84. $x^4 + 8x^2 - 20$

(9.8) *Solve each equation.*

85. $(x + 6)(x - 2) = 0$

86. $(x - 7)(x + 11) = 0$

87. $3x(x + 1)(7x - 2) = 0$

88. $4(5x + 1)(x + 3) = 0$

89. $x^2 + 8x + 7 = 0$

90. $x^2 - 2x - 24 = 0$

91. $x^2 + 10x = -25$

92. $x(x - 10) = -16$

93. $(3x - 1)(9x^2 + 3x + 1) = 0$

94. $56x^2 - 5x - 6 = 0$

95. $m^2 = 6m$

96. $r^2 = 25$

97. Write a quadratic equation that has the two solutions 4 and 5.

98. Write a quadratic equation that has two solutions, both −1.

(9.9) *Use the given information to choose the correct dimensions.*

△ **99.** The perimeter of a rectangle is 24 inches. The length is twice the width. Find the dimensions of the rectangle.

   a. 5 inches by 7 inches   **b.** 5 inches by 10 inches

   c. 4 inches by 8 inches   **d.** 2 inches by 10 inches

△ **100.** The area of a rectangle is 80 meters. The length is one more than three times the width. Find the dimensions of the rectangle.

   a. 8 meters by 10 meters   **b.** 4 meters by 13 meters

   c. 4 meters by 20 meters   **d.** 5 meters by 16 meters

Use the given information to find the dimensions of each figure.

△ **101.** The *area* of the square is 81 square units. Find the length of a side.

△ **102.** The *perimeter* of the quadrilateral is 47 units. Find the lengths of the sides.

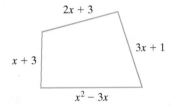

Solve.

△ **103.** A flag for a local organization is in the shape of a rectangle whose length is 15 inches less than twice its width. If the area of the flag is 500 square inches, find its dimensions.

△ **104.** The base of a triangular sail is four times its height. If the area of the triangle is 162 square yards, find the base.

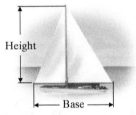

105. Find two consecutive positive integers whose product is 380.

106. Find two consecutive positive even integers whose product is 440.

107. A rocket is fired from the ground with an initial velocity of 440 feet per second. Its height h after t seconds is given by the equation $h = -16t^2 + 440t$.

   a. Find how many seconds pass before the rocket reaches a height of 2800 feet. Explain why two answers are obtained.

   b. Find how many seconds pass before the rocket reaches the ground again.

△ **108.** An architect's squaring instrument is in the shape of a right triangle. Find the length of the longer leg of the right triangle if the hypotenuse is 8 centimeters longer than the longer leg and the shorter leg is 8 centimeters shorter than the longer leg.

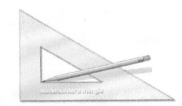

Answers to Selected Exercises

Chapter 9 Factoring Polynomials

Section 9.1

Vocabulary and Readiness Check   **1.** factors   **3.** least   **5.** false   **7.** $2 \cdot 7$ **9.** 3   **11.** 5

Exercise Set 9.1   **1.** 4   **3.** 6   **5.** 1   **7.** y^2 **9.** z^7 **11.** xy^2 **13.** 7   **15.** $4y^3$ **17.** $5x^2$ **19.** $3x^3$ **21.** $9x^2y$ **23.** $10a^6b$ **25.** $3(a + 2)$
27. $15(2x - 1)$ **29.** $x^2(x + 5)$ **31.** $2y^3(3y + 1)$ **33.** $2x(16y - 9x)$ **35.** $4(x - 2y + 1)$ **37.** $3x(2x^2 - 3x + 4)$ **39.** $a^2b^2(a^5b^4 - a + b^3 - 1)$
41. $5xy(x^2 - 3x + 2)$ **43.** $4(2x^5 + 4x^4 - 5x^3 + 3)$ **45.** $\frac{1}{3}x(x^3 + 2x^2 - 4x^4 + 1)$ **47.** $(x^2 + 2)(y + 3)$ **49.** $(y + 4)(z + 3)$
51. $(z^2 - 6)(r + 1)$ **53.** $-1(x + 7)$ **55.** $-1(2 - z)$ **57.** $-1(-3a + b - 2)$ **59.** $(x + 2)(x^2 + 5)$ **61.** $(x + 3)(5 + y)$
63. $(3x - 2)(2x^2 + 5)$ **65.** $(5m^2 + 6n)(m + 1)$ **67.** $(y - 4)(2 + x)$ **69.** $(2x + 1)(x^2 + 4)$ **71.** not factorable by grouping
73. $(x - 2y)(4x - 3)$ **75.** $(5q - 4p)(q - 1)$ **77.** $2(2y - 7)(3x^2 - 1)$ **79.** $3(2a + 3b^2)(a + b)$ **81.** $x^2 + 7x + 10$ **83.** $b^2 - 3b - 4$
85. 2, 6   **87.** $-1, -8$ **89.** $-2, 5$ **91.** $-8, 3$ **93.** d   **95.** factored   **97.** not factored   **99. a.** 22,752 thousand bales   **b.** 18,960 thousand bales
c. $-1264(x^2 - 4x - 15)$ or $1264(-x^2 + 4x + 15)$ **101.** $4x^2 - \pi x^2; x^2(4 - \pi)$ **103.** $(x^3 - 1)$ units   **105.** answers may vary
107. answers may vary

Section 9.2

Vocabulary and Readiness Check   **1.** true   **3.** false   **5.** $+ 5$ **7.** -3 **9.** $+ 2$

Exercise Set 9.2   **1.** $(x + 6)(x + 1)$ **3.** $(y - 9)(y - 1)$ **5.** $(x - 3)(x - 3)$ or $(x - 3)^2$ **7.** $(x - 6)(x + 3)$ **9.** $(x + 10)(x - 7)$
11. prime   **13.** $(x + 5y)(x + 3y)$ **15.** $(a^2 - 5)(a^2 + 3)$ **17.** $(m + 13)(m + 1)$ **19.** $(t - 2)(t + 12)$ **21.** $(a - 2b)(a - 8b)$
23. $2(z + 8)(z + 2)$ **25.** $2x(x - 5)(x - 4)$ **27.** $(x - 4y)(x + y)$ **29.** $(x + 12)(x + 3)$ **31.** $(x - 2)(x + 1)$ **33.** $(r - 12)(r - 4)$
35. $(x + 2y)(x - y)$ **37.** $3(x + 5)(x - 2)$ **39.** $3(x - 18)(x - 2)$ **41.** $(x - 24)(x + 6)$ **43.** prime   **45.** $(x - 5)(x - 3)$
47. $6x(x + 4)(x + 5)$ **49.** $4y(x^2 + x - 3)$ **51.** $(x - 7)(x + 3)$ **53.** $(x + 5y)(x + 2y)$ **55.** $2(t + 8)(t + 4)$ **57.** $x(x - 6)(x + 4)$
59. $2t^3(t - 4)(t - 3)$ **61.** $5xy(x - 8y)(x + 3y)$ **63.** $3(m - 9)(m - 6)$ **65.** $-1(x - 11)(x - 1)$ **67.** $\frac{1}{2}(y - 11)(y + 2)$
69. $x(xy - 4)(xy + 5)$ **71.** $2x^2 + 11x + 5$ **73.** $15y^2 - 17y + 4$ **75.** $9a^2 + 23ab - 12b^2$ **77.** $x^2 + 5x - 24$ **79.** answers may vary
81. $2x^2 + 28x + 66; 2(x + 3)(x + 11)$ **83.** $-16(t - 5)(t + 1)$ **85.** $\left(x + \frac{1}{4}\right)\left(x + \frac{1}{4}\right)$ or $\left(x + \frac{1}{4}\right)^2$ **87.** $(x + 1)(z - 10)(z + 7)$
89. 15; 28; 39; 48; 55; 60; 63; 64   **91.** 9; 12; 21   **93.** $(x^n + 10)(x^n - 2)$

Section 9.3

Vocabulary and Readiness Check   **1.** d   **3.** c

Exercise Set 9.3   **1.** $x + 4$ **3.** $10x - 1$ **5.** $4x - 3$ **7.** $(2x + 3)(x + 5)$ **9.** $(y - 1)(8y - 9)$ **11.** $(2x + 1)(x - 5)$ **13.** $(4r - 1)(5r + 8)$
15. $(10x + 1)(x + 3)$ **17.** $(3x - 2)(x + 1)$ **19.** $(3x - 5y)(2x - y)$ **21.** $(3m - 5)(5m + 3)$ **23.** $(x - 4)(x - 5)$ **25.** $(2x + 11)(x - 9)$
27. $(7t + 1)(t - 4)$ **29.** $(3a + b)(a + 3b)$ **31.** $(7p + 1)(7p - 2)$ **33.** $(6x - 7)(3x + 2)$ **35.** prime   **37.** $(8x + 3)(3x + 4)$
39. $x(3x + 2)(4x + 1)$ **41.** $3(7b + 5)(b - 3)$ **43.** $(3z + 4)(4z - 3)$ **45.** $2y^2(3x - 10)(x + 3)$ **47.** $(2x - 7)(2x + 3)$ **49.** $3(x^2 - 14x + 21)$
51. $(4x + 9y)(2x - 3y)$ **53.** $-1(x - 6)(x + 4)$ **55.** $x(4x + 3)(x - 3)$ **57.** $(4x - 9)(6x - 1)$ **59.** $b(8a - 3)(5a + 3)$
61. $2x(3x + 2)(5x + 3)$ **63.** $2y(3y + 5)(y - 3)$ **65.** $5x^2(2x - y)(x + 3y)$ **67.** $-1(2x - 5)(7x - 2)$ **69.** $p^2(4p - 5)(4p - 5)$ or $p^2(4p - 5)^2$
71. $-1(2x + 1)(x - 5)$ **73.** $-4(12x - 1)(x - 1)$ **75.** $(2t^2 + 9)(t^2 - 3)$ **77.** prime   **79.** $a(6a^2 + b^2)(a^2 + 6b^2)$ **81.** $x^2 - 16$
83. $x^2 + 4x + 4$ **85.** $4x^2 - 4x + 1$ **87.** no   **89.** $4x^2 + 21x + 5; (4x + 1)(x + 5)$ **91.** $\left(2x + \frac{1}{2}\right)\left(2x + \frac{1}{2}\right)$ or $\left(2x + \frac{1}{2}\right)^2$
93. $(y - 1)^2(4x + 5)(x + 5)$ **95.** 2; 14   **97.** 2   **99.** answers may vary

Section 9.4

Vocabulary and Readiness Check   **1.** a   **3.** b

Exercise Set 9.4   **1.** $(x + 3)(x + 2)$ **3.** $(y + 8)(y - 2)$ **5.** $(8x - 5)(x - 3)$ **7.** $(5x^2 - 3)(x^2 + 5)$ **9. a.** 9, 2   **b.** $9x + 2x$
c. $(2x + 3)(3x + 1)$ **11. a.** $-20, -3$ **b.** $-20x - 3x$ **c.** $(3x - 4)(5x - 1)$ **13.** $(3y + 2)(7y + 1)$ **15.** $(7x - 11)(x + 1)$
17. $(5x - 2)(2x - 1)$ **19.** $(2x - 5)(x - 1)$ **21.** $(2x + 3)(2x + 3)$ or $(2x + 3)^2$ **23.** $(2x + 3)(2x - 7)$ **25.** $(5x - 4)(2x - 3)$
27. $x(2x + 3)(x + 5)$ **29.** $2(8y - 9)(y - 1)$ **31.** $(2x - 3)(3x - 2)$ **33.** $3(3a + 2)(6a - 5)$ **35.** $a(4a + 1)(5a + 8)$ **37.** $3x(4x + 3)(x - 3)$
39. $y(3x + y)(x + y)$ **41.** prime   **43.** $6(a + b)(4a - 5b)$ **45.** $p^2(15p + q)(p + 2q)$ **47.** $(7 + x)(5 + x)$ or $(x + 7)(x + 5)$
49. $(6 - 5x)(1 - x)$ or $(5x - 6)(x - 1)$ **51.** $x^2 - 4$ **53.** $y^2 + 8y + 16$ **55.** $81z^2 - 25$ **57.** $16x^2 - 24x + 9$
59. $10x^2 + 45x + 45; 5(2x + 3)(x + 3)$ **61.** $(x^n + 2)(x^n + 3)$ **63.** $(3x^n - 5)(x^n + 7)$ **65.** answers may vary

Section 9.5

Calculator Explorations

	x^2 $2x$ 1	x^2 $2x$ 1	$(x$ $1)^2$
$x = 5$	16	14	16
$x = -3$	16	14	16
$x = 2.7$	2.89	0.89	2.89
$x = -12.1$	171.61	169.61	171.61
$x = 0$	1	-1	1

Vocabulary and Readiness Check   **1.** perfect square trinomial   **3.** perfect square trinomial   **5.** $(x + 5y)^2$ **7.** false   **9.** 8^2 **11.** $(11a)^2$ **13.** $(6p^2)^2$

Exercise Set 9.5   **1.** yes   **3.** no   **5.** yes   **7.** no   **9.** no   **11.** yes   **13.** $(x + 11)^2$ **15.** $(x - 8)^2$ **17.** $(4a - 3)^2$ **19.** $(x^2 + 2)^2$ **21.** $2(n - 7)^2$
23. $(4y + 5)^2$ **25.** $(xy - 5)^2$ **27.** $m(m + 9)^2$ **29.** prime   **31.** $(3x - 4y)^2$ **33.** $(x + 2)(x - 2)$ **35.** $(9 + p)(9 - p)$ or $-1(p + 9)(p - 9)$
37. $-1(2r + 1)(2r - 1)$ **39.** $(3x + 4)(3x - 4)$ **41.** prime   **43.** $-1(6 + x)(6 - x)$ or $(x + 6)(x - 6)$ **45.** $(m^2 + 1)(m + 1)(m - 1)$
47. $(x + 13y)(x - 13y)$ **49.** $2(3r + 2)(3r - 2)$ **51.** $x(3y + 2)(3y - 2)$ **53.** $16x^2(x + 2)(x - 2)$ **55.** $xy(y - 3z)(y + 3z)$
57. $4(3x - 4y)(3x + 4y)$ **59.** $9(4 - 3x)(4 + 3x)$ **61.** $(5y - 3)(5y + 3)$ **63.** $(11m + 10n)(11m - 10n)$ **65.** $(xy - 1)(xy + 1)$
67. $\left(x - \dfrac{1}{2}\right)\left(x + \dfrac{1}{2}\right)$ **69.** $\left(7 - \dfrac{3}{5}m\right)\left(7 + \dfrac{3}{5}m\right)$ **71.** $(9a + 5b)(9a - 5b)$ **73.** $(x + 7y)^2$ **75.** $2(4n^2 - 7)^2$ **77.** $x^2(x^2 + 9)(x + 3)(x - 3)$
79. $pq(8p + 9q)(8p - 9q)$ **81.** 6   **83.** -2 **85.** $\dfrac{1}{5}$ **87.** $\left(x - \dfrac{1}{3}\right)^2$ **89.** $(x + 2 + y)(x + 2 - y)$ **91.** $(b - 4)(a + 4)(a - 4)$
93. $(x + 3 + 2y)(x + 3 - 2y)$ **95.** $(x^n + 10)(x^n - 10)$ **97.** 8   **99.** answers may vary   **101.** $(x + 6)$ **103.** $a^2 + 2ab + b^2$ **105. a.** 2560 ft
b. 1920 ft   **c.** 13 sec   **d.** $16(13 - t)(13 + t)$ **107. a.** 1456 ft   **b.** 816 ft   **c.** 10 sec   **d.** $16(10 + t)(10 - t)$

Section 9.6

Vocabulary and Readiness Check   **1.** $(9y)^2$ **3.** $(8x^3)^2$ **5.** 5^3 **7.** $(2x)^3$ **9.** $(4x^2)^3$

Exercise Set 9.6   **1.** $(x + 3)(x^2 - 3x + 9)$ **3.** $(z - 1)(z^2 + z + 1)$ **5.** $(m + n)(m^2 - mn + n^2)$ **7.** $y^2(3 - x)(9 + 3x + x^2)$
9. $a(2b + 3a)(4b^2 - 6ab + 9a^2)$ **11.** $2(5y - 2x)(25y^2 + 10xy + 4x^2)$ **13.** $(x - 6)^2$ **15.** $2y(3x + 1)(3x - 1)$ **17.** $(3x + 7)(3x - 7)$
19. $(x^2 + 1)(x + 1)(x - 1)$ **21.** $(x^2 - y)(x^4 + x^2y + y^2)$ **23.** $(2x + 3y)(4x^2 - 6xy + 9y^2)$ **25.** $(2x + 1 + z)(2x + 1 - z)$
27. $3y^2(x^2 + 3)(x^4 - 3x^2 + 9)$ **29.** $\left(n - \dfrac{1}{3}\right)\left(n^2 + \dfrac{1}{3}n + \dfrac{1}{9}\right)$ **31.** $-16(y + 2)(y - 2)$ **33.** $(x - 5 + y)(x - 5 - y)$
35. $(ab + 5)(a^2b^2 - 5ab + 25)$ **37.** $\left(\dfrac{x}{5} + \dfrac{y}{3}\right)\left(\dfrac{x}{5} - \dfrac{y}{3}\right)$ **39.** $(x + y + 5)(x^2 + 2xy + y^2 - 5x - 5y + 25)$ **41.** $\{5\}$ **43.** $\left\{-\dfrac{1}{3}\right\}$
45. $\{0\}$ **47.** $\{5\}$ **49.** no; $x^2 - 4$ can be factored further   **51.** yes   **53.** $\pi R^2 - \pi r^2 = \pi(R + r)(R - r)$ **55.** $x^3 - y^2x; x(x + y)(x - y)$
57. $c = 9$ **59.** $c = 49$ **61. a.** $(x + 1)(x^2 - x + 1)(x - 1)(x^2 + x + 1)$ **b.** $(x + 1)(x - 1)(x^4 + x^2 + 1)$ **c.** answers may vary
63. $(x^n + 5)(x^n - 5)$ **65.** $(6x^n + 7)(6x^n - 7)$ **67.** $(x^{2n} + 4)(x^n + 2)(x^n - 2)$

Section 9.7

Vocabulary and Readiness Check   **1.** 5 and 2   **3.** 8 and 3

Exercise Set 9.7   **1.** $(x^2 + 3)(x^2 - 2)$ **3.** $(5x + 8)(5x + 2)$ **5.** $(x^3 - 4)(x^3 - 3)$ **7.** $(a - 3)(a + 8)$ **9.** $(x - 27)(x + 3)$
11. $(x - 18)(x + 3)$ **13.** $3(x - 1)^2$ **15.** $(3x + 1)(x - 2)$ **17.** $(4x - 3)(2x - 5)$ **19.** $3x^2(2x + 1)(3x + 2)$ **21.** $(x + 7z)(x + z)$
23. $(x - 4)(x + 3)$ **25.** $3(a + 2b)^2$ **27.** prime polynomial   **29.** $(2x + 13)(x + 3)$ **31.** $(3x - 2)(2x - 15)$ **33.** $(x^2 - 6)(x^2 + 1)$
35. $x(3x + 1)(2x - 1)$ **37.** $(4a - 3b)(3a - 5b)$ **39.** $(3x + 5)^2$ **41.** $y(3x - 8)(x - 1)$ **43.** $2(x + 3)(x - 2)$ **45.** $(x + 2)(x - 7)$
47. $(2x^3 - 3)(x^3 + 3)$ **49.** $2x(6y^2 - z)^2$ **51.** $2xy(x + 3)(x - 2)$ **53.** $(x + 5y)(x + y)$ **55.** $x^2 - 9$ **57.** $4x^2 + 4x + 1$ **59.** $x^3 - 8$
61. $\pm 5, \pm 7$ **63.** $x(x + 4)(x - 2)$ **65. a.** 576 ft; 672 ft; 640 ft; 480 ft   **b.** answers may vary   **c.** $-16(t + 4)(t - 9)$ **67.** $(x^n + 2)(x^n + 8)$
69. $(x^n - 6)(x^n + 3)$ **71.** $(2x^n + 1)(x^n + 5)$ **73.** $(2x^n - 3)^2$ **75.** $x^2(x + 5)(x + 1)$ **77.** $3x(5x - 1)(2x + 1)$

Section 9.8

Vocabulary and Readiness Check   **1.** quadratic   **3.** $3, -5$

Exercise Set 9.8   **1.** $2, -1$ **3.** $6, 7$ **5.** $-9, -17$ **7.** $0, -6$ **9.** $0, 8$ **11.** $-\dfrac{3}{2}, \dfrac{5}{4}$ **13.** $\dfrac{7}{2}, -\dfrac{2}{7}$ **15.** $\dfrac{1}{2}, -\dfrac{1}{3}$ **17.** $-0.2, -1.5$ **19.** $9, 4$ **21.** $-4, 2$

23. $0, 7$ **25.** $0, -20$ **27.** $4, -4$ **29.** $8, -4$ **31.** $-3, 12$ **33.** $\dfrac{7}{3}, -2$ **35.** $\dfrac{8}{3}, -9$ **37.** $0, -\dfrac{1}{2}, \dfrac{1}{2}$ **39.** $\dfrac{17}{2}$ **41.** $\dfrac{3}{4}$ **43.** $-\dfrac{1}{2}, \dfrac{1}{2}$ **45.** $-\dfrac{3}{2}, -\dfrac{1}{2}, 3$

47. $-5, 3$ **49.** $-\dfrac{5}{6}, \dfrac{6}{5}$ **51.** $2, -\dfrac{4}{5}$ **53.** $-\dfrac{4}{3}, 5$ **55.** $-4, 3$ **57.** $0, 8, 4$ **59.** -7 **61.** $0, \dfrac{3}{2}$ **63.** $0, 1, -1$ **65.** $-6, \dfrac{4}{3}$ **67.** $\dfrac{6}{7}, 1$ **69.** $\dfrac{47}{45}$ **71.** $\dfrac{17}{60}$

73. $\dfrac{7}{10}$ **75.** didn't write equation in standard form; should be $x = 4$ or $x = -2$ **77.** answers may vary, for example, $(x - 6)(x + 1) = 0$

79. answers may vary, for example, $x^2 - 12x + 35 = 0$ **81. a.** $300; 304; 276; 216; 124; 0; -156$ **b.** 5 sec   **c.** 304 ft   **83.** $0, \dfrac{1}{2}$ **85.** $0, -15$

Section 9.9

Exercise Set 9.9   **1.** width: x; length: $x + 4$ **3.** x and $x + 2$ if x is an odd integer   **5.** base: x; height: $4x + 1$ **7.** 11 units
9. 15 cm, 13 cm, 22 cm, 70 cm   **11.** base: 16 mi; height: 6 mi   **13.** 5 sec   **15.** width: 5 cm; length: 6 cm   **17.** 54 diagonals   **19.** 10 sides
21. -12 or 11   **23.** 14, 15   **25.** 13 feet   **27.** 5 in.   **29.** 12 mm, 16 mm, 20 mm   **31.** 10 km   **33.** 36 ft   **35.** 9.5 sec   **37.** 20%
39. length: 15 mi; width: 8 mi   **41.** 105 units   **43.** 1.9 million or 1,900,000   **45.** 1.9 million or 1,900,000   **47.** 2003   **49.** answers may vary
51. 8 m   **53.** 10 and 15   **55.** width of pool: 29 m; length of pool: 35 m

Chapter 9 Review   **1.** $2x - 5$ **2.** $2x^4 + 1 - 5x^3$ **3.** $5(m + 6)$ **4.** $4x(5x^2 + 3x + 6)$ **5.** $(2x + 3)(3x - 5)$ **6.** $(x + 1)(5x - 1)$
7. $(x - 1)(3x + 2)$ **8.** $(a + 3b)(3a + b)$ **9.** $(2a + b)(5a + 7b)$ **10.** $(3x + 5)(2x - 1)$ **11.** $(x + 4)(x + 2)$ **12.** $(x - 8)(x - 3)$
13. prime   **14.** $(x - 6)(x + 1)$ **15.** $(x + 4)(x - 2)$ **16.** $(x + 6y)(x - 2y)$ **17.** $(x + 5y)(x + 3y)$ **18.** $2(3 - x)(12 + x)$
19. $4(8 + 3x - x^2)$ **20.** $5y(y - 6)(y - 4)$ **21.** $-48, 2$ **22.** factor out the GCF, 3   **23.** $(2x + 1)(x + 6)$ **24.** $(2x + 3)(2x - 1)$
25. $(3x + 4y)(2x - y)$ **26.** prime   **27.** $(2x + 3)(x - 13)$ **28.** $(6x + 5y)(3x - 4y)$ **29.** $5y(2y - 3)(y + 4)$ **30.** $3y(4y - 1)(5y - 2)$
31. $5x^2 - 9x - 2; (5x + 1)(x - 2)$ **32.** $16x^2 - 28x + 6; 2(4x - 1)(2x - 3)$ **33.** yes   **34.** no   **35.** no   **36.** yes   **37.** yes   **38.** no   **39.** yes
40. no   **41.** $(x + 9)(x - 9)$ **42.** $(x + 6)^2$ **43.** $(2x + 3)(2x - 3)$ **44.** $(3t + 5s)(3t - 5s)$ **45.** prime   **46.** $(n - 9)^2$ **47.** $3(r + 6)^2$
48. $(3y - 7)^2$ **49.** $5m^6(m + 1)(m - 1)$ **50.** $(2x - 7y)^2$ **51.** $3y(x + y)^2$ **52.** $(4x^2 + 1)(2x + 1)(2x - 1)$ **53.** $(x + 10)(x - 10)$
54. $(x + 9)(x - 9)$ **55.** $2(x + 4)(x - 4)$ **56.** $6(x + 3)(x - 3)$ **57.** $(9 + x^2)(3 + x)(3 - x)$ **58.** $(4 + y^2)(2 + y)(2 - y)$
59. $(y + 7)(y - 3)$ **60.** $(x - 7)(x + 1)$ **61.** $(x + 6)(x^2 - 6x + 36)$ **62.** $(y + 8)(y^2 - 8y + 64)$ **63.** $(2 - 3y)(4 + 6y + 9y^2)$
64. $(1 - 4y)(1 + 4y + 16y^2)$ **65.** $6xy(x + 2)(x^2 - 2x + 4)$ **66.** $2x^2(x + 2y)(x^2 - 2xy + 4y^2)$ **67.** $(x - 1 + y)(x - 1 - y)$
68. $(x - 3 + 2y)(x - 3 - 2y)$ **69.** $(2x + 3)^2$ **70.** $(4a - 5b)^2$ **71.** $(x - 18)(x + 4)$ **72.** $(x - 4)(x + 20)$ **73.** $2(x - 2)(x - 7)$
74. $3(x + 2)(x + 9)$ **75.** $x(2x - 9)(x + 1)$ **76.** $(3x + 8)(x - 2)$ **77.** $(6x + 5)(x + 2)$ **78.** $(15x - 1)(x - 6)$ **79.** $2(2x - 3)(x + 2)$
80. $3(x - 2)(3x + 2)$ **81.** $(x + 6)^2(y - 3)(y + 1)$ **82.** $(x + 7)(x + 9)$ **83.** $(x^2 - 8)(x^2 + 2)$ **84.** $(x^2 - 2)(x^2 + 10)$ **85.** $-6, 2$ **86.** $-11, 7$
87. $0, -1, \dfrac{2}{7}$ **88.** $-\dfrac{1}{5}, -3$ **89.** $-7, -1$ **90.** $-4, 6$ **91.** -5 **92.** $2, 8$ **93.** $\dfrac{1}{3}$ **94.** $-\dfrac{2}{7}, \dfrac{3}{8}$ **95.** $0, 6$ **96.** $5, -5$ **97.** $x^2 - 9x + 20 = 0$
98. $x^2 + 2x + 1 = 0$ **99.** c   **100.** d   **101.** 9 units   **102.** 8 units, 13 units, 16 units, 10 units   **103.** width: 20 in.; length: 25 in.   **104.** 36 yd
105. 19 and 20   **106.** 20 and 22   **107. a.** 17.5 sec and 10 sec; answers may vary   **b.** 27.5 sec   **108.** 32 cm

Rational Expressions

10

10.1 DIVIDING POLYNOMIALS AND SYNTHETIC DIVISION

Now that we have added, subtracted, and multiplied polynomials, we will learn how to divide them.

Objective Ⓐ Dividing a Polynomial by a Monomial

Recall the following addition fact for fractions with a common denominator:

$$\frac{a}{c} + \frac{b}{c} = \frac{a+b}{c}$$

If a, b, and c are monomials, we can read this equation from right to left and gain insight into how to divide a polynomial by a monomial.

Dividing a Polynomial by a Monomial

To divide a polynomial by a monomial, divide each term in the polynomial by the monomial.

$$\frac{a+b}{c} = \frac{a}{c} + \frac{b}{c}, \quad c \neq 0$$

PRACTICE 1

Divide $16y^3 - 8y^2 + 6y$ by $2y$.

Example 1 Divide $10x^3 - 5x^2 + 20x$ by $5x$.

Solution: We divide each term of $10x^3 - 5x^2 + 20x$ by $5x$ and simplify.

$$\frac{10x^3 - 5x^2 + 20x}{5x} = \frac{10x^3}{5x} - \frac{5x^2}{5x} + \frac{20x}{5x} = 2x^2 - x + 4$$

To check, see that (quotient)(divisor) = dividend, or

$$(2x^2 - x + 4)(5x) = 10x^3 - 5x^2 + 20x$$

● **Work Practice 1**

PRACTICE 2

Divide:
$$\frac{9a^3b^3 - 6a^2b^2 + a^2b - 4a}{a^2b}$$

Example 2 Divide: $\dfrac{3x^5y^2 - 15x^3y - x^2y - 6x}{x^2y}$

Solution: We divide each term in the numerator by x^2y.

$$\frac{3x^5y^2 - 15x^3y - x^2y - 6x}{x^2y} = \frac{3x^5y^2}{x^2y} - \frac{15x^3y}{x^2y} - \frac{x^2y}{x^2y} - \frac{6x}{x^2y}$$

$$= 3x^3y - 15x - 1 - \frac{6}{xy}$$

● **Work Practice 2**

Objective Ⓑ Dividing by a Polynomial

To divide a polynomial by a polynomial other than a monomial, we use **long division.** Polynomial long division is similar to long division of real numbers. We review long division of real numbers by dividing 7 into 296.

$$\begin{array}{r} 42 \\ 7{\overline{\smash{\big)}\,296}} \end{array}$$

Divisor:

$\underline{-28}$ $4(7) = 28$

16 Subtract and bring down the next digit in the dividend.

$\underline{-14}$ $2(7) = 14$

2 Subtract. The remainder is 2.

The quotient is

$42\dfrac{2}{7}$ remainder
        divisor

To check, notice that $42(7) + 2 = 296$, which is the dividend. This same division process can be applied to polynomials, as shown next.

Example 3 Divide $2x^2 - x - 10$ by $x + 2$.

PRACTICE 3
Divide $6x^2 + 11x - 2$ by $x + 2$.

Solution: $2x^2 - x - 10$ is the dividend, and $x + 2$ is the divisor.

Step 1: Divide $2x^2$ by x.

$$x + 2 \overline{)2x^2 - x - 10} \quad \dfrac{2x}{}$$

$\dfrac{2x^2}{x} = 2x$, so $2x$ is the first term of the quotient.

Step 2: Multiply $2x(x + 2)$.

$$\begin{array}{r} 2x \\ x+2\overline{)2x^2 - x - 10} \\ 2x^2 + 4x \end{array}$$

Multiply: $2x(x+2)$. Like terms are lined up vertically.

Step 3: Subtract $(2x^2 + 4x)$ from $(2x^2 - x - 10)$ by changing the signs of $(2x^2 + 4x)$ and adding.

$$\begin{array}{r} 2x \\ x+2\overline{)2x^2 - x - 10} \\ \underline{-2x^2 - 4x} \\ -5x \end{array}$$

Step 4: Bring down the next term, -10, and start the process over.

$$\begin{array}{r} 2x \\ x+2\overline{)2x^2 - x - 10} \\ \underline{-2x^2 - 4x} \downarrow \\ -5x - 10 \end{array}$$

Step 5: Divide $-5x$ by x.

$$\begin{array}{r} 2x - 5 \\ x+2\overline{)2x^2 - x - 10} \\ \underline{-2x^2 - 4x} \downarrow \\ -5x - 10 \end{array}$$

$\dfrac{-5x}{x} = -5$ so -5 is the second term of the quotient.

Step 6: Multiply $-5(x + 2)$.

$$\begin{array}{r} 2x - 5 \\ x+2\overline{)2x^2 - x - 10} \\ \underline{-2x^2 - 4x} \\ -5x - 10 \\ -5x - 10 \end{array}$$

Multiply: $-5(x+2)$. Like terms are lined up vertically.

Step 7: Subtract by changing the signs of $-5x - 10$ and adding.

$$\begin{array}{r} 2x - 5 \\ x+2\overline{)2x^2 - x - 10} \\ \underline{-2x^2 - 4x} \\ -5x - 10 \\ \underline{+5x + 10} \\ 0 \end{array}$$

Subtract.

Remainder.

Answer
3. $6x - 1$

Then $\dfrac{2x^2 - x - 10}{x + 2} = 2x - 5$. There is no remainder.

Check this result by multiplying $2x - 5$ by $x + 2$, the divisor. Their product is $(2x - 5)(x + 2) = 2x^2 - x - 10$, the dividend.

● **Work Practice 3**

PRACTICE 4

Divide:

$(10x^2 - 17x + 5) \div (5x - 1)$

Example 4 Divide: $(6x^2 - 19x + 12) \div (3x - 5)$

Solution:

$$
\begin{array}{r}
2x \\
3x - 5 \overline{)6x^2 - 19x + 12} \\
\underline{6x^2 - 10x} \downarrow \\
-9x + 12
\end{array}
$$

Divide: $\dfrac{6x^2}{3x} = 2x$

Multiply: $2x(3x - 5)$

Subtract: $(6x^2 - 19x) - (6x^2 - 10x) = -9x$

Bring down the next term, $+12$.

$$
\begin{array}{r}
2x - 3 \\
3x - 5 \overline{)6x^2 - 19x + 12} \\
\underline{6x^2 - 10x} \\
-9x + 12 \\
\underline{-9x + 15} \\
-3
\end{array}
$$

Divide: $\dfrac{-9x}{3x} = -3$

Multiply: $-3(3x - 5)$

Subtract: $(-9x + 12) - (-9x + 15) = -3$

Check:

divisor · quotient + remainder

↓   ↓   ↓

$(3x - 5)(2x - 3) + (-3) = 6x^2 - 19x + 15 - 3$

$ = 6x^2 - 19x + 12$ The dividend

The division checks, so

$$\frac{6x^2 - 19x + 12}{3x - 5} = 2x - 3 + \frac{-3}{3x - 5}$$

Helpful Hint   This fraction is the remainder over the divisor.

● **Work Practice 4**

PRACTICE 5

Divide:

$(5x^3 - 4x^2 + 3x - 4) \div (x - 2)$.

Example 5 Divide: $(7x^3 + 16x^2 + 2x - 1) \div (x + 4)$.

Solution:

$$
\begin{array}{r}
7x^2 - 12x + 50 \\
x + 4 \overline{)7x^3 + 16x^2 + 2x - 1} \\
\underline{7x^3 + 28x^2} \\
-12x^2 + 2x \\
\underline{-12x^2 - 48x} \\
50x - 1 \\
\underline{50x + 200} \\
-201
\end{array}
$$

Divide $\dfrac{7x^3}{x} = 7x^2$.

$7x^2(x + 4)$

Subtract. Bring down $2x$.

$\dfrac{-12x^2}{x} = -12x$, a term of the quotient. $-12x(x + 4)$

Subtract. Bring down -1.

$\dfrac{50x}{x} = 50$, a term of the quotient. $50(x + 4)$

Subtract.

Answers

4. $2x - 3 + \dfrac{2}{5x - 1}$

5. $5x^2 + 6x + 15 + \dfrac{26}{x - 2}$

Thus, $\dfrac{7x^3 + 16x^2 + 2x - 1}{x + 4} = 7x^2 - 12x + 50 + \dfrac{-201}{x + 4}$ or

$$7x^2 - 12x + 50 - \frac{201}{x + 4}.$$

● **Work Practice 5**

Example 6 Divide $2x^3 + 3x^4 - 8x + 6$ by $x^2 - 1$.

Solution: Before dividing, we write terms in descending order of powers of x. Also, we represent any "missing powers" by the product of 0 and the variable raised to the missing power. There is no x^2-term in the dividend, so we include $0x^2$ to represent the missing term. Also, there is no x-term in the divisor, so we include $0x$ in the divisor.

$$
\begin{array}{r}
3x^2 + 2x + 3 \\
x^2 + 0x - 1{\overline{\smash{\big)}\,3x^4 + 2x^3 + 0x^2 - 8x + 6}} \\
\underline{3x^4 \neq 0x^3 \neq 3x^2} \qquad\qquad\quad \\
2x^3 + 3x^2 - 8x \qquad\quad \\
\underline{2x^3 \neq 0x^2 \neq 2x} \qquad\quad \\
3x^2 - 6x + 6 \\
\underline{3x^2 \neq 0x \neq 3} \\
-6x + 9
\end{array}
$$

$\dfrac{3x^4}{x^2} = 3x^2$

$3x^2(x^2 + 0x - 1)$
Subtract. Bring down $-8x$.
$2x^3/x^2 = 2x$, a term of the quotient

$2x(x^2 + 0x - 1)$
Subtract. Bring down 6.
$3x^2/x^2 = 3$, a term of the quotient

$3(x^2 + 0x - 1)$

Subtract.

The division process is finished when the degree of the remainder polynomial is less than the degree of the divisor.

Thus,

$$\frac{2x^3 + 3x^4 - 8x + 6}{x^2 - 1} = 3x^2 + 2x + 3 + \frac{-6x + 9}{x^2 - 1}$$

● **Work Practice 6**

PRACTICE 6

Divide $3x^4 + 4x^2 - 6x + 1$ by $x^2 + 1$.

Example 7 Divide $27x^3 + 8$ by $3x + 2$.

Solution: We replace the missing terms in the dividend with $0x^2$ and $0x$.

$$
\begin{array}{r}
9x^2 - 6x + 4 \\
3x + 2{\overline{\smash{\big)}\,27x^3 + 0x^2 + 0x + 8}} \\
\underline{27x^3 \neq 18x^2} \qquad\qquad\quad \\
-18x^2 + 0x \qquad\quad \\
\underline{\neq 18x^2 \neq 12x} \qquad\quad \\
12x + 8 \\
\underline{12x \neq 8}
\end{array}
$$

$9x^2(3x + 2)$

Subtract. Bring down $0x$.

$-6x(3x + 2)$

Subtract. Bring down 8.

$4(3x + 2)$

Thus, $\dfrac{27x^3 + 8}{3x + 2} = 9x^2 - 6x + 4$.

● **Work Practice 7**

PRACTICE 7

Divide $64x^3 - 27$ by $4x - 3$.

Helpful Hint The degree of the resulting polynomial (1) is the same as the degree of the divisor (1), so we continue the division process.

✔**Concept Check** In a division problem, the divisor is $4x^3 - 5$. The division process can be stopped when which of these possible remainder polynomials is reached?

a. $2x^4 + x^2 - 3$ **b.** $x^3 - 5^2$ **c.** $4x^2 + 25$

Objective ⒸUsing Synthetic Division

When a polynomial is to be divided by a binomial of the form $x - c$, a shortcut process called **synthetic division** may be used. On the left is an example of long division, and on the right is the same example showing the coefficients of the variables only.

Answers

6. $3x^2 + 1 - \dfrac{6x}{x^2 + 1}$

7. $16x^2 + 12x + 9$

✔ **Concept Check Answer**

c

$$
\begin{array}{r}
2x^2 + 5x + 2 \\
x - 3\overline{)2x^3 - x^2 - 13x + 1} \\
\underline{2x^3 - 6x^2} \\
5x^2 - 13x \\
\underline{5x^2 - 15x} \\
2x + 1 \\
\underline{2x - 6} \\
7
\end{array}
\qquad
\begin{array}{r}
2 \quad 5 \quad 2 \\
1 - 3\overline{)2 - 1 - 13 + 1} \\
\underline{2 - 6} \\
5 - 13 \\
\underline{5 - 15} \\
2 + 1 \\
\underline{2 - 6} \\
7
\end{array}
$$

Notice that as long as we keep coefficients of powers of x in the same column, we can perform division of polynomials by performing algebraic operations on the coefficients only. This shorter process of dividing with coefficients only in a special format is called synthetic division. To find $(2x^3 - x^2 - 13x + 1) \div (x - 3)$ by synthetic division, follow the next example.

PRACTICE 8

Use synthetic division to divide $3x^3 - 2x^2 + 5x + 4$ by $x - 2$.

Example 8 Use synthetic division to divide $2x^3 - x^2 - 13x + 1$ by $x - 3$.

Solution: To use synthetic division, the divisor must be in the form $x - c$. Since we are dividing by $x - 3$, c is 3. We write down 3 and the coefficients of the dividend.

The quotient is found in the bottom row. The numbers 2, 5, and 2 are the coefficients of the quotient polynomial, and the number 7 is the remainder. The degree of the quotient polynomial is one less than the degree of the dividend. In our example, the degree of the dividend is 3, so the degree of the quotient polynomial is 2. As we found when we performed the long division, the quotient is

$2x^2 + 5x + 2$,   remainder 7

or

$$2x^2 + 5x + 2 + \frac{7}{x - 3}$$

● **Work Practice 8**

Answer

8. $3x^2 + 4x + 13 + \dfrac{30}{x - 2}$

When using synthetic division, if there are missing powers of the variable, insert 0s as coefficients.

Example 9 Use synthetic division to divide $x^4 - 2x^3 - 11x^2 + 34$ by $x + 2$.

Solution: The divisor is $x + 2$, which in the form $x - c$ is $x - (-2)$. Thus, c is -2. There is no x-term in the dividend, so we insert a coefficient of 0. The dividend coefficients are $1, -2, -11, 0,$ and 34.

$$
\begin{array}{r|rrrrr}
-2 & 1 & -2 & -11 & 0 & 34 \\
   &   & -2 & 8   & 6 & -12 \\
\hline
   & 1 & -4 & -3 & 6 & 22
\end{array}
$$

The dividend is a fourth-degree polynomial, so the quotient polynomial is a third-degree polynomial. The quotient is $x^3 - 4x^2 - 3x + 6$ with a remainder of 22. Thus,

$$\frac{x^4 - 2x^3 - 11x^2 + 34}{x + 2} = x^3 - 4x^2 - 3x + 6 + \frac{22}{x + 2}$$

● Work Practice 9

PRACTICE 9

Use synthetic division to divide $x^4 + 3x^3 - 5x + 4$ by $x + 1$.

Helpful Hint

Before dividing by long division or by synthetic division, write the dividend in descending order of variable exponents. Any "missing powers" of the variable must be represented by 0 times the variable raised to the missing power.

✔ **Concept Check** Which division problems are candidates for the synthetic division process?

a. $(3x^2 + 5) \div (x + 4)$
b. $(x^3 - x^2 + 2) \div (3x^3 - 2)$
c. $(y^4 + y - 3) \div (x^2 + 1)$
d. $x^5 \div (x - 5)$

Example 10 If $P(x) = 2x^3 - 4x^2 + 5$,

a. Find $P(2)$ by substitution.
b. Use synthetic division to find the remainder when $P(x)$ is divided by $x - 2$.

Solution

a. $P(x) = 2x^3 - 4x^2 + 5$
$P(2) = 2(2)^3 - 4(2)^2 + 5$
$\quad = 2(8) - 4(4) + 5 = 16 - 16 + 5 = 5$

Thus, $P(2) = 5$.

b. The coefficients of $P(x)$ are $2, -4, 0,$ and 5. The number 0 is a coefficient of the missing power of x^1. The divisor is $x - 2$, so c is 2.

$$
\begin{array}{r|rrrr}
2 & 2 & -4 & 0 & 5 \\
  &   & 4 & 0 & 0 \\
\hline
  & 2 & 0 & 0 & 5 \;\; \text{remainder}
\end{array}
$$

The remainder when $P(x)$ is divided by $x - 2$ is 5.

● Work Practice 10

PRACTICE 10

If $P(x) = x^3 - 5x - 2$,
a. Find $P(2)$ by substitution.
b. Use synthetic division to find the remainder when $P(x)$ is divided by $x - 2$.

Answers

9. $x^3 + 2x^2 - 2x - 3 + \dfrac{7}{x + 1}$

10. a. -4 **b.** -4

✔ **Concept Check Answer**
a and d

Objective Ⓓ Using the Remainder Theorem to Evaluate Polynomials

Notice in the preceding example that $P(2) = 5$ and that the remainder when $P(x)$ is divided by $x - 2$ is 5. This is no accident. This illustrates the **remainder theorem.**

Remainder Theorem

If a polynomial $P(x)$ is divided by $x - c$, then the remainder is $P(c)$.

PRACTICE 11

Use the remainder theorem and synthetic division to find $P(3)$ if $P(x) = 2x^5 - 18x^4 + 90x^2 + 59x$.

Example 11 Use the remainder theorem and synthetic division to find $P(4)$ if

$$P(x) = 4x^6 - 25x^5 + 35x^4 + 17x^2.$$

Solution To find $P(4)$ by the remainder theorem, we divide $P(x)$ by $x - 4$. The coefficients of $P(x)$ are $4, -25, 35, 0, 17, 0,$ and 0. Also, c is 4.

```
 c
  ↘
 4 │  4   -25   35    0    17    0    0
   │       16  -36   -4   -16    4   16
   └──────────────────────────────────────
      4    -9   -1   -4     1    4   16   remainder
                                    └──┘
```

Thus, $P(4) = 16$, the remainder.

⬤ **Work Practice 11**

Answer

11. 15

10.1 Exercise Set

FOR EXTRA HELP

PRACTICE

WATCH

DOWNLOAD
READ

REVIEW

Objective A *Divide. See Examples 1 and 2.*

1. $4a^2 + 8a$ by $2a$

2. $6x^4 - 3x^3$ by $3x^2$

3. $\dfrac{12a^5b^2 + 16a^4b}{4a^4b}$

4. $\dfrac{4x^3y + 12x^2y^2 - 4xy^3}{4xy}$

5. $\dfrac{4x^2y^2 + 6xy^2 - 4y^2}{2x^2y}$

6. $\dfrac{6x^5y + 75x^4y - 24x^3y^2}{3x^4y}$

Objective B *Divide. See Examples 3 through 7.*

7. $(x^2 + 3x + 2) \div (x + 2)$

8. $(y^2 + 7y + 10) \div (y + 5)$

9. $(2x^2 - 6x - 8) \div (x + 1)$

10. $(3x^2 + 19x + 20) \div (x + 5)$

11. $2x^2 + 3x - 2$ by $2x + 4$

12. $6x^2 - 17x - 3$ by $3x - 9$

13. $(4x^3 + 7x^2 + 8x + 20) \div (2x + 4)$

14. $(8x^3 + 18x^2 + 16x + 24) \div (4x + 8)$

15. $(2x^2 + 6x^3 - 18x - 6) \div (3x + 1)$

16. $(4x - 15x^2 + 10x^3 - 6) \div (2x - 3)$

17. $(3x^5 - x^3 + 4x^2 - 12x - 8) \div (x^2 - 2)$

18. $(2x^5 - 6x^4 + x^3 - 4x + 3) \div (x^2 - 3)$

19. $\left(2x^4 + \dfrac{1}{2}x^3 + x^2 + x\right) \div (x - 2)$

20. $\left(x^4 - \dfrac{2}{3}x^3 + x\right) \div (x - 3)$

Objective C *Use synthetic division to divide. See Examples 8 and 9.*

21. $\dfrac{x^2 + 3x - 40}{x - 5}$

22. $\dfrac{x^2 - 14x + 24}{x - 2}$

23. $\dfrac{x^2 + 5x - 6}{x + 6}$

24. $\dfrac{x^2 + 12x + 32}{x + 4}$

25. $\dfrac{x^3 - 7x^2 - 13x + 5}{x - 2}$

26. $\dfrac{x^3 + 6x^2 + 4x - 7}{x + 5}$

27. $\dfrac{4x^2 - 9}{x - 2}$

28. $\dfrac{3x^2 - 4}{x - 1}$

Objectives Ⓐ Ⓑ Ⓒ **Mixed Practice** *Divide. See Examples 1–9.*

29. $\dfrac{4x^7y^4 + 8xy^2 + 4xy^3}{4xy^3}$

30. $\dfrac{15x^3y - 5x^2y + 10xy^2}{5x^2y}$

31. $(10x^3 - 5x^2 - 12x + 1) \div (2x - 1)$

32. $(20x^3 - 8x^2 + 5x - 5) \div (5x - 2)$

33. $(2x^3 - 6x^2 - 4) \div (x - 4)$

34. $(3x^3 + 4x - 10) \div (x + 2)$

35. $\dfrac{2x^4 - 13x^3 + 16x^2 - 9x + 20}{x - 5}$

36. $\dfrac{3x^4 + 5x^3 - x^2 + x - 2}{x + 2}$

37. $\dfrac{7x^2 - 4x + 12 + 3x^3}{x + 1}$

38. $\dfrac{4x^3 + x^4 - x^2 - 16x - 4}{x - 2}$

39. $\dfrac{3x^3 + 2x^2 - 4x + 1}{x - \dfrac{1}{3}}$

40. $\dfrac{9y^3 + 9y^2 - y + 2}{y + \dfrac{2}{3}}$

41. $\dfrac{x^3 - 1}{x - 1}$

42. $\dfrac{y^3 - 8}{y - 2}$

43. $(25xy^2 + 75xyz + 125x^2yz) \div (-5x^2y)$

44. $(x^6y^6 - x^3y^3z + 7x^3y) \div (-7yz^2)$

45. $(9x^5 + 6x^4 - 6x^2 - 4x) \div (3x + 2)$

46. $(5x^4 - 5x^2 + 10x^3 - 10x) \div (5x + 10)$

Objectives Ⓒ and Ⓓ *For the given polynomial P(x) and the given c, use the remainder theorem to find P(c). See Examples 10 and 11.*

47. $P(x) = x^3 + 3x^2 - 7x + 4; 1$

48. $P(x) = x^3 + 5x^2 - 4x - 6; 2$

49. $P(x) = 3x^3 - 7x^2 - 2x + 5; -3$

50. $P(x) = 4x^3 + 5x^2 - 6x - 4; -2$

51. $P(x) = 4x^4 + x^2 - 2; -1$

52. $P(x) = x^4 - 3x^2 - 2x + 5; -2$

53. $P(x) = 2x^4 - 3x^2 - 2; \dfrac{1}{3}$

54. $P(x) = 4x^4 - 2x^3 + x^2 - x - 4; \dfrac{1}{2}$

55. $P(x) = x^5 + x^4 - x^3 + 3; \dfrac{1}{2}$

56. $P(x) = x^5 - 2x^3 + 4x^2 - 5x + 6; \dfrac{2}{3}$

Review

Solve each inequality.

57. $|x + 5| < 4$ **58.** $|x - 1| \leq 8$ **59.** $|2x + 7| \geq 9$ **60.** $|4x + 2| > 10$

Concept Extensions

Solve. See the Concept Checks in this section.
Is the given division problem a candidate for the synthetic division process?

61. $(5x^2 - 3x + 2) \div (x + 2)$

62. $(x^4 - 6) \div (x^3 + 3x - 1)$

63. $(x^7 - 2) \div (x^5 + 1)$

64. $(3x^2 + 7x - 1) \div \left(x - \dfrac{1}{3} \right)$

65. In a long division exercise, if the divisor is $9x^3 - 2x$, then the division process can be stopped when the degree of the remainder is
    a. 1   **b.** 3   **c.** 9   **d.** 2

66. In a division exercise, if the divisor is $x - 3$, then the division process can be stopped when the degree of the remainder is
    a. 1   **b.** 0   **c.** 2   **d.** 3

67. A board of length $(3x^4 + 6x^2 - 18)$ meters is to be cut into three pieces of the same length. Find the length of each piece.

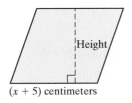

$(3x^4 + 6x^2 - 18)$ m

68. The perimeter of a regular hexagon is given to be $(12x^5 - 48x^3 + 3)$ miles. Find the length of each side.

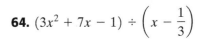

69. If the area of the rectangle is $(15x^2 - 29x - 14)$ square inches, and its length is $(5x + 2)$ inches, find its width.

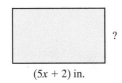

?

$(5x + 2)$ in.

70. If the area of a parallelogram is $(2x^2 - 17x + 35)$ square centimeters and its base is $(2x - 7)$ centimeters, find its height.

?

$(2x - 7)$ cm

71. If the area of a parallelogram is $(x^4 - 23x^2 + 9x - 5)$ square centimeters and its base is $(x + 5)$ centimeters, find its height.

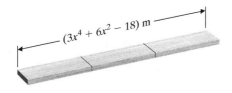

Height

$(x + 5)$ centimeters

72. If the volume of a box is $(x^4 + 6x^3 - 7x^2)$ cubic meters, its height is x^2 meters, and its length is $(x + 7)$ meters, find its width.

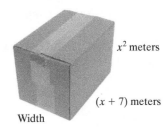

x^2 meters

$(x + 7)$ meters

Width

Divide.

73. $\left(x^4 + \dfrac{2}{3}x^3 + x\right) \div (x - 1)$

74. $\left(2x^3 + \dfrac{9}{2}x^2 - 4x - 10\right) \div (x + 2)$

75. $\left(3x^4 - x - x^3 + \dfrac{1}{2}\right) \div (2x - 1)$

76. $\left(2x^4 + \dfrac{1}{2}x^3 - \dfrac{1}{4}x^2 + x\right) \div (2x + 1)$

77. $(5x^4 - 2x^2 + 10x^3 - 4x) \div (5x + 10)$

78. $(6x^5 + 3x^4 - 2x^2 - x) \div (2x + 1)$

For each given $f(x)$ and $g(x)$, find $\dfrac{f(x)}{g(x)}$. Also find any x-values that are not in the domain of $\dfrac{f(x)}{g(x)}$. (Note: Since $g(x)$ is in the denominator, $g(x)$ cannot be 0).

79. $f(x) = 25x^2 - 5x + 30; g(x) = 5x$

80. $f(x) = 12x^4 - 9x^3 + 3x - 1; g(x) = 3x$

81. $f(x) = 7x^4 - 3x^2 + 2; g(x) = x - 2$

82. $f(x) = 2x^3 - 4x^2 + 1; g(x) = x + 3$

83. Try performing the following division without changing the order of the terms. Describe why this makes the process more complicated. Then perform the division again after putting the terms in the dividend in descending order of exponents.

$$\frac{4x^2 - 12x - 12 + 3x^3}{x - 2}$$

84. Explain how to check polynomial long division.

85. Explain an advantage of using the remainder theorem instead of direct substitution.

86. Explain an advantage of using synthetic division instead of long division.

We say that 2 is a factor of 8 because 2 divides 8 evenly, or with a remainder of 0. In the same manner, the polynomial $x - 2$ is a factor of the polynomial $x^3 - 14x^2 + 24x$ because the remainder is 0 when $x^3 - 14x^2 + 24x$ is divided by $x - 2$. Use this information for Exercises 87 and 88.

87. Use synthetic division to show that $x + 3$ is a factor of $x^3 + 3x^2 + 4x + 12$.

88. Use synthetic division to show that $x - 2$ is a factor of $x^3 - 2x^2 - 3x + 6$.

89. If a polynomial is divided by $x - 5$, the quotient is $2x^2 + 5x - 6$ and the remainder is 3. Find the original polynomial.

90. If a polynomial is divided by $x + 3$, the quotient is $x^2 - x + 10$ and the remainder is -2. Find the original polynomial.

91. eBay is the leading online auction house. eBay's annual net profit can be modeled by the polynomial function $P(x) = -7x^3 + 94x^2 - 76x + 59$, where $P(x)$ is net profit in millions of dollars and x is the number of years since 2000. eBay's annual revenue can be modeled by the function $R(x) = 939x - 194$, where $R(x)$ is revenue of millions of dollars and x is years since 2000. (*Source:* eBay, Inc.)

a. Given that

$$\text{Net profit margin} = \frac{\text{net profit}}{\text{revenue}},$$

write a function, $m(x)$, that models eBay's net profit margin.

b. Use part (a) to predict eBay's profit margin in 2010. Round to the nearest hundredth.

92. Kraft Foods is a provider of many of the best-known food brands in our supermarkets. Among their well-known brands are Kraft, Oscar Mayer, Maxwell House, and Oreo. Kraft Foods' annual revenues since 2004 can be modeled by the polynomial function $R(x) = 0.42x^3 - 1.76x^2 + 3.1x + 31.05$, where $R(x)$ is revenue in billions of dollars and x is the number of years since 2004. Kraft Foods' net profit can be modeled by the function $P(x) = 0.02x^3 - 0.11x^2 + 0.24x + 2.65$, where $P(x)$ is the net profit in billions of dollars and x is the number of years since 2004. (*Source:* Based on information from Kraft Foods)

a. Suppose that a market analyst has found the model $P(x)$ and another analyst at the same firm has found the model $R(x)$. The analysts have been asked by their manager to work together to find a model for Kraft Foods' profit margin. The analysts know that a company's profit margin is the ratio of its profit to its revenue. Describe how these two analysts could collaborate to find a function $m(x)$ that models Kraft Foods' net profit margin based on the work they have done independently.

b. Without actually finding $m(x)$, give a general description of what you would expect the answer to be.

10.2 RATIONAL FUNCTIONS AND MULTIPLYING AND DIVIDING RATIONAL EXPRESSIONS

Recall that a *rational number*, or *fraction*, is a number that can be written as the quotient $\frac{p}{q}$ of two integers p and q as long as q is not 0. A **rational expression** is an expression that can be written as the quotient $\frac{P}{Q}$ of two polynomials P and Q as long as Q is not 0.

Examples of Rational Expressions

$$\frac{8x^3 + 7x^2 + 20}{2} \qquad \frac{5x^2 - 3}{x - 1} \qquad \frac{7x - 2}{x^2 - 2x - 15}$$

Rational expressions are sometimes used to describe functions. For example, we call the function $f(x) = \frac{x^2 + 2}{x - 3}$ a **rational function** since $\frac{x^2 + 2}{x - 3}$ is a rational expression.

Objective **A** Finding Domains of Rational Functions

As with fractions, a rational expression is **undefined** if the denominator is 0. If a variable in a rational expression is replaced with a number that makes the denominator 0, we say that the rational expression is **undefined** for this value of the variable. For example, the rational expression $\frac{x^2 + 2}{x - 3}$ is undefined when x is 3, because replacing x with 3 results in a denominator of 0. For this reason, we must exclude 3 from the domain of the function $f(x) = \frac{x^2 + 2}{x - 3}$.

The domain of f is then

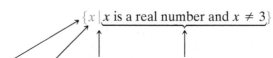

$$\{x \mid x \text{ is a real number and } x \neq 3\}$$

"The set of all x such that x is a real number and x is not equal to 3."
In this section, we will use this set builder notation to write domains.

Unless told otherwise, we assume that the domain of a function described by an equation is the set of all real numbers for which the equation is defined.

PRACTICE 1

Find the domain of each rational function.

a. $f(x) = \dfrac{x^2 + 1}{x - 6}$

b. $g(x) = \dfrac{5x + 4}{x^2 - 3x - 10}$

c. $h(x) = \dfrac{x^2 - 9}{4}$

Example 1 Find the domain of each rational function.

a. $f(x) = \dfrac{8x^3 + 7x^2 + 20}{2}$ **b.** $g(x) = \dfrac{5x^2 - 3}{x - 1}$

c. $f(x) = \dfrac{7x - 2}{x^2 - 2x - 15}$

Solution: The domain of each function will contain all real numbers except those values that make the denominator 0.

a. No matter what the value of x, the denominator of $f(x) = \dfrac{8x^3 + 7x^2 + 20}{2}$ is never 0, so the domain of f is $\{x \mid x \text{ is a real number}\}$.

b. To find the values of x that make the denominator of $g(x)$ equal to 0, we solve the equation "denominator = 0":

$$x - 1 = 0, \quad \text{or} \quad x = 1$$

The domain must exclude 1 since the rational expression is undefined when x is 1. The domain of g is $\{x \mid x \text{ is a real number and } x \neq 1\}$.

Answers

1. a. $\{x \mid x \text{ is a real number}, x \neq 6\}$
b. $\{x \mid x \text{ is a real number}, x \neq 5, x \neq -2\}$
c. $\{x \mid x \text{ is a real number}\}$

c. We find the domain by setting the denominator equal to 0.

$$x^2 - 2x - 15 = 0 \quad \text{Set the denominator equal to 0 and solve.}$$
$$(x - 5)(x + 3) = 0$$
$$x - 5 = 0 \quad \text{or} \quad x + 3 = 0$$
$$x = 5 \quad \text{or} \quad x = -3$$

If x is replaced with 5 or with -3, the rational expression is undefined.

The domain of f is $\{x \mid x \text{ is a real number and } x \neq 5, x \neq -3\}$.

● Work Practice 1

Objective Ⓑ Simplifying Rational Expressions

Recall that a fraction is in lowest terms or simplest form if the numerator and denominator have no common factors other than 1 (or -1). For example, $\dfrac{3}{13}$ is in lowest terms since 3 and 13 have no common factors other than 1 (or -1).

To **simplify** a rational expression, or to write it in lowest terms, we use a method similar to simplifying a fraction.

Recall that to simplify a fraction, we essentially "remove factors of 1." Our ability to do this comes from these facts:

- If $c \neq 0$, then $\dfrac{c}{c} = 1$. For example, $\dfrac{7}{7} = 1$ and $\dfrac{-8.65}{-8.65} = 1$.
- $n \cdot 1 = n$. For example, $-5 \cdot 1 = -5$, $126.8 \cdot 1 = 126.8$, and $\dfrac{a}{b} \cdot 1 = \dfrac{a}{b}$, $b \neq 0$.

In other words, we have the following:

$$\frac{a \cdot c}{b \cdot c} = \underbrace{\frac{a}{b} \cdot \frac{c}{c}}_{} = \frac{a}{b}$$

$$\text{Since } \tfrac{a}{b} \cdot 1 = \tfrac{a}{b}$$

Let's practice simplifying a fraction by simplifying $\dfrac{15}{65}$.

$$\frac{15}{65} = \frac{3 \cdot 5}{13 \cdot 5} = \frac{3}{13} \cdot \frac{5}{5} = \frac{3}{13} \cdot 1 = \frac{3}{13}$$

Let's use the same technique and simplify the rational expression $\dfrac{(x + 2)^2}{x^2 - 4}$.

$$\frac{(x + 2)^2}{x^2 - 4} = \frac{(x + 2)\ (x + 2)}{(x - 2)\ (x + 2)}$$

$$= \frac{(x + 2)}{(x - 2)} \cdot \frac{x + 2}{x + 2}$$

$$= \frac{x + 2}{x - 2} \cdot 1$$

$$= \frac{x + 2}{x - 2}$$

This means that the rational expression $\dfrac{(x + 2)^2}{x^2 - 4}$ has the same value as the rational expression $\dfrac{x + 2}{x - 2}$ for all values of x except 2 and -2. (Remember that when x is 2, the denominators of both rational expressions are 0 and that when x is -2, the original rational expression has a denominator of 0.)

As we simplify rational expressions, we will assume that the simplified rational expression is equivalent to the original rational expression for all real numbers except those for which either denominator is 0.

Just as for numerical fractions, we can use a shortcut notation. Remember that as long as exact factors in both the numerator and denominator are divided out, we are "removing a factor of 1." We can use the following notation:

$$\frac{(x+2)^2}{x^2-4} = \frac{(x+2)\ \boxed{(x+2)}}{(x-2)\ \boxed{(x+2)}} \qquad \text{A factor of 1 is identified by the shading.}$$

$$= \frac{x+2}{x-2} \qquad \text{"Remove" the factor of 1.}$$

In general, the following steps may be used to simplify rational expressions or to write rational expressions in lowest terms.

Simplifying or Writing a Rational Expression in Lowest Terms

Step 1: Completely factor the numerator and denominator of the rational expression.

Step 2: Divide out factors common to the numerator and denominator. (This is the same as "removing a factor of 1.")

For now, we assume that variables in a rational expression do not represent values that make the denominator 0.

Examples Simplify each rational expression.

2. $\dfrac{2x^2}{10x^3 - 2x^2} = \dfrac{2x^2 \cdot 1}{\boxed{2x^2}\,(5x-1)}$ Factor the numerator and denominator.

$$= 1 \cdot \frac{1}{5x-1} \qquad \text{Since } \frac{2x^2}{2x^2} = 1.$$

$$= \frac{1}{5x-1} \qquad \text{Simplest form.}$$

3. $\dfrac{9x^2 + 13x + 4}{8x^2 + x - 7} = \dfrac{(9x+4)\ \boxed{(x+1)}}{(8x-7)\ \boxed{(x+1)}}$ Factor the numerator and denominator.

$$= \frac{9x+4}{8x-7} \cdot 1 \qquad \text{Since } \frac{x+1}{x+1} = 1.$$

$$= \frac{9x+4}{8x-7} \qquad \text{Simplest form.}$$

● **Work Practices 2–3**

Examples Simplify each rational expression.

4. $\dfrac{2+x}{x+2} = \dfrac{x+2}{x+2} = 1$ By the commutative property of addition, $2+x = x+2$.

5. $\dfrac{2-x}{x-2}$

The terms in the numerator of $\dfrac{2-x}{x-2}$ differ by sign from the terms of the denominator, so the polynomials are opposites of each other and the expression simplifies to -1. To see this, we factor out -1 from the numerator or the denominator.

Copyright 2012 Pearson Education, Inc.

PRACTICE 2–3

Simplify each rational expression.

2. $\dfrac{3y^3}{6y^4 - 3y^3}$

3. $\dfrac{5x^2 + 13x + 6}{6x^2 + 7x - 10}$

PRACTICE 4–6

Simplify each rational expression.

4. $\dfrac{5+x}{x+5}$ **5.** $\dfrac{5-x}{x-5}$

6. $\dfrac{3-3x^2}{x^2+x-2}$

Answers

2. $\dfrac{1}{2y-1}$ **3.** $\dfrac{5x+3}{6x-5}$ **4.** 1 **5.** -1

6. $-\dfrac{3(x+1)}{x+2}$

If -1 is factored from the *numerator,* then

$$\frac{2 - x}{x - 2} = \frac{-1(-2 + x)}{x - 2} = \frac{-1\,(x - 2)}{x - 2} = \frac{-1}{1} = -1$$

If -1 is factored from the *denominator,* the result is the same.

$$\frac{2 - x}{x - 2} = \frac{2 - x}{-1(-x + 2)} = \frac{2 - x}{-1\,(2 - x)} = \frac{1}{-1} = -1$$

Helpful Hint When the numerator and the denominator of a rational expression are opposites of each other, the expression simplifies to -1.

6. $\dfrac{18 - 2x^2}{x^2 - 2x - 3} = \dfrac{2(9 - x^2)}{(x + 1)(x - 3)}$ Factor.

$$= \frac{2(3 + x)(3 - x)}{(x + 1)(x - 3)}$$ Factor completely.

Notice the opposites $3 - x$ and $x - 3$. We write $3 - x$ as $-1(x - 3)$ and simplify.

$$\frac{2(3 + x)(3 - x)}{(x + 1)(x - 3)} = \frac{2(3 + x) \cdot -1\,(x - 3)}{(x + 1)\,(x - 3)} = -\frac{2(3 + x)}{x + 1}$$

● Work Practice 4–6

Helpful Hint

Recall that for a fraction

$$\frac{a}{-b} = \frac{-a}{b} = -\frac{a}{b}$$

For example,

$$\frac{-(x + 1)}{(x + 2)} = \frac{(x + 1)}{-(x + 2)} = -\frac{x + 1}{x + 2}$$

✔**Concept Check** Which of the following expressions are equivalent to

$$\frac{x}{8 - x}?$$

a. $\dfrac{-x}{x - 8}$ **b.** $\dfrac{-x}{8 - x}$ **c.** $\dfrac{x}{x - 8}$ **d.** $\dfrac{-x}{-8 + x}$

Examples Simplify each rational expression.

7. $\dfrac{x^3 + 8}{x + 2} = \dfrac{(x + 2)\,(x^2 - 2x + 4)}{x + 2}$ Factor the sum of the two cubes.

$$= x^2 - 2x + 4$$ Simplest form.

8. $\dfrac{2y^2 + 2}{y^3 - 5y^2 + y - 5} = \dfrac{2(y^2 + 1)}{(y^3 - 5y^2) + (y - 5)}$ Factor the numerator.

$$= \frac{2(y^2 + 1)}{y^2(y - 5) + 1(y - 5)}$$ Factor the denominator by grouping.

$$= \frac{2\,(y^2 + 1)}{(y - 5)\,(y^2 + 1)}$$

$$= \frac{2}{y - 5}$$ Simplest form.

● Work Practice 7–8

PRACTICE 7–8

Simplify each rational expression.

7. $\dfrac{x^3 + 27}{x + 3}$

8. $\dfrac{3x^2 + 6}{x^3 - 3x^2 + 2x - 6}$

Answers
7. $x^2 - 3x + 9$ **8.** $\dfrac{3}{x - 3}$

✔ **Concept Check Answer**
a and **d**

✓**Concept Check** Does $\dfrac{n}{n+2}$ simplify to $\dfrac{1}{2}$? Why or why not?

Objective ⓒ Multiplying Rational Expressions

Arithmetic operations on rational expressions are performed in the same way as they are on rational numbers. To multiply rational expressions, we multiply numerators and multiply denominators.

> ### Multiplying Rational Expressions
>
> The rule for multiplying rational expressions is
>
> $$\frac{P}{Q} \cdot \frac{R}{S} = \frac{PR}{QS} \quad \text{as long as } Q \neq 0 \text{ and } S \neq 0.$$
>
> To multiply rational expressions, you may use these steps:
>
> **Step 1:** Completely factor each numerator and denominator.
>
> **Step 2:** Use the rule above and multiply the numerators and the denominators.
>
> **Step 3:** Simplify the product.

When we multiply rational expressions, notice that we factor each numerator and denominator first. This helps when we check to see whether the product is in simplest form.

PRACTICE 9–10

Multiply.

9. $\dfrac{2x - 3}{5x} \cdot \dfrac{5x + 5}{2x^2 - x - 3}$

10. $\dfrac{x^3 + 27}{-2x - 6} \cdot \dfrac{4x^3}{x^2 - 3x + 9}$

Examples Multiply.

9. $\dfrac{3n+1}{2n} \cdot \dfrac{2n-4}{3n^2 - 2n - 1} = \dfrac{3n+1}{2n} \cdot \dfrac{2(n-2)}{(3n+1)(n-1)}$ Factor.

$\qquad = \dfrac{(3n+1) \cdot 2\,(n-2)}{2\,n\,(3n+1)\,(n-1)}$ Multiply.

$\qquad = \dfrac{n-2}{n(n-1)}$ Simplest form.

10. $\dfrac{x^3 - 1}{-3x + 3} \cdot \dfrac{15x^2}{x^2 + x + 1} = \dfrac{(x-1)(x^2 + x + 1)}{-3(x-1)} \cdot \dfrac{15x^2}{x^2 + x + 1}$ Factor.

$\qquad = \dfrac{(x-1)(x^2 + x + 1) \cdot 3 \cdot 5x^2}{-1 \cdot 3(x-1)(x^2 + x + 1)}$ Factor.

$\qquad = \dfrac{5x^2}{-1} = -5x^2$ Simplest form.

● Work Practice 9–10

Objective ⓓ Dividing Rational Expressions

Recall that two numbers are reciprocals of each other if their product is 1. Similarly, if $\dfrac{P}{Q}$ is a rational expression and $P \neq 0$, then $\dfrac{Q}{P}$ is its **reciprocal,** since

$$\frac{P}{Q} \cdot \frac{Q}{P} = \frac{P \cdot Q}{Q \cdot P} = 1$$

Answers

9. $\dfrac{1}{x}$ **10.** $-2x^3$

✓ **Concept Check Answer**

no; answers may vary

The following are examples of expressions and their reciprocals.

Expression	Reciprocal
$\dfrac{3}{x}$	$\dfrac{x}{3}$
$\dfrac{2 + x^2}{4x - 3}$	$\dfrac{4x - 3}{2 + x^2}$
x^3	$\dfrac{1}{x^3}$
0	no reciprocal

Dividing Rational Expressions

The rule for dividing rational expressions is

$$\frac{P}{Q} \div \frac{R}{S} = \frac{P}{Q} \cdot \frac{S}{R} = \frac{PS}{QR} \quad \text{as long as } Q \neq 0, S \neq 0, \text{ and } R \neq 0.$$

To divide by a rational expression, use the rule above and multiply by its reciprocal. Then simplify if possible.

Notice that division of rational expressions is the same as for rational numbers.

Examples Divide.

11. $\dfrac{8m^2}{3m^2 - 12} \div \dfrac{40}{2 - m} = \dfrac{8m^2}{3m^2 - 12} \cdot \dfrac{2 - m}{40}$ Multiply by the reciprocal of the divisor.

$= \dfrac{8m^2(2 - m)}{3(m + 2)(m - 2) \cdot 40}$ Factor and multiply.

$= \dfrac{8 \; m^2 \cdot -1 \; (m - 2)}{3(m + 2) \; (m - 2) \; \cdot \; 8 \; \cdot 5}$ Write $(2 - m)$ as $-1(m - 2)$.

$= -\dfrac{m^2}{15(m + 2)}$ Simplify.

12. $\dfrac{18y^2 + 9y - 2}{24y^2 - 10y + 1} \div \dfrac{3y^2 + 17y + 10}{8y^2 + 18y - 5}$

$= \dfrac{18y^2 + 9y - 2}{24y^2 - 10y + 1} \cdot \dfrac{8y^2 + 18y - 5}{3y^2 + 17y + 10}$ Multiply by the reciprocal.

$= \dfrac{(6y - 1) \; (3y + 2) \cdot (4y - 1) \; (2y + 5)}{(6y - 1) \; (4y - 1) \cdot (3y + 2) \; (y + 5)}$ Factor.

$= \dfrac{2y + 5}{y + 5}$ Simplest form.

● Work Practice 11–12

PRACTICE 11–12

Divide.

11. $\dfrac{12y^3}{5y^2 - 5} \div \dfrac{6}{1 - y}$

12. $\dfrac{8z^2 + 14z + 3}{20z^2 + z - 1}$

$\div \dfrac{2z^2 + 7z + 6}{35z^2 + 3z - 2}$

Helpful Hint

When dividing rational expressions, do not divide out common factors until the division problem is rewritten as a multiplication problem.

Answers

11. $-\dfrac{2y^3}{5(y + 1)}$ **12.** $\dfrac{7z + 2}{z + 2}$

PRACTICE 13

Perform each indicated operation.

$$\frac{(x + 3)^2}{x^2 - 9} \cdot \frac{2x - 6}{5x} \div \frac{x^2 + 7x + 12}{x}$$

Example 13 Perform each indicated operation.

$$\frac{x^2 - 25}{(x + 5)^2} \cdot \frac{3x + 15}{4x} \div \frac{x^2 - 3x - 10}{x}$$

Solution:

$$\frac{x^2 - 25}{(x + 5)^2} \cdot \frac{3x + 15}{4x} \div \frac{x^2 - 3x - 10}{x}$$

$$= \frac{x^2 - 25}{(x + 5)^2} \cdot \frac{3x + 15}{4x} \cdot \frac{x}{x^2 - 3x - 10}$$ To divide, multiply by the reciprocal.

$$= \frac{(x + 5)\,(x - 5)}{(x + 5)\,(x + 5)} \cdot \frac{3\,(x + 5)}{4\,x} \cdot \frac{x}{(x - 5)\,(x + 2)}$$

$$= \frac{3}{4(x + 2)}$$

● **Work Practice 13**

Objective ⓔ Applications with Rational Functions

Rational functions are often used to model real-life situations. Don't forget to be aware of the domains of these functions. See the Graphing Calculator Explorations on the following page for further domain exercises.

PRACTICE 14

A company's cost per book for printing x particular books is given by the rational function $C(x) = \dfrac{0.8x + 5000}{x}$.

Find the cost per book for printing:

a. 100 books

b. 1000 books

Example 14 Finding Unit Cost

For the ICL Production Company, the rational function $C(x) = \dfrac{2.6x + 10{,}000}{x}$ describes the company's cost per disc of pressing x compact discs. Find the cost per disc for pressing:

a. 100 compact discs

b. 1000 compact discs

Solution:

a. $C(100) = \dfrac{2.6(100) + 10{,}000}{100} = \dfrac{10{,}260}{100} = 102.6$

The cost per disc for pressing 100 compact discs is $102.60.

b. $C(1000) = \dfrac{2.6(1000) + 10{,}000}{1000} = \dfrac{12{,}600}{1000} = 12.6$

The cost per disc for pressing 1000 compact discs is $12.60. Notice that as more compact discs are produced, the cost per disc decreases.

● **Work Practice 14**

Answers

13. $\dfrac{2}{5(x + 4)}$ 14. **a.** $50.80 **b.** $5.80

Calculator Explorations Graphing

Recall that since the rational expression $\dfrac{7x - 2}{(x - 2)(x + 5)}$ is not defined when $x = 2$ or when $x = -5$, we say that the domain of the rational function $f(x) = \dfrac{7x - 2}{(x - 2)(x + 5)}$ is all real numbers except 2 and -5. This domain can be written as $\{x \mid x \text{ is a real number and } x \neq 2, x \neq -5\}$. This means that the graph of f should not cross the vertical lines $x = 2$ and $x = -5$. The graph of f in *connected* mode is shown below. In connected mode the grapher tries to connect all dots of the graph so that the result is a smooth curve. This is what has happened in the graph. Notice that the graph appears to contain vertical lines at $x = 2$ and at $x = -5$. We know that this cannot happen because the function is not defined at $x = 2$ and at $x = -5$. We also know that this cannot happen because the graph of this function would not pass the vertical line test.

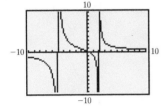

If we graph f in *dot* mode, the graph appears as below. In dot mode the grapher will not connect dots with a smooth curve. Notice that the vertical lines have disappeared, and we have a better picture of the graph. It actually appears more like the hand-drawn graph above. By using a TABLE feature, a CALCULATE VALUE feature, or by tracing, we can see that the function is not defined at $x = 2$ and at $x = -5$.

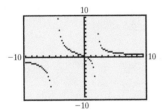

Note: Some calculator manufacturers now offer downloadable operating systems that eliminate the need to use dot mode to graph rational functions.

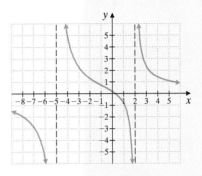

Find the domain of each rational function. Then graph each rational function and use the graph to confirm the domain.

1. $f(x) = \dfrac{5x}{x - 6}$

2. $f(x) = \dfrac{x}{x + 4}$

3. $f(x) = \dfrac{x + 1}{x^2 - 4}$

4. $g(x) = \dfrac{5x}{x^2 - 9}$

5. $h(x) = \dfrac{x^2}{2x^2 + 7x - 4}$

6. $f(x) = \dfrac{3x + 2}{4x^2 - 19x - 5}$

7. $g(x) = \dfrac{x^2 + x + 1}{5}$

8. $h(x) = \dfrac{x^2 + 25}{2}$

Vocabulary and Readiness Check

Use the choices below to fill in each blank. Not all choices will be used.

1   true   rational   simplified $\dfrac{-a}{-b}$ $\dfrac{-a}{b}$ $\dfrac{a}{-b}$

−1   false   domain   0

1. A _____ expression is an expression that can be written as the quotient $\dfrac{P}{Q}$ of two polynomials P and Q as long as $Q \neq 0$.

2. A rational expression is undefined if the denominator is _____.

3. The _____ of the rational function $f(x) = \dfrac{2}{x}$ is $\{x \mid x$ is a real number and $x \neq 0\}$.

4. A rational expression is _____ if the numerator and denominator have no common factors other than 1 or −1.

5. The expression $\dfrac{x^2 + 2}{2 + x^2}$ simplifies to _____.

6. The expression $\dfrac{y - z}{z - y}$ simplifies to _____.

7. For a rational expression, $-\dfrac{a}{b} = $ _____ $= $ _____.

8. True or false: $\dfrac{a - 6}{a + 2} = \dfrac{-(a - 6)}{-(a + 2)} = \dfrac{-a + 6}{-a - 2}$. _____

Multiply.

9. $\dfrac{x}{5} \cdot \dfrac{y}{2}$

10. $\dfrac{y}{6} \cdot \dfrac{z}{5}$

11. $\dfrac{2}{x} \cdot \dfrac{y}{3}$

12. $\dfrac{a}{5} \cdot \dfrac{7}{b}$

13. $\dfrac{m}{6} \cdot \dfrac{m}{6}$

14. $\dfrac{9}{x} \cdot \dfrac{8}{x}$

10.2 Exercise Set

FOR EXTRA HELP

 MyMathLab   PRACTICE   WATCH   DOWNLOAD   READ   REVIEW

Objective Ⓐ *Find the domain of each rational expression. See Example 1.*

1. $f(x) = \dfrac{5x - 7}{4}$

2. $g(x) = \dfrac{4 - 3x}{2}$

3. $s(t) = \dfrac{t^2 + 1}{2t}$

4. $v(t) = -\dfrac{5t + t^2}{3t}$

5. $f(x) = \dfrac{3x}{7 - x}$

6. $f(x) = \dfrac{-4x}{-2 + x}$

7. $f(x) = \dfrac{x}{3x - 1}$

8. $g(x) = \dfrac{-2}{2x + 5}$

9. $R(x) = \dfrac{3 + 2x}{x^3 + x^2 - 2x}$

10. $h(x) = \dfrac{5 - 3x}{2x^2 - 14x + 20}$

11. $C(x) = \dfrac{x + 3}{x^2 - 4}$

12. $R(x) = \dfrac{5}{x^2 - 7x}$

Objective Ⓑ *Simplify each rational expression. See Examples 2 through 8.*

13. $\dfrac{8x - 16x^2}{8x}$

14. $\dfrac{3x - 6x^2}{3x}$

15. $\dfrac{x^2 - 9}{3 + x}$

16. $\dfrac{x^2 - 25}{5 + x}$

17. $\dfrac{9y - 18}{7y - 14}$

18. $\dfrac{6y - 18}{2y - 6}$

19. $\dfrac{x^2 + 6x - 40}{x + 10}$

20. $\dfrac{x^2 - 8x + 16}{x - 4}$

21. $\dfrac{x - 9}{9 - x}$

22. $\dfrac{x - 4}{4 - x}$

23. $\dfrac{x^2 - 49}{7 - x}$

24. $\dfrac{x^2 - y^2}{y - x}$

25. $\dfrac{2x^2 - 7x - 4}{x^2 - 5x + 4}$

26. $\dfrac{3x^2 - 11x + 10}{x^2 - 7x + 10}$

27. $\dfrac{x^3 - 125}{2x - 10}$

28. $\dfrac{4x + 4}{x^3 + 1}$

29. $\dfrac{3x^2 - 5x - 2}{6x^3 + 2x^2 + 3x + 1}$

30. $\dfrac{2x^2 - x - 3}{2x^3 - 3x^2 + 2x - 3}$

31. $\dfrac{9x^2 - 15x + 25}{27x^3 + 125}$

32. $\dfrac{8x^3 - 27}{4x^2 + 6x + 9}$

Objective Ⓒ *Multiply and simplify. See Examples 9 and 10.*

33. $\dfrac{2x - 4}{15} \cdot \dfrac{6}{2 - x}$

34. $\dfrac{10 - 2x}{7} \cdot \dfrac{14}{5x - 25}$

35. $\dfrac{18a - 12a^2}{4a^2 + 4a + 1} \cdot \dfrac{4a^2 + 8a + 3}{4a^2 - 9}$

36. $\dfrac{a - 5}{a^2 + a} \cdot \dfrac{1 - a^2}{10 - 2a}$

37. $\dfrac{9x + 9}{4x + 8} \cdot \dfrac{2x + 4}{3x^2 - 3}$

38. $\dfrac{2x^2 - 2}{10x + 30} \cdot \dfrac{12x + 36}{3x - 3}$

39. $\dfrac{2x^3 - 16}{6x^2 + 6x - 36} \cdot \dfrac{9x + 18}{3x^2 + 6x + 12}$

40. $\dfrac{x^2 - 3x + 9}{5x^2 - 20x - 105} \cdot \dfrac{x^2 - 49}{x^3 + 27}$

41. $\dfrac{a^3 + a^2b + a + b}{5a^3 + 5a} \cdot \dfrac{6a^2}{2a^2 - 2b^2}$

42. $\dfrac{4a^2 - 8a}{ab - 2b + 3a - 6} \cdot \dfrac{8b + 24}{3a + 6}$

43. $\dfrac{x^2 - 6x - 16}{2x^2 - 128} \cdot \dfrac{x^2 + 16x + 64}{3x^2 + 30x + 48}$

44. $\dfrac{2x^2 + 12x - 32}{x^2 + 16x + 64} \cdot \dfrac{x^2 + 10x + 16}{x^2 - 3x - 10}$

Objective Ⓓ *Divide and simplify. See Examples 11 and 12.*

45. $\dfrac{2x}{5} \div \dfrac{6x + 12}{5x + 10}$

46. $\dfrac{7}{3x} \div \dfrac{14 - 7x}{18 - 9x}$

47. $\dfrac{a + b}{ab} \div \dfrac{a^2 - b^2}{4a^3b}$

48. $\dfrac{6a^2b^2}{a^2 - 4} \div \dfrac{3ab^2}{a - 2}$

49. $\dfrac{x^2 - 6x + 9}{x^2 - x - 6} \div \dfrac{x^2 - 9}{4}$

50. $\dfrac{x^2 - 4}{3x + 6} \div \dfrac{2x^2 - 8x + 8}{x^2 + 4x + 4}$

51. $\dfrac{x^2 - 6x - 16}{2x^2 - 128} \div \dfrac{x^2 + 10x + 16}{x^2 + 16x + 64}$

52. $\dfrac{a^2 - a - 6}{a^2 - 81} \div \dfrac{a^2 - 7a - 18}{4a + 36}$

53. $\dfrac{3x - x^2}{x^3 - 27} \div \dfrac{x}{x^2 + 3x + 9}$

54. $\dfrac{x^2 - 3x}{x^3 - 27} \div \dfrac{2x}{2x^2 + 6x + 18}$

55. $\dfrac{8b + 24}{3a + 6} \div \dfrac{ab - 2b + 3a - 6}{a^2 - 4a + 4}$

56. $\dfrac{2a^2 - 2b^2}{a^3 + a^2b + a + b} \div \dfrac{6a^2}{a^3 + a}$

Objectives Ⓑ Ⓒ Ⓓ **Mixed Practice** *Perform each indicated operation. See Examples 2 through 13.*

57. $\dfrac{x^2 - 9}{4} \cdot \dfrac{x^2 - x - 6}{x^2 - 6x + 9}$

58. $\dfrac{x^2 - 4}{9} \cdot \dfrac{x^2 - 6x + 9}{x^2 - 5x + 6}$

59. $\dfrac{2x^2 - 4x - 30}{5x^2 - 40x - 75} \div \dfrac{x^2 - 8x + 15}{x^2 - 6x + 9}$

60. $\dfrac{4a + 36}{a^2 - 7a - 18} \div \dfrac{a^2 - a - 6}{a^2 - 81}$

61. Simplify: $\dfrac{r^3 + s^3}{r + s}$

62. Simplify: $\dfrac{m^3 - n^3}{m - n}$

63. $\dfrac{4}{x} \div \dfrac{3xy}{x^2} \cdot \dfrac{6x^2}{x^4}$

64. $\dfrac{4}{x} \cdot \dfrac{3xy}{x^2} \div \dfrac{6x^2}{x^4}$

65. $\dfrac{3x^2 - 5x - 2}{y^2 + y - 2} \cdot \dfrac{y^2 + 4y - 5}{12x^2 + 7x + 1} \div \dfrac{5x^2 - 9x - 2}{8x^2 - 2x - 1}$

66. $\dfrac{x^2 + x - 2}{3y^2 - 5y - 2} \cdot \dfrac{12y^2 + y - 1}{x^2 + 4x - 5} \div \dfrac{8y^2 - 6y + 1}{5y^2 - 9y - 2}$

Objective Ⓔ *Find each function value. See Example 14.*

67. If $f(x) = \dfrac{x + 8}{2x - 1}$, find $f(2)$, $f(0)$, and $f(-1)$.

68. If $f(x) = \dfrac{x - 2}{-5 + x}$, find $f(-5)$, $f(0)$, and $f(10)$.

69. $g(x) = \dfrac{x^2 + 8}{x^3 - 25x}$; $g(3), g(-2), g(1)$

70. $s(t) = \dfrac{t^3 + 1}{t^2 + 1}$; $s(-1), s(1), s(2)$

71. The total revenue from the sale of a popular book is approximated by the rational function
$$R(x) = \dfrac{1000x^2}{x^2 + 4},$$ where x is the number of years since publication and $R(x)$ is the total revenue in millions of dollars.

   a. Find the total revenue at the end of the first year.

   b. Find the total revenue at the end of the second year.

   c. Find the revenue during the second year only.

   d. Find the domain of function R.

72. The function $f(x) = \dfrac{100,000x}{100 - x}$ models the cost in dollars for removing x percent of the pollutants from a bayou in which a nearby company dumped creosol.

   a. Find the cost of removing 20% of the pollutants from the bayou. [*Hint:* Find $f(20)$.]

   b. Find the cost of removing 60% of the pollutants and then 80% of the pollutants.

   c. Find $f(90)$, then $f(95)$, and then $f(99)$. What happens to the cost as x approaches 100%?

   d. Find the domain of function f.

Review

Perform each indicated operation.

73. $\dfrac{4}{5} + \dfrac{3}{5}$

74. $\dfrac{4}{10} - \dfrac{7}{10}$

75. $\dfrac{5}{28} - \dfrac{2}{21}$

76. $\dfrac{5}{13} + \dfrac{2}{7}$

77. $\dfrac{3}{8} + \dfrac{1}{2} - \dfrac{3}{16}$

78. $\dfrac{2}{9} - \dfrac{1}{6} + \dfrac{2}{3}$

Concept Extensions

Solve. For Exercises 79 and 80, see the first Concept Check in this section; for Exercises 81 and 82, see the second Concept Check.

79. Which of the expressions are equivalent to $\dfrac{x}{5 - x}$?

    a. $\dfrac{-x}{5 - x}$ **b.** $\dfrac{-x}{-5 + x}$

    c. $\dfrac{x}{x - 5}$ **d.** $\dfrac{-x}{x - 5}$

80. Which of the expressions are equivalent to $\dfrac{-2 + x}{x}$?

    a. $\dfrac{2 - x}{-x}$ **b.** $-\dfrac{2 - x}{x}$

    c. $\dfrac{x - 2}{x}$ **d.** $\dfrac{x - 2}{-x}$

81. Does $\dfrac{x}{x + 5}$ simplify to $\dfrac{1}{5}$? Why or why not?

82. Does $\dfrac{x + 7}{x}$ simplify to 7? Why or why not?

83. Find the area of the rectangle.

A rectangle with width $\dfrac{5x}{x^2 - 4}$ m and base $\dfrac{x + 2}{x}$ m.

84. Find the area of the triangle.

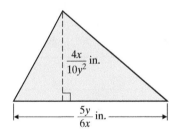

A triangle with height $\dfrac{4x}{10y^2}$ in. and base $\dfrac{5y}{6x}$ in.

85. A parallelogram has an area of $\dfrac{x^2 + x - 2}{x^3}$ square feet and a height of $\dfrac{x^2}{x - 1}$ feet. Express the length of its base as a rational expression in x. (*Hint:* Since $A = b \cdot h$, then $b = \dfrac{A}{h}$ or $b = A \div h$.)

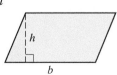

86. A lottery prize of $\dfrac{15x^3}{y^2}$ dollars is to be divided among $5x$ people. Express the amount of money each person is to receive as a rational expression in x and y.

87. In your own words explain how to simplify a rational expression.

88. In your own words, explain the difference between multiplying rational expressions and dividing rational expressions.

89. Decide whether each rational expression equals $1, -1$, or neither.

   a. $\dfrac{x + 5}{5 + x}$ **b.** $\dfrac{x - 5}{5 - x}$

   c. $\dfrac{x + 5}{x - 5}$ **d.** $\dfrac{-x - 5}{x + 5}$

   e. $\dfrac{x - 5}{-x + 5}$ **f.** $\dfrac{-5 + x}{x - 5}$

90. Find the polynomial in the second numerator such that the following statement is true.

$$\frac{x^2 - 4}{x^2 - 7x + 10} \cdot \frac{?}{2x^2 + 11x + 14} = 1$$

91. In our definition of division for

$$\frac{P}{Q} \div \frac{R}{S}$$

we stated that $Q \neq 0$, $S \neq 0$, and $R \neq 0$. Explain why R cannot equal 0.

92. In your own words, explain how to find the domain of a rational function.

Simplify. Assume that no denominator is 0.

93. $\dfrac{p^x - 4}{4 - p^x}$

94. $\dfrac{3 + q^n}{q^n + 3}$

95. $\dfrac{x^n + 4}{x^{2n} - 16}$

96. $\dfrac{x^{2k} - 9}{3 + x^k}$

97. Graph a portion of the function $f(x) = \dfrac{20x}{100 - x}$.

To do so, complete the given table, plot the points, and then connect the plotted points with a smooth curve.

x	0	10	30	50	70	90	95	99
y or $f(x)$								

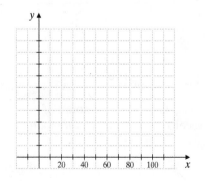

98. The domain of the function $f(x) = \dfrac{1}{x}$ is all real numbers except 0. This means that the graph of this function will be in two pieces: one piece corresponding to x values less than 0 and one piece corresponding to x values greater than 0. Graph the function by completing the following tables, separately plotting the points, and connecting each set of plotted points with a smooth curve.

x	$\frac{1}{4}$	$\frac{1}{2}$	1	2	4
y or $f(x)$					

x	-4	-2	-1	$-\frac{1}{2}$	$-\frac{1}{4}$
y or $f(x)$					

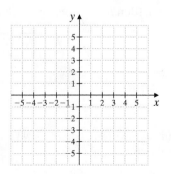

10.3 ADDING AND SUBTRACTING RATIONAL EXPRESSIONS

Objectives

A Add and Subtract Rational Expressions with the Same Denominator.

B Find the Least Common Denominator (LCD) of Two or More Rational Expressions.

C Add and Subtract Rational Expressions with Different Denominators.

Objective **A** Adding or Subtracting Rational Expressions with the Same Denominator

We add or subtract rational expressions just as we add or subtract fractions.

Adding or Subtracting Rational Expressions with Common Denominators

If $\dfrac{P}{Q}$ and $\dfrac{R}{Q}$ are rational expressions, then

$$\frac{P}{Q} + \frac{R}{Q} = \frac{P + R}{Q} \quad \text{and} \quad \frac{P}{Q} - \frac{R}{Q} = \frac{P - R}{Q}$$

To add or subtract rational expressions with common denominators, add or subtract the numerators and write the sum or difference over the common denominator.

Examples Add.

1. $\dfrac{5}{7z^2} + \dfrac{x}{7z^2} = \dfrac{5 + x}{7z^2}$ Add the numerators and write the result over the common denominator.

2. $\dfrac{x}{4} + \dfrac{5x}{4} = \dfrac{x + 5x}{4} = \dfrac{6x}{4} = \dfrac{3x}{2}$

● Work Practice 1–2

Examples Subtract.

3. $\dfrac{x^2}{x + 7} - \dfrac{49}{x + 7} = \dfrac{x^2 - 49}{x + 7}$ Subtract the numerators and write the result over the common denominator.

$$= \frac{(x + 7)(x - 7)}{x + 7}$$ Factor the numerator.

$$= x - 7$$ Simplify.

4. $\dfrac{x}{3y^2} - \dfrac{x + 1}{3y^2} = \dfrac{x - (x + 1)}{3y^2}$ Subtract the numerators.

$$= \frac{x - x - 1}{3y^2}$$ Use the distributive property.

$$= -\frac{1}{3y^2}$$ Simplify.

Helpful Hint Be sure to insert parentheses here so that the entire second numerator is subtracted.

● Work Practice 3–4

✔ **Concept Check** Find and correct the error.

$$\frac{3 + 2y}{y^2 - 1} - \frac{y + 3}{y^2 - 1}$$

$$= \frac{3 + 2y - y + 3}{y^2 - 1}$$

$$= \frac{y + 6}{y^2 - 1}$$

PRACTICE 1–2

Add.

1. $\dfrac{9}{11x^4} + \dfrac{y}{11x^4}$ **2.** $\dfrac{x}{6} + \dfrac{7x}{6}$

PRACTICE 3–4

Subtract.

3. $\dfrac{x^2}{x + 3} - \dfrac{9}{x + 3}$

4. $\dfrac{a}{5b^3} - \dfrac{a + 2}{5b^3}$

Answers

1. $\dfrac{9 + y}{11x^4}$ **2.** $\dfrac{4x}{3}$ **3.** $x - 3$ **4.** $-\dfrac{2}{5b^3}$

✔ **Concept Check Answer**

$$\frac{3 + 2y}{y^2 - 1} - \frac{y + 3}{y^2 - 1} = \frac{3 + 2y - y - 3}{y^2 - 1}$$

$$= \frac{y}{y^2 - 1}$$

815

Objective Ⓑ Finding the LCD of Rational Expressions

To add or subtract rational expressions with unlike, or different, denominators, we first write the rational expressions as equivalent rational expressions with common denominators.

The **least common denominator (LCD)** is usually the easiest common denominator to work with. The LCD of a list of rational expressions is a polynomial of least degree whose factors include all the factors of the denominators in the list.

The following steps can be used to find the LCD.

> ### Finding the Least Common Denominator (LCD)
>
> **Step 1:** Factor each denominator completely.
>
> **Step 2:** The LCD is the product of all unique factors each raised to a power equal to the greatest number of times that the factor appears in any one factored denominator.

PRACTICE 5

Find the LCD of the rational expressions in each list.

a. $\dfrac{7}{20a^2b^3}, \dfrac{9}{15ab^4}$

b. $\dfrac{6x}{x-2}, \dfrac{5}{x+2}$

c. $\dfrac{x+4}{x^2-36}, \dfrac{x}{x^2+12x+36},$ $\dfrac{x^3}{3x^2+19x+6}$

d. $\dfrac{6}{x^2-1}, \dfrac{7}{2-2x}$

Example 5 Find the LCD of the rational expressions in each list.

a. $\dfrac{2}{3x^5y^2}, \dfrac{3z}{5xy^3}$

b. $\dfrac{7}{z+1}, \dfrac{z}{z-1}$

c. $\dfrac{m-1}{m^2-25}, \dfrac{2m}{2m^2-9m-5}, \dfrac{7}{m^2-10m+25}$

d. $\dfrac{x}{x^2-4}, \dfrac{11}{6-3x}$

Solution:

a. First we factor each denominator.

$$3x^5y^2 = 3 \cdot x^5 \cdot y^2$$
$$5xy^3 = 5 \cdot x \cdot y^3$$
$$\text{LCD} = 3 \cdot 5 \cdot x^5 \cdot y^3 = 15x^5y^3$$

> **Helpful Hint** The greatest power of x is 5, so we have a factor of x^5. The greatest power of y is 3, so we have a factor of y^3.

b. The denominators $z + 1$ and $z - 1$ do not factor further.

$$(z + 1) = (z + 1)$$
$$(z - 1) = (z - 1)$$
$$\text{LCD} = (z + 1)(z - 1)$$

c. We first factor each denominator.

$$m^2 - 25 = (m + 5)(m - 5)$$
$$2m^2 - 9m - 5 = (2m + 1)(m - 5)$$
$$m^2 - 10m + 25 = (m - 5)(m - 5)$$
$$\text{LCD} = (m + 5)(2m + 1)(m - 5)^2$$

d. We factor each denominator.

$$x^2 - 4 = (x + 2)(x - 2)$$
$$6 - 3x = 3(2 - x) = 3(-1)(x - 2)$$
$$\text{LCD} = 3(-1)(x + 2)(x - 2)$$
$$= -3(x + 2)(x - 2)$$

> **Helpful Hint** $(x - 2)$ and $(2 - x)$ are opposite factors. Notice that a -1 was factored from $(2 - x)$ so that the factors are identical.

◉ **Work Practice 5**

Answers
5. a. $60a^2b^4$ **b.** $(x - 2)(x + 2)$
c. $(x - 6)(3x + 1)(x + 6)^2$
d. $-2(x + 1)(x - 1)$

Helpful Hint

If opposite factors occur, do not use both in the LCD. Instead, factor -1 from one of the opposite factors so that the factors are then identical.

Objective ⊙ Adding or Subtracting Rational Expressions with Different Denominators

To add or subtract rational expressions with different denominators, we write each rational expression as an equivalent rational expression with the LCD as the denominator. To do this, we use the multiplication property of 1 and multiply each rational expression by a form of 1 so that each denominator becomes the LCD.

Adding or Subtracting Rational Expressions with Different Denominators

Step 1: Find the LCD of the rational expressions.

Step 2: Write each rational expression as an equivalent rational expression whose denominator is the LCD found in Step 1.

Step 3: Add or subtract numerators, and write the result over the common denominator.

Step 4: Simplify the resulting rational expression.

Example 6 Add: $\dfrac{2}{x^2} + \dfrac{5}{3x^3}$

Solution: The LCD is $3x^3$. To write the first rational expression as an equivalent rational expression with denominator $3x^3$, we multiply by 1 in the form of $\dfrac{3x}{3x}$.

$$\frac{2}{x^2} + \frac{5}{3x^3} = \frac{2 \cdot 3x}{x^2 \cdot 3x} + \frac{5}{3x^3} \qquad \text{The second expression already has a denominator of } 3x^3.$$

$$= \frac{6x}{3x^3} + \frac{5}{3x^3}$$

$$= \frac{6x + 5}{3x^3} \qquad \text{Add the numerators.}$$

● **Work Practice 6**

Example 7 Add: $\dfrac{3}{x+2} + \dfrac{2x}{x-2}$

Solution: The LCD is the product of the two denominators: $(x+2)(x-2)$.

$$\frac{3}{x+2} + \frac{2x}{x-2} = \frac{3 \cdot (x-2)}{(x+2) \cdot (x-2)} + \frac{2x \cdot (x+2)}{(x-2) \cdot (x+2)} \quad \begin{array}{l}\text{Write equivalent}\\ \text{rational expressions.}\end{array}$$

$$= \frac{3x-6}{(x+2)(x-2)} + \frac{2x^2+4x}{(x+2)(x-2)} \quad \begin{array}{l}\text{Multiply in the}\\ \text{numerators.}\end{array}$$

$$= \frac{3x-6+2x^2+4x}{(x+2)(x-2)} \quad \text{Add the numerators.}$$

$$= \frac{2x^2+7x-6}{(x+2)(x-2)} \quad \text{Simplify.}$$

● **Work Practice 7**

PRACTICE 6

Add: $\dfrac{7}{a^3} + \dfrac{9}{2a^4}$

PRACTICE 7

Add: $\dfrac{1}{x+5} + \dfrac{6x}{x-5}$

Answers

6. $\dfrac{14a+9}{2a^4}$ **7.** $\dfrac{6x^2+31x-5}{(x+5)(x-5)}$

PRACTICE 8

Subtract: $\dfrac{3m - 26}{m - 6} - \dfrac{8}{6 - m}$

Example 8 Subtract: $\dfrac{2x - 6}{x - 1} - \dfrac{4}{1 - x}$

Solution: The LCD is either $x - 1$ or $1 - x$. To get a common denominator of $x - 1$, we factor -1 from the denominator of the second rational expression.

$$\frac{2x - 6}{x - 1} - \frac{4}{1 - x} = \frac{2x - 6}{x - 1} - \frac{4}{-1(x - 1)} \quad \text{Write } 1 - x \text{ as } -1(x - 1).$$

$$= \frac{2x - 6}{x - 1} - \frac{-1 \cdot 4}{x - 1} \quad \text{Write } \frac{4}{-1(x - 1)} \text{ as } \frac{-1 \cdot 4}{x - 1}.$$

$$= \frac{2x - 6 - (-4)}{x - 1}$$

$$= \frac{2x - 6 + 4}{x - 1} \quad \text{Simplify.}$$

$$= \frac{2x - 2}{x - 1}$$

$$= \frac{2(x - 1)}{x - 1}$$

$$= 2$$

● **Work Practice 8**

PRACTICE 9

Subtract:
$\dfrac{2x}{x^2 - 9} - \dfrac{3}{x^2 - 4x + 3}$

Example 9 Subtract: $\dfrac{5k}{k^2 - 4} - \dfrac{2}{k^2 + k - 2}$

Solution:

$$\frac{5k}{k^2 - 4} - \frac{2}{k^2 + k - 2} = \frac{5k}{(k + 2)(k - 2)} - \frac{2}{(k + 2)(k - 1)} \quad \begin{array}{l}\text{Factor each}\\\text{denominator to}\\\text{find the LCD.}\end{array}$$

The LCD is $(k + 2)(k - 2)(k - 1)$. We write equivalent rational expressions with the LCD as the denominator.

$$\frac{5k}{(k + 2)(k - 2)} - \frac{2}{(k + 2)(k - 1)}$$

$$= \frac{5k \cdot (k - 1)}{(k + 2)(k - 2) \cdot (k - 1)} - \frac{2 \cdot (k - 2)}{(k + 2)(k - 1) \cdot (k - 2)}$$

$$= \frac{5k^2 - 5k}{(k + 2)(k - 2)(k - 1)} - \frac{2k - 4}{(k + 2)(k - 2)(k - 1)} \quad \begin{array}{l}\text{Multiply in the}\\\text{numerators.}\end{array}$$

$$= \frac{5k^2 - 5k - 2k + 4}{(k + 2)(k - 2)(k - 1)} \quad \begin{array}{l}\text{Subtract the}\\\text{numerators.}\end{array}$$

$$= \frac{5k^2 - 7k + 4}{(k + 2)(k - 2)(k - 1)} \quad \text{Simplify.}$$

The numerator is a prime polynomial, so the expression cannot be simplified further.

● **Work Practice 9**

Answers

8. 3   **9.** $\dfrac{2x^2 - 5x - 9}{(x + 3)(x - 3)(x - 1)}$

Example 10 Add: $\dfrac{2x - 1}{2x^2 - 9x - 5} + \dfrac{x + 3}{6x^2 - x - 2}$

Solution:

$$\dfrac{2x - 1}{2x^2 - 9x - 5} + \dfrac{x + 3}{6x^2 - x - 2} = \dfrac{2x - 1}{(2x + 1)(x - 5)} + \dfrac{x + 3}{(2x + 1)(3x - 2)}$$
Factor the denominators.

The LCD is $(2x + 1)(x - 5)(3x - 2)$.

$$= \dfrac{(2x - 1) \cdot (3x - 2)}{(2x + 1)(x - 5) \cdot (3x - 2)} + \dfrac{(x + 3) \cdot (x - 5)}{(2x + 1)(3x - 2) \cdot (x - 5)}$$

$$= \dfrac{6x^2 - 7x + 2}{(2x + 1)(x - 5)(3x - 2)} + \dfrac{x^2 - 2x - 15}{(2x + 1)(x - 5)(3x - 2)} \qquad \text{Multiply in the numerators.}$$

$$= \dfrac{6x^2 - 7x + 2 + x^2 - 2x - 15}{(2x + 1)(x - 5)(3x - 2)} \qquad \text{Add the numerators.}$$

$$= \dfrac{7x^2 - 9x - 13}{(2x + 1)(x - 5)(3x - 2)} \qquad \text{Simplify.}$$

The numerator is a prime polynomial, so the expression cannot be simplified further.

● **Work Practice 10**

Example 11 Perform each indicated operation:

$$\dfrac{7}{x - 1} + \dfrac{10x}{x^2 - 1} - \dfrac{5}{x + 1}$$

Solution:

$$\dfrac{7}{x - 1} + \dfrac{10x}{x^2 - 1} - \dfrac{5}{x + 1} = \dfrac{7}{x - 1} + \dfrac{10x}{(x - 1)(x + 1)} - \dfrac{5}{x + 1}$$
The LCD is $(x - 1)(x + 1)$.

$$= \dfrac{7 \cdot (x + 1)}{(x - 1) \cdot (x + 1)} + \dfrac{10x}{(x - 1) \cdot (x + 1)} - \dfrac{5 \cdot (x - 1)}{(x + 1) \cdot (x - 1)}$$

$$= \dfrac{7x + 7}{(x - 1)(x + 1)} + \dfrac{10x}{(x - 1)(x + 1)} - \dfrac{5x - 5}{(x + 1)(x - 1)} \qquad \text{Multiply in the numerators.}$$

$$= \dfrac{7x + 7 + 10x - 5x + 5}{(x - 1)(x + 1)} \qquad \text{Add and subtract the numerators.}$$

$$= \dfrac{12x + 12}{(x - 1)(x + 1)} \qquad \text{Simplify.}$$

$$= \dfrac{12(x + 1)}{(x - 1)(x + 1)} \qquad \text{Factor the numerator.}$$

$$= \dfrac{12}{x - 1} \qquad \text{Simplify.}$$

● **Work Practice 11**

PRACTICE 10

Add:

$$\dfrac{x + 1}{x^2 + x - 12} + \dfrac{2x - 1}{x^2 + 6x + 8}$$

PRACTICE 11

Perform each indicated operation.

$$\dfrac{6}{x - 5} + \dfrac{x - 35}{x^2 - 5x} - \dfrac{2}{x}$$

Answers

10. $\dfrac{3x^2 - 4x + 5}{(x + 2)(x - 3)(x + 4)}$ **11.** $\dfrac{5}{x}$

▦ **Calculator Explorations** Graphing

A grapher can be used to support the results of operations on rational expressions. For example, to verify the result of Example 7, graph

on the same set of axes. The graphs should be the same. Use a TABLE feature or a TRACE feature to see that this is true.

$$Y_1 = \dfrac{3}{x + 2} + \dfrac{2x}{x - 2} \quad \text{and} \quad Y_2 = \dfrac{2x^2 + 7x - 6}{(x + 2)(x - 2)}$$

Vocabulary and Readiness Check

Name the operation(s) below that make each statement true.

    a. Addition   **b.** Subtraction   **c.** Multiplication   **d.** Division

1. The denominators must be the same before performing the operation. _____

2. To perform this operation, you multiply the first rational expression by the reciprocal of the second rational expression. _____

3. Numerator times numerator all over denominator times denominator. _____

4. These operations are commutative (order doesn't matter.) _____

For the rational expressions $\dfrac{5}{y}$ and $\dfrac{7}{y}$, perform each operation mentally.

5. Addition   _____

6. Subtraction   _____

7. Multiplication   _____

8. Division   _____

Be careful when subtracting! For example, $\dfrac{8}{x+1} - \dfrac{x+5}{x+1} = \dfrac{8-(x+5)}{x+1} = \dfrac{3-x}{x+1}$ *or* $\dfrac{-x+3}{x+1}$.

Use this example to help you perform the subtractions.

9. $\dfrac{5}{2x} - \dfrac{x+1}{2x} =$ _____

10. $\dfrac{9}{5x} - \dfrac{6-x}{5x} =$ _____

11. $\dfrac{y+11}{y-2} - \dfrac{y-5}{y-2} =$ _____

12. $\dfrac{z-1}{z+6} - \dfrac{z+4}{z+6} =$ _____

10.3 Exercise Set

FOR EXTRA HELP

PRACTICE   WATCH   DOWNLOAD   READ   REVIEW

Objective Ⓐ *Add or subtract as indicated. Simplify each answer. See Examples 1 through 4.*

1. $\dfrac{2}{xz^2} - \dfrac{5}{xz^2}$

2. $\dfrac{4}{x^2y} + \dfrac{2}{x^2y}$

3. $\dfrac{2}{x-2} + \dfrac{x}{x-2}$

4. $\dfrac{x}{5-x} + \dfrac{7}{5-x}$

5. $\dfrac{x^2}{x+2} - \dfrac{4}{x+2}$

6. $\dfrac{x^2}{x+6} - \dfrac{36}{x+6}$

7. $\dfrac{2x-6}{x^2+x-6} + \dfrac{3-3x}{x^2+x-6}$

8. $\dfrac{5x+2}{x^2+2x-8} + \dfrac{2-4x}{x^2+2x-8}$

9. $\dfrac{x-5}{2x} - \dfrac{x+5}{2x}$

10. $\dfrac{x+4}{4x} - \dfrac{x-4}{4x}$

Objective Ⓑ *Find the LCD of the rational expressions in each list. See Example 5.*

11. $\dfrac{2}{7}, \dfrac{3}{5x}$

12. $\dfrac{4}{5y}, \dfrac{3}{4y^2}$

13. $\dfrac{3}{x}, \dfrac{2}{x+1}$

14. $\dfrac{5}{2x}, \dfrac{7}{2+x}$

15. $\dfrac{12}{x+7}, \dfrac{8}{x-7}$

16. $\dfrac{1}{2x-1}, \dfrac{8}{2x+1}$

17. $\dfrac{5}{3x+6}, \dfrac{2x}{2x-4}$

18. $\dfrac{2}{3a+9}, \dfrac{5}{5a-15}$

📷 **19.** $\dfrac{2a}{a^2-b^2}, \dfrac{1}{a^2-2ab+b^2}$

20. $\dfrac{2a}{a^2+8a+16}, \dfrac{7a}{a^2+a-12}$

21. $\dfrac{x}{x^2-9}, \dfrac{5}{x}, \dfrac{7}{12-4x}$

22. $\dfrac{9}{x^2-25}, \dfrac{1}{50-10x}, \dfrac{6}{x}$

Objective Ⓒ *Add or subtract as indicated. Simplify each answer. See Examples 6 and 7.*

📷 **23.** $\dfrac{4}{3x} + \dfrac{3}{2x}$

24. $\dfrac{10}{7x} - \dfrac{5}{2x}$

25. $\dfrac{5}{2y^2} - \dfrac{2}{7y}$

26. $\dfrac{4}{11x^4} - \dfrac{1}{4x^2}$

📷 **27.** $\dfrac{x-3}{x+4} - \dfrac{x+2}{x-4}$

28. $\dfrac{x-1}{x-5} - \dfrac{x+2}{x+5}$

29. $\dfrac{1}{x-5} + \dfrac{2x-19}{(x-5)(x+4)}$

30. $\dfrac{4x-2}{(x-5)(x+4)} - \dfrac{2}{x+4}$

Perform the indicated operation. If possible, simplify your answer. See Example 8.

31. $\dfrac{1}{a-b} + \dfrac{1}{b-a}$

32. $\dfrac{1}{a-3} - \dfrac{1}{3-a}$

33. $\dfrac{x+1}{1-x} - \dfrac{1}{x-1}$

34. $\dfrac{5}{1-x} - \dfrac{1}{x-1}$

35. $\dfrac{5}{x-2} + \dfrac{x+4}{2-x}$

36. $\dfrac{3}{5-x} + \dfrac{x+2}{x-5}$

Perform each indicated operation. If possible, simplify your answer. See Examples 6 through 10.

📷 **37.** $\dfrac{y+1}{y^2-6y+8} - \dfrac{3}{y^2-16}$

38. $\dfrac{x+2}{x^2-36} - \dfrac{x}{x^2+9x+18}$

39. $\dfrac{x+4}{3x^2+11x+6} + \dfrac{x}{2x^2+x-15}$

40. $\dfrac{x+3}{5x^2+12x+4} + \dfrac{6}{x^2-x-6}$

41. $\dfrac{x}{x^2 + 4x + 3} - \dfrac{7}{x^2 - x - 2}$

42. $\dfrac{a}{a^2 + 10a + 25} - \dfrac{4}{a^2 + 6a + 5}$

43. $\dfrac{x}{2x^2 + x - 15} - \dfrac{x + 4}{3x^2 + 11x + 6}$

44. $\dfrac{x}{x^2 - x - 6} - \dfrac{x + 3}{5x^2 + 12x + 4}$

45. $\dfrac{2}{a^2 + 2a + 1} + \dfrac{3}{a^2 - 1}$

46. $\dfrac{9x + 2}{3x^2 - 2x - 8} + \dfrac{7}{3x^2 + x - 4}$

Objectives Ⓐ Ⓑ Ⓒ **Mixed Practice** *Add or subtract as indicated. If possible, simplify your answer. See Examples 1 through 10.*

47. $\dfrac{4}{3x^2y^3} + \dfrac{5}{3x^2y^3}$

48. $\dfrac{7}{2xy^4} + \dfrac{1}{2xy^4}$

49. $\dfrac{13x - 5}{2x} - \dfrac{13x + 5}{2x}$

50. $\dfrac{17x + 4}{4x} - \dfrac{17x - 4}{4x}$

51. $\dfrac{3}{2x + 10} + \dfrac{8}{3x + 15}$

52. $\dfrac{10}{3x - 3} + \dfrac{1}{7x - 7}$

53. $\dfrac{-2}{x^2 - 3x} - \dfrac{1}{x^3 - 3x^2}$

54. $\dfrac{-3}{2a + 8} - \dfrac{8}{a^2 + 4a}$

55. $\dfrac{ab}{a^2 - b^2} + \dfrac{b}{a + b}$

56. $\dfrac{x}{25 - x^2} + \dfrac{2}{3x - 15}$

57. $\dfrac{5}{x^2 - 4} - \dfrac{3}{x^2 + 4x + 4}$

58. $\dfrac{3z}{z^2 - 9} - \dfrac{2}{3 - z}$

59. $\dfrac{3x}{2x^2 - 11x + 5} + \dfrac{7}{x^2 - 2x - 15}$

60. $\dfrac{2x}{3x^2 - 13x + 4} + \dfrac{5}{x^2 - 2x - 8}$

Objective Ⓒ *Perform each indicated operation. Simplify each answer. See Example 11.*

61. $\dfrac{2}{x + 1} - \dfrac{3x}{3x + 3} + \dfrac{1}{2x + 2}$

62. $\dfrac{5}{3x - 6} - \dfrac{x}{x - 2} + \dfrac{3 + 2x}{5x - 10}$

63. $\dfrac{3}{x + 3} + \dfrac{5}{x^2 + 6x + 9} - \dfrac{x}{x^2 - 9}$

64. $\dfrac{x + 2}{x^2 - 2x - 3} + \dfrac{x}{x - 3} - \dfrac{x}{x + 1}$

65. $\dfrac{x}{x^2 - 9} + \dfrac{3}{x^2 - 6x + 9} - \dfrac{1}{x + 3}$

66. $\dfrac{3}{x^2 - 9} - \dfrac{x}{x^2 - 6x + 9} + \dfrac{1}{x + 3}$

67. $\left(\dfrac{1}{x} + \dfrac{2}{3}\right) - \left(\dfrac{1}{x} - \dfrac{2}{3}\right)$

68. $\left(\dfrac{1}{2} + \dfrac{2}{x}\right) - \left(\dfrac{1}{2} - \dfrac{1}{x}\right)$

Review

Use the distributive property to multiply each expression.

69. $12\left(\dfrac{2}{3} + \dfrac{1}{6}\right)$

70. $14\left(\dfrac{1}{7} + \dfrac{3}{14}\right)$

71. $x^2\left(\dfrac{4}{x^2} + 1\right)$

72. $5y^2\left(\dfrac{1}{y^2} - \dfrac{1}{5}\right)$

Concept Extensions

Find and correct each error. See the Concept Check in this section.

73. $\dfrac{2x - 3}{x^2 + 1} - \dfrac{x - 6}{x^2 + 1} = \dfrac{2x - 3 - x - 6}{x^2 + 1}$
$$= \dfrac{x - 9}{x^2 + 1}$$

74. $\dfrac{7}{x + 7} - \dfrac{x + 3}{x + 7} = \dfrac{7 - x - 3}{(x + 7)^2}$
$$= \dfrac{-x + 4}{(x + 7)^2}$$

75. Find the perimeter and the area of the square.

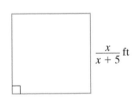

$\dfrac{x}{x + 5}$ ft

76. Find the perimeter of the quadrilateral.

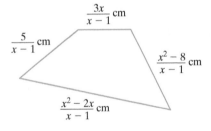

$\dfrac{3x}{x - 1}$ cm

$\dfrac{5}{x - 1}$ cm

$\dfrac{x^2 - 8}{x - 1}$ cm

$\dfrac{x^2 - 2x}{x - 1}$ cm

77. When is the LCD of two rational expressions equal to the product of their denominators? ($Hint:$ What is the LCD of $\dfrac{1}{x}$ and $\dfrac{7}{x + 5}$?)

78. When is the LCD of two rational expressions with different denominators equal to one of the denominators? ($Hint:$ What is the LCD of $\dfrac{3x}{x + 2}$ and $\dfrac{7x + 1}{(x + 2)^3}$?)

79. In your own words, explain how to add rational expressions with different denominators.

80. In your own words, explain how to multiply rational expressions.

81. In your own words, explain how to divide rational expressions.

82. In your own words, explain how to subtract rational expressions with different denominators.

Mixed Practice (Sections 10.2, 10.3) *Perform the indicated operation. If possible, simplify your answer.*

83. $\left(\dfrac{2}{3} - \dfrac{1}{x}\right) \cdot \left(\dfrac{3}{x} + \dfrac{1}{2}\right)$

84. $\left(\dfrac{2}{3} - \dfrac{1}{x}\right) \div \left(\dfrac{3}{x} + \dfrac{1}{2}\right)$

85. $\left(\dfrac{2a}{3}\right)^2 \div \left(\dfrac{a^2}{a + 1} - \dfrac{1}{a + 1}\right)$

86. $\left(\dfrac{x + 2}{2x} - \dfrac{x - 2}{2x}\right) \cdot \left(\dfrac{5x}{4}\right)^2$

87. $\left(\dfrac{2x}{3}\right)^2 \div \left(\dfrac{x}{3}\right)^2$

88. $\left(\dfrac{2x}{3}\right)^2 \cdot \left(\dfrac{3}{x}\right)^2$

89. $\left(\dfrac{x}{x + 1} - \dfrac{x}{x - 1}\right) \div \dfrac{x}{2x + 2}$

90. $\dfrac{x}{2x + 2} \div \left(\dfrac{x}{x + 1} + \dfrac{x}{x - 1}\right)$

91. $\dfrac{4}{x} \cdot \left(\dfrac{2}{x + 2} - \dfrac{2}{x - 2}\right)$

92. $\dfrac{1}{x + 1} \cdot \left(\dfrac{5}{x} + \dfrac{2}{x - 3}\right)$

Perform each indicated operation. (Hint: First write each expression with positive exponents.)

93. $x^{-1} + (2x)^{-1}$

94. $y^{-1} + (4y)^{-1}$

95. $4x^{-2} - 3x^{-1}$

96. $(4x)^{-2} - (3x)^{-1}$

Use a graphing calculator to support the results of each exercise.

97. Exercise 3

98. Exercise 4

10.4 SIMPLIFYING COMPLEX FRACTIONS

Objectives

A. Simplify Complex Fractions by Simplifying the Numerator and Denominator and Then Dividing.

B. Simplify Complex Fractions by Multiplying by the Least Common Denominator (LCD).

C. Simplify Expressions with Negative Exponents.

A rational expression whose numerator, denominator, or both contain one or more rational expressions is called a **complex rational expression** or a **complex fraction.** Examples are

$$\frac{\frac{1}{a}}{\frac{b}{2}} \qquad \frac{\frac{x}{2y^2}}{\frac{6x - 2}{9y}} \qquad \frac{x + \frac{1}{y}}{y + 1}$$

The parts of a complex fraction are

$$\frac{\left.\dfrac{x}{y + 2}\right\}}{\left.7 + \dfrac{1}{y}\right\}} \quad \begin{array}{l} \leftarrow \text{Numerator of complex fraction} \\ \leftarrow \text{Main fraction bar} \\ \leftarrow \text{Denominator of complex fraction} \end{array}$$

Our goal in this section is to simplify complex fractions. A complex fraction is simplified when it is in the form $\dfrac{P}{Q}$, where P and Q are polynomials that have no common factors. Two methods of simplifying complex fractions are introduced.

Objective A Method 1: Simplifying a Complex Fraction by Simplifying the Numerator and Denominator and Then Dividing

In the first method we study, we simplify complex fractions by simplifying and dividing.

Simplifying a Complex Fraction: Method 1

Step 1: Simplify the numerator and the denominator of the complex fraction so that each is a single fraction.

Step 2: Perform the indicated division by multiplying the numerator of the complex fraction by the reciprocal of the denominator of the complex fraction.

Step 3: Simplify if possible.

Example 1 Simplify: $\dfrac{\dfrac{5x}{x + 2}}{\dfrac{10}{x - 2}}$

Solution:

$$\frac{\dfrac{5x}{x + 2}}{\dfrac{10}{x - 2}} = \frac{5x}{x + 2} \cdot \frac{x - 2}{10} \qquad \text{Multiply by the reciprocal of } \frac{10}{x - 2}.$$

$$= \frac{5 \; x(x - 2)}{2 \cdot 5 \; (x + 2)}$$

$$= \frac{x(x - 2)}{2(x + 2)} \qquad \text{Simplify.}$$

● Work Practice 1

PRACTICE 1

Use Method 1 to simplify:

$$\frac{\dfrac{6x}{x - 5}}{\dfrac{12}{x + 5}}$$

Answer

1. $\dfrac{x(x + 5)}{2(x - 5)}$

825

✓**Concept Check** Which of the following are equivalent to $\dfrac{\dfrac{1}{x}}{\dfrac{3}{y}}$?

a. $\dfrac{1}{x} \div \dfrac{3}{y}$　　**b.** $\dfrac{1}{x} \cdot \dfrac{y}{3}$　　**c.** $\dfrac{1}{x} \div \dfrac{y}{3}$

PRACTICE 2

Use Method 1 to simplify:

$$\frac{\dfrac{x}{y^2} - \dfrac{1}{y}}{\dfrac{y}{x^2} - \dfrac{1}{x}}$$

Example 2 Simplify: $\dfrac{\dfrac{x}{y^2} + \dfrac{1}{y}}{\dfrac{y}{x^2} + \dfrac{1}{x}}$

Solution: First we simplify the numerator and the denominator of the complex fraction separately so that each is a single fraction.

$$\frac{\dfrac{x}{y^2} + \dfrac{1}{y}}{\dfrac{y}{x^2} + \dfrac{1}{x}} = \frac{\dfrac{x}{y^2} + \dfrac{1 \cdot y}{y \cdot y}}{\dfrac{y}{x^2} + \dfrac{1 \cdot x}{x \cdot x}}$$

　The LCD is y^2.

　The LCD is x^2.

$$= \frac{\dfrac{x + y}{y^2}}{\dfrac{y + x}{x^2}}$$

　Add.

　Add.

$$= \frac{x + y}{y^2} \cdot \frac{x^2}{y + x}$$　Multiply by the reciprocal of $\dfrac{y + x}{x^2}$.

$$= \frac{x^2(x + y)}{y^2(y + x)}$$

$$= \frac{x^2}{y^2}$$　Simplify.

● **Work Practice 2**

Objective Ⓑ Method 2: Simplifying a Complex Fraction by Multiplying the Numerator and Denominator by the LCD

With this method, we multiply the numerator and the denominator of the complex fraction by the least common denominator (LCD) of all fractions in the complex fraction.

Simplifying a Complex Fraction: Method 2

Step 1: Multiply the numerator and the denominator of the complex fraction by the LCD of all the fractions in both the numerator and the denominator.

Step 2: Simplify.

PRACTICE 3

Use Method 2 to simplify:

$$\frac{\dfrac{6x}{x - 5}}{\dfrac{12}{x + 5}}$$

Example 3 Simplify: $\dfrac{\dfrac{5x}{x + 2}}{\dfrac{10}{x - 2}}$

Solution: Notice we are reworking Example 1 using Method 2. The least common denominator of $\dfrac{5x}{x + 2}$ and $\dfrac{10}{x - 2}$ is $(x + 2)(x - 2)$. We multiply both the numerator, $\dfrac{5x}{x + 2}$, and the denominator, $\dfrac{10}{x - 2}$, by this LCD.

Answers

2. $-\dfrac{x^2}{y^2}$　**3.** $\dfrac{x(x + 5)}{2(x - 5)}$

✓ **Concept Check Answer**

a and **b**

$$\dfrac{\dfrac{5x}{x+2}}{\dfrac{10}{x-2}} = \dfrac{\left(\dfrac{5x}{x+2}\right)\cdot (x+2)\,(x-2)}{\left(\dfrac{10}{x-2}\right)\cdot (x+2)\,(x-2)}$$

Multiply the numerator and denominator by the LCD.

$$= \dfrac{5\,x\cdot(x-2)}{2\cdot 5\cdot(x+2)}$$

Simplify.

$$= \dfrac{x(x-2)}{2(x+2)}$$

Simplify.

● Work Practice 3

Examples 1 and 3 are the same and simplify to the same rational expression. Regardless of what method you choose to use, the simplification is the same.

Example 4 Simplify: $\dfrac{\dfrac{x}{y^2}+\dfrac{1}{y}}{\dfrac{y}{x^2}+\dfrac{1}{x}}$

Solution: The least common denominator of $\dfrac{x}{y^2}, \dfrac{1}{y}, \dfrac{y}{x^2},$ and $\dfrac{1}{x}$ is x^2y^2.

$$\dfrac{\dfrac{x}{y^2}+\dfrac{1}{y}}{\dfrac{y}{x^2}+\dfrac{1}{x}} = \dfrac{\left(\dfrac{x}{y^2}+\dfrac{1}{y}\right)\cdot x^2y^2}{\left(\dfrac{y}{x^2}+\dfrac{1}{x}\right)\cdot x^2y^2}$$

Multiply the numerator and denominator by the LCD.

$$= \dfrac{\dfrac{x}{y^2}\cdot x^2y^2 + \dfrac{1}{y}\cdot x^2y^2}{\dfrac{y}{x^2}\cdot x^2y^2 + \dfrac{1}{x}\cdot x^2y^2}$$

Use the distributive property.

$$= \dfrac{x^3 + x^2y}{y^3 + xy^2}$$

Simplify.

$$= \dfrac{x^2\,(x+y)}{y^2\,(y+x)}$$

Factor.

$$= \dfrac{x^2}{y^2}$$

Simplify.

● Work Practice 4

PRACTICE 4

Use Method 2 to simplify:

$$\dfrac{\dfrac{x}{y^2}-\dfrac{1}{y}}{\dfrac{y}{x^2}-\dfrac{1}{x}}$$

Helpful Hint

Just as for Examples 1 and 3, Examples 2 and 4 are the same and they simplify to the same rational expression. Note that regardless of what method you use, the result is the same.

Objective ⓒ Simplifying Expressions with Negative Exponents

Some expressions containing negative exponents can be written as complex fractions. To simplify these expressions, we first write them as equivalent expressions with positive exponents.

Answer

4. $-\dfrac{x^2}{y^2}$

PRACTICE 5

Simplify: $\dfrac{2x^{-1} + 3y^{-1}}{x^{-1} - 2y^{-1}}$

Example 5 Simplify: $\dfrac{x^{-1} + 2xy^{-1}}{x^{-2} - x^{-2}y^{-1}}$

Solution: This fraction does not appear to be a complex fraction. However, if we write it by using only positive exponents, we see that it is a complex fraction.

$$\frac{x^{-1} + 2xy^{-1}}{x^{-2} - x^{-2}y^{-1}} = \frac{\dfrac{1}{x} + \dfrac{2x}{y}}{\dfrac{1}{x^2} - \dfrac{1}{x^2 y}}$$

The LCD of $\dfrac{1}{x}, \dfrac{2x}{y}, \dfrac{1}{x^2}$, and $\dfrac{1}{x^2 y}$ is $x^2 y$. We multiply both the numerator and denominator by $x^2 y$.

$$\frac{\dfrac{1}{x} + \dfrac{2x}{y}}{\dfrac{1}{x^2} - \dfrac{1}{x^2 y}} = \frac{\left(\dfrac{1}{x} + \dfrac{2x}{y}\right) \cdot x^2 y}{\left(\dfrac{1}{x^2} - \dfrac{1}{x^2 y}\right) \cdot x^2 y}$$

$$= \frac{\dfrac{1}{x} \cdot x^2 y + \dfrac{2x}{y} \cdot x^2 y}{\dfrac{1}{x^2} \cdot x^2 y - \dfrac{1}{x^2 y} \cdot x^2 y} \qquad \text{Use the distributive property.}$$

$$= \frac{xy + 2x^3}{y - 1} \qquad \text{Simplify.}$$

$$\text{or } \frac{x(y + 2x^2)}{y - 1}$$

● **Work Practice 5**

PRACTICE 6

Simplify: $\dfrac{5 - 3x^{-1}}{2 + (3x)^{-1}}$

Example 6 Simplify: $\dfrac{(2x)^{-1} + 1}{2x^{-1} - 1}$

Solution: $\dfrac{(2x)^{-1} + 1}{2x^{-1} - 1} = \dfrac{\dfrac{1}{2x} + 1}{\dfrac{2}{x} - 1}$ Write using positive exponents.

$$= \frac{\left(\dfrac{1}{2x} + 1\right) \cdot 2x}{\left(\dfrac{2}{x} - 1\right) \cdot 2x} \qquad \text{The LCD of } \dfrac{1}{2x} \text{ and } \dfrac{2}{x} \text{ is } 2x.$$

$$= \frac{\dfrac{1}{2x} \cdot 2x + 1 \cdot 2x}{\dfrac{2}{x} \cdot 2x - 1 \cdot 2x} \qquad \text{Use distributive property.}$$

$$= \frac{1 + 2x}{4 - 2x} \qquad \text{Simplify.}$$

Helpful Hint   Don't forget that $(2x)^{-1} = \dfrac{1}{2x}$, but $2x^{-1} = 2 \cdot \dfrac{1}{x} = \dfrac{2}{x}$.

● **Work Practice 6**

Answers

5. $\dfrac{2y + 3x}{y - 2x}$ **6.** $\dfrac{15x - 9}{6x + 1}$ or $\dfrac{3(5x - 3)}{6x + 1}$

Vocabulary and Readiness Check

Complete the steps by writing the simplified complex fraction.

1. $\dfrac{\dfrac{7}{x}}{\dfrac{1}{x}+\dfrac{z}{x}}=\dfrac{x\left(\dfrac{7}{x}\right)}{x\left(\dfrac{1}{x}\right)+x\left(\dfrac{z}{x}\right)}=$ _____

2. $\dfrac{\dfrac{x}{4}}{\dfrac{x^2}{2}+\dfrac{1}{4}}=\dfrac{4\left(\dfrac{x}{4}\right)}{4\left(\dfrac{x^2}{2}\right)+4\left(\dfrac{1}{4}\right)}=$ _____

Write each with positive exponents.

3. $x^{-2}=$ _____

4. $y^{-3}=$ _____

5. $2x^{-1}=$ _____

6. $(2x)^{-1}=$ _____

7. $(9y)^{-1}=$ _____

8. $9y^{-2}=$ _____

10.4 Exercise Set

Objectives A B Mixed Practice *Simplify each complex fraction. See Examples 1 through 4.*

1. $\dfrac{1+\dfrac{2}{5}}{2+\dfrac{3}{5}}$

2. $\dfrac{2+\dfrac{1}{7}}{3-\dfrac{4}{7}}$

3. $\dfrac{\dfrac{4}{x-1}}{\dfrac{x}{x-1}}$

4. $\dfrac{\dfrac{x}{x+2}}{\dfrac{2}{x+2}}$

5. $\dfrac{1-\dfrac{2}{x}}{x+\dfrac{4}{9x}}$

6. $\dfrac{5-\dfrac{3}{x}}{x+\dfrac{2}{3x}}$

** 7.** $\dfrac{\dfrac{10}{3x}}{\dfrac{5}{6x}}$

8. $\dfrac{\dfrac{15}{2x}}{\dfrac{5}{6x}}$

 9. $\dfrac{\dfrac{4x^2-y^2}{xy}}{\dfrac{2}{y}-\dfrac{1}{x}}$

10. $\dfrac{\dfrac{x^2-9y^2}{xy}}{\dfrac{1}{y}-\dfrac{3}{x}}$

11. $\dfrac{\dfrac{x+1}{3}}{\dfrac{2x-1}{6}}$

12. $\dfrac{\dfrac{x+3}{12}}{\dfrac{4x-5}{15}}$

13. $\dfrac{\dfrac{2}{x}+\dfrac{3}{x^2}}{\dfrac{4}{x^2}-\dfrac{9}{x}}$

14. $\dfrac{\dfrac{2}{x^2}+\dfrac{1}{x}}{\dfrac{4}{x^2}-\dfrac{1}{x}}$

15. $\dfrac{\dfrac{1}{x}+\dfrac{2}{x^2}}{x+\dfrac{8}{x^2}}$

16. $\dfrac{\dfrac{1}{y}+\dfrac{3}{y^2}}{y+\dfrac{27}{y^2}}$

17. $\dfrac{\dfrac{4}{5-x}+\dfrac{5}{x-5}}{\dfrac{2}{x}+\dfrac{3}{x-5}}$

18. $\dfrac{\dfrac{3}{x-4}-\dfrac{2}{4-x}}{\dfrac{2}{x-4}-\dfrac{2}{x}}$

** 19.** $\dfrac{\dfrac{x+2}{x}-\dfrac{2}{x-1}}{\dfrac{x+1}{x}+\dfrac{x+1}{x-1}}$

20. $\dfrac{\dfrac{5}{a+2}-\dfrac{1}{a-2}}{\dfrac{3}{2+a}+\dfrac{6}{2-a}}$

21. $\dfrac{\dfrac{2}{x}+3}{\dfrac{4}{x^2}-9}$

22. $\dfrac{2+\dfrac{1}{x}}{4x-\dfrac{1}{x}}$

23. $\dfrac{1 - \dfrac{1}{y}}{\dfrac{1}{y^2} - 1}$

24. $\dfrac{1 - \dfrac{2}{x}}{x - \dfrac{4}{x}}$

25. $\dfrac{\dfrac{-2x}{x^2 - xy}}{\dfrac{y}{x^2}}$

26. $\dfrac{\dfrac{7y}{x^2 + xy}}{\dfrac{y^2}{x^2}}$

27. $\dfrac{\dfrac{2}{x} + \dfrac{1}{x^2}}{\dfrac{y}{x^2} + 1}$

28. $\dfrac{\dfrac{5}{x^2} - \dfrac{2}{x}}{\dfrac{1}{x} + 2}$

29. $\dfrac{\dfrac{x}{9} - \dfrac{1}{x}}{1 + \dfrac{3}{x}}$

30. $\dfrac{\dfrac{x}{4} - \dfrac{4}{x}}{1 - \dfrac{4}{x}}$

31. $\dfrac{\dfrac{x - 1}{x^2 - 4}}{1 + \dfrac{1}{x - 2}}$

32. $\dfrac{\dfrac{x - 2}{x^2 - 9}}{1 + \dfrac{1}{x - 3}}$

33. $\dfrac{\dfrac{2}{x + 5} + \dfrac{4}{x + 3}}{\dfrac{3x + 13}{x^2 + 8x + 15}}$

34. $\dfrac{\dfrac{2}{x + 2} + \dfrac{6}{x + 7}}{\dfrac{4x + 13}{x^2 + 9x + 14}}$

Objective C *Simplify. See Examples 5 and 6.*

35. $\dfrac{x^{-1}}{x^{-2} + y^{-2}}$

36. $\dfrac{a^{-3} + b^{-1}}{a^{-2}}$

37. $\dfrac{2a^{-1} + 3b^{-2}}{a^{-1} - b^{-1}}$

38. $\dfrac{x^{-1} + y^{-1}}{3x^{-2} + 5y^{-2}}$

39. $\dfrac{1}{x - x^{-1}}$

40. $\dfrac{x^{-2}}{x + 3x^{-1}}$

41. $\dfrac{a^{-1} + 1}{a^{-1} - 1}$

42. $\dfrac{a^{-1} - 4}{4 + a^{-1}}$

43. $\dfrac{3x^{-1} + (2y)^{-1}}{x^{-2}}$

44. $\dfrac{5x^{-2} - 3y^{-1}}{x^{-1} + y^{-1}}$

45. $\dfrac{2a^{-1} + (2a)^{-1}}{a^{-1} + 2a^{-2}}$

46. $\dfrac{a^{-1} + 2a^{-2}}{2a^{-1} + (2a)^{-1}}$

47. $\dfrac{5x^{-1} + 2y^{-1}}{x^{-2}y^{-2}}$

48. $\dfrac{x^{-2}y^{-2}}{5x^{-1} + 2y^{-1}}$

49. $\dfrac{5x^{-1} - 2y^{-1}}{25x^{-2} - 4y^{-2}}$

50. $\dfrac{3x^{-1} + 3y^{-1}}{4x^{-2} - 9y^{-2}}$

Review

Solve each equation for x.

51. $7x + 2 = x - 3$

52. $4 - 2x = 17 - 5x$

53. $x^2 = 4x - 4$

54. $5x^2 + 10x = 15$

55. $\dfrac{x}{3} - 5 = 13$

56. $\dfrac{2x}{9} + 1 = \dfrac{7}{9}$

Concept Extensions

Solve. See the Concept Check in the section.

57. Which of the following are equivalent to $\dfrac{\frac{x+1}{9}}{\frac{y-2}{5}}$?

   a. $\dfrac{x+1}{9} \div \dfrac{y-2}{5}$

   b. $\dfrac{x+1}{9} \cdot \dfrac{y-2}{5}$

   c. $\dfrac{x+1}{9} \cdot \dfrac{5}{y-2}$

58. Which of the following are equivalent to $\dfrac{\frac{a}{7}}{\frac{b}{13}}$?

   a. $\dfrac{a}{7} \cdot \dfrac{b}{13}$

   b. $\dfrac{a}{7} \div \dfrac{b}{13}$

   c. $\dfrac{a}{7} \div \dfrac{13}{b}$

   d. $\dfrac{a}{7} \cdot \dfrac{13}{b}$

59. When the source of a sound is traveling toward a listener, the pitch that the listener hears due to the Doppler effect is given by the complex rational compression $\dfrac{a}{1 - \frac{s}{770}}$, where a is the actual pitch of the sound and s is the speed of the sound source. Simplify this expression.

60. In baseball, the earned run average (ERA) statistic gives the average number of earned runs scored on a pitcher per game. It is computed with the following expression: $\dfrac{E}{\frac{I}{9}}$, where E is the number of earned runs scored on a pitcher and I is the total number of innings pitched by the pitcher. Simplify this expression.

61. Which of the following are equivalent to $\dfrac{\frac{1}{x}}{\frac{3}{y}}$?

   a. $\dfrac{1}{x} \div \dfrac{3}{y}$ **b.** $\dfrac{1}{x} \cdot \dfrac{y}{3}$ **c.** $\dfrac{1}{x} \div \dfrac{y}{3}$

62. Which of the following are equivalent to $\dfrac{5}{\frac{2}{a}}$?

   a. $\dfrac{5}{1} \div \dfrac{2}{a}$ **b.** $\dfrac{1}{5} \div \dfrac{2}{a}$ **c.** $\dfrac{5}{1} \cdot \dfrac{2}{a}$

63. In your own words, explain one method for simplifying a complex fraction.

64. Explain your favorite method for simplifying a complex fraction and why.

Simplify.

65. $\dfrac{\dfrac{2}{y^2} - \dfrac{5}{xy} - \dfrac{3}{x^2}}{\dfrac{2}{y^2} + \dfrac{7}{xy} + \dfrac{3}{x^2}}$

66. $\dfrac{\dfrac{2}{x^2} - \dfrac{1}{xy} - \dfrac{1}{y^2}}{\dfrac{1}{x^2} - \dfrac{3}{xy} + \dfrac{2}{y^2}}$

67. $\dfrac{1}{1 + (1 + x)^{-1}}$

68. $\dfrac{(x + 2)^{-1} + (x - 2)^{-1}}{(x^2 - 4)^{-1}}$

69. $\dfrac{x}{1 - \dfrac{1}{1 + \dfrac{1}{x}}}$

70. $\dfrac{x}{1 - \dfrac{1}{1 - \dfrac{1}{x}}}$

In the study of calculus, the difference quotient $\dfrac{f(a + h) - f(a)}{h}$ is often found and simplified. Find and simplify this quotient for each function $f(x)$ by following steps **a** through **d**.

a. Find $f(a + h)$.

b. Find $f(a)$.

c. Use steps **a** and **b** to find $\dfrac{f(a + h) - f(a)}{h}$

d. Simplify the result of step **c**.

71. $f(x) = \dfrac{1}{x}$

72. $f(x) = \dfrac{5}{x}$

73. $f(x) = \dfrac{3}{x + 1}$

74. $f(x) = \dfrac{2}{x^2}$

10.5 SOLVING EQUATIONS CONTAINING RATIONAL EXPRESSIONS

Objective

A Solve Equations Containing Rational Expressions.

Objective **A** Solving Equations Containing Rational Expressions

In this section, we solve rational equations. A *rational equation* is an equation containing at least one rational expression. Before beginning this section, make sure that you understand the difference between an *equation* and an *expression*. An **equation** contains an equal sign and an **expression** does not.

Equation	**Expression**
$\dfrac{x}{2} + \dfrac{x}{6} \underset{\uparrow}{=} \dfrac{2}{3}$	$\dfrac{x}{2} + \dfrac{x}{6}$
equal sign	

Solving an Equation Containing Rational Expressions

To solve an *equation* containing rational expressions, first clear the equation of fractions by multiplying both sides of the equation by the LCD of all rational expressions. Then solve as usual.

> **Helpful Hint**
> The method described is for equations only. It may *not* be used for performing operations on expressions.

✔**Concept Check** True or false? Clearing fractions is valid when solving an equation and when simplifying rational expressions. Explain.

Example 1 Solve: $\dfrac{4x}{5} + \dfrac{3}{2} = \dfrac{3x}{10}$

Solution: The LCD of $\dfrac{4x}{5}, \dfrac{3}{2}$, and $\dfrac{3x}{10}$ is 10. We multiply both sides of the equation by 10.

$$\frac{4x}{5} + \frac{3}{2} = \frac{3x}{10}$$

$$10\left(\frac{4x}{5} + \frac{3}{2}\right) = 10\left(\frac{3x}{10}\right) \qquad \text{Multiply both sides by the LCD.}$$

$$10 \cdot \frac{4x}{5} + 10 \cdot \frac{3}{2} = 10 \cdot \frac{3x}{10} \qquad \text{Use the distributive property.}$$

$$8x + 15 = 3x \qquad \text{Simplify.}$$

$$15 = -5x \qquad \text{Subtract } 8x \text{ from both sides.}$$

$$-3 = x \qquad \text{Solve.}$$

We verify this solution by replacing x with -3 in the original equation.

Check: $\dfrac{4x}{5} + \dfrac{3}{2} = \dfrac{3x}{10}$

$$\frac{4(-3)}{5} + \frac{3}{2} \overset{?}{=} \frac{3(-3)}{10}$$

$$\frac{-12}{5} + \frac{3}{2} \overset{?}{=} \frac{-9}{10}$$

$$-\frac{24}{10} + \frac{15}{10} \overset{?}{=} -\frac{9}{10}$$

$$-\frac{9}{10} = -\frac{9}{10} \qquad \text{True}$$

The solution set is $\{-3\}$.

🔵 **Work Practice 1**

PRACTICE 1

Solve: $\dfrac{5x}{6} + \dfrac{1}{2} = \dfrac{x}{3}$

Answer
1. $\{-1\}$

✔**Concept Check Answer**
false; answers may vary

833

The important difference about the equations in this section is that the denominator of a rational expression may contain a variable. Recall that a rational expression is undefined for values of the variable that make the denominator 0. If a proposed solution makes the denominator 0, then it must be rejected as a solution of the original equation. Such proposed solutions are called **extraneous solutions.**

The following steps may be used to solve equations containing rational expressions.

To Solve an Equation Containing Rational Expressions

Step 1: Multiply both sides of the equation by the LCD of all rational expressions in the equation.

Step 2: Simplify both sides.

Step 3: Determine whether the equation is linear, quadratic, or higher degree and solve accordingly.

Step 4: Check the solution in the original equation.

PRACTICE 2

Solve: $\dfrac{5}{x} - \dfrac{3x + 6}{2x} = \dfrac{7}{2}$

Example 2 Solve: $\dfrac{3}{x} - \dfrac{x + 21}{3x} = \dfrac{5}{3}$

Solution: The LCD of the denominators x, $3x$, and 3 is $3x$. We multiply both sides by $3x$. (We are allowed to do this as long as $x \neq 0$.)

$$\frac{3}{x} - \frac{x + 21}{3x} = \frac{5}{3}$$

$$3x\left(\frac{3}{x} - \frac{x + 21}{3x}\right) = 3x\left(\frac{5}{3}\right) \quad \text{Multiply both sides by the LCD.}$$

$$3x \cdot \frac{3}{x} - 3x \cdot \frac{x + 21}{3x} = 3x \cdot \frac{5}{3} \quad \text{Use the distributive property.}$$

$$9 - (x + 21) = 5x \quad \text{Simplify.}$$

$$9 - x - 21 = 5x$$

$$-12 = 6x$$

$$-2 = x \quad \text{Solve.}$$

The proposed solution is -2.

Check: We check the proposed solution in the original equation.

$$\frac{3}{x} - \frac{x + 21}{3x} = \frac{5}{3}$$

$$\frac{3}{-2} - \frac{-2 + 21}{3(-2)} \stackrel{?}{=} \frac{5}{3}$$

$$-\frac{9}{6} + \frac{19}{6} \stackrel{?}{=} \frac{5}{3}$$

$$\frac{10}{6} = \frac{5}{3} \quad \text{True}$$

The solution set is $\{-2\}$.

● **Work Practice 2**

Let's talk more about multiplying both sides of an equation by the LCD of the rational expressions in the equation. In Example 3 that follows, the LCD is $x - 2$, so we will first multiply both sides of the equation by $x - 2$. Recall that the multiplication property for equations allows us to multiply both sides of an equation by

Answer

2. $\left\{\dfrac{2}{5}\right\}$

any *nonzero* number. In other words, for Example 3 below, we may multiply both sides of the equation by $x - 2$ *as long as* $x - 2 \neq 0$ or as long as $x \neq 2$. Keep this in mind when solving these equations.

Example 3 Solve: $\dfrac{x + 6}{x - 2} = \dfrac{2(x + 2)}{x - 2}$

Solution: First multiply both sides of the equation by the LCD, $x - 2$. (Remember, we can only do this if $x \neq 2$, so that we are not multiplying by 0.)

$$\frac{x + 6}{x - 2} = \frac{2(x + 2)}{x - 2}$$

$$(x - 2) \cdot \frac{x + 6}{x - 2} = (x - 2) \cdot \frac{2(x + 2)}{x - 2} \qquad \text{Multiply both sides by } x - 2.$$

$$x + 6 = 2(x + 2) \qquad \text{Simplify.}$$

$$x + 6 = 2x + 4 \qquad \text{Use the distributive property.}$$

$$2 = x \qquad \text{Solve.}$$

From above, we assumed that $x \neq 2$, so this equation has no solution. This will also show as we attempt to check this proposed solution.

Check: The proposed solution is 2. Notice that 2 makes the denominators 0 in the original equation. This can also be seen in a check. Check the proposed solution 2 in the original equation.

$$\frac{x + 6}{x - 2} = \frac{2(x + 2)}{x - 2}$$

$$\frac{2 + 6}{6 - 2} = \frac{2(2 + 2)}{2 - 2}$$

$$\frac{8}{0} = \frac{2(4)}{0}$$

The denominators are 0, so 2 is not a solution of the original equation. The solution set is $\varnothing$ or $\{\ \}$.

● **Work Practice 3**

Example 4 Solve: $\dfrac{2x}{2x - 1} + \dfrac{1}{x} = \dfrac{1}{2x - 1}$

Solution: The LCD is $x(2x - 1)$. Multiply both sides by $x(2x - 1)$. By the distributive property, this is the same as multiplying each term by $x(2x - 1)$.

$$x(2x - 1) \cdot \frac{2x}{2x - 1} + x(2x - 1) \cdot \frac{1}{x} = x(2x - 1) \cdot \frac{1}{2x - 1}$$

$$x(2x) + (2x - 1) = x$$

$$2x^2 + 2x - 1 - x = 0$$

$$2x^2 + x - 1 = 0$$

$$(x + 1)(2x - 1) = 0$$

$$x + 1 = 0 \quad \text{or} \quad 2x - 1 = 0$$

$$x = -1 \qquad\qquad x = \frac{1}{2}$$

The number $\dfrac{1}{2}$ makes the denominator $2x - 1$ equal 0, so it is not a solution. The solution set is $\{-1\}$.

● **Work Practice 4**

PRACTICE 3

Solve: $\dfrac{x + 5}{x - 3} = \dfrac{2(x + 1)}{x - 3}$

PRACTICE 4

Solve: $\dfrac{3x}{3x - 1} + \dfrac{1}{x} = \dfrac{1}{3x - 1}$

Answers
3. $\varnothing$ **4.** $\{-1\}$

PRACTICE 5

Solve:

$$\frac{2x}{x-4} + \frac{10-5x}{x^2-16} = \frac{x}{x+4}$$

Example 5 Solve: $\dfrac{2x}{x-3} + \dfrac{6-2x}{x^2-9} = \dfrac{x}{x+3}$

Solution: We factor the second denominator to find that the LCD is $(x+3)(x-3)$. We multiply both sides of the equation by $(x+3)(x-3)$. By the distributive property, this is the same as multiplying each term by $(x+3)(x-3)$.

$$\frac{2x}{x-3} + \frac{6-2x}{x^2-9} = \frac{x}{x+3}$$

$$(x+3)(x-3)\cdot\frac{2x}{x-3} + (x+3)(x-3)\cdot\frac{6-2x}{(x+3)(x-3)}$$

$$= (x+3)(x-3)\left(\frac{x}{x+3}\right)$$

$$2x(x+3) + (6-2x) = x(x-3) \quad \text{Simplify.}$$

$$2x^2 + 6x + 6 - 2x = x^2 - 3x \quad \text{Use the distributive property.}$$

Next we solve this quadratic equation by the factoring method. To do so, we first write the equation so that one side is 0.

$$x^2 + 7x + 6 = 0$$

$$(x+6)(x+1) = 0 \quad \text{Factor.}$$

$$x = -6 \quad \text{or} \quad x = -1 \quad \text{Set each factor equal to 0 and solve.}$$

Neither -6 nor -1 makes any denominator 0. Check to see that the solution set is $\{-6, -1\}$.

● **Work Practice 5**

PRACTICE 6

Solve:

$$\frac{3z}{3z^2+7z-6} - \frac{1}{z} = \frac{4}{3z^2-2z}$$

Example 6 Solve: $\dfrac{z}{2z^2+3z-2} - \dfrac{1}{2z} = \dfrac{3}{z^2+2z}$

Solution: Factor the denominators to find that the LCD is $2z(z+2)(2z-1)$. Multiply both sides by the LCD. Remember, by using the distributive property, this is the same as multiplying each term by $2z(z+2)(2z-1)$.

$$\frac{z}{2z^2+3z-2} - \frac{1}{2z} = \frac{3}{z^2+2z}$$

$$\frac{z}{(2z-1)(z+2)} - \frac{1}{2z} = \frac{3}{z(z+2)}$$

$$2z(z+2)(2z-1)\cdot\frac{z}{(2z-1)(z+2)} - 2z(z+2)(2z-1)\cdot\frac{1}{2z}$$

$$= 2z(z+2)(2z-1)\cdot\frac{3}{z(z+2)} \quad \begin{array}{l}\text{Apply the distributive}\\ \text{property.}\end{array}$$

$$2z(z) - (z+2)(2z-1) = 3\cdot2(2z-1) \quad \text{Simplify.}$$

$$2z^2 - (2z^2+3z-2) = 12z - 6$$

$$2z^2 - 2z^2 - 3z + 2 = 12z - 6$$

$$-3z + 2 = 12z - 6$$

$$-15z = -8$$

$$z = \frac{8}{15} \quad \text{Solve.}$$

The proposed solution $\dfrac{8}{15}$ does not make any denominator 0; the solution set is $\left\{\dfrac{8}{15}\right\}$.

● **Work Practice 6**

Answers

5. $\{-5, -2\}$ **6.** $\left\{-\dfrac{6}{11}\right\}$

A graph can be helpful in visualizing solutions of equations. For example, to visualize the solution of the equation $\dfrac{3}{x} - \dfrac{x+21}{3x} = \dfrac{5}{3}$ in Example 2, the graph of the related rational function $f(x) = \dfrac{3}{x} - \dfrac{x+21}{3x}$ is shown. A solution of the equation is an x-value that corresponds to a y-value of $\dfrac{5}{3}$.

Notice that an x-value of -2 corresponds to a y-value of $\dfrac{5}{3}$. The solution of the equation is indeed -2 as shown in Example 2.

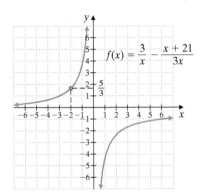

Vocabulary and Readiness Check

Determine whether each is an equation or an expression. Do not solve or simplify.

1. $\dfrac{x}{2} = \dfrac{3x}{5} + \dfrac{x}{6}$

2. $\dfrac{3x}{5} + \dfrac{x}{6}$

3. $\dfrac{x}{x-1} + \dfrac{2x}{x+1}$

4. $\dfrac{x}{x-1} + \dfrac{2x}{x+1} = 5$

5. $\dfrac{y+7}{2} = \dfrac{y+1}{6} + \dfrac{1}{y}$

6. $\dfrac{y+1}{6} + \dfrac{1}{y}$

Choose the least common denominator (LCD) for the rational expressions in each equation. Do not solve.

7. $\dfrac{x}{7} - \dfrac{x}{2} = \dfrac{1}{2}$; LCD = _____

    a. 7   **b.** 2   **c.** 14   **d.** 28

8. $\dfrac{9}{x+1} + \dfrac{5}{(x+1)^2} = \dfrac{x}{x+1}$; LCD = _____

    a. $x+1$ **b.** $(x+1)^2$ **c.** $(x+1)^3$

9. $\dfrac{7}{x-4} = \dfrac{x}{x^2-16} + \dfrac{1}{x+4}$; LCD = _____

    a. $(x+4)(x-4)$ **b.** $x-4$ **c.** $x+4$ **d.** $(x^2-16)(x-4)(x+4)$

10. $3 = \dfrac{1}{x-5} - \dfrac{2}{x^2-5x}$; LCD = _____

    a. $x-5$ **b.** $3(x-5)$ **c.** $3x(x-5)$ **d.** $x(x-5)$

10.5 Exercise Set

FOR EXTRA HELP

MyMathLab

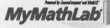 PRACTICE   WATCH   DOWNLOAD   READ   REVIEW

Objective Ⓐ *Solve each equation. See Examples 1 and 2.*

1. $\dfrac{x}{2} - \dfrac{x}{3} = 12$

2. $x = \dfrac{x}{2} - 4$

3. $\dfrac{x}{3} = \dfrac{1}{6} + \dfrac{x}{4}$

4. $\dfrac{x}{2} = \dfrac{21}{10} - \dfrac{x}{5}$

5. $\dfrac{2}{x} + \dfrac{1}{2} = \dfrac{5}{x}$

6. $\dfrac{5}{3x} + 1 = \dfrac{7}{6}$

7. $\dfrac{x^2+1}{x} = \dfrac{5}{x}$

8. $\dfrac{x^2-14}{2x} = -\dfrac{5}{2x}$

Solve each equation. See Examples 3 through 6.

9. $\dfrac{x+5}{x+3} = \dfrac{2}{x+3}$

10. $\dfrac{x-7}{x-1} = \dfrac{11}{x-1}$

11. $\dfrac{5}{x-2} - \dfrac{2}{x+4} = \dfrac{-4}{x^2+2x-8}$

12. $\dfrac{1}{x-1} + \dfrac{1}{x+1} = \dfrac{2}{x^2-1}$

13. $\dfrac{1}{x-1} = \dfrac{2}{x+1}$

14. $\dfrac{6}{x+3} = \dfrac{4}{x-3}$

15. $\dfrac{x^2-23}{2x^2-5x-3} + \dfrac{2}{x-3} = \dfrac{-1}{2x+1}$

16. $\dfrac{4x^2-24x}{3x^2-x-2} + \dfrac{3}{3x+2} = \dfrac{-4}{x-1}$

17. $\dfrac{1}{x-4} - \dfrac{3x}{x^2-16} = \dfrac{2}{x+4}$

18. $\dfrac{3}{2x+3} - \dfrac{1}{2x-3} = \dfrac{4}{4x^2-9}$

19. $\dfrac{1}{x-4} = \dfrac{8}{x^2-16}$

20. $\dfrac{2}{x^2-4} = \dfrac{1}{2x-4}$

21. $\dfrac{1}{x-2} - \dfrac{2}{x^2-2x} = 1$

22. $\dfrac{12}{3x^2+12x} = 1 - \dfrac{1}{x+4}$

Mixed Practice *Solve each equation. See Examples 1 through 6.*

23. $\dfrac{5}{x} = \dfrac{20}{12}$

24. $\dfrac{2}{x} = \dfrac{10}{5}$

25. $1 - \dfrac{4}{a} = 5$

26. $7 + \dfrac{6}{a} = 5$

27. $\dfrac{x^2+5}{x} - 1 = \dfrac{5(x+1)}{x}$

28. $\dfrac{x^2+6}{x} + 5 = \dfrac{2(x+3)}{x}$

29. $\dfrac{1}{2x} - \dfrac{1}{x+1} = \dfrac{1}{3x^2+3x}$

30. $\dfrac{2}{x-5} + \dfrac{1}{2x} = \dfrac{5}{3x^2-15x}$

31. $\dfrac{1}{x} - \dfrac{x}{25} = 0$

32. $\dfrac{x}{4} + \dfrac{5}{x} = 3$

33. $5 - \dfrac{2}{2y-5} = \dfrac{3}{2y-5}$

34. $1 - \dfrac{5}{y+7} = \dfrac{4}{y+7}$

35. $\dfrac{x-1}{x+2} = \dfrac{2}{3}$

36. $\dfrac{6x+7}{2x+9} = \dfrac{5}{3}$

37. $\dfrac{x+3}{x+2} = \dfrac{1}{x+2}$

38. $\dfrac{2x+1}{4-x} = \dfrac{9}{4-x}$

39. $\dfrac{1}{a-3} + \dfrac{2}{a+3} = \dfrac{1}{a^2-9}$

40. $\dfrac{12}{9-a^2} + \dfrac{3}{3+a} = \dfrac{2}{3-a}$

41. $\dfrac{64}{x^2-16} + 1 = \dfrac{2x}{x-4}$

42. $2 + \dfrac{3}{x} = \dfrac{2x}{x+3}$

43. $\dfrac{-15}{4y+1} + 4 = y$

44. $\dfrac{36}{x^2-9} + 1 = \dfrac{2x}{x+3}$

45. $\dfrac{28}{x^2-9} + \dfrac{2x}{x-3} + \dfrac{6}{x+3} = 0$

46. $\dfrac{x^2-20}{x^2-7x+12} = \dfrac{3}{x-3} + \dfrac{5}{x-4}$

47. $\dfrac{x+2}{x^2+7x+10} = \dfrac{1}{3x+6} - \dfrac{1}{x+5}$

48. $\dfrac{3}{2x-5} + \dfrac{2}{2x+3} = 0$

Review

Write each sentence as an equation and solve.

49. Four more than 3 times a number is 19. Find the number.

50. The sum of two consecutive integers is 147. Find the integers.

51. The length of a rectangle is 5 inches more than the width. Its perimeter is 50 inches. Find the length and width.

52. The sum of a number and its reciprocal is $\dfrac{5}{2}$. Find the number and its reciprocal.

The following graph is from a recent survey of state and federal prisons. Use this graph to answer Exercises 53 through 58.

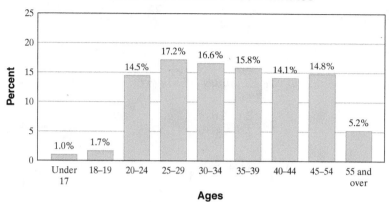

State and Federal Prison Inmates

Source: Bureau of Justice Statistics, U.S. Department of Justice

53. What percent of state and federal prison inmates are age 45 to 54?

54. What percent of state and federal prison inmates are 55 years old or older?

55. What age category shows the highest percent of prison inmates?

56. What percent of state and federal prison inmates are 20 to 34 years old?

57. At the end of 2008, there were 173,670 inmates under the jurisdiction of state and federal correction authorities in the state of California. Approximately how many 25- to 29-year-old inmates would you expect to have been held in California at the end of 2008? Round to the nearest whole. (*Source:* Bureau of Justice Statistics, U.S. Department of Justice)

58. Use the data from Exercise 57 to answer the following.

 a. Approximate the number of 35- to 39-year-old inmates you might expect to have been held in California at the end of 2008. Round to the nearest whole.

 b. Is your answer to part (a) greater than or less than your answer to Exercise 57? Is this reasonable? Why or why not?

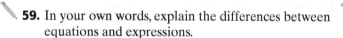

Concept Extensions

59. In your own words, explain the differences between equations and expressions.

60. In your own words, explain why it is necessary to check solutions to equations containing rational expressions.

61. The average cost of producing x game disks for a computer is given by the function $C(x) = 3.3 + \dfrac{5400}{x}$. Find the number of game disks that must be produced for the average cost to be $5.10.

62. The average cost of producing x electric pencil sharpeners is given by the function $C(x) = 20 + \dfrac{4000}{x}$. Find the number of electric pencil sharpeners that must be produced for the average cost to be $25.

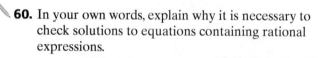

Solve each equation. Begin by writing each equation with positive exponents only.

63. $x^{-2} - 19x^{-1} + 48 = 0$ **64.** $x^{-2} - 5x^{-1} - 36 = 0$

65. $p^{-2} + 4p^{-1} - 5 = 0$ **66.** $6p^{-2} - 5p^{-1} + 1 = 0$

Solve each equation. Round solutions to two decimal places.

67. $\dfrac{1.4}{x - 2.6} = \dfrac{-3.5}{x + 7.1}$ **68.** $\dfrac{-8.5}{x + 1.9} = \dfrac{5.7}{x - 3.6}$

69. $\dfrac{10.6}{y} - 14.7 = \dfrac{9.92}{3.2} + 7.6$ **70.** $\dfrac{12.2}{x} + 17.3 = \dfrac{9.6}{x} - 14.7$

Solve each equation by substitution. For example, to solve Exercise 71, first let $u = x - 1$. After substituting, we have $u^2 + 3u + 2 = 0$. Solve for u and then substitute back to solve for x.

71. $(x - 1)^2 + 3(x - 1) + 2 = 0$ **72.** $(4 - x)^2 - 5(4 - x) + 6 = 0$

73. $\left(\dfrac{3}{x - 1}\right)^2 + 2\left(\dfrac{3}{x - 1}\right) + 1 = 0$ **74.** $\left(\dfrac{5}{2 + x}\right)^2 + \left(\dfrac{5}{2 + x}\right) - 20 = 0$

Use a graphing calculator to verify the solution of each given exercise.

75. Exercise 23   **76.** Exercise 24   **77.** Exercise 35   **78.** Exercise 36

A Solve an Equation Containing Rational Expressions for a Specified Variable.

B Solve Number Problems by Writing Equations Containing Rational Expressions.

C Solve Problems Modeled by Proportions.

D Solve Problems About Work.

E Solve Problems About Distance, Rate, and Time.

10.6 RATIONAL EQUATIONS AND PROBLEM SOLVING

Objective **A** Solving Rational Equations for a Specified Variable

In this section, we continue practicing this skill by solving equations containing rational expressions for a specified variable.

Solving an Equation for a Specified Variable

Step 1: Clear the equation of fractions or rational expressions by multiplying each side of the equation by the least common denominator (LCD) of all denominators in the equation.

Step 2: Use the distributive property to remove grouping symbols such as parentheses.

Step 3: Combine like terms on each side of the equation.

Step 4: Use the addition property of equality to rewrite the equation as an equivalent equation with terms containing the specified variable on one side and all other terms on the other side.

Step 5: Use the distributive property and the multiplication property of equality to get the specified variable alone.

PRACTICE 1

Solve $\dfrac{1}{x} + \dfrac{1}{y} = \dfrac{1}{z}$ for y.

Example 1 Solve $\dfrac{1}{x} + \dfrac{1}{y} = \dfrac{1}{z}$ for x.

Solution: To clear this equation of fractions, we multiply both sides of the equation by xyz, the LCD of $\dfrac{1}{x}, \dfrac{1}{y},$ and $\dfrac{1}{z}$.

$$\frac{1}{x} + \frac{1}{y} = \frac{1}{z}$$

$$xyz\left(\frac{1}{x} + \frac{1}{y}\right) = xyz\left(\frac{1}{z}\right) \quad \text{Multiply both sides by } xyz.$$

$$xyz\left(\frac{1}{x}\right) + xyz\left(\frac{1}{y}\right) = xyz\left(\frac{1}{z}\right) \quad \text{Use the distributive property.}$$

$$yz + xz = xy \quad \text{Simplify.}$$

Notice the two terms that contain the specified variable, x.

Next, we subtract xz from both sides so that all terms containing the specified variable x are on one side of the equation and all other terms are on the other side.

$$yz = xy - xz$$

Now we use the distributive property to factor x from $xy - xz$ and then the multiplication property of equality to solve for x.

$$yz = x(y - z)$$

$$\frac{yz}{y - z} = x \quad \text{or} \quad x = \frac{yz}{y - z} \quad \text{Divide both sides by } y - z.$$

● **Work Practice 1**

Answer

1. $y = \dfrac{xz}{x - z}$

Objective ⓑ Solving Number Problems Modeled by Rational Equations

Problem solving sometimes involves modeling a described situation with an equation containing rational expressions. In Examples 2 through 5, we practice solving such problems.

Example 2 Finding an Unknown Number

If a certain number is subtracted from the numerator and added to the denominator of $\frac{9}{19}$, the new fraction is equivalent to $\frac{1}{3}$. Find the number.

Solution:

1. **UNDERSTAND** the problem. Read and reread the problem and try guessing the solution. For example, if the unknown number is 3, we have

$$\frac{9-3}{19+3} = \frac{6}{22} = \frac{3}{11} \neq \frac{1}{3}$$

Thus, $\frac{9-3}{19+3} \neq \frac{1}{3}$ and 3 is not the correct number. Remember that the purpose of this step is not to guess the correct solution but to gain an understanding of the problem posed.

    We will let n = the number to be subtracted from the numerator and added to the denominator.

2. **TRANSLATE** the problem.

In words:	when the number is subtracted from the numerator and added to the denominator of the fraction $\frac{9}{19}$	this is equivalent to	$\frac{1}{3}$
	↓	↓	↓
Translate:	$\dfrac{9-n}{19+n}$	$=$	$\dfrac{1}{3}$

3. **SOLVE** the equation for n.

$$\frac{9-n}{19+n} = \frac{1}{3}$$

To solve for n, we begin by multiplying both sides by the LCD, $3(19+n)$.

$$3(19+n) \cdot \frac{9-n}{19+n} = 3(19+n) \cdot \frac{1}{3} \quad \text{Multiply both sides by the LCD.}$$
$$3(9-n) = 19+n \qquad \text{Simplify.}$$
$$27 - 3n = 19 + n$$
$$8 = 4n$$
$$2 = n \qquad\qquad \text{Solve.}$$

4. **INTERPRET** the results.

Check: If we subtract 2 from the numerator and add 2 to the denominator of $\frac{9}{19}$, we have $\frac{9-2}{19+2} = \frac{7}{21} = \frac{1}{3}$, and the problem checks.

State: The unknown number is 2.

 Work Practice 2

Objective ⓒ Solving Problems Modeled by Proportions

A **ratio** is the quotient of two numbers or two quantities. Since rational expressions are quotients of quantities, rational expressions are ratios, also. A **proportion** is a mathematical statement that two ratios are equal.

Let's review two methods for solving a proportion such as $\frac{x-3}{10} = \frac{7}{15}$. We can multiply both sides of the equation by the LCD, 30.

Multiply both sides by the LCD, 30.

$$30 \cdot \frac{x-3}{10} = 30 \cdot \frac{7}{15}$$
$$3(x-3) = 2 \cdot 7$$
$$3x - 9 = 14$$
$$3x = 23$$
$$x = \frac{23}{3}$$

We can also solve a proportion by setting cross products equal. Here, we are using the fact that if $\frac{a}{b} = \frac{c}{d}$, then $ad = bc$.

$$\frac{x-3}{10} = \frac{7}{15}$$

$$15(x-3) = 10 \cdot 7 \qquad \text{Set cross products equal.}$$
$$15x - 45 = 70 \qquad \text{Use the distributive property.}$$
$$15x = 115$$
$$x = \frac{115}{15} \quad \text{or} \quad \frac{23}{3}$$

A ratio of two different quantities is called a **rate.** For example $\frac{3 \text{ miles}}{2 \text{ hours}}$ or 1.5 miles/hour is a rate. The proportions we write to solve problems will sometimes include rates. When this happens, make sure that the rates contain units written in the same order.

PRACTICE 3

In the United States, 1 out of 50 homes is heated by wood. At this rate, how many homes in a community of 36,000 homes are heated by wood? (*Source:* 2000 Census Survey)

Example 3 In the United States, 7 out of every 25 homes are heated by electricity. At this rate, how many homes in a community of 36,000 homes would you predict are heated by electricity? (*Source:* Census Survey)

Solution:

1. UNDERSTAND. Read and reread the problem. Try to estimate a reasonable solution. For example, since 7 is less than $\frac{1}{3}$ of 25, we might reason that the solution would be less than $\frac{1}{3}$ of 36,000 or 12,000.

   Let's let x = number of homes in the community heated by electricity.

2. TRANSLATE.

   homes heated by electricity → $\dfrac{7}{25} = \dfrac{x}{36,000}$ ← homes heated by electricity
   total homes → ← total homes

3. SOLVE. To solve this proportion, we will set cross products equal.

$$\frac{7}{25} = \frac{x}{36,000}$$

$$7 \cdot 36,000 = 25x$$
$$\frac{252,000}{25} = x$$
$$10,080 = x$$

Answer

3. 720 homes

4. INTERPRET.

Check: To check, replace x with 10,080 in the proportion and see that a true statement results. Notice that our answer is reasonable since it is less than 12,000 as we stated above.

State: We predict that 10,080 homes are heated by electricity.

● Work Practice 3

Objective ⓓ Solving Problems About Work

The following work example leads to an equation containing rational expressions.

Example 4 Calculating Work Hours

Melissa Scarlatti can clean the house in 4 hours, whereas her husband, Zack, can do the same job in 5 hours. They have agreed to clean together so that they can finish in time to watch a movie on TV that starts in 2 hours. How long will it take them to clean the house together? Can they finish before the movie starts?

Solution:

1. Read and reread the problem. The key idea here is the relationship between the *time* (in hours) it takes to complete the job and the *part of the job* completed in 1 unit of time (1 hour). For example, if the *time* it takes Melissa to complete the job is 4 hours, the *part of the job* she can complete in 1 hour is $\frac{1}{4}$. Similarly, Zack can complete $\frac{1}{5}$ of the job in 1 hour.

   We will let t = the *time* in hours it takes Melissa and Zack to clean the house together. Then $\frac{1}{t}$ represents the *part of the job* they complete in 1 hour. We summarize the given information on a chart.

	Hours to Complete the Job	Part of Job Completed in 1 Hour
Melissa Alone	4	$\frac{1}{4}$
Zack Alone	5	$\frac{1}{5}$
Together	t	$\frac{1}{t}$

2. **TRANSLATE.**

	part of job Melissa can complete in 1 hour	added to	part of job Zack can complete in 1 hour	is equal to	part of job they can complete together in 1 hour
In words:	↓	↓	↓	↓	↓
Translate:	$\frac{1}{4}$	$+$	$\frac{1}{5}$	$=$	$\frac{1}{t}$

Continued on next page

PRACTICE 4

Greg Guillot can paint a room alone in 3 hours. His brother Phillip can do the same job alone in 5 hours. How long would it take them to paint the room if they work together?

Answer

4. $1\frac{7}{8}$ hr

3. SOLVE:

$$\frac{1}{4} + \frac{1}{5} = \frac{1}{t}$$

$$20t\left(\frac{1}{4} + \frac{1}{5}\right) = 20t\left(\frac{1}{t}\right) \qquad \text{Multiply both sides by the LCD, } 20t.$$

$$5t + 4t = 20$$

$$9t = 20$$

$$t = \frac{20}{9} \quad \text{or} \quad 2\frac{2}{9} \quad \text{Solve.}$$

4. INTERPRET.

Check: The proposed solution is $2\frac{2}{9}$. That is, Melissa and Zack would take $2\frac{2}{9}$ hours to clean the house together. This proposed solution is reasonable since $2\frac{2}{9}$ hours is more than half of Melissa's time and less than half of Zack's time. Check this solution in the originally stated problem.

State: Melissa and Zack can clean the house together in $2\frac{2}{9}$ hours. They cannot complete the job before the movie starts.

⬤ **Work Practice 4**

Objective ⓔ Solving Problems About Distance, Rate, and Time

Before we solve Example 5 on the next page, let's review the formula

$$d = r \cdot t, \quad \text{or} \quad \text{distance} = \text{rate} \cdot \text{time}$$

For example, if we travel at a rate or speed of 60 mph for a time of 3 hours, the distance we travel is

$$d = 60 \text{ mph} \cdot 3 \text{ hr}$$
$$= 180 \text{ mi}$$

The Formula $d = r \cdot t$ is solved for distance, d. We can also solve this formula for rate r or for time t.

Solve $d = r \cdot t$ for r.   Solve $d = r \cdot t$ for t.

$$d = r \cdot t \qquad\qquad\qquad d = r \cdot t$$

$$\frac{d}{t} = \frac{r \cdot t}{t} \qquad\qquad\qquad \frac{d}{r} = \frac{r \cdot t}{r}$$

$$\frac{d}{t} = r \qquad\qquad\qquad\qquad \frac{d}{r} = t$$

All three forms of the distance formula are useful, as we shall see.

Example 5   Finding the Speed of a Current

Steve Deitmer takes $1\frac{1}{2}$ times as long to go 72 miles upstream in his boat as he does to return. If the boat cruises at 30 mph in still water, what is the speed of the current?

Solution:

1. **UNDERSTAND.** Read and reread the problem. Guess a solution. Suppose that the current is 4 mph. The speed of the boat upstream is slowed down by the current: $30 - 4$, or 26 mph, and the speed of the boat downstream is speeded up by the current: $30 + 4$, or 34 mph. Next let's find out how long it takes to travel 72 miles upstream and 72 miles downstream. To do so, we use the formula $d = r \cdot t$, or $\frac{d}{r} = t$.

Upstream

$$\frac{d}{r} = t$$

$$\frac{72}{26} = t$$

$$2\frac{10}{13} = t$$

Downstream

$$\frac{d}{r} = t$$

$$\frac{72}{34} = t$$

$$2\frac{2}{17} = t$$

Since the time upstream $\left(2\frac{10}{13} \text{ hours}\right)$ is not $1\frac{1}{2}$ times the time downstream $\left(2\frac{2}{17} \text{ hours}\right)$, our guess is not correct. We do, however, have a better understanding of the problem.

     We will let

$$x = \text{the speed of the current}$$
$$30 + x = \text{the speed of the boat downstream}$$
$$30 - x = \text{the speed of the boat upstream}$$

This information is summarized in the following chart, where we use the formula $\frac{d}{r} = t$.

	Distance	**Rate**	**Time** $\left(\frac{d}{r}\right)$
Upstream	72	$30 - x$	$\dfrac{72}{30 - x}$
Downstream	72	$30 + x$	$\dfrac{72}{30 + x}$

Continued on next page

Continued on next page

PRACTICE 5

A fisherman traveling on the Pearl River takes $\frac{2}{3}$ times as long to travel 60 miles downstream in his boat than to return. If the boat's speed is 25 mph in still water, find the speed of the current.

Answer

5. 5 mph

2. **TRANSLATE.** Since the time spent traveling upstream is $1\frac{1}{2}$ times the time spent traveling downstream, we have

In words:	time upstream	is	$1\frac{1}{2}$	times	time downstream
	↓	↓	↓	↓	↓
Translate:	$\dfrac{72}{30-x}$	$=$	$\dfrac{3}{2}$	$\cdot$	$\dfrac{72}{30+x}$

3. **SOLVE.** $\dfrac{72}{30-x} = \dfrac{3}{2} \cdot \dfrac{72}{30+x}$

First we multiply both sides by the LCD, $2(30+x)(30-x)$.

$$2(30+x)(30-x) \cdot \frac{72}{30-x} = 2(30+x)(30-x)\left(\frac{3}{2} \cdot \frac{72}{30+x}\right)$$

$$72 \cdot 2(30+x) = 3 \cdot 72 \cdot (30-x) \quad \text{Simplify.}$$

$$2(30+x) = 3(30-x) \quad \text{Divide both sides by 72.}$$

$$60 + 2x = 90 - 3x \quad \text{Use the distributive property.}$$

$$5x = 30$$

$$x = 6 \quad \text{Solve.}$$

4. **INTERPRET.**

Check: Check the proposed solution of 6 mph in the originally stated problem.

State: The current's speed is 6 mph.

● **Work Practice 5**

10.6 Exercise Set

FOR EXTRA HELP

MyMathLab

 PRACTICE

 WATCH

 DOWNLOAD

 READ

REVIEW

Objective Ⓐ *Solve each equation for the specified variable. See Example 1.*

1. $F = \dfrac{9}{5}C + 32$ for C

2. $V = \dfrac{1}{3}\pi r^2 h$ for h

3. $Q = \dfrac{A - I}{L}$ for I

4. $P = 1 - \dfrac{C}{S}$ for S

5. $\dfrac{1}{R} = \dfrac{1}{R_1} + \dfrac{1}{R_2}$ for R

6. $\dfrac{1}{R} = \dfrac{1}{R_1} + \dfrac{1}{R_2}$ for R_1

7. $S = \dfrac{n(a + L)}{2}$ for n

8. $S = \dfrac{n(a + L)}{2}$ for a

9. $A = \dfrac{h(a + b)}{2}$ for b

10. $A = \dfrac{h(a + b)}{2}$ for h

11. $\dfrac{P_1 V_1}{T_1} = \dfrac{P_2 V_2}{T_2}$ for T_2

12. $H = \dfrac{k A(T_1 - T_2)}{L}$ for T_2

13. $f = \dfrac{f_1 f_2}{f_1 + f_2}$ for f_2

14. $I = \dfrac{E}{R + r}$ for r

15. $\lambda = \dfrac{2L}{n}$ for L

16. $S = \dfrac{a_1 - a_n r}{1 - r}$ for a_1

17. $\dfrac{\theta}{\omega} = \dfrac{2L}{c}$ for c

18. $F = \dfrac{-GMm}{r^2}$ for M

Objective Ⓑ *Solve. For Exercises 19 and 20, the solutions have been started for you. See Example 2.*

19. The sum of a number and 5 times its reciprocal is 6. Find the number(s).

Start the solution:

1. UNDERSTAND the problem. Reread it as many times as needed. Let's let

   x = a number. Then

   $\dfrac{1}{x}$ = its reciprocal.

2. TRANSLATE into an equation. (Fill in the blanks below.)

a number	plus	5	times	its reciprocal	is	6
↓	↓	↓	↓	↓	↓	↓
____	+	5	·	____	=	6

   Finish with:

3. SOLVE and

4. INTERPRET

20. The quotient of a number and 9 times its reciprocal is 1. Find the number(s).

Start the solution:

1. UNDERSTAND the problem. Reread it as many times as needed. Let's let

   x = a number. Then

   $\dfrac{1}{x}$ = its reciprocal.

2. TRANSLATE into an equation. (Fill in the blanks below.)

a number	divided by	9	times	its reciprocal	is	1
↓	↓	↓	↓	↓	↓	↓
____	÷	9	·	____	=	1

   Finish with:

3. SOLVE and

4. INTERPRET

21. If a number is added to the numerator of $\frac{12}{41}$ and twice the number is added to the denominator of $\frac{12}{41}$, the resulting fraction is equivalent to $\frac{1}{3}$. Find the number.

22. If a number is subtracted from the numerator of $\frac{13}{8}$ and added to the denominator of $\frac{13}{8}$, the resulting fraction is equivalent to $\frac{2}{5}$. Find the number.

Objective Ⓒ *Solve. See Example 3.*

23. An Arabian camel can drink 15 gallons of water in 10 minutes. At this rate, how much water can the camel drink in 3 minutes? (*Source:* Grolier, Inc.)

24. An Arabian camel can travel 20 miles in 8 hours, carrying a 300-pound load on its back. At this rate, how far can the camel travel in 10 hours? (*Source:* Grolier, Inc.)

25. In 2009, 12.5 out of every 100 Coast Guard personnel were women. If there were 43,628 total Coast Guard personnel on active duty, estimate the number of women. Round to the nearest whole. (*Source:* Women in Military Service for America Memorial Foundation, Inc.)

26. In 2009, 47 out of every 50 marine personnel were men. If there were 202,786 total marine personnel in 2009, estimate the number of men. Round to the nearest whole. (*Source:* Women in Military Service for America Memorial Foundation, Inc.)

Objective Ⓓ *Solve. See Example 4.*

27. An experienced roofer can roof a house in 26 hours. A beginning roofer needs 39 hours to complete the same job. Find how long it takes for the two to do the job together.

28. Alan Cantrell can word process a research paper in 6 hours. With Steve Isaac's help, the paper can be processed in 4 hours. Find how long it takes Steve to word process the paper alone.

29. Three postal workers can sort a stack of mail in 20 minutes, 30 minutes, and 60 minutes, respectively. Find how long it takes them to sort the mail if all three work together.

30. A new printing press can print newspapers twice as fast as the old one can. The old one can print the afternoon edition in 4 hours. Find how long it takes to print the afternoon edition if both printers are operating.

Objective Ⓔ *Solve. See Example 5.*

31. Mattie Evans drove 150 miles in the same amount of time that it took a turbopropeller plane to travel 600 miles. The speed of the plane was 150 mph faster than the speed of the car. Find the speed of the plane.

32. An F-100 plane and a Toyota truck leave the same town at sunrise and head for a town 450 miles away. The speed of the plane is three times the speed of truck, and the plane arrives 6 hours ahead of the truck. Find the speed of the truck.

33. The speed of Lazy River's current is 5 mph. If a boat travels 20 miles downstream in the same time that it takes to travel 10 miles upstream, find the speed of the boat in still water.

34. The speed of a boat in still water is 24 mph. If the boat travels 54 miles upstream in the same time that it takes to travel 90 miles downstream, find the speed of the current.

Objectives Ⓑ Ⓒ Ⓓ Ⓔ **Mixed Practice** *Solve. See Examples 2 through 5.*

35. The sum of the reciprocals of two consecutive integers is $-\frac{15}{56}$. Find the two integers.

36. The sum of the reciprocals of two consecutive odd integers is $\frac{20}{99}$. Find the two integers.

37. One hose can fill a goldfish pond in 45 minutes, and if a second hose is used, the two hoses can fill the same pond in 20 minutes. Find how long it takes the second hose alone to fill the pond.

38. If Sarah Clark can do a job in 5 hours and Dick Belli and Sarah working together can do the same job in 2 hours, find how long it takes Dick to do the job alone.

39. Two trains going in opposite directions leave at the same time. One train travels 15 mph faster than the other. In 6 hours the trains are 630 miles apart. Find the speed of each.

40. The speed of Alberto Contador during the fourth stage of the 2010 Paris–Nice bicycle race was 6 kilometers/hour faster than Jimmy Casper, who came in last in the stage. If Contador traveled 208 kilometers in the time that Casper traveled 181.35 kilometers, find the speed of Casper, rounded to the nearest tenth.

41. A giant tortoise can travel 0.17 miles in 1 hour. At this rate, how long would it take the tortoise to travel 1 mile? Round to the nearest tenth of an hour. (*Source: The World Almanac*)

42. A black mamba snake can travel 88 feet in 3 seconds. At this rate, how long does it take to travel 300 feet (the length of a football field)? Round to the nearest tenth of a second. (*Source: The World Almanac, 2002*).

43. Moo Dairy has three machines to fill half-gallon milk cartons. The machines can fill the daily quota in 5 hours, 6 hours, and 7.5 hours, respectively. Find how long it takes to fill the daily quota if all three machines are running.

44. The inlet pipe of an oil tank can fill the tank in 1 hour 30 minutes. The outlet pipe can empty the tank in 1 hour. Find how long it takes to empty a full tank if both pipes are open.

45. A plane flies 465 miles with the wind and 345 miles against the wind in the same length of time. If the speed of the wind is 20 mph, find the speed of the plane in still air.

46. Two rockets are launched. The first travels at 9000 mph. Fifteen minutes later the second is launched at 10,000 mph. Find the distance at which both rockets are the same distance from Earth.

47. Two joggers, one averaging 8 mph and one averaging 6 mph, start from a designated initial point. The slower jogger arrives at the end of the run a half-hour after the other jogger. Find the distance of the run.

48. A semi truck travels 300 miles through the flatland in the same amount of time that it travels 180 miles through the Great Smoky Mountains. The rate of the truck is 20 miles per hour slower in the mountains than in the flatland. Find both the flatland rate and mountain rate.

49. The denominator of a fraction is 1 more than the numerator. If both the numerator and the denominator are decreased by 3, the resulting fraction is equivalent to $\frac{4}{5}$. Find the fraction.

50. The numerator of a fraction is 4 less than the denominator. If both the numerator and the denominator are increased by 2, the resulting fraction is equivalent to $\frac{2}{3}$. Find the fraction.

51. In 2 minutes, a conveyor belt can move 300 pounds of recyclable aluminum from the delivery truck to a storage area. A smaller belt can move the same quantity of cans the same distance in 6 minutes. If both belts are used, find how long it takes to move the cans to the storage area.

52. Gary Marcus and Tony Alva work at Lombardo's Pipe and Concrete. Mr. Lombardo is preparing an estimate for a customer. He knows that Gary can lay a slab of concrete in 6 hours. Tony can lay the same size slab in 4 hours. If both work on the job and the cost of labor is $45.00 per hour, determine what the labor estimate should be.

53. The world record for the largest white bass caught is held by Ronald Sprouse of Virginia. The bass weighed 6 pounds 13 ounces. If Ronald rows to his favorite fishing spot 9 miles downstream in the same amount of time that he rows 3 miles upstream and if the current is 6 mph, find how long it takes him to cover the 12 miles.

54. An amateur cyclist training for a road race rode the first 20-mile portion of his workout at a constant rate. For the 16-mile cooldown portion of his workout, he reduced his speed by 2 miles per hour. Each portion of the workout took equal time. Find the cyclist's rate during the first portion and his rate during the cooldown portion.

55. Smith Engineering is in the process of reviewing the salaries of their surveyors. During this review, the company found that an experienced surveyor can survey a roadbed in 4 hours. An apprentice surveyor needs 5 hours to survey the same stretch of road. If the two work together, find how long it takes them to complete the job.

56. Mr. Dodson can paint his house by himself in four days. His son will need an additional day to complete the job if he works by himself. If they work together, find how long it takes to paint the house.

57. An experienced bricklayer can construct a small wall in 3 hours. An apprentice can complete the job in 6 hours. Find how long it takes if they work together.

58. A marketing manager travels 1080 miles in a corporate jet and then an additional 240 miles by car. If the car ride takes 1 hour longer, and if the rate of the jet is 6 times the rate of the car, find the time the manager travels by jet and find the time she travels by car.

Review

Solve each equation.

59. $\dfrac{x}{5} = \dfrac{x+2}{3}$

60. $\dfrac{x}{4} = \dfrac{x+3}{6}$

61. $\dfrac{x-3}{2} = \dfrac{x-5}{6}$

62. $\dfrac{x-6}{4} = \dfrac{x-2}{5}$

Concept Extensions

Calculating body-mass index (BMI) is a way to gauge whether a person should lose weight. Doctors recommend that body-mass index values fall between 19 and 25. The formula for body-mass index B is $B = \dfrac{705w}{h^2}$, where w is weight in pounds and h is height in inches. Use this formula to answer Exercises 63 and 64.

63. A patient is 5 ft 8 in. tall. What should his or her weight be to have a body-mass index of 25? Round to the nearest whole pound.

64. A doctor recorded a body-mass index of 47 on a patient's chart. Later, a nurse notices that the doctor recorded the patient's weight as 240 pounds but neglected to record the patient's height. Explain how the nurse can use the information from the chart to find the patient's height. Then find the height.

In physics, when the source of a sound is traveling toward an observer, the relationship between the actual pitch a of the sound and the pitch h that the observer hears due to the Doppler effect is described by the formula $h = \dfrac{a}{1 - \dfrac{s}{770}}$, where s is the speed of the sound source in miles per hour. Use this formula to answer Exercises 65 and 66.

65. An emergency vehicle has a single-tone siren with the pitch of the musical note E. As it approaches an observer standing by the road, the vehicle is traveling 50 mph. Is the pitch that the observer hears due to the Doppler effect lower or higher than the actual pitch? To which musical note is the pitch that the observer hears closest?

66. Suppose an emergency van has a single-tone siren with the pitch of the musical note G. If the van is traveling at 80 mph approaching a standing observer, name the pitch the observer hears and the musical note closest to that pitch.

Pitch of an Octave of Musical Notes in Hertz (Hz)	
Note	**Pitch**
Middle C	261.63
D	293.66
E	329.63
F	349.23
G	392.00
A	440.00
B	493.88

Note: Greater numbers indicate higher pitches (acoustically).

(*Source:* American Standards Association)

In electronics, the relationship among the resistances R_1 and R_2 of two resistors wired in a parallel circuit and their combined resistance R is described by the formula $\dfrac{1}{R} = \dfrac{1}{R_1} + \dfrac{1}{R_2}$. Use this formula to solve Exercises 67 through 69.

67. If the combined resistance is 2 ohms and one of the two resistances is 3 ohms, find the other resistance.

68. Find the combined resistance of two resistors of 12 ohms each when they are wired in a parallel circuit.

69. The relationship among resistance of two resistors wired in a parallel circuit and their combined resistance may be extended to three resistors of resistances R_1, R_2, and R_3. Write an equation you think may describe the relationship, and use it to find the combined resistance if R_1 is 5, R_2 is 6, and R_3 is 2.

70. For the formula $\dfrac{1}{x} = \dfrac{1}{y} + \dfrac{1}{z} - \dfrac{1}{w}$, find x if $y = 2$, $z = 7$, and $w = 6$.

10.7 VARIATION AND PROBLEM SOLVING

Objective **A** Solving Problems Involving Direct Variation

A very familiar example of **direct variation** is the relationship of the circumference C of a circle to its radius r. The formula $C = 2\pi r$ expresses that the circumference is always 2π times the radius. In other words, C is always a constant multiple (2π) of r. Because it is, we say that *C varies directly as r*, that *C varies directly with r*, or that *C is directly proportional to r*.

$$C = 2\pi r$$
constant

Direct Variation

y varies directly as x, or **y is directly proportional to x,** if there is a nonzero constant k such that

$$y = kx$$

The number k is called the **constant of variation** or the **constant of proportionality.**

In the above definition, the relationship described between x and y is a linear one. In other words, the graph of $y = kx$ is a line. The slope of the line is k, and the line passes through the origin.

For example, the graph of the direct variation equation $C = 2\pi r$ is shown. The horizontal axis represents the radius r, and the vertical axis is the circumference C. From the graph we can read that when the radius is 6 units, the circumference is approximately 38 units. Also, when the circumference is 45 units, the radius is between 7 and 8 units. Notice that as the radius increases, the circumference increases.

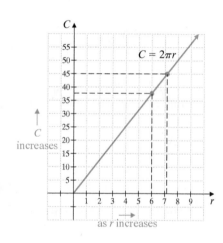

Suppose that y varies directly as x. If y is 24 when x is 8, find the constant of variation and the direct variation equation.

Example 1 Suppose that y varies directly as x. If y is 5 when x is 30, find the constant of variation and the direct variation equation.

Solution: Since y varies directly as x, we write $y = kx$. If $y = 5$ when $x = 30$, we have that

$$y = kx$$
$$5 = k(30) \quad \text{Replace } y \text{ with 5 and } x \text{ with 30.}$$
$$\frac{1}{6} = k \quad \text{Solve for } k.$$

The constant of variation is $\frac{1}{6}$.

After finding the constant of variation k, the direct variation equation can be written as $y = \frac{1}{6}x$.

● **Work Practice 1**

Answer

1. $k = 3$; $y = 3x$

854

Example 2 Using Direct Variation and Hooke's Law

Hooke's law states that the distance a spring stretches is directly proportional to the weight attached to the spring. If a 40-pound weight attached to the spring stretches the spring 5 inches, find the distance that a 65-pound weight attached to the spring stretches the spring.

Solution:

1. UNDERSTAND. Read and reread the problem. Notice that we are given that the distance a spring stretches is *directly proportional* to the weight attached. We let

    d = the distance stretched.

    w = the weight attached

The constant of variation is represented by k.

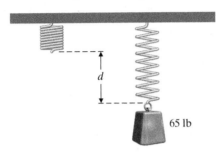

2. TRANSLATE. Because d is directly proportional to w, we write

    $d = kw$

3. SOLVE. When a weight of 40 pounds is attached, the spring stretches 5 inches. That is, when $w = 40, d = 5$.

    $5 = k(40)$ Replace d with 5 and w with 40.

    $\dfrac{1}{8} = k$ Solve for k.

    Now when we replace k with $\dfrac{1}{8}$ in the equation $d = kw$, we have

    $d = \dfrac{1}{8}w$

    To find the stretch when a weight of 65 pounds is attached, we replace w with 65 to find d.

    $d = \dfrac{1}{8}(65)$

    $= \dfrac{65}{8} = 8\dfrac{1}{8}$ or 8.125

4. INTERPRET.

Check: Check the proposed solution of 8.125 inches in the original problem.

State: The spring stretches 8.125 inches when a 65-pound weight is attached.

● Work Practice 2

Objective ⒷSolving Problems Involving Inverse Variation

When y is proportional to the *reciprocal* of another variable x, we say that y *varies inversely as* x, or that y *is inversely proportional to* x. An example of the **inverse variation** relationship is the relationship between the pressure that a gas exerts and

PRACTICE 2

Use Hooke's law as stated in Example 2. If a 56-pound weight attached to a spring stretches the spring 8 inches, find the distance that an 85-pound weight attached to the spring stretches the spring.

Answer

2. $12\dfrac{1}{7}$ in.

the volume of its container. As the volume of a container decreases, the pressure of the gas it contains increases.

> ### *Inverse Variation*
>
> ***y* varies inversely as *x*,** or ***y* is inversely proportional to *x*,** if there is a nonzero constant *k* such that
>
> $$y = \frac{k}{x}$$
>
> The number *k* is called the **constant of variation** or the **constant of proportionality.**

Notice that $y = \frac{k}{x}$ is an equation containing a rational expression. Its graph for $k > 0$ and $x > 0$ is shown. From the graph, we can see that as *x* increases, *y* decreases.

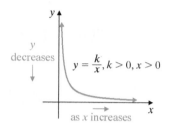

$$y = \frac{k}{x}, k > 0, x > 0$$

Example 3 Suppose that *u* varies inversely as *w*. If *u* is 3 when *w* is 5, find the constant of variation and the inverse variation equation.

Solution: Since *u* varies inversely as *w*, we have $u = \frac{k}{w}$. We let $u = 3$ and $w = 5$, and we solve for *k*.

$$u = \frac{k}{w}$$

$$3 = \frac{k}{5} \qquad \text{Let } u = 3 \text{ and } w = 5.$$

$$15 = k \qquad \text{Multiply both sides by 5.}$$

The constant of variation *k* is 15. This gives the inverse variation equation

$$u = \frac{15}{w}$$

● **Work Practice 3**

Example 4 Using Inverse Variation and Boyle's Law

Boyle's law says that if the temperature stays the same, the pressure *P* of a gas is inversely proportional to the volume *V*. If a cylinder in a steam engine has a pressure of 960 kilopascals when the volume is 1.4 cubic meters, find the pressure when the volume increases to 2.5 cubic meters.

PRACTICE 3

Suppose that *y* varies inversely as *x*. If *y* is 6 when *x* is 3, find the constant of variation and the inverse variation equation.

PRACTICE 4

The speed *r* at which one needs to drive in order to travel a constant distance is inversely proportional to the time *t*. A fixed distance can be driven in 5 hours at a rate of 24 mph. Find the rate needed to drive the same distance in 4 hours.

Answers

3. $k = 18; y = \dfrac{18}{x}$ **4.** 30 mph

Solution:

1. UNDERSTAND. Read and reread the problem. Notice that we are given that the pressure of a gas is *inversely proportional* to the volume. We will let P = the pressure and V = the volume. The constant of variation is represented by k.

2. TRANSLATE. Because P is inversely proportional to V, we write

$$P = \frac{k}{V}.$$

When P = 960 kilopascals, the volume V = 1.4 cubic meters. We use this information to find k.

$$960 = \frac{k}{1.4} \quad \text{Let } P = 960 \text{ and } V = 1.4.$$

$$1344 = k \quad \text{Multiply both sides by 1.4.}$$

Thus, the value of k is 1344. Replacing k with 1344 in the variation equation, we have

$$P = \frac{1344}{V}$$

Next we find P when V is 2.5 cubic meters.

3. SOLVE.

$$P = \frac{1344}{2.5} \quad \text{Let } V = 2.5$$

$$= 537.6$$

4. INTERPRET. *Check* the proposed solution in the original problem.

State: When the volume is 2.5 cubic meters, the pressure is 537.6 kilopascals.

● Work Practice 4

Objective ⓒ Solving Problems Involving Joint Variation

Sometimes the ratio of a variable to the product of many other variables is constant. For example, the ratio of distance traveled to the product of speed and time traveled is constantly 1:

$$\frac{d}{rt} = 1 \quad \text{or} \quad d = rt$$

Such a relationship is called **joint variation.**

Joint Variation

If the ratio of a variable y to the product of two or more variables is constant, then y **varies jointly as,** or **is jointly proportional to,** the other variables. If

$$y = kxz$$

then the number k is the **constant of variation** or the **constant of proportionality.**

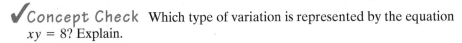 Concept Check Which type of variation is represented by the equation $xy = 8$? Explain.

a. Direct variation

b. Inverse variation

c. Joint variation

PRACTICE 5

The area of a triangle varies jointly as its base and height. Express the area in terms of base b and height h.

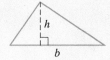

Example 5 The lateral surface area of a cylinder varies jointly as its radius and height. Express surface area S in terms of radius r and height h.

Solution: Because the surface area varies jointly as the radius r and the height h, we equate S to a constant multiple of r and h:

$$S = krh$$

Note: From actual values of S, r, and h, it can be determined that the constant k is 2π, and we then have the formula $S = 2\pi rh$.

● **Work Practice 5**

Objective ⓓ Solving Problems Involving Combined Variation

Some examples of variation involve combinations of direct, inverse, and joint variation. We will call these variations **combined variation.**

PRACTICE 6

Suppose that y varies inversely as the square of x. If y is 24 when x is 2, find the constant of variation and the variation equation.

Example 6 Suppose that y varies directly as the square of x. If y is 24 when x is 2, find the constant of variation and the variation equation.

Solution: Since y varies directly as the square of x, we have

$$y = kx^2$$

Now let $y = 24$ and $x = 2$ and solve for k.

$$y = kx^2$$
$$24 = k \cdot 2^2$$
$$24 = 4k$$
$$6 = k$$

The constant of variation is 6, so the variation equation is

$$y = 6x^2$$

● **Work Practice 6**

PRACTICE 7

The maximum weight that a rectangular beam can support varies jointly as its width and the square of its height and inversely as its length. If a beam $\frac{1}{3}$ foot wide, 1 foot high, and 10 feet long can support 3 tons, find how much weight a similar beam can support if it is 1 foot wide, $\frac{1}{3}$ foot high, and 9 feet long.

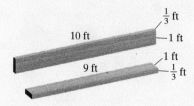

Example 7 Using Combined Variation

The maximum weight that a circular column can support is directly proportional to the fourth power of its diameter and inversely proportional to the square of its height. A 2-meter-wide column that is 8 meters in height can support 1 ton. Find the weight that a 1-meter-wide column that is 4 meters in height can support.

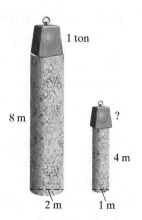

Answers

5. $A = kbh$ **6.** $k = 96; y = \dfrac{96}{x^2}$

7. $1\frac{1}{9}$ tons

Solution:

1. UNDERSTAND. Read and reread the problem. Let w = weight, d = diameter, h = height, and k = the constant of variation.

2. TRANSLATE. Since w is directly proportional to d^4 and inversely proportional to h^2, we have

$$w = \frac{kd^4}{h^2}$$

3. SOLVE. To find k, we are given that a 2-meter-wide column that is 8 meters in height can support 1 ton. That is, $w = 1$ when $d = 2$ and $h = 8$, or

$$1 = \frac{k \cdot 2^4}{8^2} \qquad \text{Let } w = 1, d = 2, \text{and } h = 8.$$

$$1 = \frac{k \cdot 16}{64}$$

$$4 = k \qquad \text{Solve for } k.$$

Now we replace k with 4 in the equation $w = \dfrac{kd^4}{h^2}$:

$$w = \frac{4d^4}{h^2}$$

To find weight, w, for a 1-meter-wide column that is 4 meters in height, we let $d = 1$ and $h = 4$.

$$w = \frac{4 \cdot 1^4}{4^2}$$

$$w = \frac{4}{16} = \frac{1}{4}$$

4. INTERPRET. *Check* the proposed solution in the original problem.

State: The 1-meter-wide column that is 4 meters in height can hold $\dfrac{1}{4}$ ton of weight.

⬤ **Work Practice 7**

Vocabulary and Readiness Check

State whether each equation represents direct, inverse, or joint variation.

1. $y = 5x$

2. $y = \dfrac{700}{x}$

3. $y = 5xz$

4. $y = \dfrac{1}{2}abc$

5. $y = \dfrac{9.1}{x}$

6. $y = 2.3x$

7. $y = \dfrac{2}{3}x$

8. $y = 3.1st$

10.7 Exercise Set

Objective A *If y varies directly as x, find the constant of variation and the direct variation equation for each situation. See Example 1.*

1. $y = 4$ when $x = 20$

2. $y = 6$ when $x = 30$

3. $y = 6$ when $x = 4$

4. $y = 12$ when $x = 8$

5. $y = 7$ when $x = \dfrac{1}{2}$

6. $y = 11$ when $x = \dfrac{1}{3}$

7. $y = 0.2$ when $x = 0.8$

8. $y = 0.4$ when $x = 2.5$

Solve. See Example 2.

9. The weight of a synthetic ball varies directly with the cube of its radius. A ball with a radius of 2 inches weighs 1.20 pounds. Find the weight of a ball of the same material with a 3-inch radius.

10. At sea, the distance to the horizon is directly proportional to the square root of the elevation of the observer. If a person who is 36 feet above the water can see 7.4 miles, find how far a person 64 feet above the water can see. Round to the nearest tenth of a mile.

11. The amount P of pollution varies directly with the population N of people. Kansas City has a population of 442,000 and produces 260,000 tons of pollutants. Find how many tons of pollution we should expect St. Louis to produce, if we know that its population is 348,000. Round to the nearest whole ton. (*Population Source: The World Almanac*)

12. Charles's law states that if the pressure P stays the same, the volume V of a gas is directly proportional to its temperature T. If a balloon is filled with 20 cubic meters of a gas at a temperature of 300 K, find the new volume if the temperature rises 360 K while the pressure stays the same.

Objective B *If y varies inversely as x, find the constant of variation and the inverse variation equation for each situation. See Example 3.*

13. $y = 6$ when $x = 5$

14. $y = 20$ when $x = 9$

15. $y = 100$ when $x = 7$

16. $y = 63$ when $x = 3$

17. $y = \dfrac{1}{8}$ when $x = 16$

18. $y = \dfrac{1}{10}$ when $x = 40$

19. $y = 0.2$ when $x = 0.7$

20. $y = 0.6$ when $x = 0.3$

Solve. See Example 4.

21. Pairs of markings a set distance apart are made on highways so that police can detect drivers exceeding the speed limit. Over a fixed distance, the speed R varies inversely with the time T. In one particular pair of markings, R is 45 mph when T is 6 seconds. Find the speed of a car that travels the given distance in 5 seconds.

22. The weight of an object on or above the surface of Earth varies inversely as the square of the distance between the object and Earth's center. If a person weighs 160 pounds on Earth's surface, find the individual's weight if he moves 200 miles above Earth. Round to the nearest whole pound. (Assume that Earth's radius is 4000 miles.)

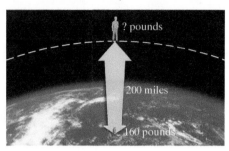

23. If the voltage V in an electric circuit is held constant, the current I is inversely proportional to the resistance R. If the current is 40 amperes when the resistance is 270 ohms, find the current when the resistance is 150 ohms.

24. Because it is more efficient to produce larger numbers of items, the cost of producing a certain computer DVD is inversely proportional to the number produced. If 4000 can be produced at a cost of $1.20 each, find the cost per DVD when 6000 are produced.

25. The intensity I of light varies inversely as the square of the distance d from the light source. If the distance from the light source is doubled (see the figure), determine what happens to the intensity of light at the new location.

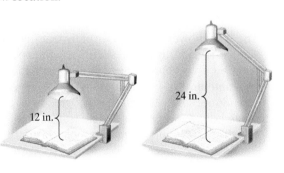

26. The maximum weight that a circular column can hold is inversely proportional to the square of its height. If an 8-foot column can hold 2 tons, find how much weight a 10-foot column can hold.

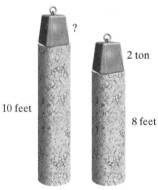

Objectives C D **Mixed Practice** *Write each statement as an equation. Use k as the constant of variation. See Example 5.*

27. x varies jointly as y and z.

28. P varies jointly as R and the square of S.

29. r varies jointly as s and the cube of t.

30. a varies jointly as b and c.

For each statement, find the constant of variation and the variation equation. See Examples 5 and 6.

31. y varies directly as the cube of x; $y = 9$ when $x = 3$

32. y varies directly as the cube of x; $y = 32$ when $x = 4$

33. y varies directly as the square root of x; $y = 0.4$ when $x = 4$

34. y varies directly as the square root of x; $y = 2.1$ when $x = 9$

35. y varies inversely as the square of x; $y = 0.052$ when $x = 5$

36. y varies inversely as the square of x; $y = 0.011$ when $x = 10$

37. y varies jointly as x and the cube of z; $y = 120$ when $x = 5$ and $z = 2$

38. y varies jointly as x and the square of z; $y = 360$ when $x = 4$ and $z = 3$

Solve. See Example 7.

39. The maximum weight that a rectangular beam can support varies jointly as its width and the square of its height and inversely as its length. If a beam $\frac{1}{2}$ foot wide, $\frac{1}{3}$ foot high, and 10 feet long can support 12 tons, find how much a similar beam can support if the beam is $\frac{2}{3}$ foot wide, $\frac{1}{2}$ foot high, and 16 feet long.

40. The number of cars manufactured on an assembly line at a General Motors plant varies jointly as the number of workers and the time they work. If 200 workers can produce 60 cars in 2 hours, find how many cars 240 workers should be able to make in 3 hours.

41. The volume of a cone varies jointly as its height and the square of its radius. If the volume of a cone is 32π cubic inches when the radius is 4 inches and the height is 6 inches, find the volume of a cone when the radius is 3 inches and the height is 5 inches.

42. When a wind blows perpendicularly against a flat surface, its force is jointly proportional to the surface area and the speed of the wind. A sail whose surface area is 12 square feet experiences a 20-pound force when the wind speed is 10 miles per hour. Find the force on an 8-square-foot sail if the wind speed is 12 miles per hour.

43. The intensity of light (in foot-candles) varies inversely as the square of x, the distance in feet from the light source. The intensity of light 2 feet from the source is 80 foot-candles. How far away is the source if the intensity of light is 5 foot-candles?

44. The horsepower that can be safely transmitted to a shaft varies jointly as the shaft's angular speed of rotation (in revolutions per minute) and the cube of its diameter. A 2-inch shaft making 120 revolutions per minute safely transmits 40 horsepower. Find how much horsepower can be safely transmitted by a 3-inch shaft making 80 revolutions per minute.

Objectives Ⓐ Ⓑ Ⓒ Ⓓ **Mixed Practice** *Write an equation to describe each variation. Use k for the constant of proportionality. See Examples 1 through 7.*

45. y varies directly as x

46. p varies directly as q

47. a varies inversely as b

48. y varies inversely as x

49. y varies jointly as x and z

50. y varies jointly as q, r, and t

51. y varies inversely as x^3

52. y varies inversely as a^4

53. y varies directly as x and inversely as p^2

54. y varies directly as a^5 and inversely as b

Review

Find the exact circumference C and area A of each circle. Use the formulas $C = 2\pi r$ and $A = \pi r^2$ where r is the radius of the circle.

△**55.**

6 cm

△**56.**

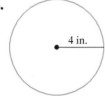

4 in.

△**57.**

7 m

△**58.**

9 cm

Find the slope of the line containing each pair of points.

59. $(3, 6), (-2, 6)$

60. $(-5, -2), (0, 7)$

61. $(4, -1), (5, -2)$

62. $(2, 1), (2, -3)$

Concept Extensions

Solve. See the Concept Check in this section. Choose the type of variation that each equation represents.
a. *Direct variation* **b.** *Inverse variation* **c.** *Joint variation*

63. $y = \dfrac{2}{3}x$

64. $y = \dfrac{0.6}{x}$

65. $y = 9ab$

66. $xy = \dfrac{2}{11}$

△**67.** The volume of a cylinder varies jointly as the height and the square of the radius. If the height is halved and the radius is doubled, determine what happens to the volume.

68. The horsepower to drive a boat varies directly as the cube of the speed of the boat. If the speed of the boat is to double, determine the corresponding increase in horsepower required.

69. Suppose that y varies directly as x^2. If x is doubled, what is the effect on y?

70. Suppose that y varies directly as x. If x is doubled, what is the effect on y?

10 Chapter Highlights

Definitions and Concepts	Examples

Section 10.1 Dividing Polynomials and Synthetic Division

DIVIDING A POLYNOMIAL BY A MONOMIAL

Divide each term in the polynomial by the monomial.

$$\frac{12a^5b^3 - 6a^2b^2 + ab}{6a^2b^2}$$

$$= \frac{12a^5b^3}{6a^2b^2} - \frac{6a^2b^2}{6a^2b^2} + \frac{ab}{6a^2b^2}$$

$$= 2a^3b - 1 + \frac{1}{6ab}$$

DIVIDING A POLYNOMIAL BY A POLYNOMIAL OTHER THAN A MONOMIAL

Use **long division.**

Divide $2x^3 - x^2 - 8x - 1$ by $x - 2$.

$$
\begin{array}{r}
2x^2 + 3x - 2 \\
x - 2 \overline{\smash{)}\ 2x^3 - x^2 - 8x - 1} \\
\underline{2x^3 - 4x^2} \\
3x^2 - 8x \\
\underline{3x^2 - 6x} \\
-2x - 1 \\
\underline{-2x + 4} \\
-5
\end{array}
$$

A shortcut method called **synthetic division** may be used to divide a polynomial by a binomial of the form $x - c$.

The quotient is $2x^2 + 3x - 2 - \dfrac{5}{x - 2}$.

Use synthetic division to divide $2x^3 - x^2 - 8x - 1$ by $x - 2$.

$$
\begin{array}{r|rrrr}
2 & 2 & -1 & -8 & -1 \\
 & & 4 & 6 & -4 \\
\hline
 & 2 & 3 & -2 & -5
\end{array}
$$

The quotient is $2x^2 + 3x - 2 - \dfrac{5}{x - 2}$.

Section 10.2 Rational Functions and Multiplying and Dividing Rational Expressions

A **rational expression** is the quotient $\dfrac{P}{Q}$ of two polynomials P and Q, as long as Q is not 0.

$$\frac{2x - 6}{7}, \frac{t^2 - 3t + 5}{t - 1}$$

SIMPLIFYING A RATIONAL EXPRESSION

Step 1. Completely factor the numerator and the denominator.

Step 2. Divide out common factors.

Simplify.

$$\frac{2x^2 + 9x - 5}{x^2 - 25} = \frac{(2x - 1)(x + 5)}{(x - 5)(x + 5)}$$

$$= \frac{2x - 1}{x - 5}$$

Definitions and Concepts	**Examples**

Section 10.2 Rational Functions and Multiplying and Dividing Rational Expressions (*continued*)

MULTIPLYING RATIONAL EXPRESSIONS

Step 1. Completely factor numerators and denominators.

Step 2. Multiply the numerators and multiply the denominators.

Step 3. Simplify the product.

Multiply: $\dfrac{x^3 + 8}{12x - 18} \cdot \dfrac{14x^2 - 21x}{x^2 + 2x}$

$= \dfrac{(x + 2)(x^2 - 2x + 4)}{6(2x - 3)} \cdot \dfrac{7x(2x - 3)}{x(x + 2)}$

$= \dfrac{7(x^2 - 2x + 4)}{6}$

DIVIDING RATIONAL EXPRESSIONS

Multiply the first rational expression by the reciprocal of the second rational expression.

A **rational function** is a function described by a rational expression.

Divide: $\dfrac{x^2 + 6x + 9}{5xy - 5y} \div \dfrac{x + 3}{10y}$

$= \dfrac{(x + 3)(x + 3)}{5y(x - 1)} \cdot \dfrac{2 \cdot 5y}{x + 3}$

$= \dfrac{2(x + 3)}{x - 1}$

$f(x) = \dfrac{2x - 6}{7}, h(t) = \dfrac{t^2 - 3t + 5}{t - 1}$

Section 10.3 Adding and Subtracting Rational Expressions

ADDING OR SUBTRACTING RATIONAL EXPRESSIONS

Step 1. Find the LCD.

Step 2. Write each rational expression as an equivalent rational expression whose denominator is the LCD.

Step 3. Add or subtract numerators and write the sum or difference over the common denominator.

Step 4. Simplify the result.

Subtract: $\dfrac{3}{x + 2} - \dfrac{x + 1}{x - 3}$

$= \dfrac{3 \cdot (x - 3)}{(x + 2) \cdot (x - 3)} - \dfrac{(x + 1) \cdot (x + 2)}{(x - 3) \cdot (x + 2)}$

$= \dfrac{3(x - 3) - (x + 1)(x + 2)}{(x + 2)(x - 3)}$

$= \dfrac{3x - 9 - (x^2 + 3x + 2)}{(x + 2)(x - 3)}$

$= \dfrac{3x - 9 - x^2 - 3x - 2}{(x + 2)(x - 3)}$

$= \dfrac{-x^2 - 11}{(x + 2)(x - 3)}$

Section 10.4 Simplifying Complex Fractions

Method 1: Simplify the numerator and the denominator so that each is a single fraction. Then perform the indicated division and simplify if possible.

Simplify: $\dfrac{\dfrac{x + 2}{x}}{x - \dfrac{4}{x}}$

Method 1: $\dfrac{\dfrac{x + 2}{x}}{\dfrac{x \cdot x}{1 \cdot x} - \dfrac{4}{x}} = \dfrac{\dfrac{x + 2}{x}}{\dfrac{x^2 - 4}{x}}$

$= \dfrac{x + 2}{x} \cdot \dfrac{x}{(x + 2)(x - 2)} = \dfrac{1}{x - 2}$

Definitions and Concepts	**Examples**

Section 10.4 Simplifying Complex Fractions (*continued*)

Method 2: Multiply the numerator and the denominator of the complex fraction by the LCD of the fractions in both the numerator and the denominator. Then simplify if possible.

Method 2:
$$\frac{\left(\dfrac{x+2}{x}\right)\cdot x}{\left(x-\dfrac{4}{x}\right)\cdot x} = \frac{x+2}{x\cdot x - \dfrac{4}{x}\cdot x}$$

$$= \frac{x+2}{x^2-4} = \frac{x+2}{(x+2)(x-2)} = \frac{1}{x-2}$$

Section 10.5 Solving Equations Containing Rational Expressions

SOLVING AN EQUATION CONTAINING RATIONAL EXPRESSIONS

Multiply both sides of the equation by the LCD of all rational expressions. Then use the distributive property and simplify. Solve the resulting equation and then check each proposed solution to see whether it makes any denominator 0. Discard any solutions that do.

Solve: $x - \dfrac{3}{x} = \dfrac{1}{2}$

$$2x\left(x-\frac{3}{x}\right) = 2x\left(\frac{1}{2}\right) \quad \text{The LCD is } 2x.$$

$$2x\cdot x - 2x\left(\frac{3}{x}\right) = 2x\left(\frac{1}{2}\right) \quad \text{Distribute.}$$

$$2x^2 - 6 = x$$

$$2x^2 - x - 6 = 0 \quad \text{Subtract } x \text{ from both sides.}$$

$$(2x+3)(x-2) = 0 \quad \text{Factor.}$$

$$x = -\frac{3}{2} \quad \text{or} \quad x = 2$$

Both $-\dfrac{3}{2}$ and 2 check. The solution set is $\left\{2, -\dfrac{3}{2}\right\}$.

Section 10.6 Rational Equations and Problem Solving

SOLVING AN EQUATION FOR A SPECIFIED VARIABLE

Treat the specified variable as the only variable of the equation and solve as usual.

Solve for x.

$$A = \frac{2x+3y}{5}$$

$$5A = 2x + 3y \quad \text{Multiply both sides by 5.}$$

$$5A - 3y = 2x \quad \text{Subtract } 3y \text{ from both sides.}$$

$$\frac{5A-3y}{2} = x \quad \text{Divide both sides by 2.}$$

SOLVING A PROBLEM THAT INVOLVES A RATIONAL EQUATION

Jeanee and David Dillon volunteer every year to clean a strip of Lake Ponchartrain beach. Jeanee can clean all the trash in this area of beach in 6 hours; David takes 5 hours. Find how long it will take them to clean the area of beach together.

1. UNDERSTAND.

1. Read and reread the problem. Let x = time in hours that it takes Jeanee and David to clean the beach together.

	Hours to Complete	Part Completed in 1 Hour
Jeanee Alone	6	$\dfrac{1}{6}$
David Alone	5	$\dfrac{1}{5}$
Together	x	$\dfrac{1}{x}$

Definitions and Concepts	**Examples**

Section 10.6   Rational Equations and Problem Solving (continued)

2. TRANSLATE.

2. In words:

part Jeanee can complete in 1 hour	+	part David can complete in 1 hour	=	part they can complete together in 1 hour
$\downarrow$		$\downarrow$		$\downarrow$

Translate:

$$\frac{1}{6} \quad + \quad \frac{1}{5} \quad = \quad \frac{1}{x}$$

3. SOLVE.

3. $\quad \dfrac{1}{6} + \dfrac{1}{5} = \dfrac{1}{x}$

$\quad 5x + 6x = 30 \qquad$ Multiply both sides by 30x.

$\quad\quad\quad 11x = 30$

$\quad\quad\quad\quad x = \dfrac{30}{11} \quad$ or $\quad 2\dfrac{8}{11}$

4. INTERPRET.

4. *Check* and then *state*. Together, they can clean the beach in $2\dfrac{8}{11}$ hours.

Section 10.7   Variation and Problem Solving

y **varies directly** as *x*, or *y* is **directly proportional** to *x*, if there is a nonzero constant *k* such that

$$y = kx$$

The circumference of a circle *C* varies directly as its radius *r*.

$$C = \underbrace{2\pi}_{k} r$$

y **varies inversely** as *x*, or *y* is **inversely proportional** to *x*, if there is a nonzero constant *k* such that

$$y = \frac{k}{x}$$

Pressure *P* varies inversely with volume *V*.

$$P = \frac{k}{V}$$

y **varies jointly** as *x* and *z*, or *y* is **jointly proportional** to *x* and *z*, if there is a nonzero constant *k* such that

$$y = kxz$$

The lateral surface area *S* of a cylinder varies jointly as its radius *r* and height *h*.

$$S = \underbrace{2\pi}_{k} rh$$

Chapter 10 Review

(10.1) *Divide*

1. $(4xy + 2x^2 - 9) \div (4xy)$

2 $12xb^2 + 16xb^4$ by $4xb^3$

3. $(3x^4 - 25x^2 - 20) \div (x - 3)$

4. $(-x^2 + 2x^4 + 5x - 12) \div (x - 3)$

5. $(2x^4 - x^3 + 2x^2 - 3x + 1) \div \left(x - \dfrac{1}{2}\right)$

6. $(x^3 + 3x^2 - 2x + 2) \div \left(x - \dfrac{1}{2}\right)$

7. $(3x^4 + 5x^3 + 7x^2 + 3x - 2) \div (x^2 + x + 2)$

8. $(9x^4 - 6x^3 + 3x^2 - 12x - 30) \div (3x^2 - 2x - 5)$

Use synthetic division to find each quotient.

9. $(3x^3 + 12x - 4) \div (x - 2)$

10. $(4x^3 + 2x^2 - 4x - 2) \div \left(x + \dfrac{3}{2}\right).$

11. $(x^5 - 1) \div (x + 1)$

12. $(x^3 - 81) \div (x - 3)$

13. $(x^3 - x^2 + 3x^4 - 2) \div (x - 4)$

14. $(3x^4 - 2x^2 + 10) \div (x + 2)$

(10.2) *Find the domain for each rational function.*

15. $f(x) = \dfrac{3 - 5x}{7}$

16. $g(x) = \dfrac{2x + 4}{11}$

17. $F(x) = \dfrac{-3x^2}{x - 5}$

18. $h(x) = \dfrac{4x}{3x - 12}$

19. $f(x) = \dfrac{x^3 + 2}{x^2 + 8x}$

20. $G(x) = \dfrac{20}{3x^2 - 48}$

Write each rational expression in lowest terms.

21. $\dfrac{x - 12}{12 - x}$

22. $\dfrac{5x - 15}{25x - 75}$

23. $\dfrac{2x}{2x^2 - 2x}$

24. $\dfrac{x + 7}{x^2 - 49}$

25. $\dfrac{2x^2 + 4x - 30}{x^2 + x - 20}$

26. The average cost of manufacturing x bookcases is given by the rational function.

$$C(x) = \frac{35x + 4200}{x}$$

a. Find the average cost per bookcase of manufacturing 50 bookcases.

b. Find the average cost per bookcase of manufacturing 100 bookcases.

c. As the number of bookcases increases, does the average cost per bookcase increase or decrease? (See parts (a) and (b).)

Perform each indicated operation. Write your answers in lowest terms.

27. $\dfrac{4-x}{5} \cdot \dfrac{15}{2x-8}$

28. $\dfrac{x^2-6x+9}{2x^2-18} \cdot \dfrac{4x+12}{5x-15}$

29. $\dfrac{a-4b}{a^2+ab} \cdot \dfrac{b^2-a^2}{8b-2a}$

30. $\dfrac{x^2-x-12}{2x^2-32} \cdot \dfrac{x^2+8x+16}{3x^2+21x+36}$

31. $\dfrac{4x+8y}{3} \div \dfrac{5x+10y}{9}$

32. $\dfrac{x^2-25}{3} \div \dfrac{x^2-10x+25}{x^2-x-20}$

33. $\dfrac{a-4b}{a^2+ab} \div \dfrac{20b-5a}{b^2-a^2}$

34. $\dfrac{3x+3}{x-1} \div \dfrac{x^2-6x-7}{x^2-1}$

35. $\dfrac{2x-x^2}{x^3-8} \div \dfrac{x^2}{x^2+2x+4}$

36. $\dfrac{5x-15}{3-x} \cdot \dfrac{x+2}{10x+20} \cdot \dfrac{x^2-9}{x^2-x-6}$

(10.3) *Find the LCD of the rational expressions in each list.*

37. $\dfrac{5}{4x^2y^5}, \dfrac{3}{10x^2y^4}, \dfrac{x}{6y^4}$

38. $\dfrac{5}{2x}, \dfrac{7}{x-2}$

39. $\dfrac{3}{5x}, \dfrac{2}{x-5}$

40. $\dfrac{1}{5x^3}, \dfrac{4}{x^2+3x-28}, \dfrac{11}{10x^2-30x}$

Perform each indicated operation. Write your answers in lowest terms.

41. $\dfrac{4}{x-4} + \dfrac{x}{x-4}$

42. $\dfrac{4}{3x^2} + \dfrac{2}{3x^2}$

43. $\dfrac{1}{x-2} - \dfrac{1}{4-2x}$

44. $\dfrac{1}{10-x} + \dfrac{x-1}{x-10}$

45. $\dfrac{x}{9-x^2} - \dfrac{2}{5x-15}$

46. $2x+1 - \dfrac{1}{x-3}$

47. $\dfrac{2}{a^2-2a+1} + \dfrac{3}{a^2-1}$

48. $\dfrac{x}{9x^2+12x+16} - \dfrac{3x+4}{27x^3-64}$

Perform each indicated operation. Write your answers in lowest terms.

49. $\dfrac{2}{x-1} - \dfrac{3x}{3x-3} + \dfrac{1}{2x-2}$

50. Find the perimeter of the heptagon (a polygon with seven sides).

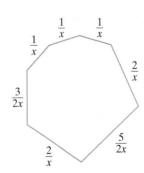

(10.4) *Simplify each complex fraction.*

51. $\dfrac{1 - \dfrac{3x}{4}}{2 + \dfrac{x}{4}}$

52. $\dfrac{\dfrac{x^2}{15}}{\dfrac{x+1}{5x}}$

53. $\dfrac{2 - \dfrac{3}{2x}}{x - \dfrac{2}{5x}}$

54. $\dfrac{1 + \dfrac{x}{y}}{\dfrac{x^2}{y^2} - 1}$

55. $\dfrac{\dfrac{5}{x} + \dfrac{1}{xy}}{\dfrac{3}{x^2}}$

56. $\dfrac{\dfrac{x}{3} - \dfrac{3}{x}}{1 + \dfrac{3}{x}}$

57. $\dfrac{\dfrac{1}{x-1} + 1}{\dfrac{1}{x+1} - 1}$

58. $\dfrac{\dfrac{x-3}{x+3} + \dfrac{x+3}{x-3}}{\dfrac{x-3}{x+3} - \dfrac{x+3}{x-3}}$

(10.5) *Solve each equation.*

59. $\dfrac{3}{x} + \dfrac{1}{3} = \dfrac{5}{x}$

60. $\dfrac{2x+3}{5x-9} = \dfrac{3}{2}$

61. $\dfrac{1}{x-2} - \dfrac{3x}{x^2-4} = \dfrac{2}{x+2}$

62. $\dfrac{7}{x} - \dfrac{x}{7} = 0$

Solve each equation or perform each indicated operation. Simplify.

63. $\dfrac{5}{x^2-7x} + \dfrac{4}{2x-14}$

64. $\dfrac{4}{3-x} - \dfrac{7}{2x-6} + \dfrac{5}{x}$

65. $3 - \dfrac{5}{x} - \dfrac{2}{x^2} = 0$

66. $2 + \dfrac{15}{x^2} = \dfrac{13}{x}$

(10.6) *Solve each equation for the specified variable.*

△ **67.** $A = \dfrac{h(a+b)}{2}$ for a

68. $\dfrac{1}{R} = \dfrac{1}{R_1} + \dfrac{1}{R_2}$ for R_2

69. $I = \dfrac{E}{R+r}$ for R

70. $A = P + Prt$ for r

71. $\dfrac{1}{x} = \dfrac{1}{y} - \dfrac{1}{z}$ for x

72. $H = \dfrac{kA(T_1 - T_2)}{L}$ for A

Solve.

73. The sum of a number and twice its reciprocal is 3. Find the number(s).

74. If a number is added to the numerator of $\dfrac{3}{7}$, and twice that number is added to the denominator of $\dfrac{3}{7}$, the result is equivalent to $\dfrac{10}{21}$. Find the number.

75. Three boys can paint a fence in 4 hours, 5 hours, and 6 hours, respectively. Find how long it will take all three boys to paint the fence.

76. If Sue Katz can type a certain number of mailing labels in 6 hours and Tom Neilson and Sue working together can type the same number of mailing labels in 4 hours, find how long it takes Tom alone to type the mailing labels.

77. The speed of a Ranger boat in still water is 32 mph. If the boat travels 72 miles upstream in the same time that it takes to travel 120 miles downstream, find the speed of the current.

78. The speed of a jogger is 3 mph faster than the speed of a walker. If the jogger travels 14 miles in the same amount of time that the walker travels 8 miles, find the speed of the walker.

(10.7) *Solve each variation problem.*

79. A is directly proportional to B. If $A = 6$ when $B = 14$, find A when $B = 21$.

80. According to Boyle's law, the pressure exerted by a gas is inversely proportional to the volume, as long as the temperature stays the same. If a gas exerts a pressure of 1250 kilopascals when the volume is 2 cubic meters, find the volume when the pressure is 800 kilopascals.

Answers to Selected Exercises

Chapter 10 Rational Expressions

Section 10.1

Exercise Set 10.1 **1.** $2a + 4$ **3.** $3ab + 4$ **5.** $2y + \dfrac{3y}{x} - \dfrac{2y}{x^2}$ **7.** $x + 1$ **9.** $2x - 8$ **11.** $x - \dfrac{1}{2}$ **13.** $2x^2 - \dfrac{1}{2}x + 5$ **15.** $2x^2 - 6$

17. $3x^3 + 5x + 4 - \dfrac{2x}{x^2 - 2}$ **19.** $2x^3 + \dfrac{9}{2}x^2 + 10x + 21 + \dfrac{42}{x - 2}$ **21.** $x + 8$ **23.** $x - 1$ **25.** $x^2 - 5x - 23 - \dfrac{41}{x - 2}$ **27.** $4x + 8 + \dfrac{7}{x - 2}$

29. $x^6 y + \dfrac{2}{y} + 1$ **31.** $5x^2 - 6 - \dfrac{5}{2x - 1}$ **33.** $2x^2 + 2x + 8 + \dfrac{28}{x - 4}$ **35.** $2x^3 - 3x^2 + x - 4$ **37.** $3x^2 + 4x - 8 + \dfrac{20}{x + 1}$ **39.** $3x^2 + 3x - 3$

41. $x^2 + x + 1$ **43.** $-\dfrac{5y}{x} - \dfrac{15z}{x} - 25z$ **45.** $3x^4 - 2x$ **47.** 1 **49.** -133 **51.** 3 **53.** $-\dfrac{187}{81}$ **55.** $\dfrac{95}{32}$ **57.** $(-9, -1)$ **59.** $(-\infty, -8] \circ [1, \infty)$

61. yes **63.** no **65.** a or d **67.** $(x^4 + 2x^2 - 6)$ m **69.** $(3x - 7)$ in. **71.** $(x^3 - 5x^2 + 2x - 1)$ cm **73.** $x^3 + \dfrac{5}{3}x^2 + \dfrac{5}{3}x + \dfrac{8}{3} + \dfrac{8}{3(x - 1)}$

75. $\dfrac{3}{2}x^3 + \dfrac{1}{4}x^2 + \dfrac{1}{8}x - \dfrac{7}{16} + \dfrac{1}{16(2x - 1)}$ **77.** $x^3 - \dfrac{2}{5}x$ **79.** $5x - 1 + \dfrac{6}{x}; x \neq 0$ **81.** $7x^3 + 14x^2 + 25x + 50 + \dfrac{102}{x - 2}; x \neq 2$

83. answers may vary **85.** answers may vary **87.** $(x + 3)(x^2 + 4) = x^3 + 3x^2 + 4x + 12$ **89.** $2x^3 - 5x^2 - 31x + 33$

91. a. $m(x) = \dfrac{-7x^3 + 94x^2 - 76x + 59}{939x - 194}$ **b.** 0.18

Section 10.2

Calculator Explorations **1.** $\{x \mid x \text{ is a real number and } x \neq 6\}$ **3.** $\{x \mid x \text{ is a real number and } x \neq -2, x \neq 2\}$
5. $\left\{x \mid x \text{ is a real number and } x \neq -4, x \neq \dfrac{1}{2}\right\}$ **7.** $\{x \mid x \text{ is a real number}\}$

Vocabulary and Readiness Check **1.** rational **3.** domain **5.** 1 **7.** $\dfrac{-a}{b}; \dfrac{a}{-b}$ **9.** $\dfrac{xy}{10}$ **11.** $\dfrac{2y}{3x}$ **13.** $\dfrac{m^2}{36}$

Exercise Set 10.2 **1.** $\{x \mid x \text{ is a real number}\}$ **3.** $\{t \mid t \text{ is a real number and } t \neq 0\}$ **5.** $\{x \mid x \text{ is a real number and } x \neq 7\}$
7. $\left\{x \mid x \text{ is a real number and } x \neq \dfrac{1}{3}\right\}$ **9.** $\{x \mid x \text{ is a real number and } x \neq -2, x \neq 0, x \neq 1\}$ **11.** $\{x \mid x \text{ is a real number and } x \neq 2, x \neq -2\}$

13. $1 - 2x$ **15.** $3 - x$ **17.** $\dfrac{9}{7}$ **19.** $x - 4$ **21.** -1 **23.** $-(x + 7)$ **25.** $\dfrac{2x + 1}{x - 1}$ **27.** $\dfrac{x^2 + 5x + 25}{2}$ **29.** $\dfrac{x - 2}{2x^2 + 1}$ **31.** $\dfrac{1}{3x + 5}$ **33.** $-\dfrac{4}{5}$

35. $-\dfrac{6a}{2a + 1}$ **37.** $\dfrac{3}{2(x - 1)}$ **39.** $\dfrac{x + 2}{x + 3}$ **41.** $\dfrac{3a}{5(a - b)}$ **43.** $\dfrac{1}{6}$ **45.** $\dfrac{x}{3}$ **47.** $\dfrac{4a^2}{a - b}$ **49.** $\dfrac{4}{(x + 2)(x + 3)}$ **51.** $\dfrac{1}{2}$ **53.** -1 **55.** $\dfrac{8(a - 2)}{3(a + 2)}$

57. $\dfrac{(x + 2)(x + 3)}{4}$ **59.** $\dfrac{2(x + 3)(x - 3)}{5(x^2 - 8x - 15)}$ **61.** $r^2 - rs + s^2$ **63.** $\dfrac{8}{x^2 y}$ **65.** $\dfrac{(y + 5)(2x - 1)}{(y + 2)(5x + 1)}$ **67.** $\dfrac{10}{3}, -8, -\dfrac{7}{3}$ **69.** $-\dfrac{17}{48}, \dfrac{2}{7}, -\dfrac{3}{8}$ **71. a.** \$200 million

b. \$500 million **c.** \$300 million **d.** $\{x \mid x \text{ is a real number}\}$ **73.** $\dfrac{7}{5}$ **75.** $\dfrac{1}{12}$ **77.** $\dfrac{11}{16}$ **79.** b and d **81.** no; answers may vary **83.** $\dfrac{5}{x - 2}$ sq m

85. $\dfrac{(x + 2)(x - 1)^2}{x^5}$ ft **87.** answers may vary **89. a.** 1 **b.** -1 **c.** neither **d.** -1 **e.** -1 **f.** 1 **91.** answers may vary **93.** -1

95. $\dfrac{1}{x^n - 4}$ **97.**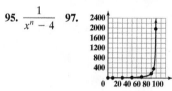

Section 10.3

Vocabulary and Readiness Check **1.** a, b **3.** c **5.** $\dfrac{12}{y}$ **7.** $\dfrac{35}{y^2}$ **9.** $\dfrac{-x + 4}{2x}$ **11.** $\dfrac{16}{y - 2}$

Exercise Set 10.3 **1.** $-\dfrac{3}{xz^2}$ **3.** $\dfrac{x + 2}{x - 2}$ **5.** $x - 2$ **7.** $\dfrac{-1}{x - 2}$ or $\dfrac{1}{2 - x}$ **9.** $-\dfrac{5}{x}$ **11.** $35x$ **13.** $x(x + 1)$ **15.** $(x + 7)(x - 7)$

17. $6(x + 2)(x - 2)$ **19.** $(a - b)(a - b)^2$ **21.** $-4x(x + 3)(x - 3)$ **23.** $\dfrac{17}{6x}$ **25.** $\dfrac{35 - 4y}{14y^2}$ **27.** $\dfrac{-13x + 4}{(x + 4)(x - 4)}$ **29.** $\dfrac{3}{x + 4}$ **31.** 0

33. $-\dfrac{x+2}{x-1}$ or $\dfrac{x+2}{1-x}$ **35.** $\dfrac{-x+1}{x-2}$ or $\dfrac{x-1}{2-x}$ **37.** $\dfrac{y^2+2y+10}{(y+4)(y-4)(y-2)}$ **39.** $\dfrac{5(x^2+x-4)}{(3x+2)(x+3)(2x-5)}$ **41.** $\dfrac{x^2-9x-21}{(x+3)(x+1)(x-2)}$

43. $\dfrac{x^2-x+20}{(2x-5)(x+3)(3x+2)}$ **45.** $\dfrac{5a+1}{(a+1)^2(a-1)}$ **47.** $\dfrac{3}{x^2y^3}$ **49.** $-\dfrac{5}{x}$ **51.** $\dfrac{25}{6(x+5)}$ **53.** $\dfrac{-2x-1}{x^2(x-3)}$ **55.** $\dfrac{b(2a-b)}{(a+b)(a-b)}$

57. $\dfrac{2(x+8)}{(x+2)^2(x-2)}$ **59.** $\dfrac{3x^2+23x-7}{(2x-1)(x-5)(x+3)}$ **61.** $\dfrac{5-2x}{2(x+1)}$ **63.** $\dfrac{2(x^2+x-21)}{(x+3)^2(x-3)}$ **65.** $\dfrac{6x}{(x+3)(x-3)^2}$ **67.** $\dfrac{4}{3}$ **69.** 10 **71.** $4+x^2$

73. $\dfrac{2x-3}{x^2+1}-\dfrac{x-6}{x^2+1}=\dfrac{2x-3-x+6}{x^2+1}=\dfrac{x+3}{x^2+1}$ **75.** $\dfrac{4x}{x+5}$ ft; $\dfrac{x^2}{(x+5)^2}$ sq ft **77.** answers may vary **79.** answers may vary **81.** answers may vary

83. $\dfrac{(x+6)(2x-3)}{6x^2}$ or $\dfrac{2x^2+9x-18}{6x^2}$ **85.** $\dfrac{4a^2}{9(a-1)}$ **87.** 4 **89.** $-\dfrac{4}{x-1}$ **91.** $\dfrac{32}{x(x+2)(x-2)}$ **93.** $\dfrac{3}{2x}$ **95.** $\dfrac{4-3x}{x^2}$

97.

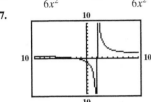

Section 10.4

Vocabulary and Readiness Check **1.** $\dfrac{7}{1+z}$ **3.** $\dfrac{1}{x^2}$ **5.** $\dfrac{2}{x}$ **7.** $\dfrac{1}{9y}$

Exercise Set 10.4 **1.** $\dfrac{7}{13}$ **3.** $\dfrac{4}{x}$ **5.** $\dfrac{9(x-2)}{9x^2+4}$ **7.** 4 **9.** $2x+y$ **11.** $\dfrac{2(x+1)}{2x-1}$ **13.** $\dfrac{2x+3}{4-9x}$ **15.** $\dfrac{1}{x^2-2x+4}$ **17.** $\dfrac{x}{5x-10}$ **19.** $\dfrac{x-2}{2x-1}$

21. $\dfrac{x}{2-3x}$ **23.** $-\dfrac{y}{y+1}$ **25.** $-\dfrac{2x^2}{y(x-y)}$ **27.** $\dfrac{2x+1}{y+x^2}$ **29.** $\dfrac{x-3}{9}$ **31.** $\dfrac{1}{x+2}$ **33.** 2 **35.** $\dfrac{xy^2}{x^2+y^2}$ **37.** $\dfrac{2b^2+3a}{b(b-a)}$ **39.** $\dfrac{x}{(x+1)(x-1)}$

41. $\dfrac{1+a}{1-a}$ **43.** $\dfrac{x(x+6y)}{2y}$ **45.** $\dfrac{5a}{2(a+2)}$ **47.** $5xy^2+2x^2y$ **49.** $\dfrac{xy}{5y+2x}$ **51.** $\left\{-\dfrac{5}{6}\right\}$ **53.** $\{2\}$ **55.** $\{54\}$ **57.** a and c **59.** $\dfrac{770a}{770-s}$

61. a and b **63.** answers may vary **65.** $\dfrac{x-3y}{x+3y}$ **67.** $\dfrac{1+x}{2+x}$ **69.** $x(x+1)$ **71. a.** $\dfrac{1}{a+h}$ **b.** $\dfrac{1}{a}$ **c.** $\dfrac{\dfrac{1}{a+h}-\dfrac{1}{a}}{h}$ **d.** $\dfrac{-1}{a(a+h)}$ **73. a.** $\dfrac{3}{a+h+1}$

b. $\dfrac{3}{a+1}$ **c.** $\dfrac{\dfrac{3}{a+h+1}-\dfrac{3}{a+1}}{h}$ **d.** $\dfrac{-3}{(a+h+1)(a+1)}$

Section 10.5

Vocabulary and Readiness Check **1.** equation **3.** expression **5.** equation **7.** 14; c **9.** $(x+4)(x-4)$; a

Exercise Set 10.5 **1.** $\{72\}$ **3.** $\{2\}$ **5.** $\{6\}$ **7.** $\{2,2\}$ **9.** $\varnothing$ **11.** $\left\{-\dfrac{28}{3}\right\}$ **13.** $\{3\}$ **15.** $\{-8\}$ **17.** $\{3\}$ **19.** $\varnothing$ **21.** $\{1\}$ **23.** $\{3\}$ **25.** $\{-1\}$

27. $\{6\}$ **29.** $\left\{\dfrac{1}{3}\right\}$ **31.** $\{-5,5\}$ **33.** $\{3\}$ **35.** $\{7\}$ **37.** $\varnothing$ **39.** $\left\{\dfrac{4}{3}\right\}$ **41.** $\{-12\}$ **43.** $\left\{1,\dfrac{11}{4}\right\}$ **45.** $\{-5,-1\}$ **47.** $\left\{-\dfrac{7}{5}\right\}$ **49.** 5

51. length: 15 in.; width: 10 in. **53.** 14.8% **55.** 25–29 **57.** 29,871 inmates **59.** answers may vary **61.** 3000 game disks **63.** $\left\{\dfrac{1}{16},\dfrac{1}{3}\right\}$

65. $\left\{-\dfrac{1}{5},1\right\}$ **67.** $\{-0.17\}$ **69.** $\{0.42\}$ **71.** $\{-1,0\}$ **73.** $\{-2\}$ **75.**

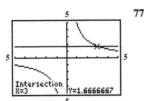

77.

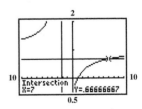

Section 10.6

Exercise Set 10.6 **1.** $C=\dfrac{5}{9}(F-32)$ **3.** $I=A-QL$ **5.** $R=\dfrac{R_1R_2}{R_1+R_2}$ **7.** $n=\dfrac{2s}{a+L}$ **9.** $b=\dfrac{2A-ah}{h}$ **11.** $T_2=\dfrac{P_2V_2T_1}{P_1V_1}$ **13.** $f_2=\dfrac{f_1f}{f_1-f}$

15. $L=\dfrac{n\lambda}{2}$ **17.** $c=\dfrac{2L\omega}{\theta}$ **19.** 1 and 5 **21.** 5 **23.** 4.5 gal **25.** 5454 women **27.** 15.6 hr **29.** 10 min **31.** 200 mph **33.** 15 mph **35.** -8 and -7

37. 36 min **39.** 45 mph; 60 mph **41.** 5.9 hr **43.** 2 hr **45.** 135 mph **47.** 12 mi **49.** $\dfrac{7}{8}$ **51.** $1\dfrac{1}{2}$ min **53.** 1 hr **55.** $2\dfrac{2}{9}$ hr **57.** 2 hr **59.** $\{-5\}$

61. $\{2\}$ **63.** 164 lb **65.** higher; F **67.** 6 ohms **69.** $\dfrac{1}{R}=\dfrac{1}{R_1}+\dfrac{1}{R_2}+\dfrac{1}{R_3}$; $R=\dfrac{15}{13}$ ohms

Answers to Selected Exercises

Section 10.7

Vocabulary and Readiness Check **1.** direct **3.** joint **5.** inverse **7.** direct

Exercise Set 10.7 **1.** $k = \dfrac{1}{5}; y = \dfrac{1}{5}x$ **3.** $k = \dfrac{3}{2}; y = \dfrac{3}{2}x$ **5.** $k = 14; y = 14x$ **7.** $k = 0.25; y = 0.25x$ **9.** 4.05 lb **11.** 204,706 tons **13.** $k = 30; y = \dfrac{30}{x}$

15. $k = 700; y = \dfrac{700}{x}$ **17.** $k = 2; y = \dfrac{2}{x}$ **19.** $k = 0.14; y = \dfrac{0.14}{x}$ **21.** 54 mph **23.** 72 amps **25.** divided by 4 **27.** $x = kyz$ **29.** $r = kst^3$

31. $k = \dfrac{1}{3}; y = \dfrac{1}{3}x^3$ **33.** $k = 0.2; y = 0.2\sqrt{x}$ **35.** $k = 1.3; y = \dfrac{1.3}{x^2}$ **37.** $k = 3; y = 3xz^3$ **39.** 22.5 tons **41.** 15π cu in. **43.** 8 ft **45.** $y = kx$

47. $a = \dfrac{k}{b}$ **49.** $y = kxz$ **51.** $y = \dfrac{k}{x^3}$ **53.** $y = \dfrac{kx}{p^2}$ **55.** $C = 12\pi$ cm; $A = 36\pi$ sq cm **57.** $C = 14\pi$ m; $A = 49\pi$ sq m **59.** 0 **61.** -1

63. a **65.** c **67.** multiplied by 2 **69.** multiplied by 4

Chapter 10 Review **1.** $1 + \dfrac{x}{2y} - \dfrac{9}{4xy}$ **2.** $\dfrac{3}{b} + 4b$ **3.** $3x^3 + 9x^2 + 2x + 6 - \dfrac{2}{x-3}$ **4.** $2x^3 + 6x^2 + 17x + 56 + \dfrac{156}{x-3}$ **5.** $2x^3 + 2x - 2$

6. $x^2 + \dfrac{7}{2}x - \dfrac{1}{4} + \dfrac{15}{8\left(x - \dfrac{1}{2}\right)}$ **7.** $3x^2 + 2x - 1$ **8.** $3x^2 + 6$ **9.** $3x^2 + 6x + 24 + \dfrac{44}{x-2}$ **10.** $4x^2 - 4x + 2 - \dfrac{5}{x + \dfrac{3}{2}}$

11. $x^4 - x^3 + x^2 - x + 1 - \dfrac{2}{x+1}$ **12.** $x^2 + 3x + 9 - \dfrac{54}{x-3}$ **13.** $3x^3 + 13x^2 + 51x + 204 + \dfrac{814}{x-4}$ **14.** $3x^3 - 6x^2 + 10x - 20 + \dfrac{50}{x+2}$

15. $\{x \mid x \text{ is a real number}\}$ **16.** $\{x \mid x \text{ is a real number}\}$ **17.** $\{x \mid x \text{ is a real number and } x \neq 5\}$ **18.** $\{x \mid x \text{ is a real number and } x \neq 4\}$

19. $\{x \mid x \text{ is a real number and } x \neq 0, x \neq -8\}$ **20.** $\{x \mid x \text{ is a real number and } x \neq -4, x \neq 4\}$ **21.** -1 **22.** $\dfrac{1}{5}$ **23.** $\dfrac{1}{x-1}$ **24.** $\dfrac{1}{x-7}$

25. $\dfrac{2(x-3)}{x-4}$ **26. a.** \$119 **b.** \$77 **c.** decrease **27.** $-\dfrac{3}{2}$ **28.** $\dfrac{2}{5}$ **29.** $\dfrac{a-b}{2a}$ **30.** $\dfrac{1}{6}$ **31.** $\dfrac{12}{5}$ **32.** $\dfrac{(x+4)(x+5)}{3}$ **33.** $\dfrac{a-b}{5a}$ **34.** $\dfrac{3(x+1)}{x-7}$

35. $-\dfrac{1}{x}$ **36.** $-\dfrac{x+3}{2(x+2)}$ **37.** $60x^2y^5$ **38.** $2x(x-2)$ **39.** $5x(x-5)$ **40.** $10x^3(x-4)(x+7)(x-3)$ **41.** $\dfrac{4+x}{x-4}$ **42.** $\dfrac{2}{x^2}$ **43.** $\dfrac{3}{2(x-2)}$

44. $\dfrac{x-2}{x-10}$ **45.** $\dfrac{-7x-6}{5(x-3)(x+3)}$ **46.** $\dfrac{2x^2 - 5x - 4}{x-3}$ **47.** $\dfrac{5a-1}{(a-1)^2(a+1)}$ **48.** $\dfrac{3x^2 - 7x - 4}{(3x-4)(9x^2 + 12x + 16)}$ **49.** $\dfrac{5-2x}{2(x-1)}$ **50.** $\dfrac{11}{x}$

51. $\dfrac{4-3x}{8+x}$ **52.** $\dfrac{x^3}{3(x+1)}$ **53.** $\dfrac{5(4x-3)}{2(5x^2 - 2)}$ **54.** $\dfrac{y}{x-y}$ **55.** $\dfrac{x(5y+1)}{3y}$ **56.** $\dfrac{x-3}{3}$ **57.** $\dfrac{1+x}{1-x}$ **58.** $-\dfrac{x^2 + 9}{6x}$ **59.** $\{6\}$ **60.** $\{3\}$ **61.** $\left\{\dfrac{3}{2}\right\}$

62. $\{-7, 7\}$ **63.** $\dfrac{2x+5}{x(x-7)}$ **64.** $\dfrac{-5(x+6)}{2x(x-3)}$ **65.** $\left\{-\dfrac{1}{3}, 2\right\}$ **66.** $\left\{\dfrac{3}{2}, 5\right\}$ **67.** $a = \dfrac{2A}{h} - b$ **68.** $R_2 = \dfrac{RR_1}{R_1 - R}$ **69.** $R = \dfrac{E}{I} - r$

70. $r = \dfrac{A-P}{Pt}$ **71.** $x = \dfrac{yz}{z-y}$ **72.** $A = \dfrac{HL}{k(T_1 - T_2)}$ **73.** 1 and 2 **74.** 7 **75.** $1\dfrac{23}{37}$ hr **76.** 12 hr **77.** 8 mph **78.** 4 mph **79.** 9 **80.** 3.125 cu m

Systems of Linear Equations

11

A Determine Whether an Ordered Pair Is a Solution of a System of Two Linear Equations.

B Solve a System of Two Equations by Graphing.

C Solve a System Using Substitution.

D Solve a System Using Elimination.

11.1 SOLVING SYSTEMS OF LINEAR EQUALITIES IN TWO VARIABLES

Recall from Chapter 3 that the graph of a linear equation in two variables is a line. Two or more linear equations form a **system of linear equations.** Some examples of systems of linear equations in two variables follow.

$$\begin{cases} x - 2y = -7 \\ 3x + y = 0 \end{cases} \qquad \begin{cases} x = 5 \\ x + \dfrac{y}{2} = 9 \end{cases} \qquad \begin{cases} x - 3 = 2y + 6 \\ y = 1 \end{cases}$$

Objective **A** Determining Whether an Ordered Pair Is a Solution

Recall that a solution of an equation in two variables is an ordered pair (x, y) that makes the equation true. A **solution of a system** of two equations in two variables is an ordered pair (x, y) that makes both equations true.

PRACTICE 1

Determine whether the ordered pair $(4, 1)$ is a solution of the system.

$$\begin{cases} x - y = 3 \\ 2x - 3y = 5 \end{cases}$$

Example 1 Determine whether the ordered pair $(-1, 1)$ is a solution of the system.

$$\begin{cases} -x + y = 2 \\ 2x - y = -3 \end{cases}$$

Solution: We replace x with -1 and y with 1 in each equation.

$$-x + y = 2 \quad \text{First equation}$$
$$-(-1) + (1) \overset{?}{=} 2 \quad \text{Let } x = -1 \text{ and } y = 1.$$
$$1 + 1 \overset{?}{=} 2$$
$$2 = 2 \quad \text{True}$$

$$2x - y = -3 \quad \text{Second equation}$$
$$2(-1) - (1) \overset{?}{=} -3 \quad \text{Let } x = -1 \text{ and } y = 1.$$
$$-2 - 1 \overset{?}{=} -3$$
$$-3 = -3 \quad \text{True}$$

Since $(-1, 1)$ makes both equations true, it is a solution.

● **Work Practice 1**

PRACTICE 2

Determine whether the ordered pair $(-3, 3)$ is a solution of the system.

$$\begin{cases} 3x - y = -12 \\ x - y = 0 \end{cases}$$

Example 2 Determine whether the ordered pair $(-2, 3)$ is a solution of the system.

$$\begin{cases} 5x + 3y = -1 \\ x - y = 1 \end{cases}$$

Solution: We replace x with -2 and y with 3 in each equation.

$$5x + 3y = -1 \quad \text{First equation}$$
$$5(-2) + 3(3) \overset{?}{=} -1 \quad \text{Let } x = -2 \text{ and } y = 3.$$
$$-10 + 9 \overset{?}{=} -1$$
$$-1 = -1 \quad \text{True}$$

Answers

1. yes, a solution   **2.** no, not a solution

$$x - y = 1 \quad \text{Second equation}$$
$$(-2) - (3) \stackrel{?}{=} 1 \quad \text{Let } x = -2 \text{ and } y = 3.$$
$$-5 = 1 \quad \text{False}$$

Since the ordered pair $(-2, 3)$ does not make both equations true, it is not a solution of the system.

● **Work Practice 2**

Objective **B** Solving a System by Graphing

The graph of each linear equation in a system is a line. Each point on each line corresponds to an ordered pair solution of its equation. If the lines intersect, the point of intersection lies on both lines and corresponds to an ordered pair solution of both equations. In other words, the point of intersection corresponds to an ordered pair solution of the system. Therefore, we can estimate the solutions of a system by graphing the equations on the same rectangular coordinate system and estimating the coordinates of any points of intersection.

Example 3 Solve the system by graphing.

$$\begin{cases} x + y = 2 \\ 3x - y = -2 \end{cases}$$

Solution: First we graph the linear equations on the same rectangular coordinate system. These lines intersect at one point as shown. The coordinates of the point of intersection appear to be $(0, 2)$. We check this estimated solution by replacing x with 0 and y with 2 in *both* equations.

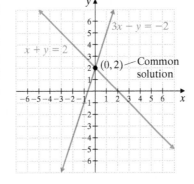

$$x + y = 2 \quad \text{First equation}$$
$$0 + 2 \stackrel{?}{=} 2 \quad \text{Let } x = 0 \text{ and } y = 2.$$
$$2 = 2 \quad \text{True}$$

$$3x - y = -2 \quad \text{Second equation}$$
$$3(0) - 2 \stackrel{?}{=} -2 \quad \text{Let } x = 0 \text{ and } y = 2.$$
$$-2 = -2 \quad \text{True}$$

The ordered pair $(0, 2)$ is the solution of the system. A system that has at least one solution, such as this one, is said to be **consistent.**

● **Work Practice 3**

    In Example 3, we have a **consistent system.** To review, a system that has at least one solution is said to be consistent.

    Later, we will talk about **dependent equations.** For now, we define an **independent equation** to be an equation in a system of equations that cannot be algebraically derived from any other equation in the system.

    Thus for:

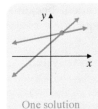

Consistent System: the system has at least one solution

One solution   Independent Equations: each equation in the system cannot be algebraically derived from the other

PRACTICE 3

Solve each system by graphing. If the system has just one solution, estimate the solution.

3. $\begin{cases} x - y = 2 \\ x + 3y = 6 \end{cases}$

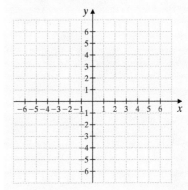

Answer
3. $(3, 1)$

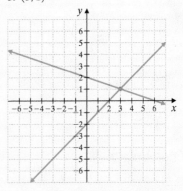

PRACTICE 4

Solve each system by graphing. If the system has just one solution, estimate the solution.

4. $\begin{cases} y = -3x \\ 6x + 2y = 4 \end{cases}$

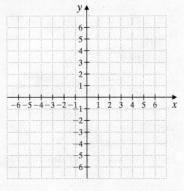

Example 4 Solve the system by graphing.

$$\begin{cases} x - 2y = 4 \\ x = 2y \end{cases}$$

Solution: We graph each linear equation.

The lines appear to be parallel. To be sure, let's write each equation in slope-intercept form, $y = mx + b$. To do so, we solve for y.

$$x - 2y = 4 \qquad \text{First equation}$$
$$-2y = -x + 4 \qquad \text{Subtract } x \text{ from both sides.}$$
$$y = \frac{1}{2}x - 2 \qquad \text{Divide both sides by } -2.$$

$$x = 2y \qquad \text{Second equation}$$
$$\frac{1}{2}x = y \qquad \text{Divide both sides by 2.}$$

$$y = \frac{1}{2}x$$

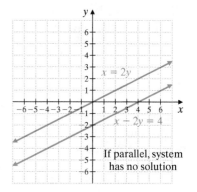

If parallel, system has no solution

The graphs of these equations have the same slope, $\frac{1}{2}$, but different y-intercepts, so these lines are parallel. Therefore, the system has no solution since the equations have no common solution (there are no intersection points). A system that has no solution is said to be **inconsistent.**

● **Work Practice 4**

In Example 4, we have an **inconsistent system.** To review, a system that has no solution is said to be inconsistent.

Let's now talk about the equations in this system. Each equation in this system cannot be algebraically derived from the other, so each equation is independent of the other.

Thus:

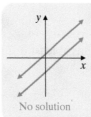

No solution

Inconsistent System: the system has no solution

Independent Equations: each equation in the system cannot be algebraically derived from the other

Answer
4. no solution, or ∅

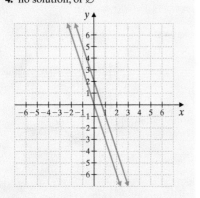

Helpful Hint

- If a system of equations has *at least one solution,* the system is *consistent.*
- If a system of equations has *no solution,* the system is *inconsistent.*

The pairs of equations in Examples 3 and 4 are called independent because their graphs differ. In Example 5, we see an example of dependent equations.

✓ **Concept Check** How can you tell just by looking at the following system that it has no solution?

$$\begin{cases} y = 3x + 5 \\ y = 3x - 7 \end{cases}$$

✓ **Concept Check Answer**

answers may vary

Example 5 Solve the system by graphing.

$$\begin{cases} 2x + 4y = 10 \\ x + 2y = 5 \end{cases}$$

Solution: We graph each linear equation. We see that the graphs of the equations are the same line. To confirm this, notice that if both sides of the second equation are multiplied by 2, the result is the first equation. This means that the equations have identical solutions. Any ordered pair solution of one equation satisfies the other equation also. These equations are said to be **dependent equations**. The solution set of the system is $\{(x, y)\,|\,x + 2y = 5\}$ or, equivalently, $\{(x, y)\,|\,2x + 4y = 10\}$ since the lines describe identical ordered pairs. Written the second way, the solution set is read "the set of all ordered pairs (x, y), such that $2x + 4y = 10$." There is an infinite number of solutions to this system.

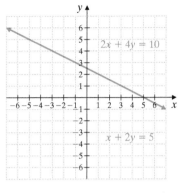

● **Work Practice 5**

In Example 5, we have a **consistent system** since the system has at least one solution. In fact, the system in Example 5 has an infinite number of solutions.

Let's now define **dependent equations**. We define a **dependent equation** to be an equation in a system of equations that can be algebraically derived from another equation in the system.

Thus:

Consistent System: the system has at least one solution

Infinite number of solutions

Dependent Equations: an equation in a system of equations can be algebraically derived from another

Helpful Hint

- If the graphs of two equations *differ*, they are *independent* equations.
- If the graphs of two equations are the *same*, they are *dependent* equations.

✓ **Concept Check** How can you tell just by looking at the following system that it has infinitely many solutions?

$$\begin{cases} x + y = 5 \\ 2x + 2y = 10 \end{cases}$$

PRACTICE 5

Solve the system by graphing.

$$\begin{cases} -2x + y = 1 \\ 4x - 2y = -2 \end{cases}$$

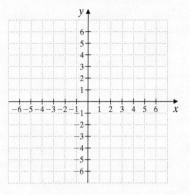

Answer

5. $\{(x, y)\,|\,-2x + y = 1\}$

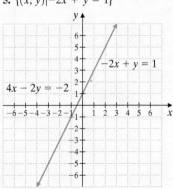

✓ **Concept Check Answer**

answers may vary

We can summarize the information discovered in Examples 3 through 5 as follows.

Possible Solutions to Systems of Two Linear Equations

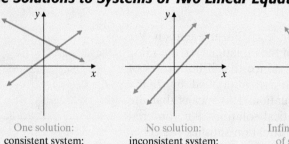

One solution:
consistent system;
independent equations

No solution:
inconsistent system;
independent equations

Infinite number
of solutions:
consistent system;
dependent equations

Objective ⊙ Solving a System Using Substitution

Graphing the equations of a system by hand is often a good method for finding approximate solutions of a system, but it is not a reliable method for finding exact solutions. To find an exact solution, we need to use *algebra*. One *algebraic* method is called the **substitution method.**

PRACTICE 6

Use the substitution method to solve the system:
$$\begin{cases} 6x - 4y = 10 \\ y = 3x - 3 \end{cases}$$

Example 6 Use the substitution method to solve the system:

$$\begin{cases} 2x + 4y = -6 & \text{First equation} \\ x = 2y - 5 & \text{Second equation} \end{cases}$$

Solution: In the second equation, we are told that x is equal to $2y - 5$. Since they are equal, we can *substitute* $2y - 5$ for x in the first equation. This will give us an equation in one variable, which we can solve for y.

$$2x + 4y = -6 \qquad \text{First equation}$$

$$2(\overbrace{2y - 5}) + 4y = -6 \qquad \text{Substitute } 2y - 5 \text{ for } x.$$

$$4y - 10 + 4y = -6$$

$$8y = 4$$

$$y = \frac{4}{8} = \frac{1}{2} \qquad \text{Solve for } y.$$

The y-coordinate of the solution is $\frac{1}{2}$. To find the x-coordinate, we replace y with $\frac{1}{2}$ in the second equation,

$$x = 2y - 5$$
$$x = 2y - 5$$
$$x = 2\left(\frac{1}{2}\right) - 5 = 1 - 5 = -4$$

The ordered pair solution is $\left(-4, \frac{1}{2}\right)$. Check to see that $\left(-4, \frac{1}{2}\right)$ satisfies both equations of the system.

▶ Work Practice 6

Answer

6. $\left(\frac{1}{3}, -2\right)$

The substitution method is summarized below. Feel free to use these steps.

Solving a System of Two Equations Using the Substitution Method

Step 1: Solve one of the equations for one of its variables.

Step 2: Substitute the expression for the variable found in Step 1 into the other equation.

Step 3: Find the value of one variable by solving the equation from Step 2.

Step 4: Find the value of the other variable by substituting the value found in Step 3 into the equation from Step 1.

Step 5: Check the ordered pair solution in *both* original equations.

Example 7 Use the substitution method to solve the system:

$$\begin{cases} -\dfrac{x}{6} + \dfrac{y}{2} = \dfrac{1}{2} \\ \dfrac{x}{3} - \dfrac{y}{6} = -\dfrac{3}{4} \end{cases}$$

Solution: First we multiply each equation by its least common denominator to clear the system of fractions. We multiply the first equation by 6 and the second equation by 12.

$$\begin{cases} 6\left(-\dfrac{x}{6} + \dfrac{y}{2}\right) = 6\left(\dfrac{1}{2}\right) \\ 12\left(\dfrac{x}{3} - \dfrac{y}{6}\right) = 12\left(-\dfrac{3}{4}\right) \end{cases}$$
simplifies to
$$\begin{cases} -x + 3y = 3 & \text{First equation} \\ 4x - 2y = -9 & \text{Second equation} \end{cases}$$

We now solve the first equation for x so that we may substitute our findings into the second equation.

$$-x + 3y = 3 \quad \text{First equation}$$
$$3y - 3 = x \quad \text{Solve for } x.$$

Next we replace x with $3y - 3$ in the second equation.

$$4x - 2y = -9 \quad \text{Second equation}$$
$$4(\overbrace{3y - 3}) - 2y = -9$$
$$12y - 12 - 2y = -9$$
$$10y = 3$$
$$y = \dfrac{3}{10} \quad \text{Solve for } y.$$

> **Helpful Hint** To avoid tedious fractions, solve for a variable whose coefficient is 1 or −1, if possible.

The y-coordinate is $\dfrac{3}{10}$. To find the x-coordinate, we replace y with $\dfrac{3}{10}$ in the equation $x = 3y - 3$. Then

$$x = 3\left(\dfrac{3}{10}\right) - 3 = \dfrac{9}{10} - 3 = \dfrac{9}{10} - \dfrac{30}{10} = -\dfrac{21}{10}$$

The ordered pair solution is $\left(-\dfrac{21}{10}, \dfrac{3}{10}\right)$. Check to see that this solution satisfies both original equations.

● **Work Practice 7**

PRACTICE 7

Use the substitution method to solve the system:

$$\begin{cases} -\dfrac{x}{2} + \dfrac{y}{4} = \dfrac{1}{2} \\ \dfrac{x}{2} + \dfrac{y}{2} = -\dfrac{1}{8} \end{cases}$$

> **Helpful Hint** If a system of equations contains equations with fractions, the first step is to clear the equations of fractions.

Answer

7. $\left(-\dfrac{3}{4}, \dfrac{1}{2}\right)$

Objective ⓓ Solving a System Using Elimination

The **elimination method,** or **addition method,** is a second algebraic technique for solving systems of equations. For this method, we rely on a version of the addition property of equality, which states that "equals added to equals are equal."

> If $A = B$ and $C = D$ then $A + C = B + D$

PRACTICE 8

Use the elimination method to solve the system:
$$\begin{cases} 3x - y = 1 \\ 4x + y = 6 \end{cases}$$

Example 8 Use the elimination method to solve the system:

$$\begin{cases} x - 5y = -12 & \text{First equation} \\ -x + y = 4 & \text{Second equation} \end{cases}$$

Solution: Since the left side of each equation is equal to the right side, we add equal quantities by adding the left sides of the equations and the right sides of the equations. This sum gives us an equation in one variable, y, which we can solve for y.

$$
\begin{array}{ll}
x - 5y = -12 & \text{First equation} \\
\underline{-x + y = 4} & \text{Second equation} \\
-4y = -8 & \text{Add.} \\
y = 2 & \text{Solve for } y.
\end{array}
$$

The y-coordinate of the solution is 2. To find the corresponding x-coordinate, we replace y with 2 in either original equation of the system. Let's use the second equation.

$$
\begin{array}{ll}
-x + y = 4 & \text{Second equation} \\
-x + 2 = 4 & \text{Let } y = 2. \\
-x = 2 & \\
x = -2 &
\end{array}
$$

The ordered pair solution is $(-2, 2)$. Check to see that $(-2, 2)$ satisfies both equations of the system.

◉ **Work Practice 8**

The steps below summarize the elimination method.

> ### Solving a System of Two Linear Equations Using the Elimination Method
>
> **Step 1:** Rewrite each equation in standard form, $Ax + By = C$.
>
> **Step 2:** If necessary, multiply one or both equations by some nonzero number so that the coefficient of one variable in one equation is the opposite of the coefficient of that variable in the other equation.
>
> **Step 3:** Add the equations. Your chosen variable should be eliminated.
>
> **Step 4:** Find the value of the remaining variable by solving the equation from Step 3.
>
> **Step 5:** Find the value of the other variable by substituting the value found in Step 4 into either original equation.
>
> **Step 6:** Check the proposed ordered pair solution in *both* original equations.

Answer

8. $(1, 2)$

Example 9 Use the elimination method to solve the system:

$$\begin{cases} 3x + \dfrac{y}{2} = 2 \\ 6x + y = 5 \end{cases}$$

Solution: If we add the two equations, the sum will still be an equation in two variables. Notice, however, that if we multiply both sides of the first equation by -2, the coefficients of x in the two equations will be opposites. Then

$$\begin{cases} -2\left(3x + \dfrac{y}{2}\right) = -2(2) \\ 6x + y = 5 \end{cases} \quad \text{simplifies to} \quad \begin{cases} -6x - y = -4 \\ 6x + y = 5 \end{cases}$$

Now we can add the left sides and add the right sides.

$$\begin{array}{r} -6x - y = -4 \\ 6x + y = 5 \\ \hline 0 = 1 \quad \text{False} \end{array}$$

The resulting equation, $0 = 1$, is false for all values of y or x. Thus, the system has no solution. The solution set is $\{\ \}$, or $\varnothing$. This system is inconsistent, and the graphs of the equations are parallel lines.

 Work Practice 9

PRACTICE 9

Use the elimination method to solve the system:

$$\begin{cases} \dfrac{x}{3} + 2y = -1 \\ x + 6y = 2 \end{cases}$$

Example 10 Use the elimination method to solve the system:

$$\begin{cases} 3x - 2y = 10 \\ 4x - 3y = 15 \end{cases}$$

Solution: To eliminate y, our first step is to multiply both sides of the first equation by 3 and both sides of the second equation by -2. Then

$$\begin{cases} 3(3x - 2y) = 3(10) \\ -2(4x - 3y) = -2(15) \end{cases} \quad \text{simplifies to} \quad \begin{cases} 9x - 6y = 30 \\ -8x + 6y = -30 \end{cases}$$

Next we add the left sides and add the right sides.

$$\begin{array}{r} 9x - 6y = 30 \\ -8x + 6y = -30 \\ \hline x \quad\quad = 0 \end{array}$$

To find y, we let $x = 0$ in either equation of the system

$$\begin{aligned} 3x - 2y &= 10 \quad \text{First equation} \\ 3(0) - 2y &= 10 \quad \text{Let } x = 0. \\ -2y &= 10 \\ y &= -5 \end{aligned}$$

The ordered pair solution is $(0, -5)$. Check to see that $(0, -5)$ satisfies both equations.

 Work Practice 10

PRACTICE 10

Use the elimination method to solve the system:

$$\begin{cases} 2x - 5y = 6 \\ 3x - 4y = 9 \end{cases}$$

Answers
9. no solution, or $\varnothing$ **10.** $(3, 0)$

PRACTICE 11

Use the elimination method to solve the system:

$$\begin{cases} 4x - 7y = 10 \\ -8x + 14y = -20 \end{cases}$$

Example 11 Use the elimination method to solve the system:

$$\begin{cases} -5x - 3y = 9 \\ 10x + 6y = -18 \end{cases}$$

Solution: To eliminate x, our first step is to multiply both sides of the first equation by 2. Then

$$\begin{cases} 2(-5x - 3y) = 2(9) \\ 10x + 6y = -18 \end{cases} \text{ simplifies to } \begin{cases} -10x - 6y = 18 \\ 10x + 6y = -18 \end{cases}$$

Next we add the equations.

$$\begin{array}{r} -10x - 6y = 18 \\ \underline{10x + 6y = -18} \\ 0 = 0 \end{array}$$

The resulting equation, $0 = 0$, is true for all possible values of y or x. Notice in the original system that if both sides of the first equation are multiplied by -2, the result is the second equation. This means that the two equations are equivalent. They have the same solution set and there are an infinite number of solutions. Thus, the equations of this system are dependent, and the solution set of the system is

$$\{(x, y) \mid -5x - 3y = 9\} \quad \text{or, equivalently,} \quad \{(x, y) \mid 10x + 6y = -18\}$$

● **Work Practice 11**

Answer

11. $\{(x, y) \mid 4x - 7y = 10\}$

Helpful Hint

Remember that not all ordered pairs are solutions of the system in Example 11—only the infinite number of ordered pairs that satisfy $-5x - 3y = 9$ or, equivalently, $10x + 6y = -18$.

 Calculator Explorations   Graphing

We may use a grapher to approximate solutions of systems of equations by graphing both equations on the same set of axes and approximating any points of intersection. For example, let's approximate the solution of the system

$$\begin{cases} y = -2.6x + 5.6 \\ y = 4.3x - 4.9 \end{cases}$$

We use a standard window and graph the equations on a single screen.

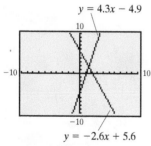

The two lines intersect. To approximate the point of intersection, we trace to the point of intersection and use an INTERSECT feature of the grapher, a ZOOM IN feature of the grapher, or redefine the window to [0, 3] by [0, 3]. If we redefine the window to [0, 3] by [0, 3], the screen should look like the following:

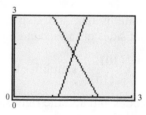

By tracing along the curves, we can see that the point of intersection has an x-value between 1.5 and 1.532. We can continue to zoom and trace or redefine the window until the coordinates of the point of intersection can be determined to the nearest hundredth. The approximate point of intersection is (1.52, 1.64).

Solve each system of equations. Approximate each solution to two decimal places.

1. $\begin{cases} y = -1.65x + 3.65 \\ y = 4.56x - 9.44 \end{cases}$

2. $\begin{cases} y = 7.61x + 3.48 \\ y = -1.26x - 6.43 \end{cases}$

3. $\begin{cases} 2.33x - 4.72y = 10.61 \\ 5.86x - 6.22y = -8.89 \end{cases}$

4. $\begin{cases} -7.89x - 5.68y = 3.26 \\ -3.65x + 4.98y = 11.77 \end{cases}$

Vocabulary and Readiness Check

Match each graph with the solution of the corresponding system.

A
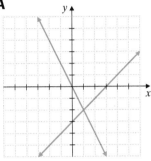

B
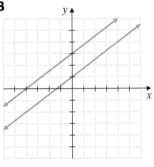

C
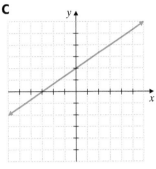

D
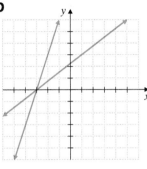

1. No solution

2. Infinite number of solutions

3. $(1, -2)$

4. $(-3, 0)$

11.1 Exercise Set

FOR EXTRA HELP

MyMathLab
Powered by CourseCompass™ and MathXL®

Math XP
PRACTICE

WATCH

DOWNLOAD

READ

REVIEW

Objective A *Determine whether the given ordered pair is a solution of the system. See Examples 1 and 2.*

1. $\begin{cases} x - y = 3 \\ 2x - 4y = 8 \end{cases}$ $(2, -1)$

2. $\begin{cases} x - y = -4 \\ 2x + 10y = 4 \end{cases}$ $(-3, 1)$

**3.** $\begin{cases} 2x - 3y = -9 \\ 4x + 2y = -2 \end{cases}$ $(3, 5)$

4. $\begin{cases} 2x - 5y = -2 \\ 3x + 4y = 4 \end{cases}$ $(4, 2)$

5. $\begin{cases} y = -5x \\ x = -2 \end{cases}$ $(-2, 10)$

6. $\begin{cases} y = 6 \\ x = -2y \end{cases}$ $(-12, 6)$

7. $\begin{cases} 3x + 7y = -19 \\ -6x = 5y + 8 \end{cases}$ $\left(\dfrac{2}{3}, -3\right)$

8. $\begin{cases} 4x + 5y = -7 \\ -8x = 3y - 1 \end{cases}$ $\left(\dfrac{3}{4}, -2\right)$

Objective B *Solve each system by graphing. See Examples 3 through 5.*

9. $\begin{cases} x + y = 1 \\ x - 2y = 4 \end{cases}$

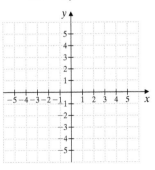

10. $\begin{cases} 2x - y = 8 \\ x + 3y = 11 \end{cases}$

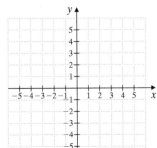

11. $\begin{cases} 2y - 4x = 0 \\ x + 2y = 5 \end{cases}$

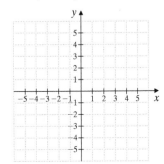

12. $\begin{cases} 4x - y = 6 \\ x - y = 0 \end{cases}$

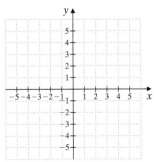

13. $\begin{cases} 3x - y = 4 \\ 6x - 2y = 4 \end{cases}$

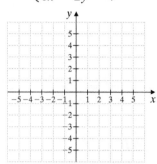

14. $\begin{cases} -x + 3y = 6 \\ 3x - 9y = 9 \end{cases}$

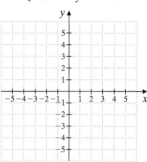

15. $\begin{cases} y = -3x \\ 2x - y = -5 \end{cases}$

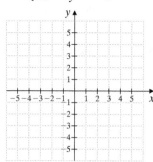

16. $\begin{cases} y = -2x \\ -3x + y = 10 \end{cases}$

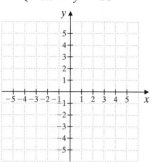

Objective Ⓒ *Use the substitution method to solve each system of equations. See Examples 6 and 7.*

17. $\begin{cases} x + y = 10 \\ y = 4x \end{cases}$

18. $\begin{cases} 5x + 2y = -17 \\ x = 3y \end{cases}$

19. $\begin{cases} 4x - y = 9 \\ 2x + 3y = -27 \end{cases}$

20. $\begin{cases} 3x - y = 6 \\ -4x + 2y = -8 \end{cases}$

21. $\begin{cases} \frac{1}{2}x + \frac{3}{4}y = -\frac{1}{4} \\ \frac{3}{4}x - \frac{1}{4}y = 1 \end{cases}$

22. $\begin{cases} \frac{2}{5}x + \frac{1}{5}y = -1 \\ x + \frac{2}{5}y = -\frac{8}{5} \end{cases}$

23. $\begin{cases} x = -3y + 4 \\ 3x + 9y = 12 \end{cases}$

24. $\begin{cases} x = 3y - 1 \\ 2x - 6y = -2 \end{cases}$

Objective Ⓓ *Use the elimination method to solve each system of equations. See Examples 8 through 11.*

25. $\begin{cases} 2x - 4y = 0 \\ x + 2y = 5 \end{cases}$

26. $\begin{cases} 2x - 3y = 0 \\ 2x + 6y = 3 \end{cases}$

27. $\begin{cases} 5x + 2y = 1 \\ x - 3y = 7 \end{cases}$

28. $\begin{cases} 6x - y = -5 \\ 4x - 2y = 6 \end{cases}$

29. $\begin{cases} 5x - 2y = 27 \\ -3x + 5y = 18 \end{cases}$

30. $\begin{cases} 3x + 4y = 2 \\ 2x + 5y = -1 \end{cases}$

31. $\begin{cases} 3x = 5y + 11 \\ 2x = 6y + 2 \end{cases}$

32. $\begin{cases} 6x = 3y - 3 \\ 4x = -5y - 9 \end{cases}$

33. $\begin{cases} x - 2y = 4 \\ 2x - 4y = 4 \end{cases}$

34. $\begin{cases} -x + 3y = 6 \\ 3x - 9y = 9 \end{cases}$

35. $\begin{cases} 3x + y = 1 \\ 2y = 2 - 6x \end{cases}$

36. $\begin{cases} y = 2x - 5 \\ 8x - 4y = 20 \end{cases}$

Objectives Ⓒ Ⓓ **Mixed Practice** *Solve each system of equations by substitution or elimination.*

37. $\begin{cases} 2x + 5y = 8 \\ 6x + y = 10 \end{cases}$

38. $\begin{cases} x - 4y = -5 \\ -3x - 8y = 0 \end{cases}$

39. $\begin{cases} x + y = 1 \\ x - 2y = 4 \end{cases}$

40. $\begin{cases} 2x - y = 8 \\ x + 3y = 11 \end{cases}$

41. $\begin{cases} \frac{1}{3}x + y = \frac{4}{3} \\ -\frac{1}{4}x - \frac{1}{2}y = -\frac{1}{4} \end{cases}$

42. $\begin{cases} \frac{3}{4}x - \frac{1}{2}y = -\frac{1}{2} \\ x + y = -\frac{3}{2} \end{cases}$

43. $\begin{cases} 4x + 2y = 5 \\ 2x + y = -1 \end{cases}$

44. $\begin{cases} 3x + 6y = 15 \\ 2x + 4y = 3 \end{cases}$

45. $\begin{cases} 10y - 2x = 1 \\ 5y = 4 - 6x \end{cases}$

46. $\begin{cases} 3x + 4y = 0 \\ 7x = 3y \end{cases}$

47. $\begin{cases} \frac{3}{4}x + \frac{5}{2}y = 11 \\ \frac{1}{16}x - \frac{3}{4}y = -1 \end{cases}$

48. $\begin{cases} \frac{2}{3}x + \frac{1}{4}y = -\frac{3}{2} \\ \frac{1}{2}x - \frac{1}{4}y = -2 \end{cases}$

49. $\begin{cases} x = 3y + 2 \\ 5x - 15y = 10 \end{cases}$ **50.** $\begin{cases} x = 7y - 21 \\ 2x - 14y = -42 \end{cases}$ **51.** $\begin{cases} \dfrac{x}{3} + y = \dfrac{4}{3} \\ -x + 2y = 11 \end{cases}$ **52.** $\begin{cases} \dfrac{x}{8} - \dfrac{y}{2} = 1 \\ \dfrac{x}{3} - y = 2 \end{cases}$

53. $\begin{cases} 2x = 6 \\ y = 5 - x \end{cases}$ **54.** $\begin{cases} x = 3y + 4 \\ -y = 5 \end{cases}$ **55.** $\begin{cases} \dfrac{x+5}{2} = \dfrac{6-4y}{3} \\ \dfrac{3x}{5} = \dfrac{21-7y}{10} \end{cases}$ **56.** $\begin{cases} \dfrac{y}{5} = \dfrac{8-x}{2} \\ x = \dfrac{2y-8}{3} \end{cases}$

57. $\begin{cases} 4x - 7y = 7 \\ 12x - 21y = 24 \end{cases}$ **58.** $\begin{cases} 2x - 5y = 12 \\ -4x + 10y = 20 \end{cases}$ **59.** $\begin{cases} \dfrac{2}{3}x - \dfrac{3}{4}y = -1 \\ -\dfrac{1}{6}x + \dfrac{3}{8}y = 1 \end{cases}$ **60.** $\begin{cases} \dfrac{1}{2}x - \dfrac{1}{3}y = -3 \\ \dfrac{1}{8}x + \dfrac{1}{6}y = 0 \end{cases}$

61. $\begin{cases} 2x - y = -1 \\ y = -2x \end{cases}$ **62.** $\begin{cases} 4y - x = -1 \\ x = -2y \end{cases}$ **63.** $\begin{cases} 0.7x - 0.2y = -1.6 \\ 0.2x - y = -1.4 \end{cases}$ **64.** $\begin{cases} -0.7x + 0.6y = 1.3 \\ 0.5x - 0.3y = -0.8 \end{cases}$

65. $\begin{cases} 4x - 1.5y = 10.2 \\ 2x + 7.8y = -25.68 \end{cases}$ **66.** $\begin{cases} x - 3y = -5.3 \\ 6.3x + 6y = 3.96 \end{cases}$

Review

Determine whether the given replacement values make each equation true or false.

67. $3x - 4y + 2z = 5$;
$x = 1, y = 2,$ and $z = 5$

68. $x + 2y - z = 7$;
$x = 2, y = -3,$ and $z = 3$

69. $-x - 5y + 3z = 15$;
$x = 0, y = -1,$ and $z = 5$

70. $-4x + y - 8z = 4$;
$x = 1, y = 0,$ and $z = -1$

Add the equations in each system. See this section.

71. $\begin{cases} 3x + 2y - 5z = 10 \\ -3x + 4y + z = 15 \end{cases}$ **72.** $\begin{cases} x + 4y - 5z = 20 \\ 2x - 4y - 2z = -17 \end{cases}$

73. $\begin{cases} 10x + 5y + 6z = 14 \\ -9x + 5y - 6z = -12 \end{cases}$ **74.** $\begin{cases} -9x - 8y - z = 31 \\ 9x + 4y - z = 12 \end{cases}$

Concept Extensions

Without graphing, determine whether each system has one solution, no solution, or an infinite number of solutions. See the Concept Checks in this section.

75. $\begin{cases} y = 2x - 5 \\ y = 2x + 1 \end{cases}$ **76.** $\begin{cases} y = 3x - \dfrac{1}{2} \\ y = -2x + \dfrac{1}{5} \end{cases}$ **77.** $\begin{cases} x + y = 3 \\ 5x + 5y = 15 \end{cases}$ **78.** $\begin{cases} y = 5x - 2 \\ y = -\dfrac{1}{5}x - 2 \end{cases}$

79. Can a system consisting of two linear equations have exactly two solutions? Explain why or why not.

80. Suppose the graph of the equations in a system of two equations in two variables consists of a circle and a line. Discuss the possible number of solutions for this system.

The concept of supply and demand is used often in business. In general, as the unit price of a commodity increases, the demand for that commodity decreases. Also, as a commodity's unit price increases, the manufacturer normally increases the supply. The point where supply is equal to demand is called the equilibrium point. The following shows the graph of a demand equation and the graph of a supply equation for previously rented DVDs. The x-axis represents the number of DVDs in thousands, and the y-axis represents the cost of a DVD. Use this graph to answer Exercises 81 through 84.

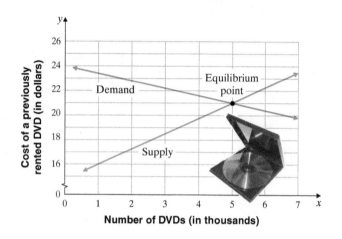

81. Find the number of DVDs and the price per DVD when supply equals demand.

82. When x is between 3 and 4, is supply greater than demand or is demand greater than supply?

83. When x is greater than 6, is supply greater than demand or is demand greater than supply?

84. For what x-values are the y-values corresponding to the supply equation greater than the y-values corresponding to the demand equation?

The revenue equation for a certain brand of toothpaste is $y = 2.5x$, where x is the number of tubes of toothpaste sold and y is the total income for selling x tubes. The cost equation is $y = 0.9x + 3000$, where x is the number of tubes of toothpaste manufactured and y is the cost of producing x tubes. The following set of axes shows the graph of the cost and revenue equations. Use this graph for Exercises 85 through 90.

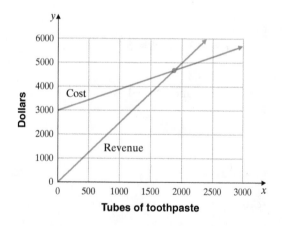

85. Find the coordinates of the point of intersection, or break-even point, by solving the system
$$\begin{cases} y = 2.5x \\ y = 0.9x + 3000 \end{cases}$$

86. Explain the meaning of the x-value of the point of intersection.

87. If the company sells 2000 tubes of toothpaste, does the company make money or lose money?

88. If the company sells 1000 tubes of toothpaste, does the company make money or lose money?

89. For what x-values will the company make a profit? (*Hint:* For what x-values is the revenue graph "higher" than the cost graph?)

90. For what x-values will the company lose money? (*Hint:* For what x-values is the revenue graph "lower" than the cost graph?)

91. Write a system of two linear equations in x and y that has the ordered pair solution $(2, 5)$.

92. Which method would you use to solve the system?
$$\begin{cases} 5x - 2y = 6 \\ 2x + 3y = 5 \end{cases}$$
Explain your choice.

93. The amount y of bottled water consumed per person in the United States (in gallons) in the year x can be modeled by the linear equation $y = 1.47x + 9.26$. The amount y of carbonated diet soft drinks consumed per person in the United States (in gallons) in the year x can be modeled by the linear equation $y = 0.13x + 13.55$. In both models, $x = 0$ represents the year 1995. (*Source:* Based on data from the Economic Research Service, U.S. Department of Agriculture)

a. What does the slope of each equation tell you about the patterns of bottled water and carbonated diet soft drink consumption in the United States?

b. Solve this system of equations. (Round your final results to the nearest whole numbers.)

c. Explain the meaning of your answer to part (b).

94. The amount of U.S. federal government income y (in billions of dollars) for fiscal year x, from 2006 through 2009 ($x = 0$ represents 2006), can be modeled by the linear equation $y = -95x + 2406$. The amount of U.S. federal government expenditures y (in billions of dollars) for the same period can be modeled by the linear equation $y = 285x + 2655$. (*Source:* Based on data from Financial Management Service, U.S. Department of the Treasury, 2006–2009)

a. What does the slope of each equation tell you about the patterns of U.S. federal government income and expenditures?

b. Solve this system of equations. (Round your final results to the nearest whole numbers.)

c. Did expenses ever equal income during the period from 2006 through 2009?

Solve each system. To do so you may want to let $a = \dfrac{1}{x}$ (if x is in the denominator) and let $b = \dfrac{1}{y}$ (if y is in the denominator.)

95. $\begin{cases} \dfrac{1}{x} + y = 12 \\ \dfrac{3}{x} - y = 4 \end{cases}$

96. $\begin{cases} x + \dfrac{2}{y} = 7 \\ 3x + \dfrac{3}{y} = 6 \end{cases}$

97. $\begin{cases} \dfrac{1}{x} + \dfrac{1}{y} = 5 \\ \dfrac{1}{x} - \dfrac{1}{y} = 1 \end{cases}$

98. $\begin{cases} \dfrac{2}{x} + \dfrac{3}{y} = 5 \\ \dfrac{5}{x} - \dfrac{3}{y} = 2 \end{cases}$

99. $\begin{cases} \dfrac{2}{x} + \dfrac{3}{y} = -1 \\ \dfrac{3}{x} - \dfrac{2}{y} = 18 \end{cases}$

100. $\begin{cases} \dfrac{3}{x} - \dfrac{2}{y} = -18 \\ \dfrac{2}{x} + \dfrac{3}{y} = 1 \end{cases}$

101. $\begin{cases} \dfrac{2}{x} - \dfrac{4}{y} = 5 \\ \dfrac{1}{x} - \dfrac{2}{y} = \dfrac{3}{2} \end{cases}$

102. $\begin{cases} \dfrac{5}{x} + \dfrac{7}{y} = 1 \\ -\dfrac{10}{x} - \dfrac{14}{y} = 0 \end{cases}$

Objective

A Solve a System of Three Linear Equations in Three Variables.

11.2 SOLVING SYSTEMS OF LINEAR EQUALITIES IN THREE VARIABLES

In this section, we solve systems of linear equations in three variables. We call the equation $3x - y + z = -15$, for example, a **linear equation in three variables** since there are three variables and each variable is raised only to the power 1. A solution of this equation is an **ordered triple (x, y, z)** that makes the equation a true statement.

For example, the ordered triple $(2, 0, -21)$ is a solution of $3x - y + z = -15$ since replacing x with 2, y with 0, and z with -21 yields the true statement

$$3(2) - 0 + (-21) = -15$$

The graph of this equation is a plane in three-dimensional space, just as the graph of a linear equation in two variables is a line in two-dimensional space.

Although we will not discuss the techniques for graphing equations in three variables, visualizing the possible patterns of intersecting planes gives us insight into the possible patterns of solutions of a system of three three-variable linear equations. There are four possible patterns.

1. Three planes have a single point in common. This point represents the single solution of the system. This system is **consistent.**

2. Three planes intersect at no point common to all three. This system has no solution. A few ways that this can occur are shown. This system is **inconsistent.**

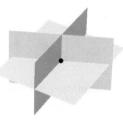

3. Three planes intersect at all the points of a single line. The system has infinitely many solutions. This system is **consistent.**

4. Three planes coincide at all points on the plane. The system is **consistent,** and the equations are **dependent.**

Objective Ⓐ Solving a System of Three Linear Equalities in Three Variables

Just as with systems of two equations in two variables, we can use the elimination or substitution method to solve a system of three equations in three variables. To use the elimination method, we eliminate a variable and obtain a system of two equations in two variables. Then we use the methods we learned in the previous section to solve the system of two equations.

Example 1 Solve the system:

$$\begin{cases} 3x - y + z = -15 & \text{Equation (1)} \\ x + 2y - z = 1 & \text{Equation (2)} \\ 2x + 3y - 2z = 0 & \text{Equation (3)} \end{cases}$$

Solution: Let's add equations (1) and (2) to eliminate z.

$$\begin{array}{l} 3x - y + z = -15 \\ \underline{x + 2y - z = 1} \\ 4x + y = -14 \quad \text{Equation (4)} \end{array}$$

Next we add two *other* equations and *eliminate z again*. To do so, we multiply both sides of equation (1) by 2 and add the resulting equation to equation (3). Then

$$\begin{cases} 2(3x - y + z) = 2(-15) \\ 2x + 3y - 2z = 0 \end{cases} \text{simplifies to} \begin{cases} 6x - 2y + 2z = -30 \\ \underline{2x + 3y - 2z = 0} \\ 8x + y = -30 \end{cases}$$

$$\text{Equation (5)}$$

We now have two equations (4 and 5) in the same two variables. This means we can solve equations (4) and (5) for x and y. To solve by elimination, we multiply both sides of equation (4) by -1 and add the resulting equation to equation (5). Then

$$\begin{cases} -1(4x + y) = -1(-14) \\ 8x + y = -30 \end{cases} \text{simplifies to} \begin{cases} -4x - y = 14 \\ \underline{8x + y = -30} \\ 4x = -16 \\ x = -4 \end{cases}$$

Add the
equations.
Solve for x.

We now replace x with -4 in equation (4) or (5).

$$\begin{array}{ll} 4x + y = -14 & \text{Equation (4)} \\ 4(-4) + y = -14 & \text{Let } x = -4. \\ y = 2 & \text{Solve for } y. \end{array}$$

Finally, we replace x with -4 and y with 2 in equation (1), (2), or (3).

$$\begin{array}{ll} x + 2y - z = 1 & \text{Equation (2)} \\ -4 + 2(2) - z = 1 & \text{Let } x = -4 \text{ and } y = 2. \\ -4 + 4 - z = 1 & \\ -z = 1 & \\ z = -1 & \end{array}$$

The ordered triple solution is $(-4, 2, -1)$.

Check: To check, we let $x = -4$, $y = 2$, and $z = -1$ in *all three* original equations of the system.

Equation (1)	**Equation (2)**
$3x - y + z = -15$	$x + 2y - z = 1$
$3(-4) - 2 + (-1) \stackrel{?}{=} -15$	$-4 + 2(2) - (-1) \stackrel{?}{=} 1$
$-12 - 2 - 1 \stackrel{?}{=} -15$	$-4 + 4 + 1 \stackrel{?}{=} 1$
$-15 = -15$ True	$1 = 1$ True

Continued on next page

PRACTICE 1

Solve the system:

$$\begin{cases} 2x - y + 3z = 13 \\ x + y - z = -2 \\ 3x + 2y + 2z = 13 \end{cases}$$

Helpful Hint   Make sure you add two other equations besides equations (1) and (2) and *also* **eliminate the same variable.** You will see why as you follow this example.

Answer
1. $(1, 1, 4)$

Equation (3)

$$2x + 3y - 2z = 0$$
$$2(-4) + 3(2) - 2(-1) \overset{?}{=} 0$$
$$-8 + 6 + 2 \overset{?}{=} 0$$
$$0 = 0 \quad \text{True}$$

All three statements are true, so the ordered triple solution is $(-4, 2, -1)$.

● **Work Practice 1**

PRACTICE 2

Solve the system:

$$\begin{cases} 2x + 4y - 2z = 3 \\ -x + y - z = 6 \\ x + 2y - z = 1 \end{cases}$$

Example 2 Solve the system:

$$\begin{cases} 2x - 4y + 8z = 2 & (1) \\ -x - 3y + z = 11 & (2) \\ x - 2y + 4z = 0 & (3) \end{cases}$$

Solution: Add equations (2) and (3) to eliminate x, and the new equation is

$$-5y + 5z = 11 \quad (4)$$

To eliminate x again, we multiply both sides of equation (2) by 2 and add the resulting equation to equation (1). Then

$$\begin{cases} 2x - 4y + 8z = 2 \\ 2(-x - 3y + z) = 2(11) \end{cases} \text{ simplifies to } \begin{cases} 2x - 4y + 8z = 2 \\ \underline{-2x - 6y + 2z = 22} \\ -10y + 10z = 24 \quad (5) \end{cases}$$

Next we solve for y and z using equations (4) and (5). To do so, we multiply both sides of equation (4) by -2 and add the resulting equation to equation (5).

$$\begin{cases} -2(-5y + 5z) = -2(11) \\ -10y + 10z = 24 \end{cases} \text{ simplifies to } \begin{cases} 10y - 10z = -22 \\ \underline{-10y + 10z = 24} \\ 0 = 2 \quad \text{False} \end{cases}$$

Since the statement is false, this system is inconsistent and has no solution. The solution set is the empty set $\{ \ \}$, or $\varnothing$.

● **Work Practice 2**

The elimination method is summarized next.

> ### Solving a System of Three Linear Equations by the Elimination Method
>
> **Step 1:** Write each equation in standard form, $Ax + By + Cz = D$.
>
> **Step 2:** Choose a pair of equations and use them to eliminate a variable.
>
> **Step 3:** Choose any other pair of equations and eliminate the *same variable* as in Step 2.
>
> **Step 4:** Two equations in two variables should be obtained from Step 2 and Step 3. Use methods from Section 11.1 to solve this system for both variables.
>
> **Step 5:** To solve for the third variable, substitute the values of the variables found in Step 4 into any of the original equations containing the third variable.
>
> **Step 6:** Check the ordered triple solution in *all three* original equations.

Helpful Hint Make sure you read closely and follow Step 3.

Answer

2. $\varnothing$

✓**Concept Check** In the system

$$\begin{cases} x + y + z = 6 & \text{Equation (1)} \\ 2x - y + z = 3 & \text{Equation (2)} \\ x + 2y + 3z = 14 & \text{Equation (3)} \end{cases}$$

equations (1) and (2) are used to eliminate *y*. Which action could be used to finish solving? Why?

a. Use (1) and (2) to eliminate *z*.

b. Use (2) and (3) to eliminate *y*.

c. Use (1) and (3) to eliminate *x*.

Example 3 Solve the system:

$$\begin{cases} 2x + 4y \quad = 1 & (1) \\ 4x \quad - 4z = -1 & (2) \\ \quad y - 4z = -3 & (3) \end{cases}$$

Solution: Notice that equation (2) has no term containing the variable *y*. Let's eliminate *y* using equations (1) and (3). We multiply both sides of equation (3) by -4 and add the resulting equation to equation (1). Then

$$\begin{cases} 2x + 4y = 1 \\ -4(y - 4z) = -4(-3) \end{cases} \text{ simplifies to } \begin{cases} 2x + 4y = 1 \\ \underline{\quad -4y + 16z = 12} \\ 2x \quad + 16z = 13 \quad (4) \end{cases}$$

Next we solve for *z* using equations (4) and (2). We multiply both sides of equation (4) by -2 and add the resulting equation to equation (2).

$$\begin{cases} -2(2x + 16z) = -2(13) \\ 4x - 4z = -1 \end{cases} \text{ simplifies to } \begin{cases} -4x - 32z = -26 \\ \underline{\quad 4x - 4z = -1} \\ -36z = -27 \\ z = \frac{3}{4} \end{cases}$$

Now we replace *z* with $\frac{3}{4}$ in equation (3) and solve for *y*.

$$y - 4\left(\frac{3}{4}\right) = -3 \quad \text{Let } z = \frac{3}{4} \text{ in equation (3).}$$
$$y - 3 = -3$$
$$y = 0$$

Finally, we replace *y* with 0 in equation (1) and solve for *x*.

$$2x + 4(0) = 1 \quad \text{Let } y = 0 \text{ in equation (1).}$$
$$2x = 1$$
$$x = \frac{1}{2}$$

The ordered triple solution is $\left(\frac{1}{2}, 0, \frac{3}{4}\right)$. Check to see that this solution satisfies *all three* equations of the system.

Work Practice 3

PRACTICE 3

Solve the system:

$$\begin{cases} 3x + 2y \quad = -1 \\ 6x \quad - 2z = 4 \\ \quad y - 3z = 2 \end{cases}$$

Answer

3. $\left(\frac{1}{3}, -1, -1\right)$

✓ **Concept Check Answer**

b; answers may vary

PRACTICE 4

PRACTICE 4

Solve the system:

$$\begin{cases} x - 3y + 4z = 2 \\ -2x + 6y - 8z = -4 \\ \dfrac{1}{2}x - \dfrac{3}{2}y + 2z = 1 \end{cases}$$

Example 4 Solve the system:

$$\begin{cases} x - 5y - 2z = 6 & (1) \\ -2x + 10y + 4z = -12 & (2) \\ \dfrac{1}{2}x - \dfrac{5}{2}y - z = 3 & (3) \end{cases}$$

Solution: We multiply both sides of equation (3) by 2 to eliminate fractions, and we multiply both sides of equation (2) by $-\dfrac{1}{2}$ so that the coefficient of x is 1. The resulting system is then

$$\begin{cases} x - 5y - 2z = 6 & (1) \\ x - 5y - 2z = 6 & \text{Multiply (2) by } -\dfrac{1}{2}. \\ x - 5y - 2z = 6 & \text{Multiply (3) by 2.} \end{cases}$$

All three resulting equations are identical, and therefore equations (1), (2), and (3) are all equivalent. There are infinitely many solutions of this system. The equations are dependent. The solution set can be written as $\{(x, y, z) | x - 5y - 2z = 6\}$.

● **Work Practice 4**

As mentioned earlier, we can also use the substitution method to solve a system of linear equations in three variables.

PRACTICE 5

Solve the system:

$$\begin{cases} 2x + 5y - 3z = 30 & (1) \\ x + y = -3 & (2) \\ 2x - z = 0 & (3) \end{cases}$$

(*Hint:* Equations (2) and (3) each contain the variable x and have a variable missing.)

Example 5 Solve the system:

$$\begin{cases} x - 4y - 5z = 35 & (1) \\ x - 3y = 0 & (2) \\ -y + z = -55 & (3) \end{cases}$$

Solution: Notice in equations (2) and (3) that a variable is missing. Also notice that both equations contain the variable y. Let's use the substitution method by solving equation (2) for x and equation (3) for z and substituting the results in equation (1).

$$\begin{aligned} x - 3y &= 0 & (2) \\ x &= 3y & \text{Solve equation (2) for } x. \\ -y + z &= -55 & (3) \\ z &= y - 55 & \text{Solve equation (3) for } z. \end{aligned}$$

Now substitute $3y$ for x and $y - 55$ for z in equation (1).

Helpful Hint
Do not forget to distribute.

$$\begin{aligned} x - 4y - 5z &= 35 & (1) \\ 3y - 4y - 5(y - 55) &= 35 & \text{Let } x = 3y \text{ and } z = y - 55. \\ 3y - 4y - 5y + 275 &= 35 & \text{Use the distributive property and multiply.} \\ -6y + 275 &= 35 & \text{Combine like terms.} \\ -6y &= -240 & \text{Subtract 275 from both sides.} \\ y &= 40 & \text{Solve.} \end{aligned}$$

To find x, recall that $x = 3y$ and substitute 40 for y. Then $x = 3y$ becomes $x = 3 \cdot 40 = 120$. To find z, recall that $z = y - 55$ and also substitute 40 for y. Then $z = y - 55$ becomes $z = 40 - 55 = -15$. The solution is $(120, 40, -15)$.

● **Work Practice 5**

Answers
4. $\{(x, y, z) | x - 3y + 4z = 2\}$
5. $(-5, 2, -10)$

Vocabulary and Readiness Check

Solve.

1. Choose the equation(s) that has $(-1, 3, 1)$ as a solution.
   a. $x + y + z = 3$ **b.** $-x + y + z = 5$ **c.** $-x + y + 2z = 0$ **d.** $x + 2y - 3z = 2$

2. Choose the equation(s) that has $(2, 1, -4)$ as a solution.
   a. $x + y + z = -1$ **b.** $x - y - z = -3$ **c.** $2x - y + z = -1$ **d.** $-x - 3y - z = -1$

3. Use the result of Exercise 1 to determine whether $(-1, 3, 1)$ is a solution of the system below. Explain your answer.

$$\begin{cases} x + y + z = 3 \\ -x + y + z = 5 \\ x + 2y - 3z = 2 \end{cases}$$

4. Use the result of Exercise 2 to determine whether $(2, 1, -4)$ is a solution of the system below. Explain your answer.

$$\begin{cases} x + y + z = -1 \\ x - y - z = -3 \\ 2x - y + z = -1 \end{cases}$$

11.2 Exercise Set

FOR EXTRA HELP

MyMathLab   Math XL   PRACTICE   WATCH   DOWNLOAD   READ   REVIEW

Objective A *Solve each system. See Examples 1 through 5.*

1. $\begin{cases} x - y + z = -4 \\ 3x + 2y - z = 5 \\ -2x + 3y - z = 15 \end{cases}$

2. $\begin{cases} x + y - z = -1 \\ -4x - y + 2z = -7 \\ 2x - 2y - 5z = 7 \end{cases}$

3. $\begin{cases} x + y = 3 \\ 2y = 10 \\ 3x + 2y - 3z = 1 \end{cases}$

4. $\begin{cases} 5x = 5 \\ 2x + y = 4 \\ 3x + y - 4z = -15 \end{cases}$

5. $\begin{cases} 2x + 2y + z = 1 \\ -x + y + 2z = 3 \\ x + 2y + 4z = 0 \end{cases}$

6. $\begin{cases} 2x - 3y + z = 5 \\ x + y + z = 0 \\ 4x + 2y + 4z = 4 \end{cases}$

7. $\begin{cases} x - 2y + z = -5 \\ -3x + 6y - 3z = 15 \\ 2x - 4y + 2z = -10 \end{cases}$

8. $\begin{cases} 3x + y - 2z = 2 \\ -6x - 2y + 4z = -4 \\ 9x + 3y - 6z = 6 \end{cases}$

9. $\begin{cases} 4x - y + 2z = 5 \\ 2y + z = 4 \\ 4x + y + 3z = 10 \end{cases}$

10. $\begin{cases} 5y - 7z = 14 \\ 2x + y + 4z = 10 \\ 2x + 6y - 3z = 30 \end{cases}$

11. $\begin{cases} x + 5z = 0 \\ 5x + y = 0 \\ y - 3z = 0 \end{cases}$

12. $\begin{cases} x - 5y = 0 \\ x - z = 0 \\ -x + 5z = 0 \end{cases}$

13. $\begin{cases} 6x - 5z = 17 \\ 5x - y + 3z = -1 \\ 2x + y = -41 \end{cases}$

14. $\begin{cases} x + 2y = 6 \\ 7x + 3y + z = -33 \\ x - z = 16 \end{cases}$

15. $\begin{cases} x + y + z = 8 \\ 2x - y - z = 10 \\ x - 2y - 3z = 22 \end{cases}$

16. $\begin{cases} 5x + y + 3z = 1 \\ x - y + 3z = -7 \\ -x + y = 1 \end{cases}$

17. $\begin{cases} x + 2y - z = 5 \\ 6x + y + z = 7 \\ 2x + 4y - 2z = 5 \end{cases}$

18. $\begin{cases} 4x - y + 3z = 10 \\ x + y - z = 5 \\ 8x - 2y + 6z = 10 \end{cases}$

19. $\begin{cases} 2x - 3y + z = 2 \\ x - 5y + 5z = 3 \\ 3x + y - 3z = 5 \end{cases}$

20. $\begin{cases} 4x + y - z = 8 \\ x - y + 2z = 3 \\ 3x - y + z = 6 \end{cases}$

21. $\begin{cases} -2x - 4y + 6z = -8 \\ x + 2y - 3z = 4 \\ 4x + 8y - 12z = 16 \end{cases}$

22. $\begin{cases} -6x + 12y + 3z = -6 \\ 2x - 4y - z = 2 \\ -x + 2y + \dfrac{z}{2} = -1 \end{cases}$

23. $\begin{cases} 2x + 2y - 3z = 1 \\ y + 2z = -14 \\ 3x - 2y = -1 \end{cases}$

24. $\begin{cases} 7x + 4y = 10 \\ x - 4y + 2z = 6 \\ y - 2z = -1 \end{cases}$

25. $\begin{cases} x + 2y - z = 5 \\ -3x - 2y - 3z = 11 \\ 4x + 4y + 5z = -18 \end{cases}$

26. $\begin{cases} 3x - 3y + z = -1 \\ 3x - y - z = 3 \\ -6x + 4y + 3z = -8 \end{cases}$

27. $\begin{cases} \dfrac{3}{4}x - \dfrac{1}{3}y + \dfrac{1}{2}z = 9 \\ \dfrac{1}{6}x + \dfrac{1}{3}y - \dfrac{1}{2}z = 2 \\ \dfrac{1}{2}x - y + \dfrac{1}{2}z = 2 \end{cases}$

28. $\begin{cases} \dfrac{1}{3}x - \dfrac{1}{4}y + z = -9 \\ \dfrac{1}{2}x - \dfrac{1}{3}y - \dfrac{1}{4}z = -6 \\ x - \dfrac{1}{2}y - z = -8 \end{cases}$

Review

Solve.

29. $2(x - 1) - 3x = x - 12$

30. $7(2x - 1) + 4 = 11(3x - 2)$

31. $-y - 5(y + 5) = 3y - 10$

32. $z - 3(z + 7) = 6(2z + 1)$

Solve.

33. The sum of two numbers is 45 and one number is twice the other. Find the numbers.

34. The difference between two numbers is 5. Twice the smaller number added to five times the larger number is 53. Find the numbers.

Concept Extensions

35. Write a single linear equation in three variables that has $(-1, 2, -4)$ as a solution. (There are many possibilities.) Explain the process you used to write an equation.

36. When solving a system of three equations in three unknowns, explain how to determine that a system has no solution.

37. Write a system of linear equations in three variables that has the solution $(-1, 2, -4)$. (There are many possibilities.) Explain the process you used to write your system.

38. Write a system of three linear equations in three variables that has $(2, 1, 5)$ as a solution. (There are many possibilities.) Explain the process you used to write an equation.

39. The fraction $\dfrac{1}{24}$ can be written as the following sum:

$$\frac{1}{24} = \frac{x}{8} + \frac{y}{4} + \frac{z}{3}$$

where the numbers x, y, and z are solutions of

$$\begin{cases} x + y + z = 1 \\ 2x - y + z = 0 \\ -x + 2y + 2z = -1 \end{cases}$$

Solve the system and see that the sum of the fractions is $\dfrac{1}{24}$.

40. The fraction $\dfrac{1}{18}$ can be written as the following sum:

$$\frac{1}{18} = \frac{x}{2} + \frac{y}{3} + \frac{z}{9}$$

where the numbers x, y, and z are solutions of

$$\begin{cases} x + 3y + z = -3 \\ -x + y + 2z = -14 \\ 3x + 2y - z = 12 \end{cases}$$

Solve the system and see that the sum of the fractions is $\dfrac{1}{18}$.

Solving systems involving more than three variables can be accomplished with methods similar to those encountered in this section. Apply what you already know to solve each system of equations in four variables.

41. $\begin{cases} x + y \quad\quad - w = 0 \\ \quad\quad y + 2z + w = 3 \\ x \quad\quad - z \quad\quad = 1 \\ 2x - y \quad\quad - w = -1 \end{cases}$

42. $\begin{cases} 5x + 4y \quad\quad\quad = 29 \\ \quad\quad y + z - w = -2 \\ 5x \quad\quad + z \quad\quad = 23 \\ \quad\quad y - z + w = 4 \end{cases}$

43. $\begin{cases} x + y + z + w = 5 \\ 2x + y + z + w = 6 \\ x + y + z \quad\quad = 2 \\ x + y \quad\quad\quad = 0 \end{cases}$

44. $\begin{cases} 2x \quad\quad - z \quad\quad = -1 \\ \quad\quad y + z + w = 9 \\ \quad\quad y \quad\quad - 2w = -6 \\ x + y \quad\quad\quad = 3 \end{cases}$

45. Write a system of three linear equations in three variables that are dependent equations.

46. What is the solution to the system in Exercise 45?

A Solve Problems That Can Be Modeled by a System of Two Linear Equations.

B Solve Problems with Cost and Revenue Functions.

C Solve Problems That Can Be Modeled by a System of Three Linear Equations.

11.3 SYSTEMS OF LINEAR EQUATIONS AND PROBLEM SOLVING

Objective A Solving Problems Modeled by Systems of Two Equations

Thus far, we have solved problems by writing one-variable equations and solving for the variable. Some of these problems can be solved, perhaps more easily, by writing a system of equations, as illustrated in this section.

Example 1 Predicting Equal Consumption of Red Meat and Poultry

America's consumption of red meat has decreased most years since 2000, while consumption of poultry has increased. The function $y = -0.56x + 113.6$ approximates the annual pounds of red meat consumed per capita, where x is the number of years since 2000. The function $y = 0.76x + 68.57$ approximates the annual pounds of poultry consumed per capita, where x is also the number of years since 2000. If this trend continues, determine the year when the annual consumption of red meat and poultry will be equal. (*Source:* USDA: Economic Research Service)

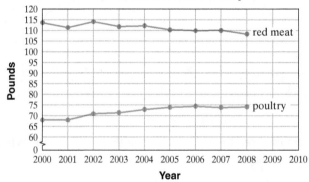

Annual U.S. per Capita Consumption of Red Meat and Poultry

PRACTICE 1

Read Example 1. If we use the years 2005, 2006, 2007, and 2008 only to write functions approximating the consumption of red meat and poultry, we have the following:

Red Meat: $y = -0.54x + 110.6$

Poultry: $y = -0.36x + 74.1$

where x is the number of years since 2005 and y is pounds per year consumed.

a. Assuming this trend continues, predict the year when consumption of red meat and poultry will be the same. Round to the nearest year.

b. Does your answer differ from the answer to Example 1? Why or why not?

Solution:

1. UNDERSTAND. Read and reread the problem and guess a year. Let's guess the year 2020. This year is 20 years since 2000, so $x = 20$. Now let $x = 20$ in each given function.

   Red meat: $y = -0.56x + 113.6 = -0.56(20) + 113.6 = 102.4$ pounds

   Poultry: $y = 0.76x + 68.57 = 0.76(20) + 68.57 = 83.77$ pounds

   Since the projected pounds in 2020 for red meat and poultry are not the same, we guessed incorrectly, but we do have a better understanding of the problem. We know that the year will be later than 2020.

2. TRANSLATE. We are already given the system of equations.

3. SOLVE. We want to know the year x in which pounds y are the same, so we solve the system:

$$\begin{cases} y = -0.56x + 113.6 \\ y = 0.76x + 68.57 \end{cases}$$

Answers

1. a. 2203 **b.** yes; answers may vary

Since both equations are solved for y, one way to solve is to use the substitution method.

$$y = -0.56x + 113.6 \quad \text{First equation}$$

$$-0.56x + 113.6 = 0.76x + 68.57 \quad \text{Let } y = -0.56x + 113.6$$

$$-1.32x = -45.03$$

$$x = \frac{-45.03}{-1.32} \approx 34.11$$

4. INTERPRET. Since we are only asked to find the year, we need only solve for x.

Check: To check, see whether $x \approx 34.11$ gives approximately the same number of pounds of red meat and poultry.

Red meat: $y = -0.56x + 113.6 = -0.56(34.11) + 113.6 \approx 94.49$ pounds

Poultry: $y = 0.76x + 68.57 = 0.76(34.11) + 68.57 \approx 94.49$ pounds

Since we rounded the number of years, the numbers of pounds do differ slightly. They differ only by 0.0048, so we can assume we solved correctly.

State: The consumption of red meat and poultry will be the same about 34.11 years after 2000, or 2034.11. Thus, in the year 2034, we predict the consumption will be the same.

◗ **Work Practice 1**

Example 2 Finding Unknown Numbers

A first number is 4 less than a second number. Four times the first number is 6 more than twice the second. Find the numbers.

Solution:

1. UNDERSTAND. Read and reread the problem and guess a solution. If one number is 10 and this is 4 less than a second number, the second number is 14. Four times the first number is 4(10), or 40. This is not equal to 6 more than twice the second number, which is 2(14) + 6 or 34. Although we guessed incorrectly, we now have a better understanding of the problem.

Since we are looking for two numbers, we will let

$x = $ first number

$y = $ second number

2. TRANSLATE. Since we have assigned two variables to this problem, we will translate the given facts into two equations. For the first statement we have

In words:	the first number	is	4 less than second number
	↓	↓	↓
Translate:	x	$=$	$y - 4$

Next we translate the second statement into an equation.

In words:	four times the first number	is	6 more than twice the second number
	↓	↓	↓
Translate:	$4x$	$=$	$2y + 6$

3. SOLVE. Now we solve the system

$$\begin{cases} x = y - 4 \\ 4x = 2y + 6 \end{cases}$$

Continued on next page

PRACTICE 2

A first number is 7 greater than a second number. Twice the first number is 4 more than three times the second. Find the numbers.

Answer
2. 17 and 10

Since the first equation expresses x in terms of y, we will use substitution. We substitute $y - 4$ for x in the second equation and solve for y.

$$4x = 2y + 6 \qquad \text{Second equation}$$

$$4(y - 4) = 2y + 6 \qquad \text{Let } x = y - 4.$$

$$4y - 16 = 2y + 6$$

$$2y = 22$$

$$y = 11$$

Now we replace y with 11 in the equation $x = y - 4$ and solve for x. Then $x = y - 4$ becomes $x = 11 - 4 = 7$. The ordered pair solution of the system is $(7, 11)$.

4. INTERPRET. Since the solution of the system is $(7, 11)$, the first number we are looking for is 7 and the second number is 11.

Check: Notice that 7 *is* 4 less than 11, and 4 times 7 *is* 6 more than twice 11. The proposed numbers, 7 and 11, are correct.

State: The numbers are 7 and 11.

● **Work Practice 2**

PRACTICE 3

Two trains leave Tulsa, one traveling north and the other south. After 4 hours, they are 376 miles apart. If one train is traveling 10 mph faster than the other, what is the speed of each?

Example 3 Finding the Rate of Speed

Two cars leave Indianapolis, one traveling east and the other west. After 3 hours they are 297 miles apart. If one car is traveling 5 mph faster than the other, what is the speed of each?

Solution:

1. UNDERSTAND. Read and reread the problem. Let's guess a solution and use the formula $d = r \cdot t$ to check. In this formula, d is distance, r is rate, and t is time. Suppose the faster car is traveling at a rate of 55 mph. This means that the other car is traveling at a rate of 50 mph since we are told that one car is traveling 5 mph faster than the other. To find the distance apart after 3 hours, we will first find the distance traveled by each car. One car's distance is rate $\cdot$ time $= 55(3) = 165$ miles. The other car's distance is rate $\cdot$ time $= 50(3) = 150$ miles. Since one car is traveling east and the other west, their distance apart is the sum of their distances, or 165 miles + 150 miles = 315 miles. Although this distance apart is not the required distance of 297 miles, we now have a better understanding of the problem.

Let's model the problem with a system of equations. We will let

x = speed of one car

y = speed of the other car

We summarize the information on the following chart. Both cars have traveled 3 hours. Since distance = rate $\cdot$ time, their distances are $3x$ and $3y$ miles, respectively.

	Rate	· Time	= Distance
One Car	x	3	$3x$
Other Car	y	3	$3y$

Answer

3. 42 mph; 52 mph

2. TRANSLATE. We can now translate the stated conditions into two equations.

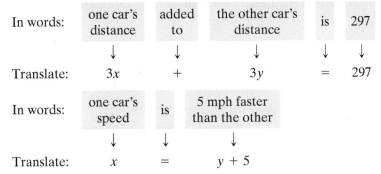

In words:

| one car's distance | added to | the other car's distance | is | 297 |

Translate: $3x + 3y = 297$

In words:

| one car's speed | is | 5 mph faster than the other |

Translate: $x = y + 5$

3. SOLVE. Now we solve the system.

$$\begin{cases} 3x + 3y = 297 \\ x = y + 5 \end{cases}$$

Again, the substitution method is appropriate. We replace x with $y + 5$ in the first equation and solve for y.

$$3x + 3y = 297 \quad \text{First equation}$$
$$3(\overbrace{y + 5}) + 3y = 297 \quad \text{Let } x = y + 5.$$
$$3y + 15 + 3y = 297$$
$$6y = 282$$
$$y = 47$$

To find x, we replace y with 47 in the equation $x = y + 5$. Then $x = 47 + 5 = 52$. The ordered pair solution of the system is $(52, 47)$.

4. INTERPRET. The solution $(52, 47)$ means that the cars are traveling at 52 mph and 47 mph, respectively.

Check: Notice that one car is traveling 5 mph faster than the other. Also, if one car travels 52 mph for 3 hours, the distance is $3(52) = 156$ miles. The other car traveling for 3 hours at 47 mph travels a distance of $3(47) = 141$ miles. The sum of the distances $156 + 141$ is 297 miles, the required distance.

State: The cars are traveling at 52 mph and 47 mph.

> **Helpful Hint**
> Don't forget to attach units, if appropriate.

⬤ **Work Practice 3**

Example 4 Mixing Solutions

Lynn Pike, a pharmacist, needs 70 liters of a 50% alcohol solution. She has available a 30% alcohol solution and an 80% alcohol solution. How many liters of each solution should she mix to obtain 70 liters of a 50% alcohol solution?

Solution:

1. UNDERSTAND. Read and reread the problem. Next, guess the solution. Suppose that we need 20 liters of the 30% solution. Then we need $70 - 20 = 50$ liters of the 80% solution. To see if this gives us 70 liters of a 50% alcohol solution, let's find the amount of pure alcohol in each solution.

number of liters	×	alcohol strength	=	amount of pure alcohol
20 liters	×	0.30	=	6 liters
50 liters	×	0.80	=	40 liters
70 liters	×	0.50	=	35 liters

Continued on next page

PRACTICE 4

One solution contains 20% acid and a second solution contains 50% acid. How many ounces of each solution should be mixed in order to have 60 ounces of a 30% acid solution?

Answer
4. 40 oz of 20% solution; 20 oz of 50% solution

Since 6 liters + 40 liters = 46 liters and not 35 liters, our guess is incorrect, but we have gained some insight as to how to model and check this problem.

We will let

x = amount of 30% solution, in liters

y = amount of 80% solution, in liters

and use a table to organize the given data.

	Number of Liters	Alcohol Strength	Amount of Pure Alcohol
30% Solution	x	30%	$0.30x$
80% Solution	y	80%	$0.80y$
50% Solution Needed	70	50%	$(0.50)(70)$

2. TRANSLATE. We translate the stated conditions into two equations.

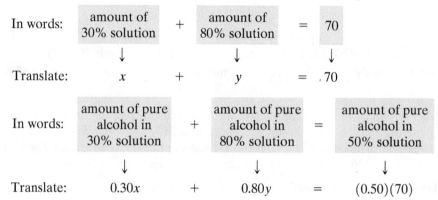

In words: amount of 30% solution + amount of 80% solution = 70

Translate: x + y =   70

In words: amount of pure alcohol in 30% solution + amount of pure alcohol in 80% solution = amount of pure alcohol in 50% solution

Translate: $0.30x$ + $0.80y$ = $(0.50)(70)$

3. SOLVE. Now we solve the system

$$\begin{cases} x + y = 70 \\ 0.30x + 0.80y = (0.50)(70) \end{cases}$$

To solve this system, we use the elimination method. We multiply both sides of the first equation by -3 and both sides of the second equation by 10. Then

$$\begin{cases} -3(x + y) = -3(70) \\ 10(0.30x + 0.80y) = 10(0.50)(70) \end{cases} \text{ simplifies to } \begin{cases} -3x - 3y = -210 \\ \underline{3x + 8y = 350} \\ \qquad\quad 5y = 140 \\ \qquad\quad\; y = 28 \end{cases}$$

Now we replace y with 28 in the equation $x + y = 70$ and find that $x + 28 = 70$, or $x = 42$. The ordered pair solution of the system is $(42, 28)$.

4. INTERPRET. The solution $(42, 28)$ means 42 liters of the 30% solution and 28 liters of the 80% solution.

Check: We check the solution in the same way that we checked our guess.

State: The pharmacist needs to mix 42 liters of 30% solution and 28 liters of 80% solution to obtain 70 liters of 50% solution.

● **Work Practice 4**

✓**Concept Check** Suppose you mix an amount of 25% acid solution with an amount of 60% acid solution. You then calculate the acid strength of the resulting acid mixture. For which of the following results should you suspect an error in your calculation? Why?

a. 14%   **b.** 32%   **c.** 55%

Objective B Solving Problems with Cost and Revenue Functions

Recall that businesses are often computing cost and revenue functions or equations to predict sales, to determine whether prices need to be adjusted, and to see whether the company is making or losing money. Recall also that the value at which revenue equals cost is called the break-even point. When revenue is less than cost, the company is losing money; when revenue is greater than cost, the company is making money.

Example 5 Finding a Break-Even Point

A manufacturing company recently purchased $3000 worth of new equipment to create new personalized stationery to sell to its customers. The cost of producing a package of personalized stationery is $3.00, and it is sold for $5.50. Find the number of packages that must be sold for the company to break even.

Solution:

1. **UNDERSTAND. Read and reread the problem.**

   Notice that the cost to the company will include a one-time cost of $3000 for the equipment and then $3.00 per package produced. The revenue will be $5.50 per package sold.

   To model this problem, we will let

   x = number of packages of personalized stationery

   $C(x)$ = total cost for producing x packages of stationery

   $R(x)$ = total revenue for selling x packages of stationery

2. **TRANSLATE.** The revenue equation is

In words:	revenue for selling x packages of stationery	=	price per package	·	number of packages
	↓		↓		↓
Translate:	$R(x)$	=	5.5	·	x

   The cost equation is

In words:	cost for producing x packages of stationery	=	cost per package	·	number of packages	+	cost for equipment
	↓		↓		↓		↓
Translate:	$C(x)$	=	3	·	x	+	3000

Continued on next page

3. SOLVE. Since the break-even point is when $R(x) = C(x)$, we solve the equation $5.5x = 3x + 3000$.

$5.5x = 3x + 3000$

$2.5x = 3000$ Subtract $3x$ from both sides.

$x = 1200$ Divide both sides by 2.5.

4. INTERPRET.

Check: To see whether the break-even point occurs when 1200 packages are produced and sold, we check to see if revenue equals cost when $x = 1200$. When $x = 1200$,

$$R(x) = 5.5x = 5.5(1200) = 6600$$

$$C(x) = 3x + 3000 = 3(1200) + 3000 = 6600$$

Since $R(1200) = C(1200) = 6600$, the break-even point is 1200.

State: The company must sell 1200 packages of stationery to break even. The graph of this system is shown.

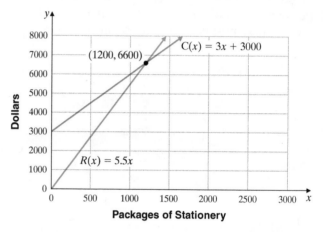

● **Work Practice 5**

Objective Ⓒ Solving Problems Modeled by Systems of Three Equations

To introduce problem solving with systems of three linear equations in three variables, we solve a problem about triangles.

Example 6 Finding Angle Measures

The measure of the largest angle of a triangle is 80° more than the measure of the smallest angle, and the measure of the remaining angle is 10° more than the measure of the smallest angle. Find the measure of each angle.

Solution:

1. UNDERSTAND. Read and reread the problem. Recall that the sum of the measures of the angles of a triangle is 180°. Then guess a solution. If the smallest angle measures 20°, the measure of the largest angle is 80° more, or 20° + 80° = 100°. The measure of the remaining angle is 10° more than the measure of the smallest angle, or 20° + 10° = 30°. The sum of these three angles is 20° + 100° + 30° = 150°, not the required 180°. We now know that the measure of the smallest angle is greater than 20°.

PRACTICE 6

The measure of the largest angle of a triangle is 80° more than the measure of the smallest angle, and the measure of the remaining angle is 40° more than the measure of the smallest angle. Find the measure of each angle.

Answer

6. 20°; 60°; 100°

To model this problem, we will let

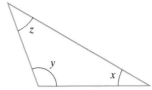

x = degree measure of the smallest angle

y = degree measure of the largest angle

z = degree measure of the remaining angle

2. **TRANSLATE.** We translate the given information into three equations.

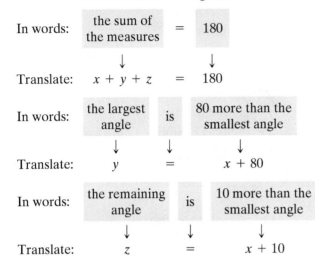

In words:	the sum of the measures	=	180

Translate: $x + y + z$ = 180

In words: | the largest angle | is | 80 more than the smallest angle

Translate: y = $x + 80$

In words: | the remaining angle | is | 10 more than the smallest angle

Translate: z = $x + 10$

3. **SOLVE.** We solve the system

$$\begin{cases} x + y + z = 180 \\ y = x + 80 \\ z = x + 10 \end{cases}$$

Since y and z are both expressed in terms of x, we will solve using the substitution method. We substitute $y = x + 80$ and $z = x + 10$ in the first equation. Then

$$x + y + z = 180 \quad \text{First equation}$$

$$x + (x + 80) + (x + 10) = 180 \quad \text{Let } y = x + 80 \text{ and } z = x + 10.$$
$$3x + 90 = 180$$
$$3x = 90$$
$$x = 30$$

Then $y = x + 80 = 30 + 80 = 110$, and $z = x + 10 = 30 + 10 = 40$. The ordered triple solution is $(30, 110, 40)$.

4. **INTERPRET.**

Check: Notice that $30° + 40° + 110° = 180°$. Also, the measure of the largest angle, $110°$, is $80°$ more than the measure of the smallest angle, $30°$. The measure of the remaining angle, $40°$, is $10°$ more than the measure of the smallest angle, $30°$.

State: The angles measure $30°$, $110°$, and $40°$.

🔵 **Work Practice 6**

11.3 Exercise Set

FOR EXTRA HELP

MyMathLab

Powered by CourseCompass™ and MathXL™

Math XP

PRACTICE   WATCH   DOWNLOAD   READ   REVIEW

Objective Ⓐ *Solve. See Examples 1 through 4. For Exercises 1 and 2, the solutions have been started for you.*

1. One number is two more than a second number. Twice the first is 4 less than 3 times the second. Find the numbers.

Start the solution:

1. UNDERSTAND the problem. Since we are looking for two numbers, let

x = one number

y = second number

2. TRANSLATE. Since we have assigned two variables, we will translate the facts into two equations. (Fill in the blanks.)

First equation:

In words:

| One number | is | two | more than | second number |

Translate: x =   ___ ___ ___

Second equation:

In words:

| Twice the first number | is | 4 | less than | 3 times the second number |

Translate: $2x$ =   ___ ___ ___

Finish with:

3. SOLVE the system and

4. INTERPRET the results.

2. Three times one number minus a second is 8, and the sum of the numbers is 12. Find the numbers.

Start the solution:

1. UNDERSTAND the problem. Since we are looking for two numbers, let

x = one number

y = second number

2. TRANSLATE. Since we have assigned two variables, we will translate the facts into two equations. (Fill in the blanks.)

First equation:

In words:

| Three times one number | minus | a second number | is | 8 |

Translate: $3x$ ___ ___   =   8

Second equation:

In words:

| The sum of the numbers | is | 12 |

Translate: x +   ___ ___   12

Finish with:

3. SOLVE the system and

4. INTERPRET the results..

3. The U.S.A. has the world's only "large deck" aircraft carriers which can hold up to 72 aircraft. The Enterprise class carrier is longest in length while the Nimitz class carrier is the second longest. The total length of these two carriers is 2193 feet while the difference of their lengths is only 9 feet. (*Source: USA Today,* May, 2001)

a. Find the length of each class carrier.

b. If a football field has a length of 100 yards, determine the length of the Enterprise class carrier in terms of number of football fields.

4. The rate of growth of participation of women in sports has been increasing since Title IX was enacted in the 1970s. In 2008, the number of women participating in swimming was 1.1 million less than twice the number participating in running. If the total number of women participating in these two sports was 50.5 million, find the number of participants in each sport. (*Source:* Sporting Goods Association of America, 2009 report)

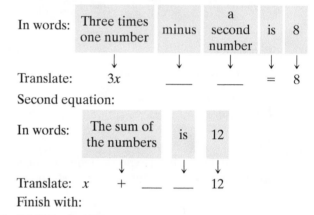

5. A Delta 727 traveled 560 mph with the wind and 480 mph against the wind. Find the speed of the plane in still air and the speed of the wind.

6. Terry Watkins can row about 10.6 kilometers in 1 hour downstream and 6.8 kilometers upstream in 1 hour. Find how fast he can row in still water, and find the speed of the current.

7. Find how many quarts of 4% butterfat milk and 1% butterfat milk should be mixed to yield 60 quarts of 2% butterfat milk.

8. A pharmacist needs 500 milliliters of a 20% phenobarbital solution but has only 5% and 25% phenobarbital solutions available. Find how many milliliters of each she should mix to get the desired solution.

9. In recent years, the United Kingdom was the most popular host country for U.S. students traveling abroad to study. Italy was the second most popular destination. A total of 64,003 students visited one of the two countries. If 2663 more U.S. students studied in the United Kingdom than Italy, how many students studied abroad in each country? (*Source:* Institute of International Education, Open Doors 2009)

10. The enrollment at both the University of Texas at El Paso (UTEP) and the University of New Hampshire at Durham (UNH) increased for the 2009–2010 school year. The enrollment at UTEP is 7981 less than twice the enrollment at UNH. Together, these two schools enrolled 35,507 students. Find the number of students enrolled at each school. (*Source:* UTEP and UNH)

11. Karen Karlin bought some large frames for $15 each and some small frames for $8 each at a closeout sale. If she bought 22 frames for $239, find how many of each type she bought.

12. Hilton University Drama Club sold 311 tickets for a play. Student tickets cost 50 cents each; nonstudent tickets cost $1.50. If total receipts were $385.50, find how many tickets of each type were sold.

13. One number is two less than a second number. Twice the first is 4 more than 3 times the second. Find the numbers.

14. Twice one number plus a second number is 42, and the first number minus the second number is −6. Find the numbers.

15. In the United States, the percent of adult blogging has changed within the various age ranges. From 2007 to 2009, the function $y = -4.5x + 24$ can be used to estimate the percent of adults under 30 who blogged, while the function $y = 2x + 7$ can be used to estimate the percent of adults over 30 who blogged. For both functions, x is the number of years after 2007. (*Source:* Pew Internet & American Life Project)

a. If this trend continues, predict the year in which the percent of adults under 30 and the percent of adults over 30 will blog at the same rate.

b. Use these equations to predict the percent of adults under 30 who blog and the percent of adults over 30 who blog for the current year.

16. The rate of fatalities per 100 million vehicle-miles has been decreasing for both automobiles and light trucks (pickups, sport-utility vehicles, and minivans). For the years 2002 through 2008, the function $y = -0.06x + 1.3$ can be used to estimate the rate of fatalities per 100 million vehicle-miles for cars during this period, while the function $y = -0.02x + 1.2$ can be used to estimate the rate of fatalities per 100 million vehicle-miles for light trucks during this period. For both functions, x is the number of years since 2002. (*Source:* Bureau of Transportation Statistics, U.S. Department of Transportation)

a. If this trend continues, predict the year in which the fatality rate for automobiles equaled the fatality rate for light trucks.

b. Use these equations to predict the fatality rate per 100 million vehicle-miles for automobiles and light trucks for the current year.

17. An office supply store in San Diego sells 7 writing tablets and 4 pens for $6.40. Also, 2 tablets and 19 pens cost $5.40. Find the price of each.

18. A Candy Barrel shop manager mixes M&M's worth $2.00 per pound with trail mix worth $1.50 per pound. Find how many pounds of each she should use to get 50 pounds of a party mix worth $1.80 per pound.

19. An airplane takes 3 hours to travel a distance of 2160 miles with the wind. The return trip takes 4 hours against the wind. Find the speed of the plane in still air and the speed of the wind.

20. Two cyclists start at the same point and travel in opposite directions. One travels 4 mph faster than the other. In 4 hours they are 112 miles apart. Find how fast each is traveling.

21. The annual U.S. per capita consumption of cheddar cheese has remained about the same since the millennium, while the consumption of mozzarella cheese has increased. For the years 2000–2009, the function $y = 0.06x + 9.7$ approximates the annual U.S. per capita consumption of cheddar cheese in pounds, and the function $y = 0.19x + 9.3$ approximates the annual U.S. per capita consumption of mozzarella cheese in pounds. For both functions, x is the number of years after 2000.

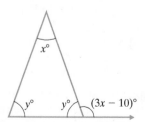

a. Explain how the given function verifies that the consumption of cheddar cheese has remained the same, while given function verifies that the consumption of mozzarella cheese has increased.

b. Based on this information, determine the year in which the pounds of cheddar cheese consumed equaled the pounds of mozzarella cheese consumed. (*Source:* Based on data from the U.S. Department of Agriculture)

22. Two of the major job categories defined by the U.S. Department of Labor are manufacturing jobs and jobs in the service sector. Jobs in the manufacturing sector have decreased nearly every year since the 1960s. During the same time period, service sector jobs have been steadily increasing. For the years from 1988 through 2009, the function $y = -0.225x + 16.1$ approximates the percent of jobs in the U.S. economy that are manufacturing jobs, while the function $y = 0.45x + 21.7$ approximates the percent of jobs that are service sector jobs. (*Source:* Based on data from the U.S. Department of Labor)

a. Explain how the decrease in manufacturing jobs can be verified by the given function, while the increase of service sector jobs can be verified by the given function.

b. Based on this information, determine the year when the percent of manufacturing jobs and the percent of service sector jobs were the same.

23. The perimeter of a triangle is 93 centimeters. If two sides are equally long and the third side is 9 centimeters longer than the others, find the lengths of the three sides.

24. Jack Reinholt, a car salesman, has a choice of two pay arrangements: a weekly salary of $200 plus 5% commission on sales, or a straight 15% commission. Find the amount of weekly sales for which Jack's earnings are the same regardless of the pay arrangement.

25. Hertz car rental agency charges $25 daily plus 10 cents per mile. Budget charges $20 daily plus 25 cents per mile. Find the daily mileage for which the Budget charge for the day is twice that of the Hertz charge for the day.

26. Carroll Blakemore, a drafting student, bought three templates and a pencil one day for $6.45. Another day, he bought two pads of paper and four pencils for $7.50. If the price of a pad of paper is three times the price of a pencil, find the price of each type of item.

27. In the figure, line l and line m are parallel lines cut by transversal t. Find the values of x and y.

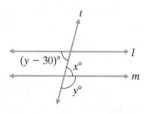

28. Find the values of x and y in the following isosceles triangle.

Objective Ⓑ *Given the cost function $C(x)$ and the revenue function $R(x)$, find the number of units x that must be sold to break even. See Example 5.*

29. $C(x) = 30x + 10,000 \ R(x) = 46x$

30. $C(x) = 12x + 15,000 \ R(x) = 32x$

31. $C(x) = 1.2x + 1500 \ R(x) = 1.7x$

32. $C(x) = 0.8x + 900 \ R(x) = 2x$

33. $C(x) = 75x + 160,000 \ R(x) = 200x$

34. $C(x) = 105x + 70,000 \ R(x) = 245x$

35. The planning department of Abstract Office Supplies has been asked to determine whether the company should introduce a new computer desk next year. The department estimates that $6000 of new manufacturing equipment will need to be purchased and that the cost of constructing each desk will be $200. The department also estimates that the revenue from each desk will be $450.
  a. Determine the revenue function $R(x)$ from the sale of x desks.
  b. Determine the cost function $C(x)$ for manufacturing x desks.
  c. Find the break-even point.

36. Baskets, Inc., is planning to introduce a new woven basket. The company estimates that $500 worth of new equipment will be needed to manufacture this new type of basket and that it will cost $15 per basket to manufacture. The company also estimates that the revenue from each basket will be $31.
  a. Determine the revenue function $R(x)$ from the sale of x baskets.
  b. Determine the cost function $C(x)$ for manufacturing x baskets.
  c. Find the break-even point. Round up to the nearest whole basket.

Objective Ⓒ *Solve. See Example 6.*

37. Rabbits in a lab are to be kept on a strict daily diet that includes 30 grams of protein, 16 grams of fat, and 24 grams of carbohydrates. The scientist has only three food mixes available with the following grams of nutrients per unit.

	Protein	Fat	Carbohydrate
Mix A	4	6	3
Mix B	6	1	2
Mix C	4	1	12

Find how many units of each mix are needed daily to meet each rabbit's dietary need.

38. Gerry Gundersen mixes different solutions with concentrations of 25%, 40%, and 50% to get 200 liters of a 32% solution. If he uses twice as much of the 25% solution as of the 40% solution, find how many liters of each kind he uses.

39. The perimeter of a quadrilateral (four-sided polygon) is 29 inches. The longest side is twice as long as the shortest side. The other two sides are equally long and are 2 inches longer than the shortest side. Find the lengths of all four sides.

40. The measure of the largest angle of a triangle is 90° more than the measure of the smallest angle, and the measure of the remaining angle is 30° more than the measure of the smallest angle. Find the measure of each angle.

41. The sum of three numbers is 40. The first number is five more than the second number. It is also twice the third. Find the numbers.

42. The sum of the digits of a three-digit number is 15. The tens-place digit is twice the hundreds-place digit, and the ones-place digit is 1 less than the hundreds-place digit. Find the three-digit number.

43. During the 2008–2009 regular NBA season, the top-scoring player was Dwyane Wade of the Miami Heat. Wade scored a total of 2386 points during the regular season. The number of free throws (each worth one point) he made was 26 less than seven times the number of three-point field goals he made. The number of two-point field goals that Wade made was 176 more than the number of free throws he made. How many free throws, two-point field goals, and three-point field goals did Dwyane Wade make during the 2008–2009 NBA season? (*Source:* National Basketball Association)

44. For 2009, the WNBA's top scorer was Cappie Poindexter of the Phoenix Mercury. She scored a total of 648 points during the regular season. The number of two-point field goals that Poindexter made was 22 fewer than five times the number of three-point field goals she made. The number of free throws (each worth one point) she made was 60 fewer than the number of two-point field goals she made. Find how many field goals, three-point field goals, and free throws Cappie Poindexter made during the 2009 regular season. (*Source:* Women's National Basketball Association)

△ **45.** Find the values of x, y, and z in the following triangle.

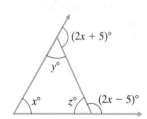

△ **46.** The sum of the measures of the angles of a quadrilateral is 360°. Find the values of x, y, and z in the following quadrilateral.

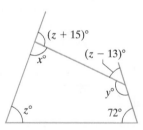

Review

Multiply both sides of equation (1) by 2, and add the resulting equation to equation (2). See Section 11.2.

47. $3x - y + z = 2$ (1)
$-x + 2y + 3z = 6$ (2)

48. $2x + y + 3z = 7$ (1)
$-4x + y + 2z = 4$ (2)

Multiply both sides of equation (1) by −3, and add the resulting equation to equation (2). See Section 11.2.

49. $x + 2y - z = 0$ (1)
$3x + y - z = 2$ (2)

50. $2x - 3y + 2z = 5$ (1)
$x - 9y + z = -1$ (2)

Concept Extensions

51. The number of personal bankruptcy petitions filed in the United States was consistently on the rise until there was a major change in bankruptcy law. The year 2007 was the year in which the fewest personal bankruptcy petitions were filed in 15 years, but the rate soon began to rise. In 2009, the number of petitions filed was 206,593 less than twice the number of petitions filed in 2007. This is equivalent to an increase of 568,751 petitions filed from 2007 to 2009. Find how many personal bankruptcy petitions were filed in each year. (*Source:* Based on data from the Administrative Office of the United States Courts)

52. In 2009, the median weekly earnings for male nurses were $89 more than the median weekly earnings for female nurses. The median weekly earnings for female nurses were 0.83 times that of their male counterparts. Also in 2009, the median weekly earnings for female architects were $257 less than the median weekly earnings for male architects. The median weekly earnings for male architects were 1.24 times that of their female counterparts. (*Source:* Based on data from the Bureau of Labor Statistics, U.S. Department of Labor)

   a. Find the median weekly earnings for female nurses in the United States in 2009. (Round to the nearest dollar.)

   b. Find the median weekly earnings for female architects in the United States in 2009. (Round to the nearest dollar.)

   c. Of the four groups of workers described in the problem, which group makes the greatest weekly earnings? Which group makes the least weekly earnings?

53. Find the values of a, b, and c such that the equation $y = ax^2 + bx + c$ has ordered pair solutions $(1, 6)$, $(-1, -2)$, and $(0, -1)$. To do so, substitute each ordered pair solution into the equation. Each time, the result is an equation in three unknowns: a, b, and c. Then solve the resulting system of three linear equations in three unknowns, a, b, and c.

54. Find the values of a, b, and c such that the equation $y = ax^2 + bx + c$ has ordered pair solutions $(1, 2)$, $(2, 3)$, and $(-1, 6)$. (*Hint:* See Exercise 53.)

55. Data (x, y) for the total number (in thousands) of college-bound students who took the ACT assessment in the year x are approximately $(3, 927)$, $(11, 1179)$, and $(19, 1495)$, where $x = 3$ represents 1993 and $x = 11$ represents 2001. Find the values a, b, and c such that the equation $y = ax^2 + bx + c$ models these data. According to your model, how many students will take the ACT in 2012? (*Source:* ACT, Inc.)

56. Monthly normal rainfall data (x, y) for Portland, Oregon, are $(4, 2.47)$, $(7, 0.58)$, $(8, 1.07)$, where x represents time in months (with $x = 1$ representing January) and y represents rainfall in inches. Find the values of a, b, and c rounded to 2 decimal places such that the equation $y = ax^2 + bx + c$ models this data. According to your model, how much rain should Portland expect during September? (*Source:* National Climatic Data Center)

11.4 SOLVING SYSTEMS OF EQUATIONS USING MATRICES

By now, you may have noticed that the solution of a system of equations depends on the coefficients of the equations in the system and not on the variables. In this section, we introduce how to solve a system of equations using a **matrix**.

Objective **A** Using Matrices to Solve a System of Two Equations

A **matrix** (plural: **matrices**) is a rectangular array of numbers. The following are examples of matrices.

$$\begin{bmatrix} 1 & 0 \\ 0 & 1 \end{bmatrix} \qquad \begin{bmatrix} 2 & 1 & 3 & -1 \\ 0 & -1 & 4 & 5 \\ -6 & 2 & 1 & 0 \end{bmatrix} \qquad \begin{bmatrix} a & b & c \\ d & e & f \end{bmatrix}$$

The numbers aligned horizontally in a matrix are in the same **row.** The numbers aligned vertically are in the same **column.**

$$\begin{array}{l} \text{Row 1} \rightarrow \\ \text{Row 2} \rightarrow \end{array} \begin{bmatrix} 2 & 1 & 0 \\ -1 & 6 & 2 \end{bmatrix}$$

This matrix has 2 rows and 3 columns. It is called a 2 × 3 (read "two by three") matrix.

Column 1   Column 2   Column 3

To see the relationship between systems of equations and matrices, study the example below.

System of Equations (in Standard Form)

$$\begin{cases} 2x - 3y = 6 & \text{Equation 1} \\ x + y = 0 & \text{Equation 2} \end{cases}$$

Corresponding Matrix

$$\begin{bmatrix} 2 & -3 & 6 \\ 1 & 1 & 0 \end{bmatrix} \begin{array}{l} \text{Row 1} \\ \text{Row 2} \end{array}$$

Notice that the rows of the matrix correspond to the equations in the system. The coefficients of the variables are placed to the left of a vertical dashed line. The constants are placed to the right. Each of the numbers in the matrix is called an **element.**

The method of solving systems by matrices is to write this matrix as an equivalent matrix from which we can easily identify the solution. Two matrices are equivalent if they represent systems that have the same solution set. The following **row operations** can be performed on matrices, and the result is an equivalent matrix.

Elementary Row Operations

1. Any two rows in a matrix may be interchanged.

2. The elements of any row may be multiplied (or divided) by the same nonzero number.

3. The elements of any row may be multiplied (or divided) by a nonzero number and added to their corresponding elements in any other row.

Helpful Hint

Before writing the corresponding matrix associated with a system of equations, make sure that the equations are written in standard form.

Helpful Hint

Notice that these *row* operations are the same operations that we can perform on *equations* in a system.

To solve a system of two equations in x and y by matrices, write the corresponding matrix associated with the system. Then use elementary row operations to write equivalent matrices until you have a matrix of the form

$$\begin{bmatrix} 1 & a & | & b \\ 0 & 1 & | & c \end{bmatrix},$$

where $a, b,$ and c are constants. Why? If a matrix associated with a system of equations is in this form, we can easily solve for x and y. For example,

Matrix   **System of Equations**

$$\begin{bmatrix} 1 & 2 & | & -3 \\ 0 & 1 & | & 5 \end{bmatrix} \text{ corresponds to } \begin{cases} 1x + 2y = -3 \\ 0x + 1y = 5 \end{cases} \text{ or } \begin{cases} x + 2y = -3 \\ y = 5 \end{cases}$$

In the second equation, we have $y = 5$. Substituting this in the first equation, we have $x + 2(5) = -3$ or $x = -13$. The solution of the system is the ordered pair $(-13, 5)$.

Example 1 Use matrices to solve the system:

$$\begin{cases} x + 3y = 5 \\ 2x - y = -4 \end{cases}$$

Solution: The corresponding matrix is $\begin{bmatrix} 1 & 3 & | & 5 \\ 2 & -1 & | & -4 \end{bmatrix}$. We use elementary row operations to write an equivalent matrix that looks like $\begin{bmatrix} 1 & a & | & b \\ 0 & 1 & | & c \end{bmatrix}$.

For the matrix given, the element in the first row, first column is already 1, as desired. Next we write an equivalent matrix with a 0 below the 1. To do this, we multiply row 1 by -2 and add to row 2. *We will change only row 2.*

$$\begin{bmatrix} 1 & 3 & | & 5 \\ -2(1) + 2 & -2(3) + (-1) & | & -2(5) + (-4) \end{bmatrix} \text{ simplifies to}$$

    ↑   ↑   ↑   ↑   ↑   ↑
Row 1 Row 2 Row 1 Row 2 Row 1 Row 2 $\begin{bmatrix} 1 & 3 & | & 5 \\ 0 & -7 & | & -14 \end{bmatrix}$
element element element element element element

Now we change the -7 to a 1 by use of an elementary row operation. We divide row 2 by -7, then

$$\begin{bmatrix} 1 & 3 & | & 5 \\ \frac{0}{-7} & \frac{-7}{-7} & | & \frac{-14}{-7} \end{bmatrix} \text{ simplifies to } \begin{bmatrix} 1 & 3 & | & 5 \\ 0 & 1 & | & 2 \end{bmatrix}$$

This last matrix corresponds to the system

$$\begin{cases} x + 3y = 5 \\ y = 2 \end{cases}$$

Thus we know that y is 2. To find x, we let $y = 2$ in the first equation, $x + 3y = 5$.

$$x + 3y = 5 \quad \text{First equation}$$
$$x + 3(2) = 5 \quad \text{Let } y = 2.$$
$$x = -1$$

The ordered pair solution is $(-1, 2)$. Check to see that this ordered pair satisfies both original equations.

⬤ **Work Practice 1**

PRACTICE 1

Use matrices to solve the system:

$$\begin{cases} x + 2y = -4 \\ 2x - 3y = 13 \end{cases}$$

Answer
1. $(2, -3)$

PRACTICE 2

Use matrices to solve the system:
$$\begin{cases} -3x + y = 0 \\ -6x + 2y = 2 \end{cases}$$

Example 2 Use matrices to solve the system:
$$\begin{cases} 2x - y = 3 \\ 4x - 2y = 5 \end{cases}$$

Solution: The corresponding matrix is $\left[\begin{array}{cc|c} 2 & -1 & 3 \\ 4 & -2 & 5 \end{array}\right]$. To get 1 in the row 1, column 1 position, we divide the elements of row 1 by 2.

$$\left[\begin{array}{cc|c} \frac{2}{2} & -\frac{1}{2} & \frac{3}{2} \\ 4 & -2 & 5 \end{array}\right] \text{ simplifies to } \left[\begin{array}{cc|c} 1 & -\frac{1}{2} & \frac{3}{2} \\ 4 & -2 & 5 \end{array}\right]$$

To get 0 under the 1, we multiply the elements of row 1 by -4 and add the new elements to the elements of row 2.

$$\left[\begin{array}{cc|c} 1 & -\frac{1}{2} & \frac{3}{2} \\ -4(1)+4 & -4\left(-\frac{1}{2}\right)-2 & -4\left(\frac{3}{2}\right)+5 \end{array}\right] \text{ simplifies to } \left[\begin{array}{cc|c} 1 & -\frac{1}{2} & \frac{3}{2} \\ 0 & 0 & -1 \end{array}\right]$$

The corresponding system is $\begin{cases} x - \frac{1}{2}y = \frac{3}{2} \\ 0 = -1 \end{cases}$. The equation $0 = -1$ is false for all y or x values; hence the system is inconsistent and has no solution. The solution set is $\varnothing$ or $\{\ \}$.

⬤ **Work Practice 2**

✔**Concept Check** Consider the system
$$\begin{cases} 2x - 3y = 8 \\ x + 5y = -3 \end{cases}$$

What is wrong with its corresponding matrix shown below?
$$\left[\begin{array}{cc|c} 2 & -3 & 8 \\ 0 & 5 & -3 \end{array}\right]$$

Objective Ⓑ Using Matrices to Solve a System of Three Equations

To solve a system of three equations in three variables using matrices, we will write the corresponding matrix in the equivalent form
$$\left[\begin{array}{ccc|c} 1 & a & b & d \\ 0 & 1 & c & e \\ 0 & 0 & 1 & f \end{array}\right]$$

PRACTICE 3

Use matrices to solve the system:
$$\begin{cases} x + 3y + z = 5 \\ -3x + y - 3z = 5 \\ x + 2y - 2z = 9 \end{cases}$$

Example 3 Use matrices to solve the system:
$$\begin{cases} x + 2y + z = 2 \\ -2x - y + 2z = 5 \\ x + 3y - 2z = -8 \end{cases}$$

Answers
2. $\varnothing$ **3.** $(1, 2, -2)$

✔**Concept Check Answer**
matrix should be $\left[\begin{array}{cc|c} 2 & -3 & 8 \\ 1 & 5 & -3 \end{array}\right]$

Solution: The corresponding matrix is $\left[\begin{array}{ccc|c} 1 & 2 & 1 & 2 \\ -2 & -1 & 2 & 5 \\ 1 & 3 & -2 & -8 \end{array}\right]$.

Continued on next page

Our goal is to write an equivalent matrix with 1s along the diagonal (see the numbers in red in the previous matrix) and 0s below the 1s. The element in row 1, column 1 is already 1. Next we get 0s for each element in the rest of column 1. To do this, first we multiply the elements of row 1 by 2 and add the new elements to row 2. Also, we multiply the elements of row 1 by -1 and add the new elements to the elements of row 3. *We do not change row 1.* Then

$$\left[\begin{array}{ccc|c} 1 & 2 & 1 & 2 \\ 2(1)-2 & 2(2)-1 & 2(1)+2 & 2(2)+5 \\ -1(1)+1 & -1(2)+3 & -1(1)-2 & -1(2)-8 \end{array}\right] \quad \text{simplifies to}$$

$$\left[\begin{array}{ccc|c} 1 & 2 & 1 & 2 \\ 0 & 3 & 4 & 9 \\ 0 & 1 & -3 & -10 \end{array}\right]$$

We continue down the diagonal and use elementary row operations to get 1 where the element 3 is now. To do this, we interchange rows 2 and 3.

$$\left[\begin{array}{ccc|c} 1 & 2 & 1 & 2 \\ 0 & 3 & 4 & 9 \\ 0 & 1 & -3 & -10 \end{array}\right] \quad \text{is equivalent to} \quad \left[\begin{array}{ccc|c} 1 & 2 & 1 & 2 \\ 0 & 1 & -3 & -10 \\ 0 & 3 & 4 & 9 \end{array}\right]$$

Next we want the new row 3, column 2 element to be 0. We multiply the elements of row 2 by -3 and add the result to the elements of row 3.

$$\left[\begin{array}{ccc|c} 1 & 2 & 1 & 2 \\ 0 & 1 & -3 & -10 \\ -3(0)+0 & -3(1)+3 & -3(-3)+4 & -3(-10)+9 \end{array}\right] \quad \text{simplifies to}$$

$$\left[\begin{array}{ccc|c} 1 & 2 & 1 & 2 \\ 0 & 1 & -3 & -10 \\ 0 & 0 & 13 & 39 \end{array}\right]$$

Finally, we divide the elements of row 3 by 13 so that the final diagonal element is 1.

$$\left[\begin{array}{ccc|c} 1 & 2 & 1 & 2 \\ 0 & 1 & -3 & -10 \\ \frac{0}{13} & \frac{0}{13} & \frac{13}{13} & \frac{39}{13} \end{array}\right] \quad \text{simplifies to} \quad \left[\begin{array}{ccc|c} 1 & 2 & 1 & 2 \\ 0 & 1 & -3 & -10 \\ 0 & 0 & 1 & 3 \end{array}\right]$$

This matrix corresponds to the system

$$\begin{cases} x + 2y + z = 2 \\ y - 3z = -10 \\ z = 3 \end{cases}$$

We identify the z-coordinate of the solution as 3. Next we replace z with 3 in the second equation and solve for y.

$y - 3z = -10$ Second equation

$y - 3(3) = -10$ Let $z = 3$.

$y = -1$

To find x, we let $z = 3$ and $y = -1$ in the first equation.

$x + 2y + z = 2$ First equation

$x + 2(-1) + 3 = 2$ Let $z = 3$ and $y = -1$.

$x = 1$

The ordered triple solution is $(1, -1, 3)$. Check to see that it satisfies all three equations in the original system.

Work Practice 3

Vocabulary and Readiness Check

Use the choices below to fill in each blank.

column   element   row   matrix

1. A(n) _____ is a rectangular array of numbers.
2. Each of the numbers in a matrix is called a(n) _____.
3. The numbers aligned horizontally in a matrix are in the same _____.
4. The numbers aligned vertically in a matrix are in the same _____.

Answer true or false for each statement about operations within a matrix forming an equivalent matrix.

5. Any two columns may be interchanged. _____
6. Any two rows may be interchanged. _____
7. The elements in a row may be added to their corresponding elements in another row. _____
8. The elements of a column may be multiplied by any nonzero number. _____

11.4 Exercise Set

FOR EXTRA HELP

MyMathLab *Powered by CourseCompass™ and MathXL®*

 PRACTICE   WATCH   DOWNLOAD   READ   REVIEW

Objective A *Use matrices to solve each system of linear equations. See Example 1.*

1. $\begin{cases} x + y = 1 \\ x - 2y = 4 \end{cases}$

2. $\begin{cases} 2x - y = 8 \\ x + 3y = 11 \end{cases}$

3. $\begin{cases} x + 3y = 2 \\ x + 2y = 0 \end{cases}$

4. $\begin{cases} 4x - y = 5 \\ 3x - 3y = 6 \end{cases}$

Use matrices to solve each system of linear equations. See Example 2.

5. $\begin{cases} x - 2y = 4 \\ 2x - 4y = 4 \end{cases}$

6. $\begin{cases} -x + 3y = 6 \\ 3x - 9y = 9 \end{cases}$

7. $\begin{cases} 3x - 3y = 9 \\ 2x - 2y = 6 \end{cases}$

8. $\begin{cases} 9x - 3y = 6 \\ -18x + 6y = -12 \end{cases}$

Objective B *Use matrices to solve each system of linear equations. See Example 3.*

9. $\begin{cases} x + y = 3 \\ 2y = 10 \\ 3x + 2y - 4z = 12 \end{cases}$

10. $\begin{cases} 5x = 5 \\ 2x + y = 4 \\ 3x + y - 5z = -15 \end{cases}$

11. $\begin{cases} 2y - z = -7 \\ x + 4y + z = -4 \\ 5x - y + 2z = 13 \end{cases}$

12. $\begin{cases} 4y + 3z = -2 \\ 5x - 4y = 1 \\ -5x + 4y + z = -3 \end{cases}$

Objectives A B Mixed Practice *Solve each system of linear equations using matrices. See Examples 1 through 3.*

13. $\begin{cases} x - 4 = 0 \\ x + y = 1 \end{cases}$

14. $\begin{cases} 3y = 6 \\ x + y = 7 \end{cases}$

15. $\begin{cases} x + y + z = 2 \\ 2x - z = 5 \\ 3y + z = 2 \end{cases}$

16. $\begin{cases} x + 2y + z = 5 \\ x - y - z = 3 \\ y + z = 2 \end{cases}$

17. $\begin{cases} 5x - 2y = 27 \\ -3x + 5y = 18 \end{cases}$

18. $\begin{cases} 4x - y = 9 \\ 2x + 3y = -27 \end{cases}$

19. $\begin{cases} 4x - 7y = 7 \\ 12x - 21y = 24 \end{cases}$

20. $\begin{cases} 2x - 5y = 12 \\ -4x + 10y = 20 \end{cases}$

21. $\begin{cases} 4x - y + 2z = 5 \\ 2y + z = 4 \\ 4x + y + 3z = 10 \end{cases}$ **22.** $\begin{cases} 5y - 7z = 14 \\ 2x + y + 4z = 10 \\ 2x + 6y - 3z = 30 \end{cases}$ 📱**23.** $\begin{cases} 4x + y + z = 3 \\ -x + y - 2z = -11 \\ x + 2y + 2z = -1 \end{cases}$ **24.** $\begin{cases} x + y + z = 9 \\ 3x - y + z = -1 \\ -2x + 2y - 3z = -2 \end{cases}$

Review

Determine the solution of each system of equations represented by the given graph. See Section 11.1.

25.

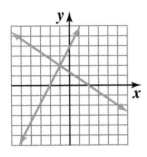

26.

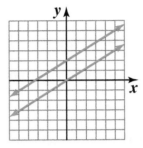

27.

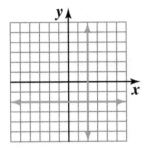

28.

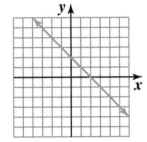

Concept Extensions

Solve. See the Concept Check in this section.

29. For the system $\begin{cases} x + z = 7 \\ y + 2z = -6 \\ 3x - y = 0 \end{cases}$, which is the correct corresponding matrix?

a. $\begin{bmatrix} 1 & 1 & 7 \\ 1 & 2 & -6 \\ 3 & -1 & 0 \end{bmatrix}$ **b.** $\begin{bmatrix} 1 & 0 & 1 & 7 \\ 1 & 2 & 0 & -6 \\ 3 & -1 & 0 & 0 \end{bmatrix}$ **c.** $\begin{bmatrix} 1 & 0 & 1 & 7 \\ 0 & 1 & 2 & -6 \\ 3 & -1 & 0 & 0 \end{bmatrix}$

30. For the system $\begin{cases} x - 6 = 0 \\ 2x - 3y = 1 \end{cases}$, which is the correct corresponding matrix?

a. $\begin{bmatrix} 1 & -6 & 0 \\ 2 & -3 & 1 \end{bmatrix}$ **b.** $\begin{bmatrix} 1 & 0 & 6 \\ 2 & -3 & 1 \end{bmatrix}$ **c.** $\begin{bmatrix} 1 & 0 & -6 \\ 2 & -3 & 1 \end{bmatrix}$

31. The amount of electricity y generated by geothermal sources (in billions of kilowatts) from 2000 to 2009 can be modeled by the linear equation $y - 0.11x = 14.05$, where x represents the number of years after 2000. Similarly, the amount of electricity y generated by wind power (in billions of kilowatts) during the same time period can be modeled by the linear equation $5.13x - y = 0.65$. (*Source:* Based on data from Energy Information Administration, U.S. Department of Energy)

    a. The data used to form these two models were incomplete. It is impossible to tell from the data the year in which the electricity generated by geothermal sources was the same as the electricity generated by wind power. Use matrix methods to estimate the year in which this occurred.

    b. The earliest data for wind power was in 1989, where 2.1 billion kilowatts of electricity was generated. Can this data be determined from the given equation? Why do you think that is?

    c. According to these models, will the percent of electricity generated by geothermal ever go to zero? Why?

    d. Can you think of an explanation why the amount of electricity generated by wind power is increasing so much faster than the amount of electricity generated by geothermal power?

32. The most popular amusement park in the world (according to annual attendance) is Tokyo Disneyland, whose yearly attendance in thousands can be approximated by the equation $y = 1201x + 16{,}507$ where x is the number of years after 2000. In second place is Walt Disney World's Magic Kingdom, whose yearly attendance, in thousands, can be approximated by $y = -616x + 15{,}400$. Find the last year when attendance in Magic Kingdom was greater than attendance in Tokyo Disneyland. (*Source:* Amusement Business)

33. For the system $\begin{cases} 2x - 3y = 8 \\ x + 5y = -3 \end{cases}$, explain what is wrong with writing the corresponding matrix as $\begin{bmatrix} 2 & 3 & 8 \\ 0 & 5 & -3 \end{bmatrix}$.

34. For the system $\begin{cases} 5x + 2y = 0 \\ -y = 2 \end{cases}$, explain what is wrong with writing the corresponding matrix as $\begin{bmatrix} 5 & 2 & 0 \\ -1 & 0 & 2 \end{bmatrix}$.

Are you preparing for your test? Use the Test Prep Videos to see the fully worked-out solutions to any of the exercises you want to review.

11 Chapter Highlights

Definitions and Concepts	Examples
Section 11.1 Solving Systems of Linear Equalities in Two Variables	

A **system of linear equations** consists of two or more linear equations.

$$\begin{cases} x - 3y = 6 \\ \quad\quad y = \dfrac{1}{2}x \end{cases} \quad\quad \begin{cases} x + 2y - z = 1 \\ 3x - y + 4z = 0 \\ \quad\quad 5y + z = 6 \end{cases}$$

A **solution** of a system of two equations in two variables is an ordered pair (x, y) that makes both equations true.

Determine whether $(2, -5)$ is a solution of the system.

$$\begin{cases} x + y = -3 \\ 2x - 3y = 19 \end{cases}$$

Replace x with 2 and y with -5 in both equations.

$$x + y = -3 \quad\quad\quad 2x - 3y = 19$$
$$2 + (-5) \overset{?}{=} -3 \quad\quad 2(2) - 3(-5) \overset{?}{=} 19$$
$$-3 = -3 \quad \text{True} \quad\quad 4 + 15 \overset{?}{=} 19$$
$$19 = 19 \quad \text{True}$$

$(2, -5)$ is a solution of the system.

Geometrically, a solution of a system in two variables is a point of intersection of the graphs of the equations.

Solve by graphing: $\begin{cases} y = 2x - 1 \\ x + 2y = 13 \end{cases}$

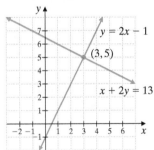

(continued)

Definitions and Concepts	**Examples**

Section 11.1   Solving Systems of Linear Equalities in Two Variables (*continued*)

A system of equations with at least one solution is a **consistent system.** A system that has no solution is an **inconsistent system.**

If the graphs of two linear equations are identical, the equations are **dependent.**

If their graphs are different, the equations are **independent.**

One solution:
Independent equations
Consistent system

No solution:
Independent equations
Inconsistent system

Infinite number of solutions:
Dependent equations
Consistent system

SOLVING A SYSTEM OF LINEAR EQUATIONS BY THE SUBSTITUTION METHOD

Step 1. Solve one equation for a variable.

Step 2. Substitute the expression for the variable into the other equation.

Step 3. Solve the equation from Step 2 to find the value of one variable.

Step 4. Substitute the value from Step 3 in either original equation to find the value of the other variable.

Step 5. Check the solution in both equations.

Solve by substitution:

$$\begin{cases} y = x + 2 \\ 3x - 2y = -5 \end{cases}$$

Since the first equation is solved for y, substitute $x + 2$ for y in the second equation.

$$3x - 2y = -5 \quad \text{Second equation}$$
$$3x - 2(x + 2) = -5 \quad \text{Let } y = x + 2.$$
$$3x - 2x - 4 = -5$$
$$x - 4 = -5 \quad \text{Simplify.}$$
$$x = -1 \quad \text{Add 4.}$$

To find y, let $x = -1$ in $y = x + 2$, so $y = -1 + 2 = 1$. The solution $(-1, 1)$ checks.

SOLVING A SYSTEM OF LINEAR EQUATIONS BY THE ELIMINATION METHOD

Step 1. Rewrite each equation in standard form, $Ax + By = C$.

Step 2. Multiply one or both equations by a nonzero number so that the coefficients of a variable are opposites.

Step 3. Add the equations.

Step 4. Find the value of the remaining variable by solving the resulting equation.

Step 5. Substitute the value from Step 4 into either original equation to find the value of the other variable.

Step 6. Check the solution in both equations.

Solve by elimination:

$$\begin{cases} x - 3y = -3 \\ -2x + y = 6 \end{cases}$$

Multiply both sides of the first equation by 2.

$$\begin{array}{r} 2x - 6y = -6 \\ \underline{-2x + y = 6} \\ -5y = 0 \quad \text{Add.} \\ y = 0 \quad \text{Divide by } -5. \end{array}$$

To find x, let $y = 0$ in an original equation.

$$x - 3y = -3$$
$$x - 3 \cdot 0 = -3$$
$$x = -3$$

The solution $(-3, 0)$ checks.

Definitions and Concepts	**Examples**
Section 11.2 Solving Systems of Linear Equalities in Three Variables	

A **solution** of an equation in three variables x, y, and z is an **ordered triple** (x, y, z) that makes the equation a true statement.

Verify that $(-2, 1, 3)$ is a solution of $2x + 3y - 2z = -7$. Replace x with -2, y with 1, and z with 3.

$$2(-2) + 3(1) - 2(3) \stackrel{?}{=} -7$$
$$-4 + 3 - 6 \stackrel{?}{=} -7$$
$$-7 = -7 \quad \text{True}$$

$(-2, 1, 3)$ is a solution.

SOLVING A SYSTEM OF THREE LINEAR EQUATIONS BY THE ELIMINATION METHOD

Step 1. Write each equation in standard form, $Ax + By + Cz = D$.

Step 2. Choose a pair of equations and use them to eliminate a variable.

Step 3. Choose any other pair of equations and eliminate the same variable.

Step 4. Solve the system of two equations in two variables from Steps 2 and 3.

Step 5. Solve for the third variable by substituting the values of the variables from Step 4 into any of the original equations.

Step 6. Check the solution in all three original equations.

Solve:
$$\begin{cases} 2x + y - z = 0 & (1) \\ x - y - 2z = -6 & (2) \\ -3x - 2y + 3z = -22 & (3) \end{cases}$$

1. Each equation is written in standard form.

2.
$$\begin{array}{l} 2x + y - z = 0 \quad (1) \\ \underline{x - y - 2z = -6} \quad (2) \\ 3x \quad - 3z = -6 \quad (4) \quad \text{Add.} \end{array}$$

3. Eliminate y from equations (1) and (3) also.
$$\begin{array}{l} 4x + 2y - 2z = 0 \quad \text{Multiply equation (1) by 2.} \\ \underline{-3x - 2y + 3z = -22} \quad (3) \\ x \quad + z = -22 \quad (5) \quad \text{Add.} \end{array}$$

4. Solve.
$$\begin{cases} 3x - 3z = -6 & (4) \\ x + z = -22 & (5) \end{cases}$$
$$\begin{array}{l} x - z = -2 \quad \text{Divide equation (4) by 3.} \\ \underline{x + z = -22} \quad (5) \\ 2x = -24 \\ x = -12 \end{array}$$

To find z, use equation (5).
$$x + z = -22$$
$$-12 + z = -22$$
$$z = -10$$

5. To find y, use equation (1).
$$2x + y - z = 0$$
$$2(-12) + y - (-10) = 0$$
$$-24 + y + 10 = 0$$
$$y = 14$$

6. The solution $(-12, 14, -10)$ checks.

Definitions and Concepts	**Examples**
Section 11.3 Systems of Linear Equations and Problem Solving	
	Two numbers have a sum of 11. Twice one number is 3 less than 3 times the other. Find the numbers.
1. UNDERSTAND the problem.	**1.** Read and reread. x = one number y = other number
2. TRANSLATE.	**2.** In words:

	sum of numbers	is	11
	↓	↓	↓
Translate:	$x + y$	$=$	11

In words:

	twice one number	is	3 less than 3 times the other number
	↓	↓	↓
Translate:	$2x$	$=$	$3y - 3$

3. SOLVE.

3. Solve the system: $\begin{cases} x + y = 11 \\ 2x = 3y - 3 \end{cases}$

In the first equation, $x = 11 - y$. Substitute into the other equation.

$$2x = 3y - 3$$
$$2(11 - y) = 3y - 3$$
$$22 - 2y = 3y - 3$$
$$-5y = -25$$
$$y = 5$$

4. INTERPRET.

Replace y with 5 in the equation $x = 11 - y$. Then $x = 11 - 5 = 6$. The solution is $(6, 5)$.

4. *Check:* See that $6 + 5 = 11$ is the required sum and that twice 6 is 3 times 5 less 3. *State:* The numbers are 6 and 5.

Section 11.4 Solving Systems of Equations Using Matrices	
A **matrix** is a rectangular array of numbers.	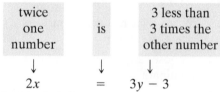
The **matrix** corresponding to a system is composed of the coefficients of the variables and the constants of the system.	The matrix corresponding to the system $\begin{cases} x - y = 1 \\ 2x + y = 11 \end{cases}$ is $\left[\begin{array}{cc\|c} 1 & -1 & 1 \\ 2 & 1 & 11 \end{array}\right]$

Definitions and Concepts	**Examples**

Section 11.4   Solving Systems of Equations Using Matrices (*continued*)

The following **row operations** can be performed on matrices, and the result is an equivalent matrix.

Elementary row operations:

1. Interchange any two rows.

2. Multiply (or divide) the elements of one row by the same nonzero number.

3. Multiply (or divide) the elements of one row by the same nonzero number and add them to their corresponding elements in any other row.

Use matrices to solve: $\begin{cases} x - y = 1 \\ 2x + y = 11 \end{cases}$

The corresponding matrix is

$$\left[\begin{array}{cc|c} 1 & -1 & 1 \\ 2 & 1 & 11 \end{array}\right]$$

Use row operations to write an equivalent matrix with 1s along the diagonal and 0s below each 1 in the diagonal. Multiply row 1 by -2 and add to row 2. Change row 2 only.

$$\left[\begin{array}{cc|c} 1 & -1 & 1 \\ -2(1) + 2 & -2(-1) + 1 & -2(1) + 11 \end{array}\right]$$

simplifies to $\left[\begin{array}{cc|c} 1 & -1 & 1 \\ 0 & 3 & 9 \end{array}\right]$

Divide row 2 by 3.

$$\left[\begin{array}{cc|c} 1 & -1 & 1 \\ \dfrac{0}{3} & \dfrac{3}{3} & \dfrac{9}{3} \end{array}\right] \text{ simplifies to } \left[\begin{array}{cc|c} 1 & -1 & 1 \\ 0 & 1 & 3 \end{array}\right]$$

This matrix corresponds to the system

$$\begin{cases} x - y = 1 \\ \phantom{x - {}} y = 3 \end{cases}$$

Let $y = 3$ in the first equation.

$$x - 3 = 1$$
$$x = 4$$

The ordered pair solution is $(4, 3)$.

(11.1) *Solve each system of equations in two variables by each method: (a) graphing, (b) substitution, and (c) elimination.*

1. $\begin{cases} 3x + 10y = 1 \\ x + 2y = -1 \end{cases}$

2. $\begin{cases} y = \dfrac{1}{2}x + \dfrac{2}{3} \\ 4x + 6y = 4 \end{cases}$

3. $\begin{cases} 2x - 4y = 22 \\ 5x - 10y = 15 \end{cases}$

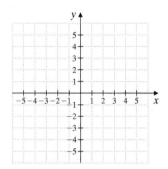
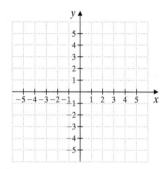
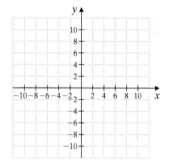

4. $\begin{cases} 3x - 6y = 12 \\ 2y = x - 4 \end{cases}$

5. $\begin{cases} \dfrac{1}{2}x - \dfrac{3}{4}y = -\dfrac{1}{2} \\ \dfrac{1}{8}x + \dfrac{3}{4}y = \dfrac{19}{8} \end{cases}$

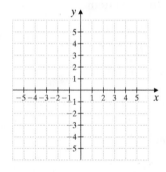
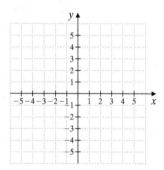

6. The revenue equation for a certain style of backpack is $y = 32x$, where x is the number of backpacks sold and y is the income in dollars for selling x backpacks. The cost equation for these units is $y = 15x + 25,500$, where x is the number of backpacks manufactured and y is the cost in dollars for manufacturing x backpacks. Find the number of units to be sold for the company to break even. (*Hint:* Solve the system of equations formed by the two given equations.)

(11.2) *Solve each system of equations in three variables.*

7. $\begin{cases} x \quad\;\; + z = 4 \\ 2x - y \quad\;\; = 4 \\ x + y - z = 0 \end{cases}$

8. $\begin{cases} 2x + 5y \quad\;\; = 4 \\ x - 5y + z = -1 \\ 4x \quad\quad - z = 11 \end{cases}$

9. $\begin{cases} 4y + 2z = 5 \\ 2x + 8y \quad\;\; = 5 \\ 6x + \quad\;\; 4z = 1 \end{cases}$

10. $\begin{cases} 5x + 7y = 9 \\ 14y - z = 28 \\ 4x + 2z = -4 \end{cases}$

11. $\begin{cases} 3x - 2y + 2z = 5 \\ -x + 6y + z = 4 \\ 3x + 14y + 7z = 20 \end{cases}$

12. $\begin{cases} x + 2y + 3z = 11 \\ y + 2z = 3 \\ 2x + 2z = 10 \end{cases}$

13. $\begin{cases} 7x - 3y + 2z = 0 \\ 4x - 4y - z = 2 \\ 5x + 2y + 3z = 1 \end{cases}$

14. $\begin{cases} x - 3y - 5z = -5 \\ 4x - 2y + 3z = 13 \\ 5x + 3y + 4z = 22 \end{cases}$

(11.3) *Use systems of equations to solve.*

15. The sum of three numbers is 98. The sum of the first and second is two more than the third number, and the second is four times the first. Find the numbers.

16. One number is three times a second number, and twice the sum of the numbers is 168. Find the numbers.

17. Two cars leave Chicago, one traveling east and the other west. After 4 hours they are 492 miles apart. If one car is traveling 7 mph faster than the other, find the speed of each.

△ **18.** The foundation for a rectangular Hardware Warehouse has a length three times the width and is 296 feet around. Find the dimensions of the building.

19. James Callahan has available a 10% alcohol solution and a 60% alcohol solution. Find how many liters of each solution he should mix to make 50 liters of a 40% alcohol solution.

20. An employee at a See's Candy Store needs a special mixture of candy. She has creme-filled chocolates that sell for $3.00 per pound, chocolate-covered nuts that sell for $2.70 per pound, and chocolate-covered raisins that sell for $2.25 per pound. She wants to have twice as many raisins as nuts in the mixture. Find how many pounds of each she should use to make 45 pounds worth $2.80 per pound.

21. Chris Kringler has $2.77 in her coin jar—all in pennies, nickels, and dimes. If she has 53 coins in all and four more nickels than dimes, find how many of each type of coin she has.

22. $10,000 and $4000 are invested such that $1250 in interest is earned in one year. The rate of interest on the larger investment is 2% more than that on the smaller investment. Find the rates of interest.

23. The perimeter of an isosceles (two sides equal) triangle is 73 centimeters. If the unequal side is 7 centimeters longer than the two equal sides, find the lengths of the three sides.

24. The sum of three numbers is 295. The first number is five more than the second and twice the third. Find the numbers.

(11.4) *Use matrices to solve each system.*

25. $\begin{cases} 3x + 10y = 1 \\ x + 2y = -1 \end{cases}$

26. $\begin{cases} 3x - 6y = 12 \\ 2y = x - 4 \end{cases}$

27. $\begin{cases} 3x - 2y = -8 \\ 6x + 5y = 11 \end{cases}$

28. $\begin{cases} 6x - 6y = -5 \\ 10x - 2y = 1 \end{cases}$

29. $\begin{cases} 3x - 6y = 0 \\ 2x + 4y = 5 \end{cases}$

30. $\begin{cases} 5x - 3y = 10 \\ -2x + y = -1 \end{cases}$

31. $\begin{cases} 0.2x - 0.3y = -0.7 \\ 0.5x + 0.3y = 1.4 \end{cases}$

32. $\begin{cases} 3x + 2y = 8 \\ 3x - y = 5 \end{cases}$

33. $\begin{cases} x + z = 4 \\ 2x - y = 0 \\ x + y - z = 0 \end{cases}$

34. $\begin{cases} 2x + 5y = 4 \\ x - 5y + z = -1 \\ 4x - z = 11 \end{cases}$

35. $\begin{cases} 3x - y = 11 \\ x + 2z = 13 \\ y - z = -7 \end{cases}$

36. $\begin{cases} 5x + 7y + 3z = 9 \\ 14y - z = 28 \\ 4x + 2z = -4 \end{cases}$

37. $\begin{cases} 7x - 3y + 2z = 0 \\ 4x - 4y - z = 2 \\ 5x + 2y + 3z = 1 \end{cases}$

38. $\begin{cases} x + 2y + 3z = 14 \\ y + 2z = 3 \\ 2x - 2z = 10 \end{cases}$

Answers to Selected Exercises

Chapter 11 Systems of Linear Equations

Section 11.1

Calculator Explorations 1. $(2.11, 0.17)$ **3.** $(-8.20, -6.30)$

Vocabulary and Readiness Check 1. B **3.** A

Exercise Set 11.1 1. yes **3.** no **5.** yes **7.** no **9.** **11.** **13.** $\varnothing$ **15.**

17. $(2, 8)$ **19.** $(0, -9)$ **21.** $(1, -1)$ **23.** $\{(x, y) \mid x = -3y + 4\}$ **25.** $\left(\frac{5}{2}, \frac{5}{4}\right)$ **27.** $(1, -2)$ **29.** $(9, 9)$ **31.** $(7, 2)$ **33.** $\varnothing$ **35.** $\{(x, y) \mid 3x + y = 1\}$

37. $\left(\frac{3}{2}, 1\right)$ **39.** $(2, -1)$ **41.** $(-5, 3)$ **43.** $\varnothing$ **45.** $\left(\frac{1}{2}, \frac{1}{5}\right)$ **47.** $(8, 2)$ **49.** $\{(x, y) \mid x = 3y + 2\}$ **51.** $(-5, 3)$ **53.** $(3, 2)$ **55.** $(7, -3)$ **57.** $\varnothing$

59. $(3, 4)$ **61.** $\left(-\frac{1}{4}, \frac{1}{2}\right)$ **63.** $(-2, 1)$ **65.** $(1.2, -3.6)$ **67.** true **69.** false **71.** $6y - 4z = 25$ **73.** $x + 10y = 2$ **75.** no solution

77. infinite number of solutions **79.** no; answers may vary **81.** 5000 DVDs; $21 **83.** supply greater than demand **85.** $(1875, 4687.5)$

87. makes money **89.** for x-values greater than 1875 **91.** answers may vary; one possibility: $\begin{cases} -2x + y = 1 \\ x - 2y = -8 \end{cases}$ **93. a.** Consumption of

bottled water is growing faster than that of carbonated diet soft drinks. **b.** $(3, 14)$ **c.** In the year 1998, per capita bottled water consumption was about

the same as per capita carbonated diet soft drink consumption. **95.** $\left(\frac{1}{4}, 8\right)$ **97.** $\left(\frac{1}{3}, \frac{1}{2}\right)$ **99.** $\left(\frac{1}{4}, -\frac{1}{3}\right)$ **101.** $\varnothing$

Section 11.2

Vocabulary and Readiness Check 1. a, b, d **3.** yes; answers may vary

Exercise Set 11.2 1. $(-1, 5, 2)$ **3.** $(-2, 5, 1)$ **5.** $(-2, 3, -1)$ **7.** $\{(x, y, z) \mid x - 2y + z = -5\}$ **9.** $\varnothing$ **11.** $(0, 0, 0)$ **13.** $(-3, -35, -7)$

15. $(6, 22, -20)$ **17.** $\varnothing$ **19.** $(3, 2, 2)$ **21.** $\{(x, y, z) \mid x + 2y - 3z = 4\}$ **23.** $(-3, -4, -5)$ **25.** $\left(0, \frac{1}{2}, -4\right)$ **27.** $(12, 6, 4)$ **29.** $\{5\}$ **31.** $\left\{-\frac{5}{3}\right\}$

33. 15 and 30 **35.** answers may vary **37.** answers may vary **39.** $(1, 1, -1)$ **41.** $(1, 1, 0, 2)$ **43.** $(1, -1, 2, 3)$ **45.** answers may vary

Section 11.3

Exercise Set 11.3 1. 10 and 8 **3. a.** Enterprise class: 1101 ft; Nimitz class: 1092 ft **b.** 3.67 football fields **5.** plane: 520 mph; wind: 40 mph
7. 20 qt of 4%; 40 qt of 1% **9.** United Kingdom: 33,333 students; Italy: 30,670 students **11.** 9 large frames; 13 small frames **13.** -10 and -8
15. a. 2010 **b.** answers may vary **17.** tablets: $0.80; pens: $0.20 **19.** speed of plane: 630 mph; speed of wind: 90 mph **21. a.** answers may vary **b.** 2003
23. 28 cm; 28 cm; 37 cm **25.** 600 mi **27.** $x = 75; y = 105$ **29.** 625 units **31.** 3000 units **33.** 1280 units **35. a.** $R(x) = 450x$
b. $C(x) = 200x + 6000$ **c.** 24 desks **37.** 2 units of Mix A; 3 units of Mix B; 1 unit of Mix C **39.** 5 in.; 7 in.; 7 in.; 10 in. **41.** 18, 13, and 9
43. free throws: 590; 2-pt field goals: 766; 3-pt field goals: 88 **45.** $x = 60; y = 55; z = 65$ **47.** $5x + 5z = 10$ **49.** $-5y + 2z = 2$

51. 2007: 775,334; 2009: 1,344,095 **53.** $a = 3, b = 4, c = -1$ **55.** $a = \frac{1}{2}; b = 24\frac{1}{2}; c = 849$ or $a = 0.5, b = 24.5, c = 849$; 1630 thousand students

Section 11.4

Vocabulary and Readiness Check 1. matrix **3.** row **5.** false **7.** true

Exercise Set 11.4 1. $(2, -1)$ **3.** $(-4, 2)$ **5.** $\varnothing$ **7.** $\{(x, y) \mid 3x - 3y = 9\}$ **9.** $(-2, 5, -2)$ **11.** $(1, -2, 3)$ **13.** $(4, -3)$ **15.** $(2, 1, -1)$
17. $(9, 9)$ **19.** $\varnothing$ **21.** $\varnothing$ **23.** $(1, -4, 3)$ **25.** 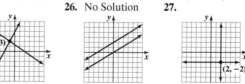 **26.** No Solution **27.** 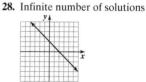 **28.** Infinite number of solutions

29. c **31. a.** in 2002 **b.** no; answers may vary **c.** no, it has a positive slope **d.** answers may vary **33.** answers may vary

Answers to Selected Exercises

Chapter 11 Review   **1.** $(-3, 1)$ **2.** $\left(0, \dfrac{2}{3}\right)$ **3.** $\varnothing$ **4.** $\{(x, y) \mid 3x - 6y = 12\}$ **5.** $\left(3, \dfrac{8}{3}\right)$ **6.** 1500 backpacks   **7.** $(2, 0, 2)$ **8.** $(2, 0, -3)$

9. $\left(-\dfrac{1}{2}, \dfrac{3}{4}, 1\right)$ **10.** $(-1, 2, 0)$ **11.** $\varnothing$ **12.** $(5, 3, 0)$ **13.** $(1, 1, -2)$ **14.** $(3, 1, 1)$ **15.** 10, 40, and 48   **16.** 63 and 21   **17.** 58 mph; 65 mph

18. width: 37 ft; length: 111 ft   **19.** 20 L of 10% solution; 30 L of 60% solution   **20.** 30 lb of creme-filled; 5 lb of chocolate-covered nuts; 10 lb of chocolate-covered raisins   **21.** 17 pennies; 20 nickels; 16 dimes   **22.** larger investment: 9.5%; smaller investment: 7.5%   **23.** two sides: 22 cm each; third side: 29 cm   **24.** 120, 115, and 60   **25.** $(-3, 1)$ **26.** $\{(x, y) \mid x - 2y = 4\}$ **27.** $\left(-\dfrac{2}{3}, 3\right)$ **28.** $\left(\dfrac{1}{3}, \dfrac{7}{6}\right)$ **29.** $\left(\dfrac{5}{4}, \dfrac{5}{8}\right)$

30. $(-7, -15)$ **31.** $(1, 3)$ **32.** $(2, 1)$ **33.** $(1, 2, 3)$ **34.** $(2, 0, -3)$ **35.** $(3, -2, 5)$ **36.** $(-1, 2, 0)$ **37.** $(1, 1, -2)$ **38.** $\varnothing$

Graphs and Functions

12

Objective

A Use Interval Notation.

12.1 SETS AND INTERVAL NOTATION

Objective **A** Using Interval Notation

Recall that a **solution** of an inequality is a value of the variable that makes the inequality a true statement. The **solution set** of an inequality is the set of all solutions. Notice that the solution set of the inequality $x > 2$, for example, contains all numbers greater than 2. Its graph is an interval on the number line since an infinite number of values satisfy the variable. If we use open/closed-circle notation, the graph of $\{x \mid x > 2\}$ looks like:

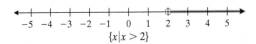

$\{x \mid x > 2\}$

In this section, a different graphing notation will be used to help us understand **interval notation.** Instead of an open circle, we use a parenthesis; instead of a closed circle, we use a bracket. With this new notation, the graph of $\{x \mid x > 2\}$ now looks like:

and can be represented in interval notation as $(2, \infty)$. The symbol ∞ is read "infinity" and indicates that the interval includes *all* numbers greater than 2. The left parenthesis indicates that 2 *is not* included in the interval. Using a left bracket, [, would indicate that 2 *is* included in the interval. The following table shows three equivalent ways to describe an interval: in set notation, as a graph, and in interval notation.

Set Notation	Graph	Interval Notation
$\{x \mid x < a\}$	⟵————————)————⟶ a	$(-\infty, a)$
$\{x \mid x > a\}$	⟵————(————————⟶ a	(a, ∞)
$\{x \mid x \le a\}$	⟵————————]————⟶ a	$(-\infty, a]$
$\{x \mid x \ge a\}$	⟵————[————————⟶ a	$[a, \infty)$
$\{x \mid a < x < b\}$	⟵———(————)———⟶ a b	(a, b)
$\{x \mid a \le x \le b\}$	⟵———[————]———⟶ a b	$[a, b]$
$\{x \mid a < x \le b\}$	⟵———(————]———⟶ a b	$(a, b]$
$\{x \mid a \le x < b\}$	⟵———[————)———⟶ a b	$[a, b)$
$\{x \mid x \text{ is a real number}\}$	⟵————————————⟶	$(-\infty, \infty)$

Helpful Hint

Notice that a parenthesis is always used to enclose ∞ and $-\infty$.

Examples Graph each set on a number line and then write it in interval notation.

1. $\{x \mid x \geq 2\}$  $[2, \infty)$

2. $\{x \mid x < -1\}$ $(-\infty, -1)$

3. $\{x \mid 0.5 < x \leq 3\}$  $(0.5, 3]$

● **Work Practice 1–3**

PRACTICE 1–3

Graph each set on a number line and then write it in interval notation.

1. $\{x \mid x > -3\}$

2. $\{x \mid x \leq 0\}$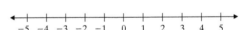

3. $\{x \mid -0.5 \leq x < 2\}$

✓**Concept Check** Explain what is wrong with writing the interval $(5, \infty]$

12.1 Exercise Set

FOR EXTRA HELP
MyMathLab   Math XP PRACTICE   WATCH   DOWNLOAD   READ   REVIEW

Objective A *Graph the solution set of each inequality on a number line and then write it in interval notation. See Examples 1 through 3.*

1. $\{x \mid x < -3\}$

2. $\{x \mid x \geq 0.3\}$

3. $\{x \mid -7 \leq x\}$

4. $\{x \mid -2 < x < 5\}$

5. $\{x \mid 5 \geq x > -1\}$

Objectives

A Define Relation, Domain, and Range.

B Identify Functions.

C Use the Vertical Line Test for Functions.

D Use Function Notation.

E Graph a Linear Function.

12.2 INTRODUCTION TO FUNCTIONS

Objective **A** Defining Relation, Domain, and Range

Equations in two variables, such as $y = 2x + 1$, describe **relations** between x-values and y-values. For example, if $x = 1$, then this equation describes how to find the y-value related to $x = 1$. In words, the equation $y = 2x + 1$ says that twice the x-value increased by 1 gives the corresponding y-value. The x-value of 1 corresponds to the y-value of $2(1) + 1 = 3$ for this equation, and we have the ordered pair $(1, 3)$. In other words, for the relationship (or relation) between x and y defined by $y = 2x + 1$, the x-value 1 is paired with the y-value 3.

There are other ways of describing relations or correspondences between two numbers or, in general, a set of first components (sometimes called the set of *inputs*) and a set of second components (sometimes called the set of *outputs*). For example,

First Set: Input	Correspondence	Second Set: Output
People in a certain city	Each person's age, to the nearest year	The set of nonnegative integers

A few examples of ordered pairs from this relation might be (Ana, 4); (Bob, 36); (Trey, 21); and so on.

Below are just a few other ways of describing relations between two sets and the ordered pairs that they generate.

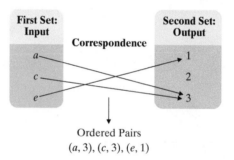

Ordered Pairs
$(a, 3), (c, 3), (e, 1)$

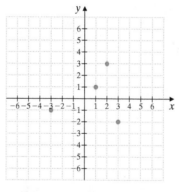

Ordered Pairs

$(-3, -1), (1, 1), (2, 3), (3, -2)$

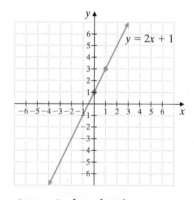

Some Ordered Pairs

$(0, 1), (1, 3)$, and so on

Relation, Domain, and Range

A **relation** is a set of ordered pairs.

The **domain** of the relation is the set of all first components of the ordered pairs.

The **range** of the relation is the set of all second components of the ordered pairs.

For example, the domain for our middle relation on the previous page is $\{a, c, e\}$ and the range is $\{1, 3\}$. Notice that the range does not include the element 2 of the second set. This is because no element of the first set is assigned to this element. If a relation is defined in terms of x- and y-values, we will agree that the domain corresponds to x-values and that the range corresponds to y-values that are paired with x-values.

Helpful Hint

Remember that the range only includes elements that are paired with domain values. For

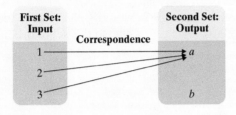

the range is $\{a\}$.

Examples Determine the domain and range of each relation.

1. $\{(2, 3), (2, 4), (0, -1), (3, -1)\}$

   The domain is the set of all first coordinates of the ordered pairs, $\{2, 0, 3\}$.
   The range is the set of all second coordinates, $\{3, 4, -1\}$.

2.
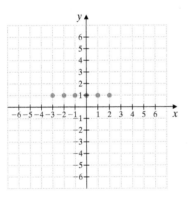

Helpful Hint Equivalent domain or range elements that occur more than once need only to be listed once.

   The relation is $\{(-3, 1), (-2, 1), (-1, 1), (0, 1), (1, 1), (2, 1)\}$.
   The domain is $\{-3, -2, -1, 0, 1, 2\}$.
   The range is $\{1\}$.

3.
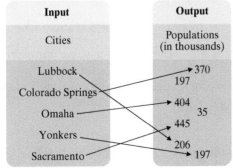

   The domain is the set of inputs {Lubbock, Colorado Springs, Omaha, Yonkers, Sacramento}. The range is the numbers in the set of outputs that correspond to elements in the set of inputs {370, 404, 445, 206, 197}.

● Work Practice 1–3

PRACTICE 1–3

Determine the domain and range of each relation.

1. $\{(1, 6), (2, 8), (0, 3), (0, -2)\}$

2.

3.
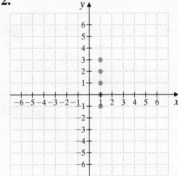

Answers

1. domain: $\{1, 2, 0\}$; range: $\{6, 8, 3, -2\}$
2. domain: $\{1\}$; range: $\{-1, 0, 1, 2, 3\}$
3. domain: {Arkansas, Texas, Oklahoma, Oregon}; range: $\{4, 5, 32\}$

A function is a special type of relation, so all functions are relations. But not all relations are functions.

Objective Ⓑ Identifying Functions

Now we consider a special kind of relation called a *function*.

Function

A **function** is a relation in which each first component in the ordered pairs corresponds to *exactly one* second component.

Examples Determine whether each relation is also a function.

4. $\{(-2, 5), (2, 7), (-3, 5), (9, 9)\}$

Although the ordered pairs $(-2, 5)$ and $(-3, 5)$ have the same *y*-value, each *x*-value is assigned to only one *y*-value, so this set of ordered pairs is a function.

5.

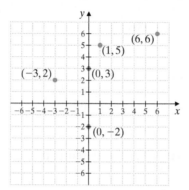

The *x*-value 0 is assigned to two *y*-values, -2 and 3, in this graph, so this relation is not a function.

6.

Input	Correspondence	Output
People in a certain city	Each person's age, to the nearest year	The set of nonnegative integers

This relation is a function because although two different people may have the same age, each person has only one age. This means that each element in the first set is assigned to only one element in the second set.

● Work Practice 4–6

✓**Concept Check** Explain why a function can contain both the ordered pairs $(1, 3)$ and $(2, 3)$ but not both $(3, 1)$ and $(3, 2)$.

Recall that an equation such as $y = 2x + 1$ is a relation since this equation defines a set of ordered pair solutions.

Example 7 Determine whether the relation $y = 3x - 5$ is also a function.

Solution: The relation $y = 3x - 5$ is a function if each *x*-value corresponds to just one *y*-value. For each *x*-value substituted in the equation $y = 3x - 5$, the multiplication and addition performed give a single result, so only one *y*-value will be associated with each *x*-value. Thus, $y = 3x - 5$ is a function.

● Work Practice 7

Example 8 Determine whether the relation $x = y^2$ is also a function.

Solution: In $x = y^2$, if $y = 3$, then $x = 9$. Also, if $y = -3$, then $x = 9$. In other words, we have the ordered pairs $(9, 3)$ and $(9, -3)$. Since the *x*-value 9 corresponds to two *y*-values, 3 and -3, $x = y^2$ is not a function.

● Work Practice 8

PRACTICE 4–6

Determine whether each relation is also a function.

4. $\{(-3, 7), (1, 7), (2, 2)\}$

5.

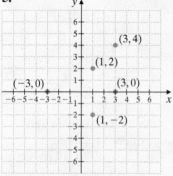

6.

Input	Correspondence	Output
People in a certain state	County/parish that a person lives in	Counties of that state

PRACTICE 7

Determine whether the relation $y = 3x + 2$ is also a function.

PRACTICE 8

Determine whether the relation $x = y^2 + 1$ is also a function.

Answers

4. function **5.** not a function

6. function **7.** function

8. not a function

✓ **Concept Check Answer**

In a function, two different ordered pairs can have the same *y*-value, but not the same *x*-value.

Objective ⓒ Using the Vertical Line Test

As we have seen, not all relations are functions. Consider the graphs of $y = 2x + 1$ and $x = y^2$ shown next. On the graph of $y = 2x + 1$, notice that each x-value corresponds to only one y-value. Recall from Example 7 that $y = 2x + 1$ is a function.

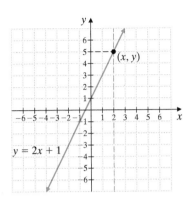

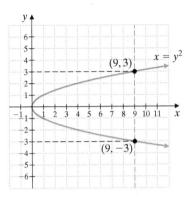

On the graph of $x = y^2$, the x-value 9, for example, corresponds to two y-values, 3 and -3, as shown by the vertical line. Recall from Example 8 that $x = y^2$ is not a function.

Graphs can be used to help determine whether a relation is also a function by the following **vertical line test.**

Vertical Line Test

If no vertical line can be drawn so that it intersects a graph more than once, the graph is the graph of a function. If such a line can be drawn, the graph is not that of a function.

Examples Use the vertical line test to determine which are graphs of functions.

9.

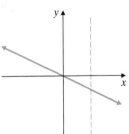

This is the graph of a function since no vertical line will intersect this graph more than once.

10.

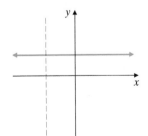

This is the graph of a function.

11.

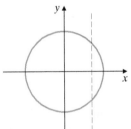

This is not the graph of a function. Note that vertical lines can be drawn that intersect the graph in two points.

PRACTICE 9–13

Use the vertical line test to determine which are graphs of functions.

9.

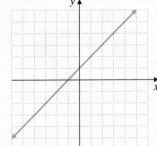

10.

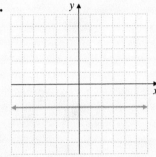

11.

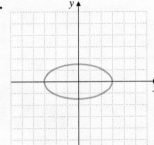

12.

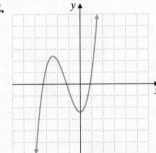

13.

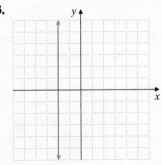

Answers

9. function   **10.** function

11. not a function   **12.** function

13. not a function

12.

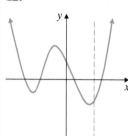

This is the graph of a function.

13.

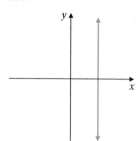

This is not the graph of a function. A vertical line can be drawn that intersects this line at every point.

 Work Practice 9–13

✓**Concept Check** Determine which equations represent functions. Explain your answer.

a. $y = 14$　　**b.** $x = -5$　　**c.** $x + y = 6$

Objective ⒟ Using Function Notation

Many times letters such as $f, g,$ and h are used to name functions.

> ### Function Notation
>
> To denote that y is a function of x, we can write
>
> $$y = \underbrace{f(x)}_{\text{Function Notation}} \text{(Read "}f\text{ of }x\text{")}$$
>
> This notation means that **y is a function of x** or that *y depends on x*. For this reason, y is called the **dependent variable** and x the **independent variable.**

For example, to use function notation with the function $y = 4x + 3$, we write $f(x) = 4x + 3$. The notation $f(1)$ means to replace x with 1 and find the resulting y- or function value. Since

$$f(x) = 4x + 3$$

then

$$f(1) = 4(1) + 3 = 7$$

This means that when $x = 1, y$ or $f(x) = 7$. The corresponding ordered pair is $(1, 7)$. Here, the input is 1 and the output is $f(1)$ or 7. Now let's find $f(2), f(0),$ and $f(-1)$.

$$\begin{array}{lll}
f(x) = 4x + 3 & f(x) = 4x + 3 & f(x) = 4x + 3 \\
f(2) = 4(2) + 3 & f(0) = 4(0) + 3 & f(-1) = 4(-1) + 3 \\
\quad = 8 + 3 & \quad = 0 + 3 & \quad = -4 + 3 \\
\quad = 11 & \quad = 3 & \quad = -1
\end{array}$$

Ordered Pairs:

$$(2, 11) \qquad\qquad (0, 3) \qquad\qquad (-1, -1)$$

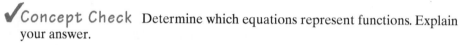 **Helpful Hint**

Note that $f(x)$ is a special symbol in mathematics used to denote a function. The symbol $f(x)$ is read "f of x." It does *not* mean $f \cdot x$ (f times x).

Examples Find each function value.

14. If $g(x) = 3x - 2$, find $g(1)$.

$g(1) = 3(1) - 2 = 1$

15. If $g(x) = 3x - 2$, find $g(0)$.

$g(0) = 3(0) - 2 = -2$

16. If $f(x) = 7x^2 - 3x + 1$, find $f(1)$.

$f(1) = 7(1)^2 - 3(1) + 1 = 5$

17. If $f(x) = 7x^2 - 3x + 1$, find $f(-2)$.

$f(-2) = 7(-2)^2 - 3(-2) + 1 = 35$

● **Work Practice 14–17**

✔**Concept Check** Suppose $y = f(x)$ and we are told that $f(3) = 9$. Which is not true?

a. When $x = 3$, $y = 9$.

b. A possible function is $f(x) = x^2$.

c. A point on the graph of the function is $(3, 9)$.

d. A possible function is $f(x) = 2x + 4$.

If it helps, think of a function, f, as a machine that has been programmed with a certain correspondence or rule. An input value (a member of the domain) is then fed into the machine, the machine does the correspondence or rule, and the result is the output (a member of the range).

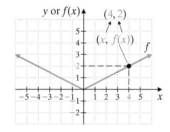 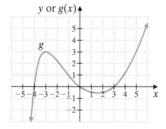

Example 18 Given the graphs of the functions f and g, find each function value by inspecting the graphs.

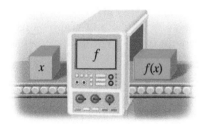 

a. $f(4)$ **b.** $f(-2)$ **c.** $g(5)$ **d.** $g(0)$

e. Find all x-values such that $f(x) = 1$.

f. Find all x-values such that $g(x) = 0$.

Solution

a. To find $f(4)$, find the y-value when $x = 4$. We see from the graph that when $x = 4$, y or $f(x) = 2$. Thus, $f(4) = 2$.

b. $f(-2) = 1$ from the ordered pair $(-2, 1)$.

c. $g(5) = 3$ from the ordered pair $(5, 3)$.

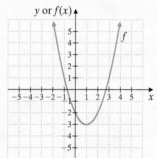
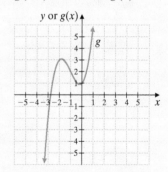

d. $g(0) = 0$ from the ordered pair $(0, 0)$.

e. To find x-values such that $f(x) = 1$, we are looking for any ordered pairs on the graph of f whose $f(x)$ or y-value is 1. They are $(2, 1)$ and $(-2, 1)$. Thus $f(2) = 1$ and $f(-2) = 1$. The x-values are 2 and -2.

f. Find ordered pairs on the graph of g whose $g(x)$ or y-value is 0. They are $(3, 0)$ $(0, 0)$ and $(-4, 0)$. Thus $g(3) = 0$, $g(0) = 0$, and $g(-4) = 0$. The x-values are $3, 0$ and -4.

○ **Work Practice 18**

Objective ⓔ Graphing Linear Functions

Recall that the graph of a linear equation in two variables is a line, and a line that is not vertical will always pass the vertical line test. Thus, *all linear equations are functions except those whose graphs are vertical lines.* We call such functions *linear functions.*

> **Linear Function**
>
> A **linear function** is a function that can be written in the form
>
> $$f(x) = mx + b$$

PRACTICE 19

Graph the function $f(x) = 3x - 2$.

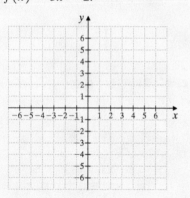

Example 19 Graph the function $f(x) = 2x + 1$.

Solution: Since $y = f(x)$, we can replace $f(x)$ with y and graph as usual. The graph of $y = 2x + 1$ has slope 2 and y-intercept $(0, 1)$. Its graph is shown.

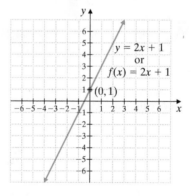

○ **Work Practice 19**

Answer

19.

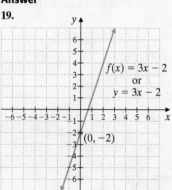

Vocabulary and Readiness Check

Use the choices below to fill in each blank. Not all choices will be used.

domain	vertical	relation	$(1.7, -2)$
range	horizontal	function	$(-2, 1.7)$

1. A _____ is a set of ordered pairs.
2. The _____ of a relation is the set of all second components of the ordered pairs.
3. The _____ of a relation is the set of all first components of the ordered pairs.
4. A _____ is a relation in which each first component in the ordered pairs corresponds to *exactly* one second component.
5. By the vertical line test, all linear equations are functions except those whose graphs are _____ lines.
6. If $f(-2) = 1.7$, the corresponding ordered pair is _____ .

 **12.2** Exercise Set

FOR EXTRA HELP

MyMathLab

 Math XP
PRACTICE

WATCH

DOWNLOAD

READ

REVIEW

Objectives **A** **B** **Mixed Practice** *Find the domain and the range of each relation. Also determine whether the relation is a function. See Examples 1 through 6.*

1. $\{(-1, 7), (0, 6), (-2, 2), (5, 6)\}$

2. $\{(4, 9), (-4, 9), (2, 3), (10, -5)\}$

3. $\{(-2, 4), (6, 4), (-2, -3), (-7, -8)\}$

4. $\{(6, 6), (5, 6), (5, -2), (7, 6)\}$

5. $\{(1, 1), (1, 2), (1, 3), (1, 4)\}$

6. $\{(1, 1), (2, 1), (3, 1), (4, 1)\}$

7. $\left\{\left(\frac{3}{2}, \frac{1}{2}\right), \left(1\frac{1}{2}, -7\right), \left(0, \frac{4}{5}\right)\right\}$

8. $\left\{\left(\frac{1}{2}, \frac{1}{4}\right), \left(0, \frac{7}{8}\right), (0.5, \pi)\right\}$

9. $\{(-3, -3), (0, 0), (3, 3)\}$

10. $\{(\pi, 0), (0, \pi), (-2, 4), (4, -2)\}$

11.

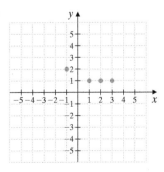

12.

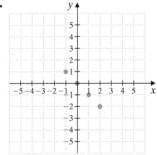

933

13.

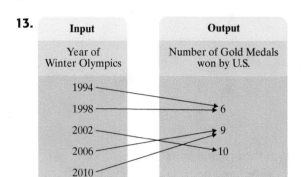

14.

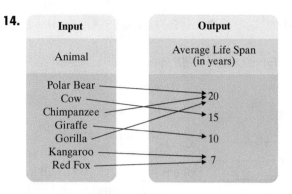

15.

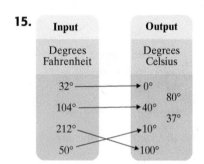

16.

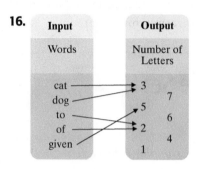

17.

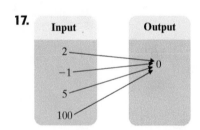

18.

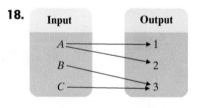

Determine whether each relation is a function. See Examples 4 through 6.

	First Set: Input	**Correspondence**	**Second Set: Output**
19.	Class of algebra students	Final grade average	nonnegative numbers
20.	People who live in Cincinnati, Ohio	Birth date	days of the year
21.	blue, green, brown	Eye color	People who live in Cincinnati, Ohio
22.	Whole numbers from 0 to 4	Number of children	50 women in a water aerobics class

Determine whether each relation is also a function. See Examples 7 and 8.

23. $y = x + 1$ **24.** $y = x - 1$ **25.** $x = 2y^2$

26. $y = x^2$ **27.** $y - x = 7$ **28.** $2x - 3y = 9$

Objective C *Use the vertical line test to determine whether each graph is the graph of a function. See Examples 9 through 13.*

29.
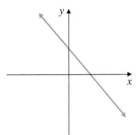

30.
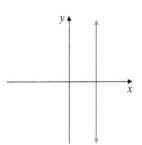

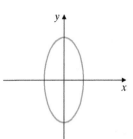**31.**

32.
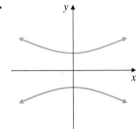

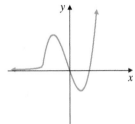**33.**

34.
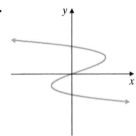

35.
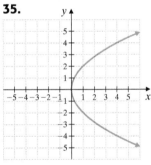

36.
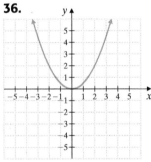

37.
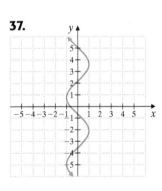

38.
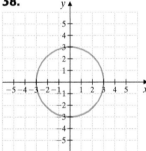

39.
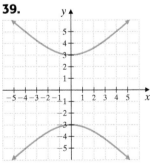

40.
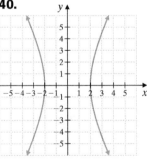

41.
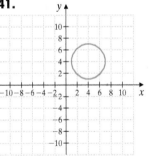

42.
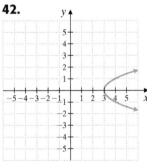

43.
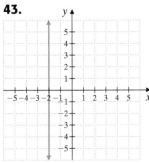

44.
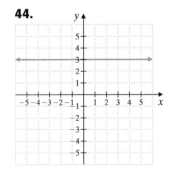

45.
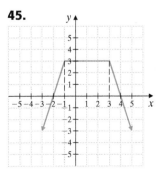

46.
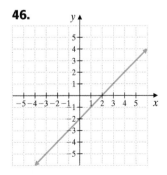

Objective Ⓓ *If* $f(x) = 3x + 3$, $g(x) = 4x^2 - 6x + 3$, *and* $h(x) = 5x^2 - 7$, *find each function value. See Examples 14 through 17.*

47. $f(4)$ **48.** $f(-1)$ **49.** $h(-3)$ **50.** $h(0)$

51. $g(2)$ **52.** $g(1)$ **53.** $g(0)$ **54.** $h(-2)$

For each function, find the indicated values. See Examples 14 through 17.

55. $f(x) = \dfrac{1}{2}x$;
   a. $f(0)$
   b. $f(2)$
   c. $f(-2)$

56. $g(x) = -\dfrac{1}{3}x$;
   a. $g(0)$
   b. $g(-1)$
   c. $g(3)$

57. $f(x) = -5$;
   a. $f(2)$
   b. $f(0)$
   c. $f(606)$

58. $h(x) = 7$;
   a. $h(7)$
   b. $h(542)$
   c. $h\left(-\dfrac{3}{4}\right)$

Use the graph of the functions below to answer Exercises 59 through 70. See Example 18.

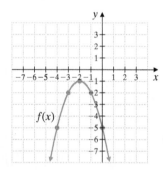
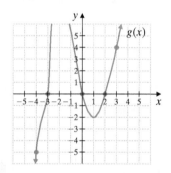

59. If $f(1) = -10$, write the corresponding ordered pair.   **60.** If $f(-5) = -10$, write the corresponding ordered pair.

61. If $g(4) = 56$, write the corresponding ordered pair.   **62.** If $g(-2) = 8$, write the corresponding ordered pair.

63. Find $f(-1)$.   **64.** Find $f(-2)$.   **65.** Find $g(2)$.

66. Find $g(-4)$.   **67.** Find all values of x such that $f(x) = -5$.   **68.** Find all values of x such that $f(x) = -2$.

69. Find all positive values of x such that $g(x) = 4$.   **70.** Find all values of x such that $g(x) = 0$.

The function $A(r) = \pi r^2$ may be used to find the area of a circle if we are given its radius. Use this function to answer Exercises 71 and 72. See Examples 14–17.

71. Find the area of a circle whose radius is 5 centimeters. (Do not approximate π.)

72. Find the area of a circular garden whose radius is 8 feet. (Do not approximate π.)

The function $V(x) = x^3$ may be used to find the volume of a cube if we are given the length x of a side. Use this function to answer Exercises 73 and 74. See Examples 14–17.

73. Find the volume of a cube whose side is 14 inches.

74. Find the volume of a die whose side is 1.7 centimeters.

Forensic scientists use the following functions to find the height of a woman if they are given the height of her femur bone (f) or her tibia bone (t) in centimeters.

$$H(f) = 2.59f + 47.24$$

$$H(t) = 2.72t + 61.28$$

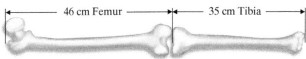

Use these functions to answer Exercises 75 and 76. See Examples 14–17.

75. Find the height of a woman whose femur measures 46 centimeters.

76. Find the height of a woman whose tibia measures 35 centimeters.

The dosage in milligrams D of Ivermectin, a heartworm preventive, for a dog who weighs x pounds is given by

$$D(x) = \frac{136}{25}x$$

Use this function to answer Exercises 77 and 78. See Examples 14–17.

77. Find the proper dosage for a dog that weighs 30 pounds.

78. Find the proper dosage for a dog that weighs 50 pounds.

Solve. See Examples 14–17.

79. The per capita consumption (in pounds) of all beef in the United States is given by the function $C(x) = -0.33x + 67.1$, where x is the number of years since 2000. (*Source:* Based on data from the Economic Research Service, U.S. Department of Agriculture, 2000–2008)

  a. Find and interpret $C(4)$.

  b. Estimate the per capita consumption of beef in the United States in 2010.

80. The amount of money (in billions of dollars) spent by the Boeing Company and subsidiaries on research and development annually is represented by the function $R(x) = 0.54x + 1.96$, where x is the number of years since 2004. (*Source:* Based on data from the Boeing Corporation)

  a. Find and interpret $R(2)$.

  b. Estimate the amount of money spent on research and development by Boeing in 2009.

Objective **E** *Graph each linear function. See Example 19.*

81. $f(x) = 2x + 3$

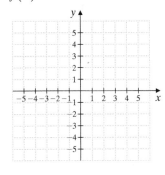

82. $f(x) = 5x - 1$

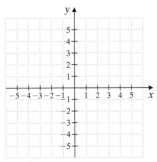

83. $f(x) = -3x$

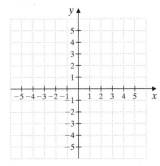

84. $f(x) = -4x$

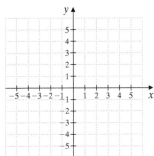

85. $f(x) = -x + 2$

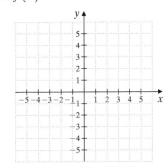

86. $f(x) = -x + 1$

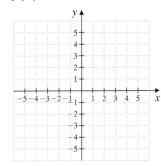

Review

Solve.

87. $2x - 7 \leq 21$

88. $-3x + 1 > 0$

89. $5(x - 2) \geq 3(x - 1)$

90. $-2(x + 1) \leq -x + 10$

91. $\dfrac{x}{2} + \dfrac{1}{4} < \dfrac{1}{8}$

92. $\dfrac{x}{5} - \dfrac{3}{10} \geq \dfrac{x}{2} - 1$

Concept Extensions

Think about the appearance of each graph. Without graphing, determine which equations represent functions. Explain each answer. See the second Concept Check in this section.

93. $x = -1$

94. $y = 5$

95. $y = 2x$

96. $x + y = -5$

Suppose that $y = f(x)$ and it is true that $f(7) = 50$. For Exercises 97–100, determine whether each statement is true or false. See the third Concept Check in this section.

97. An ordered-pair solution of the function is $(7, 50)$.

98. When x is 50, y is 7.

99. A possible function is $f(x) = x^2 + 1$.

100. A possible function is $f(x) = 10x - 20$.

101. What is the greatest number of x-intercepts that a function may have? Explain your answer.

102. What is the greatest number of y-intercepts that a function may have? Explain your answer.

103. In your own words, explain how to find the domain of a function given its graph.

104. Explain the vertical line test and how it is used.

For each function, find the indicated values.

105. $f(x) = x - 12$;

    a. $f(12)$
    b. $f(a)$
    c. $f(-x)$
    d. $f(x + h)$

106. $f(x) = 2x + 7$

    a. $f(2)$
    b. $f(a)$
    c. $f(-x)$
    d. $f(x + h)$

12.3 FINDING DOMAINS AND RANGES FROM GRAPHS AND GRAPHING PIECEWISE-DEFINED FUNCTIONS

Objectives

A Find the Domain and Range from a Graph.

B Graph Piecewise-Defined Functions.

Objective A Finding the Domain and Range from a Graph

Recall from Section 12.2 that the

> **domain** of a relation is the set of all first components of the ordered pairs of the relation and the
> **range** of a relation is the set of all second components of the ordered pairs of the relation.

In this section we use the graph of a relation to find its domain and range. Let's use interval notation to write these domains and ranges. Remember, we use a parenthesis to indicate that a number is not part of the domain and we use a bracket to indicate that a number is part of the domain. Of course, as usual, parentheses are placed about infinity symbols indicating that we approach but never reach infinity.

To find the domain of a function (or relation) from its graph, recall that on the rectangular coordinate system, "domain" is the set of first components of the ordered pairs, so this means the *x*-values that are graphed. Similarly, "range" is the set of second components of the ordered pairs, so this means the *y*-values that are graphed.

Examples Find the domain and range of each relation.

1.

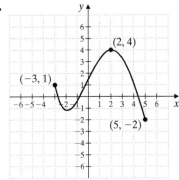

2.

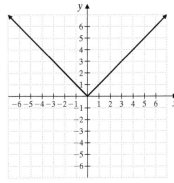

3.

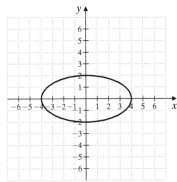

4.

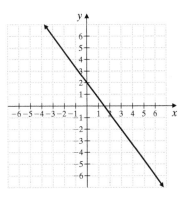

Continued on next page

PRACTICE 1–4

Find the domain and range of each relation.

1.

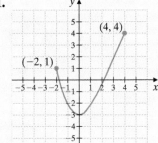

2.

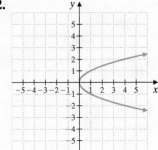

3.

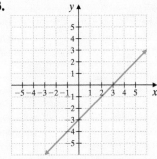

Answers

1. domain: $[-2, 4]$; range: $[-3, 4]$
2. domain: $[0, \infty)$; range: $(-\infty, \infty)$
3. domain: $(-\infty, \infty)$; range: $(-\infty, \infty)$

4.

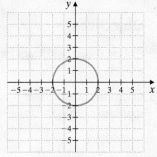

Solution: Notice that the graphs for Examples 1, 2, and 4 are graphs of functions because each passes the vertical line test.

1.

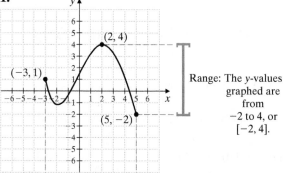

Range: The y-values graphed are from −2 to 4, or [−2, 4].

Domain:
The x-values graphed are from −3 to 5, or [−3, 5].

2.

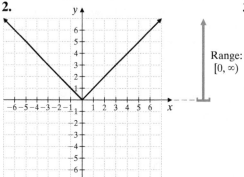

Range: [0, ∞)

Domain: (−∞, ∞)

3.

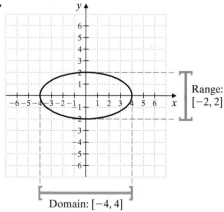

Range: [−2, 2]

Domain: [−4, 4]

4.

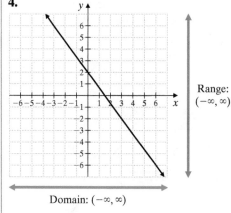

Range: (−∞, ∞)

Domain: (−∞, ∞)

🔵 **Work Practice 1–4**

Objective Ⓑ Graphing Piecewise-Defined Functions

In the last section we graphed functions. There are many special functions. In fact, sometimes a function is defined by two or more expressions. The equation to use depends upon the value of x. Before we actually graph these piecewise-defined functions, let's practice finding function values.

Answer
4. domain: [−2, 2]; range: [−2, 2]

Example 5 Evaluate $f(2), f(-6)$, and $f(0)$ for the function

$$f(x) = \begin{cases} 2x + 3 & \text{if } x \le 0 \\ -x - 1 & \text{if } x > 0 \end{cases}$$

Then write your results in ordered-pair form.

Solution: Take a moment and study this function. It is a single function defined by two expressions depending on the value of x. From above, if $x \le 0$, use $f(x) = 2x + 3$. If $x > 0$, use $f(x) = -x - 1$. Thus

$f(2) = -(2) - 1$	$f(-6) = 2(-6) + 3$	$f(0) = 2(0) + 3$
$= -3$ since $2 > 0$	$= -9$ since $-6 \le 0$	$= 3$ since $0 \le 0$
$f(2) = -3$	$f(-6) = -9$	$f(0) = 3$
Ordered pairs: $(2, -3)$	$(-6, -9)$	$(0, 3)$

● **Work Practice 5**

Now, let's graph a piecewise-defined function.

Example 6 Graph $f(x) = \begin{cases} 2x + 3 & \text{if } x \le 0 \\ -x - 1 & \text{if } x > 0 \end{cases}$

Solution: Let's graph each piece.

If $x \le 0$,
$f(x) = 2x + 3$

Values ≤ 0 {

x	$f(x) = 2x + 3$
0	3 Closed circle
−1	1
−2	−1

If $x > 0$,
$f(x) = -x - 1$

Values > 0 {

x	$f(x) = -x - 1$
1	−2
2	−3
3	−4

The graph of the first part of $f(x)$ listed will look like a ray with a closed-circle endpoint at $(0, 3)$. The graph of the second part of $f(x)$ listed will look like a ray with an open-circle endpoint. To find the exact location of the open-circle endpoint, use $f(x) = -x - 1$ and find $f(0)$. Since $f(0) = -0 - 1 = -1$, we graph the values from the second table and place an open circle at $(0, -1)$.

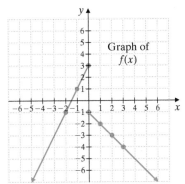

Graph of $f(x)$

Notice that this graph is the graph of a function because it passes the vertical line test. The domain of this function is $(-\infty, \infty)$ and the range is $(-\infty, 3]$.

● **Work Practice 6**

In the exercises in the next section, we shall graph piecewise-defined functions whose pieces are not necessarily pieces of lines.

PRACTICE 5

Evaluate $f(-4), f(3)$, and $f(0)$ for the function

$$f(x) = \begin{cases} 3x + 4 & \text{if } x < 0 \\ -x + 2 & \text{if } x \ge 0 \end{cases}$$

Then write your results in ordered-pair solution form.

PRACTICE 6

Graph

$$f(x) = \begin{cases} 3x + 4 & \text{if } x < 0 \\ -x + 2 & \text{if } x \ge 0 \end{cases}$$

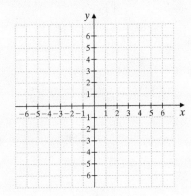

Answers

5. $f(-4) = -8; f(3) = -1; f(0) = 2;$
$(-4, -8); (3, -1); (0, 2)$

6.

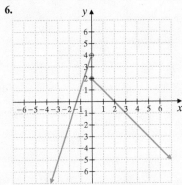

Objective Ⓐ *Find the domain and the range of each relation. See Examples 1 through 4.*

1.

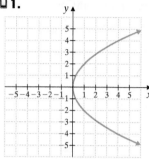

2.

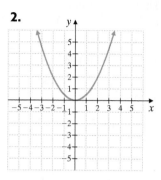

3.

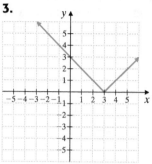

4.

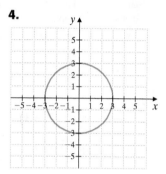

5.

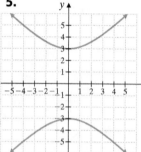

6.

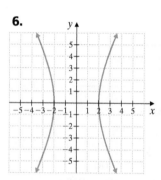

7.

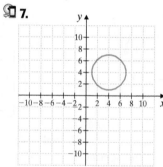

8.

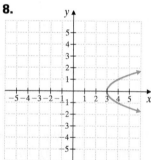

9.

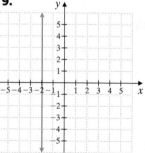

10.

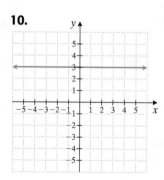

11.

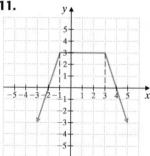

12.

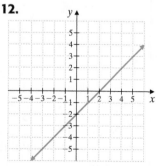

13.

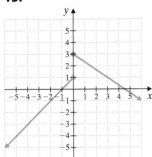

14.

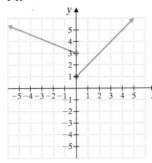

15.

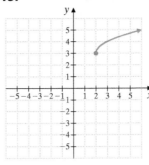

16.

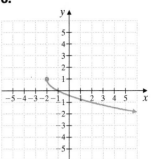

Objective **B** *Graph each piecewise-defined function. See Examples 5 and 6.*

17. $f(x) = \begin{cases} 2x & \text{if } x < 0 \\ x + 1 & \text{if } x \ge 0 \end{cases}$

18. $f(x) = \begin{cases} 3x & \text{if } x < 0 \\ x + 2 & \text{if } x \ge 0 \end{cases}$

19. $f(x) = \begin{cases} 4x + 5 & \text{if } x \le 0 \\ \dfrac{1}{4}x + 2 & \text{if } x > 0 \end{cases}$

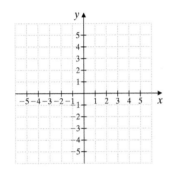

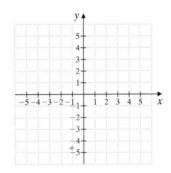

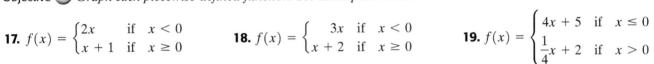

20. $f(x) = \begin{cases} 5x + 4 & \text{if } x \le 0 \\ \dfrac{1}{3}x - 1 & \text{if } x > 0 \end{cases}$

21. $g(x) = \begin{cases} -x & \text{if } x \le 1 \\ 2x + 1 & \text{if } x > 1 \end{cases}$

22. $g(x) = \begin{cases} 3x - 1 & \text{if } x \le 2 \\ -x & \text{if } x > 2 \end{cases}$

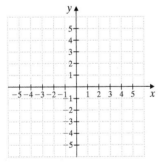

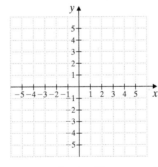

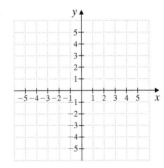

23. $f(x) = \begin{cases} 5 & \text{if } x < -2 \\ 3 & \text{if } x \ge -2 \end{cases}$

24. $f(x) = \begin{cases} 4 & \text{if } x < -3 \\ -2 & \text{if } x \ge -3 \end{cases}$

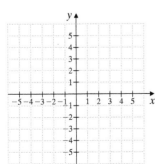

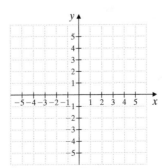

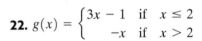

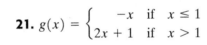

Objectives **A** **B** **Mixed Practice** *Graph each piecewise-defined function. Use the graph to determine the domain and range of the function. See Examples 1 through 6.*

25. $f(x) = \begin{cases} -2x & \text{if } x \le 0 \\ 2x + 1 & \text{if } x > 0 \end{cases}$

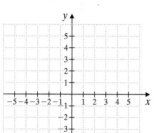

26. $g(x) = \begin{cases} -3x & \text{if } x \le 0 \\ 3x + 2 & \text{if } x > 0 \end{cases}$

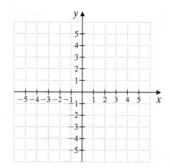

27. $h(x) = \begin{cases} 5x - 5 & \text{if } x < 2 \\ -x + 3 & \text{if } x \ge 2 \end{cases}$

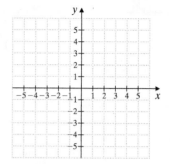

28. $f(x) = \begin{cases} 4x - 4 & \text{if } x < 2 \\ -x + 1 & \text{if } x \ge 2 \end{cases}$

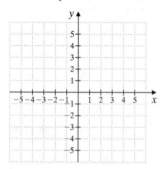

29. $f(x) = \begin{cases} x + 3 & \text{if } x < -1 \\ -2x + 4 & \text{if } x \ge -1 \end{cases}$

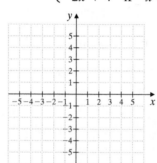

30. $h(x) = \begin{cases} x + 2 & \text{if } x < 1 \\ 2x - 1 & \text{if } x \ge 1 \end{cases}$

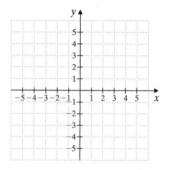

31. $g(x) = \begin{cases} -2 & \text{if } x \le 0 \\ -4 & \text{if } x \ge 1 \end{cases}$

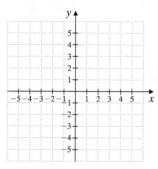

32. $f(x) = \begin{cases} -1 & \text{if } x \le 0 \\ -3 & \text{if } x \ge 2 \end{cases}$

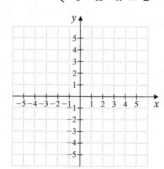

Review

Match each equation with its graph.

33. $y = -1$
A
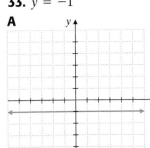

34. $x = -1$
B
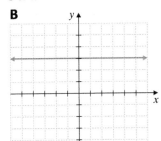

35. $x = 3$
C
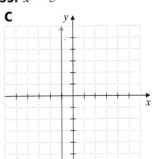

36. $y = 3$
D
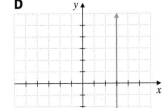

Concept Extensions

37. Draw a graph whose domain is $(-\infty, 5]$ and whose range is $[2, \infty)$. Is your graph a function? Discuss why or why not.

38. In your own words, describe how to graph a piecewise-defined function.

39. Graph: $f(x) = \begin{cases} -\dfrac{1}{2}x & \text{if } x \le 0 \\ x + 1 & \text{if } 0 < x \le 2 \\ 2x - 1 & \text{if } x > 2 \end{cases}$

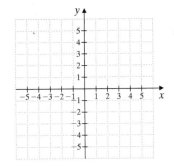

40. Graph: $f(x) = \begin{cases} \dfrac{1}{3}x & \text{if } x < 0 \\ -x + 2 & \text{if } 0 \le x < 4 \\ 3x - 10 & x \ge 4 \end{cases}$

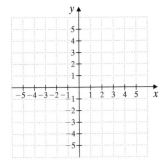

12.4 SHIFTING AND REFLECTING GRAPHS OF FUNCTIONS

In this section, we take common graphs and learn how more complicated graphs are actually formed by shifting and reflecting these common graphs. These shifts and reflections are called transformations, and it is possible to combine transformations. A knowledge of these transformations will help you simplify future graphs.

Objective **A** Graphing Common Equations

Let's begin with the graphs of four common functions.

First, let's graph the linear function $f(x) = x$, or $y = x$. Ordered-pair solutions of this graph consist of ordered pairs whose x- and y-values are the same.

x	y or $f(x) = x$
-3	-3
0	0
1	1
4	4

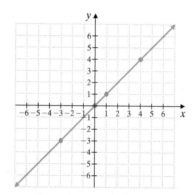

Next, let's graph the nonlinear function $f(x) = x^2$ or $y = x^2$.

This equation is not linear because the x^2 term does not allow us to write it in the form $Ax + By = C$. Its graph is not a line. We begin by finding ordered pair solutions. Because this graph is solved for $f(x)$, or y, we choose x-values and find corresponding $f(x)$, or y-values.

If $x = -3$, then $y = (-3)^2$, or 9.
If $x = -2$, then $y = (-2)^2$, or 4.
If $x = -1$, then $y = (-1)^2$, or 1.
If $x = 0$, then $y = 0^2$, or 0.
If $x = 1$, then $y = 1^2$, or 1.
If $x = 2$, then $y = 2^2$, or 4.
If $x = 3$, then $y = 3^2$, or 9.

x	$f(x)$ or y
-3	9
-2	4
-1	1
0	0
1	1
2	4
3	9

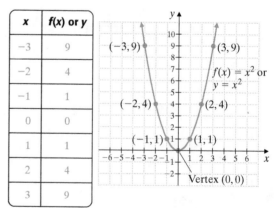

Study the table a moment and look for patterns. Notice that the ordered pair solution (0, 0) contains the smallest y-value because any other x-value squared will give a positive result. This means that the point (0, 0) will be the lowest point on the graph. Also notice that all other y-values correspond to two different x-values. For example, $3^2 = 9$ and also $(-3)^2 = 9$. This means that the graph will be a mirror image of itself across the y-axis. Connect the plotted points with a smooth curve to sketch its graph.

This curve is given a special name, a **parabola.** We will study more about parabolas in later chapters.

Next, let's graph another nonlinear function $f(x) = |x|$ or $y = |x|$.

This is not a linear equation since it cannot be written in the form $Ax + By = C$. Its graph is not a line. Because we do not know the shape of this graph, we find many ordered pair solutions. We will choose x-values and substitute to find corresponding y-values.

x	y
−3	3
−2	2
−1	1
0	0
1	1
2	2
3	3

If $x = -3$, then $y = |-3|$, or 3.

If $x = -2$, then $y = |-2|$, or 2.

If $x = -1$, then $y = |-1|$, or 1.

If $x = 0$, then $y = |0|$, or 0.

If $x = 1$, then $y = |1|$, or 1.

If $x = 2$, then $y = |2|$, or 2.

If $x = 3$, then $y = |3|$, or 3.

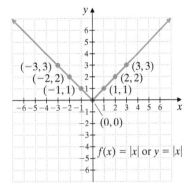

Again, study the table of values for a moment and notice any patterns.

From the plotted ordered pairs, we see that the graph of this absolute value equation is V-shaped.

Finally, a fourth common function, $f(x) = \sqrt{x}$ or $y = \sqrt{x}$. For this graph, you need to recall basic facts about square roots and use your calculator to approximate some square roots to help locate points. Recall also that the square root of a negative number is not a real number, so be careful when finding your domain.

Now let's graph the square root function $f(x) = \sqrt{x}$, or $y = \sqrt{x}$.

To graph, we identify the domain, evaluate the function for several values of x, plot the resulting points, and connect the points with a smooth curve. Since $\sqrt{x}$ represents the nonnegative square root of x, the domain of this function is the set of all nonnegative numbers, $\{x \mid x \geq 0\}$, or $[0, \infty)$. We have approximated $\sqrt{3}$ below to help us locate the point corresponding to $(3, \sqrt{3})$.

x	$f(x) = \sqrt{x}$
0	0
1	1
3	$\sqrt{3} \approx 1.7$
4	2
9	3

If $x = 0$, then $y = \sqrt{0}$, or 0.

If $x = 1$, then $y = \sqrt{1}$, or 1.

If $x = 3$, then $y = \sqrt{3}$, or 1.7.

If $x = 4$, then $y = \sqrt{4}$, or 2.

If $x = 9$, then $y = \sqrt{9}$, or 3.

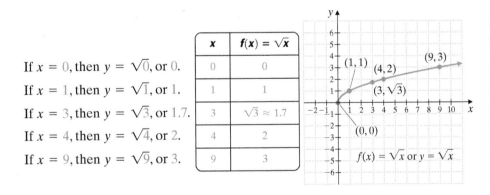

Notice that the graph of this function passes the vertical line test, as expected.

Below is a summary of our four common graphs. Take a moment and study these graphs. Your success in the rest of this section depends on your knowledge of these graphs.

Common Graphs

$f(x) = x$

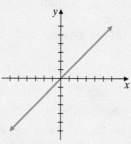

$f(x) = x^2$

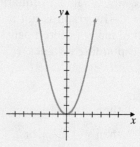

$f(x) = 1\overline{x}$

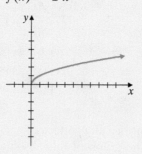

$f(x) = |x|$

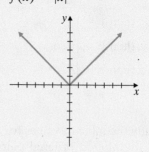

Answers

1.

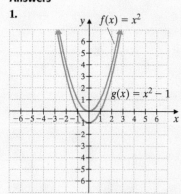

2.

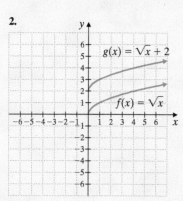

3.

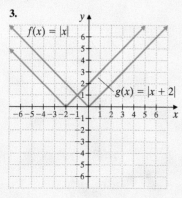

Objective B Vertical and Horizontal Shifting

Your knowledge of the slope-intercept form, $f(x) = mx + b$, will help you understand simple shifting of transformations such as vertical shifts. For example, what is the difference between the graphs of $f(x) = x$ and $g(x) = x + 3$?

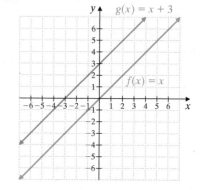

$f(x) = x$
slope, $m = 1$
y-intercept is $(0,0)$

$g(x) = x + 3$
slope, $m = 1$
y-intercept is $(0,3)$

Notice that the graph of $g(x) = x + 3$ is the same as the graph of $f(x) = x$, but moved upward 3 units. This is an example of a **vertical shift** and is true for graphs in general.

Vertical Shifts (Upward and Downward)
Let k be a Positive Number

Graph of	Same as	Moved
$g(x) = f(x) + k$	$f(x)$	k units upward
$g(x) = f(x) - k$	$f(x)$	k units downward

Examples Without plotting points, sketch the graph of each pair of functions on the same set of axes.

1. $f(x) = x^2$ and $g(x) = x^2 + 2$ **2.** $f(x) = \sqrt{x}$ and $g(x) = \sqrt{x} - 3$

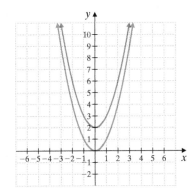   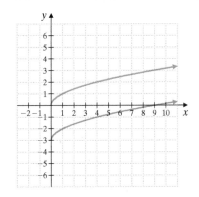

● **Work Practice 1–2**

A horizontal shift to the left or right may be slightly more difficult to understand. Let's graph $g(x) = |x - 2|$ and compare it with $f(x) = |x|$.

Example 3 Without plotting points, sketch the graphs of $f(x) = |x|$ and $g(x) = |x - 2|$ on the same set of axes.

Solution:

x	$f(x) = |x|$	$g(x) = |x - 2|$
-3	3	5
-2	2	4
-1	1	3
0	0	2
1	1	1
2	2	0
3	3	1

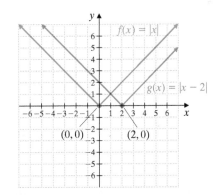

The graph of $g(x) = |x - 2|$ is the same as the graph of $f(x) = |x|$, but moved 2 units to the right. This is an example of a **horizontal shift** and is true for graphs in general. The table is provided to verify the graphs.

● **Work Practice 3**

Horizontal Shift (To the Left or Right) Let h be a Positive Number

Graph of	Same as	Moved
$g(x) = f(x - h)$	$f(x)$	h units to the right
$g(x) = f(x + h)$	$f(x)$	h units to the left

Helpful Hint

Notice that $f(x - h)$ corresponds to a shift to the right and $f(x + h)$ corresponds to a shift to the left.

Vertical and horizontal shifts can be combined.

PRACTICE 1–2

Without plotting points, sketch the graphs of each pair of functions on the same set of axes.

1. $f(x) = x^2$ and
   $g(x) = x^2 - 1$

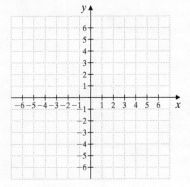

2. $f(x) = \sqrt{x}$ and
   $g(x) = \sqrt{x} + 2$

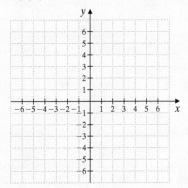

PRACTICE 3

Without plotting points, sketch the graphs of $f(x) = |x|$ and $g(x) = |x + 2|$ on the same set of axes.

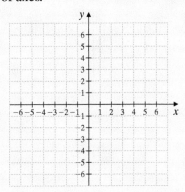

Answers
1–3. See page 958.

PRACTICE 4

Sketch the graphs of $f(x) = x^2$ and $g(x) = (x + 2)^2 - 1$ on the same set of axes.

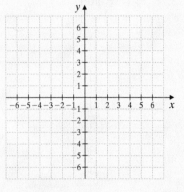

Example 4 Sketch the graphs of $f(x) = x^2$ and $g(x) = (x - 2)^2 + 1$ on the same set of axes.

Solution: The graph of $g(x)$ is the same as the graph of $f(x)$ shifted 2 units to the right and 1 unit up.

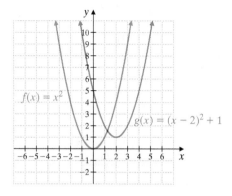

● Work Practice 4

PRACTICE 5

Sketch the graph of $h(x) = -(x - 3)^2 + 2$.

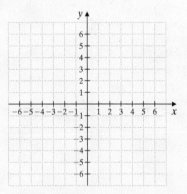

Objective ⓒ Reflecting Graphs

Another type of transformation is called a **reflection.** In this section, we will study reflections (mirror images) about the x-axis only. For example, take a moment and study these two graphs. The graph of $g(x) = -x^2$ can be found, as usual, by plotting points.

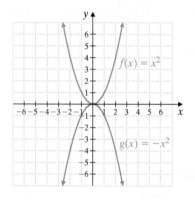

Reflection about the x-axis

The graph of $g(x) = -f(x)$ is the graph of $f(x)$ reflected about the x-axis.

Example 5 Sketch the graph of $h(x) = -|x - 3| + 2$.

Solution: The graph of $h(x) = -|x - 3| + 2$ is the same as the graph of $f(x) = |x|$ reflected about the x-axis, then moved three units to the right and two units upward.

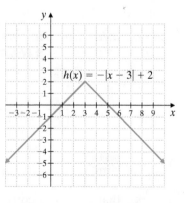

● Work Practice 5

There are other transformations, such as stretching, that won't be covered in this section. For a review of this transformation, see the Appendix.

Answers

4.

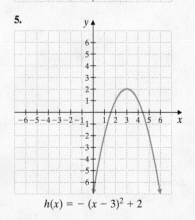

5.

$h(x) = -(x - 3)^2 + 2$

Vocabulary and Readiness Check

Match each equation with its graph.

1. $y = \sqrt{x}$ **2.** $y = x^2$ **3.** $y = x$ **4.** $y = |x|$

A 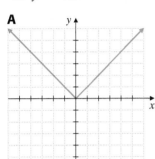   **B** 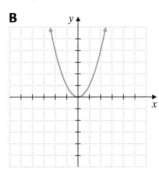   **C** 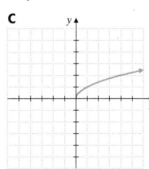   **D**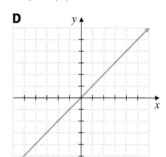

12.4 Exercise Set

FOR EXTRA HELP

MyMathLab Math XL PRACTICE WATCH DOWNLOAD READ REVIEW

Objectives Ⓐ Ⓑ **Mixed Practice** *Sketch the graph of each function. See Examples 1 through 4.*

1. $f(x) = |x| + 3$
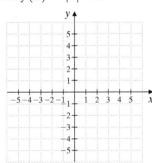

2. $f(x) = |x| - 2$
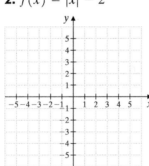

3. $f(x) = \sqrt{x} - 2$
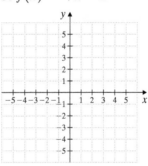

4. $f(x) = \sqrt{x} + 3$
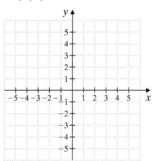

5. $f(x) = |x - 4|$
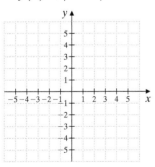

6. $f(x) = |x + 3|$
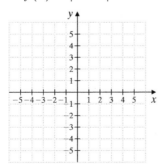

7. $f(x) = \sqrt{x + 2}$
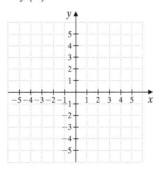

8. $f(x) = \sqrt{x - 2}$
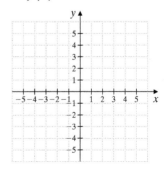

9. $y = (x - 4)^2$

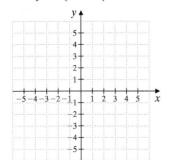

10. $y = (x + 4)^2$

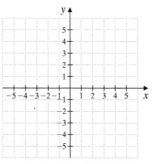

11. $f(x) = x^2 + 4$

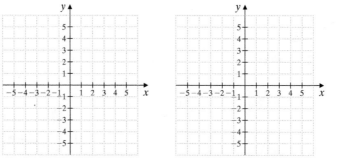

12. $f(x) = x^2 - 4$

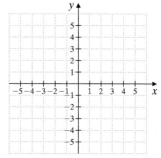

13. $f(x) = \sqrt{x - 2} + 3$

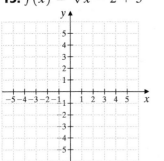

14. $f(x) = \sqrt{x - 1} + 3$

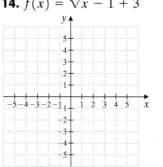

15. $f(x) = |x - 1| + 5$

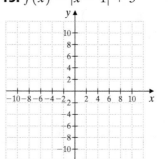

16. $f(x) = |x - 3| + 2$

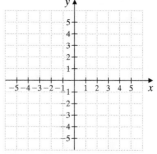

17. $f(x) = \sqrt{x + 1} + 1$

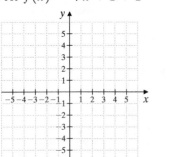

18. $f(x) = \sqrt{x + 3} + 2$

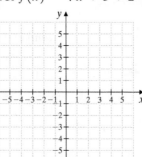

19. $f(x) = |x + 3| - 1$

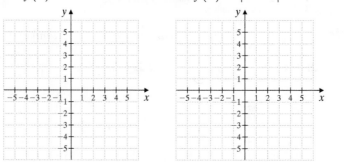

20. $f(x) = |x + 1| - 4$

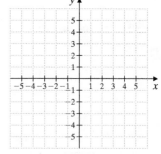

21. $g(x) = (x - 1)^2 - 1$

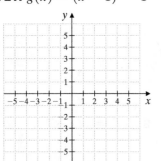

22. $h(x) = (x + 2)^2 + 2$

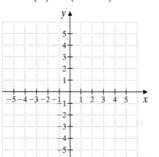

23. $f(x) = (x + 3)^2 - 2$

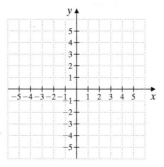

24. $f(x) = (x + 2)^2 + 4$

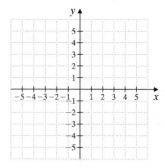

Objectives Ⓐ Ⓑ Ⓒ **Mixed Practice** *Sketch the graph of each function.*

25. $f(x) = -(x - 1)^2$

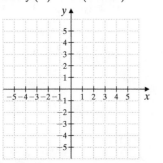

26. $g(x) = -(x + 2)^2$

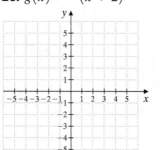

27. $h(x) = -\sqrt{x} + 3$

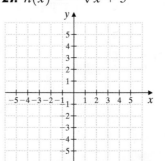

28. $f(x) = -\sqrt{x + 3}$

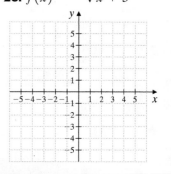

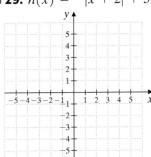 **29.** $h(x) = -|x + 2| + 3$ **30.** $g(x) = -|x + 1| + 1$ **31.** $f(x) = (x - 3) + 2$ **32.** $f(x) = (x - 1) + 4$

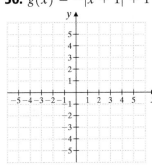

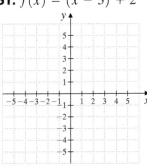

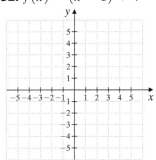

Review

Simplify.

33. $-3x^4 \cdot 5x^4$ **34.** $-3x^4 + 5x^4$ **35.** $8(y^7 + y^{11})$ **36.** $y^7 \cdot y^{11}$

Concept Extensions

Mixed Practice (*Sections 12.3, 12.4*) *Write the domain and range of the indicated function in this section.*

37. Exercise 13

38. Exercise 14

39. Exercise 29

40. Exercise 30

Without graphing, find the domain of each function.

41. $f(x) = 5\sqrt{x - 20} + 1$ **42.** $g(x) = -3\sqrt{x + 5}$ **43.** $h(x) = 5|x - 20| + 1$

44. $f(x) = -3|x + 5.7|$ **45.** $g(x) = 9 - \sqrt{x + 103}$ **46.** $h(x) = \sqrt{x - 17} - 3$

Sketch the graph of each piecewise-defined function. Write the domain and range of each function.

47. $f(x) = \begin{cases} |x| & \text{if } x \le 0 \\ x^2 & \text{if } x > 0 \end{cases}$

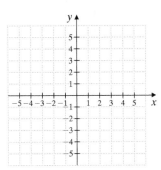

48. $f(x) = \begin{cases} x^2 & \text{if } x < 0 \\ \sqrt{x} & \text{if } x \ge 0 \end{cases}$

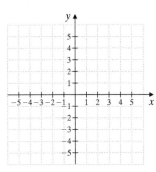

49. $g(x) = \begin{cases} |x - 2| & \text{if } x < 0 \\ -x^2 & \text{if } x \ge 0 \end{cases}$

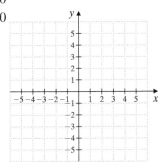

50. $g(x) = \begin{cases} -|x + 1| - 1 & \text{if } x < -2 \\ \sqrt{x + 2} - 4 & \text{if } x \ge -2 \end{cases}$

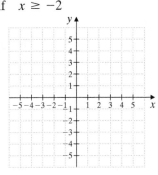

12 Chapter Highlights

Helpful Hint 📱 Are you preparing for your test? Use the Chapter Test Prep Videos to see the fully worked-out solutions to any of the exercises you want to review.

Definitions and Concepts	Examples

Section 12.1   Sets and Interval Notation

Set Notation	Graph	Interval Notation
$\{x \mid x < a\}$	*a*	$(-\infty, a)$
$\{x \mid x > a\}$	*a*	(a, ∞)
$\{x \mid x \leq a\}$	*a*	$(-\infty, a]$
$\{x \mid x \geq a\}$	*a*	$[a, \infty)$
$\{x \mid a < x < b\}$	*a* *b*	(a, b)
$\{x \mid a \leq x \leq b\}$	*a* *b*	$[a, b]$
$\{x \mid a < x \leq b\}$	*a* *b*	$(a, b]$
$\{x \mid a \leq x < b\}$	*a* *b*	$[a, b)$
$\{x \mid x \text{ is a real number}\}$		$(-\infty, \infty)$

Section 12.2   Introduction to Functions

A **relation** is a set of ordered pairs. The **domain** of the relation is the set of all first components of the ordered pairs. The **range** of the relation is the set of all second components of the ordered pairs.

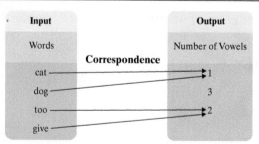

Domain: {cat, dog, too, give}
Range: {1, 2}

A **function** is a relation in which each element of the first set corresponds to exactly one element of the second set.

The previous relation is a function. Each word contains one exact number of vowels.

VERTICAL LINE TEST

If no vertical line can be drawn so that it intersects a graph more than once, the graph is the graph of a function. If such a line can be drawn, the graph is not that of a function.

Find the domain and the range of the relation. Also determine whether the relation is a function.

Range $(-\infty, 0]$

Domain: $(-\infty, \infty)$

By the vertical line test, this is the graph of a function.

954

Definitions and Concepts	**Examples**

Section 12.2   Introduction to Functions (*continued*)

The symbol $f(x)$ means **function of *x*** and is called **function notation.**

A **linear function** is a function that can be written in the form

$$f(x) = mx + b$$

To graph a linear function, use the slope and *y*-intercept.

If $f(x) = 2x^2 - 5$, find $f(-3)$.

$$f(-3) = 2(-3)^2 - 5 = 2(9) - 5 = 13$$

$$f(x) = -3, g(x) = 5x, h(x) = -\frac{1}{3}x - 7$$

Graph: $f(x) = -2x$
(or $y = -2x + 0$)

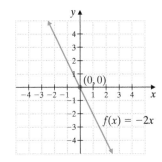

The slope is $\dfrac{2}{-1}$.

The *y*-intercept is $(0, 0)$.

Section 12.3   Finding Domains and Ranges from Graphs and Graphing Piecewise-Defined Functions

To find the domain of a function (or relation) from its graph, recall that on the rectangular coordinate system, "domain" means the *x*-values that are graphed. Similarly, "range" means the *y*-values that are graphed.

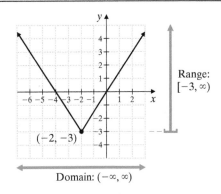

Section 12.4   Shifting and Reflecting Graphs of Functions

Vertical shifts (upward and downward) let *k* be a positive number.

Graph of	**Same as**	**Moved**
$g(x) = f(x) + k$	$f(x)$	*k* units upward
$g(x) = f(x) - k$	$f(x)$	*k* units downward

Horizontal shift (to the left or right) let *h* be a positive number.

Graph of	**Same as**	**Moved**
$g(x) = f(x - h)$	$f(x)$	*h* units to the right
$g(x) = f(x + h)$	$f(x)$	*h* units to the left

Reflection about the *x*-axis
The graph of $g(x) = -f(x)$ is the graph of $f(x)$ reflected about the *x*-axis.

The graph of $h(x) = -|x - 3| + 1$ is the same as the graph of $f(x) = |x|$, reflected about the *x*-axis, shifted 3 units right, then 1 unit up.

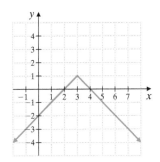

(12.1) *Find the domain and range of each relation. Use interval notation to write your answers.*

1. $\{x \mid x > 5\}$

2. $\{x \mid x < -0.2\}$

3. $\{x \mid -7 \geq x\}$

4. $\{x \mid -5 \leq x \leq -1\}$

5. $\{x \mid -3 > x \geq -7\}$

Graph each function.

6. $f(x) = \begin{cases} -3x & \text{if } x < 0 \\ x - 3 & \text{if } x \geq 0 \end{cases}$

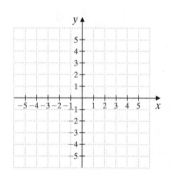

7. $g(x) = \begin{cases} -\dfrac{1}{5}x & \text{if } x \leq -1 \\ -4x + 2 & \text{if } x > -1 \end{cases}$

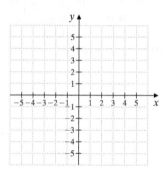

(12.2) *Find the domain and range of each relation. Then determine whether the relation is also a function.*

8. $\left\{ \left(-\dfrac{1}{2}, \dfrac{3}{4}\right), (6, 0.65), (0, -12), (25, 25) \right\}$

9. $\left\{ \left(\dfrac{3}{4}, -\dfrac{1}{2}\right), (0.65, 6), (-12, 0), (25, 25) \right\}$

10.

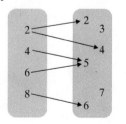

11.

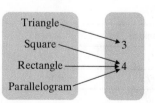

12.

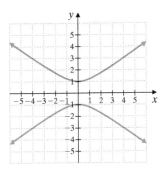

13.

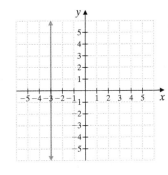

14.

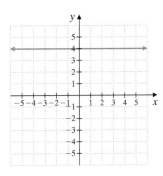

15.

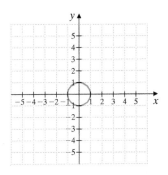

If $f(x) = x - 5$, $g(x) = -3x$, and $h(x) = 2x^2 - 6x + 1$, find each function value.

16. $f(2)$

17. $g(0)$

18. $g(-6)$

19. $h(-1)$

20. $h(1)$

21. $f(5)$

The function $J(x) = 2.54x$ may be used to calculate the weight of an object on Jupiter (J) given its weight on Earth (x).

22. If a person weighs 150 pounds on Earth, find the equivalent weight on Jupiter.

23. A 2000-pound probe on Earth weighs how many pounds on Jupiter?

Graph each linear function.

24. $f(x) = x + 2$

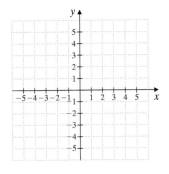

25. $f(x) = -\dfrac{1}{2}x + 3$

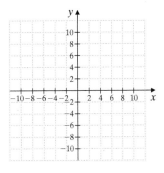

(12.3) *Find the domain and range of each relation.*

26.

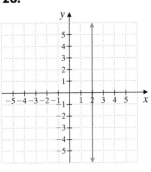

27.

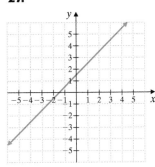

28.

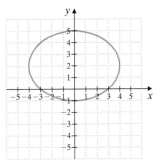

29.

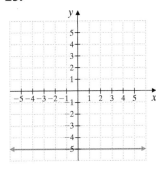

Graph each function.

30. $f(x) = \begin{cases} -3x & \text{if } x < 0 \\ x - 3 & \text{if } x \geq 0 \end{cases}$

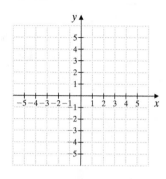

31. $g(x) = \begin{cases} -\dfrac{1}{5}x & \text{if } x \leq -1 \\ -4x + 2 & \text{if } x > -1 \end{cases}$

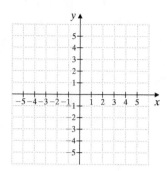

(12.4) *Graph each function.*

32. $y = \sqrt{x} - 4$

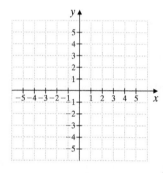

33. $f(x) = \sqrt{x - 4}$

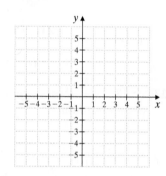

34. $g(x) = |x - 2| - 2$

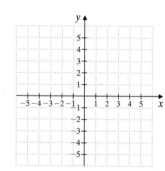

35. $h(x) = -(x + 3)^2 - 1$

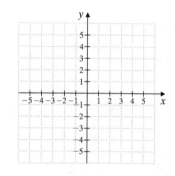

Answers to Selected Exercises

Chapter 12 Graphs and Functions

Section 12.1

Exercise Set 12.1 **1.** $(-\infty, -3)$ **3.** $[-7, \infty)$
5. $(-1, 5]$

Section 12.2

Vocabulary and Readiness Check **1.** relation **3.** domain **5.** vertical

Exercise Set 12.2 **1.** domain; $\{-1, 0, -2, 5\}$; range: $\{7, 6, 2\}$; function **3.** domain; $\{-2, 6, -7\}$; range: $\{4, -3, -8\}$; not a function **5.** domain: $\{1\}$; range: $\{1, 2, 3, 4\}$; not a function **7.** domain: $\left\{\frac{3}{2}, 0\right\}$; range: $\left\{\frac{1}{2}, -7, \frac{4}{5}\right\}$; not a function **9.** domain: $\{-3, 0, 3\}$; range: $\{-3, 0, 3\}$; function **11.** domain: $\{-1, 1, 2, 3\}$; range: $\{2, 1\}$; function **13.** domain: $\{1994, 1998, 2002, 2006, 2010\}$; range: $\{6, 9, 10\}$; function **15.** domain: $\{32°, 104°, 212°, 50°\}$; range: $\{0°, 40°, 10°, 100°\}$; function **17.** domain: $\{2, -1, 5, 100\}$; range: $\{0\}$; function **19.** function **21.** not a function **23.** yes **25.** no **27.** yes **29.** function **31.** not a function **33.** function **35.** not a function **37.** not a function **39.** not a function **41.** not a function **43.** not a function **45.** function **47.** 15 **49.** 38 **51.** 7 **53.** 3 **55. a.** 0 **b.** 1 **c.** -1 **57. a.** -5 **b.** -5 **c.** -5 **59.** $(1, -10)$ **61.** $(4, 56)$ **63.** -2 **65.** 0 **67.** $-4, 0$ **69.** 3 **71.** 25π sq cm **73.** 2744 cu in. **75.** 166.38 cm **77.** 163.2 mg **79. a.** 65.78; per capita consumption of beef was 65.78 lb in 2004 **b.** 63.8 lb

81. **83.** **85.** **87.** $(-\infty, 14]$ **89.** $\left[\frac{7}{2}, \infty\right)$ **91.** $\left(-\infty, -\frac{1}{4}\right)$ **93.** no; answers may vary

95. yes; answers may vary **97.** true **99.** true **101.** infinite number **103.** answers may vary **105. a.** 0 **b.** $a - 12$ **c.** $-x - 12$ **d.** $x + h - 12$

Section 12.3

Exercise Set 12.3 **1.** domain; $[0, \infty)$; range: $(-\infty, \infty)$ **3.** domain: $(-\infty, \infty)$; range: $[0, \infty)$ **5.** domain: $(-\infty, \infty)$; range: $(-\infty, -3] \cup [3, \infty)$ **7.** domain: $[1, 7]$; range: $[1, 7]$ **9.** domain: $\{-2\}$; range: $(-\infty, \infty)$ **11.** domain: $(-\infty, \infty)$; range: $(-\infty, 3]$ **13.** domain: $(-\infty, \infty)$; range: $(-\infty, 3]$ **15.** domain: $[2, \infty)$; range: $[3, \infty)$ **17.** **19.** **21.** 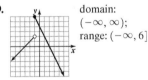 **23.**

25. domain: $(-\infty, \infty)$; range: $[0, \infty)$ **27.** domain: $(-\infty, \infty)$; range: $(-\infty, 5)$ **29.** domain: $(-\infty, \infty)$; range: $(-\infty, 6]$

31. domain: $(-\infty, 0] \cup [1, \infty)$; range: $\{-4, -2\}$ **33.** A **35.** D **37.** answers may vary **39.**

A29

Section 12.4

Vocabulary and Readiness Check   **1.** C   **3.** D

Exercise Set 12.4   **1.**   **3.**   **5.**   **7.**   **9.**   **11.**

13.   **15.**   **17.**   **19.**   **21.**   **23.**   **25.**

27.   **29.**   **31.**   **33.** $-15x^8$ **35.** $8y^7 + 8y^{11}$ **37.** domain: $[2, \infty)$; range: $[3, \infty)$
39. domain: $(-\infty, \infty)$; range: $(-\infty, 3]$ **41.** $[20, \infty)$ **43.** $(-\infty, \infty)$
45. $[-103, \infty)$

47.   domain: $(-\infty, \infty)$; range: $[0, \infty)$ **49.**   domain: $(-\infty, \infty)$; range: $(-\infty, 0] \cup (2, \infty)$

Chapter 12 Review   **6.** domain: $(-\infty, \infty)$; range: $(-\infty - 1] \cup [1, \infty)$; not a function   **7.** domain: $\{-3\}$; range: $(-\infty, \infty)$; not a function
8. domain: $(-\infty, \infty)$; range: $\{4\}$; function   **9.** domain: $[-1, 1]$; range: $[-1, 1]$; not a function
10. -3 **11.** 0   **12.** 18   **13.** 9   **14.** -3 **15.** 0   **16.** 381 lb   **17.** 5080 lb   **18.** 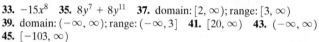   **19.**

20. domain: $\{2\}$; range: $(-\infty, \infty)$ **21.** domain: $(-\infty, \infty)$; range: $(-\infty, \infty)$ **22.** domain: $[-4, 4]$; range: $[-1, 5]$ **23.** domain: $(-\infty, \infty)$; range: $\{-5\}$
24.   **25.**   **26.** 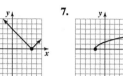 $(0, -4)$ **27.** $(4, 0)$ **28.** $(2, -2)$ **29.** $(-3, -1)$

Appendix A

A.1 LINES AND ANGLES

Objective Ⓐ Identifying Lines, Line Segments, Rays, and Angles

Let's begin with a review of two important concepts—space and plane.

Space extends in all directions indefinitely. Examples of objects in space are houses, grains of salt, bushes, your *Developmental Mathematics* textbook, and you.

A **plane** is a flat surface that extends indefinitely. Surfaces like a plane are a classroom floor or a blackboard or whiteboard.

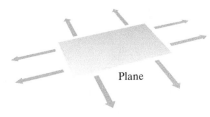

Plane

The most basic concept of geometry is the idea of a point in space. A **point** has no length, no width, and no height, but it does have location. We represent a point by a dot, and we usually label points with capital letters.

Point *P*

A **line** is a set of points extending indefinitely in two directions. A line has no width or height, but it does have length. We can name a line by any two of its points or by a single lowercase letter. A **line segment** is a piece of a line with two endpoints.

Line *AB*, $\overleftrightarrow{AB}$, or line *l**   Line segment *AB* or $\overline{AB}$

A **ray** is a part of a line with one endpoint. A ray extends indefinitely in one direction. An **angle** is made up of two rays that share the same endpoint. The common endpoint is called the **vertex.**

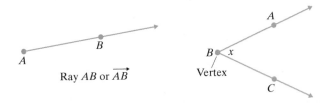

Ray *AB* or $\overrightarrow{AB}$ Vertex

*Although line *l* is also line *BA* or $\overleftrightarrow{BA}$, we will use only one order of points to name a line or line segment.

The angle in the figure on the preceding page can be named

$$\angle ABC \quad \angle CBA \quad \angle B \quad \text{or} \quad \angle x$$

The vertex is the middle point.

Rays BA and BC are **sides** of the angle.

Helpful Hint

Naming an Angle
When there is no confusion as to what angle is being named, you may use the vertex alone.

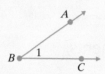

Name of $\angle B$ is all right.
There is no confusion. $\angle B$ means $\angle 1$.

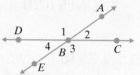

Name of $\angle B$ is *not* all right.
There is confusion. Does $\angle B$ mean $\angle 1, \angle 2, \angle 3,$ or $\angle 4$?

PRACTICE 1

Identify each figure as a line, a ray, a line segment, or an angle. Then name the figure using the given points.

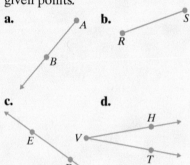

PRACTICE 2

Use the figure in Example 2 to list other ways to name $\angle z$.

Answers

1. a. ray; ray AB or $\overrightarrow{AB}$
  b. line segment; line segment RS or $\overline{RS}$
  c. line; line EF or $\overleftrightarrow{EF}$
  d. angle; $\angle TVH$ or $\angle HVT$ or $\angle V$
2. $\angle RTS, \angle STR$

Example 1 Identify each figure as a line, a ray, a line segment, or an angle. Then name the figure using the given points.

a.

b.

c.
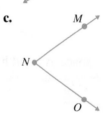

d.

Solution:

Figure (a) extends indefinitely in two directions. It is line CD or $\overleftrightarrow{CD}$.
Figure (b) has two endpoints. It is line segment EF or $\overline{EF}$.
Figure (c) has two rays with a common endpoint. It is $\angle MNO, \angle ONM,$ or $\angle N$.
Figure (d) is part of a line with one endpoint. It is ray PT or $\overrightarrow{PT}$.

● **Work Practice 1**

Example 2 List other ways to name $\angle y$.

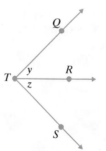

Solution: Two other ways to name $\angle y$ are $\angle QTR$ and $\angle RTQ$. We may *not* use the vertex alone to name this angle because three different angles have T as their vertex.

● **Work Practice 2**

Objective B Classifying Angles as Acute, Right, Obtuse, or Straight

An angle can be measured in **degrees.** The symbol for degrees is a small, raised circle, °. There are 360° in a full revolution, or a full circle.

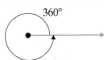

$\frac{1}{2}$ of a revolution measures $\frac{1}{2}(360°) = 180°$. An angle that measures 180° is called a **straight angle.**

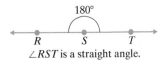

∠*RST* is a straight angle.

$\frac{1}{4}$ of a revolution measures $\frac{1}{4}(360°) = 90°$. An angle that measures 90° is called a **right angle.** The symbol ⌐ is used to denote a right angle.

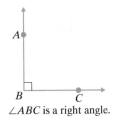

∠*ABC* is a right angle.

An angle whose measure is between 0° and 90° is called an **acute angle.**

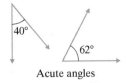

Acute angles

An angle whose measure is between 90° and 180° is called an **obtuse angle.**

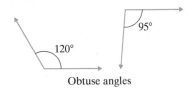

Obtuse angles

Example 3 Classify each angle as acute, right, obtuse, or straight.

a.

b.

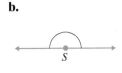

c.

d.

Continued on next page

PRACTICE 3

Classify each angle as acute, right, obtuse, or straight.

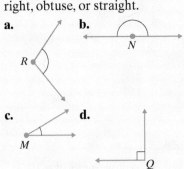

Answers

3. **a.** obtuse **b.** straight **c.** acute **d.** right

Solution:

a. $\angle R$ is a right angle, denoted by ∟. It measures 90°.

b. $\angle S$ is a straight angle. It measures 180°.

c. $\angle T$ is an acute angle. It measures between 0° and 90°.

d. $\angle Q$ is an obtuse angle. It measures between 90° and 180°.

● Work Practice 3

Let's look at $\angle B$ below, whose measure is 62°.

There is a shorthand notation for writing the measure of this angle. To write "The measure of $\angle B$ is 62°," we can write,

$$m\angle B = 62°.$$

By the way, note that $\angle B$ is an acute angle because $m\angle B$ is between 0° and 90°.

Objective ○ Identifying Complementary and Supplementary Angles

Two angles that have a sum of 90° are called **complementary angles.** We say that each angle is the **complement** of the other.

$\angle R$ and $\angle S$ are complementary angles because

$$m\angle R + m\angle S = 60° + 30° = 90°$$

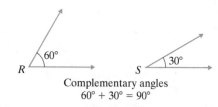

Complementary angles
60° + 30° = 90°

Two angles that have a sum of 180° are called **supplementary angles.** We say that each angle is the **supplement** of the other.

$\angle M$ and $\angle N$ are supplementary angles because

$$m\angle M + m\angle N = 125° + 55° = 180°$$

Supplementary angles
125° + 55° = 180°

PRACTICE 4

Find the complement of a 29° angle.

Example 4 Find the complement of a 48° angle.

Solution: Two angles that have a sum of 90° are complementary. This means that the complement of an angle that measures 48° is an angle that measures $90° - 48° = 42°$.

● Work Practice 4

Answer

4. 61°

Example 5 Find the supplement of a 107° angle.

Solution: Two angles that have a sum of 180° are supplementary. This means that the supplement of an angle that measures 107° is an angle that measures 180° − 107° = 73°.

● **Work Practice 5**

✓**Concept Check** True or false? The supplement of a 48° angle is 42°. Explain.

Objective ⓓ Finding Measures of Angles

Measures of angles can be added or subtracted to find measures of related angles.

Example 6 Find the measure of ∠x. Then classify ∠x as an acute, obtuse, or right angle.

Solution:
$$m\angle x = m\angle QTS - m\angle RTS$$
$$= 87° - 52°$$
$$= 35°$$

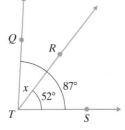

Thus, the measure of ∠x (m∠x) is 35°.
Since ∠x measures between 0° and 90°, it is an acute angle.

● **Work Practice 6**

Two lines in a plane can be either parallel or intersecting. **Parallel lines** never meet. **Intersecting lines** meet at a point. The symbol ‖ is used to indicate "is parallel to." For example, in the figure, p‖q.

Parallel lines   Intersecting lines

Some intersecting lines are perpendicular. Two lines are **perpendicular** if they form right angles when they intersect. The symbol ⊥ is used to denote "is perpendicular to." For example, in the figure below, m ⊥ n.

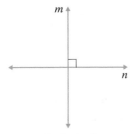

Perpendicular lines

When two lines intersect, four angles are formed. Two angles that are opposite each other are called **vertical angles.** Vertical angles have the same measure.

Two angles that share a common side are called **adjacent angles.** Adjacent angles formed by intersecting lines are supplementary. That is, the sum of their measures is 180°.

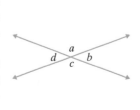

Vertical angles:
∠a and ∠c
∠d and ∠b

Adjacent angles:
∠a and ∠b
∠b and ∠c
∠c and ∠d
∠d and ∠a

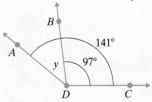
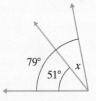

Here are a few real-life examples of the lines we just discussed.

Parallel lines

Vertical angles

Perpendicular lines

PRACTICE 7

Find the measures of $\angle a$, $\angle b$, and $\angle c$.

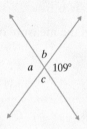

Example 7 Find the measures of $\angle x$, $\angle y$, and $\angle z$ if the measure of $\angle t$ is 42°.

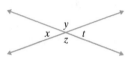

Solution: Since $\angle t$ and $\angle x$ are vertical angles, they have the same measure, so $\angle x$ measures 42°.

Since $\angle t$ and $\angle y$ are adjacent angles, their measures have a sum of 180°. So $\angle y$ measures $180° - 42° = 138°$.

Since $\angle y$ and $\angle z$ are vertical angles, they have the same measure. So $\angle z$ measures 138°.

● **Work Practice 7**

A line that intersects two or more lines at different points is called a **transversal.** Line l is a transversal that intersects lines m and n. The eight angles formed have special names. Some of these names are:

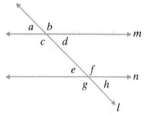

Corresponding angles: $\angle a$ and $\angle e$, $\angle c$ and $\angle g$, $\angle b$ and $\angle f$, $\angle d$ and $\angle h$

Alternate interior angles: $\angle c$ and $\angle f$, $\angle d$ and $\angle e$

When two lines cut by a transversal are *parallel,* the following statement is true:

PRACTICE 8

Given that $m \parallel n$ and that the measure of $\angle w = 45°$, find the measures of all the angles shown.

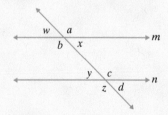

Parallel Lines Cut by a Transversal

If two parallel lines are cut by a transversal, then the measures of **corresponding angles are equal** and the measures of the **alternate interior angles are equal.**

Example 8 Given that $m \parallel n$ and that the measure of $\angle w$ is 100°, find the measures of $\angle x$, $\angle y$, and $\angle z$.

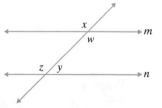

Solution:

$m\angle x = 100°$ $\angle x$ and $\angle w$ are vertical angles.

$m\angle z = 100°$ $\angle x$ and $\angle z$ are corresponding angles.

$m\angle y = 180° - 100° = 80°$ $\angle z$ and $\angle y$ are supplementary angles.

● **Work Practice 8**

Answers

7. $m\angle a = 109°$; $m\angle b = 71°$; $m\angle c = 71°$

8. $m\angle x = 45°$; $m\angle y = 45°$; $m\angle z = 135°$; $m\angle a = 135°$; $m\angle b = 135°$; $m\angle c = 135°$; $m\angle d = 45°$

Vocabulary and Readiness Check

Use the choices below to fill in each blank.

acute	straight	degrees	adjacent	parallel	intersecting
obtuse	space	plane	point	vertical	vertex
right	angle	ray	line	perpendicular	transversal

1. A(n) _____ is a flat surface that extends indefinitely.
2. A(n) _____ has no length, no width, and no height.
3. _____ extends in all directions indefinitely.
4. A(n) _____ is a set of points extending indefinitely in two directions.
5. A(n) _____ is part of a line with one endpoint.
6. A(n) _____ is made up of two rays that share a common endpoint. The common endpoint is called the _____.
7. A(n) _____ angle measures 180°.
8. A(n) _____ angle measures 90°.
9. A(n) _____ angle measures between 0° and 90°.
10. A(n) _____ angle measures between 90° and 180°.
11. _____ lines never meet and _____ lines meet at a point.
12. Two intersecting lines are _____ if they form right angles when they intersect.
13. An angle can be measured in _____.
14. A line that intersects two or more lines at different points is called a(n) _____.
15. When two lines intersect, four angles are formed, called _____ angles.
16. Two angles that share a common side are called _____ angles.

A.1 Exercise Set

FOR EXTRA HELP

MyMathLab   Math XL   PRACTICE   WATCH   DOWNLOAD   READ   REVIEW

Objective Ⓐ *Identify each figure as a line, a ray, a line segment, or an angle. Then name the figure using the given points. See Examples 1 and 2.*

1.
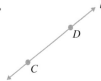

2.

3.

4.

5.
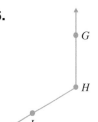

6.

7.

8.

965

List two other ways to name each angle. See Example 2.

9. ∠x

10. ∠w

11. ∠z

12. ∠y

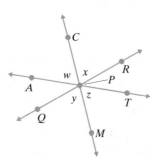

Objective Ⓑ *Classify each angle as acute, right, obtuse, or straight. See Example 3.*

13.   S

14.   H

📱**15.**   R

16.   T

📱**17.**   Q

18.   M

19.   P

20.   N

Objective Ⓒ *Find each complementary or supplementary angle as indicated. See Examples 4 and 5.*

📱**21.** Find the complement of a 23° angle.

22. Find the complement of a 77° angle.

📱**23.** Find the supplement of a 17° angle.

24. Find the supplement of a 77° angle.

25. Find the complement of a 58° angle.

26. Find the complement of a 22° angle.

27. Find the supplement of a 150° angle.

28. Find the supplement of a 130° angle.

29. Identify the pairs of complementary angles.

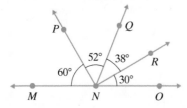

30. Identify the pairs of complementary angles.

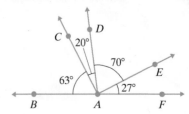

31. Identify the pairs of supplementary angles.

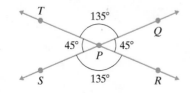

32. Identify the pairs of supplementary angles.

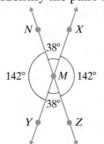

Objective **D** *Find the measure of ∠x in each figure. See Example 6.*

33.
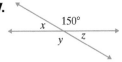

34.
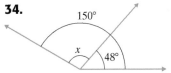

35.
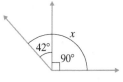

36.

Find the measures of angles x, y, and z in each figure. See Examples 7 and 8.

37.

38.
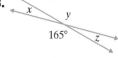

39.

40.

41. *m ∥ n*
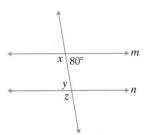

42. *m ∥ n*
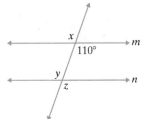

43. *m ∥ n*
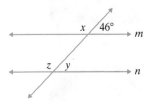

44. *m ∥ n*
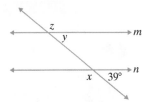

Objectives **A** **D** Mixed Practice *Find two other ways of naming each angle. See Example 2.*

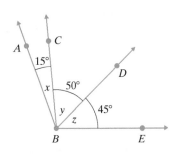

45. ∠x

46. ∠y

47. ∠z

48. ∠ABE (just name one other way)

Find the measure of each angle in the figure above. See Example 6.

49. ∠ABC

50. ∠EBD

51. ∠CBD

52. ∠CBA

53. ∠DBA

54. ∠EBC

55. ∠CBE

56. ∠ABE

Review

Perform each indicated operation. See Sections 2.4, 2.5, 2.8, and 2.9.

57. $\dfrac{7}{8} + \dfrac{1}{4}$

58. $\dfrac{7}{8} - \dfrac{1}{4}$

59. $\dfrac{7}{8} \cdot \dfrac{1}{4}$

60. $\dfrac{7}{8} \div \dfrac{1}{4}$

61. $3\dfrac{1}{3} - 2\dfrac{1}{2}$

62. $3\dfrac{1}{3} + 2\dfrac{1}{2}$

63. $3\dfrac{1}{3} \div 2\dfrac{1}{2}$

64. $3\dfrac{1}{3} \cdot 2\dfrac{1}{2}$

Concept Extensions

65. The angle between the two walls of the Vietnam Veterans Memorial in Washington, D.C., is 125.2°. Find the supplement of this angle. (*Source:* National Park Service)

66. The faces of Khafre's Pyramid at Giza, Egypt, are inclined at an angle of 53.13°. Find the complement of this angle. (*Source:* PBS *NOVA* Online)

Answer true or false for Exercises 67 through 70. See the Concept Check in this section. If false, explain why.

67. The complement of a 100° angle is an 80° angle.

68. It is possible to find the complement of a 120° angle.

69. It is possible to find the supplement of a 120° angle.

70. The supplement of a 5° angle is a 175° angle.

71. If lines *m* and *n* are parallel, find the measures of angles *a* through *e*.

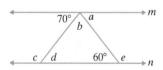

72. Below is a rectangle. List which segments, if extended, would be parallel lines.

73. Can two supplementary angles both be acute? Explain why or why not.

74. In your own words, describe how to find the complement and the supplement of a given angle.

75. Find two complementary angles with the same measure.

76. Is the figure below possible? Why or why not?

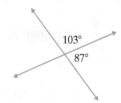

A.2 PLANE FIGURES AND SOLIDS

Objectives

A Identify Plane Figures.

B Identify Solids.

In order to prepare for the sections ahead in this chapter, we first review plane figures and solids.

Objective **A** Identifying Plane Figures

Recall from Section A.1 that a **plane** is a flat surface that extends indefinitely.

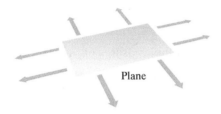

Plane

A **plane figure** is a figure that lies on a plane. Plane figures, like planes, have length and width but no thickness or depth.

A **polygon** is a closed plane figure that basically consists of three or more line segments that meet at their endpoints.

A **regular polygon** is one whose sides are all the same length and whose angles are the same measure.

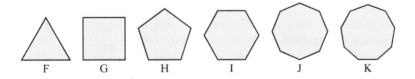

A polygon is named according to the number of its sides.

Polygons		
Number of Sides	**Name**	**Figure Examples**
3	Triangle	A, F
4	Quadrilateral	B, E, G
5	Pentagon	H
6	Hexagon	I
7	Heptagon	C
8	Octagon	J
9	Nonagon	K
10	Decagon	D

Some triangles and quadrilaterals are given special names, so let's study these polygons further. We begin with triangles.

970

The sum of the measures of the angles of a triangle is 180°.

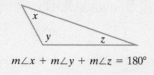

$$m\angle x + m\angle y + m\angle z = 180°$$

Copyright 2011 Pearson Education, Inc.

PRACTICE 1

Find the measure of $\angle x$.

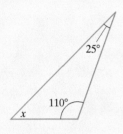

Example 1 Find the measure of $\angle a$.

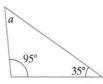

Solution: Since the sum of the measures of the three angles is 180°, we have

measure of $\angle a$, or $m\angle a = 180° - 95° - 35° = 50°$

To check, see that $95° + 35° + 50° = 180°$.

● Work Practice 1

We can classify triangles according to the lengths of their sides. (We will use tick marks to denote the sides and angles of a figure that are equal.)

Equilateral triangle
All three sides are the same length. Also, all three angles have the same measure.

Isosceles triangle
Two sides are the same length. Also, the angles opposite the equal sides have equal measure.

Scalene triangle
No sides are the same length. No angles have the same measure.

One other important type of triangle is a right triangle. A **right triangle** is a triangle with a right angle. The side opposite the right angle is called the **hypotenuse,** and the other two sides are called **legs.**

PRACTICE 2

Find the measure of $\angle y$.

Example 2 Find the measure of $\angle b$.

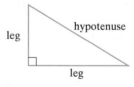

Solution: We know that the measure of the right angle, ∟, is 90°. Since the sum of the measures of the angles is 180°, we have

measure of $\angle b$, or $m\angle b = 180° - 90° - 30° = 60°$

● Work Practice 2

Answers

1. 45° **2.** 65°

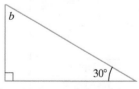

Helpful Hint

From the previous example, can you see that in a right triangle, the sum of the other two acute angles is 90°? This is because

$$90° + 90° = 180°$$

↑	↑	↑
right angle's measure	sum of other two angles' measures	sum of angles' measures

Now we review some special quadrilaterals. A **parallelogram** is a special quadrilateral with opposite sides parallel and equal in length.

A **rectangle** is a special **parallelogram** that has four right angles.

A **square** is a special **rectangle** that has all four sides equal in length.

A **rhombus** is a special **parallelogram** that has all four sides equal in length.

A **trapezoid** is a quadrilateral with exactly one pair of opposite sides parallel.

parallel sides

✓**Concept Check** True or false? All quadrilaterals are parallelograms. Explain.

In addition to triangles, quadrilaterals, and other polygons, circles are also plane figures. A **circle** is a plane figure that consists of all points that are the same fixed distance from a point c. The point c is called the **center** of the circle. The **radius** of a circle is the distance from the center of the circle to any point on the circle. The **diameter** of a circle is the distance across the circle passing through the center. Notice that the diameter is twice the radius, and the radius is half the diameter.

radius

center

diameter

✓ **Concept Check Answer**
false

$$\boxed{\text{diameter}} = \boxed{2} \cdot \boxed{\text{radius}} \qquad \boxed{\text{radius}} = \boxed{\dfrac{\text{diameter}}{2}}$$

$$d = 2 \cdot r \qquad\qquad r = \dfrac{d}{2}$$

PRACTICE 3

Find the radius of the circle.

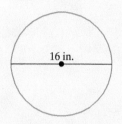

16 in.

Example 3 Find the diameter of the circle.

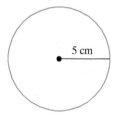

5 cm

Solution: The diameter is twice the radius.

$d = 2 \cdot r$

$d = 2 \cdot 5 \text{ cm} = 10 \text{ cm}$

The diameter is 10 centimeters.

● **Work Practice 3**

Objective Ⓑ Identifying Solid Figures

Recall from Section A.1 that space extends in all directions indefinitely.

A **solid** is a figure that lies in space. Solids have length, width, and height or depth.

A **rectangular solid** is a solid that consists of six sides, or faces, all of which are rectangles.

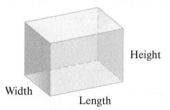

Height

Width

Length

A **cube** is a rectangular solid whose six sides are squares.

A **pyramid** is shown below. The pyramids we will study have square bases and heights that are perpendicular to their base.

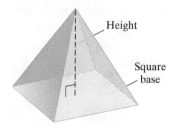

Height

Square base

Answer

3. 8 in.

A **sphere** consists of all points in space that are the same distance from a point *c*. The point *c* is called the **center** of the sphere. The **radius** of a sphere is the distance from the center to any point on the sphere. The **diameter** of a sphere is the distance across the sphere passing through the center.

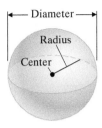

The radius and diameter of a sphere are related in the same way as the radius and diameter of a circle.

$$d = 2 \cdot r \quad \text{or} \quad r = \frac{d}{2}$$

Example 4 Find the radius of the sphere.

Solution: The radius is half the diameter.

$$r = \frac{d}{2}$$

$$r = \frac{36 \text{ feet}}{2} = 18 \text{ feet}$$

The radius is 18 feet.

Work Practice 4

The **cylinders** we will study have bases that are in the shape of circles and heights that are perpendicular to their base.

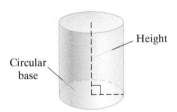

The **cones** we will study have bases that are circles and heights that are perpendicular to their base.

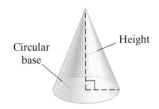

PRACTICE 4

Find the diameter of the sphere.

A.2 Exercise Set

Objective A *Identify each polygon. See the table at the beginning of this section.*

1.

2.

3.

4.

5.

6.

7.

8.

Classify each triangle as equilateral, isosceles, or scalene. Also identify any triangles that are also right triangles.

9.

10.

11.

12.

13.

14.

Find the measure of $\angle x$ in each figure. See Examples 1 and 2.

15.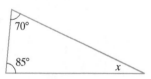
70°
85°
x

16.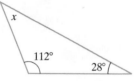
x
112°
28°

17.
95°
72°
x

18.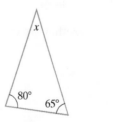
x
80°
65°

19.
x
50°

20.
x
20°

Fill in each blank.

21. Twice the radius of a circle is its _____.

22. A rectangle with all four sides equal is a(n) _____.

23. A parallelogram with four right angles is a(n) _____.

24. Half the diameter of a circle is its _____.

25. A quadrilateral with opposite sides parallel is a(n) _____.

26. A quadrilateral with exactly one pair of opposite sides parallel is a(n) _____.

27. The side opposite the right angle of a right triangle is called the _____.

28. A triangle with no equal sides is a(n) _____.

Find the unknown diameter or radius in each figure. See Example 3.

29.
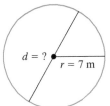
$d = ?$
$r = 7$ m

30.
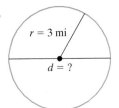
$r = 3$ mi
$d = ?$

31.
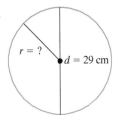
$r = ?$
$d = 29$ cm

32.
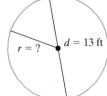
$r = ?$
$d = 13$ ft

33.
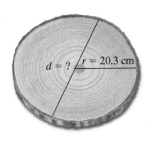
$d = ?$ $r = 20.3$ cm

34.
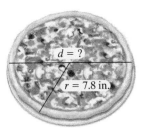
$d = ?$
$r = 7.8$ in.

35.
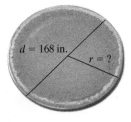
$d = 168$ in.
$r = ?$

Largest pumpkin pie (*Source:* Circleville, Ohio, Pumpkin Festival)

36.
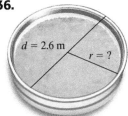
$d = 2.6$ m
$r = ?$

Largest cereal bowl (*Source: Guinness World Records*)

Objective B *Identify each solid.*

37.

38.

39.

40.

41.

42.

Identify the basic shape of each item.

43.

44.

45.

46.

47.

48.

49.

50.

Find each unknown radius or diameter. See Example 4.

51. The radius of a sphere is 7.4 inches. Find its diameter.

52. The radius of a sphere is 5.8 meters. Find its diameter.

53. Find the radius of the sphere.

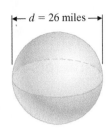

d = 26 miles

54. Find the radius of the sphere.

d = 78 cm

55. Saturn has a radius of approximately 36,184 miles. What is its diameter?

56. A sphere-shaped wasp nest found in Japan had a radius of approximately 15 inches. What was its diameter? (*Source: Guinness World Records*)

Review

Perform each indicated operation. See Sections 1.3, 1.6, 3.3, and 3.4.

57. $2(18) + 2(36)$

58. $4(87)$

59. $4(3.14)$

60. $2(7.8) + 2(9.6)$

Concept Extensions

Determine whether each statement is true or false. See the Concept Check in this section.

61. A square is also a rhombus.

62. A square is also a regular polygon.

63. A rectangle is also a parallelogram.

64. A trapezoid is also a parallelogram.

65. A pentagon is also a quadrilateral.

66. A rhombus is also a parallelogram.

67. Is an isosceles right triangle possible? If so, draw one.

68. In your own words, explain whether a square is also a rhombus.

69. The following demonstration is credited to the mathematician Pascal, who is said to have developed it as a young boy.

   Cut a triangle from a piece of paper. The length of the sides and the size of the angles are unimportant. Tear the points off the triangle as shown.

Place the points of the triangle together. Notice that a straight line is formed. What was Pascal trying to show?

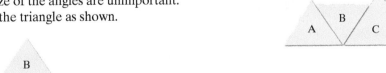

A.3 PERIMETER

Objective Ⓐ Using Formulas to Find Perimeters

Recall from Section 1.3 that the perimeter of a polygon is the distance around the polygon. This means that the perimeter of a polygon is the sum of the lengths of its sides.

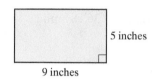

Example 1 Find the perimeter of the rectangle below.

5 inches

9 inches

Solution:

perimeter = 9 inches + 9 inches + 5 inches + 5 inches
         = 28 inches

● **Work Practice 1**

Notice that the perimeter of the rectangle in Example 1 can be written as $2 \cdot (9 \text{ inches}) + 2 \cdot (5 \text{ inches})$.

↑ length   ↑ width

In general, we can say that the perimeter of a rectangle is always

$2 \cdot \text{length} + 2 \cdot \text{width}$

As we have just seen, the perimeters of some special figures such as rectangles form patterns. These patterns are given as **formulas.** The formula for the perimeter of a rectangle is shown next:

> ### Perimeter of a Rectangle
>
> perimeter = $2 \cdot \text{length} + 2 \cdot \text{width}$
>
> In symbols, this can be written as
>
> $P = 2 \cdot l + 2 \cdot w$

length

width   width

length

PRACTICE 1

a. Find the perimeter of the rectangle.

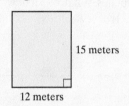

15 meters

12 meters

b. Find the perimeter of the rectangular lot shown below:

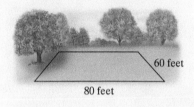

60 feet

80 feet

PRACTICE 2

Find the perimeter of a rectangle with a length of 22 centimeters and a width of 10 centimeters.

Example 2 Find the perimeter of a rectangle with a length of 11 inches and a width of 3 inches.

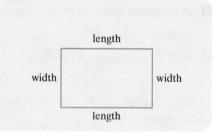

11 in.

3 in.

Solution: We use the formula for perimeter and replace the letters by their known lengths.

$P = 2 \cdot l + 2 \cdot w$
   $= 2 \cdot 11 \text{ in.} + 2 \cdot 3 \text{ in.}$ Replace *l* with 11 in. and *w* with 3 in.
   $= 22 \text{ in.} + 6 \text{ in.}$
   $= 28 \text{ in.}$

The perimeter is 28 inches.

● **Work Practice 2**

Recall that a square is a special rectangle with all four sides the same length. The formula for the perimeter of a square is shown next:

Perimeter of a Square

Perimeter = side + side + side + side
          = 4 · side

In symbols,

$P = 4 \cdot s$

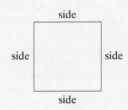

side

side   side

side

Example 3 Finding the Perimeter of a Field

How much fencing is needed to enclose a square field 50 yards on a side?

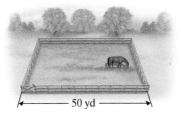

50 yd

Solution: To find the amount of fencing needed, we find the distance around, or perimeter. The formula for the perimeter of a square is $P = 4 \cdot s$. We use this formula and replace s by 50 yards.

$P = 4 \cdot s$

$= 4 \cdot 50$ yd

$= 200$ yd

The amount of fencing needed is 200 yards.

● Work Practice 3

The formula for the perimeter of a triangle with sides of lengths a, b, and c is given next:

Perimeter of a Triangle

Perimeter = side a + side b + side c

In symbols,

$P = a + b + c$

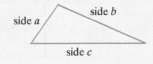

side a side b

side c

PRACTICE 3

Find the perimeter of a square tabletop if each side is 5 feet long.

5 feet

5 feet

Answer
3. 20 ft

PRACTICE 4

Find the perimeter of a triangle if the sides are 4 centimeters, 7 centimeters, and 8 centimeters in length.

Example 4 Find the perimeter of a triangle if the sides are 3 inches, 7 inches, and 6 inches.

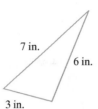

Solution: The formula for the perimeter is $P = a + b + c$, where a, b, and c are the lengths of the sides. Thus,

$$P = a + b + c$$
$$= 3 \text{ in.} + 7 \text{ in.} + 6 \text{ in.}$$
$$= 16 \text{ in.}$$

The perimeter of the triangle is 16 inches.

● Work Practice 4

Recall that to find the perimeter of other polygons, we find the sum of the lengths of their sides.

PRACTICE 5

Find the perimeter of the trapezoid shown.

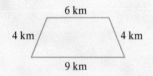

Example 5 Find the perimeter of the trapezoid shown below:

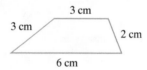

Solution: To find the perimeter, we find the sum of the lengths of its sides.

perimeter $= 3 \text{ cm} + 2 \text{ cm} + 6 \text{ cm} + 3 \text{ cm} = 14 \text{ cm}$

The perimeter is 14 centimeters.

● Work Practice 5

PRACTICE 6

Find the perimeter of the room shown.

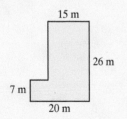

Example 6 Finding the Perimeter of a Room

Find the perimeter of the room shown below:

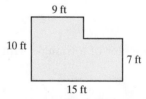

Solution: To find the perimeter of the room, we first need to find the lengths of all sides of the room.

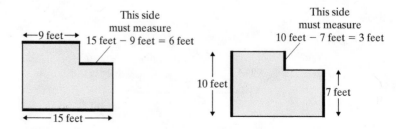

Answers
4. 19 cm 5. 23 km 6. 92 m

Now that we know the measures of all sides of the room, we can add the measures to find the perimeter.

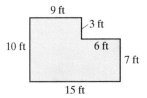

9 ft
3 ft
10 ft
6 ft
7 ft
15 ft

perimeter = 10 ft + 9 ft + 3 ft + 6 ft + 7 ft + 15 ft

= 50 ft

The perimeter of the room is 50 feet.

● **Work Practice 6**

Example 7 Calculating the Cost of Wallpaper Border

A rectangular room measures 10 feet by 12 feet. Find the cost to hang a wallpaper border on the walls close to the ceiling if the cost of the wallpaper border is $1.09 per foot.

Solution: First we find the perimeter of the room.

$P = 2 \cdot l + 2 \cdot w$

$= 2 \cdot 12 \text{ ft} + 2 \cdot 10 \text{ ft}$ Replace *l* with 12 feet and *w* with 10 feet.

$= 24 \text{ ft} + 20 \text{ ft}$

$= 44 \text{ ft}$

The cost of the wallpaper is

cost = $1.09 · 44 ft = 47.96

The cost of the wallpaper is $47.96.

● **Work Practice 7**

PRACTICE 7

A rectangular lot measures 60 feet by 120 feet. Find the cost to install fencing around the lot if the cost of fencing is $1.90 per foot.

Objective ⓑ Using Formulas to Find Circumferences

Recall from Section 3.4 that the distance around a circle is called the **circumference.** This distance depends on the radius or the diameter of the circle.

The formulas for circumference are shown next:

Circumference of a Circle

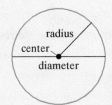

radius
center
diameter

Circumference = 2 · π · radius or Circumference = π · diameter

In symbols,

$C = 2 \cdot \pi \cdot r$ or $C = \pi \cdot d,$

where $\pi \approx 3.14$ or $\pi \approx \dfrac{22}{7}$.

Answer

7. $684

To better understand circumference and π(pi), try the following experiment. Take any can and measure its circumference and its diameter.

The can in the figure above has a circumference of 23.5 centimeters and a diameter of 7.5 centimeters. Now divide the circumference by the diameter.

$$\frac{\text{circumference}}{\text{diameter}} = \frac{23.5 \text{ cm}}{7.5 \text{ cm}} \approx 3.13$$

Try this with other sizes of cylinders and circles—you should always get a number close to 3.1. The exact ratio of circumference to diameter is π. (Recall that $\pi \approx 3.14$ or $\approx \frac{22}{7}$.)

PRACTICE 8

a. An irrigation device waters a circular region with a diameter of 20 yards. Find the exact circumference of the watered region, then use $\pi \approx 3.14$ to give an approximation.

20 yd

b. A manufacturer of clocks is designing a new model. To help the designer calculate the cost of materials to make the new clock, calculate the circumference of a clock with a face diameter of 12 inches. Give an exact circumference; then use $\pi \approx 3.14$ to approximate.

Example 8 Finding Circumference of Spa

Mary Catherine Dooley plans to install a border of new tiling around the circumference of her circular spa. If her spa has a diameter of 14 feet, find its exact circumference. Then use the approximation 3.14 for π to approximate the circumference.

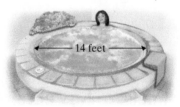

14 feet

Solution: Because we are given the diameter, we use the formula $C = \pi \cdot d$.

$$C = \pi \cdot d$$
$$= \pi \cdot 14 \text{ ft} \quad \text{Replace } d \text{ with 14 feet.}$$
$$= 14\pi \text{ ft}$$

The circumference of the spa is *exactly* 14π feet. By replacing π with the *approximation* 3.14, we find that the circumference is *approximately* 14 feet $\cdot$ 3.14 = 43.96 feet.

● **Work Practice 8**

Answers

8. a. exactly 20π yd ≈ 62.8 yd
b. exactly 12π in. ≈ 37.68 in.

✓ **Concept Check Answer**

a square with side length 5 in.

✓**Concept Check** The distance around which figure is greater: a square with side length 5 inches or a circle with radius 3 inches?

Vocabulary and Readiness Check

Use the choices below to fill in each blank.

circumference   radius π $\frac{22}{7}$

diameter   perimeter   3.14

1. The _____ of a polygon is the sum of the lengths of its sides.

2. The distance around a circle is called the_____.

3. The exact ratio of circumference to diameter is_____.

4. The diameter of a circle is double its _____.

5. Both _____ and _____ are approximations for π.

6. The radius of a circle is half its _____.

A.3 Exercise Set

FOR EXTRA HELP

MyMathLab   Powered by CourseCompass and MathXL   Math XL   PRACTICE   WATCH   DOWNLOAD   READ   REVIEW

Objective Ⓐ *Find the perimeter of each figure. See Examples 1 through 6.*

1.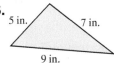
15 ft Rectangle 17 ft

2.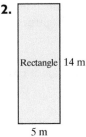
Rectangle 14 m 5 m

3.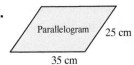
Parallelogram 25 cm 35 cm

4.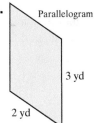
Parallelogram 3 yd 2 yd

5.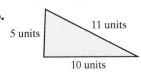
5 in. 7 in. 9 in.

6.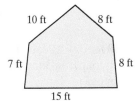
11 units 5 units 10 units

7.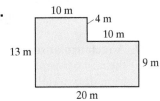
10 ft 8 ft 7 ft 8 ft 15 ft

8.
10 m 4 m 10 m 13 m 9 m 20 m

Find the perimeter of each regular polygon. (The sides of a regular polygon have the same length.)

9.
14 inches

10.
50 m

11.
31 cm

12.
15 yd

Solve. See Examples 1 through 7.

13. A polygon has sides of length 5 feet, 3 feet, 2 feet, 7 feet, and 4 feet. Find its perimeter.

14. A triangle has sides of length 8 inches, 12 inches, and 10 inches. Find its perimeter.

15. A line-marking machine lays down lime powder to mark both foul lines on a baseball field. If each foul line for this field measures 312 feet, how many feet of lime powder will be deposited?

16. A baseball diamond has 4 sides, with each side length 90 feet. If a baseball player hits a home run, how far does the player run (home plate, around the bases, then back to home plate)?

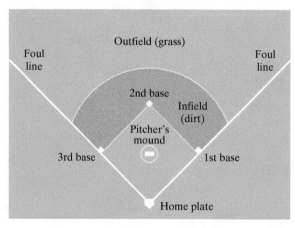

17. If a football field is 53 yards wide and 120 yards long, what is the perimeter?

18. A stop sign has eight equal sides of length 12 inches. Find its perimeter.

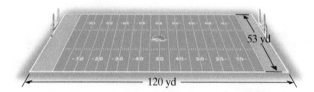

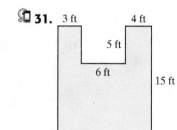

19. A metal strip is being installed around a workbench that is 8 feet long and 3 feet wide. Find how much stripping is needed for this project.

20. Find how much fencing is needed to enclose a rectangular garden 70 feet by 21 feet.

21. If the stripping in Exercise 19 costs $2.50 per foot, find the total cost of the stripping.

22. If the fencing in Exercise 20 costs $2 per foot, find the total cost of the fencing.

23. A regular octagon has a side length of 9 inches. Find its perimeter.

24. A regular pentagon has a side length of 14 meters. Find its perimeter.

25. Find the perimeter of the top of a square compact disc case if the length of one side is 7 inches.

26. Find the perimeter of a square ceramic tile with a side of length 3 inches.

27. A rectangular room measures 10 feet by 11 feet. Find the cost of installing a strip of wallpaper around the room if the wallpaper costs $0.86 per foot.

28. A rectangular house measures 85 feet by 70 feet. Find the cost of installing gutters around the house if the cost is $2.36 per foot.

Find the perimeter of each figure. See Example 6.

29.

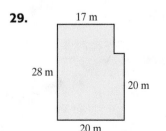

30.

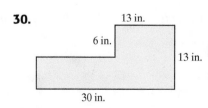

31.

32.

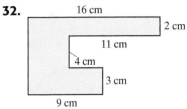

16 cm
2 cm
11 cm
4 cm
3 cm
9 cm

33.

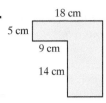

18 cm
5 cm
9 cm
14 cm

34.

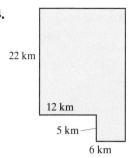

22 km
12 km
5 km
6 km

Objective **B** *Find the circumference of each circle. Give the exact circumference and then an approximation. Use π ≈ 3.14. See Example 8.*

35.

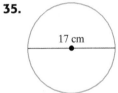

17 cm

36.

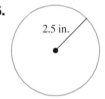

2.5 in.

37.

8 mi

38.

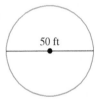

50 ft

39.

26 m

40.

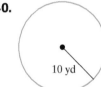

10 yd

41. Wyley Robinson just bought a trampoline for his children to use. The trampoline has a diameter of 15 feet. If Wyley wishes to buy netting to go around the outside of the trampoline, how many feet of netting does he need?

42. The largest round barn in the world is located at the Marshfield Fairgrounds in Wisconsin. The barn has a diameter of 150 ft. What is the circumference of the barn? (*Source: The Milwaukee Journal Sentinel*)

43. Meteor Crater, near Winslow, Arizona, is 4000 feet in diameter. Approximate the distance around the crater. Use 3.14 for π. (*Source: The Handy Science Answer Book*)

44. The largest pearl, the *Pearl of Lao-tze*, has a diameter of $5\frac{1}{2}$ inches. Approximate the distance around the pearl. Use $\frac{22}{7}$ for π. (*Source: The Guinness Book of World Records*)

Objectives Ⓐ Ⓑ **Mixed Practice** *Find the distance around each figure. For circles, give the exact circumference and then an approximation. Use* $\pi \approx 3.14$. *See Examples 1 through 8.*

45.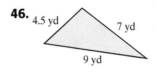
9 mi
4.7 mi
6 mi
11 mi

46.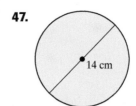
4.5 yd
7 yd
9 yd

47.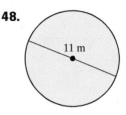
14 cm

48.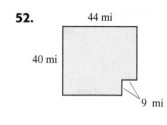
11 m

49.
Regular Pentagon
8 mm

50.
Regular Parallelogram
19 km

51.
7 ft
8 ft
22 ft
20 ft

52.
44 mi
40 mi
9 mi

Review

Simplify. See Section 1.9.

53. $5 + 6 \cdot 3$

54. $25 - 3 \cdot 7$

55. $(20 - 16) \div 4$

56. $6 \cdot (8 + 2)$

57. $72 \div (2 \cdot 6)$

58. $(72 \div 2) \cdot 6$

59. $(18 + 8) - (12 + 4)$

60. $4^1 \cdot (2^3 - 8)$

Concept Extensions

There are a number of factors that determine the dimensions of a rectangular soccer field. Use the table below to answer Exercises 61 and 62.

Soccer Field Width and Length		
Age	Width Min–Max	Length Min–Max
Under 6/7:	15–20 yards	25–30 yards
Under 8:	20–25 yards	30–40 yards
Under 9:	30–35 yards	40–50 yards
Under 10:	40–50 yards	60–70 yards
Under 11:	40–50 yards	70–80 yards
Under 12:	40–55 yards	100–105 yards
Under 13:	50–60 yards	100–110 yards
International:	70–80 yards	110–120 yards

61. a. Find the minimum length and width of a soccer field for 8-year-old children. (Carefully consider the age.)

   b. Find the perimeter of this field.

62. a. Find the maximum length and width of a soccer field for 12-year-old children.

   b. Find the perimeter of this field.

Solve. See the Concept Check in this section. Choose the figure that has the greater distance around.

63. a. A square with side length 3 inches

   b. A circle with diameter 4 inches

64. a. A circle with diameter 7 inches

   b. A square with side length 7 inches

65. a. Find the circumference of each circle. Approximate the circumference by using 3.14 for π.

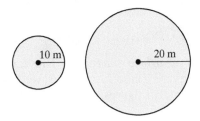

b. If the radius of a circle is doubled, is its corresponding circumference doubled?

66. a. Find the circumference of each circle. Approximate the circumference by using 3.14 for π.

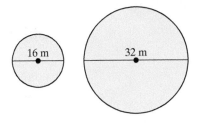

b. If the diameter of a circle is doubled, is its corresponding circumference doubled?

67. In your own words, explain how to find the perimeter of any polygon.

68. In your own words, explain how perimeter and circumference are the same and how they are different.

Find the perimeter. Round your results to the nearest tenth.

69.

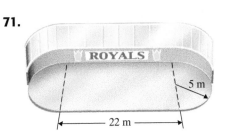

6 meters

6 meters

70.

6 meters

6 meters

71.

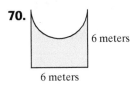

5 m

22 m

72.

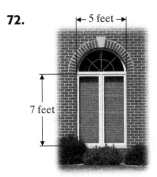

5 feet

7 feet

73. The perimeter of this rectangle is 31 feet. Find its width.

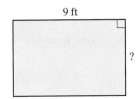

9 ft

?

74. The perimeter of this square is 18 inches. Find the length of a side.

A.4 AREA

Objective **A** Finding Areas of Geometric Figures

Recall that area measures the amount of surface of a region. Thus far, we know how to find the area of a rectangle and a square. These formulas, as well as formulas for finding the areas of other common geometric figures, are given next:

Area Formulas of Common Geometric Figures

Geometric Figure	Area Formula
RECTANGLE 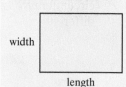	Area of a rectangle: **Area = length · width** $A = lw$
SQUARE 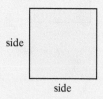	Area of a square: **Area = side · side** $A = s \cdot s = s^2$
TRIANGLE 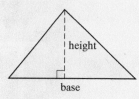	Area of a triangle: **Area = $\frac{1}{2}$ · base · height** $A = \frac{1}{2} \cdot b \cdot h$
PARALLELOGRAM 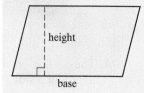	Area of a parallelogram: **Area = base · height** $A = b \cdot h$
TRAPEZOID 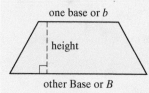	Area of a trapezoid: **Area = $\frac{1}{2}$ · (one base + other Base) · height** $A = \frac{1}{2} \cdot (b + B) \cdot h$

Use these formulas for the following examples.

Helpful Hint

Area is always measured in square units.

Example 1 Find the area of the triangle.

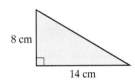

8 cm

14 cm

Solution: $A = \frac{1}{2} \cdot b \cdot h$

$= \frac{1}{2} \cdot 14 \text{ cm} \cdot 8 \text{ cm}$

$= \frac{\overset{1}{\cancel{2}} \cdot 7 \cdot 8}{\underset{1}{\cancel{2}}} \text{ sq cm}$

$= 56 \text{ square cm}$

The area is 56 square centimeters.

Helpful Hint You may see 56 sq cm, for example, written with the notation 56 cm². Both of these notations mean the same quantity.

● **Work Practice 1**

Example 2 Find the area of the parallelogram.

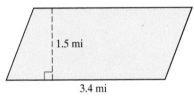

1.5 mi

3.4 mi

Solution:

$A = b \cdot h$

$= 3.4 \text{ miles} \cdot 1.5 \text{ miles}$

$= 5.1 \text{ square miles}$

The area is 5.1 square miles.

● **Work Practice 2**

Helpful Hint

When finding the area of figures, be sure all measurements are changed to the same unit before calculations are made.

Example 3 Find the area of the figure.

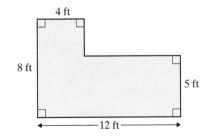

4 ft

8 ft

5 ft

12 ft

Continued on next page

PRACTICE 1

Find the area of the triangle.

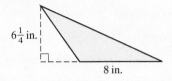

$6\frac{1}{4}$ in.

8 in.

PRACTICE 2

Find the area of the square.

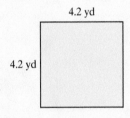

4.2 yd

4.2 yd

PRACTICE 3

Find the area of the figure.

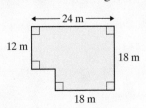

24 m

12 m

18 m

18 m

Answers

1. 25 sq in. **2.** 17.64 sq yd
3. 396 sq m

Solution: Split the figure into two rectangles. To find the area of the figure, we find the sum of the areas of the two rectangles.

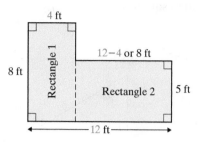

$$\text{Area of Rectangle 1} = l \cdot w$$
$$= 8 \text{ feet} \cdot 4 \text{ feet}$$
$$= 32 \text{ square feet}$$

Notice that the length of Rectangle 2 is 12 feet − 4 feet, or 8 feet.

$$\text{Area of Rectangle 2} = l \cdot w$$
$$= 8 \text{ feet} \cdot 5 \text{ feet}$$
$$= 40 \text{ square feet}$$

$$\text{Area of the Figure} = \text{Area of Rectangle 1} + \text{Area of Rectangle 2}$$
$$= 32 \text{ square feet} + 40 \text{ square feet}$$
$$= 72 \text{ square feet}$$

● **Work Practice 3**

Helpful Hint

The figure in Example 3 can also be split into two rectangles as shown:

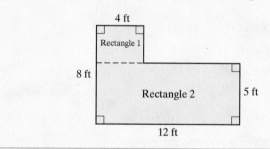

To better understand the formula for area of a circle, try the following. Cut a circle into many pieces as shown:

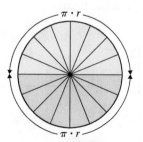

The circumference of a circle is $2 \cdot \pi \cdot r$. This means that the circumference of half a circle is half of $2 \cdot \pi \cdot r$, or $\pi \cdot r$.

Then unfold the two halves of the circle and place them together as shown:

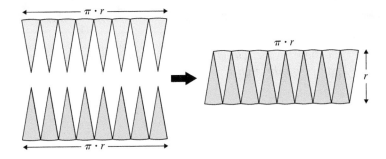

The figure on the right is almost a parallelogram with a base of $\pi \cdot r$ and a height of r. The area is

$$A = \boxed{\text{base}} \cdot \boxed{\text{height}}$$
$$ \quad \downarrow \qquad \downarrow$$
$$= (\pi \cdot r) \cdot \quad r$$
$$= \pi \cdot r^2$$

This is the formula for area of a circle.

Area Formula of a Circle

CIRCLE

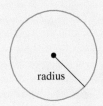
radius

Area of a circle:

Area $= \pi \cdot (\textbf{radius})^2$

$A = \pi \cdot r^2$

(A fraction approximation for π is $\dfrac{22}{7}$.)

(A decimal approximation for π is 3.14.)

Example 4 Find the area of a circle with a radius of 3 feet. Find the exact area and an approximation. Use 3.14 as an approximation for π.

Solution: We let $r = 3$ ft and use the formula.

$A = \pi \cdot r^2$
$ = \pi \cdot (3 \text{ ft})^2$
$ = \pi \cdot 9 \text{ square ft, or } 9 \cdot \pi \text{ square ft}$

To approximate this area, we substitute 3.14 for π.

$9 \cdot \pi \text{ square feet} \approx 9 \cdot 3.14 \text{ square feet}$
$\phantom{9 \cdot \pi \text{ square feet}} = 28.26 \text{ square feet}$

The *exact* area of the circle is 9π square feet, which is *approximately* 28.26 square feet.

● **Work Practice 4**

✓Concept Check Use diagrams to decide which figure would have a larger area: a circle of diameter 10 inches or a square 10 inches long on each side.

PRACTICE 4

Find the area of the given circle. Find the exact area and an approximation. Use 3.14 as an approximation for π.

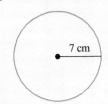
7 cm

Answer
4. 49π sq cm $\approx$ 153.86 sq cm

✓ Concept Check Answer
a square 10 in. long on each side

A.4 Exercise Set

FOR EXTRA HELP

MyMathLab

Math XL
PRACTICE

WATCH

DOWNLOAD

READ

REVIEW

Objective A *Find the area of the geometric figure. If the figure is a circle, give an exact area and then use the given* ***approximation*** *for π to approximate the area. See Examples 1 through 4.*

1.

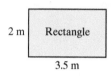

2 m | Rectangle | 3.5 m

2.

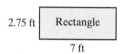

2.75 ft | Rectangle | 7 ft

3.

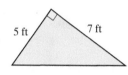

3 yd, $6\frac{1}{2}$ yd

4.

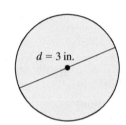

5 ft, $4\frac{1}{2}$ ft

5.

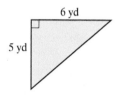

6 yd, 5 yd

6.

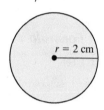

5 ft, 7 ft

7. Use 3.14 for π.

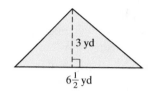

$d = 3$ in.

8. Use $\frac{22}{7}$ for π.

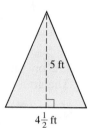

$r = 2$ cm

9.

Square | 4.2 ft

10.

Square | 2.6 m

11.

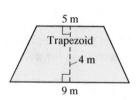

5 m, Trapezoid, 4 m, 9 m

12.

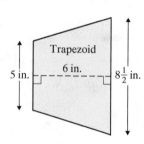

Trapezoid, 5 in., 6 in., $8\frac{1}{2}$ in.

13.

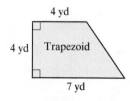

4 yd, 4 yd, Trapezoid, 7 yd

14.

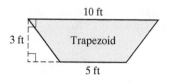

10 ft, 3 ft, Trapezoid, 5 ft

15.

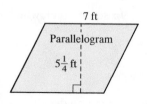

7 ft, Parallelogram, $5\frac{1}{4}$ ft

16.

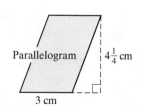

Parallelogram, $4\frac{1}{4}$ cm, 3 cm

17.

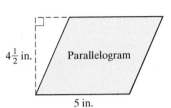
$4\frac{1}{2}$ in.   Parallelogram   5 in.

18.

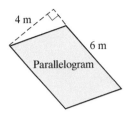
4 m   6 m   Parallelogram

19.

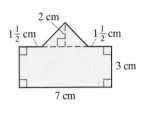
2 cm $1\frac{1}{2}$ cm $1\frac{1}{2}$ cm   3 cm   7 cm

20.

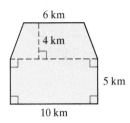
6 km   4 km   5 km   10 km

21.

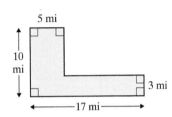
5 mi   10 mi   3 mi   17 mi

22.

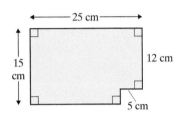
25 cm   15 cm   12 cm   5 cm

23.

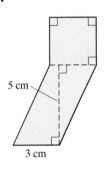
5 cm   3 cm

24.

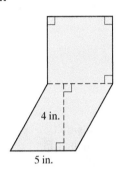
4 in.   5 in.

25. Use $\frac{22}{7}$ for π.

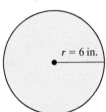
$r = 6$ in.

26. Use 3.14 for π.

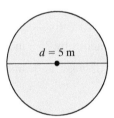
$d = 5$ m

Solve. See Examples 1 through 4.

27. A $10\frac{1}{2}$-foot by 16-foot concrete wall is to be built using concrete blocks. Find the area of the wall.

28. The floor of Terry's attic is 24 feet by 35 feet. Find how many square feet of insulation are needed to cover the attic floor.

29. The world's largest flag measures 505 feet by 225 feet. It's the U.S. "Super flag" owned by "Ski" Demski of Long Beach, California. Find its area. (*Source: Guinness World Records, 2005*)

30. The longest illuminated sign is in Ramat Gan, Israel, and measures 197 feet by 66 feet. Find its area. (*Source: The Guinness Book of Records*)

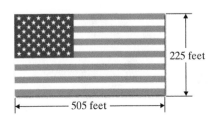
225 feet   505 feet

31. Paul Revere's Pizza in the USA will bake and deliver a pizza with a 4-foot diameter. This pizza is called the "Ultimate Party Pizza" and its current price is $99.99. Find the area of the top of the pizza. Give an exact answer and an approximate answer using 3.14 for π.

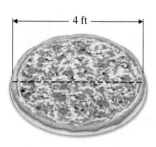

4 ft

32. The face of a watch has a diameter of 2 centimeters. What is its area? Give an exact answer and an approximate answer using 3.14 for π.

2 cm

33. One side of a concrete block measures 8 inches by 16 inches. Find the area of the side in square inches. Find the area in square feet (144 sq in. = 1 sq ft).

34. A standard *double* roll of wallpaper is $6\frac{5}{6}$ feet wide and 33 feet long. Find the area of the *double* roll.

35. A picture frame measures 20 inches by $25\frac{1}{2}$ inches. Find how many square inches of glass the frame requires.

36. A mat to go under a tablecloth is made to fit a round dining table with a 4-foot diameter. Approximate how many square feet of mat there are. Use 3.14 as an approximation for π.

37. A drapery panel measures 6 feet by 7 feet. Find how many square feet of material are needed for *four* panels.

38. A page in a book measures 27.5 centimeters by 20.5 centimeters. Find its area.

39. Find how many square feet of land are in the plot shown:

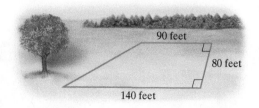

90 feet

80 feet

140 feet

40. For Gerald Gomez to determine how much grass seed he needs to buy, he must know the size of his yard. Use the drawing to determine how many square feet are in his yard.

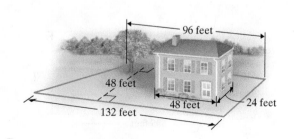

96 feet

48 feet

48 feet

24 feet

132 feet

41. The outlined part of the roof shown is in the shape of a trapezoid and needs to be shingled. The number of shingles to buy depends on the area.

   a. Use the dimensions given to find the area of the outlined part of the roof to the nearest whole square foot.

   b. Shingles are packaged in a unit called a "square." If a "square" covers 100 square feet, how many whole squares need to be purchased to shingle this part of the roof?

42. The entire side of the building shaded in the drawing is to be bricked. The number of bricks to buy depends on the area.

   a. Find the area.

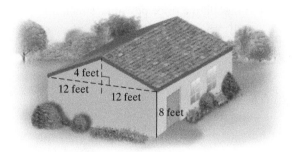

   b. If the side area of each brick (including mortar room) is $\frac{1}{6}$ square ft, find the number of bricks that are needed to brick the end of the building.

Review

Find the perimeter or circumference of each geometric figure. See Section A.3.

43. Give an exact circumference and an approximation. Use 3.14 for π.

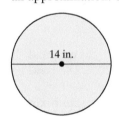

44.

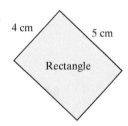

45.

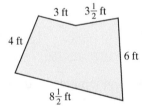

46.

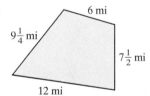

47.

48.

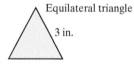

Concept Extensions

Given the following situations, tell whether you are more likely to be concerned with area or perimeter.

49. ordering fencing to fence a yard

50. ordering grass seed to plant in a yard

51. buying carpet to install in a room

52. buying gutters to install on a house

53. ordering paint to paint a wall

54. ordering baseboards to install in a room

55. buying a wallpaper border to go on the walls around a room

56. buying fertilizer for your yard

57. A pizza restaurant recently advertised two specials. The first special was a 12-inch diameter pizza for $10. The second special was two 8-inch diameter pizzas for $9. Determine the better buy. (*Hint:* First compare the areas of the pizzas in the two specials and then find a price per square inch for the pizzas in both specials.)

58. Find the approximate area of the state of Utah.

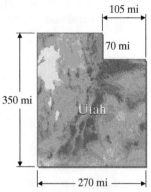

59. Find the area of a rectangle that measures 2 *feet* by 8 *inches*. Give the area in square feet and in square inches.

60. In your own words, explain why perimeter is measured in units and area is measured in square units. (*Hint:* See Section 1.6 for an introduction on the meaning of area.)

61. Find the area of the shaded region. Use the approximation 3.14 for π.

6 in.

62. Estimate the cost of a piece of carpet for a rectangular room 10 yards by 15 yards. The cost of the carpet is $6.50 per square yard.

63. The largest pumpkin pie was made for the 100th anniversary of the Circleville, Ohio, Pumpkin Festival in October 2008. The pie had a diameter of 168 inches. Find the exact area of the top of the pie, and an approximation. Use $\pi \approx 3.14$. (*Source:* Circleville, Ohio, Pumpkin Festival)

64. The largest cereal bowl in the world was made by Kellogg's South Africa in July 2007. The bowl had a 2.6-meter diameter. Calculate the exact area of the circular opening of the bowl and an approximation. Use $\pi \approx 3.14$. (*Source: Guinness Book of World Records*)

$d = 2.6$ m

Find the area of each figure. If needed, use $\pi \approx 3.14$ and round results to the nearest tenth.

65. Find the skating area.

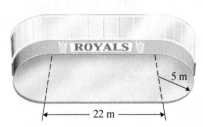

ROYALS

5 m

22 m

66.

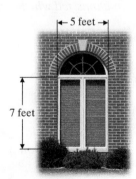

5 feet

7 feet

There are a number of factors that determine the dimensions of a rectangular soccer field. Use the table below to answer Exercises 67 and 68.

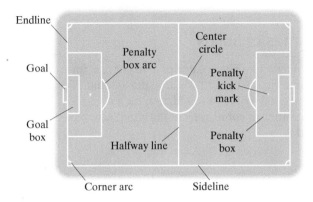

Soccer Field Width and Length		
Age	Width Min–Max	Length Min–Max
Under 6/7:	15–20 yards	25–30 yards
Under 8:	20–25 yards	30–40 yards
Under 9:	30–35 yards	40–50 yards
Under 10:	40–50 yards	60–70 yards
Under 11:	40–50 yards	70–80 yards
Under 12:	40–55 yards	100–105 yards
Under 13:	50–60 yards	100–110 yards
International:	70–80 yards	110–120 yards

67. a. Find the minimum length and width of a soccer field for 9-year-old children. (Carefully consider the age.)

b. Find the area of this field.

68. a. Find the maximum length and width of a soccer field for 11-year-old children.

b. Find the area of this field.

69. Do two rectangles with the same perimeter have the same area? To see, find the perimeter and the area of each rectangle.

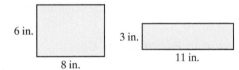

6 in.

8 in.

3 in.

11 in.

A.5 VOLUME

Objective **A** Finding Volumes of Solids

Volume is a measure of the space of a region. The volume of a box or can, for example, is the amount of space inside. Volume can be used to describe the amount of juice in a pitcher or the amount of concrete needed to pour a foundation for a house.

The volume of a solid is the number of **cubic units** in the solid. A cubic centimeter and a cubic inch are illustrated.

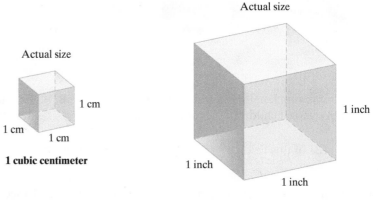

Actual size

1 cm
1 cm
1 cm

1 cubic centimeter

Actual size

1 inch
1 inch
1 inch

1 cubic inch

Formulas for finding the volumes of some common solids are given next:

Volume Formulas of Common Solids

Solid

RECTANGULAR SOLID

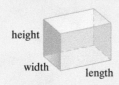

height
width
length

CUBE

side
side
side

SPHERE

radius

CIRCULAR CYLINDER

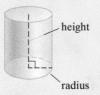

height
radius

Volume Formulas

Volume of a rectangular solid:
Volume = length · width · height
$$V = l \cdot w \cdot h$$

Volume of a cube:
Volume = side · side · side
$$V = s^3$$

Volume of a sphere:
$$\textbf{Volume} = \frac{4}{3} \cdot \pi \cdot (\textbf{radius})^3$$
$$V = \frac{4}{3} \cdot \pi \cdot r^3$$

Volume of a circular cylinder:
$$\textbf{Volume} = \pi \cdot (\textbf{radius})^2 \cdot \textbf{height}$$
$$V = \pi \cdot r^2 \cdot h$$

Volume Formulas of Common Solids (continued)

Solid

CONE

height

radius

SQUARE-BASED PYRAMID

height

side

Volume Formulas

Volume of a cone:

$$\textbf{Volume} = \frac{1}{3} \cdot \pi \cdot (\textbf{radius})^2 \cdot \textbf{height}$$

$$V = \frac{1}{3} \cdot \pi \cdot r^2 \cdot h$$

Volume of a square-based pyramid:

$$\textbf{Volume} = \frac{1}{3} \cdot (\textbf{side})^2 \cdot \textbf{height}$$

$$V = \frac{1}{3} \cdot s^2 \cdot h$$

> **Helpful Hint**
>
> Volume is always measured in cubic units.

Example 1 Find the volume of a rectangular box that is 12 inches long, 6 inches wide, and 3 inches high.

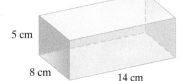
3 in.
FRAGILE
6 in.   12 in.

Solution:

$$V = l \cdot w \cdot h$$

$$V = 12 \text{ in.} \cdot 6 \text{ in.} \cdot 3 \text{ in.} = 216 \text{ cubic in.}$$

The volume of the rectangular box is 216 cubic inches.

● **Work Practice 1**

PRACTICE 1

Find the volume of a rectangular box that is 5 feet long, 2 feet wide, and 4 feet deep.

✓ **Concept Check** Juan is calculating the volume of the following rectangular solid. Find the error in his calculation.

Volume $= l + w + h$

$= 14 \text{ cm} + 8 \text{ cm} + 5 \text{ cm}$

$= 27 \text{ cu cm}$

5 cm

8 cm   14 cm

Example 2 Approximate the volume of a ball of radius 3 inches. Use the approximation $\frac{22}{7}$ for π. Give an exact answer and an approximate answer.

3 in.

PRACTICE 2

Approximate the volume of a ball of radius $\frac{1}{2}$ centimeter. Use $\frac{22}{7}$ for π. Give an exact answer and an approximate answer.

Answers

1. 40 cu ft   **2.** $\frac{1}{6}\pi$ cu cm $\approx \frac{11}{21}$ cu cm

✓ **Concept Check Answer**

Volume $= l \cdot w \cdot h$

$= 14 \text{ cm} \cdot 8 \text{ cm} \cdot 5 \text{ cm}$

$= 560 \text{ cu cm}$

Continued on next page

Solution:

$$V = \frac{4}{3} \cdot \pi \cdot r^3$$

$$= \frac{4}{3} \cdot \pi \cdot (3 \text{ in.})^3$$

$$= \frac{4}{3} \cdot \pi \cdot 27 \text{ cu in.}$$

$$= \frac{4 \cdot \pi \cdot \overset{1}{\cancel{3}} \cdot 9}{\underset{1}{\cancel{3}}} \text{ cu in.}$$

$$= 36\pi \text{ cu in.}$$

This is the exact volume. To approximate the volume, use the approximation $\frac{22}{7}$ for π.

$$V = 36\pi \text{ cu in.}$$

$$\approx 36 \cdot \frac{22}{7} \text{ cu in.} \quad \text{Replace } \pi \text{ with } \frac{22}{7}.$$

$$= \frac{36 \cdot 22}{7} \text{ cu in.}$$

$$= \frac{792}{7} \quad \text{or} \quad 113\frac{1}{7} \text{ cubic inches}$$

The volume is *approximately* $113\frac{1}{7}$ cubic inches.

● **Work Practice 2**

PRACTICE 3

Approximate the volume of a cylinder of radius 5 inches and height 7 inches. Use 3.14 for π. Give an exact answer and an approximate answer.

Example 3 Approximate the volume of a can that has a $3\frac{1}{2}$-inch radius and a height of 6 inches. Use $\frac{22}{7}$ for π. Give an exact volume and an approximate volume.

$3\frac{1}{2}$ in.

6 in.

Solution: Using the formula for a circular cylinder, we have

$$V = \pi \cdot r^2 \cdot h$$

$$3\frac{1}{2} = \frac{7}{2}$$

$$= \pi \cdot \left(\frac{7}{2} \text{ in.}\right)^2 \cdot 6 \text{ in.}$$

$$= \pi \cdot \frac{49}{4} \text{ sq in.} \cdot 6 \text{ in.}$$

$$= \frac{\pi \cdot 49 \cdot \overset{1}{\cancel{2}} \cdot 3}{\underset{1}{\cancel{2}} \cdot 2} \text{ cu in.}$$

$$= 73\frac{1}{2}\pi \text{ cu in. or } 73.5\pi \text{ cu in.}$$

Answer

3. 175π cu in. ≈ 549.5 cu in.

This is the exact volume. To approximate the volume, use the approximation $\frac{22}{7}$ for π.

$$V = 73\frac{1}{2}\pi \text{ cu in.}$$

$$\approx \frac{147}{2} \cdot \frac{22}{7} \text{ cu in.} \quad \text{Replace } \pi \text{ with } \frac{22}{7}.$$

$$= \frac{21 \cdot \overset{1}{\cancel{7}} \cdot \overset{1}{\cancel{2}} \cdot 11}{\underset{1}{\cancel{2}} \cdot \underset{1}{\cancel{7}}} \text{ cu in.}$$

$$= 231 \text{ cubic in.}$$

The volume is approximately 231 cubic inches.

Work Practice 3

Example 4 Approximate the volume of a cone that has a height of 14 centimeters and a radius of 3 centimeters. Use 3.14 for π. Give an exact answer and an approximate answer.

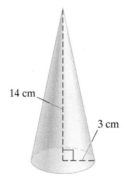

PRACTICE 4

Find the volume of a square-based pyramid that has a 3-meter side and a height of 5.1 meters.

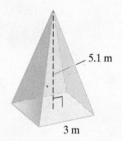

Solution: Using the formula for volume of a cone, we have

$$V = \frac{1}{3} \cdot \pi \cdot r^2 \cdot h$$

$$= \frac{1}{3} \cdot \pi \cdot (3 \text{ cm})^2 \cdot 14 \text{ cm} \quad \text{Replace } r \text{ with 3 cm and } h \text{ with 14 cm.}$$

$$= 42\pi \text{ cu cm}$$

Thus, 42π cubic centimeters is the exact volume. To approximate the volume, use the approximation 3.14 for π.

$$V \approx 42 \cdot 3.14 \text{ cu cm} \quad \text{Replace } \pi \text{ with 3.14.}$$

$$= 131.88 \text{ cu cm}$$

The volume is approximately 131.88 cubic centimeters.

Work Practice 4

Answer
4. 15.3 cu m

Vocabulary and Readiness Check

Use the choices below to fill in each blank. Some exercises are from Sections A.3 and A.4.

cubic   perimeter   volume

units   area   square

1. The measure of the amount of space inside a solid is its _____.
2. _____ measures the amount of surface enclosed by a region.
3. Volume is measured in _____ units.
4. Area is measured in _____ units.
5. The _____ of a polygon is the sum of the lengths of its sides.
6. Perimeter is measured in _____.

A.5 Exercise Set

FOR EXTRA HELP

MyMathLab   Powered by CourseCompass™ and MathXL™

Math XL   PRACTICE   WATCH   DOWNLOAD   READ   REVIEW

Objective Ⓐ *Find the volume of each solid. See Examples 1 through 4. Use $\frac{22}{7}$ for π.*

1.
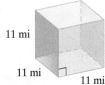
3 in.
4 in.
6 in.

2.
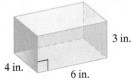
4 cm
4 cm
8 cm

3.
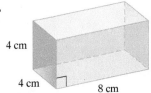
8 cm
8 cm
8 cm

4.

11 mi
11 mi
11 mi

5.
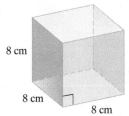
3 yd
2 yd

6.

$1\frac{3}{4}$ in.
9 in.

7.

10 in.

8.

3 mi

9.
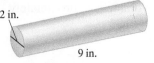
2 in.
9 in.

10.  10 ft

6 ft

11. 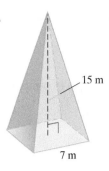 9 cm

5 cm

12. 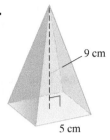 15 m

7 m

Solve.

13. Find the volume of a cube with edges of $1\frac{1}{3}$ inches.

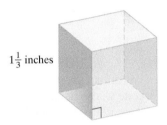

$1\frac{1}{3}$ inches

14. A water storage tank is in the shape of a cone with the pointed end down. If the radius is 14 feet and the depth of the tank is 15 feet, approximate the volume of the tank in cubic feet. Use $\frac{22}{7}$ for π.

14 ft

15 ft

15. Find the volume of a rectangular box 2 feet by 1.4 feet by 3 feet.

16. Find the volume of a box in the shape of a cube that is 5 feet on each side.

17. Find the volume of a pyramid with a square base 5 inches on a side and a height of $1\frac{3}{10}$ inches.

18. Approximate to the nearest hundredth the volume of a sphere with a radius of 2 centimeters. Use 3.14 for π.

19. A paperweight is in the shape of a square-based pyramid 20 centimeters tall. If an edge of the base is 12 centimeters, find the volume of the paperweight.

20. A birdbath is made in the shape of a hemisphere (half-sphere). If its radius is 10 inches, approximate the volume. Use $\frac{22}{7}$ for π.

10 in.

21. Find the exact volume of a sphere with a radius of 7 inches.

22. A tank is in the shape of a cylinder 8 feet tall and 3 feet in radius. Find the exact volume of the tank.

23. Find the volume of a rectangular block of ice 2 feet by $2\frac{1}{2}$ feet by $1\frac{1}{2}$ feet.

24. Find the capacity (volume in cubic feet) of a rectangular ice chest with inside measurements of 3 feet by $1\frac{1}{2}$ feet by $1\frac{3}{4}$ feet.

25. The largest inflatable beach ball has a diameter of 12 yards. Find its exact volume. (*Source: Guinness World Records*, 2010)

26. The largest free-floating soap bubble made with a wand had a diameter of almost 6 feet. Find the exact volume of a sphere with a diameter of 6 feet. (*Source: Guinness World Records*, 2010)

27. Find the exact volume of a waffle ice cream cone with a 3-in. diameter and a height of 7 inches.

28. A snow globe has a diameter of 6 inches. Find its exact volume. Then approximate its volume using 3.14 for π.

29. The largest cereal bowl in the world was made by Kellogg's South Africa in July 2007. The bowl had a 2.6-m diameter and a height of 1.5 m. If the bowl is in the shape of a cylinder, calculate the volume of cereal you could put into this bowl. Use $\pi \approx 3.14$ and round to the nearest hundredth of a cubic meter. (*Source: Guinness Book of World Records*)

30. Mount Fuji, in Japan, is considered the most beautiful composite volcano in the world. The mountain is in the shape of a cone whose height is about 3.5 kilometers and whose base radius is about 3 kilometers. Approximate the volume of Mt. Fuji in cubic kilometers. Use $\frac{22}{7}$ for π.

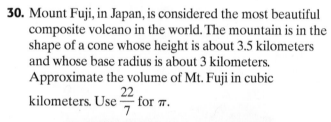

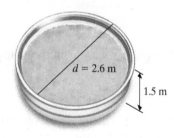

31. An ice cream cone with a 4-centimeter diameter and 3-centimeter depth is filled exactly level with the top of the cone. Approximate how much ice cream (in cubic centimeters) is in the cone. Use $\frac{22}{7}$ for π.

32. A child's toy is in the shape of a square-based pyramid 10 inches tall. If an edge of the base is 7 inches, find the volume of the toy.

The Space Cube is supposed to be the world's smallest computer, with dimensions of 2 inches by 2 inches by 2.2 inches.

33. Find the volume of the Space Cube.

34. Find the volume of an actual cube that measures 2 inches by 2 inches by 2 inches.

35. Find the volume of an actual cube that measures 2.2 inches by 2.2 inches by 2.2 inches.

36. Comment on the results of Exercises 33–35. Were you surprised when you compared volumes? Why or why not?

Review

Evaluate. See Section 1.9.

37. 5^2 **38.** 7^2 **39.** 3^2 **40.** 20^2

41. $1^2 + 2^2$ **42.** $5^2 + 3^2$ **43.** $4^2 + 2^2$ **44.** $1^2 + 6^2$

Concept Extensions

45. The Hayden Planetarium, at the Museum of Natural History in New York City, boasts a dome that has a diameter of 20 m. The dome is a hemisphere, or half a sphere. What is the volume enclosed by the dome at the Hayden Planetarium? Use 3.14 for π and round to the nearest hundredth. (*Source:* Hayden Planetarium)

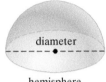

hemisphere

46. The Adler Museum in Chicago recently added a new planetarium, its StarRider Theater, which has a diameter of 55 feet. Find the volume of its hemispheric (half a sphere) dome. Use 3.14 for π and round to the nearest hundredth. (*Source:* The Adler Museum)

47. Do two rectangular solids with the same volume have the same shape? To help, find the volume of each rectangular solid.

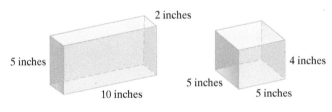

48. Do two rectangular solids with the same volume have the same surface area? To see, find the volume and surface area of each rectangular solid. Surface area is the area of the surface of the solid. To find the surface area of each rectangular solid, find the sum of the areas of the six rectangles that form each solid.

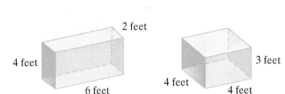

49. Two kennels are offered at a hotel. The kennels measure

a. 2'1" by 1'8" by 1'7" and
b. 1'1" by 2' by 2'8"

What is the volume of each kennel rounded to the nearest cubic foot? Which is larger?

50. The centerpiece of the New England Aquarium in Boston is its Giant Ocean Tank. This exhibit is a four-story cylindrical saltwater tank containing sharks, sea turtles, stingrays, and tropical fish. The radius of the tank is 16.3 feet and its height is 32 feet (assuming that a story is 8 feet). What is the volume of the Giant Ocean Tank? Use $\pi \approx 3.14$ and round to the nearest tenth of a cubic foot. (*Source:* New England Aquarium)

51. Find the volume of the figure below. Give an exact measure and then a whole number approximation.

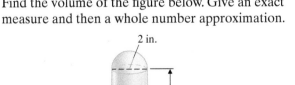

52. Can you compute the volume of a rectangle? Why or why not?

Answers to Selected Exercises

Appendix A

Section A.1

Vocabulary and Readiness Check **1.** plane **3.** Space **5.** ray **7.** straight **9.** acute **11.** Parallel; intersecting **13.** degrees **15.** vertical

Exercise Set A.1 **1.** line; line CD or line l or $\overleftrightarrow{CD}$ **3.** line segment; line segment MN or $\overline{MN}$ **5.** angle; $\angle GHI$ or $\angle IHG$ or $\angle H$
7. ray; ray UW or $\overrightarrow{UW}$ **9.** $\angle CPR$, $\angle RPC$ **11.** $\angle TPM$, $\angle MPT$ **13.** straight **15.** right **17.** obtuse **19.** acute **21.** 67°
23. 163° **25.** 32° **27.** 30° **29.** $\angle MNP$ and $\angle RNO$; $\angle PNQ$ and $\angle QNR$ **31.** $\angle SPT$ and $\angle TPQ$; $\angle SPR$ and $\angle RPQ$; $\angle SPT$ and
$\angle SPR$; $\angle TPQ$ and $\angle QPR$ **33.** 27° **35.** 132° **37.** $m\angle x = 30°$; $m\angle y = 150°$; $m\angle z = 30°$ **39.** $m\angle x = 77°$; $m\angle y = 103°$; $m\angle z = 77°$
41. $m\angle x = 100°$; $m\angle y = 80°$; $m\angle z = 100°$ **43.** $m\angle x = 134°$; $m\angle y = 46°$; $m\angle z = 134°$ **45.** $\angle ABC$ or $\angle CBA$ **47.** $\angle DBE$ or $\angle EBD$
49. 15° **51.** 50° **53.** 65° **55.** 95° **57.** $\frac{9}{8}$ or $1\frac{1}{8}$ **59.** $\frac{7}{32}$ **61.** $\frac{5}{6}$ **63.** $\frac{4}{3}$ or $1\frac{1}{3}$ **65.** 54.8° **67.** false; answers may vary **69.** true
71. $m\angle a = 60°$; $m\angle b = 50°$; $m\angle c = 110°$; $m\angle d = 70°$; $m\angle e = 120°$ **73.** no; answers may vary **75.** 45°; 45°

Section A.2

Exercise Set A.2 **1.** pentagon **3.** hexagon **5.** quadrilateral **7.** pentagon **9.** equilateral **11.** scalene; right **13.** isosceles **15.** 25° **17.** 13°
19. 40° **21.** diameter **23.** rectangle **25.** parallelogram **27.** hypotenuse **29.** 14 m **31.** 14.5 cm **33.** 40.6 cm **35.** 84 in. **37.** cylinder
39. rectangular solid **41.** cone **43.** cube **45.** rectangular solid **47.** sphere **49.** pyramid **51.** 14.8 in. **53.** 13 mi **55.** 72,368 mi **57.** 108 **59.** 12.56
61. true **63.** true **65.** false **67.** yes; answers may vary **69.** answers may vary

Section A.3

Vocabulary and Readiness Check **1.** perimeter **3.** π **5.** $\frac{22}{7}$ (or 3.14); 3.14 $\left(\text{or } \frac{22}{7}\right)$

Exercise Set A.3 **1.** 64 ft **3.** 120 cm **5.** 21 in. **7.** 48 ft **9.** 42 in. **11.** 155 cm **13.** 21 ft **15.** 624 ft **17.** 346 yd **19.** 22 ft **21.** $55
23. 72 in. **25.** 28 in. **27.** $36.12 **29.** 96 m **31.** 66 ft **33.** 74 cm **35.** 17π cm; 53.38 cm **37.** 16π mi; 50.24 mi **39.** 26π m; 81.64 m
41. 15π ft; 47.1 ft **43.** 12,560 ft **45.** 30.7 mi **47.** 14π cm $\approx$ 43.96 cm **49.** 40 mm **51.** 84 ft **53.** 23 **55.** 1 **57.** 6 **59.** 10 **61. a.** width: 30 yd;
length: 40 yd **b.** 140 yd **63.** b **65. a.** 62.8 m; 125.6 m **b.** yes **67.** answers may vary **69.** 27.4 m **71.** 75.4 m **73.** 6.5 ft

Section A.4
Exercise Set A.4 **1.** 7 sq m **3.** $9\frac{3}{4}$ sq yd **5.** 15 sq yd **7.** 2.25π sq in. $\approx$ 7.065 sq in. **9.** 17.64 sq ft **11.** 28 sq m **13.** 22 sq yd **15.** $36\frac{3}{4}$ sq ft

17. $22\frac{1}{2}$ sq in. **19.** 25 sq cm **21.** 86 sq mi **23.** 24 sq cm **25.** 36π sq in. $\approx 113\frac{1}{7}$ sq in. **27.** 168 sq ft **29.** 113,625 sq ft **31.** 4π sq ft $\approx$ 12.56 sq ft

33. 128 sq in.; $\frac{8}{9}$ sq ft **35.** 510 sq in. **37.** 168 sq ft **39.** 9200 sq ft **41. a.** 381 sq ft **b.** 4 squares **43.** 14π in. $\approx$ 43.96 in. **45.** 25 ft **47.** $12\frac{3}{4}$ ft

49. perimeter **51.** area **53.** area **55.** perimeter **57.** 12-in. pizza **59.** $1\frac{1}{3}$ sq ft; 192 sq in. **61.** 7.74 sq in.

63. 7056π sq in. $\approx$ 22,155.84 sq in. **65.** 298.5 sq m **67. a.** width: 40 yd; length: 60 yd **b.** 2400 sq yd **69.** no; answers may vary

Section A.5

Vocabulary and Readiness Check **1.** volume **3.** cubic **5.** perimeter

Exercise Set A.5 **1.** 72 cu in. **3.** 512 cu cm **5.** $12\frac{4}{7}$ cu yd **7.** $523\frac{17}{21}$ cu in. **9.** $28\frac{2}{7}$ cu in. **11.** 75 cu cm **13.** $2\frac{10}{27}$ cu in. **15.** 8.4 cu ft

17. $10\frac{5}{6}$ cu in. **19.** 960 cu cm **21.** $\frac{1372}{3}\pi$ cu in. or $457\frac{1}{3}\pi$ cu in. **23.** $7\frac{1}{2}$ cu ft **25.** 288π cu yd **27.** 5.25π cu in. **29.** 7.96 cu m **31.** $12\frac{4}{7}$ cu cm

33. 8.8 cu in. **35.** 10.648 cu in. **37.** 25 **39.** 9 **41.** 5 **43.** 20 **45.** 2093.33 cu m **47.** no; answers may vary **49.** 5 cu ft; 5.8 cu ft; (b) is larger

51. $6\frac{2}{3}\pi$ cu in. $\approx$ 21 cu in.

Appendix

B

Objectives

A Read Pictographs.

B Read and Construct Bar Graphs.

C Read and Construct Histograms.

D Read Line Graphs.

B.1 READING PICTOGRAPHS, BAR GRAPHS, HISTOGRAMS, AND LINE GRAPHS

Often data are presented visually in a graph. In this section, we practice reading several kinds of graphs, including pictographs, bar graphs, and line graphs.

Objective A Reading Pictographs

A **pictograph** such as the one below is a graph in which pictures or symbols are used. This type of graph contains a key that explains the meaning of the symbol used. An advantage of using a pictograph to display information is that comparisons can easily be made. A disadvantage of using a pictograph is that it is often hard to tell what fractional part of a symbol is shown. For example, in the pictograph below, Chinese shows a part of a symbol, but it's hard to read with any accuracy what fractional part of a symbol is shown.

Example 1 Calculating Languages Spoken

The following pictograph shows the top eight most-spoken (primary) languages. Use this pictograph to answer the questions.

Top 8 Most-Spoken (Primary) Languages

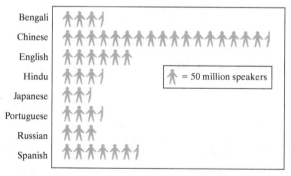

Source: www.ethnologue.com

a. Approximate the number of people who primarily speak Russian.

b. Approximate how many more people primarily speak Spanish than Russian.

Solution:

a. Russian corresponds to 3 symbols, and each symbol represents 50 million speakers. This means that the number of people who primarily speak Russian is approximately $3 \cdot (50 \text{ million})$ or 150 million people.

b. Spanish shows $3\frac{1}{2}$ more symbols than Russian. This means that $3\frac{1}{2} \cdot (50 \text{ million})$ or 175 million more people primarily speak Spanish than Russian.

● **Work Practice 1**

PRACTICE 1

Use the pictograph shown in Example 1 to answer the following questions:

a. Approximate the number of people who primarily speak English.

b. Approximate how many more people primarily speak English than Portuguese.

Answers

1. a. 300 million people

b. 125 million people

1006

Example 2 Calculating Lunar and Planetary Explorations

The following pictograph shows the approximate number of spaceflights by various countries or space consortia for lunar or planetary explorations from 1957 to the present day. Use this pictograph to answer the questions. (*Source:* University of Michigan Corporation for Atmospheric Research)

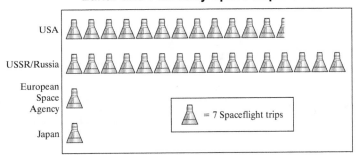

Lunar and Planetary Space Explorations

a. Approximate the number of spaceflights undertaken by the United States.
b. Approximate how many more spaceflights were undertaken by the USSR/Russia than by the United States.

Solution:

a. The United States corresponds to $12\frac{1}{2}$ symbols, and each symbol represents 7 spaceflights. This means that the United States undertook approximately $12\frac{1}{2} \cdot 7 = 87.5 \approx 88$ spaceflights for lunar and planetary exploration.

b. The USSR/Russia shows 16 symbols, or $3\frac{1}{2}$ more than the United States. This means that the USSR/Russia undertook $3\frac{1}{2} \cdot 7 = 24.5 \approx 25$ more spaceflights than the United States.

● Work Practice 2

Objective Ⓑ Reading and Constructing Bar Graphs

Another way to visually present data is with a **bar graph.** Bar graphs can appear with vertical bars or horizontal bars. Although we have studied bar graphs in previous sections, we now practice reading the height or length of the bars contained in a bar graph. An advantage to using bar graphs is that a scale is usually included for greater accuracy. Care must be taken when reading bar graphs, as well as other types of graphs—they may be misleading, as shown later in this section.

PRACTICE 2

Use the pictograph shown in Example 2 to answer the following questions:
a. Approximate the number of spaceflights undertaken by the European Space Agency.
b. Approximate the total number of spaceflights undertaken by the European Space Agency and Japan.

Answers
2. **a.** 7 **b.** 14

Copyright 2011 Pearson Education, Inc.

PRACTICE 3

Use the bar graph in Example 3 to answer the following questions:

a. Approximate the number of endangered species that are birds.

b. Which category shows the fewest endangered species?

Example 3 Finding the Number of Endangered Species

The following bar graph shows the number of endangered species in the United States in 2010. Use this graph to answer the questions.

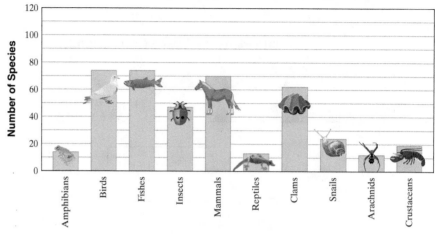

Source: U.S. Fish and Wildlife Service

a. Approximate the number of endangered species that are clams.

b. Which category has the most endangered species?

Solution:

a. To approximate the number of endangered species that are clams, we go to the top of the bar that represents clams. From the top of this bar, we move horizontally to the left until the scale is reached. We read the height of the bar on the scale as approximately 62. There are approximately 62 clam species that are endangered, as shown.

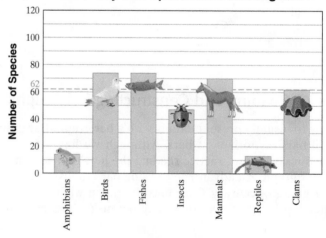

Source: U.S. Fish and Wildlife Service

b. The most endangered species is represented by the tallest (longest) bars. The tallest bars correspond to birds and fishes.

Answers

3. **a.** 74 **b.** arachnids

◗ **Work Practice 3**

Next, we practice constructing a bar graph.

Example 4 Draw a vertical bar graph using the information in the table below that gives the caffeine content of selected foods.

Average Caffeine Content of Selected Foods			
Food	**Milligrams**	**Food**	**Milligrams**
Brewed coffee (percolator, 8 ounces)	124	Instant coffee (8 ounces)	104
Brewed decaffeinated coffee (8 ounces)	3	Brewed tea (U.S. brands, 8 ounces)	64
Coca-Cola Classic (8 ounces)	31	Mr. Pibb (8 ounces)	27
Dark chocolate (semisweet, $1\frac{1}{2}$ ounces)	30	Milk chocolate (8 ounces)	9

(*Sources:* International Food Information Council and the Coca-Cola Company)

Solution: We draw and label a vertical line and a horizontal line as shown below on the left. These lines are also called axes. We place the different food categories along the horizontal axis. Along the vertical axis, we place a scale.

There are many choices of scales that would be appropriate. Notice that the milligrams range from a low of 3 to a high of 124. From this information, we use a scale that starts at 0 and then shows multiples of 20 so that the scale is not too cluttered. The scale stops at 140, the smallest multiple of 20 that will allow all milligrams to be graphed. It may also be helpful to draw horizontal lines along the scale markings to help draw the vertical bars at the correct height. The finished bar graph is shown below on the right.

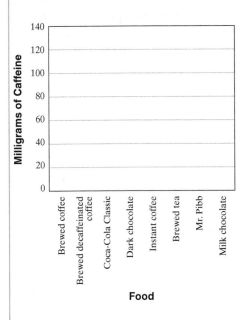

Work Practice 4

As mentioned previously, graphs can be misleading. Both graphs on the next page show the same information, but with different scales. Special care should be taken when forming conclusions from the appearance of a graph.

PRACTICE 4

Draw a vertical bar graph using the information in the table about electoral votes for President from selected states.

Total Electoral Votes by Selected States	
State	**Electoral Votes**
Texas	34
California	55
Florida	27
Nebraska	5
Indiana	11
Georgia	15

(*Source: World Almanac* 2009)

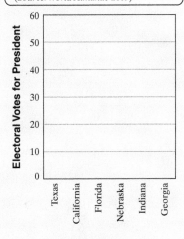

Answer

4.

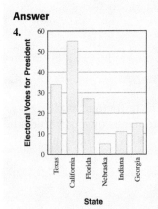

Notice the ⌇ symbol on each vertical scale on the graphs below. This symbol alerts us that numbers are missing from that scale

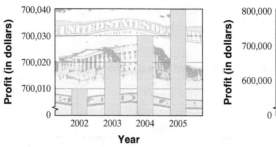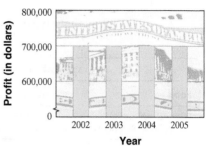

Are profits shown in the graphs above greatly increasing, or are they remaining about the same?

Objective ⒸReading and Constructing Histograms

Suppose that the test scores of 36 students are summarized in the table below:

Student Scores	Frequency (Number of Students)
40–49	1
50–59	3
60–69	2
70–79	10
80–89	12
90–99	8

The results in the table can be displayed in a histogram. A **histogram** is a special bar graph. The width of each bar represents a range of numbers called a **class interval.** The height of each bar corresponds to how many times a number in the class interval occurs and is called the **class frequency.** The bars in a histogram lie side by side with no space between them.

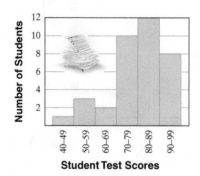

PRACTICE 5

Use the histogram on the right to determine how many students scored 80–89 on the test.

Example 5 Reading a Histogram on Student Test Scores

Use the preceding histogram to determine how many students scored 50–59 on the test.

Solution: We find the bar representing 50–59. The height of this bar is 3, which means 3 students scored 50–59 on the test.

⬤ **Work Practice 5**

Answer
5. 12

Example 6 Reading a Histogram on Student Test Scores

Use the preceding histogram to determine how many students scored 80 or above on the test.

Solution: We see that two different bars fit this description. There are 12 students who scored 80–89 and 8 students who scored 90–99. The sum of these two categories is 12 + 8 or 20 students. Thus, 20 students scored 80 or above on the test.

● Work Practice 6

Now we will look at a way to construct histograms.

The daily high temperatures for 1 month in New Orleans, Louisiana, are recorded in the following list:

85°	90°	95°	89°	88°	94°
87°	90°	95°	92°	95°	94°
82°	92°	96°	91°	94°	92°
89°	89°	90°	93°	95°	91°
88°	90°	88°	86°	93°	89°

The data in this list have not been organized and can be hard to interpret. One way to organize the data is to place them in a **frequency distribution table.** We will do this in Example 7.

Example 7 Completing a Frequency Distribution on Temperature

Complete the frequency distribution table for the preceding temperature data.

Solution: Go through the data and place a tally mark in the second column of the table next to the class interval. Then count the tally marks and write each total in the third column of the table.

Class Intervals (Temperatures)	Tally	Class Frequency (Number of Days)
82°–84°	|	1
85°–87°	|||	3
88°–90°	⊮⊮|	11
91°–93°	⊮||	7
94°–96°	⊮|||	8

● Work Practice 7

Example 8 Constructing a Histogram

Construct a histogram from the frequency distribution table in Example 7.

Solution:

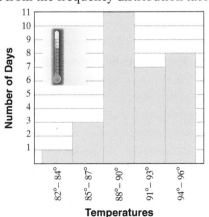

● Work Practice 8

PRACTICE 6

Use the histogram above Example 5 to determine how many students scored less than 80 on the test.

PRACTICE 7

Complete the frequency distribution table for the data below. Each number represents a credit card owner's unpaid balance for one month.

0	53	89	125
265	161	37	76
62	201	136	42

Class Intervals (Credit Card Balances)	Tally	Class Frequency (Number of Months)
$0–$49	____	____
$50–$99	____	____
$100–$149	____	____
$150–$199	____	____
$200–$249	____	____
$250–$299	____	____

PRACTICE 8

Construct a histogram from the frequency distribution table above.

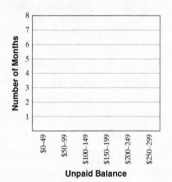

Answers

6. 16

7. table in class interval order:

8.

Tally	Class Frequency (Number of Months)
|||	3
||||	4
||	2
|	1
|	1
|	1

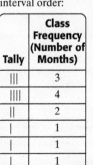

✔ **Concept Check** Which of the following sets of data is better suited to representation by a histogram? Explain.

Set 1		Set 2	
Grade on Final	# of Students	Section Number	Avg. Grade on Final
51–60	12	150	78
61–70	18	151	83
71–80	29	152	87
81–90	23	153	73
91–100	25		

Objective D Reading Line Graphs

Another common way to display information with a graph is by using a **line graph.** An advantage of a line graph is that it can be used to visualize relationships between two quantities. A line graph can also be very useful in showing a change over time.

Example 9 Reading Temperatures from a Line Graph

The following line graph shows the average daily temperature for each month for Omaha, Nebraska. Use this graph to answer the questions below.

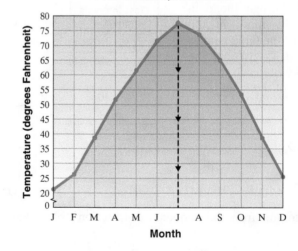

Source: National Climatic Data Center

a. During what month is the average daily temperature the highest?
b. During what month, from July through December, is the average daily temperature 65°F?
c. During what months is the average daily temperature less than 30°F?

Solution:

a. The month with the highest temperature corresponds to the highest point. This is the red point shown on the graph above. We follow this highest point downward to the horizontal month scale and see that this point corresponds to July.

PRACTICE 9

Use the temperature graph in Example 9 to answer the following questions:

a. During what month is the average daily temperature the lowest?

b. During what month is the average daily temperature 25°F?

c. During what months is the average daily temperature greater than 70°F?

Answers
9. **a.** January **b.** December
c. June, July, and August

✔ **Concept Check Answer**
Set 1; the grades are arranged in ranges of scores.

b. The months July through December correspond to the right side of the graph. We find the 65°F mark on the vertical temperature scale and move to the right until a point on the right side of the graph is reached. From that point, we move downward to the horizontal month scale and read the corresponding month. During the month of September, the average daily temperature is 65°F.

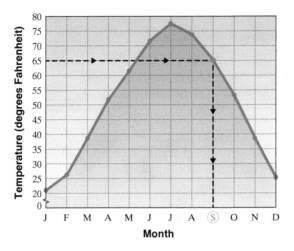

Source: National Climatic Data Center

c. To see what months the temperature is less than 30°F, we find what months correspond to points that fall below the 30°F mark on the vertical scale. These months are January, February, and December.

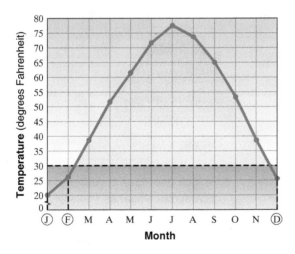

Source: National Climatic Data Center

● **Work Practice 9**

Vocabulary and Readiness Check

Fill in each blank with one of the choices below.

pictograph   bar   class frequency

histogram   line   class interval

1. A _____ graph presents data using vertical or horizontal bars.

2. A _____ is a graph in which pictures or symbols are used to visually present data.

3. A _____ graph displays information with a line that connects data points.

4. A _____ is a special bar graph in which the width of each bar represents a _____ and the height of each bar represents the _____.

FOR EXTRA HELP

MyMathLab   *Powered by CourseCompass™ and MathXL®*   MathXL®   PRACTICE   WATCH   DOWNLOAD   READ   REVIEW

B.1 Exercise Set

Objective A *The following pictograph shows the number of acres devoted to wheat production in selected states. Use this graph to answer Exercises 1 through 8. See Examples 1 and 2.* (*Source:* U.S. Department of Agriculture)

1. Which state plants the greatest quantity of acreage in wheat?

2. Which state shown plants the least amount of wheat acreage?

3. Approximate the number of acres of wheat planted in Oklahoma.

4. Approximate the number of acres of wheat planted in Kansas.

5. Which state plants about 5,000,000 acres of wheat?

6. Which state plants about 4,000,000 acres of wheat?

7. Which two states together plant about the same acreage of wheat as North Dakota?

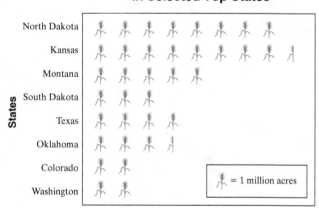

Annual Wheat Acreage in Selected Top States

8. Which two states together plant about the same acreage of wheat as Texas?

The following pictograph shows the average number of wildfires in the United States between 2003 and 2009. Use this graph to answer Exercises 9 through 16. See Examples 1 and 2. (*Source:* National Interagency Fire Center)

9. Approximate the number of wildfires in 2009.

10. Approximately how many wildfires were there in 2006?

11. Which year, of the years shown, had the most wildfires?

12. In what years were the number of wildfires greater than 72,000?

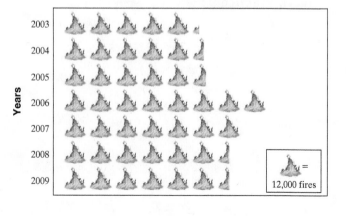

Wildfires in the United States

13. What was the amount of increase in wildfires from 2004 to 2006?

14. What was the amount of decrease in wildfires from 2006 to 2007?

15. What was the average annual number of wildfires from 2006 to 2008? (*Hint:* How do you calculate the average?)

16. Give an explanation for the large increase in the number of wildfires in 2006.

Objective **B** *The National Weather Service has exacting definitions for hurricanes; they are tropical storms with winds in excess of 74 mph. The following bar graph shows the number of hurricanes, by month, that have made landfall on the mainland United States between 1851 and 2009. Use this graph to answer Exercises 17 through 22. See Example 3.* (*Source:* National Weather Service: National Hurricane Center)

17. In which month did the most hurricanes make landfall in the United States?

18. In which month did the fewest hurricanes make landfall in the United States?

19. Approximate the number of hurricanes that made landfall in the United States during the month of August.

20. Approximate the number of hurricanes that made landfall in the United States in September.

21. In 2008 alone, two hurricanes made landfall during the month of August. What fraction of all the 76 hurricanes that made landfall during August is this?

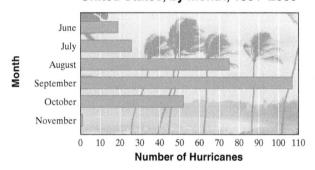

Hurricanes Making Landfall in the United States, by Month, 1851–2009

22. In 2007, only one hurricane made landfall on the United States during the entire season, in the month of September. If there have been 107 hurricanes to make landfall in the month of September since 1851, approximately what percent of these occurred in 2007?

The following horizontal bar graph shows the recent population of the world's largest cities (including their suburbs). Use this graph to answer Exercises 23 through 28. See Example 3. (*Source:* CityPopulation)

23. Name the city with the largest population, and estimate its population.

24. Name the city whose population is between 19 million and 21 million, and estimate its population.

25. Name the city in the United States with the largest population, and estimate its population.

26. Name the two cities that have approximately the same population.

27. How much larger (in terms of population) is Seoul, South Korea, than São Paolo, Brazil?

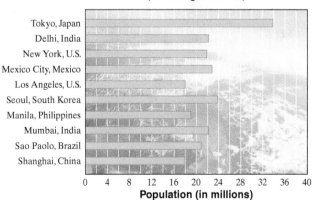

World's Largest Cities
(including Suburbs)

28. How much larger (in terms of population) is Mexico City, Mexico, than Shanghai, China?

Use the information given to draw a vertical bar graph. Clearly label the bars. See Example 4.

29.

Fiber Content of Selected Foods

Food	Grams of Total Fiber
Kidney beans $\left(\frac{1}{2}c\right)$	4.5
Oatmeal, cooked $\left(\frac{3}{4}c\right)$	3.0
Peanut butter, chunky (2 tbsp)	1.5
Popcorn (1 c)	1.0
Potato, baked, with skin (1 med)	4.0
Whole wheat bread (1 slice)	2.5

(*Sources:* American Dietetic Association and National Center for Nutrition and Dietetics)

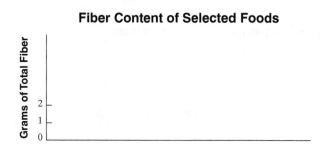

30.

U.S. Annual Food Sales

Year	Sales in Billions of Dollars
2004	915
2005	967
2006	1033
2007	1088
2008	1111
2009*	1080

(*Source:* U.S. Department of Agriculture) * predicted

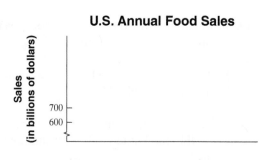

31.

Best-Selling Albums of All Time (U.S. Sales)

Album	Estimated Sales (in millions)
Pink Floyd: *The Wall* (1979)	23
Michael Jackson: *Thriller* (1982)	27
AC/DC: *Back in Black* (1980)	22
Eagles: *Their Greatest Hits* (1976)	29
Led Zeppelin: *Led Zeppelin IV* (1971)	23

(*Source:* Recording Industry Association of America)

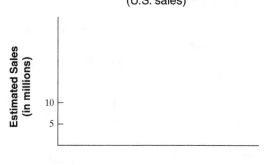

32.

Selected Worldwide Commercial Space Launches

Country	Total Commercial Space Launches 1990–2008
United States	146
Europe	132
Russia	101
China	18
Sea Launch*	30

*Sea Launch is an international venture involving 4 countries that uses its own launch facility outside national borders.
Source: Bureau of Transportation Statistics

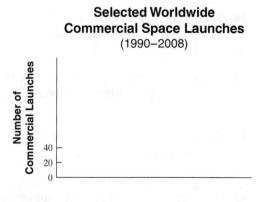

Objective **C** *The following histogram shows the number of miles that each adult, from a survey of 100 adults, drives per week. Use this histogram to answer Exercises 33 through 42. See Examples 5 and 6.*

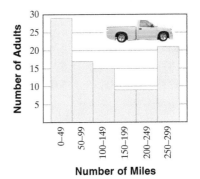

33. How many adults drive 100–149 miles per week?

34. How many adults drive 200–249 miles per week?

35. How many adults drive fewer than 150 miles per week?

36. How many adults drive 200 miles or more per week?

37. How many adults drive 100–199 miles per week?

38. How many adults drive 150–249 miles per week?

39. How many more adults drive 250–299 miles per week than 200–249 miles per week?

40. How many more adults drive 0–49 miles per week than 50–99 miles per week?

41. What is the ratio of adults who drive 150–199 miles per week to the total number of adults surveyed?

42. What is the ratio of adults who drive 50–99 miles per week to the total number of adults surveyed?

The following histogram shows the projected population (in millions), by age groups, for the United States for the year 2020. Use this histogram to answer Exercises 43 through 50. For Exercises 45 through 48, estimate to the nearest million. See Examples 5 and 6.

43. What age range will be the largest population group in 2020?

44. What age range will be the smallest population group in 2020?

45. How large is the population of 20- to 44-year-olds expected to be in 2020?

46. How large is the population of 45- to 64-year-olds expected to be in 2020?

47. How large is the population of those less than 4 years old expected to be in 2020?

48. How large is the population of 5- to 19-year-olds expected to be in 2020?

49. Which bar represents the age range you expect to be in during 2020?

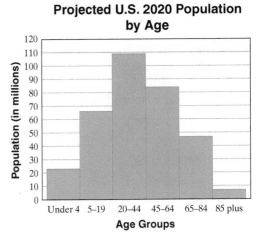

50. How many more 20- to 44-year-olds are there expected to be than 45- to 64-year-olds in 2020?

The following list shows the golf scores for an amateur golfer. Use this list to complete the frequency distribution table to the right. See Example 7.

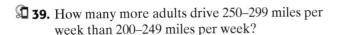

78	84	91	93	97
97	95	85	95	96
101	89	92	89	100

	Class Intervals (Scores)	Tally	Class Frequency (Number of Games)
51.	70–79		
52.	80–89		
53.	90–99		
54.	100–109		

Twenty-five people in a survey were asked to give their current checking account balances. Use the balances shown in the following list to complete the frequency distribution table to the right. See Example 7.

$53	$105	$162	$443	$109
$468	$47	$259	$316	$228
$207	$357	$15	$301	$75
$86	$77	$512	$219	$100
$192	$288	$352	$166	$292

	Class Intervals (Account Balances)	Tally	Class Frequency (Number of People)
55.	$0–$99		
56.	$100–$199		
57.	$200–$299		
58.	$300–$399		
59.	$400–$499		
60.	$500–$599		

61. Use the frequency distribution table from Exercises 51 through 54 to construct a histogram. See Example 8.

Golf Scores

62. Use the frequency distribution table from Exercises 55 through 60 to construct a histogram. See Example 8.

Account Balances

Objective Ⓓ *The following line graph shows the total points scored by both teams in the NFL Super Bowl from 2003 through 2009. Use this graph to answer Exercises 63 through 70. See Example 9.* (*Source:* National Football League)

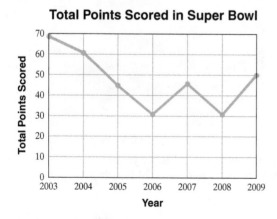

Total Points Scored in Super Bowl

63. Find the total points scored in the Super Bowl in 2003.

64. Find the total points scored in the Super Bowl in 2008.

65. During which of the years shown were the total points scored in the Super Bowl greater than 60?

66. During which of the years shown was the total score in the Super Bowl the highest?

67. During which year(s) shown was the total score in the Super Bowl the lowest?

68. Between 2005 and 2006, did the total score in the Super Bowl increase or decrease?

69. During which year(s) was the total score in the Super Bowl less than 50?

70. Between 2008 and 2009, did the total score in the Super Bowl increase or decrease?

Review

Find each percent. See Sections 4.5 and 4.6.

71. 30% of 12   **72.** 45% of 120   **73.** 10% of 62   **74.** 95% of 50

Write each fraction as a percent. See Section 4.4.

75. $\frac{1}{4}$ **76.** $\frac{2}{5}$ **77.** $\frac{17}{50}$ **78.** $\frac{9}{10}$

Concept Extensions

The following double line graph shows temperature highs and lows for a week. Use this graph to answer Exercises 79 through 84.

79. What was the high temperature reading on Thursday?

80. What was the low temperature reading on Thursday?

81. What day was the temperature the lowest? What was this low temperature?

82. What day of the week was the temperature the highest? What was this high temperature?

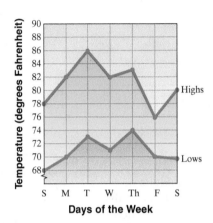

83. On what day of the week was the difference between the high temperature and the low temperature the greatest? What was this difference in temperature?

84. On what day of the week was the difference between the high temperature and the low temperature the least? What was this difference in temperature?

85. True or false? With a bar graph, the width of the bar is just as important as the height of the bar. Explain your answer.

86. Kansas plants about 17% of the wheat acreage in the United States. About how many acres of wheat are planted in the United States, according to the pictograph for Exercises 1 through 8? Round to the nearest million acre.

B.2 READING CIRCLE GRAPHS

Objective Ⓐ Reading Circle Graphs

In Exercise Set 4.3, the following **circle graph** was shown. This particular graph shows the favorite sport for 100 adults.

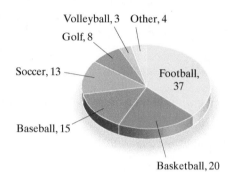

Each sector of the graph (shaped like a piece of pie) shows a category and the relative size of the category. In other words, the most popular sport is football, and it is represented by the largest sector.

PRACTICE 1

Find the ratio of adults preferring golf to total adults. Write the ratio as a fraction in simplest form.

Example 1 Find the ratio of adults preferring basketball to total adults. Write the ratio as a fraction in simplest form.

Solution: The ratio is

$$\frac{\text{people preferring basketball}}{\text{total adults}} = \frac{20}{100} = \frac{1}{5}$$

● Work Practice 1

A circle graph is often used to show percents in different categories, with the whole circle representing 100%.

PRACTICE 2

Using the circle graph shown in Example 2, determine the percent of visitors to the United States that came from Europe, Asia, and South America.

Example 2 Using a Circle Graph

The following graph shows the percent of visitors to the United States in a recent year by various regions. Using the circle graph shown, determine the percent of visitors who came to the United States from Mexico and Canada.

Solution: To find this percent, we add the percents corresponding to Mexico and Canada. The percent of visitors to the United States that came from Mexico and Canada is

$$12.3\% + 37.5\% = 49.8\%$$

● Work Practice 2

Visitors to U.S. by Region

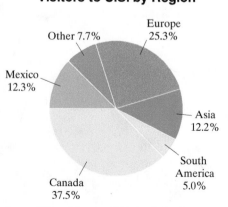

Source: Office of Travel and Tourism Industries

Helpful Hint

Since a circle graph represents a whole, the percents should add to 100% or 1. Notice this is true for Example 2.

Example 3 Finding Percent of Population

The U.S. Department of Commerce forecasts 61 million international visitors to the United States in 2011. Use the circle graph from Example 2 and estimate the number of tourists that might be from Europe.

Solution: We use the percent equation.

amount = percent · base
amount = 0.253 · 61,000,000
= 0.253(61,000,000)
= 15,433,000

Thus, 15,433,000 tourists might come from Europe in 2011.

● **Work Practice 3**

✓**Concept Check** Can the following data be represented by a circle graph? Why or why not?

Responses to the Question, "In Which Activities Are You Involved?"	
Intramural sports	60%
On-campus job	42%
Fraternity/sorority	27%
Academic clubs	21%
Music programs	14%

Objective ⓑ Drawing Circle Graphs

To draw a circle graph, we use the fact that a whole circle contains 360° (degrees).

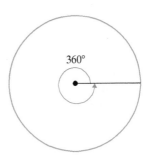

360°

PRACTICE 4

Use the data shown to draw a circle graph.

Freshmen	30%
Sophomores	27%
Juniors	25%
Seniors	18%

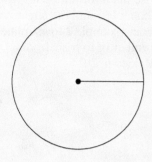

Example 4 Drawing a Circle Graph for U.S. Armed Forces Personnel

The following table shows the percent of U.S. armed forces personnel that were in each branch of service in 2009. (*Source:* U.S. Department of Defense)

Branch of Service	Percent
Army	38
Navy	23
Marine Corps	14
Air Force	22
Coast Guard	3

Draw a circle graph showing this data.

Solution: First we find the number of degrees in each sector representing each branch of service. Remember that the whole circle contains 360°. (We will round degrees to the nearest whole.)

Sector	Degrees in Each Sector
Army	$38\% \times 360° = 0.38 \times 360° = 136.8° \approx 137°$
Navy	$23\% \times 360° = 0.23 \times 360° = 82.8° \approx 83°$
Marine Corps	$14\% \times 360° = 0.14 \times 360° = 50.4° \approx 50°$
Air Force	$22\% \times 360° = 0.22 \times 360° = 79.2° \approx 79°$
Coast Guard	$3\% \times 360° = 0.03 \times 360° = 10.8° \approx 11°$

Helpful Hint

Check your calculations by finding the sum of the degrees.

$$137° + 83° + 50° + 79° + 11° = 360°$$

The sum should be 360°. (It may vary only slightly because of rounding.)

Next we draw a circle and mark its center. Then we draw a line from the center of the circle to the circle itself.

To construct the sectors, we will use a **protractor.** A protractor measures the number of degrees in an angle. We place the hole in the protractor over the center of the circle. Then we adjust the protractor so that 0° on the protractor is aligned with the line that we drew.

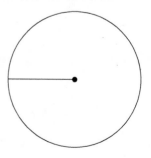

Answer

4.

Freshmen 30%
Sophomores 27%
Seniors 18%
Juniors 25%

It makes no difference which sector we draw first. To construct the "Army" sector, we find 137° on the protractor and mark our circle. Then we remove the protractor and use this mark to draw a second line from the center to the circle itself.

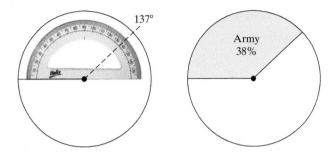

To construct the "Navy" sector, we follow the same procedure as above, except that we line up 0° with the second line we drew and mark the protractor at 83°.

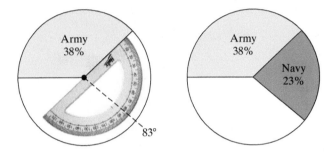

We continue in this manner until the circle graph is complete.

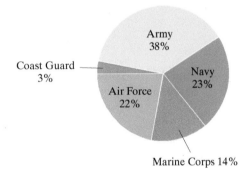

● **Work Practice 4**

✓**Concept Check** True or false? The larger a sector in a circle graph, the larger the percent of the total it represents. Explain your answer.

Vocabulary and Readiness Check

Use the choices below to fill in each blank.

   sector   circle   100   360

1. In a _____ graph, each section (shaped like a piece of pie) shows a category and the relative size of the category.

2. A circle graph contains pie-shaped sections, each called a_____.

3. The number of degrees in a whole circle is_____.

4. If a circle graph has percent labels, the percents should add up to_____.

B.2 Exercise Set

Objective A *The following circle graph is a result of surveying 700 college students. They were asked where they live while attending college. Use this graph to answer Exercises 1 through 6. Write all ratios as fractions in simplest form. See Example 1.*

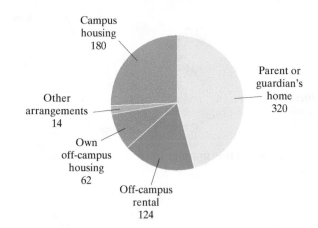

1. Where do most of these college students live?

2. Besides the category "Other arrangements," where do the fewest of these college students live?

3. Find the ratio of students living in campus housing to total students.

4. Find the ratio of students living in off-campus rentals to total students.

5. Find the ratio of students living in campus housing to students living in a parent or guardian's home.

6. Find the ratio of students living in off-campus rentals to students living in a parent or guardian's home.

The following circle graph shows the percent of the land area of the continents of Earth. Use this graph for Exercises 7 through 14. See Example 2.

7. Which continent is the largest?

8. Which continent is the smallest?

9. What percent of the land on Earth is accounted for by Asia and Europe together?

10. What percent of the land on Earth is accounted for by North and South America?

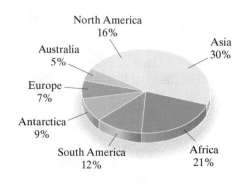

Source: National Geographic Society

The total amount of land from the continents is approximately 57,000,000 square miles. Use the graph to find the area of the continents given in Exercises 11 through 14. See Example 3.

11. Asia   **12.** South America   **13.** Australia   **14.** Europe

The following circle graph shows the percent of the types of books available at Midway Memorial Library. Use this graph for Exercises 15 through 24. See Example 2.

15. What percent of books are classified as some type of fiction?

16. What percent of books are nonfiction or reference?

17. What is the second-largest category of books?

18. What is the third-largest category of books?

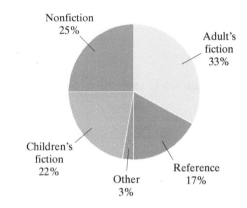

Nonfiction 25%
Adult's fiction 33%
Children's fiction 22%
Other 3%
Reference 17%

If this library has 125,600 books, find how many books are in each category given in Exercises 19 through 24. See Example 3.

19. Nonfiction   **20.** Reference   **21.** Children's fiction

22. Adult's fiction   **23.** Reference or other   **24.** Nonfiction or other

Objective Ⓑ *Fill in the tables. Round to the nearest degree. Then draw a circle graph to represent the information given in each table. (Remember: The total of "Degrees in Sector" column should equal 360° or very close to 360° because of rounding.) See Example 4.*

25.

Types of Apples Grown in Washington State		
Type of Apple	**Percent**	**Degrees in Sector**
Red Delicious	37%	
Golden Delicious	13%	
Fuji	14%	
Gala	15%	
Granny Smith	12%	
Other varieties	6%	
Braeburn	3%	
(*Source:* U.S. Apple Association)		

26.

Color Distribution of M&M's Milk Chocolate		
Color	Percent	Degrees in Sector
Blue	22.1%	
Orange	16.7%	
Green	16.7%	
Red	16.7%	
Brown	16.7%	
Yellow	11.1%	
(Source: M&M Mars)		

27.

Distribution of Large Dams by Continent		
Continent	Percent	Degrees in Sector
Europe	19%	
North America	32%	
South America	3%	
Asia	39%	
Africa	5%	
Australia	2%	
(Source: International Commission on Large Dams)		

28.

Number of Times the "Are We There Yet?" Question Is Asked of Parents During Road Trips		
	Percent	Degrees in Sector
Never	20%	
Once	11%	
2–5 times	36%	
6–10 times	14%	
More than 10 times	19%	
(Source: KRC Research for Goodyear Tire & Rubber Co.)		

Review

Write the prime factorization of each number. See Section 2.2.

29. 20

30. 25

31. 40

32. 16

33. 85

34. 105

Concept Extensions

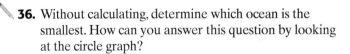

The following circle graph shows the relative sizes of the great oceans. Use this graph for Exercises 35 through 40.

35. Without calculating, determine which ocean is the largest. How can you answer this question by looking at the circle graph?

36. Without calculating, determine which ocean is the smallest. How can you answer this question by looking at the circle graph?

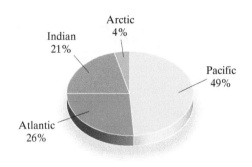

Source: Philip's World Atlas

These oceans together make up 264,489,800 square kilometers of the Earth's surface. Find the square kilometers for each ocean.

37. Pacific Ocean   **38.** Atlantic Ocean   **39.** Indian Ocean   **40.** Arctic Ocean

The following circle graph summarizes the results of a survey of 2800 Internet users who make purchases online. Use this graph for Exercises 41 through 46. Round to the nearest whole.

41. How many of the survey respondents said that they spend $0–$15 online each month?

42. How many of the survey repondents said that they spend $15–$175 online each month?

Online Spending per Month

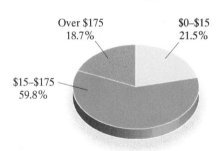

Source: UCLA Center for Communication Policy

43. How many of the survey respondents said that they spend $0 to $175 online each month?

44. How many of the survey respondents said that they spend $15 to over $175 online each month?

45. Find the ratio of *number* of respondents who spend $0–$15 online to *number* of respondents who spend $15–$175 online. Write the ratio as a fraction with integers in the numerator and denominator.

46. Find the ratio of *percent* of respondents who spend $0–$15 online to *percent* of those who spend $15–$175. Write the ratio as a fraction with integers in the numerator and denominator.

See the Concept Checks in this section.

47. Can the data below be represented by a circle graph? Why or why not?

Responses to the Question, "What Classes Are You Taking?"	
Math	80%
English	72%
History	37%
Biology	21%
Chemistry	14%

48. True or false? The smaller a sector in a circle graph, the smaller the percent of the total it represents. Explain why.

Answers to Selected Exercises

Appendix B

Section B.1

Vocabulary and Readiness Check **1.** bar **3.** line

Exercise Set B.1 **1.** Kansas **3.** 3.5 million or 3,500,000 acres **5.** Montana **7.** Montana and South Dakota **9.** 78,000 **11.** 2006 **13.** 30,000
15. 86,000 wildfires/year **17.** September **19.** 75 **21.** $\frac{1}{38}$ **23.** Tokyo, Japan; about 33.8 million or 33,800,000 **25.** New York; 21.9 million, or 21,900,000
27. approximately 3 million

29.

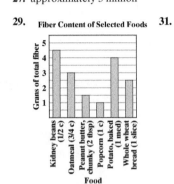

31.

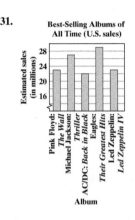

33. 15 adults **35.** 61 adults **37.** 24 adults **39.** 12 adults **41.** $\frac{9}{100}$
43. 20–44 **45.** 109 million **47.** 23 million **49.** answers may vary **51.** |; 1
53. ⫫|||; 8 **55.** ⫫|; 6 **57.** ⫫|; 6 **59.** ||; 2

61.

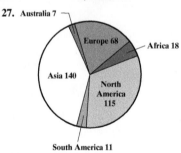

63. 69 **65.** 2003, 2004 **67.** 2006, 2008 **69.** 2005,
2006, 2007, 2008 **71.** 3.6 **73.** 6.2 **75.** 25% **77.** 34%

79. 83°F **81.** Sunday; 68°F **83.** Tuesday; 13°F
85. answers may vary

Section B.2

Vocabulary and Readiness Check **1.** circle **3.** 360

Exercise Set B.2 **1.** parent or guardian's home **3.** $\frac{9}{35}$ **5.** $\frac{9}{16}$ **7.** Asia **9.** 37% **11.** 17,100,000 sq mi **13.** 2,850,000 sq mi **15.** 55%

17. nonfiction **19.** 31,400 books **21.** 27,632 books **23.** 25,120 books

25.

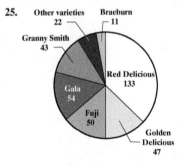

27.

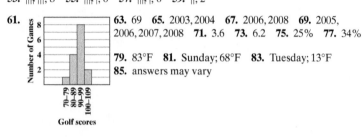

29. $2^2 \times 5$ **31.** $2^3 \times 5$ **33.** 5×17 **35.** Pacific; answers
may vary **37.** 129,600,002 sq km **39.** 55,542,858 sq km
41. 602 respondents **43.** 2276 respondents **45.** $\frac{301}{837}$

47. no; answers may vary

An Introduction to Using a Graphing Utility

Objective **A** Viewing Window and Interpreting Window Settings

In this appendix, we will use the term **graphing utility** to mean a graphing calculator or a computer software graphing package. All graphing utilities graph equations by plotting points on a screen. While plotting several points can be slow and sometimes tedious for us, a graphing utility can quickly and accurately plot hundreds of points. How does a graphing utility show plotted points? A computer or calculator screen is made up of a grid of small rectangular areas called **pixels.** If a pixel contains a point to be plotted, the pixel is turned "on"; otherwise, the pixel remains "off." The graph of an equation is then a collection of pixels turned "on." The graph of $y = 3x + 1$ from a graphing calculator is shown in Figure C-1. Notice the irregular shape of the line caused by the rectangular pixels.

Figure C-1

The portion of the coordinate plane shown on the screen in Figure C-1 is called the **viewing window** or the **viewing rectangle.** Notice the x-axis and the y-axis on the graph. While tick marks are shown on the axes, they are not labeled. This means that from this screen alone, we do not know how many units each tick mark represents. To see what each tick mark represents and the minimum and maximum values on the axes, check the *window setting* of the graphing utility. It defines the viewing window. The window of the graph of $y = 3x + 1$ shown in Figure C-1 has the following setting (Figure C-2):

$\text{Xmin} = -10$	The minimum x-value is -10.
$\text{Xmax} = 10$	The maximum x-value is 10.
$\text{Xscl} = 1$	The x-axis scale is 1 unit per tick mark.
$\text{Ymin} = -10$	The minimum y-value is -10.
$\text{Ymax} = 10$	The maximum y-value is 10.
$\text{Yscl} = 1$	The y-axis scale is 1 unit per tick mark.

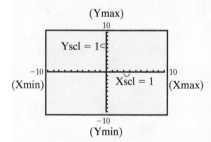

Figure C-2

By knowing the scale, we can find the minimum and the maximum values on the axes simply by counting tick marks. For example, if both the Xscl (x-axis scale) and the Yscl are 1 unit per tick mark on the graph in Figure C-3, we can count the tick marks and find that the minimum x-value is -10 and the maximum x-value is 10. Also, the minimum y-value is -10 and the maximum y-value is 10. If the Xscl (x-axis scale) changes to 2 units per tick mark (shown in Figure C-4), by counting tick marks, we see that the minimum x-value is now -20 and the maximum x-value is now 20.

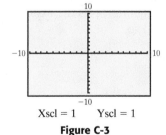

Xscl = 1	Yscl = 1		Xscl = 2	Yscl = 1
Figure C-3			**Figure C-4**	

Sometimes window settings are given in the form [Xmin, Xmax] by [Ymin, Ymax]. For example, the window setting shown in Figure C-4 can be written as $[-20, 20]$ by $[-10, 10]$.

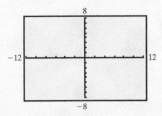

Figure C-5

It is also true that if we know the Xmin and the Xmax values, we can calculate the Xscl by the displayed axes. For example, the Xscl of the graph in Figure C-5 must be 2 units per tick mark for the maximum and minimum x-values to be as shown. Also, the Yscl of that graph must be 1 unit per tick mark for the maximum and minimum y-values to be as shown.

We will call the viewing window in Figure C-3 a *standard* viewing window or rectangle. Although a standard viewing window is sufficient for much of this text, special care must be taken to ensure that all key features of a graph are shown. Figures C-6, C-7, and C-8 show the graph of $y = x^2 + 11x - 1$ on three different viewing windows. Note that certain viewing windows for this equation are misleading.

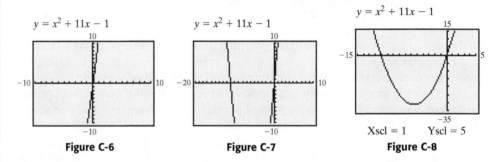

Figure C-6   Figure C-7   Figure C-8

How do we ensure that all distinguishing features of the graph of an equation are shown? It helps to know about the equation that is being graphed. For example, the equation $y = x^2 + 11x - 1$ is not a linear equation, and its graph is not a line. This equation is a quadratic equation, and therefore its graph is a parabola. By knowing this information, we know that the graph shown in Figure C-6, although correct, is misleading. Of the three viewing rectangles shown, the graph in Figure C-8 is best because it shows more of the distinguishing features of the parabola. Properties of equations needed for graphing will be studied in this text.

Objective Ⓑ Graphing Equations and Square Viewing Windows

In general, the following steps may be used to graph an equation on a standard viewing window.

> ### To Graph an Equation in x and y with a Graphing Utility on a Standard Viewing Window
>
> **Step 1:** Solve the equation for y.
>
> **Step 2:** Use your graphing utility and enter the equation in the form $Y = expression\ involving\ x$
>
> **Step 3:** Activate the graphing utility.

Special care must be taken when entering the *expression involving x* in *Step 2*. You must be sure that the graphing utility you are using interprets the expression as you want it to. For example, let's graph $3y = 4x$. To do so,

Step 1: Solve the equation for y.

$$3y = 4x \qquad \frac{3y}{3} = \frac{4x}{3} \qquad y = \frac{4}{3}x$$

Step 2: Using your graphing utility, enter the expression $\frac{4}{3}x$ after the Y = prompt.

In order for your graphing utility to correctly interpret the expression, you may need to enter $(4/3)x$ or $(4 \div 3)x$.

Step 3: Activate the graphing utility. The graph should appear as in Figure C-9.

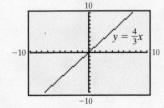

Figure C-9

Distinguishing features of the graph of a line include showing all the intercepts of the line. For example, the window of the graph of the line in Figure C-10 does not show both intercepts of the line, but the window of the graph of the same line in Figure C-11 does show both intercepts.

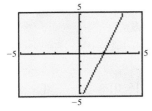

Figure C-10

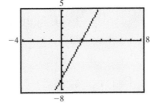

Figure C-11

On a standard viewing window, the tick marks on the *y*-axis are closer than the tick marks on the *x*-axis. This happens because the viewing window is a rectangle, and so 10 equally spaced tick marks on the positive *y*-axis will be closer together than 10 equally spaced tick marks on the positive *x*-axis. This causes the appearance of graphs to be distorted.

For example, notice the different appearances of the same line graphed using different viewing windows. The line in Figure C-12 is distorted because the tick marks along the *x*-axis are farther apart than the tick marks along the *y*-axis. The graph of the same line in Figure C-13 is not distorted because the viewing rectangle has been selected so that there is equal spacing between tick marks on both axes.

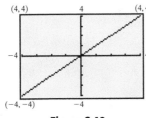

Figure C-12

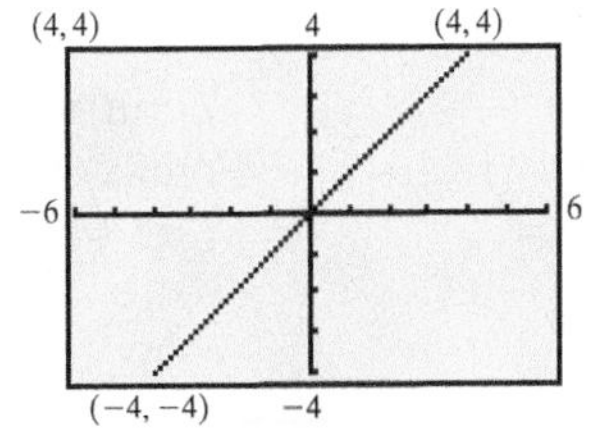

Figure C-13

We say that the line in Figure C-13 is graphed on a *square* setting. Some graphing utilities have a built-in program that, if activated, will automatically provide a square setting. A square setting is especially helpful when we are graphing perpendicular lines, circles, or when a true geometric perspective is desired. Some examples of square screens are shown in Figures C-14 and C-15.

Other features of a graphing utility such as Trace, Zoom, Intersect, and Table are discussed in appropriate Graphing Calculator Explorations in this text.

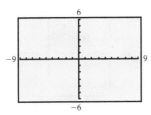

Figure C-14

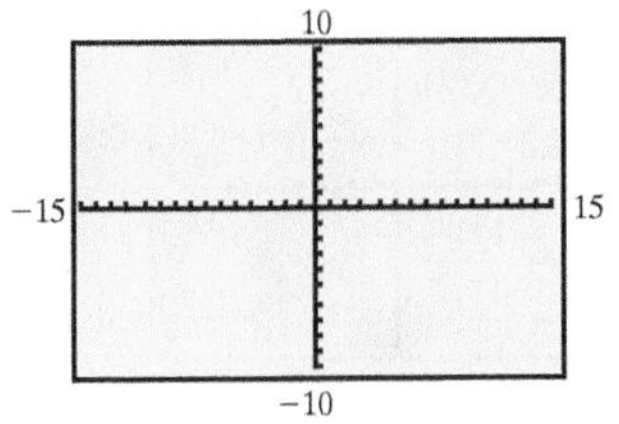

Figure C-15

C EXERCISE SET

FOR EXTRA HELP

MyMathLab   PRACTICE   WATCH   DOWNLOAD   READ   REVIEW

Objective Ⓐ *In Exercises 1–4, determine whether all ordered pairs listed will lie within a standard viewing rectangle.*

1. $(-9, 0), (5, 8), (1, -8)$

2. $(4, 7), (0, 0), (-8, 9)$

3. $(-11, 0), (2, 2), (7, -5)$

4. $(3, 5), (-3, -5), (15, 0)$

In Exercises 5–10, choose an Xmin, Xmax, Ymin, and Ymax so that all ordered pairs listed will lie within the viewing rectangle.

5. $(-90, 0), (55, 80), (0, -80)$

6. $(4, 70), (20, 20), (-18, 90)$

7. $(-11, 0), (2, 2), (7, -5)$

8. $(3, 5), (-3, -5), (15, 0)$

9. $(200, 200), (50, -50), (70, -50)$

10. $(40, 800), (-30, 500), (15, 0)$

Write the window setting for each viewing window shown. Use the following format:

Xmin =	Ymin =
Xmax =	Ymax =
Xscl =	Yscl =

11.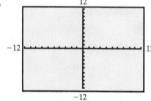

12.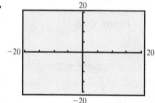

13.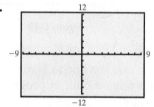

14.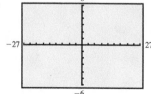

15.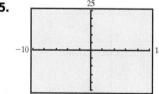

16.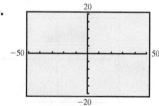

1032

17.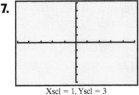
Xscl = 1, Yscl = 3

18.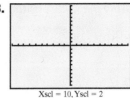
Xscl = 10, Yscl = 2

19.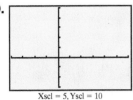
Xscl = 5, Yscl = 10

20.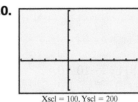
Xscl = 100, Yscl = 200

Objective Ⓑ *Graph each linear equation in two variables, using the two different window settings given. Determine which setting shows all intercepts of the line.*

21. $y = 2x + 12$
   Setting A: $[-10, 10]$ by $[-10, 10]$
   Setting B: $[-10, 10]$ by $[-10, 15]$

22. $y = -3x + 25$
   Setting A: $[-5, 5]$ by $[-30, 10]$
   Setting B: $[-10, 10]$ by $[-10, 30]$

23. $y = -x - 41$
   Setting A: $[-50, 10]$ by $[-10, 10]$
   Setting B: $[-50, 10]$ by $[-50, 15]$

24. $y = 6x - 18$
   Setting A: $[-10, 10]$ by $[-20, 10]$
   Setting B: $[-10, 10]$ by $[-10, 10]$

25. $y = \frac{1}{2}x - 15$
   Setting A: $[-10, 10]$ by $[-20, 10]$
   Setting B: $[-10, 35]$ by $[-20, 15]$

26. $y = -\frac{2}{3}x - \frac{29}{3}$
   Setting A: $[-10, 10]$ by $[-10, 10]$
   Setting B: $[-15, 5]$ by $[-15, 5]$

The graph of each equation is a line. Use a graphing utility and a standard viewing window to graph each equation.

27. $3x = 5y$ **28.** $7y = -3x$ **29.** $9x - 5y = 30$ **30.** $4x + 6y = 20$

31. $y = -7$ **32.** $y = 2$ **33.** $x + 10y = -5$ **34.** $x - 5y = 9$

Graph the following equations using the square setting given. Some keystrokes that may be helpful are given.

35. $y = \sqrt{x}$ $[-12, 12]$ by $[-8, 8]$

Suggested keystrokes: $\sqrt{x}$

36. $y = \sqrt{2x}$ $[-12, 12]$ by $[-8, 8]$

Suggested keystrokes: $\sqrt{(2x)}$

37. $y = x^2 + 2x + 1$ $[-15, 15]$ by $[-10, 10]$

Suggested keystrokes: $x \wedge 2 + 2x + 1$

38. $y = x^2 - 5$ $[-15, 15]$ by $[-10, 10]$

Suggested keystrokes: $x \wedge 2 - 5$

39. $y = |x|$ $[-9, 9]$ by $[-6, 6]$

Suggested keystrokes: ABS (x)

40. $y = |x - 2|$ $[-9, 9]$ by $[-6, 6]$

Suggested keystrokes: ABS $(x - 2)$

Graph the line on a single set of axes. Use a standard viewing window; then, if necessary, change the viewing window so that all intercepts of the line show.

41. $x + 2y = 30$

42. $1.5x - 3.7y = 40.3$

Answers to Selected Exercises

Appendix C

Exercise Set Appendix C   **1.** yes   **3.** no   **5.** answers may vary   **7.** answers may vary   **9.** answers may vary

11. Xmin $= -12$ Ymin $= -12$
Xmax $= 12$ Ymax $= 12$
Xscl $= \dfrac{6}{5}$ Yscl $= \dfrac{6}{5}$

13. Xmin $= -9$ Ymin $= -12$
Xmax $= 9$ Ymax $= 12$
Xscl $= 1$ Yscl $= 2$

15. Xmin $= -10$ Ymin $= -25$
Xmax $= 10$ Ymax $= 25$
Xscl $= 2$ Yscl $= 5$

17. Xmin $= -5$ Ymin $= -15$
Xmax $= 5$ Ymax $= 15$
Xscl $= 1$ Yscl $= 3$

19. Xmin $= -20$ Ymin $= -30$
Xmax $= 30$ Ymax $= 50$
Xscl $= 5$ Yscl $= 10$

21. Setting B   **23.** Setting B   **25.** Setting B

27.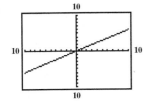

29.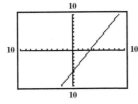

31.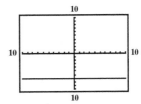

33.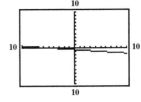

35.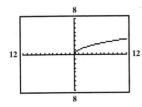

37.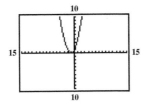

39.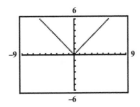

41.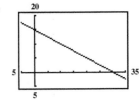

Stressing and Compressing Graphs of Absolute Value Functions

In Section 12.4, we learned to shift and reflect graphs of common functions: $f(x) = x$, $f(x) = x^2$, $f(x) = |x|$ and $f(x) = \sqrt{x}$. Since other common functions are studied throughout this text, in this appendix we concentrate on the absolute value function.

Recall that the graph of $h(x) = -|x - 1| + 2$, for example, is the same as the graph of $f(x) = |x|$ reflected about the x-axis, moved 1 unit to the right and 2 units upward. In other words,

$$h(x) = -|x - 1| + 2$$

opens   (1, 2) location of vertex of
downward   V-shape

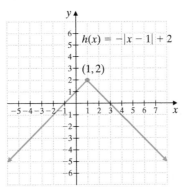

Let's now study the graphs of a few other absolute value functions.

Example 1   Graph $h(x) = 2|x|$, and $g(x) = \frac{1}{2}|x|$

Solution: Let's find and plot ordered-pair solutions for the functions.

x	h(x)	g(x)
−2	4	1
−1	2	$\frac{1}{2}$
0	0	0
1	2	$\frac{1}{2}$
2	4	1

Notice that the graph of $h(x) = 2|x|$ is narrower than the graph of $f(x) = |x|$ and the graph of $g(x) = \frac{1}{2}|x|$ is wider than the graph of $f(x) = |x|$.

● **Work Practice 1**

PRACTICE 1

Graph $h(x) = 4|x|$ and $g(x) = \frac{1}{5}|x|$ on the same set of axes.

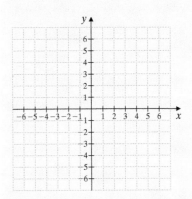

Answer

1.

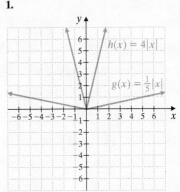

In general, for the absolute function, we have the following:

> ## The Graph of the Absolute Value Function
>
> The graph of $f(x) = a|x - h| + k$
> - Has vertex (h, k) and is V-shaped.
> - Opens up if $a > 0$ and down if $a < 0$.
> - If $|a| < 1$, the graph is wider than the graph of $y = |x|$.
> - If $|a| > 1$, the graph is narrower than a graph of $y = |x|$.

PRACTICE 2

Graph $f(x) = -\dfrac{1}{2}|x + 1| + 3$

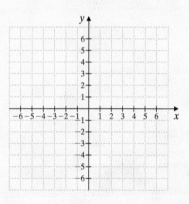

Example 2 Graph $f(x) = -\dfrac{1}{3}|x + 2| + 4$

Solution: Let's write this function in the form $f(x) = a|x - h| + k$. For our function, we have $f(x) = -\dfrac{1}{3}|x - (-2)| + 4$. Thus:

- vertex is $(-2, 4)$
- since $a < 0$, V-shape opens down
- since $|a| = \left|-\dfrac{1}{3}\right| = \dfrac{1}{3} < 1$, the graph is wider than $y = |x|$

We will also find and plot ordered-pair solutions.

If $x = -5$, $f(-5) = -\dfrac{1}{3}|-5 + 2| + 4$, or 3

If $x = 1$, $f(1) = -\dfrac{1}{3}|1 + 2| + 4$, or 3

If $x = 3$, $f(3) = -\dfrac{1}{3}|3 + 2| + 4$, or $\dfrac{7}{3}$, or $2\dfrac{1}{3}$

x	f(x)
−5	3
1	3
3	$2\dfrac{1}{3}$

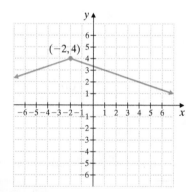

● **Work Practice 2**

Answer

2.

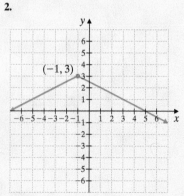

Sketch the graph of each function. Label the vertex of the V-shape. See Examples 1 and 2.

1. $f(x) = 3|x|$

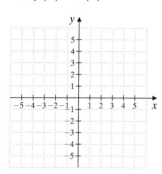

2. $f(x) = 5|x|$

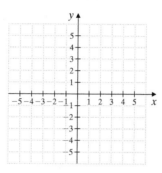

3. $f(x) = \frac{1}{4}|x|$

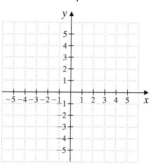

4. $f(x) = \frac{1}{3}|x|$

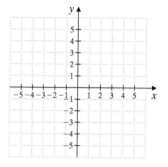

5. $g(x) = 2|x| + 3$

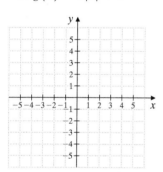

6. $g(x) = 3|x| + 2$

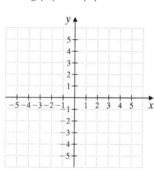

7. $h(x) = -\frac{1}{2}|x|$

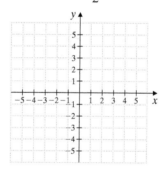

8. $h(x) = -\frac{1}{3}|x|$

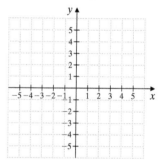

9. $f(x) = 4|x - 1|$

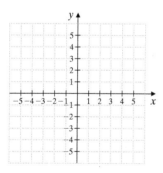

10. $f(x) = 3|x - 2|$

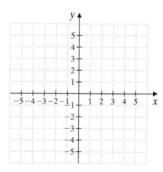

11. $g(x) = -\frac{1}{3}|x| - 2$

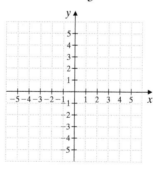

12. $g(x) = -\frac{1}{2}|x| - 3$

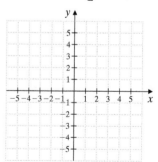

13. $f(x) = -2|x - 3| + 4$

14. $f(x) = -3|x - 1| + 5$

15. $f(x) = \frac{2}{3}|x + 2| - 5$

16. $f(x) = \frac{3}{4}|x + 1| - 4$

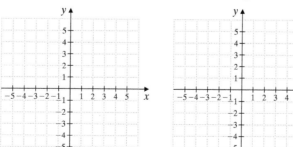
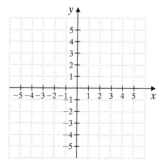

Answers to Selected Exercises

Appendix D

Exercise Set Appendix D

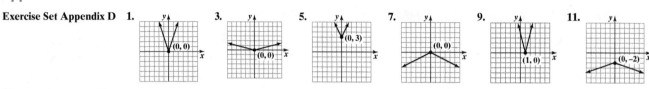

1. (0, 0) **3.** (0, 0) **5.** (0, 3) **7.** (0, 0) **9.** (1, 0) **11.** (0, −2)

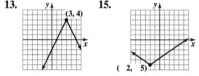

13. (3, 4) **15.** (−2, −5)

Appendix

E

E TABLE OF SQUARES AND SQUARE ROOTS

Squares and Square Roots					
n	n^2	$\sqrt{n}$	n	n^2	$\sqrt{n}$
1	1	1.000	51	2601	7.141
2	4	1.414	52	2704	7.211
3	9	1.732	53	2809	7.280
4	16	2.000	54	2916	7.348
5	25	2.236	55	3025	7.416
6	36	2.449	56	3136	7.483
7	49	2.646	57	3249	7.550
8	64	2.828	58	3364	7.616
9	81	3.000	59	3481	7.681
10	100	3.162	60	3600	7.746
11	121	3.317	61	3721	7.810
12	144	3.464	62	3844	7.874
13	169	3.606	63	3969	7.937
14	196	3.742	64	4096	8.000
15	225	3.873	65	4225	8.062
16	256	4.000	66	4356	8.124
17	289	4.123	67	4489	8.185
18	324	4.243	68	4624	8.246
19	361	4.359	69	4761	8.307
20	400	4.472	70	4900	8.367
21	441	4.583	71	5041	8.426
22	484	4.690	72	5184	8.485
23	529	4.796	73	5329	8.544
24	576	4.899	74	5476	8.602
25	625	5.000	75	5625	8.660
26	676	5.099	76	5776	8.718
27	729	5.196	77	5929	8.775
28	784	5.292	78	6084	8.832
29	841	5.385	79	6241	8.888
30	900	5.477	80	6400	8.944
31	961	5.568	81	6561	9.000
32	1024	5.657	82	6724	9.055
33	1089	5.745	83	6889	9.110
34	1156	5.831	84	7056	9.165
35	1225	5.916	85	7225	9.220
36	1296	6.000	86	7396	9.274
37	1369	6.083	87	7569	9.327
38	1444	6.164	88	7744	9.381
39	1521	6.245	89	7921	9.434
40	1600	6.325	90	8100	9.487
41	1681	6.403	91	8281	9.539
42	1764	6.481	92	8464	9.592
43	1849	6.557	93	8649	9.644
44	1936	6.633	94	8836	9.695
45	2025	6.708	95	9025	9.747
46	2116	6.782	96	9216	9.798
47	2209	6.856	97	9409	9.849
48	2304	6.928	98	9604	9.899
49	2401	7.000	99	9801	9.950
50	2500	7.071	100	10,000	10.000

Index